83d CONGRESS, 1st SESSION

HOUSE DOCUMENT NO. 122

the yearbook of agriculture

1953

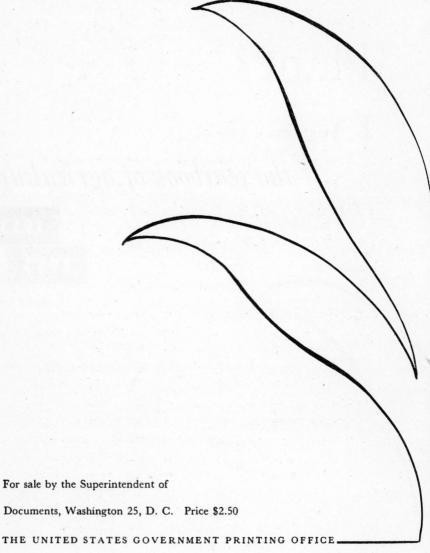

For sale by the Superintendent of

Documents, Washington 25, D. C.   Price $2.50

THE UNITED STATES GOVERNMENT PRINTING OFFICE

Plant
Diseases

the yearbook of agriculture

1953

UNITED STATES

DEPARTMENT OF

AGRICULTURE

WASHINGTON, D. C.

the yearbook

committee

Bureau of Plant Industry, Soils, and Agricultural Engineering

CURTIS MAY, *chairman*

PHILIP BRIERLEY

EDWARD E. CLAYTON

JOHN C. DUNEGAN

KERMIT W. KREITLOW

W. D. McCLELLAN

PAUL R. MILLER

H. A. RODENHISER

W. J. ZAUMEYER

Office of Experiment Stations

C. L. LEFEBVRE

Bureau of Entomology and Plant Quarantine

WILLIS H. WHEELER

Office of Information

ALFRED STEFFERUD, *editor*

Ezra Taft Benson
Secretary of Agriculture

To me the most startling aspect of plant diseases is that they cost us an estimated three billion dollars a year.

The tragic aspect is that much of the loss is a waste that can be prevented. Waste is contrary to the laws of Nature and the conscience of man. Waste is unworthy of a great people.

To conquer some of the diseases will not be easy. New diseases and new races of old disease-producing organisms appear all the time; race 15B of wheat stem rust and race 101 of crown rust of oats, for instance, appeared just when we thought we had rust under control. When we extend the production of a crop, the number and prevalence of diseases seem also to grow—as has happened to soybeans.

Some diseases still outside our borders remain a threat as communications expand. Some (like tristeza disease of citrus crops) are new to our country or new to a region. Our buying and selling of more goods—fruits, vegetables, nursery stock, seeds—enlarges the risk of spreading diseases even though the facilities for transportation and marketing them have been greatly improved.

The cost of materials and equipment for fighting the diseases has become enormous. And, finally, our efforts against plant diseases are made harder by the lack of information about them among many persons who have to do with plants and plant products.

Nevertheless, I am greatly encouraged by a number of developments. Plant breeders have perfected varieties of wheat, oats, strawberries, and other crops that can withstand, for a while at least, the ravages of a disease. More effective chemicals have been discovered for use against the fungi, viruses, bacteria, and nematodes, and others are in process of development. Our people give an ever-increasing measure of cooperation to regulatory procedures designed to halt the importation and spread of diseases. The handling of perishable foods has made great strides in markets, stores, and homes in a few years.

Much remains to be done, however.

The program I suggest looks toward an intensification of those efforts and greater efficiency in them.

One requirement is steady, continuous research in plant industry, geared to immediate problems and to the building up of basic knowledge that will be of use in solving problems of the future.

We need to give more attention to solving permanently the problems of plant diseases and not to be satisfied with palliatives that at best provide only temporary relief. Here, as elsewhere in agriculture, we should be mindful of the biological balance—the balance of Nature—which our modern practices of plowing, domestication of plants, fast travel, intensive cultivation, and clearing of land keep in constant jeopardy. Our attempts to improve the health of crops have to recognize man's relationship with Nature.

Another requirement is that the information be made available to all farmers and everyone else to whom it will be useful. Historically, the function of the Department of Agriculture is to gather information—do research—of value to farmers and to disseminate that information as widely as possible. The lag in time between the acquisition of knowledge and the time it is made use of often is greater than it should be. We need to give more attention to ways to shorten that interval.

A third facet is the closer integration of these new developments into our agriculture and into the segments of our national life that are most closely tied to agriculture.

They are part of our goal for American agriculture: Ample food for all, efficient farm production and marketing, prosperity for farmers, economy in administering sound agricultural programs, continuing cooperation among all segments of society.

This Yearbook, devoted to an important subject with so many ramifications, will help greatly in the achievement of the goal.

Alfred Stefferud, Editor

This preface may be the proper place to answer some questions from readers and others about how and why the Yearbook of Agriculture is produced.

The Yearbook of Agriculture is an institution older than the Department of Agriculture itself. It can be said to date from 1849, when the Commissioner of Patents, the forerunner of the Secretary of Agriculture, began to devote one part of his annual report to agricultural matters. The first annual report of the newly named Commissioner of Agriculture, issued under authority of the act that established the Department of Agriculture, was dated 1862.

The publication of the Yearbook of Agriculture is required by the Act of January 12, 1895, which provided:

"The Annual Report of the Secretary of Agriculture shall hereafter be submitted and printed in two parts, as follows: Part one, which shall contain purely business and executive matter which it is necessary for the Secretary to submit to the President and Congress; part two, which shall contain such reports from the different bureaus and divisions, and such papers prepared by their special agents, accompanied by suitable illustrations, as shall, in the opinion of the Secretary, be specially suited to interest and instruct the farmers of the country, and to include a general report of the operations of the Department for their information. . . ."

The preface to the Yearbook dated 1894 said: "The present volume represents but imperfectly the ideal of what such a yearbook should be . . . . It is believed that the character of the volume can be improved from year to year until it shall become finally a standard book of reference for American farmers. . . ."

The foundations of the Yearbook of Agriculture as it is now were laid by Milton S. Eisenhower, its editor from 1928 to 1935, and Gove Hambidge, the editor from 1936 to 1942. Since 1936 each volume has been devoted to discussions bearing on a single field of knowledge instead of to miscellaneous articles on year-to-year developments in a few phases of farming. The subjects of the new series are: Plant and animal genetics, 1936 and 1937; soils, 1938; human and animal nutrition, 1939; agricultural economics and history, 1940; climate, 1941; diseases of animals, 1942; recent developments in agricultural science, 1943–1947; grassland agriculture, 1948; trees, 1949; the processing of agricultural products, 1950–1951; and insects, 1952.

For many years the Yearbook of Agriculture has been the main (and at times the only) means of announcing and summarizing comprehensively the results of agricultural research—for which (as an example) $42,874,000 was spent in the United States Department of Agriculture in 1952.

As a book of science, the Yearbook is prepared with no thought of influencing farm policies inside or outside the Department of Agriculture. Its aim is to give complete, practical discussions of one topic in clear (but not elementary) language. It is prepared primarily for American farmers, but changes in the farm population and the increasing interest of nonfarm citizens in food, clothing, conservation, processing, and many other related topics mean that they also enter into our considerations when we plan and prepare a volume. *Crops in Peace and War* (1950–1951) and *Science in Farming* (1943–1947), for example, dealt with many aspects of agriculture of interest and value to the whole population.

Because most of the chapters are

later reprinted separately, an attempt is made to make each part of the book self-contained, even at the cost of some duplication. Other than the basic requirements of accuracy, completeness, and propriety, the writers of the chapters—who receive no payment for their contributions and who include employees of the United States Department of Agriculture, research men in universities, experiment stations, and industry, and other qualified persons— are subject to no limitations in the way they handle their assignments.

An editor and an editorial assistant comprise the Yearbook staff.

The Yearbooks of Agriculture, which are congressional documents, are distributed mainly by Members of the Congress. Of the current volume, 230,850 copies were printed for the Congress; 12,000 copies for Department agencies, State and county extension agents, and agricultural libraries; and about 40,000 copies for sale by the Superintendent of Documents. Income from the sales by the Superintendent of Documents returns to the United States Treasury.

Besides the books themselves, the materials in the Yearbooks have even wider dissemination—as reprints, in magazines, in anthologies, and as background for articles in magazines and books. Material in the Yearbooks is not copyrighted, and permission to reprint it is usually given, with certain restrictions, upon request.

Grass, the 1948 Yearbook of Agriculture, exemplifies the influence the Yearbooks have, even though—to repeat—our purpose is to report developments in research. It was the first major publication to recognize the importance of grassland farming and for many persons was their introduction to the production and values of grass crops.

The American Institute of Graphic Arts chose *Insects* as one of the "Fifty Books" of 1952 because of its typographic design. It was also chosen as an outstanding textbook of 1952. No thought, however, is given to making the book merely a beautiful one—it is planned with functional considerations only in mind. The cover, for example, is made of the cheapest available binding cloth, which is impregnated to make it resistant to insects and dampness and is inexpensively printed over with color because otherwise it would be an impractical, easily soiled white.

As to the present volume:

Weather, insects, and plant diseases often are called the worst natural hazards in farming. The 1941 Yearbook of Agriculture, *Climate and Man*, summarized our knowledge about the first. *Insects*, in 1952, considered the second. This book completes the triad.

Some 30,000 different diseases attack our economic plants—the plants grown for sale or use as foods, feeds, clothing, and lumber. Others spoil or destroy our flowers, shade trees, and shrubs.

In this book we present information on the causes and control of many diseases of our important crop plants. We emphasize practical details, but we also discuss fundamental biological facts that underlay the comparatively new science of phytopathology.

We use trade names solely to provide specific information. Such use does not constitute a guarantee or warranty of the products named and does not signify that the products are approved to the exclusion of others of suitable composition.

We hope this volume will enhance the prosperity of American agriculture and fulfill the expectations of the many farmers, Congressmen, students, extension workers, and others who have written us that a Yearbook on plant diseases is needed.

Many persons have had a part in its preparation, and to them thanks are given. The work of outlining and writing the material began in June 1951; typesetting and similar work began in August 1952. The final proofs were approved and made up-to-date in June of 1953.

contents

GROWING HEALTHIER PLANTS

GRASSES AND LEGUMES

COTTON

xii

FOOD AND FEED GRAINS

VEGETABLE CROPS

FRUITS AND NUTS

AFTER HARVEST

SOME OTHERS

color plates

plant diseases

Three Billion Dollars a Year

Jessie I. Wood

A farmer in Pennsylvania in 1928 sprayed his apple orchard with materials other than those tested and recommended by the experiment station.

The result was an attack of apple scab that caused the loss of 80 percent of his crop. He had expected 1,500 bushels, but he got only 300 bushels of poor apples.

Furthermore, the trees were so badly weakened that yields in after years were low. Because of their poor condition, 15 percent of the trees died during drought in 1930 and 1932. Even 20 years afterward, the orchard had not returned to its original healthy, profitable state.

But that is not all. The financial setback forced the farmer to borrow heavily every year in order to produce a crop. As a result, the farm became so debt-ridden that he would gladly have sold it for the amount of indebtedness. In order to make a living, he had to seek outside employment and finally became a full-time worker at another occupation. Thus one bad attack of a plant disease turned a debt-free enterprise into a liability and wrecked the owner's independence and security.

Another instance: A farmer had owned his farm in South Dakota all his life. In 1914–1918, leaf and stem rust caused losses to small grains. The yield of barley was reduced from 50 bushels an acre to 10; oats dropped from 40 to 60 to 5 to 15 bushels; wheat, from 20 to 30 bushels to 2 to 5 bushels an acre.

costs

and causes

I

The financial loss amounted to $1,000 to $3,000 every year. He borrowed money during this time of crop failure. A series of years of low prices added to his loss. The debt caused foreclosure in 1934, when the depression was at its worst. Here again, a plant disease gave the downward push that decided the fate of this farm home and business.

Stem rust caused almost 60 percent loss to the wheat crop in Minnesota and some of the neighboring States in the epidemic year of 1935, and the loss for the whole country was almost a quarter of the crop. Obviously, that heavy reduction in over-all yield means that some individual farmers sustain disastrous losses. Witness the following accounts of farm losses due to stem rust in Minnesota that year. In one county a $4,000 loss was the final factor, although not the only one, in foreclosure on one farm; a $2,000 loss caused foreclosure of a 400-acre farm valued at $16,000; a $4,000 loss caused foreclosure of a 1,100-acre farm worth $25,-000. In another county the wheat crop on some 700 farms was practically a complete failure because of stem rust. The average yield expected was 20 bushels to the acre, but the actual yield ranged from nothing at all to about 10 bushels an acre. The total loss for the area amounted to about $400,000. Some farmers had to give up farming. Others did not recover financial stability for 5 years or longer.

About 50 years ago Granville wilt, or bacterial wilt, of tobacco appeared in the southern part of Granville County, N. C., where about 7,000 acres of tobacco were grown on 1,500 farms, some of which had been owned and operated by the same families for generations. The disease increased until it was destroying 20 to 50 percent of the crop each year; the loss amounted to 1 to 2 million dollars annually. All attempts at control failed. Many farmers lost their farms, farmsteads deteriorated, the morale of the farm population dropped, education was neglected, and living and health standards went down. Between 1920 and 1940, when the dis-ease was at its peak, total loss from forced sale of farms at sacrifice and from reduced tobacco production amounted to 30 to 40 million dollars. All this because of one plant disease in one community!

Those are some of the cases reported by county agents. By no means were all of the losses involved so severe or lasting as the ones I have mentioned, but in many other instances a plant disease was partly or wholly the cause of serious difficulty.

Possibly you think that those farmers must not have been very skillful, that good farmers would not have such trouble, or perhaps that they did not arrange their financial affairs very well. Undoubtedly poor judgment was a factor sometimes.

But how about the tobacco farms that had been owned by the same families for generations, only to be lost when a disease-producing organism invaded the soil and could not be checked? The obvious remedy would have been to change to some other main crop or to vary the crops, but a region that is suited to and derives most of its income from one major profitable cash crop does not easily make such a change, for the change involves much more than just growing a different plant. Moreover, the bacterium that causes the disease has so many other hosts besides tobacco (such as peanuts and potatoes) that a change might merely be from the frying pan into the fire.

With farming, as with any occupation, many factors make success or failure. The farmer, no less than everyone else, is affected by the ups and downs of the general economic situation. In good times he can absorb or recover quickly from large losses due to any cause. In hard times small losses may be enough to shove him under. As for the individual economic circumstances, good financial management is as essential as fertile soil and skillful farming to be sure of leeway enough to meet all chances of loss and take advantage of all opportunities for profit. Lacking any of those qualities, a farmer may barely make a living in the best of times and certainly will possess no margin for emergencies.

Granted all that: The fact remains that agriculture is subject to numerous risks, which at times endanger the prosperity of the best of farms or of whole areas. Economic fluctuation is just one of the risks; it is shared with the rest of the population. Others are peculiarly agricultural. Among them are plant diseases.

Weather, insects, and plant diseases are the three great natural hazards of crop production. Weather is perhaps the chief one, but the order of importance is not certain. The interrelation between weather and disease and between weather and insects and among all three, if the disease is caused by a pathogen carried by insects, is so close and so complicated that sometimes it is hard to determine the actual origin of trouble. Moreover, the causes of plant diseases are mostly not obvious to the unaided eye, and loss due to them may be ascribed to the more conspicuous insects or to weather conditions. In any event, the relative importance of the three factors is not fixed but varies according to season and location, and the total loss due to each one by itself is quite enough to make comparisons superfluous.

In the United States the average annual loss from plant diseases is estimated to be about 3 billion dollars.

We have no way of establishing a precise figure, and this one is based on many assumptions but it could well be under rather than over the real amount. Without the control measures we do have, the loss would be much greater.

The primary reason for the importance of plant diseases or of anything else that affects plant growth is not economic. We are apt to take green plants for granted, so familiar are they. We use them for food and clothing and many other things, but we seldom consider their true significance. Green plants alone, save for some negligible

exceptions, manufacture the basic materials of life; the existence of animals and human beings depends on the products of these living green factories. Any serious breakdown in this process threatens life itself. The famines that periodically cause so much suffering in many regions of the earth prove that.

Disease is a cause of lowered efficiency or final breakdown in the plant's functions. Disease, literally "dis-ease," is one of those terms that are very hard to define although everybody knows what they mean. Broadly speaking, it means disturbance in functioning and growth. Whether the result of the disturbance is important to us depends on how seriously it affects the yield and quality of the product for which we grow the plant.

The reaction of the affected plant to the cause of the disturbance produces the various symptoms and consequences that we recognize as the effects of disease, such as wilting, dieback, root and stem rots, damping-off, cankers, witches'-brooms, stunting, unthriftiness, poor yields, shriveled kernels, blighted, spotted, discolored, or deformed foliage, fruit decay, and the numerous other manifestations of abnormal condition.

Diseases do not just happen; they are always the result of a cause. The causes are divided into two broad groups, namely, parasitic and nonparasitic.

Man and animals are not the only kinds of life that depend on green plants for their existence. Minute living organisms may invade and grow within the plant tissue and obtain their nourishment from it. Sometimes the involuntary plant "host" tolerates the existence of the invader within its body without apparent harm; in fact, there may be a reciprocal benefit from the association. More often the parasitic organism interferes with the functioning of the affected plant, and disease is the result. From our point of view that is bad, although the parasites are doing the same thing we do—living on the products of the green plant.

But they both lodge and board with their host, as it were, and they eat at the first table. We get what is left. Sometimes that is a very small portion.

Parasites that cause diseases through their growth in their hosts are called "pathogens," and the diseases that they cause are "pathogenic" or "parasitic" diseases. Because in this instance the diseases are the result of infection that may spread from plant to plant, they are also called the "infectious" diseases.

The nonparasitic diseases are due to environmental or nutritional factors unfavorable to the plant, or to some abnormality in the constitution of the plant itself. Nutritional disturbance arising from either actual deficiency or unbalanced supply of essential nutrient materials is one of the most important causes of plant disease. Deficiency diseases are some of the most common manifestations. In some places they are recognized as the most troublesome plant disease problems, and it has been suggested that they are probably much more widespread and significant generally than has been realized.

Our cultivated plants have inherited disorders from their wild ancestors, which are just as susceptible as any garden, field, or orchard crop to the attack of parasites or to functional disturbance from other causes. Cultivation, however, greatly increases liability to the development of disease, for various reasons.

Although many parasitic organisms can attack a great number of different kinds of plants, most of them are limited to a narrow range—sometimes to only one species. On anything else they cannot grow.

In the wild, mixed growth of different kinds of plants as well as natural genetic variation in the susceptibility among individuals of the same species interpose many barriers to the spread of pathogens that attack any one host. But in cultivation numerous individuals of one kind of plant grow near each other, sometimes almost to the exclusion of any other plant over a wide area. Moreover, consciously or unconsciously, from the very beginning crop plants have been selected for propagation on the basis of one or another desirable characteristic, so that much of the original diversity is lost, including variation in reaction to pathogens. Both the chances for infection and opportunities for spread by a pathogen to which a crop is vulnerable are therefore multiplied enormously.

Not only does cultivation enhance the local spread of disease. Crops accompany agriculture to new locations far distant from their original homes. If a pathogen is equipped to survive the journey and if it meets with favorable conditions in the new location, it, too, will become established in the new home.

But that is not all. Wild plants in the new place may harbor a pathogen that finds the introduced crop much more vulnerable to its attack than its original hosts. For example, the fire blight bacterium is indigenous to this country, where it infects various native plants of the rose family without damaging them too much. Pear trees and apple trees brought by settlers from abroad proved to be very susceptible; pear trees are so susceptible that it is hard to grow them in many parts of the country. Many "new" diseases appear in this manner; they are not really new but are transferred from wild plants.

Many a plant pathogen is inconspicuous in its effects until it meets a susceptible new host or perhaps until it acquires an efficient vector.

The susceptible new host may be a native plant and the pathogen an introduced organism. Plant disease problems are by no means limited to cultivated crops. When a wild species has rather uniform susceptibility to one kind of pathogenic organism, disease caused by the organism can become as destructive in natural stands as, for instance, rust is in the occasional widespread outbreaks in wheatfields of the Great Plains. Wild stands may suffer even greater destruction, in fact, because ordinarily there is not much that can be done to stop the spread of the pathogen.

The chestnut blight is an example. In the 40 years or so since it was first discovered in this country, the disease has practically killed the American chestnut throughout its native range. If it were not for cultivated plantings and artificial hybridization with other species of chestnut, none of the good qualities of this useful, handsome tree could be preserved for future generations. Who knows how often similar events in ages past may have caused other potentially valuable plants to become extinct?

Good nutrition is as necessary to the health of plants as it is to ours. In the natural environment, materials used by the plant in its growth are constantly being returned to the soil in decaying plant debris, but usually in cultivation they are removed from the soil, and little such natural replacement takes place. Moreover, even in the natural state some soils lack one or another of the essential elements, and cultivation may increase the deficiency to the danger point. The amount and particular combination of nutrients required for proper growth vary according to the kind of plant, and crops will not always be planted in soils suited to their special needs. Maintaining and improving the supply of plant foods in the soil to prevent the development of nutritional disease is a major agricultural problem.

Thus, when men first thought to insure themselves a food supply by growing instead of gathering it, they encountered difficulties. They wore out their soil—and then more soil, as they abandoned their clearings and moved on to fresh land. Along with the plants they found most useful, they unwittingly started cultivating the parasites that affected their chosen crops. It was ages before they recognized the cause or could combat the trouble from the parasites. The failure of staple crops due to severe outbreaks of disease must often have caused famine and suffering long before the beginning of recorded history.

Ancient literature contains many accounts of maladies in crops. Among them we can most surely identify the rust (probably both leaf and stem rust) of grains. From our own experience with its destructiveness, we can understand the ancient fear of the disease. It was all the more frightening because its origin was a mystery.

Its appearance in the fields was believed to be evidence of the displeasure of the gods. The early Romans called the disease "robigo" because of the redness. Their corn god, Robigus, was named for the rust.

This god, in their belief, possessed the power of inflicting or withholding the scourge of the disease. He was so important to them that every year they staged a festival, the Rubigalia, in his honor with ceremonial offerings and sacrifices to ward off his displeasure and seek his favor for the crops.

We know now that there is nothing mysterious about the causes of plant diseases. Even if we have not yet been able to discover with modern techniques the origin of some one disease, we know that it has a natural explanation. Modern knowledge has removed the fear of the supernatural and it has given us the means by which to reduce the damage due to plant diseases, but it has not made them less important.

One of the most tragic events in history led to the beginning of real knowledge about plant diseases and to the development of the science of plant pathology. That was the Irish famine in the middle of the nineteenth century. Two circumstances were responsible. First, the impoverished population had become almost wholly dependent on their potato gardens for food. Second, the potato crop for 2 years, 1845 and 1846, was almost wholly destroyed by late blight. Accounts of physical misery and spiritual anguish suffered because of the devastation caused by this one disease go far beyond anything that ordinary experience equips one to understand. Ireland lost almost a third of its population between 1845 and 1860 as a direct result of the outbreak of late blight. A million people died from starvation or from disease following malnutrition. A million and a half more emigrated.

The outbreak in Ireland was part of a pandemic—that is, the disease suddenly became widespread and destructive almost simultaneously in several European countries and in the United States as well. As far as can be determined, the disease had appeared in these regions not more than 2 or 3 years previously. In the meantime, the pathogen evidently increased and became widely distributed, so that when the weather became generally and extremely favorable, as happened during the years of the pandemic, it could attack rapidly and in force over a wide area at once.

Why did this outbreak overwhelm the Irish and affect other peoples much less? The answer is not simple. It lies partly in agricultural and partly in political history. But essentially it is that miserable economic conditions led to the almost sole reliance of the Irish peasantry on the easily grown, productive, and filling potato for their main food.

In other places food resources were more varied so that destruction of the potato crop did not have anywhere near the same importance.

Even after this grimmest of epidemics abated, its consequences remained. The disease had become a fixture in potato culture. It was more or less evident almost every year, and serious outbreaks, although none again so disastrous as the great pandemic, occurred from time to time whenever the weather was favorable. The tragic drama of the famine was one of the decisive factors in subsequent social and economic policy. Its influence on British-Irish relations is still felt.

Of course, circumstances must be unusual indeed for such extreme disaster to be caused by the attack of a plant disease, or, for that matter, by anything else. There have been other records of famine due to the severe occurrence of a plant disease. In 1733, more than a century before the Irish famine, 12,000 persons on one Japanese island died because of failure of the rice crop, caused perhaps by stunt, a virus disease. Early settlers in Australia are said to have suffered more than once from lack of food because their grain crops were destroyed by leaf rust. Actually, however, except for the toll of human lives that make it so terrifying and so impressive, famine is comparatively minor as an expression of the importance of plant diseases.

Nowadays help can reach victims quickly almost anywhere in the world, and there is less and less likelihood of famine or excuse for it.

THAT LAST STATEMENT is true except in times of stress and emergency, of disrupted transportation and world upheaval. Late blight is said to have had a place in the defeat of Germany in the First World War. In 1917 it destroyed about a third of the potato crop, which made up a large part of the wartime diet of the Germans. Reduction in the already scanty food supply contributed to the breakdown in morale and physical endurance that led to the end of the war. Here again, this required a favorable combination of circumstances; seldom does a single plant disease influence military affairs to that extent. Plant diseases can cause or aggravate serious shortages in wartime, however, all the more so because then fewer varieties of crops are apt to be grown; their products, whether for food or other consumption, are urgently needed in greater quantity than usual; replacements or substitutes are hard to get or are unsatisfactory; diversion of chemicals necessary in the manufacture of fertilizers and fungicides to other use hampers control of parasitic and nonparasitic diseases; and the overloaded transportation facilities multiply the effects of all the other factors.

Diseases that bring illness and death to persons and animals that eat affected products make up a special category, of which ergot is a good example. Ergot is caused by a fungus that infects the flowers of many grasses, including the cereal grains, and replaces the seed kernels with its sclerotia. The sclerotia contain alkaloids, which have a powerful action on the nervous system and can produce gangrene or convulsions and, in severe cases, death.

Rye is especially susceptible to ergot. Ergotism in man is associated mostly with its use. In most of Europe throughout the Middle Ages rye was the main food cereal for many people. Many severe epidemics of ergotism cost thousands of lives. Later, after the cause became known, standards for permissible ergot content of grain made ergotism rare in human beings. In years favorable to ergot attack, infected grass in pastures frequently causes considerable loss of livestock, however, especially from abortion.

There is another side to the ergot story. The specific action of its alkaloid content makes it valuable in medicine, particularly in childbirth. Ergot is supplied commercially from several regions where the climate regularly favors it. Elsewhere in epidemic years a rye crop may be more valuable for its ergot content than for the grain. In regions where the climate does not favor ergot, or in times of scarce production, or when the regular source is shut off for some reason, artificial infection of rye fields is resorted to in order to obtain a supply of the drug. The only ergot used in medicine is rye ergot.

"Intoxicating bread," which produces symptoms of weakness, vertigo, headache, and nausea, results when bread is made from rye grain heavily infected with one or more species of *Fusarium*. Cases have occurred in Europe from time to time. "Scabby" grain, due to *Gibberella zeae*, so prevalent in warmer parts of our humid eastern and central region, is toxic to hogs; in epidemic years considerable loss of hogs follows feeding of infected grain, especially barley.

It should be noted that among all the thousands of plant diseases only an infinitesimal number cause harm to animals or man in any way other than through their effect on abundance of wanted products.

Famine and war shortages, tragic or dangerous though they may be, are really special instances of the importance of plant diseases. So also is toxicity to human beings or animals. Usually, the consequences are not so impressive, although in the long run they are as significant.

Many times in history a thriving agricultural industry has been threatened or destroyed because of severe losses caused by plant diseases. Recovery of a region so affected may be difficult. It involves, among other things, the search for an acceptable substitute crop equally adaptable to the region and equally profitable, the learning of new techniques of cultivation and handling, and the developments of markets for disposal of the new product. The change may never be completely successful, and as a consequence agriculture deteriorates or is abandoned. Perhaps soil or climate is particularly suited to the original crop and no other proves economically successful; or markets for an otherwise suitable crop may already be preempted; or the new crop itself be attacked by devastating disease. As a rule, a readjustment means much hardship for the affected populations, either the farmers themselves or persons otherwise employed in the crop industry.

Before 1870 Ceylon was preeminent in coffee production. The coffee rust fungus, a native parasite on wild coffee trees, about that time invaded the plantations and could not be controlled. The disease spread throughout the East, and yields dropped so low that the industry could not maintain itself. South America, particularly

Brazil, thereupon became the coffee empire of the world. Ceylon planters started growing the tea bush.

In our own country the virus disease peach yellows was a main factor in the great reduction in peach culture in Michigan, Maryland, and Delaware in the 1800's. Commercial production of peaches has never again attained the same importance there. In Berrien County, Mich., between 1874 and 1884, the acreage in peaches dropped from 6,000 to 500 acres, and the number of peach trees from 654,000 to fewer than 55,000. In 1920 there were only one-tenth as many peach trees in Delaware as there had been in 1890. In Maryland, Kent and Queen Annes Counties grew nearly one-half of the peaches in 1890, but only 5 percent in 1920. Not only did the disease ruin the peach industry; it also lowered the value of the farms. Before the onset of the disease, peach farms in northern Delaware sold for high prices, but usually paid for themselves in peaches within a few years. Fifteen or twenty years later they dropped to 50 to 80 dollars an acre. In some regions where the disease was most destructive, it was hard to sell a peach farm at any price.

The important sugar beet industry in the Western States was almost destroyed by another virus disease, curly top, until, after long research, resistant varieties were developed. An additional protection to both sugar beets and the many other plants affected by the curly top virus is the spraying of Russian-thistle, the most abundant overwintering host of the insect vector, with some of the new weed killers. Without resistant varieties and reduction in vector movement, curly top would make it impossible to produce profitably many of the important vegetables, including beans, tomatoes, and muskmelons, which harbor it.

One could go on and on, multiplying illustrations, big and little, temporary or permanent, past or present, mere threat or realized actuality. For instance: Pierce's disease of grapes in California; the deficiency diseases,

which are particularly important in Western States; cranberry false blossom in New Jersey; fire blight of pear, because of which "one of the greatest industries of the San Joaquin valley vanished like a dream"; verticillium wilt of cotton in the El Paso region of Texas; melon mosaic in the Imperial Valley of California; and many, many others throughout the world.

The essential feature of plant diseases however, is that they deprive everybody, not just farmers, of the plant products they destroy. The loss from all diseases of all crops is estimated to be about 10 percent. That is an average. Some crops suffer more loss.

Others are negligibly affected. The importance of any one disease depends on the value of the crop it attacks, the severity of the disease, and the ease with which it can be controlled.

Diseases that attack the basic food crops, such as the cereals, especially wheat and rice, potatoes, or others according to regional use, are naturally of greatest concern. Epidemics in the chief centers of production can cause scarcity, with serious national and (especially with wheat) international consequences. Prices of the affected crop and of substitutes for it go up. The amount of money available for buying other commodities, whether food or any other, consequently is reduced. It is a chain; in our present national and world economy, no part is separate.

For the farmer, the labor employed in planting and caring for an affected crop is wasted; income is reduced and uncertain. With epidemic diseases he may suffer disastrous losses in one season. The less variable diseases take a constant toll that in total amount could make the difference between success or failure in the long run. The lesser continual losses may be sufficient to prevent the building-up of reserve for emergencies, and thus the effects of the occasional severe losses are enhanced. The instability of farm income is reflected in the national condition. Losses from plant diseases do not stop when a product is harvested. Fruits and vegetables spoil in transportation, market, and storage. Infection may have started in the field before harvest or it may be acquired later. Whatever the reason, the food supply is further depleted and food bills increased.

If all the waste that is due to plant disease could be prevented, it would mean an increase of 10 percent over our present crop production, or, alternatively, 10 percent of the land could be used for other purposes or 10 percent of the farm population could engage in other occupations and we would still have as much of everything as we do now.

It should be emphasized that the plant disease situation is always changing. No matter how up-to-date our information, there is always some new problem to meet. Pathogens are as variable in genetic make-up as any other organism, and new races able to attack hitherto resistant varieties of crop plants appear frequently. Wheat stem rust is a familiar example. A crop variety developed for resistance to one pathogen may be extremely susceptible to a previously entirely negligible organism, as happened with the Victoria blight of oats that flared up so suddenly and destructively a few years ago. Pathogens are carried from country to country in many ways and in spite of careful precautions. Examples of entry into this country are numerous. White pine blister rust is one; potato bacterial ring rot is another.

A grower, noting accounts of disease causing devastation in some other place, may consider that it has nothing to do with him, since crops in his region or his own fields are not affected; perhaps, even, he may rejoice because scarcity has led to higher prices for his own crop. Temporarily he may be justified, but it is never safe for growers or regions to be complacent about freedom of their crops from plant diseases. To maintain this position takes constant watchfulness.

If nothing could be done about plant diseases, there would be little point in discussing their importance. We would just have to take the loss and get along with it as best we could. We have seen how that works in some instances. We do know how to reduce the effects of most diseases, however. Increasing our knowledge about diseases will allow us to gain more advantage over them, provided we make use of it. The available control measures are not nearly so often or so efficiently used as they should be.

Diseases are too often taken for granted until irreparable harm has been done. Recognition of their importance is the first step in doing something about them.

JESSIE I. WOOD *is an associate pathologist in the Plant Disease Survey, Bureau of Plant Industry, Soils, and Agricultural Engineering. She obtained her master's degree from Stanford University in 1916 and has been with the Department of Agriculture since 1919.*

Ergot sclerotia and barley kernels.

Bacteria—
Small and
Mighty

A. J. Riker, A. C. Hildebrandt

Bacteria are an important part of the world we live in. They cause diseases in man such as tuberculosis, typhoid fever, and diphtheria, and in animals such as anthrax, brucellosis, and swine erysipelas.

Many bacteria are helpful to man. They produce useful food and chemicals, assist in the decomposition of wastes, and increase the fertility of soil. Most of us know about the nitrogen-accumulating root nodules of clover, alfalfa, and other legumes that are produced by bacteria growing in their roots.

Bacteria also cause disease in plants. The discovery of this role was made only 75 years ago. After Louis Pasteur proved that bacteria could produce animal disease, Professor T. J. Burrill, of Illinois, who studied in Europe, was filled with enthusiasm. He began working with a devastating disease of unknown cause that was sweeping through pear and apple orchards of the Midwest. Burrill soon proved that the disease, which we now call fire blight, was caused by bacteria. Burrill's brilliant pioneer discovery swept aside earlier speculation and ignorance. It pointed the way.

But Burrill's work did not go unchallenged. Many doubters spoke up. Dr. Erwin F. Smith and his associates of the United States Department of Agriculture carried the work forward meanwhile. They overcame the opposition, scorn, and derision of some distinguished scientists. They proved that bacteria caused many plant diseases. Such researches provided a solid background for later work on plant bacteria. In his book, *Bacterial Diseases of Plants*, in 1920 Dr. Smith summarized much of this work. Now we have knowledge of more than 170 different kinds of bacteria, which cause diseases in flowering plants belonging to 150 genera of 50 families.

Among living agents that cause plant disease, bacteria are perhaps the smallest (if we do not consider viruses as living). Such bacteria are so minute that about 25,000 laid side by side and 8,000 to 12,000 laid end to end would not measure more than an inch.

Each bacterial cell is an independent plant. If many cells adhere to one another, a mass of cells may be formed. But each cell acts independently; the numbers of bacterial cells increase when the cells cut themselves into two. They multiply by dividing, so to speak. Under favorable circumstances reproduction by cell division may happen as often as three times in an hour, and enormous numbers of bacteria may be produced within 2 or 3 days.

The large surface area of each bacterial cell and the myriad bacteria usually present in diseased plants give the invading bacteria a great advantage as they attack the cells of the affected plant. That helps to explain the rapid progress a bacterial disease makes under favorable conditions.

Their survival depends upon their ability to utilize the living or dead organic compounds they find in their host plants.

The bacteria that live only on dead animal or plant remains are termed saprophytes. Those that produce disease are parasites or pathogens. Many kinds of bacteria, especially those that cause plant disease, can live either as parasites or as saprophytes. Many disease-inciting bacteria are able to overwinter or maintain themselves between successive susceptible crops by living saprophytically on plant refuse.

Bacteria that induce plant disease

are all more or less short and cylindrical. They are described as rodlike. None is spherical like the coccus forms, which cause some animal or human diseases. Some species of plant parasitic bacteria have one to several filamentous, or hairlike, motile appendages called flagella, which they can wave or vibrate and by them move for short distances in water or in plant juices. Some kinds have flagella at one end or both ends (polar). Still others develop flagella at many places on the surface of the cell (peritrichous). Even those that have no flagella, however, can be carried rapidly from one place to another by flowing or splashing water, or by wind-blown droplets of moisture, by insects, and by various agricultural operations. Any agricultural practice that involves the transport of soil may serve to carry pathogenic bacteria from one place to another.

Bacteria gain entrance to plants through uninjured tissue, natural openings, and wounds. The potato scab organism usually enters through lenticels but can penetrate thin-skinned tubers directly. Root-nodule bacteria of legumes enter through the fragile root hairs. The small natural openings to the atmosphere—the stomata—in the leaves are the ports of entrance for the bacteria that cause angular leaf spot of cotton. The bean blight organism may also enter through stomata. The bacteria that cause blackleg of cabbage enter through hydathodes. Hydathodes, if present, usually are found at the edge or tip of the leaf. They are specialized gland cells that excrete fluids. Often under highly humid conditions small droplets of water may be seen adhering to the margins of such leaves as cabbage or wheat. As these droplets later may be resorbed by the leaf, any bacteria present may also gain entrance and multiply. The bacteria that cause fire blight of pear, apple, and quince trees enter at blossomtime through the specialized cells of the flower that produce nectar. This type of environment is especially suited to the growth and multiplication of the parasites.

Many kinds of bacteria enter their host plants through wounds. Those producing soft rots of fruits and vegetables and the species causing crown gall of several kinds of plants are good examples.

Once bacteria get into a plant, some may be carried along with or move in the sap stream. Others may move short distances in plant juices by swimming or be pulled about by the movement of fluids between or in the cells. Capillary attraction and changes in the pressures and tensions on fluids that sometimes flood the spaces between the cells move the bacteria from place to place inside the plant. Flooding of plant tissues often increases as certain bacteria withdraw liquid from plant cells bordering the invaded tissue. In early stages of disease, bacteria commonly develop in the spaces between the cells. But as cell walls are injured and the cells of the plant are killed, they become perforated by bacterial action. Then the bacteria may penetrate inside the cells and continue the disintegration.

PLANTS RESPOND in many ways to invasion by bacteria. Their response often is so specific that the disease they cause can be identified by the symptoms. Among the symptoms of bacterial infections are galls, wilts, slow growth, dwarfing, imperfect fruits or ears, rots, color changes of various plant parts, retarded ripening, distortion of leaves, cankers, brooming, fasciation, and leaf spots. Rots may be either localized at one place or in one tissue or may involve the whole plant. Wilts generally affect the whole plant. Galls often affect only a part of the plant.

Among the many well-known bacterial galls are olive knot, cane gall, beet pocket rot, sweet pea fasciation, hairy root, and crown gall. All contain large swollen cells and small, rapidly dividing cells along with vascular cells in a relatively disorganized arrangement. Eventually these gall structures may interfere with the normal transmission of water and food supplies, and the plants may wilt and die. Of these, crown gall, which has a very wide host range, has been studied extensively because of the opportunity it provides for clarifying basic principles of diseased growth as a biological phenomenon. The legume root nodules are usually beneficial through their ability to fix nitrogen. They have great economic importance.

Bacterial wilts may be quite destructive—for example, in sweet corn, cucumber, tobacco, and related plants. Such bacteria may produce a slime, which helps to plug the water-conducting tissue of the invaded plant. Closely related are such diseases as black rot of cabbage, ring rot of potatoes, and tomato canker, which may start in the water-conducting tissue but subsequently result in disintegration of surrounding tissue.

Cankers develop from the extensive tissue destruction, for example, by the fire blight bacteria, or from the lesions of the tomato canker organism. This latter bacterium may produce only local spots on the tomato fruits. Thus the symptoms induced by one organism may be quite different, depending on the plant tissue infected and other variables.

Local spots occur most commonly on the leaves, but sometimes appear elsewhere, as, for example, on many fruits. Symptoms of black arm of cotton show when the angular leaf spot bacteria enter the stem and girdle it. Bacterial blight of beans, halo blight of oats, potato scab, and many others appear primarily as local spots. The bacteria causing halo blight of oats and wildfire of tobacco produce toxic substances that are responsible for the yellowish areas immediately around the dead spots where the bacteria have invaded the tissue.

Soft rots develop in relatively fleshy tissues when certain bacteria invade them extensively. Such bacteria produce an enzyme that dissolves the pectic substance that cements plant cell walls together. The result is a slimy, often foul-smelling mass. The cell-wall-dissolving enzymes and toxins often destroy cells and tissues a short distance ahead of the bacteria that produce them. The soft rots often follow and extend invasion and damage by some other pathogen. For example, black rot of cabbage and late blight of potatoes would be much less serious except for the subsequent soft rot.

Symptoms of disease appear at varying lengths of time after bacteria attack and grow in a plant. Soft rots are sometimes evident within a day or so, angular leaf spot of cotton within 10 days, corn wilt within 1 to 2 months. Crown gall of orange may take 2 years. The time between first establishment of bacteria or fungi in the plant and the appearance of symptoms of disease is called the incubation period.

In some diseases bacterial ooze comes to the surface of affected plant parts. The exudate is often slimy and sticky and contains numberless bacteria. The ooze may come out of stomata or other natural openings, or may form on the surface of cankers or other lesions.

WE RECOGNIZE three major variables that influence the eventual severity of an outbreak of disease—the host plant, the pathogen, and environmental conditions. They form an eternal triangle, each affecting the other within certain limits.

The variables among the host plants are substantial and important. They make possible selection and breeding for disease resistance. The origin of disease-resistant breeding material, plant structures that affect resistance, and control of disease through the use of disease-resistant plants are discussed in detail in other articles in the Yearbook. All ages of plants are affected from the seedling stage through to maturity. Fruits and seeds may be attacked. Juiciness of tissue, however, may predispose a plant to severe attacks by bacteria.

The relationship of the pathogenic

bacteria to the host plant involves a chain of events, each link of which may be critical in determining the severity of an epidemic. Among the more important parts of this chain are the entrance of the bacteria into the host plant, their establishment within the plant tissues, their exit again to the surface of the plant, and their distribution to another plant. This chain of events may be repeated over and over again during a growing season. Moreover, the bacteria must be able to overwinter successfully if the epidemic is to develop the next year. Overwintering may be accomplished in the seed (bean blight, cabbage black rot); in tissue of perennial plants (fire blight of pear and apple, crown gall of brambles, roses, and many other kinds of plants); plant refuse (tomato wilt, potato ring rot); or the soil (crown gall, tomato wilt).

An understanding of the cyclic chain of events necessary to produce a severe outbreak of disease often enables us to select its weakest link and suggests ways of breaking the infection cycle and thus of controlling a disease. Because infected seed carry the organisms causing bean blight and cabbage black rot from one crop year to the next, we can use disease-free seed to break the chain and avoid heavy losses from those diseases. The bacteria that cause cucumber wilt are carried from plant to plant by cucumber beetles, and so control measures for the wilt include spraying to control the beetles. Losses from other diseases can be reduced through treatment of seed, selection of disease-resistant stock, and crop rotation. More effective, less expensive, and more easily applied control measures are needed for many diseases, however.

A later article explains how the variability of fungi affects the control of plant diseases. We know much less about variability in the plant disease bacteria. The vigorous pathogens apparently survive in largest numbers. This continual selection makes pathogenicity—the ability to cause disease—possibly the most stable characteristic in nature.

BACTERIAL DISEASES of plants occur in almost every place that is reasonably moist or warm. Their destructiveness varies from year to year and place to place. A part of this variation can be attributed to presence or absence of a critical environmental condition under which the bacteria operate on the host plant.

Along with temperature, moisture is extremely important. Abundant water in the soil and high relative humidity in the air encourage the plants to take in as much liquid as possible. The leaves are usually covered easily with water and any chemicals that might resist bacterial action are diluted. This often predisposes the cells to pathogenic invasion. Likewise, under those conditions, the stomata of the leaves may be wide open. Many of the pathogenic bacteria are spread from one plant to another by the distribution of splashing rain and running water. In fact, under the influence of beating rain, leaves may become partly watersoaked. Then most any soil bacterium—particularly a pathogenic form—is able to grow and to produce a necrotic lesion. Conversely, carrots and potatoes, for example, that have dried properly after digging are quite resistant to soft rot.

Temperature has an especially important part in the development of most bacterial diseases. This is seen in the tomato wilt disease, which may be present in various plantings but may not become epidemic until the warm weather raises the temperature of the soil. Bean blight is also a high-temperature disease. Infection, however, may actually take place over a wide range of temperatures, but the high temperature is needed for typical symptoms. Temperature is likewise a critical item in the development or lack of development of crown gall. Tomato plants grown at 89° F. failed to develop galls while those at 82° produced typically large cells. Air and soil temperatures are important for the tomato canker disease which develops best at a soil temperature of 82°. Cold storage effectively inhibits the bacterial rots that develop so rapidly with suitable warmth.

Mineral nutrition may influence disease development. Stewart's wilt disease of corn increases as the nitrogen level increases, within limits. At high levels of nitrogen, infected plants die in a few weeks. Virulent strains of this bacterium grow well on inorganic nitrogen, while avirulent strains require organic nitrogen. Weakly and highly virulent strains are equally destructive in nitrogen-deficient plants, but highly virulent strains are much more so in plants that receive liberal amounts of nitrogen. The tomato wilt disease is affected strikingly by the nutrient level of the plants.

The number of hours of sunlight during any season of the year also influences disease development. In the greenhouse less tomato wilt develops during an 18-hour day (simulating summer conditions) than under a 12-hour day (winter or spring conditions).

Nutrition, length of daylight, and temperature are all closely associated in the development of disease conditions. It is hard to assess the intensity of the effects of each taken alone. The three conditions influence the balance of inorganic and organic nitrogen and the carbohydrate supply in the plant sap and thereby favor or inhibit the pathogenic bacteria, depending on their requirements.

IN STUDIES of bacterial plant diseases, the scientist must identify the organism causing the disease and be certain that his cultures have not become contaminated with an unwanted species. Studies under the microscope of properly prepared samples of the growth developing in cultures and of bacterial ooze or tissue from diseased plants furnish some evidence.

Because the simple cells of the pathogenic bacteria are so similar in appearance, however, additional tests of the effects of their action on various substances must be used to identify them. Their type of growth and colony formation on various semisolid or liquid culture media in petri plates or test tubes, their ability to ferment selected nutrient substances or to produce acids or gas on them, and their ability to withstand more or less unfavorable physical conditions (such as high and low temperatures or certain chemicals) are among the reactions that are commonly used in identification. Their ability to cause plant diseases is the factor chiefly responsible for our present interest in them. That factor also is an aid in identifying an unknown organism.

TO DETERMINE the identity of bacteria, one has to have laboratory equipment for making culture media and maintaining cultures, for microscopic examinations, and for various physiological determinations.

Suitable precautions and special techniques also are necessary to get and maintain cultures and media that are free from contaminations.

The Committee on Bacteriological Technique of the Society of American Bacteriologists, Biotech Publications, Geneva, N. Y., publishes a series of frequently revised leaflets about the latest techniques. Most up-to-date bacteriologists follow Bergey's *Manual of Determinative Bacteriology*, published by Williams and Wilkins, Baltimore, Md., as the standard textbook on identification. The sixth edition of this book was published in 1948. In that manual the plant pathogenic bacteria are classified into seven genera—*Agrobacterium*, *Bacterium*, *Corynebacterium*, *Erwinia*, *Pseudomonas*, *Streptomyces*, and *Xanthomonas*.

Charlotte Elliott, a former associate of Dr. Erwin F. Smith in the Department of Agriculture, wrote a book, *Manual of Bacterial Plant Pathogens*. The second edition, published in 1951 by the Chronica Botanica Company, of Waltham, Mass., gives the names and descriptions of plant pathogenic bacteria, their reactions on culture media, symptoms of the diseases they produce, their host plants, geographical distribution, control methods if known, and citations to research literature.

How DOES a plant pathologist make sure that a plant disease is caused by a given species of bacterium? Robert Koch in 1882 worked out the rules of proof to follow for animal diseases. The rigid logic of his requirements applies equally well to bacteria causing plant disease.

Briefly stated, the postulates of Koch require that: (1) The bacterium must be associated in every case with the disease, and conversely the disease must not appear without it. (2) The micro-organism must be isolated in pure culture and its specific morphological and physiological characteristics determined. (3) When the host is inoculated with the bacterium under favorable conditions, the characteristic symptoms of the disease must develop. (4) The micro-organism must be reisolated from the inoculated plant and identified as that first isolated from the diseased host.

In this brief review we have not attempted to present detailed information on individual diseases. Losses caused by various important bacterial diseases, symptoms, means of spread and control measures when known are given in other articles on specific crops.

A. J. RIKER *is a member of the department of plant pathology, University of Wisconsin. He has made many contributions to our knowledge of bacterial diseases of plants and has conducted research on the basic reasons for diseased growth. Dr. Riker is also an authority on the diseases of forest trees.*
A. C. HILDEBRANDT, *also of the department of plant pathology, University of Wisconsin, conducts research on fundamental phases of bacterial diseases of plants with special emphasis on factors affecting the growth of organisms and plant tissue in culture media.*

Viruses, a Scourge of Mankind

C. W. Bennett

Few kinds of living organisms are immune to viruses. Man, domesticated and wild animals, insects, plants, and even bacteria succumb to their attack. They have been a scourge of mankind since before the dawn of recorded history. Smallpox, for example, existed in China in 1700 B. C. Measles, mumps, influenza, and scarlet fever are other virus diseases that plague humans.

The virus diseases of plants also probably have existed for many centuries. Their importance on crop plants has increased tremendously in the past 50 years—since 1900 more than 200 new plant viruses have been discovered. Many of them have done widespread damage to crop plants.

Curly top caused almost complete abandonment of the sugar beet industry in parts of western United States from 1916 to 1932 and still causes severe injury to tomatoes, beans, and a number of other crops. Sugarcane mosaic caused extensive losses to the sugarcane industry in the United States, Argentina, Brazil, and other countries beginning about 1917. Spotted wilt has become widespread and now causes losses to tomato and other crops in many parts of the world. Since 1940, swollen shoot has caused extensive damage to the cacao industry of west Africa. Virus diseases of citrus have become more destructive and from 1936 to 1946 tristeza caused the loss of 7 million orange trees in the state of São Paulo, Brazil, alone. It has attacked or now threatens other millions of trees in various tropical and subtropical areas.

This increase in destructiveness of virus diseases and in the number of known viruses has come about largely as a result of the expansion of agricultural enterprises and the increased movement of plants and plant products in recent years.

Disease-producing agents—particularly viruses—apparently have originated in local areas all over the world. Probably through long association have native plants developed a tolerance to the local viruses that enables infected individuals to survive with little injury and often with but little evidence of being carriers of viruses.

When crop plants are introduced into areas where they have not been grown before, they frequently become subject to infection with the native viruses, against which they have had no opportunity to develop resistance. Such a virus may cause extensive losses to a crop plant, not only in the areas of original distribution of the virus, but also in the other areas to which it may spread on the recently attacked crop plant.

The appearance of the yellow wilt virus on sugar beet in the Rio Negro Valley of Argentina when attempts were made to develop a sugar beet industry there in 1929 probably is a typical example of the transfer of a virus from wild plants to a new crop plant. From the beginning of the attempt to establish the sugar beet industry there, the sugar beets were attacked by a virus disease, previously unknown on sugar beet or on any other plant. It caused a yellowing, wilting, and death of all infected plants. Injury was so severe that attempts to grow sugar beets were abandoned about 10 years later after considerable loss to growers and processors. This disease appears still to be limited to South America, but it continues to constitute a potential threat to sugar beets elsewhere.

Many plant viruses have spread over extensive areas from their points of origin. The movement of the tristeza virus of citrus is an example of the extensive spread of a destructive virus disease. Tristeza virus probably originated in South Africa or in southwestern Asia. For many years, possibly for centuries, it appears to have had a limited distribution but since 1930 it (or a similar malady or maladies) has been reported in Australia, Java, California, Louisiana, Argentina, Uruguay, and Brazil. Apparently the chief method of long-distance spread has been by means of infected budwood or nursery stock moved from infested to noninfested areas. After it was introduced into Brazil and Argentina it was spread rapidly by the oriental citrus aphid, *Aphis citricidus*.

Virus diseases produce a wide range of symptoms and types of injury on plants. Sometimes they kill the plant in a short time, as with spotted wilt and curly top on tomato. More often they cause lesser injuries that result in reduced yields and lower quality of product. With respect to general type of the symptoms produced, most viruses are of two rather clearly defined groups: Those that cause mottling or spotting of leaves and those that cause a yellowing, leaf curling, dwarfing, or excessive branching, but little or no mottling or spotting.

The first group, by far the larger, includes such important viruses as those causing cucumber mosaic, peach mosaic, and the tomato spotted wilt. Mosaic diseases are characterized by the production of chlorotic, or yellowish, areas in the leaves and sometimes in the blossoms and other parts. The chlorotic areas may be more or less circular or they may be irregular. The spots vary in size from very small areas to large blotches. Sometimes the chlorotic areas cover a large share, or even all, of the surface of individual leaves.

Some of the mosaic viruses cause conspicuous mottling, spotting, or striping of petals of flowers of some ornamental plants. Many of the variegated tulips are only virus-infected plants of nonvariegated varieties. The Rembrandt variety is a virus-infected strain of the variety Princess Elizabeth. Variegation, or "breaking," of blossoms due to viruses commonly occurs also in wallflower, stock, gladiolus, and flowering peach.

The attractively variegated leaves of the ornamental shrub *Abutilon striatum* are also the result of a virus infection. In the United States the causal virus apparently has no insect vector and variegated and nonvariegated plants of *A. striatum* grow side by side indefinitely with no spread of the variegated condition to the nonvariegated plants. In Brazil the virus is transmitted by the whitefly, *Bemisia tabaci*, and there healthy plants may soon become variegated.

Other mosaic-type viruses cause circular or irregular necrotic—dying—or chlorotic spots on leaves, stems, and fruits, as in spotted wilt on tomato. Ring spots and oak-leaf patterns are symptoms of other virus diseases.

Some viruses produce all these types of symptoms and others as well under specific conditions or on different host plants.

Diseases of the leaf curl and yellows group are caused by viruses that appear to be associated with the vascular system of the plant and produce symptoms that are characteristic of disturbances in this type of tissue. With the leaf curl diseases, such as raspberry leaf curl, sugar beet curly top, and tobacco leaf curl, growth of veins is retarded and the leaves roll or become crinkled. Leaves are sometimes deeper green than normal. The yellows types, such as aster yellows and sugar beet yellow wilt, cause yellowing, stunting, and various types of leaf deformations. Other diseases, such as strawberry stunt, cause dwarfing of the plant and some leaf rolling and thickening. Still others stimulate the production of clusters of thin, wiry shoots as in witches'-broom of oceanspray, or they cause the production of wiry shoots on stems or on main limbs and trunks if

trees are attacked. Viruses of the leaf curl and yellows group seem to persist in their insect vectors for longer periods than do viruses of the mosaic group.

Some viruses produce symptoms only under certain environmental conditions or on certain host plants or host combinations. Red raspberry mosaic causes mottling only on leaves produced at low temperatures. Symptoms usually appear therefore only on leaves formed in early spring or late fall. Curly top virus is present in many plants of tree tobacco, *Nicotiana glauca*, in California, but no symptoms are evident. Tristeza virus produces marked symptoms only on citrus trees of certain top and root combinations. For example, both sweet and sour orange trees grow well even though infected with the tristeza virus. Also, trees of sour orange that are grafted onto sweet orange rootstocks show little evidence of injury. However, if the positions of the two types of orange are reversed in the grafted tree so that the top of the tree is of sweet orange and the rootstock is of sour orange, the tristeza virus causes yellowing and dropping of the leaves, gradual dying back of twigs, production of weak shoots on the main limbs, and eventual death of the tree.

Plants may be infected with two or more viruses at the same time. When a plant with one virus disease is attacked by another, usually symptoms of the second disease are merely superimposed on those produced by the first. Occasionally, however, infection by two viruses results in added symptoms. An example is double-virus streak in tomato caused by infection with both tobacco mosaic virus and potato virus X. Tobacco mosaic virus causes mottling and a certain amount of dwarfing. Potato virus X induces mild mottling. When both viruses are present in the same tomato plant a marked increase in injury occurs with the production of extensive necrosis on leaves and stems not characteristic of either virus alone.

Transmission of virus diseases may be

brought about in a number of different ways. Under experimental conditions, many of the mosaic-type viruses can be transmitted mechanically by rubbing juice from diseased plants over the surface of leaves of healthy plants. The addition of a small amount of an abrasive such as carborundum to the juice frequently increases the amount of infection. This method of transmission is of great value in studies of properties, characteristics, and host range of viruses. The majority of viruses, however, have not been transmitted by juice inoculation.

Transmission of sugar beet curly top virus and cucumber mosaic virus by means of dodder, *Cuscuta subinclusa*, was reported in 1940, and a number of other viruses have been transmitted since by it and other species.

The species of dodder used for virus transmission are members of a group of interesting parasitic seed plants belonging to the same family as morning-glory and sweetpotato. They sometimes cause extensive injury by parasitizing clover, alfalfa, and other plants. They attach themselves to their host plants by a type of natural graft union. Because species of dodder have extensive host ranges, plants widely different botanically may be united by a type of natural graft in which dodder forms a connecting link through which several viruses have been found to pass. Thus dodder provides a medium through which viruses may be transferred from diseased to healthy species that cannot be infected by juice inoculation or by insect vectors.

Under field conditions only a few viruses are disseminated by mechanical transfer. Most natural spread takes place through the use of infected vegetative parts for propagation, through infected seeds, and by insects.

The virus of tobacco mosaic probably is the only plant virus spread extensively and chiefly by mechanical means. It occurs in such high concentrations in infected plants, persists for such long periods in infested plant material, and is so easily spread by contact that extensive transmission in tobacco may occur in operations involving handling plants at planting time and in the cultural operations throughout the growing season. Also, it is spread in greenhouse tomatoes when they are cultivated, pruned, tied to supports, or harvested.

Propagation of plants by vegetative means results in the spread of many virus diseases. Most viruses invade plants so extensively that they occur in all parts of the plant, and many of them undoubtedly invade nearly all of the living cells. When buds or scions from virus-infected plants are used for propagation, the new plants are nearly always infected. Likewise, the tubers, roots, offshoots, or other vegetative parts used for propagation carry all of the viruses present in the parent plant. For this reason transmission by vegetative propagation is important in the dissemination of virus diseases of strawberry, raspberry, potato, tree fruits, and many ornamentals. Most of the viruses of those plants are spread by other agencies as well.

Seed transmission of viruses occurs only in relatively few cases. Seeds, for the most part, have a remarkably effective mechanism that prevents the passage of virus into the young embryo from the mother plant. The nature of this mechanism is imperfectly understood, but its effectiveness may be illustrated by the reaction of sugar beet to curly top virus. The curly top virus is known to spread throughout the plant, and seeds of diseased plants carry high concentrations of virus. Despite this fact, however, the virus does not enter the embryo and the infected seeds always produce virus-free plants.

Even the relatively few viruses known to be seed-borne, such as bean mosaic virus, cucumber mosaic virus, lettuce mosaic virus, peach ring spot virus, and dodder latent mosaic virus, are carried only in a portion of the seeds of diseased plants. In most instances, in fact, only a low percentage of such seeds produce infected plants.

Transmission in seed, however, may be important, particularly with diseases like lettuce mosaic, a few diseased seedlings of which may be the source for extensive spread by insects.

Some of the seed-borne viruses are carried in the pollen. When healthy bean plants are fertilized by pollen from mosaic plants, a certain proportion of seeds from the healthy plants produce diseased seedlings. This, however, appears not to be an important method of virus spread.

Insects are by far the most important agents of transmission. Few viruses could persist for long without them.

PROPERTIES AND CHARACTERISTICS of plant viruses have been subjects of study and speculation for many years. Information has increased with more extensive investigations and with the development of new techniques and instruments.

It was learned more than 50 years ago that viruses are very minute entities capable of passing filters so fine that they retained common forms of bacteria and that viruses apparently do not increase outside of living cells.

Further studies made in plants and with plant juices revealed that viruses vary widely in their reactions to a number of environmental conditions. Many appear to be inactivated almost immediately in juice after it is pressed from diseased plants. This probably accounts in part for the fact that many viruses cannot be transmitted by juice inoculation. Other viruses retain activity in plant juice for different periods. Cucumber mosaic virus remains active for only a few hours, sugar beet mosaic virus for 1 to 2 days, and curly top virus for 2 to 5 days. Tobacco mosaic virus is much more resistant, however, and may retain its activity in juice from diseased tobacco plants for several months.

Some viruses that can be transmitted by the juice cannot be recovered from diseased plants after they are dried. Others retain activity in dried plants longer than in plant juice. Curly top

virus was recovered from dry sugar beet plants after 8 years, and tobacco mosaic virus has retained its activity in dried tobacco leaves for more than 50 years.

Peach yellows virus is sensitive to high temperatures and can be inactivated in young peach trees by growing them at a temperature of 95° F. for 3 weeks or by immersing dormant trees in water at 122° for 10 minutes. It is destroyed by summer temperatures that prevail for extended periods in some parts of the United States. Aster yellows virus also is inactivated at relatively low temperatures, and its spread is reported to be more extensive in the spring and fall than during the summer because of inactivation of the virus in the leafhopper vector during periods of high temperatures. Most viruses, however, have thermal inactivation points well above the temperatures required to kill the host plants. Some viruses are very resistant to heat. Sugar beet curly top virus is inactivated between 167° and 176°, and tobacco mosaic virus is not inactivated until the temperature rises to 192°.

As a rule, the viruses resist the action of the common germicides. Usually they are not inactivated by the concentrations of bichloride of mercury, carbolic acid, copper, formaldehyde, and alcohol that kill most bacteria. Curiously enough, tobacco mosaic virus, in other respects one of the most stable of viruses, is easily inactivated with alcohol.

The isolation and purification of the tobacco mosaic virus by Dr. W. M. Stanley in 1932 opened the way for more direct and more comprehensive studies of the nature and characteristics of viruses than had been possible by use of earlier methods. The purification of tobacco mosaic virus was soon followed by purification of other plant viruses, some by chemical means and others by sedimentation in high-speed centrifuges.

Most of the viruses that have been obtained in relatively pure condition have been found to aggregate to form crystals or crystal-like bodies that are readily visible under low magnification. Some are even large enough to be seen with the unaided eye. The crystals differ in size and shape depending on the virus and the conditions under which they are formed. Crystals of tobacco mosaic virus are needle-shaped; those of tobacco necrosis virus lozenge-shaped, and those of tomato bushy stunt virus are dodecahedral.

Even after viruses were purified, the virus particles themselves could not be seen because their sizes are below the limits of resolution of the ordinary microscope. That deficiency was overcome with the perfection of the electron microscope, which utilizes radiations of shorter wavelength than those of light. This microscope permitted particles in the size range of viruses to be photographed. For the first time it was possible to determine what viruses look like in photographs, even if not actually to see them.

The plant viruses that have been photographed by means of the electron microscope, numbering a dozen or more, extend over a considerable range in size and shape. Some are long, straight, or tenuous rods. Some are shorter rods. Others are spherical. Tobacco mosaic virus particles are relatively straight rods about 15 millimicrons in thickness and varying in length up to 300 millimicrons, or more. (One millimicron is one-millionth of a millimeter or about one twenty-five-millionth of an inch.) The potato virus X also has rodlike particles, which vary greatly in length and appear to be more flexible than the tobacco mosaic virus particles. Among the viruses that appear to have spherical particles are alfalfa mosaic virus, with a diameter of about 17 millimicrons; tobacco ring spot virus, with a diameter of about 19 millimicrons; and bushy stunt virus, with a diameter of about 26 millimicrons.

The smallest plant viruses are somewhat smaller than some protein molecules. The largest ones are smaller than the smallest known bacteria.

Thus, viruses as a group cover a size range between chemical molecules and bacteria, with some overlapping in the lower size range.

All plant viruses so far isolated are similar in chemical composition and contain two essential constituents, nucleic acid and protein.

Nearly all of the plant viruses that have been studied extensively have been found to be complexes of strains. The strains vary in virulence, kind of disease produced, host range, or other characteristics. Curly top virus and tobacco mosaic virus are made up of innumerable strains. Some of these are weak and cause little injury even on susceptible plants. Others are more virulent and cause severe injury. Some strains of curly top virus attack tobacco and tomato; others do not. Two strains of potato yellow dwarf virus appear to be transmitted by different specific vectors.

It may be assumed that these strains have arisen, one by one, from parent strains during the course of years by a process similar to mutation. The relatively large numbers of strains of some of the more common viruses may indicate that some viruses are less stable than others, under the environmental conditions to which they are subjected, hence mutate more readily. This tendency to mutate gives to viruses a degree of adaptability that may be comparable to that possessed by plants and animals.

Recovery from the more severe phases of virus disease is a rather common phenomenon in plants but is limited usually to partial or complete recovery from obvious symptoms and very rarely extends to loss of the virus by infected plants.

One of the first examples of recovery to be discovered was that of the recovery of tobacco from ring spot. A few days after plants become infected with this virus, marked necrosis is produced on a ring of new leaves, but subsequent growth is normal or nearly normal. Plants from cuttings of recovered plants remain free of severe symptoms, and the diseased plants may be propagated indefinitely by vegetative means without the reappearance of the severe phase of the disease.

Turkish tobacco recovers to a very high degree from curly top. Tomato plants are killed by curly top if the virus is introduced by means of the beet leafhopper; if it is introduced by means of scions from recovered tobacco, however, they usually show only mild symptoms.

Water pimpernel, *Samolus parviflorus*, also shows a high degree of recovery from most strains of curly top virus. Recovery in sugar beet is much less marked. Plants of susceptible varieties usually show little evidence of improvement after they become diseased.

With some viruses and perhaps with most of them, infection by one strain protects against infection or injury from a second strain of the same virus, but no protection is afforded against infection with a totally different virus. Protection of this type is very marked between strains of the tobacco mosaic virus. Juice from a plant with tobacco mosaic, when rubbed gently over the surface of a leaf of a healthy plant of *Nicotiana sylvestris*, produces many small necrotic lesions, which mark points of separate infections. If the inoculated plant has already been invaded by a strain of tobacco mosaic virus, however, no lesions are produced by reinoculation with a second strain of the same virus.

After recovery from one strain of curly top virus, Turkish tobacco plants are very resistant to injury by other strains of this virus. Also, when tomato plants are inoculated with one strain of the curly top virus by means of scions from recovered tobacco plants, they are very resistant to injury by most other strains. Tomato plants "immunized" in this way have been grown successfully under field conditions where all the nonprotected plants were killed.

In contrast, the plants of *Nicotiana glutinosa* and water pimpernel, although they recover from the severe effects of most strains of the curly top virus, are not protected against injury by strains of the virus more virulent than the one already present. No strain of curly top virus offers appreciable protection against either infection or injury in sugar beet.

Although protection between related strains of some viruses is not always evident or complete, cross-protection tests have been of value in identification and classification of viruses from different sources and host plants.

The cross-protection phenomenon may prove to be of value also in certain phases of control of virus disease, particularly diseases such as swollen shoot of cacao and tristeza of citrus. Where either is present, it is known that all susceptible trees must sooner or later become infected from virus sources that are impossible to eliminate. Since this is true, it may prove worth while first to infect all the young planting stock with a weak and relatively harmless strain of virus in order to protect against later infection by more virulent strains of the same virus.

After a plant is infected with a virus disease nothing, as a rule, can be done to restore its health. Therefore, methods of control are directed almost wholly toward prevention of infection or toward development of disease-resistant varieties.

Many practices and precautions are employed to prevent infection with virus diseases. Control of mosaic on tobacco and tomato is obtained largely by avoiding spread of virus by contact during transplanting and cultural operations. Fortunately, few of the virus diseases are so easily transmitted and ordinary cultural operations can be carried on with most plants without danger of spreading virus diseases by contact.

Destruction of plants that serve as sources of infection is of value in the control of a number of virus diseases. Spring infection of fields of sugar beets with mosaic and virus yellows comes largely from infected beets that survive the winter or from beets that are carried through the winter for seed production. Elimination of such sources of virus usually gives a high degree of control. The spread of X-disease on peach can be prevented by removing all infected chokecherries within 500 feet of peach orchards, and the virus diseases of raspberries can be controlled, in most instances, by destroying all wild and escaped brambles in the immediate vicinity of plantings, provided the plantings themselves are not already infected.

Reducing the population of insect vectors by spraying or by other means has value in the control of some virus diseases. Usually it is not possible, however, to reduce the insect populations sufficiently or soon enough to obtain completely satisfactory results. Some virus diseases can be partly controlled by destruction of the hosts of the insect vectors. Extensive reduction of the weed hosts of the beet leafhopper in the Western States would correspondingly reduce the amount of curly top virus carried from desert plants to cultivated fields. In much of this area, reduction in weed hosts comes about naturally under systems of land management in which annual and perennial grasses and other nonhost plants are allowed to replace the weed hosts of the beet leafhopper. Fall spraying to kill leafhoppers on weeds in uncultivated areas has been resorted to also in the program to control curly top.

Virus-free nursery stock is extremely important in the control of virus diseases of strawberry and raspberry. Natural virus spread often is not extensive enough to cause serious damage during the life of plantings started with virus-free nursery stock. That is true also of some of the virus diseases of tree fruits.

C. W. BENNETT *is a pathologist of the division of sugar plant investigations, Bureau of Plant Industry, Soils, and Agricultural Engineering, who has had more than 30 years of experience in the study of plant viruses and virus diseases.*

How Insects Transmit Viruses

L. M. Black

Most viruses that cause plant disease are transmitted by insects, principally those that have sucking mouth parts— aphids, leafhoppers, white flies, mealybugs, and tingids. Leafhoppers and aphids are the most important.

Although many plant viruses are without known insect vectors, it is generally expected that insect carriers will eventually be discovered for most of them. There are exceptions. Tobacco mosaic virus and potato latent virus are two viruses that occur in high concentration in infected plants and are stable enough to be spread readily from one plant to another by almost any means that releases juice from a wound in an infected plant and transfers the juice to a fresh wound in a healthy plant. Tobacco mosaic virus is thus transferred by the hands of men working with tobacco plants even though the wounds may be only microscopic in size. It can also be thus transferred by the mouth parts of grasshoppers. Potato latent virus can be transferred from plant to plant when the wind blows the leaves of diseased plants against healthy ones so as to injure both. The mystery about these two viruses is not their transmission by such methods but why potato latent virus is apparently not transmitted by sucking insects and why tobacco mosaic virus is so poorly transmitted.

A few viruses, such as wheat rosette virus and lettuce big-vein virus, contaminate the soil in which diseased plants are grown and infect healthy plants subsequently grown therein. Just how inoculation takes place in such diseases is not known. Dodders (*Cuscuta* species), parasitic flowering plants, can transmit plant viruses by means of the natural graft unions they make with their hosts. Most plant viruses, however, depend on insects for their dispersal.

APHIDS transmit more plant viruses than any other group. Aphid-borne viruses induce in plants a great variety of symptoms, the most important of which are the mosaics. One of the most efficient aphid vectors is the green peach aphid, *Myzus persicae*, which transmits more than 50 different plant viruses.

Much remains to be learned about what actually occurs during transmission by aphids. Many aphid vectors transmit virus after very brief feedings on diseased plants. Studies on this type of transmission have reached a point where the feeding intervals of individual aphids are closely observed and timed by a stop watch. For example, the vector of beet mosaic virus requires an acquisition feeding of only 6 to 10 seconds. During subsequent consecutive inoculation feedings of 10 seconds each on healthy plants, the virus is gradually lost by the aphids and fewer than 2 percent of them can transmit to more than four plants without fresh access to virus. This virus is said to be nonpersistent in the vector. Usually such a virus is lost more rapidly from feeding aphids than from fasting ones—the virus of cucumber mosaic disease, for instance, is lost by the aphid within 6 to 8 hours when fasting, but within 10 to 20 minutes when feeding on healthy plants. In other instances this relation may be reversed. The loss of virus from aphids during feeding may be due to a virus-inactivating enzyme secreted by the aphids while feeding but not while fasting. Such a substance has not been demonstrated, however, and in reality we do not know the explanation for

such loss and for many other features of aphid transmission. A virus transmitted by aphids, particularly if it is of this nonpersistent type, is usually transmissible by several or, indeed, many species. The virus of onion yellow dwarf can be transmitted by more than 50 species of aphids, but not by thrips, mites, grasshoppers, beetles, caterpillars, or maggots.

That kind of transmission is in contrast to another type in which, following acquisition of virus, a latent period must elapse before the aphid is able to transmit. The aphid may then do so for many days without fresh access to virus. A minority of viruses transmitted by aphids are spread in that manner. One of them, the virus of potato leaf roll, is not transmitted by the aphid until 24 to 48 hours have elapsed after acquisition. The virus may then be retained by the insect for 7 to 10 days, even through molts, without fresh access to virus from plants.

That an aphid may transmit one virus in the persistent manner and another in the nonpersistent from the same host plant clearly indicates that persistence or nonpersistence is determined by the virus.

Why do we concern ourselves with such minute details of transmission? Simply because such knowledge may make the difference between success and failure in finding a vector of a virus. For instance, no transmission of a certain mosaic virus could be obtained after extensive trials with three species of aphids when they were fed one day on diseased plants and then transferred to healthy ones. When the aphids were fasted for 30 minutes before an acquisition feeding of 5 to 10 minutes and were then allowed an inoculation feeding of 5 to 10 minutes, however, transmissions were obtained.

LEAFHOPPERS, next to aphids, are the most important vectors of plant viruses. Experiments by a Japanese grower in 1884 demonstrated a connection between rice stunt and leafhoppers. That might be considered the first virus shown to be insect-transmitted, but actually it was not realized until more than 20 years later that the causal agent of the disease was not the leafhopper but some autonomous agent carried by the insect.

Viruses transmitted by leafhoppers cause a variety of symptoms in plants, including chlorotic streaking of leaves (as in corn streak), necrosis or death of tissues (as in elm phloem necrosis), tumors (as in wound-tumor disease), and yellows (as in aster yellows). All known vectors for virus diseases with a symptom picture like that of aster yellows are leafhoppers.

Although many aphid-borne viruses can be transmitted by rubbing leaves with juice from diseased plants, only two leafhopper-borne viruses have been so transferred. In other cases transmission has been accomplished only by the use of insects, dodder, or grafting. This has accordingly made the study of the viruses themselves very difficult. For such researches it has been necessary to permit the leafhoppers to feed on virus solutions through membranes or to inject the virus solution into leafhoppers. The insects must then be tested for infectivity on plants because none of the leafhoppers themselves has ever been observed to be diseased.

Practically all of the leafhopper-borne viruses (alfalfa dwarf virus is apparently an exception) are considered to have a latent or incubation period in their vectors. In some, this latent period may be so short (curly top virus) as to suggest that the virus does not multiply in the insect. Nevertheless, it reaches relatively high concentrations and is retained for weeks, not only in the beet leafhopper, which transmits it, but also in a number of other arthropods that cannot do so.

In most leafhopper vectors that have been studied, however, the period that occurs between acquisition of the virus and its transmissibility by the vector is much longer. In many it varies from 1 to 2 weeks or more. This is a true incubation period, during which the viruses multiply to an infective concentration in their vectors.

Although most leafhopper vectors do not transmit virus to their progeny through the egg, certain exceptions exist. Rice stunt virus and clover club leaf virus may be passed to 95 or 100 percent of young insects through the eggs of the vectors. A single female leafhopper carrying clover club leaf virus has originated at least 21 generations of infective progeny during a 5-year period without fresh access to virus from plants. The virus in the original female had been diluted at least 100,000,000,000,000,000,000,000,000 times. That would be impossible had not the virus multiplied in the leafhopper.

There may be, then, two main types of transmission of virus by leafhoppers. One type, exemplified by curly top virus, may be characterized by a very short incubation period and no multiplication in the vector; the other type by a long period of incubation and multiplication in the vector.

Once infective, leafhoppers tend to remain so for many days without fresh access to virus, often until they die. Nevertheless, such insects may fail to infect susceptible plants for many days in succession. Some that obtain virus from their parent through the egg may in turn pass virus to their progeny through the egg and yet may fail to infect any susceptible plants although fed on them for their entire life.

Often scientists have tested so many species of insects before finding a leafhopper vector that when they attained success they regarded the vector as specific. Only one species is known even today to transmit North American curly top virus. Very likely that is because it is the only species of the genus that occurs in North America where tests have been made.

The concept of specificity which envisioned a single leafhopper species as the vector of a virus has been broken down by recent research. For example, it is now known that Pierce's disease of grapes is transmitted by 24 different species of leafhoppers in two families. On the other hand, work with yellow dwarf and with curly top viruses has revealed a new type of specificity, of considerable complexity. In the former, there are two varieties of virus, each specifically transmitted by related leafhoppers. In the case of curly top, we have evidence of a complex of related viruses, with different vector and plant-host relationships.

Much of the wide variation observed in vector efficiencies of individuals within a leafhopper species may be genetic. For example, ability to transmit corn streak virus can be determined by a single sex-linked dominant gene in the insect vector. In the case of the leafhopper that carries New York potato yellow dwarf, multiple factors are involved, the virus having been transmitted by 80 percent of the "active" insects, 2 percent of the "inactives," and 30 percent of hybrids.

Considerable experimental work has been done on various aspects of the transmission process by the leafhopper. The mechanics of the mouth parts, the tissues of the plants reached by the mouth parts, and the location of the virus within the insect vector have all been subjects of investigation. Most leafhoppers apparently acquire virus from and introduce virus into the phloem. However, some vectors feed on the xylem and acquire virus from and inoculate it into this tissue. Some viruses show a corresponding specialization in regard to the tissues they attack.

WHITE FLIES transmit a number of plant viruses. Nymphs of the white fly are attached to the plant and therefore cannot themselves spread virus, but virus can be acquired by the nymphs, can pass through the pupal stage, and can be transmitted by the adults. The adults also can acquire the virus directly from plants.

When white flies were shown in 1946 to be vectors of a virus of abutilon, a puzzle of long standing was partly solved. Variegated abutilon had been used as an ornamental for many years in Europe and other parts of the world where the variegation never spread naturally to nonvariegated plants.

Since there was no natural spread of the condition, the disease was sometimes set somewhat apart from other virus diseases even though the variegation could be transmitted by grafting. It is now evident that in some countries a virus causing a similar variegation is disseminated in the field by a white fly.

MEALYBUGS, tended and transported by ants, are the vectors of destructive viruses that attack cocoa trees. Some of the viruses are closely related; in other cases relationships are uncertain. The viruses, which are not transmissible to plants by juice inoculations, do not remain long in the mealybugs unless they fast before the acquisition feeding; then virus may be retained about 36 hours. In spite of the nonpersistence of the virus, there is some specificity of transmission—certain mealybug species transmit certain of the virus strains not transmitted by others, and vice versa. Moreover, some strains of one of the mealybug species failed to transmit a virus that other strains of the same species transmitted.

THE ONLY VIRUS definitely known to be transmitted by thrips is the one that causes tomato spotted wilt. Forty-one different plant viruses have been tested for transmission by thrips with negative results. Although three species of thrips are vectors of tomato spotted wilt, several other thrips species are not. Tomato spotted wilt virus can be acquired only by larvae, but it passes through the pupal stage, so that both adults and larvae can inoculate plants. After an incubation period of 5 days or more the insects remain infective for life.

We have relatively few authenticated accounts of transmission by insects with biting mouth parts. In some of these isolated cases, there is better transmission of the virus by biting insects than by those with sucking mouth parts. The virus of turnip yellow mosaic is an example of this kind of virus. It apparently is not transmissible by insects with sucking mouth parts but is transmitted by a number of insects with biting mouth parts. The most important of these are flea beetles, the larvae of which may retain virus for as long as 4 days. It is believed that the insects regurgitate the virus.

All viruses of this sort are readily transmitted by rubbing juice from diseased plants on the leaves of healthy ones, and some are readily isolated.

UNTIL RECENTLY the only viruses photographed under the electron microscope were the more stable ones, which are readily transmitted mechanically and occur in relatively high concentration in plants. Some are insect-transmitted. Among them are the tobacco mosaic and squash mosaic viruses. Less stable and less concentrated viruses that have a more intimate relationship with their vectors have been identified recently under the electron microscope. Considerable interest attaches to the nature of those viruses that are known to reproduce in both plants and animals.

When one considers that the occurrence of a virus disease of plants usually involves three entities—the virus, the plant, and the vector—and may involve more than one of each, it should at once be apparent that the interactions between them and their environment may be exceedingly complex. In the laboratory, certain single factors may be demonstrated to be decisively important. Thus the virus of aster yellows is inactivated at 89° F. But when one tries to explain the vagaries of the spread of virus diseases in the field, relationships are not always readily discerned. For example: Northern regions and high altitudes with climates inimicable to aphids generally favor the production of potatoes with a low virus content, but hot and dry climates are also unfavorable for aphids and under certain conditions can be used to produce seed potatoes with a low incidence of virus.

The flight habits of aphids in the field in relation to the spread of potato virus diseases have been extensively studied at Rothamsted in England and the Maine Agricultural Experiment Station. It was determined in Maine that early and sustained flights containing a high proportion of *Myzus persicae*, an aphid vector of leaf roll disease of potatoes, were associated with considerable spread of the disease. But flights late in August or in September usually resulted in little or no spread.

Detailed work has been done on the ecology of the vector of the curly top virus. This leafhopper is an active flier, and large numbers can easily be borne long distances by the wind. It often multiplies in the spring on a variety of succulent weeds on uncultivated or abandoned lands. If those plants dry up after the insects have reached the winged adult stage, the insects take flight. One such migratory flight was estimated at 60 miles. Forecasts of leafhopper invasions based on studies of the breeding areas have been used to reduce losses.

In general the insect vectors of a virus tend to be confined to one of the major phylogenetic divisions, such as the families of the Hemiptera or the order Thysanoptera. Some of the viruses multiply in their insect carriers and more may be expected to be placed in this category. The vector relationships of such viruses are obviously quite different from those of the viruses that do not multiply in the vector. Although more extensive research on certain viruses has greatly increased the number of known vectors for each, other research has at the same time indicated more highly specific virus-vector relationships than were indicated in early work.

L. M. BLACK *is a professor in the department of botany in the University of Illinois. Before joining the University in 1952, he was curator of plant pathology in the Brooklyn Botanic Garden.*

The Fungi Are Living Organisms

Russell B. Stevens

Most fungi can be easily seen. Some are large and conspicuous, like the fleshy mushrooms of field and forest.

Some are stout and woody, like the bracket fungi on rotting timber. The pathogenic fungi, the ones that produce disease, more closely resemble the molds that overrun our shoes and stored leather goods in damp weather, damage foods, rot fabrics, and, in happier circumstances, produce valuable drugs and chemicals and give the desired flavor to our choicest cheeses.

The most important detail to remember about fungi is that they are living organisms. They require, therefore, a source of energy. Like animals, but unlike green plants, fungi cannot convert the energy of the sun and thus synthesize the food they need. They must therefore get food from some external source. In so doing, the slender, infinitely tiny, often colorless threads that make up the fungus itself live and grow at the expense of the environment in which they exist. If the environment is another plant, particularly if it is one of our cultivated agricultural plants, the resulting situation is regarded as a plant disease. Thus the apple scab fungus, familiar to anyone who has tried to raise apples in practically any part of the United States, forms olive-green patches on the leaves and fruits of its host and profits at its expense. The same is true of the grain rust fungi, the corn smut fungus, and a myriad of others. They grow thus because by their very nature they can grow successfully nowhere else.

A pathogenic fungus is but one of countless individuals in the organic world. To maintain its position it must live and grow, reproduce, be scattered about, and, under certain circumstances, survive periods during which the environment is relatively unfavorable to it. When one knows the essentials of how fungi accomplish this assignment, one knows the essentials of how fungi cause disease in plants.

Structurally, fungi are mostly very tiny—but very complex. Most of them are composed of microscopic filaments, which may be colorless or variously colored but which never contain chlorophyll, the green pigment responsible for binding the sun's energy in the formation of sugar. Considered individually, the filaments are called hyphae (singular: *hypha*). In the aggregate they are spoken of as a mycelium. The filaments are essentially like the cells of which other plants are composed, each being surrounded by a thin membranous wall and composed of a jellylike living protoplasm.

Although the filamentous growth form is common to practically all plant pathogenic fungi, the actual appearance of the fungi is enormously varied.

Some, like the rhizopus soft rot fungi of sweetpotatoes and strawberries or the scab fungi of wheat, have no particularly characteristic form and appear as a downy growth over the surface of the affected host.

Others develop aggregates of filaments with a recognizable size and shape, of distinctive color, and often decidedly firm to the touch. Such aggregates are commonly associated with the actively reproducing phase of development, and the "fruiting body" so formed serves as one of the most useful means of distinguishing one plant pathogenic fungus from another.

The physiology of fungi (like the physiology of all plants and animals) is by no means completely understood. We have enough information to suggest that the physical and chemical processes that take place in the protoplasm of the fungi are essentially the same as those of any other living organism. Indeed, those processes, summed up in the term metabolism, are strikingly similar throughout the organic world. Because the fungi lack chlorophyll, their nutrition is most like that to be found in the colorless, or rather nongreen, parts of higher plants, except that many fungi secrete digestive enzymes as do the cells of the digestive tract of man and other animals.

Because fungi depend for their food on outside sources, and because some establish themselves on other living plants and some on nonliving food sources, a great deal has been made of the terms *parasite* and *saprophyte*, supposedly to describe these two alternative conditions. Attempts to apply the terms soon demonstrate their inadequacy, at least when used in unmodified form. It is much more useful to speak of *obligate parasites*, which can grow only on living host plants, and *facultative parasites*, which can grow on nonliving food supplies but which at times do establish themselves on a living host. True saprophytes, which live exclusively on nonliving substrata, can hardly be of importance in a discussion of plant diseases.

Besides an ability to utilize food and grow, a fungus must reproduce. Because it is the most intriguing phase of the life history and because it furnishes most of the information necessary for identification, the reproductive aspects of fungi have received much attention.

By reproduction we ought always to mean an increase in the total number of individuals of a given species, a process which usually represents successive generations and thus assures the perpetuation of the species in time as well as its maintenance in space. It is an error in logic, however, to conclude that fungi reproduce in order to survive; one can say simply that they survive because they reproduce.

Characteristically, fungi reproduce by the formation of microscopic bodies collectively called spores.

Such spores, depending on the type and the particular pathogen by which formed, assume an impressive array of different characteristics. They vary greatly in size, although always tiny in terms of more familiar objects, measuring several hundreds or even thousands to the inch. Some spores are one-celled. Some are two-celled. Some have many cells. Some are completely colorless. Some are only lightly tinted, others dark. Still others are coal black. Some are extremely fragile and are killed by exposure to dry air in less than a minute. Some can withstand boiling temperatures for brief periods. A few types are capable of independent movement, but most of them drift passively on wind or water, although often they are forcibly ejected when first mature. Finally, they are formed in myriad different ways by the parent organism. Detailed consideration of specific diseases is by all odds the best way to comprehend the complexity and variability of spore formation.

No one, be he beginner or experienced professional, can truly appreciate the astonishing abundance in which spores are formed by fungi, even though they are produced on fruiting bodies so small as to be scarcely visible to the unaided eye. Total numbers from a single diseased plant must be estimated in millions, billions, even trillions, yet so little is the likelihood of survival that only the tiniest fraction of them are destined to give rise to a subsequent generation.

Fungus spores are often formed vegetatively; that is, they develop at the ends of the filaments by constriction of the walls, or their appearance may follow as the direct result, more or less, of some form of sexual activity. Those of the former type may occur pretty much at random over the surface of the relatively undifferentiated mass of hyphae, or they may be more or less enclosed in a fruiting body, which in turn is made up of nonsporebearing filaments.

The manner in which the spores are produced, and the appearance of the fruiting body, is the primary type of information upon which virtually all classification schemes are based. This is particularly true of the sexual spores. We thus have four groups of fungi:

The Phycomycetes—the filaments have no cross walls, and sexual activity consists of the fusion of many-nucleated male and female cells. In this group alone the nonsexual spores are frequently capable of swimming about, and these fungi are primarily found in very moist situations.

The Ascomycetes—sexual spores, typically in groups of eight, are to be found within a tiny sac, or ascus.

The Basidiomycetes—sexual spores, two or four, are borne upon the end of a tiny club, or basidium. The rust and smut fungi, which make up an important segment of this group, have a modified type of basidium clearly homologous to the true basidium.

The Fungi Imperfecti—only the nonsexual type of spore is known for this group, which otherwise greatly resembles the Ascomycetes.

Within the group of the Ascomycetes, particularly, further subdivisions are made on the basis of the type of fruiting body in association with which the sexual spores are produced.

THE NONSEXUAL type of spore formation generally is typical of the early stages of disease, often during the active growing season.

Sexual reproduction, on the other hand, characteristically occurs in the later phases of disease development, preliminary to a period of dormancy during the winter. Of the common diseases, the brown rot of stone fruits illustrates the point as well as any.

Here, the fruit as it approaches maturity will be literally enshrouded with a soft, velvety mass of nonsexual spores, millions of them, which are responsible for the rapid spread of the pathogen during the summer. Only after the decayed fruit has shriveled, dropped, and lain on the ground for a full winter do the fragile trumpets of the fruiting bodies appear, bearing their countless sacs of ascospores. These, in turn, carry the disease back to the budding and blossoming trees in springtime.

NOT ONLY must an organism survive in point of time; it must also be distributed in space. With the exception of fragile motile cells in certain Phycomycetes (and then only for very limited absolute distances) fungi are not self-propelled. They depend, therefore, on chance distribution by exterior forces—wind, water movement, activity of birds and animals, insect carriers, dissemination of host plants and plant parts, and so on. To a large extent the dissemination of fungi is through the medium of their spores, tiny objects often ideally suited for the purpose. Fragments of hyphae, hard masses of mycelium known as sclerotia (singular: *sclerotium*), and possibly other entities account for the remainder.

Spore movement in the bulk of fungus species is passive, although flagellated forms occur in a few species and in many others the initial discharge is forcible. The distance to which fungus spores may be carried by air currents, for example, is very great. Because of this, and because of the astonishing productivity of some pathogens, we are witness to occasional dramatic epidemics of disease. No better illustrations of this exist in the United States than the northward sweep of the cereal stem rusts in the Great Plains area, and the march of potato late blight, tobacco blue mold, and cucurbit downy mildew up the eastern seaboard.

Assuming the successful growth, reproduction, and the dissemination of fungi, and their establishment upon a host plant, there must yet be times when their continued existence depends upon their surviving a period of relatively unfavorable conditions. This can mean either extremes of temperature, moisture deficiency, oxygen inadequacy, or simply a period during which there are no available host plants. Survival may depend upon the presence of thick-walled spores, of sclerotia, or upon the ability to live for some time as a saprophyte upon the organic matter in the soil.

MUCH EMPHASIS is placed, in teaching plant pathology, for example, on the life history, or life cycle, of each fungus. On that basis, one may think of diseases as developing during that part of the life of a fungus when it is actively growing in association with a host plant.

Pathogenic disease, after all, is not a thing but a condition—a state of unstable equilibrium that results from the interaction of at least two living organisms.

Numerous technical terms have come into wide usage. A few at least are instructive:

Inoculation—that circumstance whereby the pathogen and host come intimately into contact, as by the falling of an airborne spore onto a leaf surface. Inoculation might also be accomplished through the intervention of man or animal.

Invasion—entry, passive or active, of the pathogen into the host.

Establishment—development by the fungus of a successful association with the host tissues, enabling further development of the pathogen.

Incubation—development of pathogen, in association with the host, prior to the appearance of conspicuous, recognizable symptoms of disease.

Characteristics of host (age, abundance, presence of wounds, degree of resistance) as well as of the pathogen enter into the above-mentioned events, as do considerations of the environment. Not infrequently a third organism—man, insect, bird, nematode, or other animal—may have a decisive role. Whatever the factors involved, and at whatever stage, the final development of well-defined disease is the result of a vast complex of elements.

Sporulation, important as it is from other viewpoints, is of little significance with regard to the particular host plant involved. Damage is done during the essentially vegetative phase of pathogen development and is largely realized by the time spore formation commences.

The very core of the whole problem of fungi as causal agents of plant disease lies in the phrase "host-parasite relation." It is disappointing, but not surprising, to realize that of all phases this is presently the least well known. We do not even know, in the vast majority of cases, in just what way a given pathogen is harmful to its host, whether it is a matter of food competition, toxin secretion, enzyme disturbance, or the like. Some specific considerations are nonetheless useful.

Parasitism may be either obligate, in the sense that the pathogen will not grow actively save on living tissue; or facultative, indicating that it may grow well at certain stages of its life cycle on nonliving organic matter. The obligate parasites usually have a very specific association with their hosts, the cells of the latter being invaded by microscopic outgrowths of the hyphae called haustoria. These are thought, but not fully proved, to be absorptive in function. Facultative parasites, on the other hand, often injure by the secretion of extracellular enzymes.

CERTAIN FUNGI are strictly local in their effect, producing lesions on leaf, stem, or root system, though their localism may at times be an expression of host resistance. Other fungi are selective with respect to particular tissues, as exemplified by the vascular wilt organisms, which are confined to the water-conducting tissues, or the chestnut blight fungus, injuring the cambium layer. Still others are indiscriminate, establishing themselves at various points, and at times destroying the entire plant.

There is the anticipated correlation between the mode of dissemination of the fungus and its relation to the host.

In general, leaf, stem, and fruit diseases are caused by airborne or insect-carried fungi, root diseases by soil-inhabiting species. Some vascular wilts are caused by soil fungi, some by fungi possessing insect vectors.

While there is probably no really simple host-pathogen relation, the complexity achieved in certain instances is truly impressive. Possibly the best understood instances of a complex interrelationship are to be found in the so-called heteroecious rusts. Here one is confronted with a pathogen that is an obligate parasite, having as many as five distinct spore types, and compelled to alternate from season to season between two botanically very different host species. How such a situation evolved over the past ages remains a complete mystery.

It goes almost without saying that critically accurate knowledge of the details of pathogen life cycles is essential to the development and application of effective control measures.

The attention given the fungi as causes of plant disease seems in large measure due to two further characteristics. In the first place, it is the fungus diseases of plants (by contrast with those of bacterial and virus origin) that are most easily controlled by chemical applications in the form of sprays and dusts. Added to this is the fact that fungi are responsible for a much larger number of the rapidly spreading, hence epidemic, diseases than are viruses or bacteria.

Whatever the reason, it is the sporadic diseases of this nature that bring about the greatest hardships on the individual farmer. Small wonder then that our most publicized maladies are wheat rust, apple scab, potato blight, and the like.

RUSSELL B. STEVENS *is associate professor of botany in the University of Tennessee. He obtained his doctorate at the University of Wisconsin in 1940 and served in the Army Medical Department during the Second World War. He is author with his late father of a textbook,* Disease in Plants.

Identifying a Pathogenic Fungus

William W. Diehl

From the beginning to the end of its life the health of every seed plant, wild or cultivated, is affected by fungi.

Even though a seed within a fruit or capsule may be sterile, it comes into contact with fungal spores and hyphae as soon as it is exposed to the air or is in contact with the ground. Spores are microscopic, seedlike, reproductive bodies, and hyphae are the microscopic vegative growths of fungi.

The air is literally charged with spores, and the soils of the whole earth are full of living spores and hyphae of different kinds of fungi. Most of the fungi are innocuous. Many are beneficial. But some thousands of recognizably different kinds of fungi are now known to be pathogens, or agents of disease, in plants.

Practical measures for the prevention and control of plant diseases depends in large part upon scientific knowledge of each pathogen and its role in nature. Since there are more than 100,000 recorded names of supposedly different kinds or species of fungi, the specific identification of a single specimen or culture of a fungus involves the exclusion of some 99,999 names. That is a technical problem akin in complexity and difficulty to the isolation and identification of any one out of 100,000 chemical compounds.

But the problem is not insuperable. There is a general procedure that leads the way out of the apparent chaos of more than 100,000 names.

First of all the specimen must be subjected to critical examination in order to determine any and all features that characterize it. Spores and fructifications, or spore-bearing structures, are the most significant features for diagnostic purposes.

To see the features to best advantage under the different powers of the compound microscope requires special preparation for each kind of material. The form as well as the texture of a fungal fructification, whether moldlike and fluffy or a solid structure, will determine the best method of treatment.

Most fructifications of microfungi are best viewed at first in place by reflected light with a hand lens or, better yet, a stereoscopic microscope, followed by examination under the different powers of the compound microscope of a very minute fragment mounted in water or in a staining medium.

Molds are more or less easily mounted in water or special mounting media, although they frequently require preliminary treatment with a fixing fluid to prevent a loss of spore heads, chains, or other delicately attached structures. Nevertheless, if immature stages are placed directly in the mountant, those structures that are too readily detached when mature often tend to remain in place so that their genesis is more readily observed.

If a fructification is large and opaque its anatomy can be discerned only in sections. Microtome sections made from materials imbedded in paraffin or nitrocellulose are the acme in elegance and are essential if good photomicrographic records are desired. Under ordinary circumstances, however, their preparation is too time-consuming to be justified, since for most practical purposes satisfactory sections are quickly made free-hand or by means of the freezing microtome. With moderate practice, excellent free-hand sections can be made using elder pith, carrot, or other convenient plant material as a clamp to hold a fragment firmly while slicing a number of sec-

tions among which only the best need be selected for study. If the material is too scanty to permit wastage or if the operator has not mastered the more rapid technique of free-hand sectioning, recourse may be had to the freezing microtome. Although a second-rate instrument as microtomes go, it has its advantages. Fungal structures that are too hard for easy sectioning or, after sectioning, are too impenetrable to transmitted light may usually be softened or cleared by soaking for a suitable period in some softener or clearing agent, such as a solution of potassium hydroxide or chloral hydrate. Clearing agents effectively remove fats and oils. Often after their use, structural details not otherwise evident are rendered more distinguishable, especially if they are stained. Certain mounting media, which clear and stain at one operation, are distinctly advantageous although the unstained aqueous mounts are usually satisfactory, especially so for water molds if the microscope illuminant is properly adjusted. A phase microscope is of decided advantage for living materials.

If the living specimen or culture possesses well-marked, matured spore-bearing structures, it is usually adequate for study. But if it bears no fructifications or only immature ones, they may often be produced or forced into recognizable maturity by such expedients as immersing them in water or keeping them in a moist atmosphere for a convenient period. Moist chambers are easily improvised by placing wet blotting paper under a bell jar or in a closed mason jar. It is sometimes preferable to keep specimens moist by having them wrapped in a wet towel. If there is any likelihood that the fungus requires an especially low or high temperature for maturation, that condition should be met.

Diagnostic features of many fungi are best developed through pure culture on selected artificial media in petri dishes. Standard media are particular combinations of nutrients and agar gel, but there is a wide choice of formulas. The growth reactions of some species are characteristic on certain media and not on others. In pure culture on artificial media a species may, furthermore, present a different appearance from that in nature. Hence it may be needful to grow it upon the natural substrate to obtain the development of normal fructifications.

Having observed and interpreted the more significant morphological features, one records them, at least tentatively, by means of sketches and notes. One pays special attention to measurements.

In general, spores and spore-bearing structures are preferably measured in water mounts, because published descriptions of these features have usually included dimensions determined from material mounted in water. The recorded characters are then utilized in tracing through analytical keys of the fungi to the several classes, orders, families, and genera, and finally to a species.

There are several standard keys in general use that lead to families and genera. G. W. Martin's key to families in the very useful *Dictionary of the Fungi* (third edition, 1950), by G. C. Ainsworth and G. R. Bisby, is a simplified and modern presentation, but for keys to genera one is forced to seek elsewhere. The keys to be found in E. A. Bessey's *Morphology and Taxonomy of the Fungi* (1950) are valuable for teaching purposes, but lead to representative genera only. The key to *The Genera of Fungi* (1931), by F. E. Clements and C. L. Shear, and those to be found in Engler and Prantl's *Naturlichen Pflanzenfamilien* (1897–1900), although today somewhat outmoded, are still essential references.

When a decision is reached as to the genus to which the fungus under consideration belongs, the problem remains of finding suitable literature bearing specific descriptions. The *Guide to the Literature of the Fungi*, the last chapter in Bessey's book, lists the more useful monographs and compendia as references. Yet one cannot depend upon compendia and monographs alone. They are out of date as soon as printed. It is therefore necessary to take account of the numerous increments constantly being published —hence the need for access to well-cataloged library facilities.

Host indexes as short cuts are legitimate aids in quickly finding specific names that might apply. A pathogen may, of course, have thus far escaped record as upon the particular host, but it is likely to be recorded, if at all, on some related host. A. B. Seymour's *Host Index* (1929), based upon a complete but unpublished catalog of records up to 1924 and partly through 1926, is supplemented by the later detailed cumulative *Index of Plant Diseases in the United States* (1950) by F. Weiss and (1952, 1953) by F. Weiss and M. J. O'Brien. Various foreign lists of fungi and plant diseases, notably the anonymous *List of Common British Plant Diseases* (University Press, Cambridge, 1944) and the *Enumeratio Fungorum* (1919–1924), by C. A. J. A. Oudemans, are useful because most fungi tend to be cosmopolitan.

Actually, host indexes, like regional lists, are merely suggestions in determining identities, and one must ultimately depend on monographs, supplemented by the comparisons with herbarium specimens, including cited *fungi exsiccati*. *Fungi exsiccati* are standard replicate herbarium specimens of definite reference value, but comparisons with authentic specimens and with types constitutes a court of last resort.

Considerable information on taxonomic techniques with fungi is to be found in G. R. Bisby's *Introduction to the Taxonomy and Nomenclature of the Fungi* (1945) and in M. Langeron's *Precis de Mycologie* (1945). Whether a fungus in culture is an exact replicate of a species with ample record of pathogenicity can of course be determined only by means of culture studies with inoculation experiments in order to reveal comparable growth reactions and host symptoms.

When the identity of the fungus seems assured, there is still the question whether its name is acceptable. Even if a specific name (epithet) has been found entirely applicable to the specimen at hand—that is, its features agree in all details with those noted in the description and it very closely resembles the type and other specimens regarded as authentic—there is always the likelihood that there may be other names (synonyms) that might apply equally well. If one or more names are found to be synonyms, a decision must be made as to which is the correct one to use, according to the current *International Code of Botanical Nomenclature* (1952). Each of the several synonyms may be valid—that is, it has been properly published—but conformity with the Code will determine which combination of generic and specific names is legitimate and, therefore, the proper choice. The present Code epitomizes the evolution in the nomenclature of fungi that began with the pioneer work of the eighteenth century.

Some persons, even specialists themselves, at times assume that the most expeditious way to get specimens or cultures identified is to refer them to individuals in other institutions. If the recipient is both competent and obliging, he is soon so overburdened with requests, many of them trivial but time consuming, that his own effectiveness in service and research is vitiated. Actually, the number of experienced mycologists equipped with laboratory, catalogs, and library facilities adequate for this kind of service in the United States, or in any other country for that matter, is limited to a few persons in a few institutions.

The taxonomist's concern, as well as his experience, is generally limited to particular genera or families. He naturally welcomes specimens and cultures that apply to his specialty; for him they are relatively easy to determine or else they challenge his mettle. Of course, no taxonomist can avoid a certain amount of drudgery; yet he should not be expected to determine the many common pathogens that ought to be more familiar to the senders. Some fairly common pathogens are often less familiar to the mycologist and can pose for him as much of a problem as any other unknown fungus. The sender is morally obligated to explain the significance and importance of his request, to supply the specimen or culture in good condition and in ample amount, as well as to accompany it with all pertinent data: Substrate, locality, date, etc. Since specimens and even cultures too often include more than one organism always possible as later contaminants, the sender should send microscopic preparations and sketches, sometimes even photographs, to avoid any possible confusion. Obviously, any materials entrusted to the mails should be so prepared that on receipt they will be in good order and not an unrecognizable mass mixed with broken glass.

As Bisby has remarked, "it is a matter of professional etiquette not to send parts of the same collection [or duplicate cultures] to be named by different experts"—to which may be added, "unless the different experts are so notified." It is almost universally considered unethical for one to publish without acknowledgment a determination provided by another. It is furthermore a convention that, lacking special agreement to the contrary, any specimens sent to another for determination become the property of the recipient for deposit in the herbarium where he is employed and that he has the right to publish at his own discretion the result of his researches upon such materials.

WILLIAM W. DIEHL *is a mycologist in the division of mycology and disease survey at the Plant Industry Station, Beltsville, Md. He has served the Department of Agriculture in Washington and at Beltsville since 1917. He is a graduate of Miami University and holds advanced degrees from Iowa State College and Harvard University.*

Problems of Variability in Fungi

E. C. Stakman, J. J. Christensen

Many plant disease fungi are known to be complex and variable, but the degree of complexity is imperfectly known for most of them and is not well enough known for any of them.

This complexity is not surprising because many of the crop plants in which the fungi live are equally complex. There are more than 14,000 varieties of wheat; there are un-numbered varieties of apples, beans, corn, roses, iris, and other cultivated and wild plants. Moreover, man and Nature are continually making new varieties by mutation and by hybridization and selection.

Plant disease fungi also are plants. They are parasitic on higher plants. Most are microscopic in size and relatively simple in structure, but they are plants nevertheless. They germinate, grow, and fructify; they multiply by the countless billions; they mutate and hybridize; consequently Nature has made countless kinds in the past and is continually making more kinds through mutation and hybridization. As plant breeders produce better kinds of useful plants, therefore, Nature may produce more destructive fungi. It is the job of plant pathologists to learn what the parasitic fungi are now doing and what they may do in the future to jeopardize or nullify man's success in plant improvement. To understand present plant disease situations and to predict possible future developments, it is essential to learn as much as possible about the variability in fungi pathogenic to plants. Other kinds of causal agents of plant diseases, such as viruses and bacteria, must be studied similarly, but the present discussion is restricted to fungi.

The principles of growth and reproduction in plant pathogenic fungi are similar to those for higher plants, except that fungi have no chlorophyll, which enables green plants to make their food from simple materials in the soil and air. The fungi therefore must live on living plants or animals or their products. The fungus parasites of plants live in or on living plants and get their nourishment from them by means of minute tubes, or hyphae, that grow, branch, and form a network known as the mycelium, which finally produces many tiny spores.

Spores serve the same propagative and reproductive function as the seeds of higher plants, but spores are much smaller and simpler in structure than seeds. Spores usually have one or at most a few cells and do not contain an embryo as do seeds. Nevertheless they germinate and produce new fungus plants with the parental characters. The conditions required for germination are similar to those for seeds, moisture and suitable temperature being the most important. The time needed for germination varies with the kind of spore and the temperature; it varies from about an hour to several days. Many fungi produce millions or even billions of spores in a few days to a few weeks and can therefore produce countless numbers in a few short generations. That is one reason why they are so dangerous.

Some spores are produced asexually and some only as a result of sexual fusions. The same fungus may produce several kinds of spores asexually, but usually produces only one kind sexually. Successive crops of asexual spores are generally produced abundantly and quickly when conditions favor growth of the fungus, and the sexual spores are usually formed when the vegetative period is terminating. Each kind of spore has a special name; thus some of the rusts produce five kinds of spores or sporelike bodies—teliospores, sporidia, pycniospores, aeciospores, and uredospores, each with special form and function.

The principles and procedures in classifying and naming fungi are similar to those for higher plants. Species of higher plants are determined by morphologic characters of the vegetative and fruiting structures, including seeds. Similarly species of fungi are determined by the characters of the mycelium, of the spore-producing organs, and of the spores themselves. The unit of measurement for fungus spores is the micron, which is one one-thousandth of a millimeter; 25 millimeters make an inch. The range in size is from about 4 microns to more than 100 microns and, together with shape, color, and certain other characters, is characteristic for each species.

Visible characters are used for grouping higher plants and plant pathogenic fungi into classes, orders, families, genera, species, and varieties. Thus it is easy to distinguish larger groups of agricultural plants, such as grasses and legumes. It is equally easy to distinguish larger groups of fungi, such as smuts and rusts. But there are many kinds of wild and cultivated grasses, such as timothy, bromegrasses, oats, barley, rye, rice, corn, and wheat; and there are many kinds of legumes, such as beans, peas, soybeans, alfalfa, and clover. Likewise, there are many kinds of smuts, such as the loose smut of wheat, the stinking smuts of wheat, common corn smut, and rye smut, and there are more than 3,000 kinds of plant rusts. It is relatively easy to recognize these major groups of higher plants and of fungi, but it becomes increasingly harder to classify the smaller groups, such as species and varieties.

The agronomist must know not only wheat, a genus scientifically designated by its Latin name *Triticum*, but he must know the species of wheats, such as the common bread wheat, *Triticum vulgare;* the durum wheats, *T. durum;* and several other species or subspecies. He must know also thousands of varieties of bread wheats and hundreds of varieties of durum. And he must learn about the new lines and potential varieties that continually are being produced. Likewise the plant pathologist must know the genera, species, varieties, and "lines" of the fungi that parasitize different kinds of wheat, and he must learn about the new ones that continually appear.

Moreover, the agronomist must know not only what crop plants look like, but also how they behave and what they are good for. He must know whether a variety of wheat is a winter wheat or a spring wheat, whether it is winter hardy, where it grows well, whether it makes good flour or poor flour, and whether it is susceptible or resistant to disease; and the plant pathologist must know not only what species of plant disease fungi look like but must also know their pathogenicity for the many different kinds and varieties of plants.

Most species of plant pathogenic fungi are equally as complex in composition as species of crop plants, and it is therefore necessary to find out what is within the species. As an example, the species *Puccinia graminis*, the stem rust of small grains and grasses, is recognized easily by its general appearance and by certain characters of its spores. But there are several varieties within the species that are alike in some characters and different in others, including the kinds of crop plants that they can attack. Thus the variety *tritici* of *Puccinia graminis* parasitizes wheat, barley, and many wild grasses; the variety *avenae* parasitizes oats and certain wild grasses but not wheat and barley; within the *tritici* variety there are races that differ in their ability to attack certain varieties of wheat; within the variety *avenae* there are races that differ in ability to attack varieties of oats. Kanred, as an example, is immune to some races of the variety *tritici* and susceptible to others. These rust races in turn can be subdivided into the ultimate subdivisions, the biotypes.

A biotype is a population of individuals that are identical genetically. The descendants of a single nonsexually produced stem rust spore constitute a biotype, unless mutation occurs to cause genetic diversity. The test of genetic purity of a population of a pathogenic fungus is the consistency of its behavior. Most species of plant pathogenic fungi comprise many biotypes, and attempts are made to group the most closely related ones into races and then to group the most closely related races into varieties, which in turn are grouped into species. Actually the procedure usually is in the reverse direction: The larger groups are recognized first, and the successively smaller groups are discovered by successively more refined methods. This can be illustrated by results of investigations of *Puccinia graminis*, the fungus that causes stem rust of small grains and grasses. (The discussion of stem rust is based on results of cooperative investigations between the United States Department of Agriculture and the University of Minnesota, which were begun in 1914 and continued by many investigators under the general supervision of the senior author, who regrets that the contributions of the many administrators and investigators cannot be specifically mentioned without interrupting the continuity of the discussion.)

Puccinia graminis is a good species within which there are clearly recognizable varieties, races, and biotypes. There are at least six rather distinct varieties that differ in size of spores and in the kinds of plants that they can attack: (1) *tritici* (wheat), whose host plants are wheat, barley, and many wild grasses; (2) *secalis* (rye), rye, barley, and many wild grasses like those attacked by *tritici*; (3) *avenae* (oats), oats and wild grasses different from those attacked by *tritici*; (4) *phleipratensis* (timothy), timothy and certain wild grasses; (5) *agrostidis* (redtop), redtop and other species of

Agrostis; (6) *poae* (bluegrass), Kentucky bluegrass (*Poa pratensis*) and related species.

There probably are more varieties than the six listed, and new ones may appear in future as a result of mutation or hybridization. Races are known within the varieties *tritici, avenae,* and *secalis.* Although there sometimes are at least slight morphologic differences between races within a variety, the most important and most easily recognizable differences are in the degree of infection (pathogenicity) on certain varieties within the genera *Triticum* (wheat), *Avena* (oats), and *Secale* (rye), respectively. The crop varieties, designated as differential varieties, now used to distinguish races within the *tritici* and *avenae* varieties, were selected from hundreds that were tested, and, at the time of selection, appeared to be representative and adequate for distinguishing races.

The differential varieties of wheat are:

Triticum compactum (club wheats): Little Club, C. I. 4066 (Cereal Investigations accession number, Department of Agriculture). (Certain lines of Jenkin, C. I. 5177, notably Hood, C. I. 11456, may be substituted for Little Club.)

Triticum vulgare (bread wheats): Marquis, C. I. 3641; Reliance, C. I. 7370 (certain lines of Kanred, C. I. 5146, can generally be substituted for Reliance); Kota, C. I. 5878.

Triticum monococcum (Einkorn): Einkorn, C. I. 2433.

Triticum durum (durum or macaroni wheats): Arnautka, C. I. 1493; Mindum, C. I. 5296; Spelmar, C. I. 6236; Kubanka, C. I. 2094; Acme, C. I. 5284.

Triticum dicoccum (emmer): Vernal, C. I. 3686; Khapli, C. I. 4013.

When inoculated with different races, these varieties may be susceptible (S), resistant (R), or heterogeneous (mesothetic) (M). Each of these classes is subdivided into infection types, based on size of pustules (small blisterlike eruptions containing from a few to 250,000 rust spores), and the condition of the wheat tissue in which pustules are formed. The rust stage which is used in identification is the repeating or summer-spore stage, called also the uredial stage; and the pustules of this stage are called also uredia (singular, uredium).

(o) *Immune*—No rust pustules developed; small flecks of dead host tissue sometimes present and designated by a semicolon, thus, o;.

(1) *Very Resistant*—Rust pustules extremely small and surrounded by dead areas.

(2) *Moderately Resistant*—Pustule small to medium; usually in green islands of host tissue surrounded by a band of yellowish (chlorotic) or dead tissue.

(3) *Moderately Susceptible*—Pustules medium in size; usually separate, no dead areas, but yellowish (chlorotic) areas may be present, especially under unfavorable conditions.

(4) *Very Susceptible*—Pustules large and often united; no dead tissue, but there may be leaf yellowing under unfavorable growing conditions.

(x) *Heterogeneous*—Size of pustules variable, sometimes including all of the above types and intergradations between them on the same leaf.

THAT grouping indicates the types of infection produced by rust races on the differential varieties of wheat. As indicators of resistance or susceptibility of the wheat varieties, the infection types are grouped as follows: Types 0, 1, and 2 are resistant (R); types 3 and 4 are susceptible types (S); and type x is mesothetic (variable) (M).

It will be seen, therefore, that varieties are considered resistant when the rust is unable to grow extensively and produce pustules on them or when the pustules are extremely small, as indicated by types 1 and 2. The small pustules are likely to be surrounded by discolored or dead host tissue, but the areas killed are almost always very small, so that the rust actually

does very little damage to the variety. The production of infection types 3 and 4 on varieties indicates that they are susceptible, because the rust can grow well and produce large pustules with large numbers of spores, without killing the host tissues of the wheat plant quickly and thus limiting its own growth, as the rust cannot grow in dead tissue. The infection type x is variable and therefore is an indication that the resistance or susceptibility of the variety is also variable.

To identify rust races, seedling plants of the 12 differential varieties are inoculated in the greenhouse by applying rust spores to them, after which the inoculated plants are kept in a moist chamber for 24 hours to provide moisture for the spores to germinate and cause infection. It takes 1 to 2 weeks for the rust to produce a new crop of spores. For the identification of races, only three reaction classes are used, namely: resistant (R), susceptible (S), and mesothetic (M). The races are designated by numbers; the differences between races 56 and 59 are shown in the table:

	Race 56	Race 59
Little Club	S	S
Marquis	S	R
Reliance	S	R
Kota	S	R
Arnautka	R	R
Mindum	R	R
Spelmar	R	R
Kubanka	S	M
Acme	S	S
Einkorn	R	S
Vernal	R	R
Khapli	R	R

The table shows that there are decided differences between races 56 and 59. Both races attack Little Club normally. Marquis, Reliance, and Kota are susceptible to race 56 and resistant to race 59. Arnautka, Mindum, and Spelmar are resistant to both races. They differ again on Kubanka and are the same on Acme. They differ on Einkorn and produce the same effect on Vernal and Khapli. They produce the same effect on seven varieties but differ on five of them. They are therefore distinctly different races, as determined by their ability to attack certain varieties of wheat.

RACE 59 comprises several known biotypes. The collections of rust from the United States and Mexico that were identified by E. C. Stakman and colleagues as race 59 between 1929 and 1944 produced the infection types given in the foregoing. Collections of rust taken from the field may contain several races, which are separated from each other by appropriate inoculations on differential varieties and the different races can then be isolated and cultured separately. Each purified culture is called an isolate. During a season when many collections of rust are identified, many isolates of the same race are made, and a number of them usually are kept for comparative tests at the same time and under the same conditions.

In 1944 an isolate from a collection that was obtained directly from barberry bushes in Massachusetts produced infection type 2 on Reliance wheat instead of the type 0, which was characteristic of the race; soon thereafter a similar isolate was obtained from a collection of rusted barberry leaves from Washington State. When comparative tests were made between isolates that produced type 0 and those that produced type 2, the difference proved to be consistent, indicating that the isolates were genetically different. As the isolates could not be subdivided further, it was concluded that each was pure genetically, and they were considered as two biotypes of the same race, 59, because they were alike on 11 varieties and the difference on the one variety, Reliance, was slight; Reliance was immune to one and highly resistant to the other. The new biotype was therefore designated as race 59A. Later in 1944 two other isolates, also from barberry, differed slightly but consistently from the other two on Kota wheat, and they were designated as 59B, and 59C, respectively. The infection types produced by the four biotypes on Reliance and Kota are:

	Reliance	Kota
59	0	0;
59A	2	0;
59B	2	2
59C	0	2

(The semicolon after 0 indicates that there were small flecks of dead wheat tissue, but no pustules.)

These minor differences in infection types on Reliance and Kota seemed scientifically interesting rather than practically important until it was found that 59A is much more virulent than 59 on certain previously resistant varieties of barley. Clearly, then, the differences between at least two biotypes of race 59 on the differential varieties of wheat are not the only differences between them, and, if they could be tested on all known varieties of wheat and barley, additional differences might be found which would justify considering them as separate races. As new varieties of wheat are produced, rust isolates that now appear identical may prove to be different. Race 15 is a good example.

Race 15 of wheat stem rust was discovered in 1918. The race was easy to identify; all of the 12 differential varieties of wheat except Khapli are susceptible to it. The identification of rust collections from different places in the United States disclosed that some isolates of race 15 were slightly more virulent than others, but the differences were neither great nor consistent enough to justify the conclusion that they were genetically different—that is, different biotypes. The first conclusive evidence that some isolates were less virulent than others was obtained by studying a collection from Japan, which produced smaller pustules on some differential wheat varieties than any of the United States collections. All of the differential varieties except Khapli were susceptible, but some were distinctly less susceptible than to isolates from the collections previously studied. The Japanese rust was therefore designated as 15A, a distinct biotype.

Race 15 therefore included at least two biotypes, and it was suspected but not proved that there were still others. In 1937, however, an isolate was obtained that was distinctly more virulent on some differential wheat varieties than any previously studied, and it was therefore designated as 15B, a third biotype within race 15.

Although clearly different genetically, the known differences between the biotype originally designated as race 15 and those subsequently found and designated as 15A and 15B were not great enough to justify considering them as separate races. As 15B appeared to be a potential menace to resistant varieties grown in northern United States, attempts were made to learn as much as possible about it. As it occurred only sparingly in nature, however, studies had to be limited to the very few isolates that could be obtained. Attempts were made to find varieties that would distinguish more clearly between 15 and 15B. After extensive investigation, research workers found that a relatively new variety, Rival, and an Australian hybrid, Kenya x Gular, were fairly good differentials. Finally the new variety Lee (Hope x Timstein), released to growers by the Minnesota Agricultural Experiment Station and the Department of Agriculture in 1951, proved resistant to 15 and susceptible to 15B, thus serving as a new indicator or differential variety for distinguishing clearly between 15 and 15B on the basis of resistance and susceptibility instead of on the less satisfactory basis of degrees of susceptibility. That seemed like progress in understanding a complex situation, but the situation itself soon became more complex.

In 1950 race 15B became widespread and prevalent in North America for the first time—at least since races of wheat stem rust were recognized. Previously it had been found occasionally near barberry bushes, especially in the Eastern States; consequently it had not been possible to study many collections of 15 or 15B, either because they did not exist or could not be found among the approximately 1,000 collections of wheat stem rust identified each year. But in 1950 there was abundant material because 15B caused a destructive epidemic on previously resistant varieties in parts of Minnesota and the Dakotas and was isolated from 317 of the 810 samples of wheat rust obtained from 17 States.

All of the 317 isolates that were identified as 15B in 1950 produced essentially the same infection types on the 12 differential varieties of wheat and on Lee wheat; otherwise they would not have been designated as 15B.

There were some indications, however, that some of the isolates were not completely identical. These results were obtained by the senior author and his colleagues at the Federal Rust Laboratory, University Farm, St. Paul, Minn. Therefore 17 selected isolates were tested on 99 additional varieties of wheat and on 17 varieties of barley. Those tests—which were made by Rosendo Postigo, a graduate student at the University of Minnesota, with the collaboration of Helen Hart and E. C. Stakman—disclosed that 14 of the 17 isolates differed clearly in their effects on one or more of these varieties, some of which had been produced recently. It is evident, then, that biotypes of rust that seem to be identical because of their identical behavior on many varieties may prove to be different if additional biologic indicators can be found. The wheat varieties are, of course, really biologic indicators or testers, and must be depended on for distinguishing between rust biotypes, because the rust grows only on living plants and there is no known method of distinguishing between biotypes except by their effects on varieties of living plants.

The experience with race 15 and 15B shows that recognition of differences between biotypes and between races depends on the availability of host varieties that react differently to them, and new varieties may serve as additional differentials. Conclusions regarding rust races therefore are limited by the varieties available at a given time; furthermore, as new races are continually being produced, it is necessary periodically to revise the classification of races.

Puccinia graminis is a good example of the complexity within the species, within the variety *tritici*, and even within races. There are a great many biotypes, and their recognition and grouping into races for practical purposes are subject to limitations of suitable differential varieties at any given time and place. To recognize the differences between all biotypes in existence would require that all varieties of wheat, barley, and many grasses be inoculated under several combinations of environmental conditions with an adequate sample of rust collections from the world—and while that was being done, many new biotypes probably would have been produced by mutation and hybridization.

The problem of identifying races is difficult not only because different biotypes may appear alike on many varieties and under many environmental conditions. It is difficult also because the infection types produced by a single biotype on a single variety may vary widely with environmental conditions. As an example, Australian and American isolates of race 34 of *P. graminis tritici* differ in temperature relations and in color, thus suggesting that different biotypes may behave alike at certain temperatures but not at others. Certain races produce a type x infection under some conditions but not under others. Thus the only known difference between races 17 and 37 of *P. graminis tritici* is that the latter produces type x on Kubanka while race 17 produces type 3 to 4. Likewise, the difference between races 56 and 125 is that the latter produces type x on Kubanka; the difference between the races is genetic, but it is slight and variable enough to be obscured by differ-

ences in light and temperature. The same is true of some of the races of oats stem rust, *Puccinia graminis avenae.*

Despite the difficulties, it has been possible in the past to explore within the species *Puccinia graminis* sufficiently to explain differences in behavior of stem rust of wheat and oats in different times and places and to predict what is likely to happen in the future. Some races are relatively stable genetically and therefore are consistent in behavior historically and geographically; others are unstable and variable.

Knowledge regarding the diversity within the species is incomplete. Were it possible to grow all stages of the rust on artificial media, it probably would be possible to recognize many more biotypes than is now possible.

Although most plant scientists are familiar with the life history of *P. graminis*, its relation to genetic studies deserves emphasis. There are five stages: Telial, sporidial, pycnial, aecial, and uredial. The mature black spores or teliospores are diploid, but reduction division occurs when they germinate, and the sporidia formed on the four-celled promycelia are haploid and of two sex groups. The sporidia can infect only certain species of barberry (species of *Berberis* and *Mahonia*) on which they produce pycnia containing pycniospores, which are in reality specialized sex cells or gametes.

Although the pycnia and pycniospores all look alike, they are of two kinds sexually, having been produced by sporidia of different sex. All the pycniospores produced within a single pycnium are of the same sex, so that pycniospores from pycnia of different sex must be brought together (in nature this is usually done by insects) in order to initiate the sexual stage. This is therefore roughly analogous to cross-pollination in dioecious higher plants. The nuclei of opposite sex pair at the base of the aecium, divide simultaneously, but do not fuse for a long time.

From the "fertilized" pycnia are formed the cluster cups or aecia on the barberry, and in them are produced the aeciospores, each with paired nuclei of opposite sex. The aeciospores cannot infect the barberry, but only appropriate grains and grasses on which the uredospores are produced in pustules, or uredia. The uredospores contain paired nuclei also, and they can infect only grains and grasses, but this is the repeating stage of the fungus, and successive generations of uredospores can be produced indefinitely, provided susceptible kinds of grains or grasses are available and in vegetative condition. When conditions become unfavorable for the development of the uredial stage, the telial stage is formed. The young teliospores have paired nuclei, which fuse within the spore, and thus the final stage in the long sexual process results in the formation of diploid nuclei. As the fused nuclei may differ in factors for pathogenicity, segregation and recombination can result in the production of new biotypes.

The fact that the uredial stage of the rust is the only one that can be clonally propagated means that races must be identified in this stage, and, since it has paired nuclei of opposite sex that later fuse in the telial stage, a single heterozygous race may yield many different races as a result of segregation and recombination even if it is selfed. In reality so many biotypes often can be isolated from or near barberry that it is extremely difficult to group them into races, because many are so nearly alike and because it often is hard to find varieties that show even the larger differences.

The common corn smut, *Ustilago zeae*, is suitable for studying biotypes within species. The smut spores (chlamydospores) result from the fusion of haploid nuclei. Accordingly the chlamydospore nucleus has a set of chromosomes from each parental line—that is, double the number (diploid) in each sex cell (gamete). On germination, the spore sends out a four-celled tube, the promycelium, like that produced by teliospores of stem rust. Each cell likewise produces a small, sporelike body, known as a

sporidium, which has a single nucleus with half as many chromosomes (haploid) as there are in the chlamydospore nucleus; this results from reduction division early in the process of germination. The sporidia are therefore sex cells or gametes, like sperms and eggs, except that those of different sex cannot be distinguished by appearance; they look alike, but those of opposite sex will conjugate (fuse) while those of the same sex will not. The test of sex, therefore, is behavior and not appearance.

But these gametic sporidia are unlike most specialized sex cells because they can either multiply by yeastlike budding or germinate like spores and produce an extensive mycelium. This stage of the smut can be grown on or in sterilized nutrient media. Although only about 8 microns long (one three-thousandth of an inch), single sporidia can be picked up with a micromanipulator and placed on solid nutrient media in sterilized flasks; within about 3 weeks colonies have formed, consisting of about 2 billion sporidia or a network of hyphae comprising a billion or more cells, all derived from a single, haploid cell. Such cultures are called monosporidial lines and are a single biotype, unless new biotypes are formed by mutation. There is no chance for segregation, because the original sporidia themselves are the product of segregation. The colonies produced from different sporidia often differ in many characters, such as size, color, and surface patterns. It is like looking at different kinds of forests from an airplane, with each forest comprising one kind of tree.

E. C. Stakman and L. J. Tyler at the University of Minnesota in 1934 crossed two monosporidial lines with five clearly contrasting characters. By 1952 many investigators there had produced about 10 thousand different biotypes from recombinations and mutations among the descendants of the two original sporidia. These biotypes differ from each other in one or many major or minor characters, including size, color, and topography of colonies, many other cultural characters, sporidial or mycelial growth type, many physiologic characters, mutability, and sex and pathogenicity. Occasional monosporidial lines are diploid instead of haploid, but they are exceptional.

Color of colonies among these biotypes ranges from aniline black through many shades and tints of purple, brown, pink, drab, and white. Innumerable patterns and combinations of topographic patterns are superimposed on the profuse array of colors—various kinds of concentric bands and ridges and many kinds of radial lines, folds, furrows, and ridges, some straight, some curving clockwise and some counterclockwise. There are many types of marginal growth. Some biotypes produce sporidia only. Others produce mycelium only. There also are many intermediate kinds, in which the growth type is determined by the amount of sugars in the medium.

Temperature requirements differ and may affect relative survival in mixtures of biotypes.

There are multiple sex groups and many gradations in pathogenicity.There are wide differences in mutability, and it is becoming evident that in cultures of some of the most constant monosporidial lines there are mutants whose presence is masked under most conditions by the growth of the original lines. These masked mutants may persist indefinitely without betraying their presence unless special methods or media are used to detect them.

Several significant facts have been obtained from investigations of *Ustilago zeae*. There are thousands of haploid biotypes within the species. Biotypes may differ from each other in one or more of all known characters, including pathogenicity. Differential media may be necessary to distinguish between biotypes, just as differential varieties of crop plants are necessary to distinguish between physiologic races and biotypes of rusts. The asexually produced progeny of a single

haploid sporidium, which should constitute a single biotype if there were no mutation, rarely do constitute a single biotype, even when the line appears pure and constant, because mutation occurs so commonly and many mutants may be masked. The virtual impossibility of guaranteeing genetic purity of the cultures suggests caution in interpreting results of experiments. Despite the vast diversity within the species, the characters of the spores (the chlamydospores) have been remarkably uniform, even though produced by thousands of different combinations of haploid lines.

Possibly *Ustilago zeae* represents the extreme of intraspecific diversity, or possibly it is only better known than many other plant pathogens. Covered kernel smut of sorghum, *Sphacelotheca sorghi*, and the grass smuts, *Sorosporium syntherismae* and *Ustilago sphaerogena*, also comprise many biotypes. Some smuts, however, such as loose smut of barley (*Ustilago nuda*), loose smut of wheat (*U. tritici*), loose smut of oats (*U. avenae*), and covered smut of barley (*U. hordei*) seem to be somewhat more homogeneous and constant.

Investigations on rusts and smuts have been mutually complementary in explaining variability of pathogenic behavior. In the rusts only the binucleate uredial stage can be propagated clonally. In the smuts only the haplophase can be so propagated.

In the smuts and rusts, three distinct phases correspond with the nuclear condition: The haplophase, in which the cells have nuclei with the reduced number of chromosomes, such as the sporidia of both groups and the pycnial stage in the rusts; the dicaryophase, in which two nuclei of opposite sex are paired in the cells but not fused; and the diplophase, in which the two nuclei of the dicaryophase have fused. The haplophase in the rusts (sporidia and pycnial stage) is restricted almost entirely to a sexual function. In some of the smuts, however, the sporidia (haplophase) can function both as propagative cells and as sex cells, but the ability of the haplophase to grow parasitically is limited. In both the smuts and rusts, the dicaryophase is the important parasitic phase, and it is important to realize that there are dicaryotic hybrids. This simply means that each cell can contain two nuclei of different sex and with different factors for pathogenicity and for other characters. The final hybridizing act is not complete until the two nuclei fuse to form the diplophase, which is restricted largely to the resting spores, the teliospores of the rusts and the chlamydospores of the smuts, except that diploid sporidial lines of smuts are encountered occasionally.

The uredial stage of rusts can be propagated indefinitely on appropriate hosts; hence, repeated experiments can be made on the pathogenicity of dicaryotic hybrids, where minor differences in pathogenicity are perceptible. In the smuts, on the other hand, the gametic haplophase can be propagated saprophytically on the artificial media where conditions can be varied and controlled, but the pathogenic dicaryophase cannot be propagated clonally even on living plants. It comes to an end with the formation of diploid spores. Accordingly the progeny of a single uredospore in the rusts constitute a biotype, barring mutation; in the smuts the progeny of a single haploid sporidium constitute a biotype, barring mutation. Likewise the monosporidial diploid lines that occasionally appear in smuts are biotypes, barring mutation and segregation. A physiologic race in the rusts, then, can be purified to a single biotype, while in the smuts the most practicable way of determining the parasitism of so-called physiologic races is to inoculate differential varieties with successive crops of chlamydospores.

The term physiologic race, then, does not have the same genetic connotation in the rusts and smuts. In many of the Fungi Imperfecti, which are imperfectly known genetically, the only criterion of races must be behavior in culture and on host plants. As commonly used, therefore, the term physiologic race means a biotype or group of biotypes that can be distinguished with reasonable certainty and facility by its physiologic characters, including pathogenicity, and, in some fungi, growth characters on artificial media.

Under that definition, most species of plant pathogenic fungi comprise physiologic races. Some of the downy mildews (including *Phytophthora infestans*, which causes late blight of potato), some of the powdery mildews, and several of the wood-rotting fungi comprise many races. The species of *Helminthosporium* that cause leaf spots, seedling blights, and root rots of small grains and corn all are complex in composition. *Helminthosporium sativum*, *H. gramineum*, *H. teres*, *H. carbonum*, and *H. victoriae* comprise many races, whether judged by behavior on artificial media or on host plants or both; *H. sativum* is known to be in the same category as *Ustilago zeae* with respect to diversity. Various species of *Fusarium*, such as those that cause flax wilt, melon wilt, tomato wilt, and head blight or scab of cereals, comprise many races. *Colletotrichum lini*, which causes anthracnose of flax, *C. lindemuthianum*, the cause of bean anthracnose, *Rhizoctonia solani*, which causes blights and rots of hundreds of kinds of plants, the apple scab fungus, the fungus causing brown rot of stone fruits, and many others comprise numerous physiologic races.

THE DETERMINATION of phenotypic variability of fungi—the temporary changes in appearance or behavior due to environment—is relatively easy when the fungi can be grown on nutrient media, as environmental factors usually affect the fungus and not the medium. Similar determinations are more difficult when the fungus is growing on living plants, because environment affects the fungus, the host plant, and the interactions between the two.

The phenotypic variability caused by nutrients, temperature, and other factors is often so great as to obscure genetic differences between biotypes or races when they are determined partly by cultural characters and by pathogenicity. It is essential therefore to standardize media and other conditions with varying degrees of exactness, depending on the fungus and the objectives of the investigation. A primary requisite is to determine the limits of phenotypic variability of isolates before making conclusions regarding genetic differences between them.

Variability in growth type of corn smut due to nutrition, temperature, and other factors can be wide or narrow, depending on the biotype. An example: Mycelial patches or sectors in colonies of certain sporidial lines seemed to be mutants until it was found that subcultures from dissimilar sectors sometimes were identical. Physiologic and genetic experiments by M. F. Kernkamp, at the University of Minnesota, then showed that there are strict sporidial lines that cannot produce mycelium, strict mycelial lines that do not produce the sporidia, and sporidial-mycelial lines that can produce both sporidia and mycelium. The relative tendency toward sporidial or mycelial production in the latter group differs in different lines, but a high content of sugar in the nutrient medium favors production of sporidia and a low content of sugar favors formation of mycelium. Change from one type of growth to another may result from mutation also; hence it is always important to find out whether the change is temporary and nonheritable or whether it is permanent and heritable.

The same biotypes, then, may have several distinctly different phenotypes. Conversely, different biotypes may appear alike on certain media and not on others. Phenotypic differences may persist to some extent for one or more cultural generations; consequently the classification of groups of isolates should be made only after they have been grown for one or more generations under identical conditions.

Variability in development of fungus pathogens on living hosts can be studied advantageously in some of the rust fungi because of the distinct infection types produced. From investigations by W. L. Waterhouse and associates at Sydney University, in Australia, Thorvaldur Johnson and others at the Dominion Laboratory of Plant Pathology, Winnipeg, and by Helen Hart and associates at the University of Minnesota, it is now known that temperature and light can cause fundamental differences in the development of certain races of stem rust on certain varieties of wheat and oats. Certain Kenya wheats and some hybrids, for example, are almost immune to race 15B of wheat stem rust at 65° F. and completely susceptible at 85°. Conversely, race 34 develops best on some varieties of wheat at moderate temperatures and relatively low light intensity, and the infection type is depressed by high temperature and high light. The oats variety Hajira is resistant to known races of *P. graminis avenae* below about 80° but it is susceptible to race 6 at 85° and to races 7 and 8 at 90°. The implications of phenotypic variability in the identification of races are important, because a given rust race may produce infection type 1 on a host variety at temperatures as high as 75° and type 4 at 85°. This is true of some race-variety combinations but not of others, and must therefore be studied for each combination.

THE TERM ADAPTATION, as used here, means the capacity of a single biotype to acquire and transmit the ability to do something that it either could not do originally or could not do well. Thus, race 19 of wheat stem rust can produce only small pustules on Marquis wheat. It would be a case of adaptation if genetically pure race 19 were grown on Marquis several successive rust generations and produced successively larger pustules until it acquired the ability to grow well on this variety, or at least better than it did originally. Likewise it would be adaptation if a single biotype of the corn smut fungus (*Ustilago zeae*) were grown for several successive generations on a medium containing arsenic and thus acquired the ability to tolerate several times as much arsenic as it did originally.

Between 1900 and 1910 the question of adaptation was studied by several investigators, who concluded that certain rust fungi and powdery mildews could adapt themselves quickly to resistant varieties.

Marshall Ward made many experiments with rust of bromegrasses (*Puccinia dispersa*) at Cambridge University, England, and published a paper on adaptive parasitism in 1903. He concluded that the brome rust could develop the ability to grow well on a resistant species of *Bromus* if grown on the resistant species for one or more successive rust generations. He also concluded that there were "bridging species" of *Bromus* that enabled the rust to attack very resistant varieties; for example, the rust could grow well on variety A but not on variety C. If, then, a variety B could be found that was intermediate taxonomically between A and C, the rust could be grown on B and there it acquired the ability to infect C. Variety B, therefore, was considered a bridge or "bridging host" between the susceptible A and the resistant C.

Ward's general conclusions were soon supported by results of experiments made by E. S. Salmon with powdery mildew (*Erysiphe graminis*), also at Cambridge; by those of E. M. Freeman and E. C. Johnson with *Puccinia graminis* at the University of Minnesota; and by experiments of I. B. Pole-Evans with stem rust of wheat in South Africa. Salmon concluded that the powdery mildew could attack injured plants of a normally resistant species and thus acquire the ability to infect noninjured plants of that species. Pole-Evans applied the principle of bridging to

the breeding of stem rust resistant varieties of wheat. He stated that some hybrids between resistant and susceptible parents were more susceptible than the susceptible parent and even enabled the rust to increase its virulence for the resistant parent.

In cooperative investigations between the United States Department of Agriculture and the University of Minnesota, E. C. Stakman, F. J. Piemeisel, and M. N. Levine studied the possible adaptation of stem rust of wheat and other cereals and grasses and of powdery mildew of wheat and barley, but obtained no evidence that these fungi could adapt themselves to resistant varieties by any of the methods previously tried nor by any new methods that could be devised.

In a paper published in 1918 they stated: "The facts given in this paper do not support the conclusions of previous workers that the pathogenicity of biologic forms is easily changed by host influence. . . . From the practical standpoint the constancy of biologic forms is of great importance. Breeding for rust resistance can proceed with considerable assurance that the same rust will not adapt itself quickly to new varieties."

They also pointed out that differential hosts must be used to separate different biologic forms from mixtures before making experiments on adaptation; otherwise what appears to be adaptation may be merely the result of the selective effect of host plants on a mixed population of the pathogen. At that time, the now obsolete term "biologic form" was used to designate what are now called varieties of stem rust; races were just being discovered within the *tritici* and other "biologic forms"; and eventually new facts led to new concepts and to changed terminology.

These results seemed to prove that stem rust and powdery mildew of cereal grains did not change by adaptation. But the rusts and powdery mildews are obligate parasites; it has not been possible to grow them on anything except living plants. Accordingly it was desirable to study possible adaptation or changes in virulence in fungi that can grow both in living host plants and on nutrient media—that is, both as parasites and as saprophytes.

The results of extensive experiments made by J. J. Christensen and C. L. Schneider at the University of Minnesota from 1946 to 1950 with *Helminthosporium sativum*, which causes leaf spots, foot rots, and root rots of barley, wheat, and other cereals and grasses, support the view that genetically pure lines of fungi do not change their virulence easily. The isolate of *H. sativum* they studied had been grown on artificial nutrient media for 28 years and had been purified by making many successive single-spore isolations. Wheat plants were inoculated with single spores; when new spores were produced, single ones were again picked and inoculated into plants with a fine needle. This process was repeated ten times in succession, and there never was any evidence of change in virulence. This extreme refinement of method was necessary because *H. sativum* mutates rather freely, producing many mutants that are less pathogenic and a few that are more pathogenic than the parental line. Some of the less pathogenic lines grow very rapidly and therefore tend to overgrow the original parental line. Unless the fungus is grown under conditions that permit the recognition of mutants and their separation from the parental line, an initially pure isolate may soon comprise a diverse mixture of mutant lines, and the original line may even have been lost in the process of making periodic transfers to new tubes of nutrient media. Obviously, then, an isolate of *H. sativum* derived from a single spore may change in virulence, but the change is due to the production of new biotypes resulting from mutation and not to a change in virulence of the original biotype.

It would be easy to conclude that some of the smut fungi increased in virulence for resistant varieties as a result of successive passages through those varieties if the intraspecific complexity of smut species were not known. Many investigators, notably W. A. R. Dillon-Weston in England, tested the resistance of varieties of wheat, barley, oats, and other crop plants to various smuts. When first inoculated with a collection of smut spores (chlamydospores), very little smut develops on some varieties. If the smut from a resistant variety is used to inoculate plants of the same variety, heavy infection may result, because nonpurified collections of smut spores are likely to comprise many parasitic races that can be separated from each other by certain varieties. Assuming that three wheat varieties, A, B, and C, are inoculated with a smut collection containing races 1, 2, and 3 in the ratio of 90:9:1 and assuming that all three races infect variety A normally, that race 2 infects B but not C, and that race 3 infects C and not B, the percentages of infection theoretically should be the following:

	A	B	C
Percentage of infection..	100	9	1
Races..............	1, 2, 3	2	3
Percentage of each race.	90:9:1	100	100

Obviously, if plants of variety A are then inoculated with the smut produced on A, spores of all three races will again be produced. But if variety B is inoculated with spores from B, 100 percent of them will be of race 2; and if variety C is inoculated with spores from C, 100 percent of the spores will be of race 3, the only one in the original mixture that can attack C. Thus, varieties B and C are biologic indicators, or differential varieties, that make it possible to find out not only which races were present in the original smut collection but also the relative percentages of each. Moreover, the apparent adaptation of the smut to varieties B and C is not adaptation at all but is due to selection of the races that can attack those varieties out of a mixture in which they were present in small amounts only.

Even after races of smuts have been isolated and purified as we have described, the degree and permanence of purity are only relative because the spores are not always exactly alike. And, even if they were, the chlamydospores of smuts are the result of sexual fusions. When the spores germinate, segregation and recombination usually occur, so that the progeny of a single spore might be diverse genetically. For practical purposes, physiologic races of smuts are usually considered to be collections of chlamydospores that behave with relative constancy in successive generations. Because of sexual recombinations and mutations within the races, however, they often comprise many biotypes, usually closely enough related so that the race behaves fairly consistently. The degree of refinement commonly practiced in classifying smut races usually suffices for determining the relative resistance of crop varieties, but certainly not for studies on adaptation or other physiologic and genetic phenomena. It suffices for practical procedures but not for scientific understanding.

There are several other reasons why races or biotypes of fungi may appear to have changed, when in reality there has been a change in the kinds of biotypes. It has been pointed out in the discussion of *Helminthosporium sativum* that apparent changes in a monosporous line may be due to the production of new biotypes by mutation, so that the culture soon comprises not only the original biotype but several others in addition; it becomes a mixed or heterogeneous population instead of a pure or homogeneous one. That the original biotype may even be lost has been shown by many experiments. And even if it is not, the behavior of mixtures of biotypes cannot be predicted.

Different races or biotypes of pathogenic fungi may not survive equally well in mixtures. This is to be expected if the environmental conditions favor one race more than the others. But it is sometimes true when conditions, as far as can be determined, are equally favorable to the different races. Extensive studies of the relative survival of races of wheat stem rust have been made at the University of Minnesota and at Sydney University, and typical results were published by I. W. Watson in 1942 and by W. Q. Loegering in 1951. As the principle is more important than the details, which must be ascertained for each individual mixture of each fungus, a few examples are given to illustrate differential survival of crop plants and of fungi.

H. V. Harlan and Mary L. Martini of the Department of Agriculture published in 1938 the results of experiments on the relative survival of barley varieties in a mixture grown in successive years. H. H. Lande and A. F. Swanson made similar experiments on winter wheats in Kansas and published their results in 1942. The experiments with barley and winter wheats established the important principle that certain varieties persisted better than others in mixtures in which the relative percentage of each variety was determined in the first year and in each successive year, when seed was taken each year and used for the next year's planting. The Darwinian principles of competition, natural selection, and survival of the fittest applied to these mixtures of varieties of barley and of wheat. Watson and Loegering tested the validity of the same principle on mixtures of races of wheat stem rust.

Loegering prepared an approximately 50:50 mixture of races 17 and 19 of wheat stem rust and grew it for six successive uredospore generations on Little Club, Fulcaster, and Mindum wheats, all of which appeared to be equally susceptible to the two races. In each generation the mixture was tested on Marquis wheat, on which race 17 produces type 4 and 19 produces type 2 infection, thus making it possible to determine the percentages of each race in the mixture. On Mindum the two races persisted almost equally well, although race 17 persisted slightly better than 19. But on Little Club and Fulcaster the percentage of race 17 increased rapidly and that of 19 decreased correspondingly. In the second generation more than 80 percent of the rust was race 17 and less than 20 percent was race 19, and within 6 generations or fewer all or almost all of the rust was race 17 and none or almost none was race 19. In similar experiments with races 17 and 56 on Ceres, Little Club, and Fulcaster wheats, all apparently equally susceptible to the two races, race 17 survived only slightly better than 56 on Ceres, but on the other two varieties it survived far better than race 56, which had disappeared completely or almost completely at the end of seven generations. These results are being fully confirmed by James W. Broyles at the University of Minnesota, who is using a yellow-spore biotype of race 11 of wheat stem rust in mixtures with other races. As the pustules produced by race 11 are yellow and those produced by other races are brick red, the percentages of race 11 can be determined without the necessity of inoculating special differential varieties. Many experiments have been made to find out why some races of wheat stem rust persist better than others in mixtures, but no obvious reasons have been discovered.

Mixtures of other fungi may behave like those of wheat stem rust, which have been used as an example because of the relative ease and precision of identification. Paul E. Hoppe at the University of Wisconsin inoculated corn with equally pathogenic strains of *Diplodia zeae*, which causes ear rot and stalk rot, and the antagonism between strains was so great that only one survived. Similarly V. F. Tapke made experiments with different races of covered smut of barley and observed that there was differential survival of races.

It appeared for a number of years that *Phytophthora infestans*, the fungus that causes late blight of potatoes, could adapt itself to resistant varieties, as Donald Reddick and associates, in their attempts to develop blight-resistant varieties in New York, observed that resistant varieties might be slightly infected when first inoculated with certain races of the blight fungus, but became more severely infected when successive inoculations were made with the blight fungus from the same variety or certain others. Helena L. G. DeBruyn made similar experiments in the Netherlands and confirmed the results of Reddick and others.

H. D. Thurston and C. J. Eide, at the University of Minnesota, have obtained results that indicate that the apparent adaptation of the potato blight fungus is due, in some cases at least, to the selective effect of varieties on a mixed population of biotypes. As an example, two races of the blight fungus infect Irish Cobbler equally well, but one attacks Cherokee and the other does not. When these races were grown in mixture on Irish Cobbler, the Cherokee race decreased rapidly in prevalence but did not disappear entirely; consequently, when the Cherokee variety is inoculated with the blight fungus from the Cobbler variety the infection is very light, because so small a proportion of the racial mixture can attack it. But the blight that does develop is caused by the Cherokee race, and when this is used to inoculate Cherokee again, there is abundant infection because all of the inoculum is potentially effective.

The present authors and some of their associates began a comprehensive investigation of adaptation in 1935. As they had not been able to obtain evidence for adaptive changes in parasitism, they investigated the possibility of adaptation to chemicals in nutrient media. Certain protozoa and bacteria were reputed to develop the ability to adapt themselves to deleterious chemicals; therefore studies were made independently by three groups of investigators to find out if this were true also of fungi. The results were not uniform. In some instances mutation clearly accounted for what could have been considered adaptation. In other instances visible mutation did not account for the results. The results that were obtained by the three groups are given below.

J. J. Christensen and several associates grew the asexual (*Fusarium*) stage of *Gibberella zeae*, which parasitizes corn and causes head blight of wheat and barley, on nutrient media containing, respectively, ethyl mercury phosphate, a widely used seed disinfectant; mercury bichloride; and malachite green in concentrations that dwarfed the growth of the fungus. The fungus produced numerous clearly visible mutants on each medium. Some grew more poorly than the parent on the special media. Some grew about equally well. Some made from 5 to 15 times as much growth as the parent. Some of the mutants, in fact, grew so much faster on the mercury and malachite green media that they soon overgrew the original line completely. The relative ability of the original line and its mutants to tolerate these chemicals persisted through many generations. In the experiments there was no increase in ability to tolerate the chemicals tried, except as a result of visible mutations, which might easily have been overlooked if special methods had not been used to detect them.

E. O. Mader and C. L. Schneider grew the asexual, or conidial, stage (*Monilia*) of *Sclerotinia fructicola*, the cause of brown rot of peaches, plums, and similar fruits, on nutrient media containing injurious amounts of copper sulfate. Some of their results were comparable with those of Christensen: Mutants were produced that grew much better than the parent on the copper media and they differed also in appearance. The increased tolerance for copper was persistent and constant in the mutant lines. But the fungus also acquired increasing tolerance for copper sulfate, without visible mutation, when grown in successive transfer generations on copper-containing media. When the fungus was grown for successive generations on copper-free media, however, it lost the acquired ability.

The third series of Minnesota experiments were made by Coyt Wilson, Frank Stevenson, Donald Munnecke, J. M. Daly, Elisa Hirschhorn, and E. C. Stakman. This group studied the adaptation of corn smut (*Ustilago zeae*) to arsenic. They grew mutable and relatively nonmutable monosporidial lines on nutrient media containing 2,400 parts per million of calcium arsenite. All lines grew poorly at first, but after having been transferred successively for about 10 generations to increasing concentrations of arsenic, all lines eventually grew as well on media containing 12,000 parts per million of calcium arsenite as they had originally grown on 2,400 parts per million, and some lines even grew on 14,000 parts per million. When grown for five successive generations or more on arsenic-free media, the arsenic-adapted lines lost their acquired ability. Numerous mutants appeared in the mutable line growing on arsenic media. Some appeared in the relatively stable line, but only two grew slightly better than the parents on arsenic. It was the consensus of this group of investigators, some of whom worked independently at different times with different lines and with different methods, that perceptible mutations did not account for the results. All smut lines that were tried, including the least mutable ones among thousands that were studied by Stakman and many associates for more than 20 years, increased their ability to grow on arsenic. It is possible that there had been unseen mutation in physiologic characters, but, if so, these mutants escaped detection.

From extensive experiments with several fungi, at Michigan State College about 25 years ago, P. D. Caldis and G. H. Coons concluded that white variants that appeared in single-spore cultures of several fungi were "semipermanent" variations, which differed from the parent form somatically rather than genetically and were comparable with the "dauermodifications" described for paramecia by Victor Jollos. The genetic explanation for this type of semipermanent change is still lacking. It is commonly observed that there may be what is sometimes called a "hangover" effect when fungi are grown for some time on one kind of nutrient medium and then transferred to another kind. This may be accounted for partly by the production of adaptive enzymes or other chemical substances, but the exact explanation cannot be given for many of these temporary changes.

Although it cannot be asserted categorically that parasitic fungi never adapt themselves to resistant varieties of plants, there is convincing evidence that apparent adaptation often is due to the selective effect of crop varieties on a mixed population of biotypes, either because the isolate or line of the fungus was genetically diverse at the beginning, even though it appeared pure by all tests then available, or because it became mixed as a result of inconspicuous mutations. The apparent loss of virulence in a single biotype frequently unquestionably is due to the production of mutants that look like the original biotype but have lost genetic factors for virulence. The apparent acquisition of ability to tolerate injurious chemicals certainly is due to mutation in some instances but appears to occur independently of mutation in others. This is still an unsolved problem and one that requires intensive research. The difficulty of obtaining and maintaining genetically pure cultures of pathogenic fungi cannot be overemphasized in research of this kind.

MANY PATHOGENIC FUNGI MUTATE abundantly on nutrient media. There is evidence that mutation occurs also on host plants in nature. The frequency of mutation differs greatly with the species, with the line or biotype within a species, and with environmental conditions, including some mutagenic agents. In *Ustilago zeae* (corn smut), *Puccinia graminis* (stem rust), and *Venturia inaequalis* (apple scab), the factors for mutant characters have been shown to be inherited through the sexual stage. Factors for mutability in *U. zeae* are inherited just as are factors for other characters.

Mutation has been observed most commonly in cultures on solid nutrient media, where the mutants often appear as conspicuous sectors or patches in the colony. Many mutants remain unobserved, either because the medium on which they appear is not suitable for their growth, or because mutation in physiologic characters and in pathogenicity may occur without change in color, growth type, or other visible characters or because mutants may be obscured by the growth of the parental line.

Mutants of obligate parasites, such as rusts, must manifest themselves on living hosts and often are not easily detected unless they cause conspicuously different infection types or are different in color.

Mutant factors usually are recessive. The parasitic stages of rusts are mostly dicaryotic, and mutation for a single factor in the dicaryophase can remain unexpressed until the factors are brought together in a homozygous condition in a new dicaryotic hybrid. The mutant characters can be expressed immediately in the dicaryophase if the rust is in a heterozygous condition at the respective loci; or if a double mutation occurs, once for each locus in the two conjugate nuclei. A mutation, even if not expressed immediately in the dicaryophase, may be expressed after recombination and segregation of factors during the sexual stage. Certain types of mutation, such as albinism, can be observed easily in haploid pycnia.

MUTATION FOR CULTURAL CHARACTERS is common in all classes of fungi, but the frequency of mutation differs greatly in different species of the same genus and in different lines or biotypes within the species. Among the smuts, as examples, mutation is relatively infrequent in *Ustilago kolleri*, covered smut of oats; *U. avenae*, loose smut of oats; and *Urocystis occulta*, stem smut of rye. On the other hand, it is extremely common in *U. zeae*, common corn smut; *Sphacelotheca sorghi*, covered kernel smut of sorghum; and *Sorosporium reilianum*, head smut of sorghum and corn.

The relative mutability of different biotypes of *Ustilago zeae*, according to Stakman and others, is due to heritable genetic factors. There is clear-cut segregation for mutability and constancy in some crosses between mutable and constant lines, but in other crosses segregates have many degrees of mutability. Mutability and constancy, respectively, were increased by crossing mutable x mutable lines and constant x constant lines, in extensive experiments made by Stakman and others. These investigators isolated the four primary sporidia (gametic segregates) from the promycelium of one of the chlamydospores resulting from a mutable x constant cross. Twenty-five (24 in one case) single sporidia were then isolated from the progeny of each of the four sporidia, and the resulting lines were grown on nutrient agar in duplicate flasks. In the 100 colonies derived from sporidia 1 and 2 there were no mutants, but there were 360 in the 98 colonies derived from sporidia 3 and 4.

Little is known about the numerical frequency of mutation in pathogenic fungi, but it falls well within the range reported for higher plants and for insects. Twenty or more sectors may appear in a single colony of a fungus growing on nutrient agar, but the colony may comprise millions of spores and hyphal cells so that the actual rate of mutation may not be so high as it seems. Christensen and Schneider calculated the frequency of mutation, based on the number of spores in colonies of certain lines of *Helminthosporium sativum* on nutrient agar, as from 1:2,400 to 1:20,000, depending on conditions; and on living plants the rate was approximately 1:2,900. S. P. Chilton, G. B. Lucas, and C. W. Edgerton, at the University of Louisiana, have concluded that certain factors in *Glomerella* sp. mutate at the rate of about 1:1,700. Studies now being made at Minnesota indicate that rate of mutation in some biotypes of *Ustilago zeae* is much higher than in *H. sativum*. In one biotype of *U. zeae*, 0.8 percent of the sporidia derived from a single sporidium were different genetically from the original sporidium. Thus, in a flask of liquid nutrient broth there were about 10 billion sporidia, all derived from one original sporidium; 80 million of the 10 billion were genetically different from the original. There had been at least five different kinds of mutations based on the character of color alone.

Mutation may be important in the plant rusts even though the rate of mutation appears to be low, because there are at least 50,000 billion uredospores of stem rust on an acre of moderately rusted wheat, and even a few mutants per acre could multiply so rapidly under favorable conditions as to produce an extremely numerous population in one growing season.

MUTATION IN FUNGI can occur for most physiological and morphological characters. The change may be in one or more characters and in many degrees of magnitude. Mutation is common for cultural characters, including color, topography, consistency of colonies, direction of growth, nature of margin, zonation, rate of growth, type of growth, and amount of sporulation. There is mutation for physiological characters (such as enzyme production), reaction to known chemicals and to toxic substances, in temperature requirements, and in tendency to mutate. There often is mutation for morphological characters, principally size, shape, and color of spores, fruiting bodies, and resting bodies. Mutation in sexual vigor and in pathogenicity also is common.

Mutation in *Ustilago zeae*, *Helminthosporium sativum*, and many other fungi has been studied at the University of Minnesota continuously for more than 30 years, and many thousands of mutants have been isolated and studied. The number and kinds of mutants produced by *U. zeae* and *H. sativum* are indefinite. Mutants may differ widely or very slightly from their parents. As one example, a series of mutants from a single brown monosporidial line of *U. zeae* ranged from near black through a score of tints to colorless. From another line, a white mutant was isolated from a pigmented line of *U. zeae*, and this white mutant in turn produced white mutants, which in turn produced additional ones. The original mutant was then crossed with certain pigmented lines to find out its breeding behavior, and all of the white segregates from the cross were isolated and kept. In this way, 98 clearly distinct white lines, mutants and segregates, were obtained, which comprised a number of sex groups. Some of the numerous white x white crosses produced large galls, but none produced chlamydospores. When some of the white lines were crossed with pigmented lines, however, both galls and chlamydospores were produced. Evidently, therefore, the original white mutant had lost factors for color production and for nuclear fusion and consequent production of chlamydospores, although the nuclei of opposite sex in some of its progeny had the necessary factors for pairing. Certain of the white x white crosses therefore had the necessary factors for pairing of nuclei and for pathogenicity, but not for the final stage in the sexual process; hence there had been a loss of some but not all of the factors for sex. Although mutation in factors for sex and pathogenicity are common in smuts, complete sex reversal has not been reported.

It is harder to observe mutation for pathogenicity than for cultural characters. When it does occur, however, there usually is partial or complete loss in pathogenicity and only occasionally is there a gain. This is conspicuously true of *H. sativum* and of *U. zeae*, probably the most thoroughly studied in this respect. When successive mutants of *U. zeae* are isolated (that is, mutant from mutant from mutant and so on), a clearly descending series from strongly pathogenic to nonpathogenic is likely to result. Occasional mutants, however, are decidedly and consistently more pathogenic than the parental line. This is true also of other fungi.

Color mutations are not uncommon in rusts, and at least two such recorded cases also involved changes in pathogenicity. There is evidence that uredospores of orange and white races of *Puccinia graminis* are destroyed more easily by ultraviolet light than those with the normal darker color. This may partly account for the relatively poor survival ability and infrequent occurrence of the abnormally light-colored races in nature.

Mutation in pathogenicity occurs occasionally in rusts and it probably is fairly common, although minor mutations are hard to detect. In cooperative investigations between the Department of Agriculture and the University of Minnesota, E. C. Stakman, M. N. Levine, and R. U. Cotter studied four distinct mutations for pathogenicity in race 1 of *Puccinia graminis tritici*, and two of the mutants differed so much from anything previously described that they were designated as new races, numbers 60 and 68. Margaret Newton and Dr. T. Johnson, at the Dominion Laboratory of Plant Pathology, reported two separate mutations for pathogenicity in *Puccinia graminis*, one in the variety *tritici* and the other in the variety *avenae*. Mutation for pathogenicity also has been reported for *Puccinia hordei*, leaf rust of barley; *P. glumarum*, stripe rust of wheat and other cereals; and *P. rubigo-vera tritici*, orange leaf rust of wheat. Some of these rust mutants were less virulent than their parents on some varieties, but some were more virulent than their parents on some varieties of host plants.

IN SOME FUNGI the number of visible mutants produced differs on different media. Whether this is always due to different rates of mutation or to differences in the conspicuousness of the mutants on different media is not known in all instances. Certain sugars, potassium salts, uranium and polonium salts, salts of some of the heavy metals, and some other chemicals generally increase the number of visible mutants. Either high or low temperature may also increase the number, depending on the species or biotype of the fungus. Ultraviolet light, radiations, and some of the bacterial products also are mutagenic.

J. J. Christensen observed that mercury bichloride, ethyl mercury phosphate, and malachite green in nutrient media were decidedly mutagenic to *Gibberella zeae, Helminthosporium sativum, H. carbonum, Fusarium moniliforme,* and *Colletotrichum lini.* The most significant fact derived from these experiments has been discussed in the section on adaptation, where it was pointed out that some of the mutants grew from 5 to 15 times as fast as the parental lines on these chemicals. Christensen and F. R. Davies also found that bacteria-staled media caused very abundant mutation in monosporous lines of *H. sativum.* Among the mutants there were zero, plus, and minus deviations from the original lines in tolerance for the bacterial products, in pathogenicity, in rate of growth, and in many cultural characters.

M. L. Gattani, E. C. Stakman, J. M. Daley, Shih I. Lu, and J. B. Rowell, at Minnesota , increased the rate of mutation in haploid and diploid lines of *Ustilago zeae* by adding uranyl nitrate, at the rate of about one gram per liter, to potato-dextrose agar. Most mutants grew as well as or better than the parental lines on the mutagenic medium. Lu studied 13 characters in 198 uranium-induced mutants from a monosporidial haploid line of *U. zeae* and summated algebraically the zero, plus, and minus deviations for each of the 13 characters for each mutant. About 20 percent had a net minus deviation, 20 percent a plus deviation, and 60 percent a zero deviation, although all were, of course, different from the parent in one or more characters.

Thus, deviation would be zero if a mutant exceeded the parent in size of colonies and in two other characters, had lost some factors for color and for two other characters, but was like the parent in the other seven characters. There would be a plus deviation if the mutant exceeded the parent in two characters, had lost in one, and remained the same in 10, and there would be a minus deviation if the plus and minus numbers were reversed. In similar studies on a solopathogenic (diploid) line, 10 percent of the mutants had a net minus deviation, 30 percent plus, and 60 percent were zero. In similar experiments I. Wahl, also at Minnesota, produced mutants of the common mushroom, *Agaricus campestris,* that were much more vigorous than the original line and that produced mushrooms of more desirable color.

Uranyl nitrate is not equally mutagenic to all fungi, being effective in about 10 percent of 194 species and lines studied by E. C. Stakman, J. B. Rowell, Howard Ehrlich, and others in an investigation made cooperatively at the University of Minnesota by the United States Atomic Energy Commission and the University. Polonium salts have been found more effective than uranium salts as mutagenic agents in the investigations.

From the studies of *Ustilago zeae* it is evident that even the most constant lines may contain mutants that may be unobserved in many serial transfers on nutrient media and become visible only under special conditions or when dilution plates are made from shake-cultures in liquid media. This fact has many obviously important implications. Although there are many known mutations in physiologic characters, there undoubtedly are many more that are not detected because there are no visible evidences of their existence in ordinary cultures. Several mutants with decreased pathogenicity may be present in a flask culture of a monosporidial line of *U. zeae* containing about 10 billion cells. This could result in lowered pathogenicity of a line that originally comprised a single biotype, but a tremendous amount of work would be required to isolate the less virulent mutants if they were slow growing and like the original line in all observable characters except pathogenicity; if the less pathogenic mutants were exceptionally fast growers on artificial media, they would tend to predominate in the culture; and the pathogenicity of the original line would appear to have been lost, when actually the line itself had been suppressed or lost. There is abundant evidence that this is fact, not mere theory.

H. sativum and *U. zeae* have been discussed so fully merely because they have been studied extensively and continuously by many investigators at Minnesota, under the general supervision of the writers, for about a quarter of a century, and because evidence is increasing that the principles derived from them apply in varying degrees to many plant pathogens. Above all, it is noteworthy that in *U. zeae* where single, haploid sporidia can be isolated and propagated asexually, thus theoretically establishing single-biotype cultures, it is extremely difficult, because of visible or invisible mutations, to maintain the genetic purity even of the apparently least-mutable monosporidial lines. At best, purity appears to be relative only.

STABILITY among mutants differs greatly: Many mutants continue mutating indefinitely. Others are relatively stable. There are many intermediate degrees of mutability. Many mutants of *Helminthosporium sativum*, *H. oryzae*, *H. carbonum*, *Gibberella zeae*, and *Fusarium lini* have been grown side by side with their parental lines for many years and have retained their distinctive characters. Some have been grown on many kinds of media several years, and have retained their distinctive cultural characters. Many mutant lines of *Ustilago zeae* have been grown under a wide range of conditions for many years without perceptible change, but others continue to mutate abundantly. C. S. Holton, in longtime experiments started at the University of Minnesota and continued under State and Federal cooperation at Washington State College, maintained an albino mutant of covered smut of oats, *Ustilago kolleri*, through many asexual and sexual generations during the past 18 years.

G. W. Keitt and M. H. Langford, at the University of Wisconsin, passed three haploid lines of *Venturia inaequalis* through the leaves of the McIntosh apples four successive times without perceptible change in cultural characters. J. J. Christensen obtained similar results by passing mutants of *Diplodia zeae*, *Gibberella zeae*, *Helminthosporium sativum*, and *H. oryzae* through their respective hosts, although in one case the cultural characters of a mutant of *H. sativum* were changed slightly. Mutant characters of *Ustilago zeae* have persisted through the sexual stage on corn plants, even though they sometimes were recombined with other characters.

HETEROCARYOSIS means that condition in which the hyphae, or individual cells of the hyphae, contain nuclei with different genetic factors. Heterocaryosis can come about independently of sex. From extensive investigations by H. N. Hansen and W. C. Snyder at the University of California, it appears that heterocaryosis is common in many of the fungi in which the sexual stage is not known, the Fungi Imperfecti. This condition can result from ordinary fusions between hyphae of different kinds or lines of fungi, and would be roughly comparable with natural grafts in higher plants.

Sydney Dickinson, in experiments

at the University of Minnesota, grew a red *Fusarium* and a white one side by side, watched some of the hyphae fuse, and then cut off hyphal tips produced by the fused hyphae and transplanted them to nutrient agar. Some of the hyphal tips produced pink colonies, all of which, however, later separated into red and white. It appears, therefore, that nuclei from the red and white lines were associated for a time and then became dissociated. Even if a hyphal branch started with a single nucleus, mutation could occur during successive nuclear divisions and result in heterocaryosis.

Whatever the origin of the heterocaryotic condition, there is likely to be dissociation or regrouping of the different kinds of nuclei. An example: If the different kinds of nuclei in a hypha are designated as A, B, and C, branches may be produced which contain any one of the three, or any combination of two, or all three of them. Consequently, lines with different characters can be isolated from such cultures. Heterocaryosis is to be distinguished from the dicaryotic condition in which two nuclei of opposite sex are paired and divide simultaneously during growth of the fungus, so that all of the derivatives of a given dicaryotic cell also have paired nuclei of opposite sex that are kept close together by some attraction which seems to be lacking when sex is not involved as in heterocaryosis.

VARIATION DUE TO HYBRIDIZATION is common and extensive in plant pathogenic fungi. Many recombinations result from crosses between different biotypes, races, and varieties within some species, between species, and between some genera. Intraspecific hybridization has been studied especially in certain rusts, smuts, and in *Venturia* spp. that cause scab of apples and pears. Interspecific and intergeneric crosses have been studied most extensively in the smuts.

Hybridization within species can result in changes of pathogenicity because of the production of numerous new biotypes and races, with a widening of host range or increase of virulence for certain varieties of crop plants. It also can result in recombinations for many physiologic and morphologic characters. The practical importance of hybridization in nature is clearly apparent in certain smuts and rusts, and, together with mutation, may result in important changes in the reaction of varieties of crop plants to disease. In the smuts, recombination of morphologic characters used in identification of species can complicate problems of classification.

In the rusts and smuts there are dicaryotic hybrids, as the two nuclei of opposite sex remain associated without fusing during the parasitic life of the fungus. In some fungi, including the smuts and rusts, distinct phases in the life cycle are associated with the nature and number of nuclei in the cells, as explained partly earlier. The terms used to designate these phases are haplophase, dicaryophase, and diplophase.

In the haplophase of smuts and rusts, each cell has a single nucleus in the haploid condition—it has half as many chromosomes as the diploid nuclei and is therefore comparable with either a sperm nucleus or an egg nucleus. Prerequisite to sexual reproduction and to hybridization, therefore, are nuclei of at least two kinds sexually. In the smuts and rusts there are no visible differences between the sexes. The only known test of sexual difference is performance, the pairing and fusion of the haploid nuclei. In both of these groups the sexual process extends over a long time because nuclei of opposite sex pair and remain paired a long time before they complete the sexual act by fusing.

The phase of development in which the cells and spores have paired haploid nuclei of opposite sex is the dicaryophase, which means the two-nuclei phase. The mycelium in this condition is sometimes called a dicaryophyte. When the two haploid nuclei fuse, they produce diploid nuclei, containing double the number of chromosomes, half from one haploid nucleus and half from the other. The stage in which the cells have diploid nuclei is the diplophase. Thus, if black and pink haploid sporidial lines of smut of opposite sex are mixed together, the sporidia will conjugate in pairs and thus bring together the nuclei B and P. The dicaryophase then has paired nuclei, B+P, and is called a dicaryotic hybrid because the hybridization is not complete until the B and P fuse to make BP. Similarly, if races 1 and 2 of the wheat stem rust are crossed, the resulting dicaryotic hybrid has in each cell one nucleus of race 1 and one of race 2, and the pathogenicity is determined by this dicaryotic hybrid. The nuclei of races 1 and 2 do not fuse until teliospores are formed. The diploid nucleus resulting from the fusion has factors for pathogenicity from both race 1 and race 2; the hybridization is complete and segregation and recombination of factors can occur, and new races can result.

In the rusts the aecial and uredial stages are dicaryotic. As the parasitic uredial stage can propagate asexually, the characters of dicaryotic hybrids (dicaryophytes) can be studied. In the smuts, only the saprophytic haplophase can be propagated clonally, except for some diploid lines of Ustilago zeae. In both groups the parasitic dicaryophase terminates with the fusion of the two nuclei in the cells and the production of the diploid teliospores, usually called chlamydospores in smuts, which produce only a promycelium, or basidium, on which the gametic sporidia are formed following reduction division. In these fungi, then, the terms dicaryotic hybrids, hybrid teliospores, and hybrid chlamydospores are often used.

STUDIES OF HYBRIDIZATION between biotypes within species are most feasible in those smut fungi that produce haploid sporidia on a four-celled promycelium, such as Ustilago zeae and Sphacelotheca sorghi. When two haploid lines are crossed and the four primary sporidia from promycelia of the resulting diploid chlamydospores are removed and permitted to multiply on nutrient media, segregation for cultural characters is evident in the resulting colonies. When the haploid segregates are mated, the results of segregation for sex factors are evident. All possible segregation ratios for cultural characters, for sex, and for mutability may occur. All four lines may be different, all may be alike, or there may be a 2:2, 3:1, or 1:3 segregation for each character, with all possible combinations between characters. All four lines may appear sexually identical on the basis of intragroup matings, but they may prove different when mated with other tester lines, as there are multiple sex groups in both species. As many as 40 to 60 haploid segregates from a single cross of Ustilago zeae have been studied and all were different and did not include parental types. Although mutation may account for some of this diversity, there is conclusive evidence that there can be very extensive recombinations of almost all characters studied, as shown by investigations made at the University of Minnesota by L. J. Tyler, Syed Vaheeduddin, M. A. Petty, and M. F. Kernkamp, which will be summarized.

Tyler made 10 crosses between monosporidial lines from the promycelia of three chlamydospores of Sphacelotheca sorghi taken from a single smutted kernel. The progeny differed from each other in size of chlamydospores, size and hardness of sori (smutted kernels of sorghum), time required for spore germination, and degree of pathogenicity. Vaheeduddin produced gray, brown, and gray-brown peridia (the membrane surrounding smutted kernels) by inoculating sorghum with different combinations of these monosporidial lines and also produced a parasitic race clearly different from anything previously described. Had this race been produced in nature, it would have increased the pathogenicity of the "chlamydospore race," and appropriate differential hosts would have been needed to detect and separate it.

Petty and Kernkamp proved that promycelial characters of *U. zeae* varied with the combinations of monosporidial lines that produced them, and other investigators have shown that pathogenicity, chlamydospore production, size and color of sporidia, and tendency to produce sporidia or mycelium vary widely with the cross. Kernkamp, as an example, crossed sporidial and mycelial lines of *U. zeae*, and sporidia and hyphal branches were formed in all possible ratios on the promycelia of the hybrid chlamydospores.

Despite the wide diversity of haploid lines in smuts, group characters may be fairly constant. In experiments made at the University of Minnesota, chlamydospore collections of *U. zeae* from Ohio, Kansas, Minnesota, and other States retained their distinctive pathogenicity when several varieties and lines of corn were inoculated with three successive annual crops of chlamydospores. Likewise, collections from Minnesota, Wisconsin, Louisiana, and Mexico tended to produce haploid lines with group cultural characters: Most lines from Wisconsin were light in color; those from Louisiana were predominantly dark; those from Minnesota were intermediate. There appear, therefore, to be group characters, with great diversity within the group; and the group may change with varying degrees of readiness. The new race of *Sphacelotheca sorghi* synthesized by Vaheeduddin, for example, easily could have changed the group character and could have been isolated from the group only by the selective effect of differential hosts.

At the University of Wisconsin, G. W. Keitt and others made crosses between single ascospore cultures of the apple scab fungus, *Venturia inaequalis*. From the resulting perithecia the parental types and new types were isolated. Factors for pathogenicity segregated in the first or second nuclear division in the ascus, and factors for the infection type produced by each segregate on a given host appeared to be in a single locus, with multiple alleles determining infection types on different varieties of apples. Langford and Keitt made crosses similarly between single-ascospore lines of *V. pyrina*, pear scab, and segregates differed in pathogenicity for certain varieties of pears, in time required for formation of the perithecia, and in numbers of ascospores produced.

S. P. Chilton and others at the University of Louisiana also obtained evidence for hybridization between different isolates of *Glomerella*.

In 1928 V. Goldschmidt in Germany crossed two races of *Ustilago violacea* smut of pinks, one of which attacked *Silene saxifraga* but not *Melandrium alba;* and the other attacked *Melandrium* but not *Silene*. The hybrid, however, attacked both hosts. Similarly, C. S. Holton and H. A. Rodenhiser, of the Department of Agriculture, crossed race T8 with T9 and race T8 with T10 of *Tilletia caries*, the reticulate-spore stinking smut of wheat. Some of the hybrids attacked the wheat cross Hussar x Hohenheimer, hitherto resistant to all known races of both *T. caries* and *T. foetida*, the smooth-spore species of stinking smut.

Races of wheat stem rust can cross readily and thus result in the production of many biotypes or races, including some that are new. Races of rust may or may not be dicaryotic hybrids. Some are homozygous and others are very heterozygous. Thus, races 9 and 36 are relatively homozygous and usually breed true when they are selfed; but race 53, which is highly heterozygous, has segregated into as many as 18 races when "selfed" in the sexual stage on barberry. Many experiments have been made to determine the results of crossing races of wheat stem rust, and in 1929 W. L. Waterhouse concluded from experiments made at Sydney University that new races could be produced by crossing known races. Similarly, Margaret Newton and T.

Johnson made extensive experiments at the Dominion Laboratory of Plant Pathology to determine the number and kinds of races produced by crossing known races and to discover the genetic principles involved. When the relatively homozygous races 9 and 36 were crossed, the first generation hybrid was race 17, but when this was selfed it produced race 36, race 17, and six other races. Newton and Johnson studied the dominance of factors for virulence by crossing races, one of which could attack certain varieties that the other could not. Thus, the nonvirulence of race 9 for Kanred wheat was dominant over the virulence of race 36, but the virulence of race 9 for three varieties of durum was dominant over the nonvirulence of race 36, and the nonvirulence of race 36 for Vernal emmer was dominant over the virulence of race 9. If factors for virulence in one of the nuclei of the dicaryophase are recessive and dominated by those for nonvirulence, a race may produce races more virulent than itself after being "selfed" in the sexual stage on the barberry, because the more virulent races could be "double recessives."

That hybridization and segregation in *Puccinia graminis* are going on in nature is clear from studies of races and biotypes on and near barberry bushes. E. C. Stakman and W. Q. Loegering, in extensive studies made cooperatively by the Department of Agriculture and the University of Minnesota, identified 43 races and biotypes of *P. graminis tritici*, wheat stem rust, in 1949, in the immediate vicinity of three groups of barberry bushes in Lebanon County, Pa., and only five races in nonbarberry areas of the State. In 1940 they isolated races 9, 10, 14, 24, 40, 55, 69, 77, 79, 83, 117, 125, 126, 140, 146, and 147 from or near barberry bushes but not elsewhere in the United States and Mexico. The ratio between races and uredial collections is about 1:50; that for aecial material is about 1:5 or less. Although only 14 races of *P. graminis avenae* are known, the presently de-structive races 7, 8, 10, and 12 were found repeatedly near barberry before they became generally distributed; the potentially dangerous races 6 and 13 were still found only on or near barberry bushes during the growing season of 1952, but they are likely to become more widely distributed in future.

That there are extensive recombinations in the sexual stage of autoecious rusts, those that produce all stages on the same plants, is shown by the researches of H. H. Flor on flax rust, *Melampsora lini*, made at the North Dakota Agricultural Experiment Station. Flor isolated 64 races from the F_2 progeny of a cross between race 22 from South America and race 24 from the United States. Of these, 62 were previously unknown, and some were more virulent on certain varieties of flax than either parental race.

MANY CROSSES have been made between varieties of *Puccinia graminis*, principally between the varieties *tritici* and *secalis*. Although there is considerable information on parasitic behavior of the immediate crosses, little is known about their subsequent progenies. Many of the varietal hybrids possessed the pathogenic capabilities of one or the other parental variety, while others were less pathogenic, being more or less intermediate between the two parents; but a few differed strikingly in their parasitic capabilities. In some crosses, many new races were produced in the F_1 generation, which is expected if one or both of the parents are heterozygous.

At the University of Minnesota nine physiologic races were obtained by crossing the homozygous race 36 of the *tritici* variety with *agrostidis* (redtop) variety. All of the nine races infected wheat, but none infected redtop or other grasses of the genus *Agrostis*. From a cross between race 36 of wheat stem rust (*tritici*) and race 11 of rye stem rust (*secalis*), eight races of *tritici* and two of *secalis* were isolated. Two of the *tritici* races were new and intermediate in pathogenicity between the parents. Similar results have been obtained at the Dominion Laboratory of Plant Pathology at Winnipeg, Canada. The varieties *tritici* and *secalis* are highly interfertile and seem closely related, as both can infect barley and several grasses about equally well. One hybrid between the two attacked barley, but not wheat or rye, and could therefore be designated as variety *hordei*. From another cross between the *tritici* and *secalis* varieties, M. N. Levine and R. U. Cotter isolated a hybrid race that attacked wheat, rye, and barley heavily, thus combining the pathogenicity of both parents.

T. Johnson and Margaret Newton in Canada crossed *tritici* and *avenae* (oats variety) and obtained a hybrid that attacked certain varieties of both wheat and oats, which neither of the parents could do. Although the host range of the hybrid was wider than that of either parent, pathogenicity was weaker than that of the parents on their respective hosts. More studies on varietal crosses are needed.

AT LEAST EIGHT SPECIES and genera of cereal and grass smuts have been crossed:

Ustilago avenae x *U. kolleri* (loose smut x covered smut of oats).

Ustilago avenae x *U. perennans* (loose smut of oats x smut of tall oatgrass).

Ustilago hordei x *U. nigra* (covered smut x false loose smut of barley).

Tilletia caries x *T. foetida* (low bunt x high bunt of wheat).

Sphacelotheca sorghi x *S. cruenta* (covered kernel smut x loose kernel smut of sorghum).

Sphacelotheca sorghi x *Sorosporium reilianum* (covered kernel smut x head smut of sorghum).

Sphacelotheca cruenta x *Sorosporium reilianum* (loose kernel smut x head smut of sorghum).

Sphacelotheca destruens x *S. syntherismae* (two head smuts of grasses).

Species involved in interspecific crosses differ considerably in morphological and physiological characters;

therefore they are suitable for studying the recombination and segregation of two or more distinct characters, such as type and consistency of the sori (spore masses), markings and color of chlamydospores, and pathogenicity.

Fertile interspecific dicaryotic hybrids are easily made between the eight combinations listed above. In some instances the F_1 chlamydospores germinate normally; in some cases chlamydospores and sporidia germinate poorly or abnormally.

THE INHERITANCE of factors for spore-wall markings of hybrid chlamydospores of smuts usually is simple. When one with smooth-walled spores is crossed with one that has spiny-walled spores (echinulate), factors for spiny wall tend to dominate over those for smooth wall, but in crosses between species of *Tilletia* with smooth and reticulate-walled spores (those with netlike ridges) more than one set of factors apparently is involved. In some crosses smooth completely dominates over reticulate, and in others reticulate is partly dominant over smooth, and intergrading types of reticulation may occur in the F_1 and F_2 chlamydospore generations.

The F_1 sori (spore masses) produced by interspecific crosses of smuts tend to be intermediate between the two parents. There may, however, be considerable variation, depending on the species involved in the cross. Different dicaryophytes of the same cross also may produce sori of several shapes and sizes. In the F_2 generation, and sometimes in later ones, there frequently are many diverse types. The factors for different sorus characters are usually inherited independently of each other and of those for sex and pathogenicity; hence, new combinations of morphological and pathogenic characters are common.

The range of variation in types of smut is well illustrated in crosses between the loose and covered smuts of oats. When varieties of oats are inoculated with different combinations of monosporidial lines of *Ustilago avenae*, loose smut, and *U. kolleri*, covered smut, many kinds of smutted heads (panicles) may be produced, ranging from loose to covered, through many intermediate types. One combination may produce loose smut on one variety and covered smut on another, and another combination may produce the same type of smut on both varieties, which indicates that the type of smutted panicles is determined by both the fungus and the variety of oats.

In interspecific crosses between the barley smuts *Ustilago hordei* (covered type) and *U. nigra* (false loose type), made by C. C. Allison at Minnesota, the F_1 head types were intermediate, but tended toward the loose type. The progeny from the F_1 chlamydospores produced not only the parental types of sori, compact heads with smooth spores and loose heads with echinulate spores, but several new types, including intermediates with smooth or echinulate spores, compact heads with echinulate spores, and loose heads with smooth spores.

L. J. Tyler and C. P. Shumway, at Minnesota, made crosses between the sorghum smuts *Sphacelotheca sorghi* (covered kernel smut) and *Sorosporium reilianum* (head smut). The characters of the F_1 sori and of the chlamydospores tended to be intermediate between those of the parents. Syed Vaheeduddin crossed *Sorosporium reilianum* (head smut of sorghum) with *Sphacelotheca cruenta* (loose kernel smut of sorghum). Different combinations of monosporidial lines produced sori differing in shape and size. Some of the F_1 sori resembled one or the other parent, while others were intermediate. Similar types were obtained again in F_2 from inoculating with different combinations of f_1 (gametic) segregates. Naturally, there was segregation of factors for many other characters also, such as size and echinulation of chlamydospores, cultural characters, sex, and pathogenicity. Some of the hybrids between the two smuts had pronounced hybrid

vigor. They caused extreme elongation of the ovaries of sorghum, thus producing an effect similar to that caused by the long smut of sorghum, *Tolyposporium filiferum*. Moreover, the chlamydospores, although intermediate in size between the sizes of the parental spores, germinated over an exceptionally wide range of temperature and produced promycelia two and a half to three times as long as those of either parent, and the sporidia and hyphal branches were correspondingly large. In addition, some haploid segregates had extraordinary tolerance for certain chemicals. Since sporidia and promycelial cells are haploid, not diploid as in higher plants, a study of hybrid vigor in smut fungi may aid in interpreting that in higher plants.

INTERSPECIFIC HYBRIDIZATION apparently produces new parasitic races of some smuts in nature. New virulent races of buff smuts of oats have been produced artificially by crossing *Ustilago avenae* with *U. kolleri*. Some of the hybrids had a wider host range than either parent. Some of the hybrid races of the buff smut attacked both the susceptible variety Monarch, and the variety Gothland, which was immune to the parental buff race. The interspecific hybrids combined some of the factors for pathogenicity of both parents. It appears that new races of buff smut can be produced readily by crossing any buff race with normal black races of *U. avenae* or of *U. kolleri*.

Many new parasitic races of *Tilletia* that cause bunt or stinking smut of wheat have been produced by hybridization between *T. caries* and *T. foetida*. Although some hybrid races are less virulent than either parent, others combine factors for pathogenicity of both parents. Crosses between *T. foetida* and *T. caries* can result in new morphologic types also. As an example, the hybrid sori and chlamydospores were smaller in one cross than those of either parent. Hybrids also may have varying degrees of spore-

wall reticulations, and size of chlamydospores can vary considerably. Such
hybrids occur in nature also, and in
some cases have been given taxonomic
rank, such as *T. caries intermedia.*

That there are innumerable species,
parasitic races, and biotypes of plant
disease fungi is a banal truism. That
innumerable new biotypes and races
can be produced by mutation, hybridization, and heterocaryosis has been
shown by extensive experimentation.
That new biotypes and parasitic races
often appear in nature is known from
long-continued observation. The new
biotypes and races, even though they
were produced infrequently, could still
become widely prevalent in a short
time because many fungi are prodi-
giously prolific and can be disseminated widely and quickly by the wind.
A single kernel of smutted wheat
contains between 2 million and 12
million spores; a single pustule of
wheat stem rust may contain a quarter
of a million spores; stem rust may
produce 70 billion spores on a single
barberry bush; there are about 50,000
billion rust spores on one acre of fairly
heavily rusted wheat. Countless billions of spores are literally carried on
the wings of the wind. Many of the
new biotypes that are produced in
these enormous populations are not
dangerous, but some are. The potentially rapid multiplication of new
biotypes and parasitic races of the
fungi and the potentially rapid spread
make the more virulent ones potentially dangerous, and too often potentiality has become reality.

The practical implications of the vast
variation in plant pathogenic fungi are
manifold, but the most important is
the menace to food supplies. Some of
the most devastating epidemic diseases
of basic food and feed crops can be
controlled economically only by the
development of disease-resistant varieties. New parasitic races have repeatedly appeared to attack these
varieties in the past and the menace
still exists for the future. The genetic
diversity and phenotypic variability of

many of the most destructive pathogens are so great as to create extremely complex problems of disease control
in the present and to raise the question
as to how complex they can become in
the future. How much virulence can
nature put into plant pathogens and
how much resistance can man put into
crop plants? This is one of the most
important questions for present and
future agriculture. It can be answered
only by basic studies to determine the
limits of genic combinations for virulence in pathogens and for productivity and disease resistance in crop plants.

E. C. STAKMAN *is head of the department
of plant pathology and botany, University
of Minnesota, and an agent in the United
States Department of Agriculture. He has
devoted his professional life principally to
basic and practical studies of diseases of
crop plants and the fungi that cause them.
He is widely known for investigations on
the epidemiology and physiologic specialization in stem rust of wheat and the genetics of
the smut fungi. At Minnesota and elsewhere
he has participated in breeding programs for
disease-resistant varieties, particularly of
wheat and oats. He was president in 1949 of
the American Association for the Advance-
ment of Science. His current activities include membership in the executive committee
of the National Science Board, in the
Advisory Committee for Biology and Medicine of the United States Atomic Energy
Commission, and chairmanship of the Committee on International Cooperation of the
American Phytopathological Society.*

J. J. CHRISTENSEN *is professor of plant
pathology at the University of Minnesota,
where he obtained the doctor of philosophy
degree in 1925. He has made extensive
studies of cereal diseases and the genetics of
plant pathogens in relation to breeding for
resistance, and has participated in cereal
breeding programs. In addition to work at
Minnesota, Dr. Christensen has studied
genetics of plant pathogens in Europe, has
been adviser to SCAP on plant diseases in
Japan, and has traveled extensively in
South America on a study of cereal diseases.
He is past president of the American
Phytopathological Society.*

Bacteria, Fungi, and Insects

J. G. Leach

Insects influence fungus and bacterial diseases of plants in several ways.

Without disseminating the microorganisms themselves, insects may make wounds on a plant through which fungi or bacteria may enter. An example is white grubs, which often feed on the roots of raspberry plants and make wounds through which the bacteria that cause crown gall gain entrance from the soil. We have no evidence, however, that the white grubs are involved in the spread of the bacteria. Curculios that feed on young peaches and plums likewise make wounds through which windborne spores of the brown rot fungus enter and cause infection.

But some insects spread pathogens from diseased plants to healthy plants without wounding the plants. When bees transmit the bacteria causing fire blight of apples and pears from diseased to healthy blossoms, they make no wounds on the blossoms but introduce the bacteria into the nectar, where they grow and later penetrate the tissues through the nectar glands. Another example is the relationship between flies and the ergot disease of rye. In early stages of infection, the fungus produces large quantities of spores in a sugary exudate, which has a foul and carrionlike odor and attracts flies. The flies feed on it and become contaminated with the fungus spores. They transport the spores to healthy flowers, where infection takes place without the need of any wounds.

More efficient is the insect that transmits the pathogen from plant to plant and also makes the wound through which infection takes place. That kind of relationship exists between the elm bark beetles and the Dutch elm disease, the striped cucumber beetle and the bacterial wilt of cucurbits, and many other diseases transmitted by insects that feed upon the plants by chewing the tissues or sucking the sap.

In a few instances insects may influence the development of a disease although they neither disseminate the pathogen nor make wounds through which it enters the plant. So it is when beetles of *Monochamus* species bore into the heartwood of trees or logs already infected with wood-rotting fungi and hasten the growth of the fungi and consequently the rotting of the log.

Almost everywhere, except possibly the humid Tropics, some period of the year is unfavorable for the growth of fungi and bacteria. Then the pathogen has the problem of survival. In the North the critical period is winter, when temperatures are too low for growth of both pathogen and host. In the warmer, drier regions, heat and drought may be limiting factors. The successful pathogens are the ones that have some special adaptations that enable them to survive winter cold and summer heat so that they are ready to cause infection when conditions again are favorable. Some pathogens are adapted to survival in the soil. Others survive in roots or stems of perennial plants or in the seeds of annual plants. Some produce resistant spores that withstand unfavorable conditions.

Some fungus and bacterial pathogens that are transmitted primarily by insects can survive within the body of the insects that transmit them. The bacteria that cause wilt of sweet corn survive the winter in the bodies of the corn flea beetle. Those that cause the wilt of cucurbits survive in the bodies of the striped and spotted cucumber beetles. The fungus that causes the Dutch elm disease may overwinter in the body of the elm bark beetle. Fungi that cause the blue stain disease of pines survive in the bodies of the pine bark beetles. Pathogens like these, which survive within the bodies of their insect vectors, withstand the digestive fluids in the insects, while many other micro-organisms are killed and digested.

When fungi and bacteria survive in the bodies of their insect carriers, there is often a mutualistic symbiotic relationship—a mutual aid arrangement. The fungi or bacteria may supply digestive enzymes or vitamins that the insect needs. They may condition trees so that insects may breed in them or they may provide a more concentrated source of nitrogen for the insects. In return, the insect protects the micro-organism against unfavorable environments, transmits them to susceptible plants, and often makes the wounds through which they infect.

Such associations between insects and plant pathogens are not matters of chance. They are the result of a long evolutionary process. Sometimes insects have developed special organs in their bodies for the purpose of harboring the micro-organism in relatively pure culture. The females of some species that have become dependent upon micro-organisms have special organs and devices in their bodies designed to contaminate the eggs so that the new generation will have a supply of the necessary micro-organisms. A rot of apples associated with the apple maggot fly is caused by bacteria that are transmitted in this way. The female fly has special pouches in the walls of the oviduct that harbor the bacteria and are so arranged that they provide a mechanism that contaminates each egg with the bacteria as it is deposited into the tissues of the apple.

Wind, water, man, and animals also spread plant diseases. Only a few fungus and bacterial diseases depend entirely on insects for their spread and development. Wind scatters spores of pathogenic fungi, but only a small percentage of them fall upon the proper plant under conditions necessary for infection. Most of them are wasted. But spores that are adapted to dissemination by insects are taken usually directly to a plant that is susceptible to their attack and are often deposited in wounds where infection occurs immediately. Thus, wind dissemination is much more wasteful of inoculum and is more subject to the vagaries of the weather; insect dissemination leaves less to chance and is more economical of inoculum. The situation is like the pollination of flowering plants by wind and by insects. The highly developed adaptive mechanisms of insect pollination have evolved from the more primitive and less efficient mechanisms of wind pollination. A similar evolutionary trend appears to exist in the methods of dissemination of fungus and bacterial diseases.

A more striking parallel with insect pollination is found in the rust fungi, in which insects are instrumental in transporting the sexual elements of the pathogen in a manner quite comparable to insect pollination of flowering plants. Many of the rust fungi are heterothallic, which means that they form two kinds of mycelium that differ sexually. Before the rust fungus can complete its entire life cycle, pycniospores of one sex must be transported to receptive hyphae of the opposite sex so that fertilization can be accomplished.

The phenomenon has been studied in the black stem rust of cereals (*Puccinia graminis*). The rust is heteroecious, which means that it lives part of its life on cereals and grasses and part on the common barberry (*Berberis vulgaris*). The spores that infect the barberry leaf are of two sexes, designated as + and −. They are in the haploid condition and neither one can complete the life cycle until there has been a sexual fusion of the two. The + or − spore infects the barberry leaf and forms a mycelium of its own kind (+ or −). From them are formed (on the upper side of the barberry leaf) small fruiting bodies (pycnia), each of which produces myriads of pycniospores of the corresponding sex. Each pycnium produces also a number of short hyphae, which protrude from the pycnium and serve as receptive organs comparable to the stigma of flowering plants. They are known as receptive hyphae. Before aeciospores can be produced on the under side of the leaf, a pycniospore of one sex must reach a receptive hyphae of the opposite sex and fuse with it. The nucleus from the pynciospore passes into the receptive hypha and fuses with a nucleus of the opposite sex. In this process it fertilizes or "diploidizes" the mycelium within the leaf tissues so that aeciospores can be formed.

Since the pycnia producing these sexual organs of different sexes are often separated on a leaf or occur on different leaves, a way is needed to bring the pycniospores to the right kind of receptive hypha. Nature has provided a mechanism that tends to insure successful fertilization. The pycnia are produced on the upper leaf surface on a bright orange spot. The pycniospores are liberated in a drop of nectar that has a high sugar content and a fragrant odor. The bright spots, the fragrance, and the food attract insects of many kinds, especially flies. The insects in feeding move from one pycnium to another and by transporting the spores to receptive hyphae bring the opposite sexes together.

Since individual diseases may be transmitted in several ways, it is desirable to know the relative importance of the different methods. Such information often is necessary for working out effective control measures. It has been proved that the bacteria causing wilt of cucurbits survive the winter only within the bodies of cucumber beetles and in nature are transmitted only by the beetles. It is obvious therefore that effective control of the beetles will control the disease. But when insect transmission is one of several methods, the relative importance of

each must be established and control measures modified accordingly. An example: The seed-corn maggot is known to transmit blackleg of potatoes and other bacterial soft rots, but it is only one of several means of transmission and even though the insects were completely controlled the diseases would be spread to some extent by other means.

It is especially difficult to determine accurately the importance of an insect vector in relation to other means of spread if one cannot control the vector. We knew for a long time, for example, that the brown rot of peaches might have some connection with the feeding and egg-laying of the curculio, but since no effective means of controlling the insect was available we could get no accurate data as to its importance. When the newer organic insecticides like DDT became available, however, better control of the curculio was possible, and we learned that less brown rot occurred in orchards in which the curculio was checked.

We have no evidence that the curculio is of great importance in disseminating the spores of the brown rot fungus, which are readily wind-borne, but it is obvious that the curculio influences the development of brown rot by making wounds on immature fruits through which the wind-blown spores are able to infect. The brown rot fungus has difficulty in infecting immature fruits if the skin is uninjured, but it grows readily in punctures made by the curculio. Spores formed early on the injured green fruits provide an abundant source of inoculum for the ripening fruit later in the season.

Often more than one kind of insect may transmit the same disease. Since 1891, when M. B. Waite, a pioneer in the Department of Agriculture, first showed that the honey bee could transmit fire blight of orchard fruits, much has been written, pro and con, about the role of bees in the spread of the disease. The importance of the bee is often overemphasized by failure to recognize that other insects regularly transmit the disease and that wind, rain, and other agents also are involved. The bacteria commonly live over winter in cankers on the larger branches of the tree from which they are liberated in early spring in a sticky exudate.

Flies and ants that feed on the exudate are chiefly responsible for transporting bacteria from the cankers to the blossom and for initiating the first blight infection of the new growth. Bees and wasps, flies, and other insects that visit the blossoms transmit the disease from blossom to blossom. Aphids, leafhoppers, and other sucking insects transmit it to the young green shoots. In the meantime, wind-blown rain may also spread the bacteria throughout the tree and man in his pruning operations may aid in spreading it throughout the orchard. Transmission of this disease is a complicated process, and proper evaluation of the different means of spread, although difficult, is essential to an understanding of its nature.

Those who have studied the Dutch elm disease have shown that several different insects under some conditions may transmit the disease. In the United States the principal vector is the smaller European elm bark beetle (*Scolytus multistriatus*). The native elm bark beetle (*Hylurgopinus rufipes*) may also transmit the disease, but is much less effective. The greater efficiency of the former is due to its feeding habits.

Both insects breed under the bark of infected trees and the fungus pathogen grows and forms spores in their breeding tunnels so that the new broods of each species have equal opportunities for becoming contaminated with the fungus spores. But when the new crops of beetles emerge, their behavior is quite different. Those of the European species fly to healthy trees and feed on the young branches and in the process inoculate the tree with the disease. Those of the native species, however,

do not feed on young twigs. They may bore into the trunk of healthy trees but they rarely penetrate deep enough to reach the sapwood and inoculate the tree. Neither insect is able to establish breeding tunnels in healthy trees, but those trees which were inoculated by the European species when it fed on the small branches are weakened so that they are subject to the attack of both species. These diseased and beetle-infested trees supply a new brood of contaminated beetles. Thus a slight difference in feeding habit may greatly influence the efficiency of an insect vector.

In a study of insect transmission of plant diseases, consideration must therefore be given to the feeding and breeding habits of all the insects that are potential vectors. Many other insects develop in infected trees and have abundant opportunities to become contaminated with the pathogens but are of no significance as vectors. For example, the wood-boring beetles (Buprestidae and Cerambycidae) breed in infected trees and come in contact with the pathogenic fungus, but when they attack the new tree the adult female of the wood-boring beetle does not bore into the tree but deposits her eggs on the surface or in niches in the bark. When the eggs hatch the young larvae bore into the tree, and because they have had little or no opportunity to become contaminated with the fungus they rarely serve as vectors.

More than 40 species of insects visit rye blossoms and feed on the spores of the ergot fungus, but not all have equal importance as carriers of ergot. Among those that feed on the spores are certain species of pollen-eating flies. They also regularly visit healthy flowers and feed on the pollen. In doing so they transmit the disease. Thus they are more effective vectors than those that do not eat pollen and visit healthy flowers only by chance or not at all.

An important aspect of plant pathology is the study of the influence of environment on disease. When the diseases are caused by fungi or bacteria the study is complicated by the effect of the environment on two different organisms, the micro-organism and the crop plant, and also on the interaction of the two. If the disease is transmitted by an insect, one has to study three different organisms and their interactions.

The prevalence of a plant disease can be determined more by the influence of the environment on the insect vector than by its influence on the disease itself. That is obvious in such diseases as bacterial wilt of cucurbits, for which insects are the only known means of transmission. Any weather condition that influences the abundance of the cucumber beetles must also influence the prevalence of the disease.

Bacterial wilt of sweet corn is more prevalent following mild winters than it is following cold winters. It is generally agreed that this is because of the survival in mild winters of a greater number of contaminated flea beetles.

Unexpected situations often happen when environment modifies strikingly the activities of insect vectors. The soft rot of vegetables, caused by bacteria, is usually favored by wet weather, but when the disease occurs as a heart rot of celery it is most destructive in dry weather. It was hard to understand why until it was discovered that, on celery, the disease is transmitted by insects of the fruit fly group. The flies deposit their eggs on the celery leaves. When the eggs hatch, the young maggots burrow into the leaves and inoculate the plant with the bacteria. The insects will deposit their eggs only on moist leaves. In wet weather the eggs are deposited on the outer leaves of the celery plant where the decay causes little damage to the plant because the outer leaves are resistant to decay and are removed and discarded at harvest. In dry weather, however, when the outer leaves are not wet, the insects seek the moist heart leaves on which to lay their eggs. When the larvae inoculate the heart leaves with the bacteria the growing point is killed and stem elongates, so that the plant has no

market value. Thus a disease that normally is favored by moist weather is, in this case, more destructive in dry weather.

Insects also may indirectly influence the spread of diseases by birds. Chestnut blight is spread over short distances by wind and water, but spot infections have appeared 100 miles or more from known infected areas. They were started by the woodpeckers and sapsuckers whose beaks had been contaminated with spores while feeding on insects that were breeding in cankers on infected trees. Since the birds feed on both insects and healthy cambium, they are effective vectors. After feeding on insects in a canker and contaminating their beaks with spores, they would continue their migrations and fly many miles before pecking holes in the bark of healthy chestnut trees to feed on the cambium. But in so doing they would effectively inoculate the trees with the spores adhering to their beaks.

It is evident from this brief review that insects play an important role in the spread and development of plant diseases. Successful control of many plant diseases depends upon the control of the insects that spread them or otherwise influence their development. Sometimes the insect that transmits a plant disease is not directly injurious and would be of no economic importance if it did not transmit the disease. Frequently there is a symbiotic relationship between the insect and the disease that it transmits in which both the insect and the micro-organism derive mutual benefits.

J. G. LEACH *has been head of the department of plant pathology and bacteriology in West Virginia University since 1938. Earlier he was professor of plant pathology in the University of Minnesota. He has done extensive research with insects in relation to plant diseases. In 1940 he published a textbook,* Insect Transmission of Plant Diseases. *He is a former president of the American Phytopathological Society.*

Crown Gall — a Malignant Growth

A. J. Riker, A. C. Hildebrandt

Crown galls are diseased growths that occur on peaches, apples, raspberries, roses, sugar beets, and a great many other broadleaved plants. The galls appear commonly where the plants come out of the ground, the crown—hence the name.

They ordinarily are quite soft. They have neither a definite exterior like a bark layer nor a woody interior like a stem. Having no protection against secondary invaders, the galls become hosts to various bacteria, fungi, and even insects, particularly during wet weather. A type of decay like soft rot sets in.

A gall contains a disorganized mixture of large, swollen cells; small cells that divide rapidly; and sap-conducting cells, which have a ladderlike thickening in the walls. The gall may seem hard if the woody cells are abundant.

The nonparasitic bur knots, callus overgrowths, and infectious hairy root are common diseases that have been mistaken for the true crown gall.

The disease occurs the world over. Infected nursery stock easily could have carried it from one place to another. Its economic importance varies. In irrigated districts and other sections with abundant moisture, the disease may occur so often that an uninfected plant is hard to find. A gall that develops on a lateral root may cause little damage. A gall that occurs on the main stem near the crown and involves a considerable part of the circumference of the stem, may weaken the stem, disrupt the flow of sap, and favor the progress of a cortical rot. Such a plant usually dies.

Crown gall is caused by the bacterium *Agrobacterium tumefaciens*, a small Gram-negative rod. It is closely related to the bacteria that produce root nodules on leguminous plants and to bacteria of the colon-typhoid group.

The crown gall bacteria grow readily on any of the common bacterial media. They do well on nitrate-sucrose-mineral salt agar.

The infection cycle is relatively simple. The bacteria enter the tissues apparently only through wounds, most commonly through wounds caused by insects or cultivation. Once inside the tissue, they occur primarily between the cells, from which they stimulate the surrounding cells to divide. In the earlier stage, that looks like the response to a wound, but it never heals. As the galls increase in size, some of the larger cells apparently are crushed by the pressure, and the bacteria move into other tissues for further activity. The bacteria occur usually in abundance on the surface, from which they may be washed off and distributed by flowing water. Chewing insects may carry them from one plant to another and also may introduce them into wounds. Over long distances the bacteria travel on the surface of nursery stock or inside the tissue. Symptoms may not develop for several weeks, depending on temperature, humidity, and the growth of the host. They may not show during nursery inspection.

Galls ordinarily develop better as the temperatures increase up to a certain point. However, on tomato, *Kalanchoe*, and certain other plants studied in experiments, the galls fail to develop much, if any, above 83° F., although plants and bacteria do well at the higher temperatures.

Moisture, light, and mineral nutrients may influence the development of the galls. Frequently, since no growth means no gall, that merely reflects the growth of the plant itself.

Various insects living in the ground seem important, especially those on raspberries. They chew on the roots and the galls. They open infection courts and may actually transmit the bacteria from one injury to another. Cultural practices likewise may be important. Obviously a type of cultivation that encourages insects or produces many injuries on the roots or crowns may encourage infection.

The means for combatting crown gall are closely tied in with the environment and the way the disease develops. Perhaps one of the best control measures is to grow a crop that is not susceptible for several years between crops that are susceptible. A crop that reduces the presence of root-chewing insects likewise discourages this means of transmission. Sometimes, if the infection is carried on the surface of the planting stock, a surface disinfectant may be helpful—but not fully reliable, because in some instances the bacteria may enter a wound and be protected against the disinfectant. Such infections are impossible to detect during nursery inspection because frequently the period of incubation is not long enough to permit gall development. Galls that develop in the nursery on the unions of piece-root apple grafts have been controlled by special adhesive tape wrappers. They may contain the disinfectant, corrosive sublimate, in the adhesive mixture.

WHILE THE ECONOMIC importance of crown gall makes it a critical disease, particularly on sugar beets, fruits, and some types of nursery stock, it has still greater importance as a tool for work dealing with the fundamentals of diseased growth. Erwin F. Smith called crown gall a "plant cancer."

The changes from normal growth to diseased growth involve many fundamental biological problems. The more one learns about biochemistry the greater appear the parallels between plants and animals—between cabbages and kings. From the standpoints of growth stimulation and, what is much more important, growth inhibition, many basic substances, including various carbohydrates, fats, proteins and their derivatives, mineral salts, vitamins, and enzymes, are common factors occurring both in plant and animal cells. Admittedly, a description of such fundamental work becomes a bit technical. Its importance extends far beyond the agricultural field.

For fundamental work on growth, plants have certain advantages over animals. The plants have no complex nervous, digestive, and circulatory systems, which complicate the basic physiology. Large numbers of plants may be used at a relatively low cost. The possibilities for genetic purity with plant material are real and important. Many inbred lines are available for use. Still better, various plants, such as many fruits, are ordinarily reproduced by vegetative propagation. Thus, the different individuals are genetically identical. For details of tissue metabolism, tissue cultures from higher plants offer a relatively simple and direct approach not yet possible with tissue from higher animals. These cultures grow indefinitely upon media which contain only nutrients with known chemical formulas. Ordinarily the tissues grow well without a change of nutrient for some weeks. The growing tissue develops in a compact mass easily separated from the medium. Thus, any change in growth may be determined merely by weighing the tissue pieces. Many ways are available for inducing at will one or another kind of diseased growth.

What actually initiates these diseased growths, what keeps them going, and especially how they can be inhibited are critical questions. They have stimulated much speculation and many experiments. One may approach this problem from the standpoint that the bacteria start off the diseased development. They may or may not be necessary to keep the diseased growth going. To make a comparison with firearms, one might consider that the causal agent operates as a trigger mechanism to set things off. However, a trigger alone is not enough. The gun must be loaded. Also important are the amount of the load, the character of the load, the amount of dampening the load carries, and so on.

Detailed data on the metabolism of the plant, of the causal agent, and of both together are necessary.

As the crown gall bacteria develop in suitable culture media, a number of physical and chemical changes occur. Knowing what happens in such media may help to clarify the action of the bacteria as they work in host tissue.

Among the critical physico-chemical changes are the modification of the hydrogen-ion concentration, a reduced oxidation-reduction potential, a decreased osmotic pressure, and an increased viscosity.

Among the chemical factors are the ability to use an unusually large number of different sources of carbon and nitrogen. Likewise these bacteria tolerate many kinds of inhibiting substances.

The metabolic products known to be formed by crown gall bacteria have thus far been surprisingly simple, principally carbon dioxide. No volatile organic material has been detected. By far the most common residual metabolite is a bacterial gum. In culture its weight is considerably greater than that of the bacterial cells. One molecule of this gum contains approximately 24 glucose molecules. The gum is viscous, takes up moisture, and is chemically rather inert. Apparently neither the bacteria nor the host plant has an enzyme system capable of attacking it.

The metabolites resulting from nitrogen in the medium have received much less attention. Ammonia was one of the first products reported and has come the nearest to being a common factor of any found among the various cell-stimulating bacteria.

The crown gall bacteria have been shown to produce the vitamins biotin, riboflavin, pantothenic acid, and thiamine. Since they grow in synthetic media, they produce any other such material needed for their metabolism.

An analysis of large quantities of the crown gall bacteria has revealed the presence of various lipids. These are more or less toxic when strong preparations are placed upon host plants.

The attenuation of the virulent culture by means of certain amino acids and related compounds has an interesting bearing upon this problem. The cultures were grown in media with a relatively alkaline reaction and only a tiny bit of the amino acid, glycine, but enough to reduce but not to stop growth. After a series of 15 or more successive transfers made at intervals of several days, the cultures gradually lost their capacity to induce gall formation. In some cases, if the attenuation was not carried through too many transfers, virulence was restored by a series of transfers on ordinary media. In other cases where the cultivation on glycine was carried several transfers beyond the point of attenuation, such restoration did not occur in 4 years.

A restoration of virulence has been accomplished also by irradiating partly attenuated cultures with ultraviolet light so as to kill all but one in a thousand. The survivors commonly showed a conspicuous increase in virulence.

The morphological responses of the plant tissue to crown gall bacteria show important changes. The wound that introduced the bacteria flooded the intercellular spaces and provided a culture medium for the bacteria. The cells around the bacteria enlarged within 2 days and the adjacent cell walls turned somewhat brown and took ordinary stains more intensely than normal walls. Within 4 days new crown gall cells had formed. In the early stages of development the new cell walls were laid down in somewhat the same manner as those from a wound.

This 4-day interval was determined independently with inoculated periwinkle plants in which the bacteria were killed by exposing the plants to high temperature. Plants heated after 3 days developed only small galls, but those heated after 4 days went on to develop galls which were free from the crown gall bacteria.

The old ideas about continuing diseased growth without the causal agent, once disease in the tissue was started, thus have received experimental evidence with periwinkle. This brings closer still the comparison between crown gall and certain diseased growths in animals. How frequently such autonomous growth also occurs in other plants remains uncertain. The failure of many "secondary" crown galls on sunflower, Paris-daisy, and marigold to continue development after the bacteria have died has suggested caution about too broad inferences.

The differences in chemical compositions between the galls and correspondingly healthy tissue have been examined. Approximate analysis indicated that the gall tissues resemble those of young plants, being high in nitrogen and low in fibrous material. Considerable variations were observed, depending on the time of collection and on the species of plant. The actively growing tissues contained more ascorbic acid. An increase of thiamine appeared in the gall tissue within a week.

The enzyme content of the galls was different from that of the healthy tissue. The galls contained 86 and 57 percent more than the stems of catalase and peroxidase on a total nitrogen basis. The galls had active tyrosinase, while the stems had little, if any. Furthermore, the galls contained relatively much more glutathione than the stems.

Reduced respiration levels by the gall tissues have appeared important. With the considerable excess of oxidizing enzymes, the suggestion has appeared that the basic metabolic activity of the galls may be relatively anaerobic in comparison with that of the neighboring tissue. This condition deserves further study as a causal factor for cell stimulation. It may be correlated perhaps with the earlier observations that the tissues involved had flooded intercellular spaces. The diffusion of oxygen through normal tissue is 2,000 to 3,000 times greater than that in tissue with water in the intercellular spaces.

As the amount of hyperplastic tissue increases in size, more difficulty with gas exchange doubtless also develops. The crown gall bacteria lower the oxidation-reduction potentials of the material in which they are growing. The formation of ammonia and the consequent change of the pH in an alkaline direction also lowers the oxidation-reduction potential. The bacteria and gum block certain intercellular spaces. The presence of gummy materials, which are hygroscopic, might cause the cells to swell and to metabolize more slowly. The reduced oxygen uptake in the presence of 3-indoleacetic acid at a gall-inducing concentration has added interest.

Among the well-known growth substance effects are increased epinasty, adventitious roots, cambial activity, bud inhibition, and delayed abscission. All were found associated with crown gall on tomato. The presence in galls has been amply demonstrated of something like 3-indoleacetic acid at approximately 6 to 12 parts per billion—an amount comparable to that in some actively growing and normal plant parts. While these extremely small amounts strikingly affect certain tissues, much stronger and almost lethal concentrations are needed to induce chemical galls.

The stimulation of tissue about inoculations with the attenuated crown gall bacteria has been possible not only with the virulent culture higher on the stem but also with galls induced by certain chemicals. However, no correlation has appeared between the formation of these chemical galls and any other growth substance effects.

The possibility of studying the physiology of these diseased tissues has been greatly enhanced by the development of tissue cultures. These consist of masses of largely undifferentiated callus that grow indefinitely on synthetic media. Thus, science has an important tool to determine which substances the tissues can use, which are not available, and particularly which are inhibiting.

The diseased tissues in culture have been derived commonly from crown galls that were free from bacteria, or from growths having a comparable origin. Extensive studies have been made in relation to the best physical conditions, the importance of plant and bacterial products, the influence of different concentrations of various mineral salts, the responses to the more common growth substances, and the activity of different sources of nitrogen and different sources of carbon—the latter including sugars and polysaccharides, alcohols, and the salts of organic acids. Some of the common metabolites appear particularly important, either for the stimulation or inhibition of growth. Likewise, the concentrations of certain metabolites seem as important as the substances themselves.

These tissue-culture studies also have shown some striking differences between the tissues from different species. Are they opening further the door for physiological as well as morphological understanding of tissues? In any case, many interesting possibilities appear for studying various aspects of tissue metabolism in health and disease, for clarifying the relations between host and pathogen, and especially for learning more about diseased growths.

Growth inhibitions from certain amino acids and organic acids have led to the hope that still other and more powerful agents would soon be found. The most active inhibition came with analogs of pteroylglutamic acid. These inhibited callus growth at 10 to 100 parts per billion. The 4-amino-N^{10}-methyl-pteroylglutamic acid applied locally to young crown galls on sunflower at 0.1 milligram per milliliter completely inhibited gall development. Certain nitrogen mustards, penicillin, 8-azaguanine, and cortisone also have inhibited crown gall.

Many trigger agents have been associated with diseased plant growths. Whether they operate by providing stimulation or by removing inhibitors remains to be determined. However, as mentioned earlier, the trigger is not enough. What happens depends on the kind of load and the amount and whether it is dampened by inhibitors. The use of tissue cultures has opened the way for determining much about the load, about dampening materials, and about the amounts of both necessary for effectiveness.

Basic information is being developed not only for the influence of common mineral salts, sources of carbon, sources of nitrogen, and various metabolites, but also for concentrations that encourage or inhibit growth.

The idea that diseased growth develops from a lack of balance among critical factors fits well into this concept. While we shall continue to analyze individual factors that by their presence or absence may change normal into pathological growth or keep it going, no one thing may be responsible. For normal growth, a number of factors operate in a suitable balance. However, in pathological growth of one kind a group of these factors may be out of balance. Likewise, in pathological growth of another kind, the balance may be disturbed in some other way.

A. J. RIKER *has been professor of plant pathology in the University of Wisconsin since 1931. He is the author of* Introduction to Research on Plant Diseases *(with R. S. Riker) and many research reports on bacterial plant diseases, diseases of forest trees, and factors that influence pathological growth. For 7 years he was an editor of* Phytopathology.

A. C. HILDEBRANDT *is an assistant professor of plant pathology in the University of Wisconsin. After earning his doctorate at Wisconsin in 1945, he has been engaged in research on crown gall, mineral and carbohydrate metabolism of tissue cultures, environmental factors affecting plant tissue culture growth, vitamins, and growth-regulating substances.*

Broomrapes, Dodders, and Mistletoes

Lake S. Gill

Parasites are plants and animals that get their living at the expense of other organisms, which are called the hosts. Usually we think of parasites as lower forms of life, such as fungi and bacteria. A number of flowering, or seed plants, however, are parasitic on vegetation. Parasitism appears in varying degrees in several widely separated botanical families and is regarded generally as a degenerative process in species that once were free-living. A higher plant that has become parasitic does not, as far as we know, return to independence.

The parasite depends physiologically for its existence on the host plant. The host may incidentally supply protection or physical support, although plants that derive only those benefits are not classed as parasites but are called epiphytes. Examples of epiphytes are Spanish-moss and some tropical orchids that attach themselves to trees but are physiologically independent even though they maintain no contact with the soil.

The parasitic seed plants vary widely in their dependence. The more independent ones are referred to as hemiparasites, half-parasites, or waterparasites. All of them produce chlorophyll and therefore are capable of manufacturing food from carbon dioxide and water, although they depend on the host for certain dissolved minerals and perhaps organic substances. Some absorb from their hosts all the water they need for transpiration and the manufacture of food.

The mildest hemiparasites look like normal green plants growing in soil. They steal their food through root connections, often inconspicuous, from surrounding host plants, which may suffer little or no harm from the arrangement. Notable parasites of this type are the sandalwood tree of India and its near relative *Commandra* (falsetoadflax), a common herb in North America. The mistletoes illustrate the opposite extremes of this group, having lost contact with the soil and being dependent on their hosts for all water and dissolved minerals even though the chlorophyll-containing species can manufacture sugars and starches in their green leaves and stems.

The complete parasites have no chlorophyll and therefore depend wholly on their hosts for nourishment. Plants that have degenerated to this extent are never green. Their leaves usually are reduced to inconspicuous scales and they exhibit a marked modification of their functional root system, which develops entirely inside the host tissues.

Parasitic seed plants important to agriculture, forestry, and arboriculture in North America are relatively few and can be classified broadly in three groups: (1) Mistletoes are green, yellowish, or brownish plants growing on the stems and branches of trees or shrubs. (2) Dodders are slender, twining, orange or yellowish, rarely white or purplish, leafless, threadlike stems often forming dense tangled mats over host plants. (3) Broomrapes are clumps of whitish, yellowish, brownish, or purplish stems that arise from the roots of host plants.

THE NAME MISTLETOE is derived from the Saxon *mistl-tan*, meaning "different twig" an indication that the ancients recognized it as something apart from the branches of the host tree. It was featured in the Greek, Norse, and Germanic legends as a plant vested with supernatural powers for good and evil. The Druids and other pagan peoples of Europe used it as a sacred emblem in their religious rites. The herbalists of the early Christian era claimed that mistletoe was once a forest tree but became dwarfed out of shame when its wood was used to make the cross at Calvary. They called it *guidhel* or *all heal* and prescribed it as an antidote for poisons and a cure for falling sickness and epilepsy. Amulets made of the plant were often worn to ward off disease.

The early American settlers considered our leafy mistletoe of the East to be identical with the *Viscum* of their homeland and thus it, too, became vested with much of the traditional symbolism that had developed about the European plant. Today it is highly prized for Christmas decorations and during the holiday period it may shed blessings on those who stand beneath it.

About 305 B. C., Theophrastus, the Greek botanist, recorded technical observations which indicated that he recognized mistletoe as a parasitic plant. In the eighteenth century, Carolus Linnaeus, the great Swedish botanist, described and named the principal European species *Viscum album*. The name was doubtless selected because the white berries of the plant were then used in the manufacture of bird lime. Strictly speaking, this plant is the true mistletoe, although today the name is loosely applied to many members of the botanical family Loranthaceae, which embraces about 900 species, mostly tropical tree-inhabiting hemiparasites. About 35 species are known in temperate North America. Five of these are in the genus *Arceuthobium*, also called dwarfmistletoe; the remainder are in the genus *Phoradendron*, often called leafy mistletoe, true mistletoe, or Christmas mistletoe. The latter genus was set apart from the Old World *Viscum* in 1847 by Thomas Nuttall, first director of the Harvard Botanical Gardens; the Greek origin of the name means "tree thief."

The Phoradendrons attack chiefly broadleaved trees, although in the far West certain conifers, especially juniper and its near relatives, are common hosts.

All species are regarded as half-parasites that produce clusters of green, perennial, jointed stems on the branches and trunks of trees or large shrubs. The stems mostly bear conspicuous deep green, leathery leaves, which persist for several seasons. A few species, notably some of those on conifers and desert plants in the West, are virtually leafless.

The stems are supplied from an absorbing system, which develops in the bark and wood of the host and takes water and whatever else may be required to supplement the food manufactured in the aerial green parts of the parasite. The flowers are dioecious; that is, the staminate or male and the pistillate or female flowers occur on separate plants. They are borne at the base of the leaves where (among pistillate plants only) the familiar translucent, whitish berries develop in the late fall or early winter. In some western species the berries are straw to pinkish in color and mature in midwinter.

Within the tough outer coat of the berry is a single seed, which is embedded in viscin, a sticky substance. Birds feed on the sticky pulp of the berries. Some of the discarded seeds stick to their bills, feet, and other parts of the body. Thus the seeds are carried to other trees or other parts of the same tree, where they may be brushed off on a branch or twig, germinate, and perhaps develop into a new mistletoe plant. If the berries are left undisturbed they disintegrate and release the sticky seeds, which may fall and adhere to a limb or twig below. Seeds that pass through the digestive tracts of birds may also germinate and start new mistletoe plants.

In most parts of the country the leafy mistletoes are relatively scarce and are regarded more as botanical curiosities than as serious pests. Because of their value as holiday decorations, some interest has been shown in their culture but thus far there have been no practical developments in that field. Most of the mistletoe for the Christmas trade is gathered in the forests of the Southern and Southwestern States where it is abundant in some localities and where it provides off-season income for agricultural workers. The berries of *Phoradendron flavescens* are a recognized source of a pressor compound (parahydroxyphenylethyl amine) of limited pharmaceutical value.

In certain arid or semiarid places in the West, notably in Texas, New Mexico, Arizona, and California, mistletoe has become so abundant as to warrant control measures for the preservation of shade and horticultural trees. The natural woodland species that are most heavily attacked—notably juniper and mesquite—generally have such low economic value that large-scale control operations cannot be justified except possibly in public parks where the primary aim is to preserve natural vegetation for the enjoyment of generations to come. In some parts of the Midwest, such hardwoods as walnut and elm are sometimes severely parasitized by mistletoe.

The spread of mistletoe can be reduced somewhat by breaking off the pistillate shoots. That must be done periodically because it does not destroy the absorbing system from which the shoots develop; it merely discourages the parasite from producing berries, which may spread about the infected tree or to other host plants. It is practical only if little mistletoe is present and the danger of reinfection from outside is remote.

When infections are moderate, one can prune off the affected limbs and thus free the host plant entirely of the parasite. Sometimes severe trunk infections can be destroyed by removing the invaded bark. If hopelessly infected trees occur near others worthy of preservation, it would perhaps be best to remove the infected ones entirely.

Although a single species of *Phoraden-* *dron* may attack a variety of trees, strong host affinities are usually developed within a species in a given region. The extent to which crossing from one host species to another occurs in nature is not known exactly, although there are strong indications it is quite limited. In regions where mistletoe is a serious pest, it would seem advisable to favor tree species that are naturally immune or highly resistant to attack in that particular area even though they are congenial hosts elsewhere.

The dwarfmistletoes are found only on conifers. In North America they do not attack juniper and related species, which are common hosts of *Phoradendron*. The mistletoe shoots themselves vary in color from green to yellow or brown. Less conspicuous than those of the true mistletoes, they range from tiny scattered outgrowths about one-fourth inch high to coarse, jointed stems up to 12 inches long. The seeds are borne in explosive, berrylike fruits. At maturity they may be shot 50 or more feet away from the host tree and thus gradually encroach on the surrounding forest. The seeds are covered with sticky viscin and adhere to any surface on which they may alight.

New infections are most likely to develop when the seeds germinate on young twigs of a suitable host plant. In that case an absorbing root penetrates the tender bark and develops a system of strands that attack the living phloem of the host. They absorb from it what is needed for the development of the parasite. Some of the strands reach the cambium layer of the host and are permanently embedded in the wood as it is laid down each year. They retain their connection with the strands in the phloem indefinitely and are called sinkers. After the absorbing system is well established, it produces buds from which shoots develop. That may occur the year after infection or it may be delayed for a decade or more. Flowers are borne on the shoots and, like *Phoradendron*, are dioecious. Insects carry the pollen from the male to the female flowers and the fruits mature 5 to 16 months later.

Forests heavily infected with dwarf-mistletoe do not produce top yields. The greatest losses occur in the far West. One species (*Arceuthobium pusillum*) is recognized as a serious agent of disease in black spruce (*Picea mariana*), especially in the Lake States. The greatest economic damage occurs in ponderosa pine (*Pinus ponderosa*), lodgepole pine (*P. contorta*), and western larch (*Larix occidentalis*). The effects of infection of the host plants include premature death, reduced growth, poor seed production, poor form, low quality of wood products, and increased susceptibility to attack by insects and other diseases.

Physical removal of the parasite is the only known means of controlling it. In heavily infected stands it is usually necessary to depart from normal forest management practices to obtain adequate protection for the future forest—exceptionally heavy harvest cuttings, followed by stand improvement designed to reduce mistletoe in the unmerchantable trees. At least one cleaning subsequent to the initial eradication will be desirable to remove the infections that originated before control work was started but which were invisible at the time. Economic justification for control will depend on the value of the stand attacked. A knowledge of the biology of the particular mistletoe species involved will aid in developing the most efficient control techniques.

DODDER belongs to the genus *Cuscuta*, a close relative of the familiar morning-glories. It is sometimes referred to as love vine, strangleweed, devil's-guts, goldthread, pull-down, devil's-ringlet, hellbine, hairweed, devil's-hair, and hailweed. It commonly appears as dense tangles of leafless, orange or yellow strands on its host plants. Sometimes it is tinged with red or purple. Occasionally it is almost white. The strands develop from seed, which germinate on the

soil. The leafless yellowish stem gropes in the air until it makes contact with a host plant. The contact is made firm by one or more coils about the host stem after which haustoria—the absorbing organs—are produced. The haustoria invade the host tissues and absorb the food required for the dodder to continue its twining growth. The basal part of the parasite soon shrivels away, so that no connection with the soil remains. Growth continues with the aid of more and more haustoria, which are produced at intervals as the stem elongates. From the original host plant, the twining stems reach out to attack others in the vicinity, so that a single dodder plant may parasitize several hosts simultaneously. Many minute flowers occur in clusters on the stems; they develop tiny seeds, which fall to the ground at maturity. The seed may remain viable without germinating for 5 years.

Of the 100-odd recognized species of *Cuscuta*, 32 are reported as being native to the United States; 18 others have been introduced. The parasite is particularly troublesome in regions where clover and alfalfa are grown extensively, although it is not to be feared in America to the same degree as in some European countries, where the production of clover seed has been abandoned because of its ravages.

Dodder also attacks flax, sugar beets, and onions. A large number of both cultivated and wild plants also are its hosts, but little or no economic loss results from the association. Cereal plants are never attacked.

Dodder is most frequently carried to a farm in impure seed. It may also be carried in hay, manure, and irrigation water and on vehicles and animals. Prevention is therefore the first principle of control. Once established, it usually appears in small scattered patches. Cutting the patches before the seed matures will often eliminate the parasite. After the seed has matured it will be necessary to burn the infested area. Heavily infested fields should be plowed under or used for hay; the stubble should be grazed closely, preferably by sheep. The safest method is to cut the crop and burn it in place when it dries. If conditions permit, an infested field can be planted to immune or resistant crops such as cereals, corn, soybeans, velvetbeans, or cowpeas. Chemical control is feasible but is not recommended because of the high cost.

THE NAME BROOMRAPE is generally applied to the genera *Orobanche* and *Phelipaea*. The 90-some species are mostly in the temperate parts of the world. Both belong to the botanical family Orobanchaceae, all members of which are complete root parasites. The family also includes the genus *Epifagus*, commonly known as beech-drops, which appears under beech trees. From an evolutionary standpoint, the group is closely related to the snapdragons and foxgloves (Scrophulariaceae). Some species of the parasites produce just as showy flowers as their independent relatives. Several members of the Scrophulariaceae exhibit mild degrees of root parasitism similar to that previously mentioned in the case of sandalwood and false-toadflax.

The broomrapes appear as clumps of whitish, yellowish, brownish, or purplish annual stems arising from the ground at or near the base of their host plants. The stems are 6 to 18 inches high. They have bractlike leaves and numerous showy flowers somewhat like those of the snapdragon. An abundance of minute seeds is produced in capsular fruits. The seeds germinate in the soil if the fibrous roots of a congenial host plant are nearby. Otherwise they remain dormant until they lose their viability, which can be retained as long as 13 years. When the primary root, or radicle, of a germinating seed makes contact with a fibrous root of its host, it forms a nodule of tissue, which becomes fused with tissues of the host. New roots and a stem of the parasite develop at that point. The stem emerges while the roots form new contacts with other host roots at each of which new roots and stems of the parasite are produced.

About 16 species of broomrape are regarded as pests of many crop plants. Three are found in the United States. The damage caused by broomrape in America does not approach the situation in Europe. Our most troublesome species, hemp broomrape (*Orobanche ramosa*), was perhaps introduced on hempseed from China or Japan. It attacks a number of unrelated crops, but it is serious only on our hemp. A native species, Louisiana broomrape (*O. ludoviciana*), sometimes damages tobacco. Beyond these, the losses caused by broomrape are negligible and sporadic.

CLEAN SEED is the best protection against broomrape in hemp culture. The seeds of the parasite can be separated mechanically. Contaminated lots may be treated with hot water or a strong bluestone solution, both of which kill the parasite without damaging the hemp. Rotation with immune or resistant crops is perhaps the most practical procedure in heavily infested fields, but it should be remembered that the seeds of the parasite remain viable in the soil for many years. Small infections of broomrape can usually be eliminated by destroying the aerial stems before the seeds ripen.

LAKE S. GILL, *senior pathologist of the division of forest pathology, Bureau of Plant Industry, Soils, and Agricultural Engineering, is an authority on the diseases of forest trees in the Southwest and the Rocky Mountains. He has made comprehensive studies of mistletoe and developed methods for its control. He is stationed in Albuquerque, N. Mex. He contributed "Arceuthobium in the United States" to Transactions of the Connecticut Academy of Arts and Science (volume 32, pages 111–245, 1935). With J. L. Bedwell he wrote "Dwarf Mistletoes" for Trees, the Yearbook of Agriculture 1949 (pages 458–461).*

The Tiny but Destructive Nematodes

Albert L. Taylor

Nematodes differ from most of the other organisms that cause plant diseases in that they belong to the animal kingdom, not the plant kingdom.

The plant parasitic nematodes, or eelworms, are representatives of a large group of species that the zoologist considers quite different from the other kinds of animals called worms. That is, they are not closely related to the earthworms, flat worms, wireworms, grubs, and cutworms, but are in a class apart. They have no close relatives.

Several thousands of species of nematodes are known. They differ in form, habits, and habitat. Some are parasites of animals and of man. Others live in the fresh waters of rivers, ponds, and lakes. Many live in the salt waters of the sea. A great number live in the soil. Most of those living in the soil can be classed as harmless and some even as distinctly beneficial, but several hundred species are known to feed on living plants as parasites and to be the causes of a variety of plant diseases.

Plant parasitic and free-living nematodes occur in enormous numbers in all kinds of soil in which plants can grow. A single acre of cultivated soil may contain hundreds of millions, but they are seldom if ever seen, even by the farmer who is constantly working with the soil. The reason is simply that, although they are thousands of times larger than bacteria, they are just a little too small to be easily seen with the naked eye, even when separated from the soil. The length of the full-grown plant parasitic nematode may be less than one sixty-fourth of an inch and seldom exceeds one-eighth inch.

Most are very slender, as the name eelworm suggests. Nevertheless, they have a highly complex organization. Their small bodies have muscular systems, specialized organs for feeding, a digestive system, a nervous system, an excretory system, and a well-developed reproductive system. Both males and females occur in most species, but reproduction without the males is not unusual.

The life history of plant parasitic nematodes is simple enough. Eggs may be deposited in the soil or in the plant on which the female feeds. In the eggs the immature forms, the larvae, develop and eventually hatch. If plants on which they can feed are available, they may begin to feed immediately, developing through several distinct stages. At the end of each of these, a molt takes place. After the last molt, the nematode becomes sexually mature and able to reproduce.

Most of the forms that have been closely studied have a minimum length of life cycle, from egg to egg-laying female, of several days to several weeks. The maximum time may be much longer, as sexual maturity is not reached until the nematode begins to feed on a living plant. Until then it remains in the larval stage and lives on a reserve supply of food originally derived from the egg. The length of time this reserve food supply lasts depends on circumstances. In warm, damp soil, the nematode will be very active and use it up in a few weeks or months. In cool or dry soil, activity is less and the food supply lasts longer. The species found in cold climates can easily live over winter and are not killed by freezing of the soil. Some species are killed if subjected to drying, but others enter a dormant state in which they can remain alive for years and from which they can revive in a short time if moistened. The most remarkable of these are parasites of wheat, rye, and other grains and grasses. The wheat nematode has been revived after dry storage for 28 years. A species that parasitizes rye has been revived after 39 years. Certain species can live a long time outside in moist soil. Females of the golden nematode of potatoes and its relatives become transformed at death into highly durable cysts. Because few or none of their eggs are deposited, the cysts contain eggs with unhatched larvae, which may remain alive for 10 years or more.

As plant parasitic nematodes neither feed nor reproduce except on living plants, survival of the individual depends on its reaching a plant on which it can feed before its reserve food supply is finally exhausted. Unless hatched in a plant, that means that the nematode must travel through the soil in search of food. This movement seems to be more or less random wandering and, since nematodes are small, is confined to a small area of soil. Perhaps most nematodes never get more than a foot or two from the spot where they were hatched. Therefore nematodes spread very slowly by their own efforts.

Plant parasitic nematodes have many enemies in the soil. At any stage of their life they may be captured and devoured by other soil animals, such as insects or predatory free-living nematodes. Certain soil fungi have traps that seem especially designed to catch nematodes. Some are loops which close when a nematode starts to crawl through. Others have sticky surfaces to which nematodes adhere. In either instance, the fungus grows into the body of the nematode and kills it.

Even though the accidents of life take a large toll of the plant parasitic nematodes, a field population is seldom exterminated. Like other parasites, the nematodes manage to reproduce just a little faster than they can be wiped out. A single female root knot nematode may produce more than 500 eggs. If only a few of them survive to reproduce in turn, a great increase in the population of a field can take place during a summer when several generations follow one another.

Information accumulated during the past century indicates that all of the crop and ornamental plants grown in the world can be attacked by plant parasitic nematodes. If there are exceptions to this rule, they must be very few, indeed. Probably most weeds and wild plants are also attacked.

That does not imply that any species of plant parasitic nematode can attack any kind of plant. All plant parasitic nematodes are more or less specialized, attacking some plants freely and others not at all, even when given every opportunity to do so and when no other source of food is available. So far as a given species of nematode is concerned, different kinds of plants may have varying degrees of suitability as food. On some they will not attempt to feed. On others they will feed, but seem unable to reproduce. Such plants are called immune to the nematode species concerned. On other plants reproduction is inhibited to various degrees; they are called resistant. Plants on which normal reproduction takes place are called susceptible. It should be emphasized that any such classification of plants can be taken as applying to only a single species of nematode. Plants immune to attack by one species of nematode may be highly susceptible to attack by others.

The species range from highly specialized (those that attack only a few kinds of plants) to polyphagous (those that attack a great many different kinds of plants). The reasons therefor are not known. In practice there seems to be no way of knowing which plants might be attacked by a given species except by experiment. Resistance to nematodes sometimes can be found in horticultural varieties of crops or in other species of the same plant genus. Advantage is taken of this fact in the development of nematode-resistant crop varieties.

Plants almost invariably become infected by nematodes that move into them from the soil. As would be expected, the underground parts of plants, roots, tubers, corms, and rhizomes are more apt to be infected than above-ground parts. Infection of stems, leaves, and flower parts is fairly common, however.

Damage to plants attacked by nematodes is due primarily to the feeding of the nematodes on the plant tissues. All the important plant parasitic nematode species have a special feeding organ, known as a stylet or spear. As seen in profile under the high-power microscope, the typical stylet resembles a nail with a thickened head, although close examination reveals that the head is composed of three more or less distinct knobs. Stylets, highly variable in size and shape according to the species of nematode, range from comparatively long to very short, and the knobs have a variety of forms, ranging from large and distinct to nearly absent. Those differences are useful in the identification of genera and species. The stylet really is more like a hypodermic needle than a nail. It is hollow, and the nematode uses it to pierce plant tissue or cell walls. With the stylet pushed into a cell, the nematode can suck out the cell contents. In preparation for this, it may inject a digestive secretion into the cell, evidently to liquefy and partly digest the food before it is ingested. Nematodes may enter the plant to feed, may feed from the outside, or be only partially embedded. Feeding habits vary according to species.

The feeding of a nematode may kill the cell or may simply interfere with its normal functioning. If the cell is killed, it often is quickly invaded by bacteria or fungi. If the cell is not killed, it and the adjacent cells may be stimulated to enlarge or multiply. Consequently the most common types of nematode damage are manifest as rotting of the attacked parts and adjacent tissue or the development of galls and other abnormal growths. Either can interfere with the orderly development of the plant and cause shortening of stems or roots, twisting, crinkling or death of parts of stems and leaves, and other abnormalities.

Those symptoms often are complicated by the presence of secondary invaders in the affected parts and, particularly in advanced cases, may present a confusing picture. Consequently the specialist depends only partly on symptoms for diagnosis and searches for nematodes in the plant or in the nearby soil.

The following representative nematode diseases are common and can be recognized fairly easily. It should be remembered that it is easy to mistake nematode diseases for those caused by some other organisms, and vice versa. Merely finding nematodes in diseased plant tissue or the soil is not conclusive evidence that they are the cause of the trouble. Nonparasitic types of nematodes often are found in great numbers in decaying plants and the soil always contains a variety of free-living nematodes. Positive identification should always be obtained before starting expensive or troublesome control measures. On the other hand, nematodes should always be considered as a possible cause of plant diseases when root systems are galled, shortened, or reduced by rotting; when the stems are shortened and thickened and the leaves do not grow normally; and some other abnormal growth is noted.

Probably the easiest of the nematode diseases to recognize is root knot, caused by nematodes of the various species of the genus *Meloidogyne* (formerly grouped under the name *Heterodera marioni*). They are called root knot nematodes. As the name implies, they cause the formation of knots or galls on roots of a great variety of crop and ornamental plants, including trees and shrubs. The typical simple galls are best observed on the younger roots, where they may look like beads on a string. Galls caused by at least one species of the genus commonly have several short, adventitious roots that rise from the upper part and produce a bushy appearance of the root.

On larger roots, compound galls may be an inch or more in diameter. Severely infected roots have a rough, clubbed appearance. Often there is considerable rotting of the roots, particularly late in the season. Galls may also be formed on tubers and on parts of the stem in contact with the soil. Positive identification of the galls is made by breaking them open and looking for the nematodes; usually the adult females are found. They are pear-shaped and not eel-shaped, like most nematodes. They are pearly white and about as big around as the shank of a common pin. That is, they are large enough to be seen with the naked eye and quite easy to see with a magnifying glass, particularly in a portion of the root that has begun to rot so that they are in contrast with the brown root tissue. The egg masses of the root knot nematode are also fairly easy to see. These are brown in color, often as large as the nematodes, and are found clinging to the side of roots. When lifted off, the female will be found embedded in the root tissue. A microscope allows one to see the eggs in various stages of development and the hatched larvae in the egg mass. Sometimes the male, a slender worm quite different from the female, can also be found in the egg mass.

Nematodes of the genus *Pratylenchus*, known as meadow or root lesion nematodes, are another common type of root parasites. They feed in the cortex of roots and destroy the cells on which they feed. Fungi then attack the dead tissue. In the early stages the only visible symptom of attack is a small, reddish-brown lesion on the root. The lesion later enlarges, often girdles the root, and eventually severs it. Heavily attacked plants have greatly reduced root systems; most of the feeder roots are destroyed late in the season. The same sort of damage is also caused by other nematodes and by other types of soil organisms; positive diagnosis depends therefore on identifying the meadow nematode.

Stubby root nematodes (species of the genus *Trichodorus*) and sting nematodes (*Belonolaimus gracilis*) are external parasites, which apparently feed mostly on root tips. The feeding causes the root tip to stop growing and turn brown. Parts of the root may then die, probably because of attacks of secondary invaders. The final result is a reduced root system with many short root stubs. The attacks are particularly damaging to seedlings. Being external parasites, these nematodes will be found only in the soil.

Bulb and stem nematodes, species of the genus *Ditylenchus*, cause more or less localized deformations of stems and leaves. Stems are shortened and thickened; leaves are twisted, shortened, and otherwise distorted; and bulbs, such as narcissus and onion, become soft. In the later stages there may be rotting of the infected tissues. Nematodes can be found in large numbers in the affected parts, but are very slender and difficult to see without a microscope.

The wheat nematode, *Anguina tritici*, causes deformation of leaves of wheat and other grains in the early stages of growth. The nematode later invades the developing ear, causing the formation of galls in place of grain. The galls are shorter than normal wheat grains and look much like smut balls. But smut balls are soft enough to crush with the fingers and nematode galls are hard. If the gall is cut open and placed in a little water, the contents spill out and can be seen under the microscope to be thousands of minute worms, the larvae of the nematode. If still alive, they will start active movement in a few hours.

THE VARIOUS KINDS of nematode damage interfere with the growth of plants. Reduction in the size of the root system by rotting or galling restricts its efficiency in obtaining the food and water the plant must get from the soil.

Root knot galls distort the tissue that has the function of conducting food and nutrients to the upper part of the plant. Damage to stems and leaves also interferes with normal growth. Consequently the yield of crop plants is reduced. Crippled plants cannot produce a high-quality crop. With some crops, such as carrots and white potatoes, galls and rot caused by nematodes can make culls out of what would otherwise be salable produce.

The general appearance of a crop heavily attacked by nematodes that damage roots gives the impression that it is suffering from lack of fertilizer and water, even when they are available in the soil in abundance. The color is a lighter or more yellowish green than normal. Nematodes are seldom evenly distributed in the soil, so the growth of plants is uneven and patches of stunted plants appear here and there. Heavily infected plants may die prematurely, because of rotting of the roots, while clean or lightly infected plants are still growing normally.

The relation of nematodes to other soil-borne diseases, such as fusarium wilt of cotton, is not clearly defined. It is certain that plants attacked by both nematodes and bacterial or fungus diseases often suffer severe injury and that control of nematodes has often resulted in fair control of the other disease. The usual theory is that nematodes, by damaging the plant tissue, prepare the way for infections by bacteria and fungi, which would not occur otherwise, but it has been difficult to demonstrate this relationship experimentally.

I have no reliable estimates of the amount of damage nematodes do to crops in the United States each year, but there is general agreement that it is at least several hundred million dollars. The use of soil fumigants for nematode control during the past several years has often produced dramatic proof that nematodes in the soil can make the difference between a good crop and one not worth harvesting. Yield increases of 25 percent to 50 percent after soil fumigation are common. Experiments with soil fumi-

gation have also made it evident that severe nematode damage can occur in any part of the United States on a great variety of crops, including tree crops. It is also evident that severe nematode damage is not confined to the farm. Home gardens and ornamental plantings in city yards also are often damaged; there may even be damage to the flower pots on the window sill. New kinds of plant parasitic nematodes are constantly being found as are new locations for the more familiar species.

Little is known of the origins of the plant parasitic nematodes, but information as to their distribution in 1953 indicates that man has been largely responsible for their multiplication and spread from place to place. Being so very small, they are often unnoticed contaminants of plants, roots, bulbs, and tubers used for planting. It is probable that some of the worst of the nematode pests have moved from country to country around the world with such material. Soil moved from place to place, purposely or accidentally, may also contain plant parasitic nematodes. They are transported over long and short distances in soil adhering to farm implements and vehicles or to the feet of men and animals. Drainage water carries them from field to field. Certain species may be blown about by the wind.

After plant parasitic nematodes are introduced into a field, it may be a long time before their presence is noted. This is partly because increase from a small number is a slow process. Even when some damage to the crop is noted, the trouble may be attributed to declining soil fertility or to a succession of unfavorable growing seasons.

ALBERT L. TAYLOR *is a member of the division of nematology investigations of the Bureau of Plant Industry, Soils, and Agricultural Engineering. He has done experimental work on soil fumigation and, while employed by the Shell Chemical Corporation from 1946 to 1949, did research and development work on the soil fumigant D-D.*

The Effect of Weather on Diseases

Paul R. Miller

Three things must happen at exactly the same time if an infectious plant disease is to occur. One, a susceptible plant must be in a vulnerable state. Two, the parasite that causes the disease must be in an infective stage. Three, environmental conditions must be favorable for disease development.

The environment of a plant consists of the air around it and the soil in which it grows. The environment of a parasite alternates between the body of its host and either air or soil, according to whether it attacks plants above or below ground.

The aerial environment actually is the weather. It is made up of light, temperature, snow, rain, atmospheric humidity, dew, cloudiness, sunshine, wind, air currents, evaporation, and atmospheric pressure. Perhaps each element of weather affects the occurrence of disease in some way, but temperature and moisture apparently are the limiting factors for most diseases.

The amount of heat and moisture available in the soil environment depends on weather (or on irrigation), together with the ability of individual soil types to absorb and retain heat and moisture.

The surface of the soil affects the air in contact with it and a short distance above it. The state of the atmosphere near the ground, therefore, is different from that higher up. Depending on topography, the direction of exposure, the color, type, and moisture content of the soil, the amount and kind of plant cover, and other circumstances, entirely different environments—microclimates—can exist close to each other. As all plants live wholly or partly within this lowest zone, the weather in it affects them and their diseases.

The weather of any one region fluctuates over a rather definite range and averages up into a characteristic climate. For any given period, however, weather may not conform to the regional climate at all. That is why forecasts are indispensable to any undertaking that is greatly influenced by weather conditions. If weather progressed exactly according to climatic specifications, forecasts would not be needed. The same thing is true of many plant diseases.

The effect of weather on a plant disease is a consequence of its action on the susceptible plant (the host); on the parasitic organism (the pathogen that causes the disease); and on the relation between host and parasite.

One of the most noticeable things about plant diseases is that some of them occur wherever the host plant is grown and that others are restricted to certain parts of the host territory. Again, a disease that is more or less constantly present over a wide area may always be destructive in some locations but normally insignificant in others. That is because of the action of climate.

Climate is the average weather of a locality or region. It includes the seasonal progress of the weather as well as the extremes. For a season, a year, or a series of years, weather may vary in one respect or another from the "normal" for the climate of which it is a part, but over a long period climate is as definite a feature of a region as its soils, rivers, and forests. In fact, climate is largely responsible for the regional characteristics expressed in the landscape.

So it is with a plant disease. The total effect of weather upon it is summed up in its geographical distribution. We cannot always be sure of the precise explanation, but we know that most diseases flourish best in certain kinds of climate. Just as with the plants that they attack, some pathogens prefer cool regions and others are restricted to warmer areas; some require a great deal of moisture and others get along with less.

Thus the climate of a region determines the crops that can profitably be grown there and also the diseases to which the crops are subject. To put it the other way around: Given the presence of susceptible plants, the area of occurrence of a plant disease depends primarily on the climate. The outside boundaries of distribution generally are the extremes of hot and cold and wet and dry that the parasite can endure.

Within a range of conditions that permit its existence, a plant disease may be an insignificant or an important factor in crop production, depending on how exactly the local or seasonal conditions fit the requirements for its development and spread. Also, within this range, some factor other than weather may assume the decisive role—susceptibility of host varieties, for example, or the type or reaction of soil, or cultural management.

A few examples illustrate some ways in which climate is responsible for the distribution and importance of plant disease.

Apple scab, caused by the fungus *Venturia inaequalis*, occurs almost everywhere apples are grown. It is absent or unimportant only in hot or very dry regions. In areas with cool, rainy springs, it becomes a limiting factor and constant attention is required to control it. In the Northeastern and North Central States, climate is especially favorable to scab, which is by far the most important apple disease there.

During a series of surveys to determine the incidence of cotton seedling diseases and boll rots, technicians discovered that the occurrence and

nonoccurrence of anthracnose caused by *Glomerella gossypii* were definitely separated by a line running through eastern Texas and Oklahoma. The line nearly coincided with the boundary between below 10 and over 10 inches of average summer rainfall. Anthracnose is a constant and important factor under high summer rainfall in the eastern part of the Cotton Belt, but is practically nonexistent in the western part, which has lower rainfall.

Onion plants are susceptible to infection by the soil-borne spores of the smut fungus, *Urocystis cepulae*, for only a very short period in the seedling stage before emergence. Warm soils hasten the growth of the seedling and allow it to escape infection. In the South, onion seed mostly is planted in the fall and germinates in warm soil. Smut is scarcely known in the South, therefore, although it must have been introduced time after time with onion sets. By contrast, the disease is important in old established onion-growing districts from Kentucky northward, and is still spreading in northern sections.

Some diseases occur widely because the time of year at which susceptible plants are grown in different regions favors their development.

Potato late blight, caused by the fungus *Phytophthora infestans*, which requires cool and moist weather, is one such disease. Most races of the fungus cannot survive high summer temperatures. The disease occurs in the South because potatoes are a winter and spring crop there and because the organism is reintroduced with infected seed tubers each season.

Climate can constitute an effective barrier against the advance of a plant disease from one region to another. For instance, the Great Plains seems to act as a barrier against curly top of sugar beets. The virus that causes the disease affects many other kinds of plants, including tomato, cucurbits, and beans. The disease occurs in the intermountain region and westward from north to south, but not farther east than the western edge of the Great Plains. Its failure to spread eastward may be due to some climatic relation of the insect that carries the virus, the beet leafhopper *Circulifer tenellus*.

Several important soil-borne organisms cannot stand low temperatures for long. Among them are the bacterium *Xanthomonas solanacearum*, which causes Granville wilt of tobacco and attacks many other kinds of plants; *Sclerotium rolfsii*, the cause of southern blight; *Macrophomina phaseoli*, which causes charcoal root rot or ashy stem blight; and *Phymatotrichum omnivorum*, to which the so-called Texas root rot of cotton is due. All attack many kinds of plants. All are practically restricted to the southern part of the country. The cotton root rot fungus is further limited to the southwestern region, where it is native to certain types of soil. The first three organisms have been carried by various means to more northern areas but are not likely to become constantly present there because of their temperature limitations.

A soil-borne organism that prefers cool temperatures but can endure warm periods can achieve a much wider permanent distribution. *Sclerotinia sclerotiorum*, another fungus with a long list of hosts, occurs in nearly all parts of the country. In the South it is active during cool weather.

A DISEASE and the pathogen that causes it pass through a series of stages: Carry-over of the pathogen from one season to another; primary (first-season) infection of the host by the pathogen; growth of the pathogen within the tissues of the host; reproduction of the pathogen and secondary spread to new host plants; and finally production of the carry-over stage of the pathogen again.

At each of these stages temperature and moisture must be within a range (depending on the particular disease) that permits the process to continue. A cumulation of favorable stages induces severe disease. Unfavorable conditions at any of the stages retard development of the disease or may stop it entirely.

Either temperature or moisture can be decisive in the initiation, development, and spread of disease. If one is constantly favorable, the other becomes the limiting factor. If both temperature and moisture fluctuate, both must be favorable at critical times. If both are constantly favorable, the disease becomes serious.

The amount of inoculum (infective stage of the pathogen) that will be available to start new infections at the beginning of a season depends on the extent of infection at the end of the preceding season and on how well the pathogen can overwinter. Abundant overwintering and favorable conditions for infection in the early part of the season lead to heavy primary infection; if conditions remain favorable, the advantage of the early start is maintained throughout the growing period of the crop.

Some pathogens overwinter in the tissues of their hosts—for example, the potato late blight fungus in infected tubers, the peach bacterial spot organism, *Xanthomonas pruni*, in cankers, and the numerous seed-borne pathogens in seeds. Soil fungi and bacteria may overwinter on host debris. Many fungi, for instance many of the cereal smuts, produce a particular kind of spore that is able to survive the winter temperatures. Some of the spores will not germinate unless they have been subjected to low temperatures. Sometimes alternating warm and cool or wet and dry periods are required for spore germination or to complete the development of primary inoculum.

Some fungi, in addition to or instead of spores, develop a different kind of special organ to carry them over unfavorable periods of various kinds; these are sclerotia.

A pathogen may overwinter in different forms in different regions. In the United States the apple scab fungus overwinters and completes its development in fallen leaves, and spring infection is started by spores of the perithecial, or perfect, stage—the ascospores. In England the perithecial stage is rare, and the vegetative stage (mycelium) of the fungus is carried through the winter in infected twigs and buds, producing the ordinary summer spores, or conidia, when growth begins again.

Another example is the cereal stem rust fungus, *Puccinia graminis*. The summer spores, or uredospores, which are responsible for continuous spread of summer infection, can survive the winter in southern Texas and sometimes somewhat farther north. In northern areas, however, the winter spores, or teliospores, are necessary for winter survival. This fungus is a rather special case, since its winter spores infect not grains but barberry, on which another kind of spore is produced that will infect grains and grasses in the early part of the season.

During periods of high temperatures or dry weather, many disease-producing pathogens cease progress and remain quiescent in established infections or exist as saprophytes in host debris. The cotton anthracnose fungus is an example. Between seedling infection and boll infection, it resumes active growth and spread with every rainy period.

The microclimate furnished by the host plant itself undoubtedly aids survival of many pathogens in hot, dry weather. Within the plant, air is humid, shaded, and comparatively cool, quite different from the outside atmosphere.

The period of primary infection is a critical stage. No matter how abundant overwintering may have been, if weather then is not favorable the pathogen cannot infect its host. Take apple scab as an example. Primary infection by the pathogen requires that ascospores produced in the fallen leaves mature at the same time that unfolding leaves and buds on apple trees are susceptible to infection, which is only during the short period of their active growth. Further, there must be a rainy period lasting long enough to keep the new host surfaces constantly wet for some hours, at a high enough temperature. Ordinarily in the Northeastern and North Central States the time of ascospore production, progress of host development, and spring weather all favor the disease. In a dry spring, however, dissemination and germination of ascospores are inhibited. In some exceptional seasons, also, most of the ascospores may "shoot" before trees are ready for infection; that is, before foliage is produced. When primary infection is reduced or delayed, subsequent spread is likely to be reduced also, unless a very favorable period occurs later in the season.

Later stages in disease development are similarly affected by weather, although some diseases (after infection by the pathogen is established) are relatively indifferent to subsequent conditions. Other diseases, however, respond quickly to any change in temperature or moisture. Rather uniform environment throughout their course favors some pathogens. Others grow well under one set of conditions but may require the stimulus of a sudden decided change to induce sporulation, while still a different combination may be necessary for spore germination and for infection.

Often the connection between disease and weather is obvious—the attacks of potato late blight following a cool rainy period, for instance, or the dependence of the apple scab on rain. With other diseases, however, the critical period has been passed long before the attack becomes evident. For example, the temperature of the preceding winter is the decisive factor in the occurrence of bacterial wilt of sweet corn (caused by *Bacterium stewartii*); on the other hand, the severity of wheat leaf rust depends on temperature and moisture during late winter and early spring. The weather at the time that a plant disease is most conspicuous is not necessarily a reliable clue to the conditions that encourage disease development. Moreover, we cannot generalize from one disease to another. Each one must be studied separately.

It is hard to determine the exact relationship of disease to weather because of the variability of the weather, the lag between the critical period for infection of the host by the pathogen and subsequent development of disease symptoms, and the fact that best conditions for production of a disease may not coincide with best conditions for growth of its causal organism. This last apparently paradoxical situation exists because disease is the result of interaction between host and pathogen. Conditions that are most favorable for growth of the pathogen in artificial culture may allow the host to withstand or escape attack. In such cases disease can occur only with some other combination at which the host will be vulnerable and the pathogen will still be active. Therefore, the disease-producing requirements of the pathogen must be a compromise between what is most desirable for its own processes and what is actually possible in its relations with its host. Change in the intensity of one weather element brings about changes in the whole disease relationship. A change in temperature may make existing moisture conditions more or less favorable to attack by the pathogen, or it may increase or decrease the vulnerability of the host. Conversely, change in moisture supply may require a corresponding change in temperature if the disease is to progress unchecked. The struggle between host and pathogen is sometimes so delicately balanced that a very small alteration in only one condition is enough to assure victory to one side or the other.

If both a host and its parasite in their separate existence are favored by the same range of conditions, and if this range does not also enable the host to resist attack, then the disease caused by the pathogen is apt to become a limiting factor in the culture of the host, in any place where these conditions are usual. So we have the seemingly contradictory fact that best yields will be obtained under circumstances known not to be particularly favorable to the host. On the other hand, if best conditions for the host are different from those most favoring growth of the pathogen by itself, or if conditions suiting both make the host more resistant, the disease will result only when the pathogen gains the advantage over its host—for example, when the growth rate of the host is slowed down so that it remains in a susceptible state for a long enough time to allow infection by the pathogen, or when injury from suffocation by waterlogged soil permits root-rotting fungi to invade the rootlets, or when the chemical or mechanical constitution of host tissues is affected in such a way as to favor the pathogen.

A good example of the differential effect of temperature on host and pathogen and on the development of disease is given by the fungus *Gibberella zeae*, which is seed-borne and also overwinters in debris left in the soil. It is widely distributed throughout our more humid corn and wheat sections and causes seedling blight and other diseases of corn and small grains. In artificial culture it grows best at 75.2° to 80.6° F.; the minimum and maximum are 37.4° and 89.6°. Wheat likes fairly low soil temperatures. Corn prefers warmer soils. If other growing conditions are favorable, little or no seedling blight develops on wheat at 53.6°. As the temperature increases, so does the amount and severity of the disease, up to as high as 80.6°. With corn, no seedling blight results above 75.2°, and the most favorable range for the disease is from 46.4° to 68°. The explanation is that with each host grown under its most favorable conditions, the cell walls of the host tissue are more resistant and the reserve food supply is less attractive to the pathogen. With wheat, higher temperatures alter composition of cell walls and food supply to make this host more vulnerable to infection and the more

suited to the pathogen's food requirements. The reverse is true with corn;
high temperatures make it more resistant. Evidently, in both instances,
the temperature effect is due to action
on the growth processes of the host.
The practical result is that seedling
blight due to this fungus attacks wheat
mostly in the southern part and corn
in the northern part of the range of
the host.

Cabbage yellows is caused by a
soil-borne fungus, *Fusarium oxysporum*
f. *conglutinans*. The fungus grows best
in warm temperatures. The disease is
associated with warm weather. Here
it is the fungus that is affected by
temperature: Yellows is rare in southern cabbage-growing areas because
cabbage is a winter crop there and
grows in cool soils.

Some diseases caused by soil-borne
organisms are more closely dependent
on moisture than on temperature. One
such disease is the avocado root rot,
caused by *Phytophthora cinnamomi*, in
California. Plantings on overirrigated
or flooded locations are severely
affected. Excess moisture prevents
soil aeration. The rootlets are injured
by lack of oxygen, and the fungus
gains entry to the roots through the
injured portions. The disease does not
occur on waterlogged soils that do
not contain the fungus, although the
rootlets are as badly injured.

For pathogens that affect the above-
ground parts of plants, environment
is much more complex and variable
than for the soil-borne organisms.
Alternation of night and day is accompanied by changes of temperature as
well as light. Cool air can hold less
water vapor than warm air. If the
difference between day and night
temperatures is great enough in relation to daytime humidity, dew forms
on the plants. Quiet air preserves
vertical and horizontal differences in
temperature and moisture. Air movement mixes cool and warm, wet and
dry air. It aids evaporation by preventing accumulation of moisture-
saturated air and promotes drying of

moist surfaces. Dew will not form on
windy nights. Moving air carries infective stages of pathogens from place
to place. Rain, dew, and fog wet the
surfaces of plants and supply moisture
for germination of fungus spores and
multiplication of bacteria. Inoculum
on the soil surface may be borne to
low stems or leaves or low-hanging
fruit with splashing raindrops. Dripping moisture from fog or rain can
carry infection from tree tops to lowest limbs. Wind-driven rain may
transport spores and bacteria for considerable distances. Cloudiness and
sunshine affect temperature, evaporation, humidity, air movement.

The constant trouble that plant diseases cause might lead us to think
every bit of infective material succeeds
in producing infection. That is not so.
Most of the countless fungus spores
every season fail to survive all the hazards against them and reach the right
part of the right kind of plant during
the life period of the spore. If it falls on
anything else, a spore is so much dust.
If it does finally fall on the surface of its
host, it must be on a part and during a
stage vulnerable to infection, without
a coating of fungicide that would kill
the spore, and with sufficient moisture
or humidity and the proper temperature lasting for a long enough period to
allow the spore to germinate and penetrate the host tissue.

A pathogen carried by an insect, as
are most viruses and many fungi and
bacteria, has an advantage over airborne organisms. The insects take the
pathogen more or less straight to the
proper host, and in most cases inoculate it directly into the host tissues.
Such pathogens and the diseases they
cause are nevertheless just as subject to
the effect of weather. The vectors, indeed, add a third organism to be included in the disease-weather relation.
Weather affects survival, increase, and
activity of the insects, as well as direction, distance, and intensity of migration and flight. Overwintering of the
insect vector is as important as survival
of the pathogen itself. Some of the

pathogens even overwinter in the vector.

SOME OF THE MOST DREADED diseases of crops are of moderate importance or are scarce or even absent a good part of the time. But they can attack with great suddenness and destructiveness in certain seasons, or perhaps during several consecutive years. Among them are wheat stem rust and potato late blight, which are probably the most famous of plant diseases because of the importance of the hosts almost everywhere and because of the extraordinary severity of epidemic outbreaks of either disease.

The incidence of stem rust in our central Wheat Belt goes sharply up and down from high peaks in favorable seasons to low troughs in years when the disease is negligible or absent. Widespread outbreaks are less frequent than formerly because of the use of varieties resistant to the predominant physiologic races of the organism and because of the eradication of barberry, which was an important source of early-season infection in the northern part of the region. Nevertheless, every once in a while the chain of circumstances still favors the disease and an epidemic results.

The essential features are: Rapid build-up of a physiologic race of stem rust, to which the wheat varieties predominantly grown are susceptible; mild winter weather, which allows abundant uredospore overwintering, perhaps as far north as Oklahoma; favorable damp and not too warm weather for early infection in the southern part of the region and continuing favorable weather along the way, as spores are borne northward by the wind, to produce infection step by step until the northern wheatfields are reached. Finally, hot, dry weather is necessary during the period when the wheat kernels are forming on the rusted plants to produce maximum damage. Such a favorable combination resulted in the 1935 epidemic, which cost the country almost a quarter of the crop for that year. In Minnesota and North Dakota the loss was almost 60 percent.

A graph of the occurrence of potato late blight would show as pronounced ups and downs as for stem rust. In the East, primary outbreaks follow two weeks of rainy or foggy, cool weather. The earlier in the season primary infection occurs, the more severe the outbreak will be, if moisture and temperature are at the required levels. In extremely favorable seasons, late blight spreads with explosive rapidity. The very conditions that favor the disease make it exceedingly difficult to keep plants protected by fungicides.

Naturally, the same conditions, when they exist, would induce severe attack in the Central States also. A more frequent favorable combination in that region, however, is alternation of high daytime temperatures with low night temperatures and high relative humidity during the day. The marked temperature fall at night stimulates sporulation and forces excess water vapor out of the air as dew, which supplies moisture for germination and infection. The microclimate furnished by the plant may be an important factor in the region. The result is serious, continued spread under conditions that, without analysis, would appear unfavorable.

In any area, really dry weather, or constantly high temperatures, and especially a dry, hot season will prevent the occurrence of late blight or check its spread. Severe epidemics result from an early start with abundant inoculum and continuous favorable temperature and moisture.

Late blight has a habit of appearing suddenly and destructively in regions where it had not previously been considered a factor. The epidemic in the southern potato crop in the winter and spring of 1943-1944 is a good illustration. Contributing factors in that outbreak were: The especially abundant supply of inoculum that resulted from wartime relaxation of seed requirements; exceptionally wet weather; favorable temperatures; lack of experience with the disease; and difficulty of control, the result of the early heavy attack, weather that prevented efficient application, and scarcity of control materials. The total result was the most severe and widespread epidemic ever known in the South. Losses were heavy in some States where the disease had not been seen for 30 years or more.

Late blight is also a disease of tomato. Since 1940 or so several severe outbreaks have caused heavy losses to tomato growers. In 1946 the disease caused an estimated loss of 40 million dollars and brought sharply to attention our need to use all the knowledge that we already possess about weather and disease and to learn a great deal more, if we are not to be at the mercy of late blight and other epidemic diseases.

Tomato late blight had been severe in various limited areas at different times before 1946. In 1946, however, all factors worked together and the result was unprecedented severity and heavy loss along the Atlantic coast from Florida to New England. The outbreak extended as far west as Minnesota in the North and Texas in the South. Again, late blight demonstrated its capacity to move rapidly and destructively into sections previously free of it.

The disease was severe on the winter and spring crop in the South. Plants grown in Georgia and other Southern States for early planting in northern fields became generally infected. Weather at the time of planting in the North favored the spread of infection from this very abundant and active source of inoculum and continued to favor the disease for most of the season. As usual with such sudden, widespread outbreaks, preparations for control—equipment, materials, and experience—were inadequate.

Late blight belongs to a group of diseases, the downy mildews, that are especially sensitive to weather. An-

other member of this group is the blue mold or downy mildew of tobacco, the causal fungus of which is *Peronospora tabacina*. Thirty years of records have shown that in southern tobacco-growing sections the incidence of blue mold is greatly influenced by temperature in January. Above-average temperatures are followed by early appearance; with low temperatures, infection is slow to develop. Subsequent conditions also affect severity; the most widespread, severe attacks occur in years when high January temperatures permit early infection, and temperature and moisture conditions afterward favor continued spread.

Experience with sweet corn bacterial wilt shows how we can make use of observed facts and records about weather and occurrence even though at first we do not know the explanation for the behavior of the disease. Bacterial wilt is constantly present on susceptible varieties in the South, but as a rule it occurs only occasionally farther north. During the early 1930's general and severe attacks made it the major disease of the crop in north central and northeastern sections of the country.

Study of a long series of observations recorded in Connecticut, together with the weather records, indicated that the disease followed warm winters and was scarce or absent after average or cold winters. The seasons during which bacterial wilt had become increasingly severe were preceded by unusually warm winters.

It was found that summation of the average temperatures for December, January, and February for any given place would show very accurately whether or not the disease could be expected during the following season and how much damage it would cause. If the sum, which is called the "winter temperature index," is 100 or above, the disease will be destructive; with lesser sums, incidence is correspondingly less severe.

Since the correlation between winter temperature and disease incidence was established, it has been found that it depends on winter survival of the insect vector, the flea beetle *Chaetocnema pulicularia*. This fact explains certain small discrepancies between observed occurrence and the original statement of the correlation. In some seasons following a very warm winter, incidence of bacterial wilt was less than was to be expected. These seasons usually were preceded by one or several during which the disease was minor. More than one favorable season is required for both the vector and the bacterium to build up sufficiently to result in maximum disease incidence.

The correlation is so regular that it is used as a guide to planting. Resistant sorts are used when severe occurrence is indicated.

Several points need to be noticed about this disease-weather relationship. First, it required study of *both* disease occurrence *and* weather records to establish it. Second, it was useful even before the explanation was known. Third, it involves a third organism, the vector. Fourth, it gives a chance to take measures against the disease even before seed is planted.

In many ways, the fact that diseases are so dependent on weather is a great advantage to us in our fight against them, as we shall see now.

ONE CANNOT STUDY a parasitic plant disease without taking into account the influence of temperature and moisture on the pathogen, on the reaction of the host, and on consequent disease development. Obviously, a connection so regular must have great practical significance.

One way in which we can make the disease-weather relationship work for us is in the management of various agricultural operations to take advantage of temperature and moisture conditions unfavorable to disease development. Thus, the way in which irrigation, surface or overhead, is used can either favor or discourage attack by pathogens. Many diseases attacking

through the seedling can be controlled by so timing planting that the seed will start growth under conditions inhibiting infection by the pathogen. Temperature and humidity in greenhouses and storage houses can be maintained at levels that will prevent or control disease. Arid and semiarid locations are ideal for the production of seed free from seed-borne pathogens, since the requisite moisture for spore germination and bacterial spread is lacking in their climates.

Chemical control measures can be used with precision when climatic relationships are taken into account. For example, seed treatment for cotton seedling disease gave varying results before surveys showed that seed-borne anthracnose was by far the most important cause in the humid Southeast, and that soil-borne organisms predominated in drier regions westward. When this different disease distribution was known, seed treatment could be applied specifically for each type of cause and was much more effective.

We can avoid the inevitable failure that would result from planting a crop in a region where it would be subject to a disease hazard because of weather. We can be watchful also to prevent the introduction of new diseases that would create new hazards in favorable climates.

It does not take very much imagination to realize that many of the diseases we have already discussed would constitute hazards in particularly favorable regions, if the control measures were not known. In fact, after a series of seasons when weather especially suits disease attack and makes control efforts arduous, expensive, and inefficient, growing of the host may have to be abandoned or greatly reduced for a while.

If we can tell when an outbreak is likely to happen, we can prepare for it and reduce losses. In particular, we can overcome the difficulty in the use of expensive chemical control measures arising from the fact that routine application is wasted in years when the disease is absent, but, on the other hand, when it does attack protection must be prompt and continuous to do any good. With such a choice farmers are apt to take a chance and often will sustain severe losses. Forecasting enables sound judgment instead of wasteful guessing on the need for control measures.

Prediction does not always help in control but does enable farmers to reduce their losses in other ways. For instance, there is no practicable short-time control measure available for wheat leaf rust, but forecasts issued early in the season allow farmers to plow up their wheat and plant some other crop or to pasture their fields if a serious outbreak is indicated. Thus they can recover at least part of their season's investment.

Predictions can never be entirely right. This is just as true of plant disease forecasting as of weather or political polls or anything else. The average correctness for the limited number of plant diseases that are being forecast so far is more than 80 percent. The possible accuracy depends on how complicated the critical periods are and on how far in advance they operate. For instance, if winter temperature by itself determines the amount of the disease for the following season, a prediction is a simple matter of calculation and can be made with practically complete certainty that it will be right. In contrast, if the pathogen can cause disease at any time that its temperature or moisture demands or both are met, both disease and weather must be watched throughout the season, and frequently revised short-term forecasts are necessary.

Forecasting plant disease occurrence on the basis of known weather requirements is well established. In this country apple scab spray warning services have been routine for almost 30 years. Some other diseases for which forecasting is regularly a part of the control program in one region or another include bacterial wilt of sweet corn, wheat leaf rust, late blight, tobacco blue mold, cucurbit downy mildew (*Pseudoperonospora cubensis*), and lima bean downy mildew (*Phytophthora phaseoli*). The weather relations that make it possible to predict for some of these diseases have already been indicated.

The 1946 tomato late blight outbreak proved beyond doubt that diseases that spread so rapidly, and attack so destructively, require more than local attention to cope with them adequately. As a result, the Crop Plant Disease Forecasting Project of the Plant Disease Survey, Bureau of Plant Industry, Soils, and Agricultural Engineering, was organized. The project is a concrete expression of the importance of the weather-disease relation. It was set up especially to keep watch over circumstances that might lead to outbreaks of plant diseases, to use all available information about conditions favoring diseases as an immediate basis for making forecasts, and to study the requirements for development and spread so that predictions can be improved in accuracy and duration.

The chart on the next page shows how the warning service of the project operates. A pathologist in each State works with it and performs the same task for his own State that the project does for regions. Because information is obtained from such a wide area, ample time is given for local warning and preparation if a disease outbreak seems likely. An indispensable feature of the project, noted in the chart, is the cooperation of fungicide and equipment manufacturers, which assures availability of chemicals and control equipment wherever and whenever they are needed. The role of the Weather Bureau, in a program that has weather as one of its components, is obvious.

Late blight, tobacco blue mold, and cucurbit downy mildew, up to now, have been the chief diseases considered by the warning service. Regional forecasting for potato late blight has been tried in the North Central States,

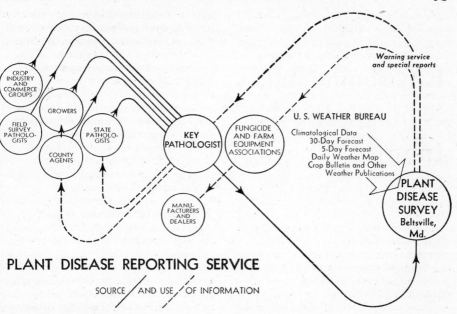

PLANT DISEASE REPORTING SERVICE

SOURCE / AND USE / OF INFORMATION

with good results. The forecasts are based on temperature and humidity recorded by hygrothermographs placed in potato fields in various parts of the region, on the weather forecasts, and on observations on the prevalence of the disease in selected locations. This regional forecasting on the basis of instrumental recording, much the same as for weather, is a new trend and shows promise of further development.

We can make useful predictions without knowing all the reasons for the observed reaction of disease to weather. Neither do we need to know at the time of predicting exactly what the weather will be. We can say that on the basis of what we know now, *if* the weather is this, *then* the disease will be that, and even the conditional forecast will be helpful. Obviously, however, the more we know about the operation and timing of the factors favoring or inhibiting the development and spread of disease, and the longer ahead of time we can be sure of the weather, the more accurate our predictions will be and the earlier we can make them. Improvement and extension of the long-range weather

forecasts is the answer to the latter need. The research program of the forecasting project is designed to add to our knowledge on the connection between environment and disease. Detailed and continuous observation of weather and microclimate is as much a part of its investigation as are the purely disease factors. By means of weather-recording instruments, the weather can be correlated directly with the development of the disease in experimental fields. The regional late blight forecasts in the Central States are a result of this sort of study.

PAUL R. MILLER, *a pathologist in charge of the Plant Disease Survey, Bureau of Plant Industry, Soils, and Agricultural Engineering, has spent 16 years developing survey techniques and conducting field studies of diseases that occur on major economic crops, including peanuts, tobacco, cotton and truck crops. Dr. Miller directs a plant disease forecasting service in cooperation with the agricultural experiment station pathologists of the 48 States, the United States Weather Bureau, and the National Fungicide and Farm Equipment Association.*

Environmental, Nonparasitic Injuries

J. E. McMurtrey, Jr.

Bad weather, air pollution, growth regulators, and the deficiencies or excesses of minerals in the soil can cause a group of diseases of plants that we classify as environmental and nonparasitic.

They are related closely to diseases brought about by parasitic organisms. Often we can regulate plant growth so as to control them and thereby control somewhat the diseases attributed to parasites. Symptoms associated with nonparasitic diseases frequently are confused with those caused by fungi, bacteria, and viruses. Often the injury from nonparasitic disturbances permits fungi, bacteria, or viruses to enter and damage the plant.

The severity and type of injury vary with the plant, its stage of maturity when the disturbance occurs, and the part of the plant involved.

LIGHTNING, hail, wind-blown rain, drowning, frost, and drought are among the elements of weather that may harm plants.

Lightning may tear large trees apart or it may only injure a few limbs. It may kill the stem tissue of annual plants, such as tobacco, so that the leaves get a shrunken, dark midrib. Damage to plants by lightning is local and usually not extensive.

Hail may cause only small holes in a few leaves or complete defoliation and destruction of plants. A striking instance of hail damage is the destruction of an entire field of shade-grown tobacco and the shade cloth over it. Usually hail does damage in limited areas only.

Heavy rains may break young, tender leaves or puncture holes in them. Wind-blown rain also causes water soaking of the intercellular spaces of the leaves. Sometimes, if micro-organisms are present, the damage may be severe. Plants blow over; leaves and grain in contact with the soil may rot; it might be impossible to use machinery to harvest the crop.

Most crop plants grow well on relatively well-drained soil that may be subject to leaching or temporary flooding, but most plants will not survive persistent flooding, which drowns and destroys the root system. If a part of the root system is damaged, growth is reduced and micro-organisms may invade the tissues. Temporary wilting is often evident. In sandy soils the rapid loss of water by percolation—leaching—causes the loss of soluble plant foods, particularly nitrogen and possibly magnesium.

Not uncommonly are plants injured on days of high temperature and bright sunshine. Sunscald is the permanent wilting of young leaves. Another type of injury results in a drying of the lower or older leaves. Such conditions are more common with temporary shortages of water. Corn, for example, first shows rolling of leaves; if the drought continues it may suffer to the degree that the upper part of the plant, including the staminate inflorescence, dries up and fertilization cannot take place. In extreme droughts trees and other plants may die.

In cold weather growth may be delayed so that parasites develop. Losses from late spring and early fall freezes are an ever-present threat in most of the Temperate Zone. Small grains, corn, and other crops often fail to reach proper maturity before being killed by freezes in some seasons in northern latitudes. Following frost and freezing injury, plants may suffer death of twigs and branches, splitting of trunks, and the loss of fruit crops when flowers are killed.

FACTORIES may release concentrations of gases that are toxic to plant growth. Sulfur dioxide is an example. In many places the vegetation around industrial establishments—such as factories that make sulfuric acid or smelters of sulfide ores—has been almost entirely wiped out. Smoke from coal sometimes contains sulfur dioxide in amounts that may injure plants if it is not dissipated by wind.

Fluorine, as hydrofluoric acid gas, is injurious to plants near chemical works that release it into the air. The injury often appears only as marginal lesions or necrosis, but sometimes the entire leaf dies prematurely. Low concentrations of fluorine often cause leaves to turn yellow.

Smog is a still, heavy mixture of fog and various contaminants, such as sulfur oxides, ammonia, fluorides, filterable oils, gaseous hydrocarbons, oxides of nitrogen, and hydrogen sulfide. It is not known for certain which one of those gases is the culprit or whether two or more act simultaneously to injure plants. In the south coastal area of California, for example, Romaine lettuce, endive, and spinach suffer extreme injury from smog; beet, celery, oats, Swiss chard, and alfalfa suffer moderate injury. Barley, onion, parsley, radish, tomato, turnip, and rhubarb suffer slight injury. Cabbage, cantaloup, carrot, cauliflower, cucumber, pumpkin, squash, and broccoli suffer no injury. Bleaching and scorching sometimes are evident.

INSECTICIDES may injure plants. Arsenicals used improperly may cause shedding of leaves. The effect of arsenicals, particularly lead arsenate, may be cumulative and in time may kill fruit trees. Calcium arsenate, as used on cotton, may temporarily sterilize the soil. Oil sprays may damage fruit trees. Parathion and some of the other newer synthetic insecticides may

cause the russeting of some varieties of apples. Benzene hexachloride may cause the formation of strap-leaf and off-flavors, particularly in potatoes.

All parts of plants, notably orchard trees, might be injured by bordeaux sprays and dusts. The leaves may show burning, shot holing, spotting, discoloration, and defoliation. The blossoms may be injured so that no fruit is set. The fruit may show spotting, russeting, malformation, cracking, and shedding. The twigs may have injuries of various kinds, or the entire tree may die if damage is unusually severe. Lime-sulfur also might cause lesions on foliage or fruit and premature fruit drop. The most common injury is a dull-brown spotting of the leaves or burning of margins and tips.

Many injuries have followed the extensive use of the growth-regulator herbicides, especially 2,4-D. Minute amounts of them are enough to produce ill effects on plants—even the tiny residue in a sprayer that has not been cleaned thoroughly with plenty of hot water and ammonia. Injury also may occur from the drift of herbicide spray when the wind is blowing. Leaf malformations occur in sensitive species around factories that prepare 2,4-D. The injury may be only a slight rat-tail type of growth of the leaves or the death of trees.

A DEFICIENCY of any one of the chemical elements necessary for plant growth may reduce total growth of plants. To distinguish the effect of one element from that of another, one must examine closely the affected plant. For example, it is not enough to say that a leaf is chlorotic; a detailed description of the chlorotic pattern is necessary and the age of the leaf must be known. A shortage of any one of the elements—boron, calcium, copper, iron, magnesium, manganese, molybdenum, nitrogen, phosphorus, potassium, sulfur, and zinc—may produce malnutritional diseases of plants.

A shortage of boron in the soil results in poor growth of tops and roots. Top sickness in tobacco, heart and dry rot of sugar beets, internal cork of apples, internal browning of cauliflower (which first occurs as small, concentric, water-soaked areas in the stem and central branches of the curd), and cracked stem of celery are boron-deficiency diseases. Poor growth, yellowing of the terminal growth, and death of the terminal buds are typical symptoms in most plants. The affected terminal growth becomes brittle, breaks easily, and shows discoloration of vascular tissues.

A deficiency of calcium shows up first near the growing point on the young leaves. The growing point dies and the young leaves often are severely distorted and show a hooked tip. When later growth takes place, the margins are irregular because of the failure in early development. The leaf petioles of many plants collapse when the growing points die. The floral parts, including corolla and calyx, may show abnormalities. Shedding and little or no seed set may follow. Tobacco, tomato, and potato plants show distinctive deficiency effects. Tomatoes show pronounced dieback of stems, leaves, and fruiting branches and blossom-end rot of fruits. Potatoes form few tubers, show bushy vines, and develop leaflets near the shoot tips that are small, chlorotic, and roll inward toward the midveins. Beans, peas, clovers, and other legumes have pale-green leaves with necrotic margins. The stems may collapse near growing points, petioles, and pedicels. Pods and seeds are few and poorly developed. The growing points of sugar beet, carrot, parsnip, and other root crops may die. The tree fruits undergo death of the terminal shoots. The tip leaves have a scorched and ragged appearance, and the margins roll inward. Calcium deficiency in most plants results in breakdown of the meristematic tissues in stem, root, or any part of the plant where the deficiency occurs. Extreme shortages of calcium commonly mean the early death of the plant.

Years ago growers learned that the dieback, or exanthema, of citrus trees in Florida could be corrected by the use of copper compounds, although the ailment was not recognized at first as due to a copper deficiency.

Apple, pear, and plum trees show much the same symptoms when they lack copper. Tobacco plants deficient in copper suffer a breakdown of older leaves and wilting of younger leaves. When the shortage of copper operates after flowering, the seed head cannot stand erect and the seed stalk bends to one side. The cereals show much the same symptoms—withering of tips of the younger leaves, wilting of the foliage, dwarfing, distorting of seed heads, and less formation of grain. The lower leaves and tillers on such plants tend to remain green. Copper is essential for normal color and growth of lettuce and onions, particularly when they are grown on peat soils.

The first deficiency disease of plants to be recognized was the one caused by too little iron. It was first reported in France, and the remedy was iron salts. Yellowing of the young growth is the first sign of the disease. Some necrosis may occur. In extreme cases the young leaves may become almost white. In milder cases there is a mottled pattern; the primary and secondary veins tend to retain the green color. Sometimes there is drying or scorching of leaf tips and margins. In extreme cases dieback of twigs may extend to large branches of trees. Fruit and shade trees are often more commonly affected than field or vegetable crops. The typical chlorosis due to iron deficiency often occurs on soils of high lime content and has been termed "lime-induced." The typical chlorosis of pineapples in Hawaii occurs on soils high in manganese and has been corrected by the use of sprays that contain iron.

Magnesium deficiency causes a chlorosis that first affects the older leaves. Magnesium is a component of chlorophyll. Sand drown, the distinctive chlorosis of tobacco, is caused by magnesium deficiency. The lowermost leaves of the plant first lose their normal green color at the tips and margins and between the veins. The primary and secondary veins and the nearby tissue tend to retain the normal green color long after the remaining leaf tissue has become pale green or almost white. The deficiency rarely occurs until the plants have attained considerable size. It is called sand drown because it is more prevalent in deep, sandy soils and during seasons of excessive rainfall. Corn has streaks on the lower leaves when magnesium is deficient. The cotton plant shows chlorosis, and a purplish-red color develops in the yellow areas. Leaves of vegetables turn yellow and die. Citrus trees develop a chlorosis known as bronzing. Leaves of deficient apple trees turn yellow and unhealthy and drop if the shortage is acute.

Chlorosis and necrosis of young leaves are early symptoms of manganese deficiency. Tomato plants growing in calcareous soils in Florida showed retarded growth, failure to blossom, chlorosis, and a necrotic spotting of the younger leaves until manganese was supplied. The gray speck disease of oats is due to too little manganese. The first seedling leaves of the oat plant are of a normal green; later leaves are faintly yellow and develop necrotic spots. "Pahala blight" of sugarcane arises from too little manganese. Snap beans show a chlorosis of the young leaves; each new leaf shows more chlorosis, and affected plants finally die. Young leaves of an ailing tobacco plant lose color in even the smallest veins; the contrast between the green and yellow places gives a checkered effect to the leaf. Chlorotic leaves develop small lifeless spots, which may enlarge and fall out. The spots are distributed over the leaf—not only at the tip and margin, as with potassium deficiency. The acidity or alkalinity of the soil on which the plant grows appears to dominate manganese absorption, as most instances of deficiency of manganese have been reported on neutral or alkaline soils.

The effect of molybdenum deficiency was first mentioned as a cause of the whiptail disease of cauliflower in New Zealand and Australia. The disease restricts the development of the leaf lamina, so that sometimes the midribs are left bare. In extreme cases the growing point dies. The effects of a shortage of molybdenum on tobacco and tomatoes has been reported for plants grown in nutrient solutions. The tomato plant shows a mottling of the lower leaves, followed by necrosis and crinkling. The fruit set is poor because most of the blossoms shed. Tobacco shows much the same symptoms when molybdenum is deficient; the shedding of flower buds leads to a reduction in amount of seed. Various crops, particularly legumes, have responded favorably to the addition of molybdenum on serpentine and ironstone soils in some areas.

Shortage of nitrogen, perhaps the most common of the deficiencies, shows up at any time from the seedling stage to maturity. First the plant loses its normal green color. The growth rate slows down. Then lemon, orange, red, or purple tints develop and the older leaves dry or drop. Leaves that develop later when nitrogen is transferred to them from the older leaves are small; the production of fruit or seed is correspondingly reduced. The growth of nitrogen-deficient plants is sparse, spindly, and erect. The roots may be long and little branched; the twigs of trees are short and small. Small grains show a marked reduction in number of tillers and consequently yield poorly. Not all effects of nitrogen deficiency are bad, however. The growth of broadleaved plants, such as tobacco, can be regulated by withholding nitrogen to produce leaf of a certain type, such as the bright lemon-colored leaf known as the flue-cured type. Fruit trees on nitrogen-deficient soil may produce highly colored fruits that store well.

Shortages of phosphorus lower plant growth markedly. The symptoms are not always clearly defined. Usually the leaves are small and erect, the lateral buds are few, and the roots may be sparsely branched. But most of the effects of phosphorus deficiency apparently are more general. The leaves usually are dark green, but in later stages or in extreme cases they may be dull green and may show purplish tints. Sometimes necrosis is evident. When the older leaves dry up or shed they are dark brown to almost black. The cereals often show purpling on older leaves. Tobacco leaves are a dark gray green and maturity is delayed. Production of fruit and seed is reduced and slow.

Chlorosis, commonly beginning on the older leaves at their tips and margins, is typical of potassium deficiency. Necrosis follows, first as small areas that gradually enlarge and merge. The dead areas may fall out so the leaves get a ragged appearance. Grasses, when potassium is deficient, show a yellowish streaking which, on older leaves, may develop into scorching. The stalks on such plants are short, roots are poor, and the ears are poorly filled at the tip. The tobacco plant becomes bluish green, mottled, and chlorotic. Generally the lower leaves show the first symptoms, but if the shortage operates during later growth stages of the plant, when growth is rapid, the upper leaves may show the first symptoms. Mottling is followed quickly by necrotic spotting at the leaf tips and margins between the veins. Tomato and the potato plants show much the same symptoms as tobacco. Tomato fruits fail to ripen evenly; often greenish-yellow patches are intermingled with the red of the red-fruited varieties. Cotton and the sweetpotato develop chlorosis and necrosis of the older leaves and some leaf shedding. Cotton rust is associated with potassium deficiency. Foliage of deciduous fruit trees becomes bluish green; intervein chlorosis, necrosis, and marginal scorch occur on older leaves; extreme cases involve dieback of shoots and branches and fruits of poor quality. Citrus fruits display small leaves, fluting or tucking along the midrib, small and poor fruit, and dieback in serious disorders.

The effects of sulfur deficiency on plant growth generally resemble those caused by shortage of nitrogen. The younger leaves display a pronounced yellowing with little or no drying of older leaves. While nitrogen shortage is accentuated and sometimes brought about by excessive rainfall, sulfur shortage is often more apparent during dry periods and in dry areas, since sulfur dioxide, a common air contaminant, is brought down by rainfall. Grasses lose their normal green color when sulfur is withheld. Leaves of legumes become yellow and develop brown spots; the plants are less succulent and have thin stems. The tobacco plant first shows light-green leaves; veins and the tissue between the veins lose their green color when sulfur is deficient. Much the same symptoms have been reported for the tomato. The tobacco plant recovers quickly from sulfur deficiency in times of adequate rainfall. Citrus trees show a marked yellowing of the younger leaves in the early stages of the deficiency. Some dieback of the twigs may occur later. A disease known as tea yellows is caused by sulfur deficiency. The initial stages of sulfur deficiency generally are marked by a yellowing of the younger leaves. When the condition becomes acute and lasting, the older leaves may turn yellow. Leaves of citrus and the tea bush may die back.

The initial effects of zinc deficiency, most evident on the older leaves of many plants, are chlorosis, necrosis, shedding of leaves, and, in extreme cases, dieback of twigs in trees. Pecan rosette, citrus mottling, littleleaf, and citrus rosette are due to zinc deficiency. The corn plant shows yellow streaks on the older leaves when zinc is deficient. The streaks later become necrotic; the young leaves unfolding in the bud may be white or yellow and produce the white-bud disease. Sugar beet and potato develop leaf spots on the older leaves. The leaves of the potato are thickened and curled. Tobacco grown in purified, zinc-free sand or solutions in the greenhouse has shown deficiency symptoms—first a faint chlorosis on the older leaves at the leaf tip and margins between the veins. Necrosis soon develops as small areas that rapidly enlarge to involve the veins or the entire leaf. The leaves are thick, internodes are short, and the corolla appears to be shortened.

IT IS NOT POSSIBLE to distinguish clearly between the disorders that are due to a deficiency as such and the disorders that are due to too much of another element. A deficient supply of one element implies an excess of other elements. A mass-action effect may arise as when too much of one element may interfere with the solubility, absorption, and utilization of another element to the extent of developing acute deficiency effects. The effects often may result from the acidity or alkalinity of the culture medium.

Many of the nutrient elements in excess may cause symptoms of toxicity. For example, boron in any considerable amounts results in a marginal necrosis of the older leaves followed often by stunting and death. Those symptoms often have been seen following the use of irrigation water that carried toxic amounts of boron. The use of potash salts in fertilizers containing excessive amounts of boron has caused serious losses.

Calcium, if present in amounts that cause alkalinity of the soils when the levels of iron, manganese, boron, or zinc are low, often results in deficiency symptoms previously described as typical for the deficiency of each of those elements.

An excess of copper causes necrosis, wilting, reduced growth, and death of plants.

Too much iron may induce a deficiency of phosphorus or manganese.

Magnesium present in large amounts may accentuate potassium deficiency if the potassium supply is low. An excess of magnesium may operate in much the same manner for calcium and show the calcium-deficiency symptoms.

Manganese when present in excess may bring about iron deficiency. Manganese is often present in acid soils in amounts sufficient to reduce plant growth. Low calcium is often associated with this condition so that plant growth will be improved by liming to neutralize soil acidity.

Excess amounts of nitrogen stimulate excessive growth and frequently may cause a deficiency of another element that is present in small amount. Often the other element is potassium; then the plant is commonly more susceptible to rusts (in the case of the small grains and cotton) and to leaf spots (tobacco). Sulfur often is added to acidify alkali soil to improve plant growth. Sometimes the continued use of ammonium sulfate and other sulfates brings about a low pH, which often is unfavorable to plant growth. Excess sulfates bring into solution the extra manganese and aluminum that may be present in the soil and thus injure plant growth.

Actually, most effects associated with soil reaction are related to solubility of nutrient or toxic ions rather than injuries associated with the hydrogen ion. Since the acidity or alkalinity of soils in humid areas may range between pH 4.0 and 8.0, most plants can grow successfully at that range if there are no complications in regard to availability and toxicity of the ions present. The so-called alkali soils show a much higher pH and present a different problem.

SALINITY is a serious problem in many arid areas and in places where ocean spray or salt water floods agricultural soils. Excessive fertilization with soluble salts sometimes causes much the same kind of injury. The effect may vary according to the plants in question and the salts and concentrations that are involved. Sometimes the effect is merely one of concentration of soluble salts, but again, if alkali salts are present in excess, the soils are said to be alkali. The actual salts present may vary, but the three common ones are sodium chloride (table salt), sodium sulfate (Glauber's salt), and sodium carbonate (sal soda). Various other salts of sodium, calcium, magnesium, and potassium may also be present.

Most of our common crop plants are sensitive to salts. Seed germination may be retarded or prevented. Young seedlings may die. When the plants do survive, the growth rate commonly is slow, the plant wilts, and the leaves burn at the tips and margins. Fruit or shade trees may survive for a time on saline soils and show chlorosis, possibly caused by induced shortages of iron brought about by alkaline soil conditions. Their growth is reduced, leaves drop, and eventually the trees die. If conditions are not too severe, the more resistant types of plants may have drought-resistant characteristics. The leaves are small and have a thicker cuticle. Waxy coatings are more developed and the breathing pores are sunken below the outer surface, so that evaporation or transpiration are reduced.

Among the crop plants, sugar beets, Rhodes grass, and Bermuda-grass have the strongest tolerance to saline conditions. Those with medium-strong tolerance to saline conditions are alfalfa, cotton, kale, barley as a hay crop, rape, and sorgo. The crops with medium tolerance include onions, squash, flax, Ladino clover, sunflowers, rice, and rye as a grain crop. Those with the weakest tolerance include red clover, snap beans, navy beans, vetch, and wheat as a grain crop.

J. E. McMurtrey, Jr., *is principal physiologist and project leader of investigations of production, breeding, disease, and quality of tobacco in the Bureau of Plant Industry, Soils, and Agricultural Engineering. He is stationed at Beltsville, Md. Dr. McMurtrey has degrees from the University of Kentucky and the University of Maryland.*

The Effects of Soil Fertility

George L. McNew

Many farmers and gardeners have observed that plant diseases have become more prevalent and soils less fertile than they used to be. Some have argued that the two phenomena are related and that diseases are more destructive because the plants have been weakened by poor mineral nutrition. A few have even maintained that there would be no serious disease problems if plants were grown in properly conditioned soil, but evidence obtained in hundreds of experiments throughout the world does not uphold this extreme viewpoint.

Soil fertility does affect the prevalence and severity of some plant diseases, but it is only one of several factors that predispose plants to infection by fungi, bacteria, viruses, and nematodes. We can make no sweeping generalizations about the effect of fertilizers on diseases because of the extreme differences in crop plants, their special nutritional requirements, the soil types upon which they are grown, and the diversity of the pathogens that attack them. Some diseases are severe on weakened, undernourished plants. Many others are most destructive when plants are growing vigorously.

If wheat on a moderately fertile soil, for example, is given an extra supply of nitrogen it probably will escape seedling diseases more readily, be more subject to pythium root rot, suffer less from take-all disease, and be more subject to infection by leaf rust and powdery mildew. Phosphorus and potassium fertilizers would have an entirely different effect on those same diseases. The addition of barnyard manure to wilt-infested cottonfields will reduce the amount of wilt in places in Arkansas where potassium and nitrogen are deficient but will increase the severity of the same disease on the delta of the Nile, where nitrogen is readily available.

Such effects of soil fertility on plant diseases must be understood in this age when fertilizer practices are being changed so rapidly. More than 18 million tons of commercial fertilizer and 25 million tons of agricultural lime were used in 1948. That is about twice as much as was required before the Second World War. Less barnyard manure is being added to the soil each year. Not enough green manure from cover crops is being plowed under to maintain the organic matter content of soils on most of our farms. Under such conditions, both the balance of the various nutrient elements and the total supply of nutrients available to the plant can be expected to fluctuate appreciably from year to year and during the growing season.

THE PRIMARY CONSIDERATION in fertilizing soil is to use such materials, in combination with suitable crop rotations and other soil management practices, as are necessary to promote the maximum productivity of the plant. Disease control is a secondary consideration beyond the fact that one must avoid certain conditions, such as an excess of nitrogen or other available nutrients, a deficiency of potassium, or changes in soil reaction that affect diseases of a crop.

Fertilizer materials that leave acid residues (such as those from ammonium sulfate, potassium sulfate, sulfur, and calcium sulfate) should be employed where neutral or alkaline soils favor diseases like potato scab.

Sodium nitrate, calcium phosphate, limestone, and similar materials that leave alkaline residues should be used where diseases such as clubroot of cabbage and some wilt diseases are suppressed by alkaline soils.

Residues from organic matter are valuable for stimulating the growth of beneficial micro-organisms in the soil. They may destroy or prevent the growth of some plant parasites that are not well adjusted to living in the soil environment.

When diseases become a serious problem on properly nourished, productive plants, other control measures such as spraying, crop rotation, or use of disease-escaping varieties will have to be employed. There is no sound reason for starving the plant into an unproductive state in order to escape disease. If the plant is properly nourished and capable of full development, the disease control measures, such as spraying or soil disinfestation, are fully justified. They are a form of crop insurance. They pay the largest dividends on productive soils. Often they are not worth applying to weak and undernourished plants.

Several plant diseases are influenced so seriously by soil deficiencies that much of the damage from them can be avoided by soil treatment. The outstanding examples, which are discussed here, are take-all disease of wheat, wheat root rot, Texas root rot of cotton, sugar beet seedling diseases, fusariam wilt of cotton, wildfire disease of tobacco, clubroot of cabbage, common scab of potatoes, bacterial leaf spot of peaches, and powdery mildew and rusts of cereals.

A deficiency of any plant nutrient may influence disease development. Nitrogen, phosphorus, and potassium, the primary elements, are mentioned most often. The secondary elements, calcium, sulfur, silicon, manganese, and boron also have been observed to exert appreciable influence on the prevalence of plant diseases.

Nitrogen is supplied in the form of

sodium nitrate (Chilean nitrate), ammonium sulfate, urea, organic nitrogen, or anhydrous ammonia. It promotes vigorous growth and is essential for production of amino acids, growth regulants, and new protoplasm. Used to excess, it encourages rank, vegetative growth, delays maturity, and tends to cause thin cell walls. Fungi may penetrate the thin walls more readily than normal ones. Infected plants collapse more easily. Cereal plants lodge. Lesions on leaves elongate rapidly. Because nitrogen in a proper combination with other nutrients often speeds up growth of seedlings and roots, the plants escape severe damage from pathogens that develop slowly. But because nitrogen may prolong vegetative growth, leaves are exposed to infection over a longer season. The roots, water-conducting tissues, leaves, and fruits of plants that are supplied with nitrogen are more nutritious to most pathogens, which grow better in them than in nitrogen-deficient plants.

Phosphorus is applied as rock phosphate, superphosphate, ammonium phosphate, basic slag, or bonemeal. Phosphorus is essential for utilization of carbohydrates and for cell division because it combines with carbohydrate materials to form nucleic acids. Adequate supplies of phosphorus promote root growth and seed development. Applications of it are most beneficial against seedling diseases and certain root rots where vigorous development of roots permits the plants to escape destruction. It is essential for multiplication of viruses in host cells and may increase susceptibility to viruses and other disease agents if too abundant. Because of its use in building new cells, any imbalance with nitrogen may cause disease losses to increase.

Potassium (potash) is supplied to soils as potassium chloride (Kainit, muriate of potash), potassium sulfate, potassium nitrate, or wood ashes. Unlike other essential nutrients, it does not become a structural part of the plant cell. It is a mobile regulator of cell activity and promotes the reduction of nitrates and the synthesis of amino acids from carbohydrate and inorganic nitrogen. Potassium promotes the development of thicker outer walls in the epidermal cells and firm tissues, which are less subject to collapse.

A deficiency of potassium enforces the accumulation of carbohydrates and inorganic nitrogen in the plant. Eventually it retards photosynthesis and production of new tissues. More plant diseases have been retarded by use of potash fertilizers than any other substance, perhaps because potassium is so essential for catalyzing cell activities. It is unavailable in many soils of light texture because its salts are so water-soluble they readily leach from the soil.

Calcium is added to the soil as ground limestone, hydrated lime, gypsum, or calcium phosphate. It is essential for normal growth since it regulates chromosome development in cell division and is assimilated into the middle lamellae of new cell walls. It is therefore important for cell division and cell development. It also may neutralize acid byproducts of cell metabolism that could become harmful if not precipitated in an insoluble condition. Calcium also influences plant diseases indirectly by its effect on soil acidity, by neutralizing toxins produced by wilt-inducing fungi, and by affecting cell division in those diseases where abnormal growth of tissues is important. Its balance with potassium becomes a primary consideration in gall development because both materials contribute to the growth and division of cells.

Silicon affects the availability of potassium. It also may be combined with other materials to give the cell walls greater structural strength. The primary effect on plant diseases apparently is in the prevention of infection by powdery mildew, a disease in which the fungus develops externally and usually penetrates the host cell through the outer wall. Sulfur is oxidized to sulfates and thereby promotes soil acidity, which discourages growth and survival of some bacteria and fungi.

Soil reaction (the hydrogen-ion concentration, expressed in terms of pH units) influences the growth and persistence of some fungi and bacteria. The parasitic organisms that depend on delicate bodies, such as thin-walled swarmspores, may have difficulty in multiplying and infecting roots in soils at unfavorable hydrogen-ion concentrations. Hydrogen-ion concentration may change the ability of pine tree roots to resist invasion, but that, if true, is an exceptional case. Soil reaction also may affect the availability of essential nutrients in the soil and the biological balance between plant parasites and saprophytic soil-inhabiting fungi and bacteria.

Although organic matter contributes essential nutrients to the crop, it probably exerts more influence through the physical and biological changes that it brings about in the soil. The carbohydrates and proteins in animal and plant byproducts provide nourishment to soil organisms that fix nitrogen from the air, tie up available nitrates in the soil, and frequently suppress plant parasites by antibiotic activity.

The humus from lignified plant tissues and other residual products promotes the massing together of soil particles and thereby improves aeration and water-holding capacity of soils. Organic matter may promote the growth of plant parasites or even facilitate their dispersal. Some of the decomposition products may increase the susceptibility of roots to invasion.

YOUNG SEEDLINGS of most crops are attacked by fungi that live in the soil or are carried on the seed.

Fungi such as *Pythium debaryanum*, *P. ultimum*, and *Rhizoctonia solani* live in most agricultural soils since they compete successfully for space with other soil saprophytes. They are stimulated to growth by organic matter around the germinating seed. If seed germination or seedling development is delayed by excessive moisture or low temperature, the fungi may invade the seed or girdle the young shoot before the plant can establish itself. These fungi become progressively less aggressive as the plant begins to synthesize its own food and its underground tissues become lignified.

Sugar beet seedlings are particularly susceptible to these damping-off fungi and *Aphanomyces cochlioides*. Failure to secure a suitable stand occurs in Montana, Colorado, Iowa, Ohio, and elsewhere whenever heavy rains fall after seeding. The usual preventive measure employed is to coat the seed with a fungicidal chemical, which prevents seed decay and protects the seedling near the seed ball. Seed dressings do not always prevent the post-emergence damping-off if the weather conditions are favorable for the soil-inhabiting fungi.

Much of the damage can be avoided by fertilizing the soil so as to promote vigorous growth of the seedlings. Phosphates alone at the rate of 400 to 800 pounds an acre in moderately fertile soils are decidedly beneficial in preventing severe losses from *Aphanomyces cochlioides* at low soil temperatures. In Montana, where seedling losses of 75 percent were common on a soil of low fertility, the application of manure, superphosphate, and sodium nitrate reduced losses to 21 percent and increased yields of roots from 7.47 tons to 18.23 tons.

The application of potash or nitrogen alone is not effective. Moderate improvements have been obtained from manure alone. Manure and phosphate or a combination of manure, phosphate, and nitrate are definitely superior. Such treatments combined with a desirable rotation such as beets-potato-oats or a 3-year cycle of beets-alfalfa-oats-potatoes eliminated most of the seedling diseases in the experiments in Montana.

Attempts to apply fertilizers as a seed dressing have not been uniformly

successful. Highly soluble materials injure the young plants, and phosphate
on the seed is not so effective as it is in
soil treatments.

Although fertilizer treatments have
not proved so successful on other
crops, there are reports of benefits
from fall application of balanced
fertilizers to clover seedlings in Russia
and from calcium on soybeans in the
United States. Nitrogen applied to
cucumber seedlings reduced the severity of damping-off, presumably by
accelerating the lignification of underground portions of the stems. Most
observers have reported, however,
that application of nitrogen alone
or in excessive proportions makes
seedlings more susceptible to attack.
The damping-off of pines, other conifers, and cotton is increased by
nitrogen fertilizers. Sodium nitrite,
however, applied at the rate of 4 to 8
ounces to the square yard, several
weeks before planting, destroys nematodes as well as damping-off fungi and
then oxidizes to harmless nitrates,
which may be used as a source of nitrogen by the young plants.

Australian workers reported that
seed decay of peas was more severe
in poor soils than in fertile ones, but
emergence of peas was not improved in
Colorado by application of different
fertilizers to poor gravelly soil. Seed
decay of peas may be increased by
applying fertilizers in direct contact
with seed. The injury can be attributed
largely to the water-soluble nitrogen
in balanced fertilizers, because phosphorus alone causes little damage and
potassium salts are only slightly injurious. Decay increases in proportion
to the percentage of nitrogen in the
formula and the total amount applied.

Tomato seedlings are also more
subject to damping-off when soluble
salts accumulate around the tender
stem and roots. The concentration of
salt seems to be more important than
the kind of compound, except that
potassium salts are tolerated in fairly
heavy concentrations.

A severe root rot of wheat in Saskatchewan and other areas on the
Great Plains, known as the browning
disease, is caused by *Pythium arrhenomanes*. The same fungus attacks sugarcane in Louisiana and Hawaii. Studies
made on the two crops have tended to
confirm each other on the effects of
soil fertility.

The disease is most severe on sugarcane and wheat in poorly drained,
wet soils. Such soils have many
products of anaerobic respiration,
such as salicylic aldehyde, present in
concentrations of 50 parts per million
or more. Salicylic aldehyde is ordinarily oxidized by species of *Penicillium*
and *Actinomyces* in well-aerated soil,
but the growth of these fungi is
suppressed by the anaerobic conditions
in wet fields. The salicylic aldehyde
does not affect the growth of either
the roots or the root-rotting fungus,
but it does predispose plants to attack.
Injurious concentrations of salicylic
aldehyde may be avoided by draining
the soil or using fertilizers that promote oxidation.

Wheat plants that have severe root
rot usually contain nitrogen in adequate to excess amounts but are
deficient in phosphorus. The disease
is particularly severe on fields that
were held under fallow cultivation
the preceding years. The nitrogen-
fixing bacteria increase the supply of
nitrates during the fallow period and
these are readily available to the
next crop. Severe damage from root
rot can usually be avoided by adding
phosphates to the soil or by reducing
the supply of nitrates available so as
to restore a normal balance between
the two nutrients.

Wheat straw, plowed under, stimulates the growth of soil micro-organisms, which assimilate the available
nitrogen and thereby reduce the
amount immediately available to the
new wheat crop. So the balance with
phosphorus is temporarily restored during the period when the young plant is
most susceptible. The same result is
achieved in Hawaii by applying to the
soil press cake from the cane extracting

plant or crude cane sirup wastes. Besides promoting growth of soil bacteria, the materials provide extra potassium, which also helps reduce loss from root rot. Barnyard manure, sweetclover, or weed hay may also be used to advantage.

Nitrogen added alone to infertile soil increases the susceptibility of roots to invasion by *Pythium*. The plants are not capable of developing new roots and consequently are severely injured. When phosphorus and nitrogen are added simultaneously the roots are still susceptible to infection, but new growth develops so rapidly that the plant escapes severe damage. The ability of plants to produce new roots explains the beneficial effect from balanced fertilizers.

Several other root rot and foot rot diseases of cereals are caused by species of *Fusarium*, *Cercosporella*, and *Helminthosporium*. The diseases usually are found to be most severe on dwarfed, undernourished plants or on plants receiving an excess of nitrogen. Field tests with phosphates and balanced fertilizers, however, have failed to prevent losses in many localities. In at least one locality in Canada excess soluble salts in the soil increased the severity of helminthosporium and fusarium root rots.

THE TAKE-ALL DISEASE of wheat causes severe losses in the United States, Canada, and Australia. Much of the damage can be avoided by maintaining a proper balance of soil nutrients. The soil requirements seem to differ in different areas. Decided benefits from nitrogen fertilizers have been obtained in England and Canada. Phosphates have proved beneficial in Kansas and Australia.

Some of the benefits from soil fertilization have been phenomenal. In an Arkansas field where 80 percent of the plants were infected, on an unfertilized plot, the application of 10 tons of barnyard manure or 400 pounds of 4-8-3 fertilizer to the acre reduced infection to 45 and 7 percent, respectively.

Experiments in sand cultures have shown that a suitable balance among nitrogen, phosphorus, and potassium must be maintained if losses from take-all are to be avoided. Severe infection occurs when all three nutrients are inadequate, or phosphorus and potassium are in short supply. Nitrogen may increase the incidence of root infection. As in pythium root rot, however, if phosphorus is also present the plant develops new roots to replace the infected ones and produces a good crop.

Readily available nitrogen has three effects on the development of take-all. An adequate supply during the fall and winter permits the causal fungus, *Ophiobolus graminis*, to prolong its existence on infested stubble. Therefore the fungus often lives longer in soil under fallow culture than in soils seeded to cover crops or oats, which utilize all available nitrogen. If nitrogen is made available to young plants, the roots are more readily invaded. Adequate nitrogen, however, will also permit the rapid replacement of diseased roots with new ones if phosphorus is present.

Because of these various effects, S. D. Garrett suggested in the Annals of Applied Biology for 1948 that trefoil was the ideal cover crop to precede wheat. Plowed under in the fall, it stimulated growth of micro-organisms so all available nitrogen in the soil would be incorporated into their bodies and the survival of the take-all fungus would be reduced. The plant residues and micro-organisms would then decompose the following spring and summer to provide a continuous, uniform supply of nitrogen to promote disease-escaping ability in the wheat crop.

For some time it was believed that organic matter reduced the severity of take-all by encouraging the multiplication of soil micro-organisms that were antagonistic to *Ophiobolus graminis*. Many carbohydrate-rich materials do increase the soil flora, but most of their effect is now attributed to uniform supply of nitrogen and phosphorus. There is very little change in the population of bacteria and fungi in the immediate vicinity of the roots where the take-all fungus attacks and all effective materials, such as chicken manure, chopped alfalfa, horse manure, and barley or oat grain, increase the amount of available nitrate and phosphate in the soil.

TEXAS ROOT ROT has been one of the more difficult diseases to control. There is little chance of obtaining disease-resistant varieties because the fungus attacks more than a thousand species of plants. As the fungus spreads slowly in the soil by mycelial growth, infested areas gradually enlarge each year. But it is a poor soil invader when divorced from plant roots and does not compete well with other soil-inhabiting organisms. Consequently it often diminishes after 2 or 3 years.

The disease is most prevalent in alkaline soils. Its radial spread may be controlled by increasing the soil acidity through use of sulfur. The fungus grows better in soils made alkaline by calcium carbonate than in soils receiving calcium nitrate, calcium sulfate, or calcium phosphate. The bark of infected roots usually is rich in phosphorus but deficient in nitrogen.

The disease can be controlled by adding nitrogenous fertilizers to the soil. The use of 15 to 20 tons of barnyard manure or green manure an acre will permit production of a good crop on infested soil. Ammonium sulfate and balanced fertilizers such as 9–3–3 at 600 to 900 pounds to the acre have been recommended for silt loam soils of Texas. Phosphate fertilizers increase the severity of root rot. A potassium deficiency reduces slightly the severity of the disease.

Many of the effects of fertilizers can be attributed to changes in the soil microflora that destroy the sclerotia—the resting bodies—of the pathogen and otherwise reduce its prevalence, The reduction of sclerotia is in proportion to the amount of organic supplements used over a range of 0.5 to 5.0 percent in clay, sandy loam, or sandy soils. Crop refuse, green manure, and such materials as starch, cellulose, and peptone promote the destruction of the root rot fungus. If soil microorganisms are not present, the organic matter alone will not destroy the sclerotia.

The amount of carbohydrate in the root bark affects the severity of disease. Because a moderate amount is necessary for invasion, young seedlings escape infection until they begin to synthesize their own foods. Later in the season carbohydrates begin to accumulate in the bark and escape into the surrounding soil. Thus the growth of soil organisms, which apparently can inhibit the root rot fungus, is promoted. High carbohydrate levels in the roots induced by extra light, less growth of twigs, reduced set of bolls, or temporary deficiency of nitrogen lower the amount of infection. Further support for this observation has been obtained by studying the relationship of the soil organisms to the resistance of corn roots. Corn secretes carbohydrates from the roots and is resistant under normal circumstances but becomes susceptible when grown in the absence of soil saprophytes that can inhibit the fungus.

THE COTTON WILT caused by *Fusarium vasinfectum* can be controlled by the use of resistant varieties if nematodes are not present in soil. The disease is most severe in the potash-deficient soils of the United States. It is very destructive on light, sandy soils such as the alluvial deposits along streams, where soluble nutrients have been lost by leaching. It is severe also on the fertile, heavy soils of the Nile Delta in Egypt, presumably because of the availability of nitrogen. Barnyard manure has been known to reduce the severity of cotton wilt in the United States since 1907, presumably because it corrects potash deficiency. Its use in Egypt, however, has been reported to increase the severity of wilt. The disease may occur in soils ranging in reaction from pH 4.6 to

3.4 but is most common on the more acid soils of Arkansas because most of them are deficient in potash.

Wilt can be reduced by application of 20 to 100 pounds of potash to the acre, but best results are had on most light soils from use of a balanced fertilizer, such as 6–8–8 or 4–10–7, at the rate of 300 to 400 pounds to the acre. On moderately fertile soils nitrogen should be omitted or used sparingly because an excess of nitrogen will increase the severity of wilt. A surplus of phosphate may be harmful but usually is not so influential as the balance between nitrogen and potash. Ammonium nitrogen is more conducive to wilt than nitrate salts.

Much of the wilting promoted by nitrogen fertilization can be avoided by using calcium nitrate in alkaline nutrient solutions or by plowing under green manure crops.

The wilt of cotton caused by *Verticillium albo-atrum* does not respond to soil treatments in the same way as the fusarium wilt. Application of potassium does not reduce infection and may even increase the severity of wilting. Nitrogen treatments increase the severity of the disease. Tomatoes infected by the fungus respond to nitrogen and potassium fertilizers much as cotton does. On both crops, plant residues are beneficial because they lower the availability of soluble nitrogen compounds.

CLUBROOT OF CABBAGE and other cruciferous crops is caused by a fungus (*Plasmodiophora brassicae*) that survives for several years in infested soil. The fungus produces free-swimming swarmspores that infect roots and root hairs. The swarmspores are released most readily in neutral or acid soils and may be inhibited in alkaline soils. Therefore, and because cabbage can grow well in calcareous soils, many investigators have recommended that soils be limed to pH 7.0 to 7.2 in order to escape the disease.

Turnip growers 200 years ago learned to use marl or alkaline clay on their fields. Ground limestone or hydrated lime is commonly recommended today. Comparable amounts of gypsum and calcium chloride are relatively ineffective. Although the hydrogen-ion concentration of soils does affect clubroot, the disease has been observed in alkaline soils of pH 7.8 to 8.1. Other contributory factors consequently must also be involved.

The disease is most severe on cabbage that gets abundant supplies of balanced nutrients. A deficiency of potassium suppresses infection on cabbage, mustard, and turnip. The disease is most severe when there is a deficiency or excess of nitrogen or an excess of potassium. Infection occurs most readily on large, actively growing roots, but mineral nutrients obviously influence the disease by changing the physiological balance within the host tissue because nitrogen deficiency promotes infection on poorly nourished roots.

Apparently the ratio of calcium to potassium may be more important than soil reaction in determining the severity of clubroot. Clubroot infection diminishes on moderately fertile silt loam soil as the ratio of calcium to potassium is decreased either by adding calcium or using less potassium while the other constituent is held constant at nominal concentrations. The effects of calcium and potassium have been observed in acid, neutral, and alkaline soils, but the general severity of the disease increases as soils become more acid.

THE COMMON SCAB of potato (*Streptomyces scabies*) is usually avoided by growing potatoes in acid soils. Scab rarely occurs in soils at pH 4.8 or below and is not serious at pH 4.8 to 5.1. It increases in prevalence and destructiveness at pH 5.4 to 7.0. Potatoes grow best at pH 5.0 to 5.5, but tolerate a range of pH 4.6 to 6.1 without loss of yield. The usual recommendation for potatoes on scab-infested soil is to adjust the reaction to pH 5.0 to 5.2. That may be done by applying sulfur or using acidic fertilizers such as ammonium sulfate and potassium sulfate in preference to sodium nitrate and other materials that leave alkaline residues.

The sulfur treatment, which is also used for the control of soil pox of sweetpotatoes caused by *Streptomyces ipomoea*, consists of applying 500 to 3,000 pounds an acre well in advance of planting so it will be converted to acid by the soil organisms. It may produce microbicidal concentrations of hydrogen sulfide. J. H. Muncie and his co-workers in Michigan reported in 1944 that the scab organism may become adjusted to the sulfur treatment and not be controlled by a second application even when soil is made acid. Heavy applications of sulfur may suppress growth of potatoes; so sulfur-tolerant crops such as cotton have been recommended for use the first year after treating the soil. In the Florida potato-growing areas, sulfur-treated soils receive an application of lime before planting to potatoes and related crops.

Barnyard manure often increases scab, but we do not fully understand the exact role of various nutrient elements. The ratio of calcium to potassium is important. One can assume that one of the major effects of hydrogen-ion concentration is on this ratio because it affects the mobilization of cationic plant nutrients. In tests by R. A. Schroeder and W. A. Albrecht, of Missouri, where exchangeable ions were controlled by the colloidal clay technique, infection increased as supplies of either calcium or potassium were increased in the presence of an adequate supply of the other. Infection was about equally prevalent at pH 5.2 and 6.8 when the calcium-potassium balance remained constant. Scab was least severe at either reaction when the two elements were balanced. Those observations were repeated and extended by G. A. Gries, J. G. Horsfall, and H. G. M. Jacobson, of Connecticut.

THE ANGULAR LEAF SPOT and wildfire disease of tobacco is caused by a bacterium (*Pseudomonas tabaci*) that invades the leaf through the stomata. Infection often is restricted to a small spot around the stomata unless the leaf tissues have become water-soaked either by driving rainstorms or root pressure during rainy periods. The disease is most severe in the Southeastern States in soils that are deficient in potassium.

Potassium fertilizers do encourage thicker cell walls, heavier cuticle, and stronger mechanical tissues in tobacco. The leaves of such plants are less easily water-soaked. Consequently they are less likely to be seriously injured by the wildfire bacterium. Plants receiving an excess of nitrogen have thinner cell walls and more succulent tissue and are more subject to water soaking and invasion.

Balanced supplies of potassium and nitrogen are essential if wildfire is to be avoided. As barnyard manure contains both elements, the application of 6 to 8 tons an acre has been effective in Kentucky and other areas where both elements are deficient. Balanced fertilizers like 4-10-6 or 6-2-3 are more effective than nitrogen and potassium alone in preventing wildfire. Most soils in the tobacco-growing areas require about 40 to 60 pounds of potash an acre. The usual recommendation is for an application of 600 to 1,500 pounds of mixed fertilizer.

PEACHES AND PLUMS frequently are defoliated in late summer by *Xanthomonas pruni*. The bacteria from overwintering cankers on the twigs invade the leaf through the stomata and cause irregular circular lesions about one-quarter inch or more in diameter. The infected area dies and falls out, thereby producing a shot-hole appearance. Sometimes the infected leaves become yellow and fall from the tree; on other trees they continue to function. Usually the nitrogen-deficient leaves in the center of the crown and on the lower branches are the first to fall. The most severe damage occurs to trees on infertile, light, sandy soils.

Vigorous, healthy leaves in an orchard in Pennsylvania had more potassium than infected leaves. Applications of potassium and magnesium, however, failed to reduce the severity of disease. Excellent results have been obtained from six applications of sodium nitrate each at the rate of 1 pound to a tree. The added nitrate does not prevent infection, but it does reduce defoliation so that trees retain their leaves throughout the summer and fall.

W. D. Valleau concluded from his observations in Kentucky that trees supplied with adequate nitrogen have ability to excise infected spots and retain their leaves longer than undernourished trees.

Moderate applications of ammonium sulfate will reduce the bacterial canker of prunes, according to E. E. Wilson. The treatment did not prevent infection through the lenticels but it did encourage the development of periderm and the cankers healed more promptly. The bacterial canker of plums in England caused by *Pseudomonas morsprunorum* differs from the disease caused by *Xanthomonas pruni* in that nitrogen has no beneficial effects, the largest cankers occurring on plants receiving generous supplies of balanced fertilizers. The smallest lesions are on plants deprived of phosphorus.

POWDERY MILDEW OF CEREALS is caused by highly specialized races of *Erysiphe graminis,* an obligate parasite that lives predominantly on the surface of leaves and sends haustoria (rootlike appendages) into the epidermal cells, where they procure foods. Either mechanical resistance of the cell wall to penetration by the haustoria or an undesirable nutritional balance inside the cell may restrict mildew development.

Heavy application of nitrogen to soil promotes rapid growth of cereals and increases the severity of mildew. Because the outer walls of the epidermal cells in such plants are thinner, it has been assumed that that change facilitates infection. Thicker walls may be developed by balancing the nitrogen with adequate supplies of potassium and phosphorus. The potassium increases resistance, but phosphorus-fed plants are more susceptible despite the thicker cell walls. Although the thickness of cell wall undoubtedly influences the susceptibility of wheat and barley, other factors (such as the chemical composition of the cell contents) also regulate the development of mildew.

Potassium has beneficial effects on cereals. Potassium silicate is particularly effective in improving resistance of wheat and barley but not oats. The outer cell membranes of the epidermis are perceptibly thickened, presumably by depositing silicates and changing the functions of the cell protoplasm. Similar effects have been reported from use of silica gel on rye, barley, and wheat. Low concentrations of nitrogen and adequate supplies of potassium promote silicification of cell walls. Silicates, however, do not improve the resistance of rye to rust, oats to helminthosporium blight, or corn to smut and anthracnose.

Secondary nutrients also influence resistance of cereals to mildew. A deficiency of boron in California and deficiency of manganese in Australia were found to increase disease.

THE CEREAL RUSTS consist of many physiologic races that are intensely specialized in their parasitic behavior. They multiply when in contact with living cells and become dormant or die when the host cells die because they cannot utilize decaying organic matter readily.

As early as 1903 J. C. Arthur commented: "So intimate is the association of parasite and host as a rule the vigor of the parasite is directly proportional to the vigor of the host."

If growth of the plants is retarded by too much nutrients, the fungus may be less fruitful.

The leaf rusts of wheat, oats, and corn are influenced by mineral nutrition. Heavy supplies of nitrogen increase the susceptibility of foliage when supplied through the roots or by leaf immersion. The nitrogenous materials, in descending order of effectiveness for accentuating rust, are ammonium nitrate, ammonium sulfate, ammonium chloride, urea, glycol, ammonium phosphate, magnesium nitrate, asparagin, calcium nitrate, potassium nitrite, and sodium nitrate. Resistance is impaired the least by these materials when supplied with adequate carbohydrates. Excessively heavy applications of sodium nitrate or potassium nitrate reduce infection of wheat.

Potassium salts in moderate amounts increase the resistance of wheat, rye, and oats to leaf rusts. Moderately resistant varieties may be made susceptible by depriving them of potassium. The reaction of very resistant varieties is not affected materially and susceptible varieties do not become immune when supplied with potassium salts. Although phosphorus has little effect on the severity of leaf rusts, it may increase resistance slightly when other nutrients are available in adequate amounts. Heavier infection usually is promoted by increasing the amount of balanced nutrients available to the plant.

The reason has not been fully explained. Any deficiency that retards growth of the host may reduce the severity of rust infection, as was observed by E. B. Mains for calcium, iron, magnesium, potassium, phosphorus, nitrogen, and sulfur deficiencies in the greenhouse. The albumen content of leaves is increased by heavy nitrogen fertilization and lowered by potassium; consequently it might regulate susceptibility. The production of a rust-inhibiting toxin by the plant may be affected. A. F. Parker-Rhodes found that extra nitrogen or a deficiency of minor elements enhanced the ability of wheat to produce a toxin for *Puccinia glumarum*. The toxins possibly are produced by the autolysis of proteins in the infected leaf.

Black stem rust may be influenced by mineral nutrition of wheat, according to C. R. Hursh. A moderate supply of nitrogen increases the incidence of stem rust. Heavy applications weaken the straw and predispose the plants to severe damage from enlarged pustules and lodging. Potassium and, to a less extent, phosphorus increase resistance when a moderate supply of nitrogen is available. Calcium phosphate in the absence of nitrogen rendered plants very resistant. He believes the mineral nutrients affect resistance by changing the thickness of epidermal walls, the number of stomata, or the amount of reenforcing tissue (sclerenchyma), which limits the size of pustules.

No change in the proportion of sclerenchyma to collenchyma that could be correlated with resistance was found by Helen Hart, of the University of Minnesota, except in the variety Kota during one season. Plants receiving treble superphosphate were less severely infected and had a larger percentage of collenchymatous tissue. The pustules in the plants were small and well separated by sclerenchyma. Plants receiving ammonium phosphate or balanced nitrogen, phosphorus, and potassium had more collenchyma tissue. She concluded, however, that nitrogen probably did not increase the amount of susceptible tissue in most varieties of wheat.

The type of reaction in very resistant or very susceptible varieties of wheat cannot be changed materially, according to J. M. Daly. The variety Thatcher, however, grown at 65° to 75° F. in the greenhouse was completely resistant to race 56 when supplied with ammonium nitrogen and partly susceptible when supplied nitrate nitrogen. Mindum wheat was resistant regardless of nitrogen source. The reaction of Marquis, Mindum, or Thatcher under field conditions was not altered by different amounts of nitrogen.

No fundamental change in resistance of wheat to *Puccinia graminis* was observed from use of fertilizers by E. C. Stakman and O. S. Aamodt in field trials that continued 8 years. Plants receiving nitrogen often had more infection, but that could be attributed to heavier growth of plants and delayed maturity. Their general conclusion was that the wheat farmer should give the soil the fertilizers that the wheat needs but avoid too much nitrogen; add potash and phosphates judiciously—and the best results are likely to be obtained.

PLANT VIRUSES are most evident in young, rapidly growing tissues and may be masked in older tissues, particularly if they are exposed to intense sunlight. Because the virus increases only in the living cells of the plant, any change in host physiology might be expected to affect the multiplication of viruses. Most of the information available on effect of mineral nutrition has been obtained from studying various strains of tobacco mosaic in hosts that develop local lesions or systemic mottling of the leaves.

The yellow strain of tobacco mosaic has been studied extensively by E. L. Spencer on plants in sand culture and nutrient-deficient soil. The virus creates local lesions most readily in Turkish tobacco supplied with abundant nitrogen, phosphorus optimum for vegetative development, and potassium at minimum concentration for full growth of the plant.

Increasing the supply of nitrogen beyond the optimum for growth increases susceptibility if all growth of the plant is not inhibited by nitrogen toxicity. Phosphorus increases susceptibility directly in proportion to plant growth. A moderate surplus of potassium suppresses susceptibility to infection. The effect of the three nutrients on the development of systemic symptoms is not closely correlated with susceptibility to initial infection. Moderate or heavy application of potassium or phosphorus delays incubation by 7 or 10 days. Either a deficiency or excess of nitrogen accelerates the appearance of systemic symptoms.

Neither infection nor systemic spread of the virus was completely controlled by the growth rate of the host induced by supply of nutrient. The local lesions formed on *Nicotiana glutinosa*, however, depend on vigorous growth of the host. A sevenfold increase in lesions occurred when ammonium phosphate was added to depleted soil.

F. C. Bawden and B. Kassanis confirm that observation. They report greatest susceptibility in *N. tabacum* and *N. glutinosa* to tobacco mosaic and tomato aucuba mosaic when plants were supplied nitrogen and phosphorus in concentrations optimum for plant growth. They feel phosphorus is more important than nitrogen or potassium in regulating host susceptibility.

As the virus protein contains both nitrogen and phosphorus, the two elements might be expected to control its multiplication. E. L. Spencer found that Turkish tobacco that had ample supplies of nitrogen had about 80 times as much virus as nitrogen-deficient plants. Furthermore, the total virus content of deficient plants apparently declined after initial systemic development. Multiplication of virus did not depend on growth of the host since the virus multiplied rapidly in plants retarded by excessive nitrogen supply. The virus concentration remained almost constant in infected plants that were deprived of nitrogen after inoculation. Apparently, therefore, the host did not assimilate virus protein and the virus cannot multiply at the expense of protein in nitrogen-starved host cells.

These studies were based on the infectivity of extracted juice and may have to be modified when virus protein is precipitated and measured directly. Spencer reported that virus preparations from young lesions purified by ultracentrifugation had less intrinsic infectivity than virus from older infections. This increase in infectivity did not occur when plants were deprived of nitrogen shortly after inoculation. These observations were not confirmed by F. C. Bawden and B. Kassanis, who suggested that Spencer may have recovered something other than the virus protein by ultracentrifugation. Dr. Spencer recognized this possibility and suggested that precursor macromolecules that could be activated into virus might have been present. This possibility has recently found support in the discovery of a noninfectious macromolecule similar to virus particles in tobacco leaves by Takihashi and Ishii. Bawden and Kassanis also differ with Spencer in their belief that virus can multiply at the expense of normal protein because they found the ratio of virus to other constituents was greatest in nitrogen-deficient tobacco. They also found that phosphorus increased both the growth of plants and concentration of virus in the sap.

More data are needed on the effect of mineral nutrients on virus diseases. There is fair agreement that vigorously growing plants are most subject to infection and injury particularly if either nitrogen or balanced nutrients are in excess supply. The lower specific activity of virus from nitrogen-deficient plants has been confirmed by M. Chessin, who found no difference in the size of virus particles from plants receiving nitrogen and those deprived of it.

THE PRINCIPAL EFFECTS of soil fertility on disease development are exemplified by the diseases I have discussed. These particular diseases have been among the more thoroughly investigated and economically important ones. Many more plant diseases are known to be affected by soil conditions but little would be gained by discussing other individual cases. A brief summary of some of the general principles involved may be of value in understanding how various types of diseases are influenced by soil fertility.

Different fertilizer procedures are to be employed for damping-off and root rot, the wilts, the galls and other overgrowth disease, and the leaf mildews and rusts caused by obligate parasites.

Damage from damping-off and root rot is avoided by promoting disease-escaping growth habits, such as rapid development of roots. The critically important nutrients for such growth are nitrogen and phosphorus; consequently properly balanced nitrate and phosphate fertilizers are beneficial.

The wilt diseases are most critically affected by the ratio of nitrogen and potassium. The gall and overgrowth diseases are appreciably affected by the calcium-potassium ratios, partially modified by hydrogen-ion effects. Potassium and nitrogen are decisive factors in influencing infection of leaves by obligate parasites.

None of these treatments completely alters the inherent reaction of a plant to pathogens. Immune plants are not attacked regardless of the soil they are grown in. Extremely susceptible varieties cannot be immunized by fertilizing the soil. The greatest benefits from soil fertilizers have been observed on moderately susceptible to partially resistant varieties. Most horticultural varieties are in this latter class since they often escape infection or recover from disease. Proper fertilizers improve their opportunities to escape destruction and produce a profitable crop.

The concentration of properly balanced nutrients in the soil may influence the severity of disease. As growth is promoted by more liberal fertilizer applications, the damping-off and root rot diseases become less serious, but the galls, clubroot, and scab diseases become more conspicuous and leaf rust and powdery mildew caused by obligate parasites flourish. If sufficient balanced fertilizers are applied to injure the plant and retard growth, damping-off and seed decay are more destructive and the obligate parasites may be less active.

The balance of nutrients may be

more important than concentration of total fertilizer when plants are exposed to attack by parasites. A deficiency or surplus of any one element often promotes disease.

All classes of diseases—from those caused by the facultative saprophytes that destroy stored fruits and vegetables to those caused by the obligate parasites—are most severe when nitrogen is overly abundant. Although it encourages infection of wheat roots by the fungi that cause the browning disease and take-all, its over-all effects may be beneficial if it promotes growth of new roots. If phosphorus, however, is not available to facilitate root development, the excess nitrogen is fatal to the root system of the plant.

An excess of nitrogen promotes wilt diseases by providing better nourishment for the vascular parasites. Ammonium salts are usually more readily used by the parasite so they are more damaging than nitrates unless the latter are reduced to nitrites, which are poisonous to plants. A deficiency of potassium, which automatically creates an excess of nitrogen and carbohydrates in the plant, also increases wilting by most vascular parasites.

A deficiency of potassium increases the severity of many diseases. Potash fertilizers have alleviated damage from more diseases than any other nutritional treatment. The importance of potassium has not been explained, but it is probably due to its ability to regulate chemical reactions in the cells of the plant. A deficiency of potassium under most circumstances implies an excess of nitrates and phosphorus; thinner cell walls in epidermal tissues; reduced production of amino acids because nitrate reduction is suppressed; accumulation of carbohydrates which cannot be synthesized into proteins; failure to produce new cells for want of essential amino acids for the protoplasm; and slower growth of meristematic tissues that would permit replacement of diseased tissues. These changes may facilitate penetration of the epidermis by plant parasites, increase their metabolism and growth in plant tissues, or promote destruction of the entire plant because it cannot develop new tissue to replace those lost by ravages of the pathogens.

The only diseases that are consistently suppressed by potassium deficiency are the galls and overgrowths that depend upon multiplication of cells. Most of the overgrowths increase conspicuously as the potassium supply is increased while wilts and leaf diseases diminish.

Soil reaction and organic matter content of soils must be considered as regulants of soil fertility because they affect the availability of the nutrient elements. Such materials as the phosphates, calcium, iron, manganese, and boron are not available to plants in alkaline soils since they may be precipitated as insoluble salts. Applications of organic matter contribute nutrients, mostly nitrogen and potassium, but the immediate effect is to remove all surplus available nitrogen by combining with it or by promoting growth of soil micro-organisms that assimilate nitrogen to the point of temporarily depleting the soil supply. The effect on diseases may be good or bad, depending upon the type of disease and the stage of its development.

Soil reaction and organic matter also influence the prevalence of plant pathogens. Some pathogens prefer alkaline soils and others thrive in acid soils so no general rule can be laid down. If soils are extremely acid or alkaline soil micro-organisms may be eliminated. Organic matter is essential for growth of most soil inhabitants irrespective of whether they are beneficial or destructive.

Many plant parasites increase and are disseminated on organic matter, such as plant refuse, manures, and compost. The addition of organic matter to soil, however, often suppresses pathogens if they are poor soil invaders. The organic matter stimulates growth of soil saprophytes that deprive the less aggressive pathogens of mineral nutrients or else they secrete toxic antibiotics. Only a few plant disease agents are affected appreciably, since most of them are effective soil inhabitants and compete successfully with the saprophytic micro-organisms.

Probably the greatest benefits derived from organic matter are in soil stabilization. The humus from lignified tissues improves the physical structure of soil so it does not erode and will hold more moisture. Application of barnyard manure, straw, crop residues, or even carbohydrates such as starch and sugar stimulates the soil micro-organisms to growth so they often synthesize all available nitrates into their bodies. This removes surplus nitrates from the soil; later they are released gradually so that the plants have a more continuous supply of nitrogen; excessive concentrations, which predispose them to so many diseases, are avoided.

This ability of organic matter to stabilize the soil solution and make the soil into a desirable medium for root growth fully justifies its use. The material may not have any unusual properties that would make plants resistant to all diseases. It can and does increase the severity of some diseases, particularly when applied to soils at the wrong time, but it can also be used to advantage for other diseases. There is no evidence that it encourages soil bacteria and fungi to produce antibiotics that are taken into the plant and help immunize it. As a matter of fact, there is evidence that some antibiotics are inactivated when added to soil.

No general rules can be laid down about fertilizing soils so as to avoid disease. Each disease must be considered by itself.

Any sound recommendation must be based on the type of soil, the availability of essential nutrients in the soil, and the character of the disease agents that are most likely to strike plants in the area. Conspicuous soil deficiencies, particularly in potash, should be corrected.

Every effort should be made to avoid surpluses of nitrogen that are not needed for steady and strong growth of the plant. Fertilizers may often be used to advantage in controlling acidity so the soil reaction will be favorable to the crop and unsuited to maximum development of the plant pathogens.

GEORGE L. McNEW *is managing director of the Boyce Thompson Institute for Plant Research at Yonkers, N. Y. Before taking that position in 1949, he was professor and head of the botany department at Iowa State College and manager of agricultural chemical research and development of the United States Rubber Company at Bethany, Conn. Earlier he conducted research on vegetable crop diseases at the New York Agricultural Experiment Station, Geneva, N. Y., and on the fundamental nature of parasitism in bacterial plant pathogens at the Rockefeller Institute for Medical Research at Princeton, N. J.*

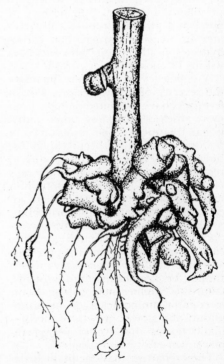

Diseased root of cabbage plant.

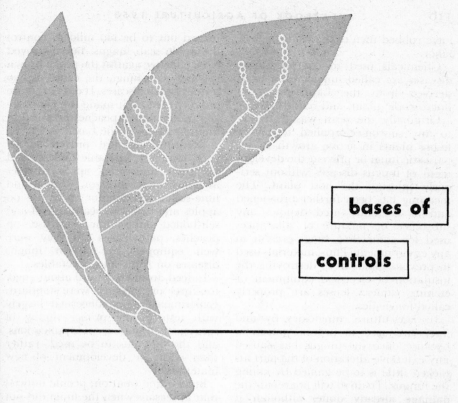

How Fungicides Have Been Developed

John C. Dunegan, S. P. Doolittle

How to keep school boys from pilfering their grapes had been a problem of French peasants in the Médoc region for a long time.

For the pilferers they found the answer, a poisonous-looking mixture of lime and copper sulfate that stuck tenaciously to the leaves when sprinkled on vines near the roadsides.

Pilfering was not the peasants' only worry, for mildew—*mildiou*, they called it—every year defoliated the vines in early fall. Professor P. M. A. Millardet,

of the University of Bordeaux, was commissioned to study this disease recently introduced from America.

One day, in 1882, as he walked through the Médoc countryside, he noticed that there was less mildew on the sprinkled vines.

The professor put two and two together: The cure for pilfering might be the cure for the mildew. The next year he started tests that confirmed his guess. He and his colleague, U. Gayon, in 1885 published illustrations of treated and untreated vines. By 1887 they claimed unqualified success.

The mixture became famous as "Bouillie Bordelaise"—bordeaux mixture—and was applied with fiber brooms or, later, with sprayers in vineyards ravaged by vine mildew and also in blighted fields of potatoes and tomatoes.

Thus only 70-odd years ago chemical weapons came into use to control blights, rusts, mildews, and fungus diseases that for countless centuries have robbed men of the fruits of their labor.

Chemicals used to control fungus diseases are called fungicides, a word derived from the Latin *fungus*, a microscopic plant, and *caedo*, "I kill."

Originally the term was restricted to any substance applied to higher living plants in active growth to kill parasitic fungi or prevent the development of fungus diseases without seriously injuring the host plant. The meaning has been further broadened and as currently used denotes any substance or mixture of substances used for controlling fungi present in any environment. Thus, materials used to prevent molds from destroying the insulation of electrical equipment or etching camera lenses are properly called fungicides.

In agriculture, fungicides by and large are used to prevent infection, because once the fungus has caused any extensive alteration of the part attacked little is to be gained by killing the fungus. To do so will not repair the damage already done, although it may prevent the further spread of the fungus.

The virtues of bordeaux mixture were soon demonstrated, but so were its faults. On certain plants the mixture produced injury. Attention was turned to other materials. In 1905 A. B. Cordley introduced lime-sulfur solution, a mixture of calcium polysulfides formed by boiling sulfur and lime together in water. The material proved to be exceptionally efficient against the apple scab fungus and eliminated the russeting of the fruit that followed the use of bordeaux mixture early in the season.

Lime-sulfur solution, however, proved to be too caustic to use on peaches. In 1907 W. M. Scott and T. W. Ayers introduced another sulfur mixture they called "self-boiled lime-sulfur." They made it by adding sulfur to stone lime slaking in water. Enough heat was produced by the slaking of the stone lime to cause a mild chemical reaction. The mixture turned out to be too mild to control the apple scab fungus, but it proved to be effective against the peach brown rot and scab fungi, the cause of two serious peach diseases. It did not injure peach trees and it made the commercial production of peaches practical in humid sections of the East.

Bordeaux mixture proved to be good for most vegetable diseases and for such midseason apple diseases as blotch and bitter rot. With it and lime-sulfur solution for early use on apples and pears for scab control and self-boiled lime-sulfur for use on peaches, pathologists felt they were well equipped to prevent fungus diseases on fruits and vegetables.

Indeed, from 1907 until about 1930, the three preparations were standard. Experiments were concerned largely with tests of the proper timing of sprays, the number of applications, and the amounts to be used, rather than with the development of new materials.

But as time went on, people noticed that in seasons when the fungi did not develop extensively the yield from unsprayed tomato plants frequently was better than from those protected by the bordeaux mixture. Probably it was the result of physiological changes induced by the residue of copper and lime on the plants. Also, they found that the lime-sulfur solution affected the leaf and shoot growth early in the season and had an adverse effect on the setting of the fruit of certain apple varieties. Bordeaux mixture too frequently caused a russeting of the fruit, severe injury to the leaves, and a premature defoliation. The main objection to self-boiled lime-sulfur was the need of stone, or unslaked, lime, which was cumbersome to handle and had to be stored in sealed containers.

Those defects led to the development of entirely new compounds as technicians began to explore the fungicidal properties of other inorganic compounds such as the fixed (relatively insoluble) copper compounds and the organic compounds. The latter compounds exist in almost countless numbers. Some 25,000 have already been tested as possible fungicides and new compounds are constantly being synthesized in the research laboratories.

Obviously, with such a multitude of compounds available, some orderly testing or screening procedure is necessary to expedite the big task. It would be physically and financially impossible to test each compound by actual spraying tests in the fields.

In these screening tests, spores of certain disease-producing fungi are suspended in solutions or suspensions of the chemical. They are removed at stated intervals, and their viability is tested. An alternate method is to expose spore suspensions of the test organisms to the chemical on glass slides and later determine whether the spores have been killed by contact with the chemical.

The test can be further improved by determining the effect of environment upon the dried deposits of the chemicals exposed on glass slides outdoors for varying periods. Tests are made at fixed intervals, frequently at the end of 7, 14, and 21 days and are compared with the effects of freshly prepared residues on the fungus spores. The tests tell whether the exposure outdoors has affected the fungicidal activity of the chemical and have eliminated unstable compounds that appear promising when freshly prepared. Other phases of the screening procedure deal with the physical properties (particle size, solubility, tenacity) of the material. As the result of these various laboratory studies it is now possible to compare the effectiveness of various compounds at different dosage rates and even to determine the portion of the complex organic molecule that actually kills the fungus.

Special types of spraying and dusting equipment have been devised for laboratory use that deliver known amounts of material with great precision. These machines make it possible to duplicate in the laboratory or greenhouse many of the factors that occur in the normal use of the compound and are an important part of the screening procedure.

Compounds that have passed through the various screening tests must still surmount the final barrier of actual field usage. They must control the fungus diseases, must be compatible with compounds added for the control of insects, and must not, either alone or in combination, produce injury to the treated plants. Furthermore, the new compounds must not be so toxic that their widespread use presents dangerous hazards either to the user or the consumer and finally their price must be such that they can compete with other compounds currently in use.

The development of a new compound therefore is a tedious and expensive process. On the average this development involves an investment between 250,000 and 350,000 dollars and may even exceed a million dollars.

"Many are tested but few are chosen," to modify an old adage, aptly applies to the development of new fungicide materials. Less than 0.1 percent of the many thousands of compounds tested are in general use.

SINCE 1930, many new materials for use on fruits and vegetables have been developed. They include:

Copper (silicates, basic sulfates, chlorides, oxides, phosphate, and certain copper organic combinations).

Mercury (phenyl derivatives—lactates, acetates, formamides).

Dithiocarbamates (thiuram disulfides—tetramethyl and morpholine; metallic methyl derivatives—iron, zinc, and lead; metallic ethylene derivatives—sodium, zinc, manganese).

Chlorinated quinones (tetrachloroquinone).

Chlorinated naphthoquinones (dichloronaphthoquinone).

Quinolinolates (copper and zinc compounds).

Quaternary compounds (quinoline, isoquinoline).

Glyoxalidines.

Nitrated phenols (dinitro compounds).

Chlorinated phenols (pentachlorophenates).

Thalamides (N-trichloromethylthio tetrahydrophthalimide).

Chromium compounds (complex double salts with other metals).

The control obtained with some of these new compounds is outstanding. The effect of ferric dimethyl dithiocarbamate (ferbam) on cedar-apple rust is an example. Before it was introduced, sulfur gave only indifferent control of this disease, but this iron dithiocarbamate has practically solved the problem of cedar-apple rust for the commercial apple grower. The same compound has eliminated the spray-injury problem in the production of high-quality pears in the Pacific Northwest.

Many of the new compounds have proved satisfactory for the control of plant diseases in the Tropics. An immense potential demand exists for the products in the Tropics, but their widespread use is limited by the relatively low purchasing power of many of the tropical farmers. Strangely enough, no organic compound has been found to replace bordeaux mixture for the control of the very destructive Sigatoka disease of bananas. So intensive is the attack of the fungus causing this leaf disease, banana plantations must be sprayed 15 to 17 times a year. Approximately 45 million pounds of copper sulfate are required each year to protect the 130 thousand acres of bananas growing in tropical America.

While these new compounds have given better control of the fungi, they have been less satisfactory against plant diseases caused by bacteria. Those diseases present a particularly difficult problem, for the bacteria are present in such enormous numbers that it is difficult to kill all of them by ordinary procedures.

Current research for the control of bacterial diseases of plants is centered on the possible use of antibiotics. These materials, derived from the fungi themselves, have given brilliant results in the field of human pathology, and research workers in various parts of the world are trying to determine if they are just as effective in their action against the bacteria that cause plant disease. The investigations are still in the preliminary stages, but even so it is evident that some antibiotics are absorbed by the plant and transported into the newly developing leaves and stems. This absorption suggests the possibility of protecting the entire plant against invasion by disease-producing bacteria.

Those tests are not limited to the use of antibiotics. The action of chemicals injected into the stem of living plants or applied as solutions to the soil around the roots also is being investigated as a possible mode of attack against virus diseases of plants—a group of important and destructive maladies that are difficult to control.

The improvements in fungicide materials would be of little value had they not been accompanied by an analogous development in the machines used for applying them. Bordeaux mixture was first applied by sprinkling it on the plants with brooms or brushes. This tedious procedure soon led to the development of simple, hand-operated hydraulic pumps. The spray material was forced, under pressure from the pump, through a jet-tipped rod and deposited on the various plant parts as the operator moved the spray rod among the plants. The bucket pump, the knapsack sprayer, the barrel-type sprayer, and the one- or two-cylinder hydraulic pumps (either hand-operated or driven by a chain-drive sprocket connected to one wheel of the wagon carrying the pump and spray supply in a barrel) are representative of the pioneer types of spraying equipment.

The gallons-per-minute output of all these rigs was low, operating them was hard work, and the acreage they could cover was limited. Nevertheless the benefit obtained, particularly when diseases required only one or two applications, was striking, indeed. Sprayed plants remained healthy and produced good crops, while the unsprayed plantings had to be abandoned because of disease.

Just as the development of some of the new organic fungicides evolved from compounds used in the manufacture of automobile tires, so did the development of efficient spray machinery evolve with the development of the gasoline engine for automobiles. Indeed, modern control of plant diseases on a large scale became feasible just as soon as the gasoline engine was substituted for manpower. Pumps were redesigned to operate at higher speeds, develop more pressure, and have a higher gallons-per-minute output than was possible with manually operated machines. The gasoline engine also permitted the introduction of a power-driven agitator to keep the spray materials thoroughly in suspension, a feature that was inadequately provided for in the manually operated machines.

At first there were rather cumbersome rigs powered by heavy, one-cylinder, two-cycle engines of low horsepower. The machines gradually were more refined. Wooden wheels on the truck were supplanted by steel wheels, which in turn were replaced by rubber-tired wheels. The heavy, one-cylinder engines were replaced by two-cylinder and four-cylinder engines, which developed increasing horsepower. Pump pressures increased from 100 to 600 pounds pressure to the square inch, and the output in gallons a minute from 2 to 3 to as high as 40 or 50, with the present-day high-capacity machines.

The increase in pump capacity necessitated larger tanks, and machines with 400- and 600-gallon tanks became standard equipment. The limit on tank size appears to be 600 gallons —because the weight of that much water, 4,800 pounds, is about the maximum that can be drawn over

soft ground. Some large commercial orchards use pumps in a central station and a network of pipes with suitable outlets or risers spaced through the planting. It would seem to be an ideal solution, but large investment in pipes and machinery is required, pipes break in winter, and the spray chemicals corrode equipment all the time. Stationary spray plants are practical only in the very large commercial operations. They probably reached their maximum use in the banana plantings in Central America.

Power-driven spray machines also have been developed for use with vegetable crops. The problem there is to cover each plant in the rows adequately with fungicides. That is done by a series of nozzles on horizontal booms arranged so that the spray envelopes the plants. In some machines the booms simultaneously spray all plants in a swath 40 feet wide. Their development has made possible the protection of extensive acreages of row crops.

Likewise, for use in vineyards and plantings of brambles on trellises, spray machines have been devised with vertical instead of horizontal booms. Some machines are designed to cover both sides of an individual row. Others spray on both sides of the machine as it moves up the rows.

The motor-driven spray rigs required two or three men. Wartime manpower shortages and high wages meant that faster and cheaper ways of applying sprays had to be found. First in citrus orchards and then in peach, apple, and pear orchards a new machine was put into operation. It was called a speed sprayer. It had a 600-gallon tank, an engine of 80 horsepower or more, conventional pumps, and spray nozzles arranged as adjustable arcs on both sides of the machine. Men were not needed to direct the spray to various parts of the tree. The spray, as it was forced from the nozzles, was caught in the blast of air from a rapidly revolving propeller and blown into the trees.

The machine was so heavy that it could be pulled only by a tractor, but the controls were so arranged that the driver could spray the trees.

Many years earlier, the use of fine powders or dusts had cut the cost of operation and reduced the amount of water needed. But the method has faults: The deposits of fungicidal dusts apparently do not adhere quite so well as spray deposits. Because of the lighter weight of the equipment and the speed of application, however, dusting is used often with success.

All in all, the trend in 1953 was to combine the advantages of several methods. One was to increase the adherence and effectiveness of dusts by injecting water and adhesives into the dust stream under relatively low pressure (70 pounds the square inch). Another was to use machines equipped with highly efficient fans or specially designed turbines, which develop high-velocity air blasts carrying either dust or liquid particles to all parts of the plants to be protected. Sometimes these modern efficient blowers were available as units for the modernization of older equipment at a minimum cost. Still another procedure was to use sprays in concentrated form. If, say, 20 gallons of dilute spray were needed to protect a given area, the same amount of fungicide was applied in 5 gallons of water—a 4 times (or 4x) concentration. Such concentrated sprays reduce the amount of water needed, but to get proper protection the rate of delivery of the pumps and nozzles and the forward movement of the spray machine must be in careful adjustment.

JOHN C. DUNEGAN *is a pathologist in charge of investigations of fungus and bacterial diseases of deciduous fruit trees in the division of fruit and nut crops and diseases, Bureau of Plant Industry, Soils, and Agricultural Engineering.*

S. P. DOOLITTLE *is a pathologist in charge of investigations of diseases of tomatoes, peppers, cucurbits, and certain other vegetable crops in the division of vegetable crops and diseases in the same bureau.*

Using Chemicals To Combat Root Diseases

Jesse R. Christie

Many of the myriad of organisms that inhabit the soil subsist on living plants. They may injure the roots and other underground parts of the plants and interfere seriously with growth. The damage they cause is likely to become more serious the longer the land is in cultivation, especially if the same crops are grown repeatedly in the same place.

Their control is a problem that we have not yet solved entirely. Suitable crop rotations and the elimination of weeds that may serve as the hosts for the disease organisms, the planting of resistant varieties, and other cultural practices help reduce losses of crops, but often they are not enough.

Control by the use of chemicals has met with considerable success, especially with vegetables. Volatile liquids that function as soil fumigants have come into use extensively since 1945. Thousands of acres are fumigated annually, and the acreage is increasing. Apparently growers have found the procedure profitable. Soil fumigation is costly, but the increased yield afterwards may have a cash value very much more than the investment. Sometimes fumigation makes the difference between a profitable crop and none at all.

To the bacteria, fungi, nematodes, and insects, to which most of the noxious organisms belong, it will be practical for us to add weed seed. Soil fumigation has been most successful in controlling nematodes; some of the fumigants kill other pests; some other methods are as effective as fumigation and less expensive. When one has to fumigate for nematodes, however, the control at the same time of insects and other pests is important.

Soil fumigants are sold under various trade names, but only four distinctly different kinds are in general use. They are composed of (or have as their active ingredient) methyl bromide (bromomethane), chloropicrin (trichloronitromethane), dichloropropene (1,3-dichloropropene), and ethylene dibromide, which is 1,2-dibromoethane.

For seedbeds, soil fumigation or any other chemical treatment should be effective against a variety of organisms.

Damping-off is notoriously serious in seedbeds, and failure to control it or reduce losses from it is a serious defect of a treatment.

A soil treatment that will kill weed seed and thereby eliminate the cost of weeding may effect savings that more than pay the cost of even an expensive chemical.

Root knot is an ever-present problem in the South. Its control in seedbeds is especially important. Other nematode problems may be equally serious in some regions—for example, control of the stubby root nematode (species of *Trichodorus*) in the seedbeds of certain celery-growing regions in Florida. Of the fumigants in general use, methyl bromide and chloropicrin come nearest to fulfilling those requirements.

Methyl bromide, a highly volatile compound, has a boiling point of about 40° F. In order to inject it into the soil, in the manner that most fumigants are applied, it must be mixed with a diluent having a higher boiling point. Such mixtures have been in use for some years, but with them it is hard to keep the gas in the soil long enough to obtain the desired results.

A newer method makes it possible to utilize, to a much greater degree,

the killing power of the chemical. Undiluted methyl bromide is evaporated in shallow trays placed on the surface of the soil under a gastight cover. The cover is held up a few inches by supports, so there is a shallow air space between it and the surface of the soil. The edges of the cover are buried. The rate for most purposes is 1 pound to 100 square feet, but for controlling the more resistant fungi, rates up to 4 pounds to 100 square feet are recommended. The cover should remain in place for 48 hours. Usually seed can be planted 2 to 3 days after the cover is removed. Penetration of the gas into the soil is surprisingly good. Under favorable conditions, the sterilizing effect extends to a depth of 12 inches or more. Most or all of the insects are killed. Miscellaneous soil nematodes are nearly eradicated. Control of root knot is usually good, although not always complete. All living plants are killed, including the most tenacious of the grasses and all but a few of the more resistant weed seed. On the basis of some tests, the control of fungi seems satisfactory. The main disadvantage of the method is cost of the cover and equipment needed to treat large seedbeds and the amount of time and labor involved in moving equipment from place to place.

Chloropicrin has been on the market longer than any other soil fumigant in general use. It is expensive and disagreeable to handle, but many vegetable growers prefer it for fumigating seedbeds. Properly applied, it will kill insects, nematodes, most weed seed, and all except a few of the more resistant fungi. Chloropicrin is injected into the soil in the same manner as most other fumigants. Injection points—or continuous streams if power equipment is used—should be spaced 10 inches apart. The recommended rate of application is 2 cubic centimeters to 3 cubic centimeters (about one-half teaspoonful) at each point.

A water seal must be applied immediately. For best results, the area should be covered with burlap sacks, canvas, newspaper, or something like them, which, in turn, should be sprinkled with water. The cover, when it is used, may be removed after 4 or 5 days. The soil is allowed to aerate. Seed must not be planted until every trace of the gas has disappeared, which usually takes 8 to 12 days; in wet, cool weather it may take longer.

Chloropicrin forms a gas that is extremely toxic to plants, in both the soil and the air. Under certain weather conditions, a blanket of gas may collect over a fumigated bed near the ground, then drift slowly over a nearby area, and cause severe injury to the plants growing there, especially at night when foliage is wet with dew. That does not always happen, but it is a risk that should be remembered when one fumigates seedbeds near growing crops.

Chlorobromopropene, commonly called CBP, is a promising new chemical for the treatment of seedbeds. When emulsified with water and applied as a drench it has given good control of nematodes, fungi, and weeds in tests conducted on the sandy soils of central Florida. Equipment that has a small gasoline-driven pump, which mixes the chemical with water and delivers the mixture through a plastic hose to a sprinkling nozzle, makes application quite easy.

Mixtures containing dichloropropene or those containing ethylene dibromide are also used for fumigating seedbeds. They give good control of nematodes and soil insects but neither has much effect on weed seed or fungi.

The practice in some regions is to prepare beds that are 6 inches or more higher than the walkways between. When methyl bromide, chloropicrin, or CBP are used, the beds are first prepared and then treated. The walkways are not treated. When ethylene dibromide or dichloropropene are used, a common practice is to fumigate the entire area, and prepare the beds afterward. The rates usually recommended are higher than those for

ordinary field applications: 35 to 45 gallons an acre of a dichloropropene fumigant or 30 to 40 gallons of 40 percent ethylene dibromide.

Ethylene dibromide and mixtures containing dichloropropene are generally used for fumigating fields. Both are excellent nematocides and good insecticides, but at ordinary rates neither has much value as a fungicide or herbicide. Ethylene dibromide is more effective against wireworms. Either fumigant substantially reduces the population of the mole crickets in Florida by killing the insects or else driving them to the surface, where they are eaten by crows and blackbirds.

All dichloropropene fumigants have about the same strength—the same percentage of active ingredients. Ethylene dibromide fumigants are mixtures of ethylene dibromide and a diluent, usually naphtha. The diluent adds nothing to the efficacy. It is used merely to increase volume and thereby facilitate accurate and uniform application. The different trade-marked fumigants of this kind differ in the amount of ethylene dibromide they contain. The two most commonly used for field-scale applications contain either 41 percent or 83 percent of ethylene dibromide by weight. The 83 percent fumigants usually are diluted by the dealer or by the farmer before applying. If proper equipment is available, they may be applied without diluting.

The entire area of a field may be fumigated. The procedure is called solid, or broadcast, application. Or the fumigant may be applied only in the rows or hills where the plants are to grow. For solid application, standard practice is to space injections 12 inches apart. The recommended dosage for a dichloropropene fumigant is 20 to 25 gallons an acre. For a 41-percent ethylene dibromide fumigant it is 15 to 20 gallons an acre. For row fumigation a single stream is applied along each row. The usual rate for either of the materials is about 2 cubic centimeters (about one-half teaspoonful) per linear foot of row or 1 gallon to 1,900 feet of row. If rows are 3 feet apart, an acre will require about 8 gallons. Row fumigation has given satisfactory control of root knot on tomatoes and some other crops.

A few tomato growers have adopted the practice of applying two streams, 12 inches apart, along each planting row, but no one seems to have demonstrated that applying two streams is very much more effective than applying about the same amount of fumigant in one stream. Good control of root knot on watermelons has been obtained by making a single injection in each hill.

Row or hill fumigation will prove effective, no doubt, for controlling many—but not all—kinds of nematodes. In experiments conducted in Florida for controlling the stubby root nematode on sweet corn, row fumigation failed completely. Those nematodes move into the fumigated area from the surrounding unfumigated soil so quickly that the plants are given only very brief protection.

Soil fumigation has been in use long enough and has been tested extensively enough to demonstrate that it is an effective and useful method, but requirements for success are somewhat exacting and the factors influencing efficacy are numerous and not fully understood. Failures may occur for many reasons, among them faulty diagnosis (attempting to correct troubles not caused by organisms that fumigation will control), faulty application, and insufficient aeration of the soil between application and planting.

In places where crop failures are not caused by organisms that fumigants will control but occur for some other reason, soil fumigation is a waste of time and money. It is not advisable to fumigate on general principles. Diagnosis should precede treatment. Often, however, determining the cause of crop failures is more easily said than done. When the cause of the trouble is in doubt, a wise procedure is to make trial applications on a small scale.

Fumigants to be successful must be properly applied. The requirements are not unduly difficult to fulfill and the reasons for them are easy to understand, but more failures have resulted from faulty application than from any other cause.

The land should be thoroughly and properly prepared. The soil should be reasonably free from lumps and clods and should be moderately, not excessively, loose. Very light, sandy soils should be compact. When seedbeds are prepared with a rotary tiller, a few days should be allowed for the soil to settle, except if methyl bromide is to be evaporated under a cover.

The soil should be moist but not wet. When the soil is even moderately dry, the efficacy of fumigants in killing most organisms is somewhat reduced, and ample moisture is especially important for effective control of weeds and certain fungi. The nearer a weed seed is to germination, the easier it is to kill, and fumigants are more likely to kill the sclerotia produced by some fungi if those structures have been wet for a few days.

The soil should be warm. Some fumigants are more effective than others at low temperatures, but generally the temperature of the soil should be at least 50° F. and preferably 60° or above.

The fumigant should be injected at a uniform depth. If the ground is uneven, the chisels of a power applicator will inject the fumigant too near the surface or even on the surface when they pass over low spots. The proper depth varies with conditions and the pests to be controlled. When chemicals are injected into the soil, organisms located near the surface are often not killed. This is an inherent weakness of soil fumigation regardless of the pests involved, and it is especially serious when attempting to control weeds or damping-off in seedbeds.

In order to overcome this difficulty by increasing the concentration of gas near the surface, shallow application is recommended, with injection 3 or 4 inches deep. For field application under most conditions, 6 inches is usually recommended. In the sandy soils of Florida, roots that grow in the upper 2 or 3 inches escape injury by nematodes to a marked degree. Celery plants, growing on land that is heavily infested with the stubby root nematode, may produce a thick mat of more or less healthy roots in the upper 3 inches of soil, although all the roots deeper than that are completely destroyed. The same is true, though to a somewhat lesser degree, for plants injured by the root knot nematodes. Hence, for field applications in Florida, fumigants should be deeply injected, never less than 6 inches deep and preferably 7 or 8 inches.

Holes or furrows made by the applicator should be promptly and firmly filled. If loosely filled, the gas, instead of diffusing into the surrounding soil, will escape upward into the air.

Fumigants are toxic to plants and should have diffused out of the soil before a crop is planted. Otherwise the plants may be stunted. The time required for adequate aeration of the soil varies greatly and is influenced by many factors, including the kind of soil, the condition of the soil (especially temperature and water content), the fumigant used, the rate of application, weather conditions following application, and the crop planted. Chloropicrin, being extremely toxic, must be followed by thorough aeration. Some kinds of plants will tolerate low concentrations of ethylene dibromide without being seriously injured. The toxicity of dichloropropene mixtures is intermediate between those two extremes, but, to avoid all danger of injury, aeration must be fairly thorough. Methyl bromide is highly toxic, but the gas leaves the soil so quickly that aeration for 2 or 3 days is usually adequate.

The usual recommendation for dichloropropene fumigants is to allow 1 week for every 10 gallons per acre. For 41 percent ethylene dibromide, one should allow similarly varied but slightly shorter intervals. For most conditions, this rule allows a reasonable margin of safety, but there are exceptions. If the soil is wet or cool and if the content of organic matter is high, those intervals may not be long enough. On the other hand, if the soil is light and the conditions are hot and dry, shorter intervals may be enough.

The question has been raised as to the possibility of injury to the soil by use of soil fumigants and whether their continued application will result in chemical, physical, or biological changes that may have a deleterious effect on the growth of plants.

Three possibilities have been suggested: That the continued application of fumigants may eventually result in the accumulation of toxic residues; that the chemicals will kill beneficial organisms and thereby seriously interfere with the normal biochemical changes that occur in the soil; and that after land has been once fumigated the treatment must be repeated each year, otherwise injurious organisms may become more serious than would have been the case had the land never been treated.

Experiments have not been numerous enough or of sufficient duration to provide a final answer to the question of toxic residues, but results indicate that, with the fumigants now in use, we have little to fear on this score. Very definitely, fumigation kills beneficial organisms, but most of them seem able to reestablish themselves rather quickly. The effect of fumigation on the nonparasitic organisms of the soil generally is more transient than is its effect on the parasites. Obligate parasites, such as many of the nematodes, cannot reproduce except on a suitable host plant, and, although fumigation rarely exterminates them, at least one crop can be grown before their numbers increase sufficiently to cause serious damage.

The conversion of nitrogen from an ammoniacal to a nitrate form is a biological process. Destruction of nitrifying bacteria by fumigation may retard the process and result in an accumulation of nitrogen in the form of ammonia. Different plants differ in their ability to utilize nitrogen in this form. Tomatoes are reported as able to absorb ammoniacal nitrogen readily if the soil is neutral but not if it is acid. Hence it appears that the extent to which fumigation may possibly have an adverse effect on crops by reducing the nitrifying bacteria of the soil depends on at least two factors—the kind of crop and the condition of the soil. I know of no instance in which fumigation has caused an accumulation of ammoniacal nitrogen sufficient to interfere seriously with the successful growing of any crop.

Fear that soil fumigation, if once begun but not continued, will be followed by an abnormal build-up of noxious organisms seems to have had its origin in results of experiments with the sugar beet nematode. Where land is heavily infested with that pest, the crop of sugar beets on fumigated areas may be very good, but the crop on unfumigated areas may be a failure. When sugar beets are grown on this same land the following year without fumigation, the situation may be reversed and the crop may be more severely damaged on the areas that were fumigated the previous year than on those where no fumigant was applied.

A suggested explanation is that during the first season on the unfumigated areas a huge number of nematode larvae hatched, attacked the roots of the plants, destroyed them, and, in so doing, eliminated their own food supply and thereby destroyed themselves. On the fumigated areas the plants made an abundance of roots, so that the residual population of nematodes not killed by the treatment could build up rapidly. By the end of the season more cysts had been produced in the fumigated than in the unfumigated areas. If this is the correct explanation, these results are scarcely an indictment of soil fumigation. That treatment of the soil

with chemicals may permit populations of plant parasitic nematodes to build up by destroying their natural enemies is a possibility. Not a great deal is known about these natural enemies and virtually nothing is known about the extent to which they hold the parasites in check.

Research laboratories are active as never before in a search to find new and more effective chemicals for controlling pests of all kinds and those that inhabit the soil are not being slighted. Compounds under test in different localities show promise of being useful additions to the ones in use, especially for controlling fungi both in seedbeds and in the field. Some can be applied to the soil in powdered or granular form. Others can be mixed with water and applied as a drench, a procedure that may have advantages for certain purposes. Chemicals that will kill some organisms and not others and can be applied around the roots of living plants seem a possibility.

Root diseases are so serious and the need of better methods for controlling them is so pressing that new chemicals are certain to come into use either with or without the sanction of experiment stations. While the purpose of such chemicals is to bring about desirable changes in the biology of the soil they may at the same time have other and undesirable effects. What these effects are, how serious they may become, and how they can be avoided or minimized are questions that provide a research problem for the future.

JESSE R. CHRISTIE, *a native of New Hampshire, is a nematologist in the Bureau of Plant Industry, Soils, and Agricultural Engineering, which he joined in 1922. He is now stationed at the Central Florida Experiment Station, Sanford, Fla., and is in charge of the Bureau's nematode investigations in the Southeastern States. He holds degrees from the University of Kentucky, the University of Illinois, and George Washington University.*

Fumigation of Soil in Hawaii

Walter Carter

As agricultural soils become older and cultivation continuous and more intensive, some soil amendment often is needed to offset the unfavorable effects on plants of the growing complex of pathogenic soil organisms or little known nutritional factors.

If that can be achieved by adding large amounts of organic matter—such as green-manure crops—or if crop rotations are established, the need for soil amendment is not so great as in areas where similar methods are not used.

Some crops, however, cannot be grown successfully except occasionally in a long rotation. In many places in Great Britain, potatoes can be grown on the same land only one year in seven. In Utah, sugar beets require a 4-year or a 5-year rotation with other crops. Nematodes are the limiting factor. In tropical or subtropical areas, where active organic matter decomposes rapidly, the need for a soil amender is acute.

Hawaii is no exception. Truck crops, particularly those that are susceptible to nematodes, cannot be grown profitably in succession on the same soils without the use of fumigants or other control methods. Pineapples have been grown in Hawaii for more than 40 years on the same land without the addition of organic matter other than the residues of the previous crop, and the decline of productivity before fumigation became an established

practice had been noted with increasing concern. One notable exception is a plantation where grass is grown for 2 years between pineapple plantings.

An early attempt at soil amendment by fumigation in Hawaii in 1926 was directed primarily against insects and nematodes in sugarcane soil. A still earlier study, in 1910, was concerned with molasses as a fertilizer for sugarcane. Fumigants were used in those experiments. The effect of fumigation with carbon bisulfide on nitrifying organisms was recognized as significantly affecting the availability of nutrients to the plant. The chemical did not destroy the micro-organisms but caused a reproportioning of them. The term is significant: It is not considered practical to eradicate a micro-organism, but its position relative to that of the other organisms can be changed.

Usually soil amendment by fumigation in Hawaii and elsewhere has been approached from the standpoint of control of nematodes and soil insects. As early as 1931, however, stimulation of the growth of pineapples was recognized as being the result of partial soil sterilization. In 1933 increased yields were recorded as having been obtained despite damage by nematodes.

The first approach to the current viewpoint on soil fumigation in Hawaii was by the late Maxwell O. Johnson in experiments begun in 1927. He got striking increases in plant growth and yields of pineapples by the use of chloropicrin—tear gas. In his first experiments he applied this liquid to pineapple fields by means of a Vermorel injector, a French device originally used for the injection of carbon bisulfide into soil and stored grain.

The first effect of the treatment was to produce a dark-green growth of the plant. Sometimes the fruit was larger. We now know that this was due, at least partly, to the killing of the nitrifying organisms in the soil by the chloropicrin. That meant that the plant used ammonium nitrogen rather than nitrate nitrogen. The pineapple plant fortunately is well adapted to ammonium nitrogen nutrition. Johnson patented the use of chloropicrin as a soil fumigant in U. S. Patent No. 1,983,546, which makes numerous claims, all of them concerned with plant stimulation. The killing by chloropicrin of such organisms as nematodes was known previously, at least academically, and it was therefore not included among the allowed claims.

Chloropicrin has disadvantages. It is an extremely pungent and tear-making gas. It has always been relatively expensive, so that its field-scale use is limited, especially as soil cover with water seals or with more or less impermeable papers was essential to best results. Furthermore, at the time Johnson first used chloropicrin in Hawaiian pineapple soils, the favorable response to fumigation, so generally experienced now, was not consistent. Many applications failed to give economic returns.

The whole question of the field-scale use of the fumigants was completely changed by the discovery in 1940 that a mixture of 1,2-dichloropropane and 1,3-dichloropropene is an effective soil amender. The discovery of its efficacy came about in an interesting way.

The mealybug wilt of pineapple had been seen to be much less serious in virgin lands in Hawaii; the point was confirmed in other tropical countries. As a result, a continuous search was made for soil amenders that might restore some of the qualities of virgin soil that produced more wilt-resistant pineapple plants. The study had gone on more than 5 years with no satisfactory results, when a number of chlorinated hydrocarbons were provided by the Shell Development Co. for trial. None of them had any effect on the susceptibility of pineapple plants to mealybug wilt, but one of them, the mixture I referred to, which now is known as D-D mixture, proved to be the most practical and successful soil amender known up to that time.

The first results with pineapple plants were available shortly after the outbreak of the Second World War, when the domestic production of vegetables became of great importance. Soil treated with D-D mixture and planted to carrots and other vegetables produced much more heavily than nontreated check plots. The result undoubtedly was due to the measure of control of nematodes that had been achieved.

D-D thus proved to be a most effective nematocide, although the discovery was purely by chance. Perhaps that was all to the good, for it gave an opportunity for the soil-amendment qualities of the material to be recognized early in its development. A logical consequence was the added recognition of growth response beyond that due to nematode control as one basic requirement for an effective soil fumigant.

HAWAII HAS ALSO PIONEERED in the development of suitable injection machinery. Injection is a problem when large acreages have to be treated and planted in a short season. Probably the first large-scale field fumigation machine was the one engineered by the California Packing Corp. for use with chloropicrin. The development of the field injectors was not easy. D-D is relatively corrosive and requires special metals. Pumps and delivery systems had to be devised—and then redesigned to get the most efficiency. The use of check rows has long been dropped as unnecessary in pineapple fields, but many an example is still provided unwittingly when application is faulty and long rows or partial rows are left untreated. From them the increasing necessity for soil fumigation, as time goes on, is demonstrated.

The methods available for small growers of truck crops have been greatly improved by the development of more effective hand injectors by firms on the United States mainland. With those new methods and new machinery, D-D and other fumigants, such as ethylene dibromide, have been found to be economical and practical as nematocides and as soil amenders.

The use of D-D mixture has become standard practice in Hawaii on pineapple lands. Some 7 million pounds are used in that way each year. The fact that in 1942, when the first results were obtained, only laboratory quantities were available as byproducts from a pilot plant used for other syntheses underscores the remarkableness of the development. Furthermore, the total volume of fumigants used on a field scale is evidence that Hawaii has pioneered in a development of vast significance to agriculture.

Perhaps a more important result of the discovery of D-D mixture was the stimulus given to the whole problem of soil amendment by fumigation for field crops in the United States and in many other countries. Other fumigants, particularly ethylene dibromide, have appeared on the market and are competitive with D-D mixture.

Some ethylene dibromide has been used in Hawaii on pineapple soils as a preplanting fumigant in place of D-D. An exact evaluation of the relative merits of the two compounds for the purpose is difficult because EDB is more sensitive to soil-moisture conditions than is D-D. With appropriate soil moisture, EDB has given excellent response. As most of the pineapple acreage is planted during dry seasons, however, D-D is perhaps the most reliable general preplanting fumigant. EDB has found a place in the postplanting fumigation of pineapple fields. Ethylene chlorobromide (ECB) is also promising for this purpose. The process involves some risk to the growing plant but growth stimulation usually has been pronounced. Sometimes profitable increases in fruit weight have followed.

Methods of testing soil fumigants have been dominated by the microbiologists' need for data on specific organisms, and the small pot test has been standard. New fumigants usually are screened by that method. Quantitative results have accrued, but the interpretation of the results in terms that the grower can use is difficult,

for the method at best is artificial and of too short duration. Field-plot tests furnish a more reliable criterion for the growers because ultimate crop yield must determine the economic feasibility of the practice.

Future advances will come by understanding how fumigants affect growth.

There is, first, the effect on specific organism-nematodes, soil insects such as wireworms, and bacteria and fungi, both pathogenic and beneficial.

Second, there is growth stimulation. Plants may be stimulated because the development of root systems is hastened and improved, either by removing root pathogens or by supplying necessary factors for their growth. Possibly there is release of root-promoting hormones in the soil.

Nutrients may be more readily available because of depression of the nitrifying organisms in the soil. That is true of the early stages of growth, but growth stimulation of pineapple plants continues sometimes for the whole 4-year growth period and is often more pronounced in the second crop than in the first. Furthermore, soil fumigation after the plant has been established for several months will favorably affect the root system by stimulating or permitting new active white root tips for that portion of the whole root system that is near the point of injection of the fumigant. This suggests the possibility that soil fumigation makes nutrients available that are needed in small quantity for vigorous plant growth.

These problems of growth stimulation are closely related to a third consideration; namely, the effect of the fumigant on fertilizer practices. That is a practical point because the effects may govern dosages to be used and the economic position of the chemical in the production of the crop.

WALTER CARTER *is a graduate of Montana State College and holds advanced degrees from the University of Minnesota. He is head of the entomology department of the Pineapple Research Institute of Hawaii.*

More About the Control of Nematodes

Albert L. Taylor

The control of nematodes requires clean soil, clean planting stock, and sanitation. Plant parasitic nematodes are eliminated from the soil by crop rotation, chemicals, heat, bare fallow, and a few other methods.

The use of crop rotations to control nematodes is based on the fact that nematodes are obligate parasites and can neither live indefinitely nor reproduce unless they can feed on living plants. Furthermore, all have a degree of host specialization: Any given species can feed and reproduce only on certain plant species. Without those plants, the nematodes starve or succumb to parasites, predators, and diseases, even though other plants are grown nearby.

The main disadvantage of crop rotations for control is the time required and the loss of income if the rotation crops are less profitable than the main crop. When crops of low or moderate value are concerned, it is the only practical method of control.

Chemicals used to kill nematodes in the soil must be efficient for killing the nematodes and must leave no residue that can harm plants. They should be easy to apply and inexpensive. Many chemicals have been tested for the purpose. Four are in general use: Chloropicrin and mixtures that contain methyl bromide, chlorobromopropene, ethylene dibromide, or dichloropropene. One type of methyl bromide mixture is a gas at ordinary temperatures. The others are liquids. The liquids are applied by injection into the soil. The methyl bromide gas is released under a cover placed above the soil. In either case, the fumes permeate the upper layers of the soil, killing the nematodes by contact.

Each has advantages and disadvantages. Prices also vary, so the choice of one for any given plot of soil involves consideration of the organisms to be controlled, the local conditions, and the relation of the cost of the fumigant to the value of the crop.

Chloropicrin applied at 200 pounds an acre is an excellent nematocide and insecticide. Applications of two or three times that amount also control some fungi, bacteria, and weeds. Because chloropicrin does not penetrate undecayed plant material readily, it should be used only after the residues of a crop have had time to decay. Because its fumes in the air will damage plants, chloropicrin cannot be used in one part of a greenhouse while crops are growing in nearby sections— a difficulty that may also be encountered outside.

After chloropicrin is applied, it must be confined to the soil. The usual method is to apply a "water seal" by sprinkling with enough water to wet the top inch or two of soil. An interval of 5 to 25 days must be allowed between application of the fumigant and planting. The exact time depends on the amount applied, the soil moisture, and the type of soil.

Extreme precautions must be used in handling chloropicrin. Small amounts of the fumes in the air will cause profuse watering of the eyes. Larger concentrations cause violent coughing, vomiting, or even death. Nevertheless, chloropicrin is not dangerous to use. In fact, the opposite is true to a certain degree, because the watering of the eyes gives preliminary warning of the presence of fumes before the more serious effects ensue. No one will voluntarily remain in even a low concentration of chloropicrin fumes. Gas masks of the proper type give full protection. Chloropicrin is not inflammable. The shipping containers are heavy cylinders for large quantities and sealed cans for 1-pound bottles.

The 98 percent methyl bromide fumigants, applied at rates of 1 or 2 pounds for each 100 square feet, give good control of nematodes, soil insects, and most weed seeds, fungi, and bacteria. The 10 to 15 percent methyl bromide mixtures are good nematocides and insecticides at the rate of 78 to 100 gallons to the acre. Methyl bromide penetrates undecayed roots readily. Small amounts of fumes in the air do not damage growing plants. Crops can be planted 2 to 4 days after application. It is particularly useful for greenhouse fumigation. If reasonable precautions are taken, methyl bromide is neither unpleasant nor dangerous to use. The 98 percent methyl bromide fumigants are obtainable in 1-pound cans. The 10-percent or 15-percent mixtures are shipped in drums.

Ethylene dibromide soil fumigants usually contain 41 percent to 83 percent of the chemical by weight, the diluent being naphtha. The rates usually recommended to control nematodes and soil insects are 10 to 20 gallons an acre of the 41-percent mixture and proportionately less of the 83-percent material. The latter is often diluted for convenience in application. Penetration of undecayed crop residues is good and small concentrations of fumes in the air are not toxic to plants. No water seal or cover is necessary. The soil can be planted 10 to 14 days after application of the fumigant. Ethylene dibromide fumigants are not dangerous or unpleasant to handle if used with care. The shipping containers are drums of various sizes.

Dichloropropene fumigants have about 50 percent of this chemical mixed with dichloropropane. Applications of 20 gallons an acre are used against nematodes and soil insects. The kill of nematodes in undecayed crop residues is good. Fumes in the air do not injure plants. At least 2 weeks must be allowed between application of the fumi-

gant and planting of the crop. No cover or water seal is necessary. The shipping containers are steel drums.

Chlorobromopropene can be used effectively against nematodes, insects, and soil fungi.

All soil fumigants are poisonous to man and animals. They must be handled with care lest the liquid come in contact with the skin or clothing and the fumes inhaled. If the fumigants are accidentally splashed on the skin, they should be washed off immediately with soap and water. If clothing or shoes become wet, they should be removed instantly and not worn again until clean. Stored fumigants should be kept tightly sealed. With the ones that are inflammable or have inflammable diluents, precautions should be taken against fire or explosion. Most of the soil fumigants are corrosive to metals, particularly in moist air, so applicators should always be cleaned thoroughly after use and partly empty containers should be tightly closed.

Besides fumigants, a few other materials have limited use in the control of nematodes, the greater part of the applications being to soil used for tobacco and other seedbeds. Urea controls nematodes when applied at rates of 8 ounces to 1 pound the square yard and is often mixed with calcium cyanamide for weed control. Sodium azide is also an effective nematocide when used at the rate of 4 ounces to the square yard. These materials are used in powder form, which is mixed with the upper layers of the soil.

Liquid soil fumigants are put 6 to 8 inches beneath the soil surface. The applications are made 10 to 12 inches apart horizontally. On a small scale that can be done with improvised equipment, but large-scale applications require special applicators. For areas of less than an acre, hand applicators that have a calibrated pump to deliver measured amounts of the fumigant through a hollow spike thrust into the soil are satisfactory. For larger areas, applicators drawn by tractors or mounted on tractors are used.

They are of two general types. One type delivers the fumigant in continuous streams behind shanks that run through the soil. The other delivers the stream of fumigant ahead of a plow which immediately turns the soil to cover it. If a shank applicator is used, the soil is prepared in advance by plowing, harrowing, and leveling. If a plow applicator is used, the harrowing and leveling follow immediately after application. Shank applicators can be made in any convenient size, but usually have six to eight shanks and can cover an acre or more an hour.

The essential points in soil fumigation are good preparation of the soil, application of the exact amount of fumigant desired with correct spacing and at the proper depth, and promptness in carrying through the operations necessary after application. Soil preparation includes cutting up of weeds, trash, and crop residues, which might interfere with the smooth operation of the applicator. After the application of the fumigant, the soil should be left smooth with all clods well broken up. This is usually accomplished by a drag behind the shanks of the applicator or by a harrow and drag after use of a plow applicator.

GASEOUS FUMIGANTS, such as 98 percent methyl bromide, are applied in a different manner. The soil is prepared as for planting. A gas-impervious cover, usually a specially treated paper, such as Sisalkraft, or plastic tarpaulins (Fumi Cover and others), is placed over the area to be fumigated. The cover is not in contact with the soil surface, but is supported a few inches above it. The edges of the cover are buried. The methyl bromide is then introduced by means of a plastic tube into an open container placed underneath this cover on the soil surface. Inexpensive applicators especially made for the purpose make it a simple operation. The cover is left in place for 24 to 48 hours. This method is limited to rather small plots.

It is used mostly to fumigate seedbeds, greenhouses, and nursery plots.

When the best possible control of nematodes or other soil pests is desired or when the crop is to be planted in rows less than 24 inches apart, the fumigant is applied to the whole area to be planted. This is called solid, area, over-all, or broadcast fumigation.

Row fumigation is used where crops are to be planted in rows more than 24 inches apart. One or two lines of fumigant are centered on the row. It requires some definite method of marking the rows so that they can be located for planting. The usual procedures are to form a raised bed when the fumigant is applied, to mark the rows by shallow furrows, or to locate them with reference to the tracks left by a tractor applicator.

Strip applications of fumigant may be used when orchards are to be planted. A strip of soil 6 to 8 feet wide is fumigated for each row of trees.

Site fumigation is used in orchards or when individual trees or shrubs are to be planted. An area 6 to 8 feet in diameter centered on the planting spot is fumigated by means of a hand applicator.

If crops are to be planted in widely spaced hills, spot fumigation can be used. The locations of the hills are marked and the fumigant placed with hand applicators.

The advantage of strip, row, site, or spot fumigation is the saving in the amount of fumigant required. At the same time the plants are protected from serious infection when they are small and most vulnerable. Often they are the most advantageous methods of using soil fumigants.

Best results with soil fumigation are had on soils of the lighter types, such as sandy loams. Fumigation of heavy soils is often disappointing. Muck or peat soils require an increase of 50 percent to 100 percent in the amount of fumigant applied to obtain results comparable to those obtained on light mineral soils. The soil should be neither very wet nor very dry when the fumigant is applied, but should have a moisture content about right for planting seed. The soil temperature at a depth of 6 inches should be above 50° F., though some fumigants can be applied at temperatures as low as 40°.

As all of the fumigants are somewhat toxic to plants, they must be applied far enough in advance of planting to allow them to have their effect and then diffuse out of the soil. This aeration time depends on the type and amount of fumigant used, the type of soil, and the temperature and moisture conditions. Fumigants disappear more quickly from warm soils than from cold soils and more quickly from dry or moist soils than from wet soils. Plowing or otherwise working the soil will hasten aeration, but should not be done until at least a week after application. It should be emphasized that the number of days between application of fumigant and planting as given in the preceding discussion are minimum times. It is often convenient to fumigate the soil several months in advance of planting. Soil can be fumigated in the fall for planting in the spring without serious loss of efficiency.

The effect of successful soil fumigation is the elimination of enough of the nematodes and other soil pests so that the crop is not seriously damaged. Since the damage from nematodes is usually the formation of galls or the partial destruction of the root system, there will be a marked increase in the number and extent of the roots, improved growth and vigor of the plant, and a tendency toward more uniform growth. If other conditions are favorable, yields will increase. Yield increases of several hundred percent are not uncommon when heavily infested soil is fumigated, but usually yield increases are from 20 percent to 50 percent. With root or tuber crops, the percentage of culls drops. Such beneficial effects are most conspicuous on the first crop following fumigation, but are often seen on subsequent crops.

Optimum applications of soil fumigants are not assumed to eradicate the nematodes but to provide the degree of control that will produce the most cash return in proportion to the cost of the fumigation. Usually it is better to use a moderate amount of fumigant for each crop than to attempt a higher degree of control with a larger amount in the hope that several crops can be raised before it is necessary to repeat the fumigation.

Ethylene dibromide and dichloropropene fumigants are the least expensive. The average cost of moderate applications is about 35 or 40 dollars an acre. The two fumigants are widely used on crops of moderate to high value when the increase of salable produce will be more than twice or three times the cost of the fumigation. The cost of applying 500 pounds of chloropicrin to the acre is 400 dollars. Liquid methyl bromide fumigants applied at the usual rates cost about 175 dollars an acre, and 98 percent methyl bromide fumigants cost about 80 cents per 100 square feet when 1 pound per 100 square feet is applied. The use of these fumigants is confined to crops of very high value, to greenhouses, seedbeds, and nurseries. Weed control by fumigation, since it eliminates expensive hand weeding, is often an important consideration.

The principal question in the practical use of soil fumigants is that of the possible profit to be obtained from their use—whether the increase in salable crops as a result of the fumigation will pay for the cost of the fumigant, the expense of application, and a reasonable profit. The best guide is experience with similar crops and conditions. Lacking that, trial plots can be used to compare yields from fumigated or unfumigated areas and to compare different fumigants or different rates of application of one fumigant. Such trials are advised if plant parasitic nematodes are known to be present in significant numbers, if yields of crops have declined over a period of years, and if the growth of crops is not uniform or root systems are poor.

All plant parasitic nematodes are killed almost instantly when heated to about 140° F. Several methods of heating soil for nematode control have been devised. The most common is steam, released from pipes buried in the soil or under a steam pan. Steam pans, usually of metal, are about 8 inches deep and 6 to 8 feet wide by 8 to 10 feet long. They are closed above and open below. The edges of the pan are buried 3 or 4 inches deep. Steam is released under the pan until the top 6 or 8 inches of the soil is heated to the required degree.

Other methods of applying heat are used with small lots of potting soil, which are heated by steam in a closed chamber, exposed to dry heat in shallow layers, drenched with hot water, or heated by electricity.

Many species of plant parasitic nematodes can be killed by drying. Small lots of soil can be air-dried by spreading out in thin layers. In favorable climates, the method can be applied on a large scale, the usual procedure being repeated plowing of the soil during the dry season of the year. In any climate it is good practice to remove the roots of a nematode-infected crop from the soil as soon after harvest as possible and to allow them to dry before plowing under.

In low, flat fields, flooding is sometimes used. We have little information on the effect of the method, but farmers who use it generally agree that flooding for several weeks is necessary.

Another possible method is bare fallow. Keeping the soil free of all vegetation deprives the nematodes of the opportunity to feed and reproduce. But because of the labor required for weed control and possible deleterious effects on the soil, this is seldom practical even for small plots.

One of the main sources of nematode infestation is planting stock, particularly plants used for transplanting, bulbs, tubers, corms, and roots. Some species of nematodes, such as the wheat nematode, *Anguina tritici*, and related forms, may be located in galled kernels mixed with seed, cysts of the genus *Heterodera* may be mixed with seed, or nematodes such as the rice nematode (*Aphelenchoides oryzae*) may be found between the seed and its enclosing glumes. Soil clinging to roots of transplants may be infested.

Other important sources of nematode infestation are soil brought into a field on vehicles or farm implements, or washed in by running water. Compost made from infected plants may also be infested. If a field is fumigated, special care should be taken to see that the seedbed is also fumigated. In fact, seedbed fumigation or sterilization by other means is excellent practice under any conditions.

It is best to discard infected planting stock, although it is sometimes possible and worth while to attempt to kill the nematodes in it and so save exceptionally valuable material. The hot-water treatment is extensively used for killing nematodes in narcissus and other bulbs, which, especially when dormant, can stand enough heat to kill the contained or adhering nematodes without serious harm to the plants themselves. Narcissus bulbs are presoaked in water with a wetting agent added, placed in water heated to 110° F. for 4 hours, and immediately dried or planted. Similar treatments have been worked out for other bulbs and planting stock.

Attempts to kill nematodes in planting stock by means of chemicals have been made, but always—so far—with serious injury to the plants. When the nematode is one of the ectoparasitic species—that is, one that does not enter the plant—it can be removed from transplants by simply washing off the adhering soil with cold water.

Only a few satisfactory and practical methods of controlling nematodes on growing plants are known. Such methods would find widespread use in orchards, in growing perennial shrubs, and even for annual crops. Where orchards or perennial ornamentals are to be planted, the only precautions that can be taken are to make sure that the soil is not infested before planting and that the transplants are free of nematodes.

The type of cover crop used in peach orchards can have a considerable effect on the degree of attack by root knot nematodes and consequently on the growth and yield of the trees. In experimental plots in Georgia, trees on plots where root knot resistant cover crops were planted produced about six times as many peaches in four seasons as trees on control plots where cover crops highly susceptible to root knot were planted. Where no cover crops at all were used and the plots were kept free of weeds, about five times as many peaches were produced as on the control plots.

Some species of the nematode *Aphelenchoides*, which parasitize the aboveground parts of such plants as strawberries and chrysanthemums, can be controlled by repeated spraying of the plants with parathion.

Undoubtedly the simplest method of preventing nematode damage is the use of plant varieties or rootstocks which are not susceptible to attack. Examples are the Shalil, Yunnan, and S–37 peach rootstocks, which are highly resistant to attack by some of the most common species of root knot nematodes in this country, though not to all of the root knot nematode species. Some advances have been made in the development of varieties of other crops resistant to root knot and other nematodes, but progress is necessarily slow and it will be many years before satisfactory nematode-resistant varieties of all crops will be available.

ALBERT L. TAYLOR *joined the division of nematology investigations of the Bureau of Plant Industry, Soils, and Agricultural Engineering in 1935. He did experimental work on soil fumigation in Tifton, Ga., until 1946 when he joined the Shell Chemical Company to do research and development work on the soil fumigant D-D. He returned to the division of nematology in 1949 and is now stationed in Beltsville, Md.*

Treating Seeds To Prevent Diseases

R. W. Leukel

Sometimes chemicals are applied to seeds, bulbs, corms, tubers, and roots to prevent their decay after planting and to control seed-borne and soil-borne plant diseases.

To be satisfactory, a seed treatment has to be effective yet reasonably safe from seed injury in case of overdosage; economical, readily available, easily applied, and chemically stable; and not overly poisonous or disagreeable to operators or corrosive to metal.

FUNGICIDES may be classified as seed disinfestants, disinfectants, or protectants, according to the location of the organisms to be combatted.

Disinfestants inactivate organisms, such as bunt spores, that are borne on the surface of the seed.

Disinfectants are effective against those located deeper within the seed.

Protectants protect the seeds from attack by organisms that are present in the soil.

Practically all effective seed-treatment materials are disinfestants. Many are also disinfectants and protectants. The formaldehyde and hot-water treatments, however, are disinfestants and disinfectants but are not seed protectants. In fact, seeds that have been treated with formaldehyde or hot water frequently are attacked by soil-borne fungi more severely than are untreated seeds and therefore should be treated also with a protectant before planting.

BASED ON COMPOSITION, fungicides may be organic or inorganic, mercurial or nonmercurial, and metallic or nonmetallic. There are organic mercurials (Ceresan) and inorganic mercurials (calomel); there are nonmercurial metallic organics (Fermate) and nonmetallic organics (Spergon); there are metallic inorganics (copper carbonate) and nonmetallic inorganics (sulfur).

Fungicidal seed treatments may be dry or wet according to the form in which the fungicide is applied to the seed.

In a dry treatment, the fungicide is applied in dust form, usually in a mechanical mixer at rates ranging from ½ to 4 ounces or more to the bushel.

Wet treatments once meant soaking the seed in a water solution of the fungicide for a certain period, after which the seed was allowed to drain and dry. Wet treatments now are applied mostly by the slurry method or the "quick-wet" method.

In the slurry method, the fungicide is applied to the seed as a soup-like water suspension, which is mixed with the seed in a special slurry treater. The seed requires no drying but may be bagged immediately for sowing or storage.

In the "quick-wet" method, a concentrated solution of a volatile fungicide is applied to the seed and thoroughly mixed with it. The dosage may range from ½ to 5 fluid ounces to a bushel. As in the slurry treatment, that adds less than 1 percent of moisture to the seed. The well-known formaldehyde spray treatment of oats is essentially a "quick-wet" treatment. So also is the method recommended for applying Panogen, Mercuran, Setrete, and several other materials.

Inorganic mercurials used for treating seed are limited practically to mercuric chloride, mercurous chloride (calomel), and mercuric oxide.

Mercuric chloride, as a 1 to 1,000 solution, may be used for treating potato seed pieces, sweetpotatoes, and rhubarb roots for planting. It is also used for seed of crucifers (plants of the mustard or cabbage family), celery, cucumber, pepper, tomato, watermelon, and certain other vegetables. Most seeds are more or less susceptible to injury by mercuric chloride.

Calomel is used on seeds of crucifers, celery, and onion. Mercuric oxide may be used as a dip treatment for sweetpotatoes (1 pound to 30 gallons of water).

ORGANIC MERCURIALS are more numerous and more widely used than the inorganics just mentioned. They are used on seed of small grains, legumes, grasses, cotton, beets, flax, sorghum, and some other field crops, and also on certain corms, bulbs, tubers, and roots and the seeds of some vegetables.

Ceresan, 2 percent ethyl mercury chloride, introduced in 1926, was the first organic mercurial widely used in the United States. It is applied at 2 ounces a bushel. It was followed and largely replaced in 1933 by New Improved Ceresan, 5 percent ethyl mercury phosphate, which is applied at ½ ounce per bushel. Both were used mostly on small grains, flax, cotton, peas, hemp, and sugar beets.

Ceresan M, 7.7 percent ethyl mercury p-toluene sulfonanilide, appeared in 1948. It largely replaced the two previous Ceresans because of several advantages over them, including its application as a slurry.

Leytosan and Agrox, 7.2 percent and 6.8 percent phenyl mercury urea, respectively, are applied to small grains, peas, rice, and sorghum at ½ ounce to the bushel and to flax at 1½ ounces. They may be applied in dust or slurry form.

Mercuran, 3.5 percent mercury as methoxy ethyl mercuric acetate, is used at the rate of ½ ounce per bushel on small grains. It may be applied as a dust, in concentrated solution by the "quick-wet" method, or in a more dilute solution with a slurry machine.

Panogen, 2.2 percent methyl mercury dicyan diamide, is a concentrated liquid applied at ¾ fluid ounce per bushel to small grains, 1½ fluid ounces to flax, and 4 fluid ounces per 100 pounds of segregated beet seed. It is applied in a special Panogen treater, but can be successfully applied in a slurry treater if diluted with water.

Setrete, 7 percent phenyl mercury ammonium acetate, is a concentrated liquid that may be applied as such at ½ ounce per bushel, or it may be diluted 1 to 9 with water and applied in a slurry treater.

Mersolite, 5 percent phenyl mercury acetate, is used as a dip treatment (1 pound to 800 gallons) for narcissus corms to combat basal rot.

Merthiolate, sodium ethyl mercury thiosalicylate, is used to prevent corm rot and yellows in gladiolus.

Sanoseed, 7.9 percent ethanol mercury chloride, and Corona P. D. 7, 5 percent mercury in a mercury bromine-phenol compound, are used as dip treatments for seed potatoes.

Semesan, 30 percent hydroxy mercuric chlorophenol (19 percent Hg), is an excellent mercurial used as a wet soak treatment for bulbs, tubers, and corms and as a dust treatment for seeds of flowers and vegetables.

Semesan Bel, a mixture of 2 percent hydroxy mercurichlorophenol and 12 percent hydroxymercurinitrophenol, is used as a dip treatment for seed potatoes.

Puratized N–5–E, 10 percent phenyl mercury triethanol ammonium lactate, is used for treating seed potatoes and lily bulbs.

L–224, an experimental mercury-zinc-chromate material, is an excellent treatment for seed corn.

Aagrano, 3.5 percent ethoxy propyl mercury bromide, is effective against cereal diseases, especially when it is applied in slurry form.

Semenon, 2 percent isopropyl methyl mercury acetate, gave excellent results in controlling diseases of small grains and sorghum. Both Aagrano and Semenon are European products. They were not available in the United States in 1953.

NONMERCURIAL organic fungicides have increased greatly in number since 1945. Generally they are less effective than the mercurials, but as a rule they are less injurious to seeds and less dangerous to persons using them. The organic sulfurs and quinones are prominent ingredients in these compounds and often are combined with phenol, chlorine, bromine, quinoline, zinc, iron, copper, sodium, or other materials.

Spergon, 98 percent chloranil (tetrachloro-*p*-benzoquinone), was among the first nonmetallic organics to be widely used for treating seed, especially peas and beans. It is used for vegetable seeds, corn, sorghum, peanuts, alfalfa, clover, soybeans, and some other crops. It may be applied as a dust or as a slurry.

Arasan, 50 percent thiram (tetramethylthiuram disulfide), still another early organic fungicide, is used for the same crops as Spergon. Both will also control bunt in wheat, but are not recommended for treating oats or barley.

Arasan SFX, 75 percent thiram, is the wettable form of Arasan for treating seeds by the slurry method. Tersan, also a wettable form of thiram, is used for the control of diseases of turf and lawn grass.

Phygon (formerly Phygon XL) consists of 50 percent 2,3-dichloro-1,4-napthoquinone and 50 percent talc. It is an effective seed treatment for corn, peanuts, rice, sorghum, and most vegetables. It controls bunt in wheat, but is not recommended for other small grains.

Zerlate, 70 percent ziram (zinc dimethyl dithiocarbamate), is effective as a prebedding dip for controlling black rot in sweetpotatoes. It is similar to Zincate, Methasan, Zimate, and Karbam, as all contain ziram as the active ingredient.

Fermate, 70 percent ferbam (ferric dimethyl dithiocarbamate), like Zerlate, is used as a prebedding dip for sweetpotatoes. Both materials are used also as foliage dusts or sprays.

Dow 9–B, 50 percent zinc trichlorophenate, has been used to treat gladiolus bulbs and seed of cotton, corn, and sorghum.

Dithane Z–78, 65 percent zinc ethylene bisdithiocarbamate, has shown promise as a disinfestant and chemotherapeutic fungicide.

Mycon, 7.7 percent methyl arsenisulfide, in extensive field tests, has been found effective in controlling those seed-borne diseases of wheat, oats, and barley that are amenable to control by fungicides.

Seedox, 50 percent 2,4,5-trichlorophenyl acetate, has been used to treat cottonseed. Mycotox is similar to Seedox. Neither is effective as a seed treatment for small grains.

Anticarie, 40 percent hexachlorobenzene, is effective as a seed treatment for the control of bunt in wheat. When applied to the soil it also prevents infection due to bunt spores in the soil. It is not recommended for treating seeds of other cereals.

Pentachloronitrobenzene (50 percent) controlled covered kernel smut in kafir and a 20-percent product controlled bunt in wheat. In Europe this chemical is reported as having controlled infection from soil-borne spores of both common bunt and dwarf bunt when it was applied to the soil at planting time at the rate of about 50 pounds an acre.

INORGANIC NONMERCURIALS are few. Copper carbonate, the first dust seed treatment to be widely used in agriculture, and basic copper sulfate are still used on wheat as bunt preventives. Copper sulfate (bluestone) solution, once a popular seed treatment for wheat, now is used for that purpose to a very limited extent.

Cuprous oxide (yellow or red) serves as a seed protectant for vegetable seeds to prevent seed decay and preemergence damping-off. It is injurious to seeds of lettuce, crucifers, and onions.

Vasco 4, a mixture of zinc oxide and zinc hydroxide, is used on seed of crucifers, spinach, and other vegetables that are sensitive to cuprous oxide.

OTHER SEED-TREATMENT MATERIALS, some effective and some experimental, may be mentioned. The hot-water treatment remains the standard method for controlling the flower-infecting loose smuts of wheat and barley. It is effective also for treating seed of crucifers, onion, tomato, and some other vegetables.

Some gases, such as chlorine, have been suggested for treating large quantities of seed, but their effectiveness has not been proved.

Hot vapor was described in 1944 as being applied to tons of seed exposed on a moving belt. Ultraviolet and infrared rays, short waves, Hertzian waves, diathermy, X-rays, and other similar devices have been tried as seed disinfectants, but none has been proved practicable. Like hot water, these materials would not act as seed protectants, and so a supplementary treatment would be necessary to guard against soil-borne fungi.

TESTING THE EFFECTIVENESS of fungicides in the control of seed-borne diseases presents two chief difficulties: Obtaining a supply of suitable seed that is sufficiently infected to furnish an adequate test for the fungicides, and obtaining environmental conditions after planting that favor infection in the plants.

In diseases like bunt of wheat, in which the causal spores are located on the surface of the seed, clean seed can be infested artificially if a supply of spores is available. But many disease organisms are located deeper within the seed in a manner that cannot be duplicated artificially. So one has to get seed from a badly infected crop, or, better still, from the seed lot that produced that crop. At times seed obtained from a heavily infected field may be infected too lightly to serve as an adequate test for seed treatment because conditions for infection may have been very unfavorable at the critical period.

We must observe certain precautions in testing fungicides for seed treatment. The seed should be thoroughly cleaned, before treatment, to remove dust, chaff, weed seeds, and other substances, all of which take up much of the fungicide. Proper dosage is important because the seed sample used usually is relatively small and hence the amount of fungicide applied must be carefully weighed or measured. In treating cereal seeds experimentally, 500 cubic centimeters is a convenient sample. This volume, which is 1/70 of a bushel, simplifies the conversion of ounces-per-bushel to grams-per-sample. If the desired rate of application is one ounce (28.34 grams) per bushel, 1/70 of a bushel will require 1/70 of 28.34 grams, or 0.4 grams. Rates of ½, 2, 3, and 4 ounces per bushel are easily converted to 0.2, 0.8, 1.2 and 1.6 grams per sample, respectively. Differences in bushel weight among different seeds or seed lots then can be ignored. It also avoids the error involved in treating samples of light, chaffy seed as compared with plump, heavy seed. The light seed should receive more fungicide for each weighed bushel than the heavy seed.

When small samples of seed are treated, the capacity of the container should be such that it is only half filled by the sample. It should be first "conditioned" by treating in it a sample of seed at a rate sufficient to coat the inside with the fungicide. This seed is then discarded.

After the fungicides have been applied to the different samples, the containers should be shaken in some mechanical contrivance so that all receive the same amount of mixing. Thorough mixing is especially essential when applying the nonvolatile materials.

Between the treatment and sowing, the treated and untreated samples should be stored at a moderate temperature and preferably at a low humidity. Metal or glass containers are preferable to paper envelopes because if the envelopes are stored in contact with one another, the fumes from a volatile mercurial fungicide in one envelope will treat the seed in the adjoining envelope. If this envelope contains the untreated check sample, it will be rendered useless for that purpose.

The effects of the treatments on germination of the seed, seedling emergence, disease control, and plant growth and yield are among the details usually desired from seed-treatment experiments.

Germination tests, to study any harmful effects of the fungicides on the seed itself, may be made on wet blotters placed in incubators (in which temperature and humidity are controlled) or in steamed wet sand or soil. Relatively disease-free seed and disinfected soil should be used in the tests, because the harmful effects of a fungicide on the seed may be masked by its protective effect against seed-borne or soil-borne fungi that cause seed rot or preemergence damping-off.

The use of infested soil is essential for determining the effect of the seed-protectant qualities of treatments on emergence. That may involve the isolation and culture of soil-borne fungi such as species of *Pythium, Fusarium, Helminthosporium,* and *Rhizoctonia,* and using the pure cultures to inoculate soil in which the treated (and untreated) seed is to be planted. Such tests may be made in the greenhouse in pots, flats, or beds. The soil should be steamed or chemically fumigated before being inoculated in order to determine the effectiveness of the fungicides against each specific soil-borne fungus culture.

The effectiveness of fungicides in the control of seed-borne diseases such as the smuts of cereals, that are not apparent in the seedling stage usually is studied in field plots. The seed should be sown at the proper date so that the soil temperature as well as moisture before emergence are conducive to infection. For the cereal that calls for soil that is not too moist for aeration and germination of the seed-borne spores. Along with the somewhat submedium moisture content of the soil, the temperatures considered conducive to infection by cereal diseases are: Bunt of wheat, 41° to 50° F.; barley covered smut, 50° to 68°; false loose smut of barley, 59° to 68°; the smuts of oats, about 54° to 72°; the barley stripe disease, 46° to 59°; and kernel smuts of sorghum, 75° to 86°. Periods favorable to infection cannot be predicted with certainty. Frequently, because of the absence of such conditions, significant field data are not obtained.

The effect of the seed treatment on yield should be obtained by treating and sowing relatively disease-free seed in replicated plots along with untreated seed. Increases in yield from such treated seed presumably reflect the seed-protectant qualities of the fungicide used.

CEREAL SEED TREATMENT was rather widely practiced for quite a few years before the treatment of other crop seeds was generally recommended.

The reasons perhaps were that smuts could be seen in cereals and that it was discovered early that some of them could be prevented by seed treatment.

The beneficial effects of the treatment of cereal seeds may result from the elimination of seed-borne diseases, the prevention of seed rot and seedling blight, and the suppression of weeds by better and more even stands.

One of the greatest benefits lies in the elimination of some seed-borne fungi or bacteria that cause primary infection lesions from which the disease spreads to other plants. Outstanding examples are certain helminthosporium diseases of wheat, oats, and barley. This spread by secondary infection may cause heavy loss, although only a small percentage of the seed sown may have been infected. Annual seed treatment of cereal seed is now considered a wise farm practice because the use of disease-free or treated seed one year does not insure the production of disease-free seed for the next year's crop. Airborne spores from neighboring fields may contaminate the heads of grain grown from disease-free seed, so that seed from these heads, if sown untreated, may produce a diseased crop the following year. Growers of certified seed have found it wise to guard against this source of infection, as it may disqualify their fields for certification.

Wheat is treated mostly for the control of bunt, which if only seed-borne is the most easily controlled of all the seed-borne cereal smuts. Ceresan M, Agrox, Setrete, Panogen, Leytosan, Mercuran, Aagrano, and some other organic mercurial compounds are generally most effective in bunt control, especially if infection is severe. Most are applied at less than an ounce to the bushel. Many nonmercurials also are effective—copper carbonate, basic copper sulfate, Arasan, Spergon, Phygon, Anticarie, Mycon, and several experimental materials. The mercurials by and large are preferable because they eliminate also some of the pathogens borne more deeply within the seed. Loose smut (caused by *Ustilago tritici*) is prevented only by the hot-water treatment.

Rye may be treated to prevent the spread of seed-borne diseases, like stalk smut and bunt. The treatments for wheat may be used also for rye.

Barley is treated largely for the prevention of covered smut, black or false loose smut, and stripe disease. Seed treatment also reduces the amount of primary infection from such diseases as bacterial blight, scab, net blotch, and spot blotch. The fungicides recommended are restricted largely to the organic mercurials such as Ceresan M, Panogen, Leytosan, and Agrox. The nonmercurial organics may improve stands and reduce infection by these diseases to some extent but, with a few exceptions, they seldom control them satisfactorily. The flower-infecting loose smut (caused by *Ustilago nuda*) is controlled only by the hot-water treatment.

Seed of oats, like that of barley, is treated most frequently for the prevention of the smut diseases, which are visible at heading time. The effective treatments are restricted largely to the organic mercurials, although the formaldehyde spray treatment is widely used. It is cheap and effective but may injure the seed. Also it is not a seed protectant. The effective organic mercurials also prevent primary infection from seed-borne halo blight, fusarium blight, anthracnose, and the helminthosporium diseases; they will not prevent these diseases, however, if the causal organisms are present in the soil.

Corn, a warm-season crop, is subject to many diseases, most of which cannot be prevented by seed treatment. Disease control or prevention is largely a matter of developing disease-resistant strains and providing favorable growing conditions for the plants. The chief purpose of corn seed treatment is to prevent seed rot and seedling blight caused by seed-borne and soil-borne fungi, especially when cold, wet weather follows planting. For many years Semesan Jr. (1 percent ethyl mercury phosphate) was most widely used for the purpose, but it has been supplanted largely by the nonmercurial organics, such as Arasan, Spergon, Phygon, and Dow 9-B. The experimental compound, L-224, a mercury zinc chromate, and Dithane also have proved to be effective. Mercury compounds may injure corn seeds that have been damaged near the embryo by rough handling, especially if planting is delayed after treating.

Hybrid corn seed, which constitutes about 80 percent of the corn seed planted, is treated at the seed houses before it is sold to the growers; thus the work of seed treatment of corn mostly has been taken out of the hands of individual growers.

Treatment of rice seed was not a generally recommended farm practice until about 1947. Experiments proved that the treatments increased stands, especially in the early seedings when the soil was cold and wet. Often yields also were improved. Best results were obtained with Ceresan M, Phygon, Arasan, and Spergon. Ceresan M prevented seedling blight caused by *Helminthosporium oryzae*. Dow 9-B injured the seed after long storage. Cuprocide (cuprous oxide) seemed best for seed sown in water, but it may injure presprouted seed. Rice may be fumigated with methyl bromide to combat the seed-borne rice nematode. Exposure to a concentration of 1½ pounds of methyl bromide to 1,000 cubic feet of space for 12 to 15 hours will kill the seed-borne nematode without injuring the seed seriously.

Sorghum, like corn, is benefited most by seed treatment when cold, wet weather follows planting. It reduces seed rot and seedling blight and prevents infection by the kernel smuts. The nonmercurial organics, such as Phygon and Arasan, have been found beneficial in improving stands and controlling smut. In varieties whose seeds have persistent glumes, however, the kernel smuts are controlled more effectively by the use of volatile organic mercurials, such as Ceresan M and Panogen.

Sugar beet seed is treated mostly to combat seed-borne infection by *Phoma betae* and *Cercospora beticola*. Seed treatment is effective in preventing preemergence damping-off caused either by seed- or soil-borne fungi. Materials used for beet seed treatment include the organic fungicides N. I. Ceresan, Ceresan M, Panogen, Phygon, and Arasan. Inorganic mercury compounds, cuprous oxide, and various mixtures of mercurials with copper carbonate have proved effective experimentally but never have come into widespread commercial use.

Preemergence and postemergence damping-off have been successfully combatted in greenhouse experiments by applying an Arasan-fertilizer mixture to the soil so that the sugar beet seed germinated in the soil impregnated with the mixture and the seed lings grew through it. The Arasan was used at a rate of about 4 pounds an acre. Field experiments to control black root by Arasan-fertilizer mixtures have not given consistently favorable results.

Seed treatments for the control of damping-off caused by *Pythium* species, *Phoma betae*, and the *Rhizoctonia* species are beneficial unless soil infestation is severe or soil moisture conditions are unfavorable. Black root, caused by *Aphanomyces cochlioides*, however, is not prevented by seed treatment.

Proper soil management helps reduce the soil populations of sugar beet pathogens. Adequate drainage and heavy application of commercial fertilizers, especially phosphate, are important. Of great importance also is a rotation in which sugar beets do not immediately follow a legume sod crop but follow an early fall-plowed legume. Such handling of the legume crop is necessary because clovers, sweetclover, and alfalfa harbor the various pathogens that cause damping-off. Their sods, if spring-plowed, produce peak populations of the fungus at the period corresponding to planting time for sugar beets. If associated with proper soil management, control of excessive soil moisture by drainage, and a good fertilizer practice, seed treatments show value.

Cotton, flax, and hemp respond to seed treatment in the order named. The diseases of cotton that are reduced somewhat by seed treatment are bacterial blight or angular leaf spot (*Xanthomonas malvacearum*), anthracnose (*Colletotrichum gossypii*), sore shin (*Rhizoctonia solani*), and seedling blight caused by species of *Aspergillus, Fusarium, Diplodia, Sclerotium*, and other fungi.

Seed of cotton is generally delinted before being treated because seed-borne infection is more easily eliminated in delinted seed. Delinting may be done mechanically by reginning or chemically by acid treatment. Mechanical delinting may injure the seed and impair its germination. Acid-delinted seed germinates better than fuzzy seed, but it rots more easily, especially in cold, wet soil. Effective seed treatments largely prevent that. Organic mercurials (such as the Ceresans) with some exceptions have generally been more effective than the nonmercurial organics (such as Spergon, Dow 9–B, Phygon, Arasan, and Seedox) in eliminating seed-borne infection. Some growers object to the use of poisonous fungicides, such as the mercurials, however, because excess treated seed may become mixed with untreated seed used for making cottonseed meal or oil. The nonmercurials are especially useful as seed protectants for acid-delinted seed.

Treatment of flaxseed is made necessary largely because seed, especially of large-seeded kinds, may be injured in threshing. Many of the fractured seeds rot after planting, particularly in heavy soils, unless they are first treated with an efficient protectant, which prevents invasion by species of *Alternaria, Penicillium, Fusarium*, and *Pythium*. Several seed-borne diseases of flax are alleviated by seed treatment. Pasmo (*Mycosphaerella linorum*), when seed-borne, causes primary infection lesions, which initiate secondary infection in other plants. Browning and stem break (*Polyspora lini*) and anthracnose (*Colletotrichum linicolum*) also may be seed-borne.

One of the difficulties in treating flaxseed is the failure of dry fungicides to adhere to the smooth seed coat. The seed therefore requires a much heavier dosage of dusts than is applied to most other seeds. Wet treatments cause gumming of the seed because of the mucillaginous coat. The organic mercury dusts usually are applied at 1½ ounces per bushel. Nonmercurials are applied somewhat more heavily.

Seed treatment of flax may increase stands, but increased yields do not always follow unless an abundance of weeds prevents sufficient branching to compensate for the thinner stands from untreated seed.

Treatment of hempseed with New Improved Ceresan, Spergon, and Arasan was found to improve stands when planting was followed by unfavorable conditions for germination and growth.

Treatment of seeds of forage crops controls some diseases, such as certain smuts in slender wheatgrass, millet, Canada wildrye, and Sudangrass. Seed treatment sometimes has increased stands in some species of *Lespedeza, Lotus, Medicago, Melilotus,* and *Trifolium*. Other species are injured by certain treatments when the treated seed is sown in dry soil.

Seed of winter peas, mung beans, cowpeas, hop clover, hairy vetch, and alfalfa gave better germination, improved stands, and superior plants when treated with Spergon, Arasan, Phygon, or Dow 9–B in extensive field and greenhouse tests in 1949. Nodulation was not inhibited by treatment when the nitrogen-fixation culture was applied to the treated seed immediately before sowing. Some investigators, however, say that legume seed should not be treated before being inoculated if it is to be sown in soil not previously cropped to legumes.

Experiments with treating soybean seeds have been more numerous and extensive than with those of almost any other legume. In general, improved stands were had after the use of Arasan, Spergon, Phygon, and Dow 9–B. Organic mercurials are sometimes injurious. Increased stands due to treatment were not always followed by increased yields, probably because branching of the plants often compensates for thinner stands and because a higher percentage of the soybean flowers in a thin stand of plants will form pods.

Treatment of peanut seed is a profitable farm practice, especially when mechanically shelled seed is used. Increases in stand have ranged from 30 to 100 percent. Uninjured hand-shelled seed frequently gets no benefit from seed treatment except when unfavorable growing conditions follow planting. Arasan, Spergon, Phygon, Dow 9–B, and Ceresan M are commonly recommended.

Vegetable seeds are treated primarily to prevent seed rot and damping-off. Sometimes the control of seed-borne diseases is a major aim. The materials so used include Arasan, Phygon, Spergon, Fermate, Semesan, Dow 9–B, N. I. Ceresan, Ceresan M, Cuprocide, zinc oxide, zinc hydroxide, mercuric and mercurous chlorides, copper sulfate, phenothiazine, Zerlate, Dithane, and others.

Arasan and Spergon are two widely used fungicides for vegetable seeds. Arasan seems most suitable for seed of beets, chard, and spinach. Spergon seems best for legumes.

Some fungicides display differential benefit or injury toward the seed of certain crops. Cuprocide, for example, is injurious to seed of crucifers and lima beans and causes necrosis, delayed absorption, and delayed seedling growth in peas. It is especially beneficial, however, to lettuce seed, which in turn is injured somewhat by Arasan and Fermate. Zinc oxide is injurious to peas but is highly beneficial to seed of spinach and crucifers.

Potato tubers often are treated before planting. Fifteen or more diseases of potatoes may be transmitted in or on the tubers. Few of them are amenable to control by treating the tubers before planting. Scab, rhizoctonia or black scurf, and fusarium seed-piece decay respond to seed treatment if they are seed-borne. The principal treatments recommended are hot formaldehyde dip, cold formaldehyde soak, hot mercuric chloride dip, cold mercuric chloride soak, yellow oxide of mercury dip, and the hydrochloric acid-mercuric dip. Several organic mercury fungicides also are used. Among them are Semesan Bel, Sanoseed, and Corona P. D. 7, all of which are made specifically for treating potato seed pieces. Beneficial results have been obtained also from the use of Fermate, Semesan, Spergon, and Dithane.

Sweetpotatoes used for planting are treated to prevent injury due to seed-borne black rot, scurf, and stem rot and soil-infesting pathogens as species of *Pythium, Rhizoctonia,* and *Sclerotium.* The standard treatment is one 10-minute dip in a 1 to 1,000 mercuric chloride solution, or a dip in Semesan Bel solution (1 pound to 7½ gallons of water). Both are effective but sometimes they delay or reduce the production of sprouts. Fairly good results without injury have been had with Spergon, Phygon, Fermate, Zerlate, Tersan, and Pura-tized N–5–E.

Some vegetable diseases, caused by soil infestation, are partly or wholly prevented by applying fungicides to the soil, usually with the fertilizer. Clubroot of cabbage has been controlled by adding calomel to the soil along with fertilizer and hydrated lime. Onion smut has been controlled by applying sodium nitrite, calcium nitrite, potassium nitrite, or Fermate to the soil a few days before sowing. Arasan, similarly applied, controls onion smut and damping-off. Phygon, applied to the soil in fertilizer, controls damping-off in eggplant, pepper, beet, cucumber, and tomato. Different formulations of Dithane, applied to the soil, are said to be effective against red stele in strawberries, downy mildew in lettuce, blight in peppers, bed diseases of mushrooms, and damping-off in peas. The material acts either as a soil disinfectant or as a therapeutic agent.

Treating the seeds of ornamentals is a common practice. Semesan has been widely used for this purpose. The nonmercurial organics, such as Arasan and Spergon, also are satisfactory.

ORNAMENTALS grown from bulbs, corms, tubers, and roots also are benefited somewhat by the use of fungicides. Gladiolus corms, for example, are helped by a 15-minute dip in a solution of 1 pound of New Improved Ceresan in 50 gallons of water just before planting. The standard mercuric and mercurous chloride solutions also are used. Dipping the corms in slurries of Spergon, Fermate, or Dow 9–B after digging is beneficial.

Tulip bulbs have not responded very well to treatment. Some fungicides have lowered the yield of bulbs. Dipping bulbs in slurries of Spergon or Fermate has increased some yields. Narcissus bulbs may be dipped in a phenyl mercury acetate solution (1 pound to 800 gallons) for 5 minutes, after digging in spring and again before planting in fall, to control fusarium basal rot. Arasan SFX, Dow 9–B, and New Improved Ceresan also are beneficial.

HORMONES IN SEED TREATMENTS have been tried often. Results have varied. Of 30 investigators whose work was reviewed, 10 reported beneficial results from the use of growth-promoting substances on seeds. Twenty failed to obtain any benefits. Apparently the conditions under which hormones may or may not be beneficial in seed treatments are not fully understood.

Growth-promoting substances are used commercially to induce root formation in cuttings, prevent fruit drop in apple orchards, induce fruit formation without pollination in some plants, and to prevent sprouting in stored potato tubers. It seems reasonable that under proper conditions the materials may improve seed germination and early growth of the seedlings. Definite and reliable recommendations cannot be made until more extensive research has been carried out.

SYNERGISM AND ANTAGONISM between different fungicides, when mixed together, has been demonstrated often enough to restrain one from mixing fungicides with one another or with insecticides without knowing how they will affect each other and the seeds on which they are to be used.

A few examples of the effects of such

mixing may be mentioned. The addition of New Improved Ceresan to DDT reduced both the fungicidal action of Ceresan and the insecticidal action of DDT. Magnesium oxide, added to copper carbonate or to Spergon, reduced the beneficial effect of those materials on emergence in wheat and on smut control in sorghum. Magnesium oxide also reduced the fungicidal efficiency of cuprous oxide and of Dow 9–B, but seemed to increase the fungicidal effectiveness of sulfur. Pyrophyllite containing 3 percent DDT when mixed with Dow 9–B reduced the control of sorghum kernel smut from 0.3 percent to 40 percent, with 60 percent infection in the check. Copper compounds in general are reduced in effectiveness when mixed with materials high in protein.

A good fungicide, prepared especially for seed treatment, usually is a well-balanced combination of active ingredients and suitable diluents, perhaps with the addition of wetting and dispensing agents, dyes, and other materials in proper proportion. The addition of other materials, such as insecticides or other fungicides, may cause chemical reactions and the formation of compounds that are ineffective as fungicides or injurious to the seed.

The labels on containers for fungicides used for dusting or spraying vegetation often mention the insecticides with which they are not to be used. Labels for seed-treatment fungicides, however, do not include such directions because, as a rule, those fungicides are not mixed with insecticides or other fungicides. That may change, however, with the growing need for combatting insects that attack seeds after they have been planted. Experiments in New York showed that Arasan SFX mixed with chlordane, lindane, or aldrin and applied to lima beans prevented both seed rot caused by fungi and seed injury due to the seed-corn maggot. Mergamma, a treatment for cereal seed, contains phenyl mercury urea for the control of certain cereal diseases and benzene hexachloride for wireworm control. The number of these insecticidal-fungicidal seed-treatment combinations doubtless will increase, but their use in combination should follow careful chemical and biological experiments.

SEED INJURY following treatment was common when the treatments were mostly copper sulfate solutions, formaldehyde, or mercuric chloride, especially when planting was delayed after treatment.

When copper carbonate dust began to be used to treat wheat, it was found that delayed planting after treatment caused no injury to the seed but actually protected it against rodents and insects in storage. The more volatile organic mercury treatments, however, occasionally lowered the viability of seed after storage periods of more than a few days, especially when the moisture content of the seed was high. Several factors govern the degree of such injury: The moisture content of the seed; the volatility of the fungicide and the rate at which it is applied; the length of the storage period; the temperature, humidity, and aeration during storage; the kind of seed (seed of some genera, species, or varieties are more susceptible to chemical injury than are those of others); and the condition of the seed coat (cracked, chipped, or broken seed coats are conducive to seed injury).

IF SEED IS TO BE STORED for a while after treatment with a volatile fungicide, its moisture content should be relatively low—13 percent or less for cereals—and a lighter rate of application used. Different portions of oats of 12 percent moisture content were treated with New Improved Ceresan at 1/2 and 1/8 ounce per bushel and either sown at once or stored for several weeks. The seed treated at the 1/2-ounce rate yielded better when sown the day after treatment. The seed that got the lighter application yielded better when sowing was delayed for several weeks after treatment. Several experiments proved that sound seed of wheat, oats, and barley of good quality and proper moisture content, treated with one of the better organic mercury disinfectants at the recommended rate and properly stored for a year, was not injured in viability but yielded better than did untreated seed similarly stored. Occasionally in the more humid areas of the Southeast, treated seed is stored with a too-high moisture content and the poor viability is ascribed to the treatment. Subsequent tests often show that the viability of the untreated seed is equally poor.

PRETREATMENT OF SEED sold by seed dealers has been advocated for years. Some large seed houses pretreat seed of some field crops, such as cereals, flax, cotton, sugar beets, peas, corn, broomcorn, and some forage crops, either as a general practice or on a buyer's request.

Pretreatment of seeds by all dealers would mean cheaper but more general and more effective seed treatment; fewer outbreaks of preventable diseases; less waste of chemicals; less need of storing large stocks of chemicals in many places; more economical packaging, distribution, and use of seed-treatment chemicals; the use of the proper disinfectant at the proper rate for each type of seed; and many other advantages.

Some objections to general pretreatment of seed are valid enough. There is no general agreement as to what treatment is best for each kind of seed. Some buyers object to planting "poisoned" seed. Some persons might not realize that treated seed is sometimes poisonous and they might suffer injury. I think, though, that all the advantages of pretreating seed outweigh the objections.

Continued advances in seed treatment doubtless will bring new and better fungicides, better apparatus, and improved procedures into use. Fungicidal materials that promise to be more effective but less costly and less poisonous and disagreeable are sought. Slurry treaters that are more accurate and less troublesome are promised. A process that will fix the slurry fungicide to the seed and prevent its dusting off when the dried seed is handled will rid the slurry method of its chief shortcoming.

The possibility of systemic fungicides and chemotherapeutic disease prevention has been suggested and has been demonstrated in a few instances. This might eventually lead to the prevention of such Nation-wide calamities as epidemics of stem rust of cereals. Such fungicides would be applied to the soil and, when taken up by the plant, would render it resistant or fatal to the fungus attacking it. The fact that a tiny amount (3 parts per million) of selenium in soil is fatal to aphids and spider mites feeding on plants grown in the treated soil should encourage the search for fungicides equally effective against fungus infection but not poisonous to humans and animals. Such fungicides would be a tremendous advance in our war against plant diseases.

R. W. LEUKEL *is a plant pathologist in the division of cereal crops and diseases at the Plant Industry Station, Beltsville, Md. He has been engaged in the study of the cause and control of cereal diseases since 1919 and is the author of more than 50 articles on the subject.*

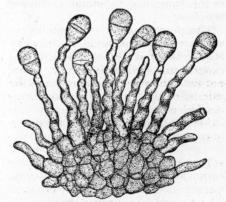

Conidia and conidiophores.

Making Sure of Healthy Seed

Erwin L. LeClerg

The primary purpose of seed certification is to maintain and to make available to our farmers crop seeds, tubers, or bulbs of good seeding value and true to name. The factors considered in determining good seeding value or quality include viability, content of weed seeds, and freedom from seed-borne pathogens or viruses.

The production of certified seed of superior varieties of field and forage crops involves the cooperative effort of many State, Federal, and private agencies. Among them are State agricultural experiment stations and extension services, State departments of agriculture, State crop improvement associations, the International Crop Improvement Association, the seed trade, and the United States Department of Agriculture. The work started at a meeting in 1919 of representatives of the States and Canadian certifying agencies.

The determination of eligibility of varieties for certification is the chief responsibility of the State agricultural experiment station in every State. Factors considered in determining the suitability of a crop variety for inclusion in a certified-seed program include yield, adaptation, and resistance to diseases and insects.

THE REQUIREMENTS for eligibility for certification vary as to type of crop. Certification for such cereal crops as wheat, oats, or barley, because of their limited area of adaptation, is relatively simple and frequently is conducted on a local-area basis. But the distribution of good seed of perennial forage crops—alfalfa, red clover, the grasses—requires the effort of many persons in widely separated areas because most of such seed is not produced in the locality where it is used for hay and pasture seedings.

The farmer may make application for inspection but is under no obligation to do so.

Varieties of field crops must be approved by a State agricultural experiment station before they are eligible to be considered for certification. In general, only one variety of the same crop, for seed production, is permitted on a farm except by prior approval of the certifying agency.

Field inspection is an important phase of the certification procedure. The International Crop Improvement Association has established certain minimum field standards, which form the basis for the regulations adopted by State certifying agencies. The standards take into consideration the type of crop, the degree of isolation necessary to prevent cross-pollination, and the class of seed produced.

Four classes of seed are recognized in seed certification of field and forage crops: Breeder seed, foundation seed, registered seed, and certified seed. The International Crop Improvement Association defines them thus:

"Breeder seed is seed or vegetative propagating material directly controlled by the originating, or in certain cases the sponsoring plant breeder or institution, and which provides the source for the initial and recurring increase of foundation seed.

"Foundation seed shall be seed stocks that are so handled as to most nearly maintain specific genetic identity and purity and that may be designated or distributed by an agricultural experiment station. Production must be carefully supervised or approved by representatives of an agricultural experiment station. Foundation seed shall be the source of all other certified seed classes, either directly or through registered seed.

"Registered seed shall be the progeny of foundation or registered seed that is so handled as to maintain satisfactory genetic identity and purity and that has been approved and certified by the certifying agency. This class of seed should be of a quality suitable for the production of certified seed.

"Certified seed shall be the progeny of foundation, registered, or certified seed that is so handled as to maintain satisfactory genetic identity and purity and that has been approved and certified by the certifying agency."

State and Federal plant breeders for years have been developing superior varieties of forage crops. For a long time, however, less than 1 percent of the legume and grass seed produced in the United States was of improved varieties.

The great demand for seed of the newer varieties in forage-producing areas meant the draining away of the early generations of seed stocks, which should have been used to increase seed. The small supply of breeder seed has been the principal limiting factor in production of adequate supplies of foundation seed of some varieties of legumes and grasses. But, equally important, no procedure for maintaining and distributing foundation seed of forage crops on a Nation-wide basis was available.

The Foundation Seed Project was initiated in 1948 to set up the organization and financial procedure whereby foundation seed stocks of improved varieties of legumes and grasses could be rapidly produced from breeder seed and distributed. Methods necessary to maintain genetic purity of the varieties were devised. It is a cooperative effort utilizing the facilities of State and Federal agencies and the commercial seed trade. In 1952, 34 States participated. The cooperating agencies include State experiment stations, State extension services, State seed certifying agencies, State foundation seed organizations,

the International Crop Improvement Association, the American Seed Trade Association, and the Department of Agriculture.

The operational phases of the program are concerned with producing, assembling, distributing, and limited stockpiling of breeder and foundation seed. The coordination of those functions is the responsibility of the Bureau of Plant Industry, Soils, and Agricultural Engineering of the Department of Agriculture. Financial assistance for contracting for the maintenance of adequate reserves of breeder and foundation seed stocks is provided by the Grain Branch of the Production and Marketing Administration, representing the Commodity Credit Corporation of the Department of Agriculture. Each State is represented by a State foundation seed representative, who is responsible for initiating the foundation seed work and handling operations in his State.

Direction of the program is the responsibility of a 16-man advisory group. Its members serve without pay. It is known as the Planning Conference and includes two representatives of each of these organizations: Northeastern Experiment Station Region, Southern Experiment Station Region, North Central Experiment Station Region, Western Experiment Station Region, International Crop Improvement Association, American Seed Trade Association, Production and Marketing Administration, and Bureau of Plant Industry, Soils, and Agricultural Engineering.

A superior variety developed by a plant breeder is tested for regional adaptation under the supervision of the Regional Forage Crops Technical Committee. A new variety found to be good in part or all of a region is then recommended by this technical committee to the Planning Conference for inclusion in the Project.

The Planning Conference determines the areas for foundation seed production for each new variety, estimates the requirements for breeder and foundation seed stocks, and co-operates with State workers in the areas of production in the development of the seed-increase program.

The breeders' seed of a new variety is assigned by the Planning Conference to State foundation seed representatives in the States where it has been determined that foundation seed is to be produced. All foundation seed is grown under contract with individual growers, who are selected by the State foundation seed representative. Because the number of growers needed is small, only the most dependable growers, located in an area with favorable soil and climate, are chosen.

The foundation seed of all varieties included in the program is allocated by the Planning Conference to State foundation seed representatives for planting to produce registered seed. The registered seed is handled by commercial seedsmen, who sell it to growers for the production of certified seed. The certified seed, which is subsequently used by farmers for forage plantings, is distributed through regular seed trade channels.

The 12 varieties included in the program in 1952 were Atlantic, Buffalo, Narragansett, and Ranger alfalfas; Kenland red clover; Tift Sudangrass; Climax lespedeza; and five blend lines of Midland red clover.

The 27 million pounds of certified seed of Ranger alfalfa available for 1953 planting was the largest amount ever produced of an improved alfalfa variety. It was almost double the amount farmers had the previous year. The market had almost twice as much Buffalo alfalfa seed in 1952 as was available in 1951. The supply of certified Atlantic alfalfa for hay and pasture seedings had increased from 150,818 pounds in 1950 to 1,511,000 pounds in 1952. Narragansett alfalfa was added to the list of varieties in the Project in 1951. Yet it was possible to produce more than 5,000 pounds of certified seed the first year in addition to increasing breeder and foundation seed supplies.

Enough stock seed of Kenland red clover was distributed to make available 215,000 pounds of certified seed in 1950, the first large-volume production. Yet in 1952, only 2 years later, there was a tenfold increase in certified seed production, which meant farmers had 2,000,000 pounds of planting. The increase of Tift Sudangrass has been comparable.

THE POTATO TUBER is subject to many diseases caused by fungus and bacterial pathogens and viruses. Disease-free seed is important.

The quality of seed potatoes has greatly improved since 1925 through the elimination of tuber-transmitted virus diseases by roguing, tuber-unit planting, tuber indexing, early harvest and pulling or killing vines; the use of winter field test plots; the use of immune or resistant varieties; the enforcement of high standards of certification; the production and use of better foundation seed; and the production of certified seed.

Many tuber-transmitted diseases of potatoes, like mosaic, curly dwarf, spindle tuber, leaf roll, and blackleg (*Erwinia atroseptica*), cannot be controlled by spraying or dusting. The only way is to remove the diseased plants from the field, a procedure that is commonly termed roguing. Seed pieces, tops, and tubers are removed sufficiently far from the field and destroyed to prevent winged aphid vectors from migrating from the rogued plants or parts back to the potato field. Roguing usually commences when the plants are 4 to 6 inches above the ground. The first roguing is followed by roguing at weekly or 10-day intervals throughout the season.

TUBER-UNIT planting and tuber indexing have been generally used as an aid in the detection and elimination of virus diseases in the production of high-quality seed stocks. Tuber-unit planting, first practiced in 1908, is commonly used for seed plots and the production of foundation seed. The method consists of planting all the seed pieces (usually four) cut from a single tuber one after another in the row, with a space separating them from the sets of the next tuber. Ready and accurate recognition of weak or diseased units thus is possible. All plants from the same tuber are removed if any one of them is weak or shows symptoms of a virus disease.

Tuber indexing, first described by F. M. Blodgett and Karl H. Fernow at Cornell University in 1921, has been generally adopted in seed-producing areas. It consists of removing a small piece bearing a single eye from each tuber and planting it in the greenhouse in winter. Only the tubers whose seed pieces produced normal and healthy plants are retained for field increase the following spring.

Foundation seed plots a mile away from other potato fields can become infected with virus diseases transmitted by winged aphids. As the growing season progresses, insect vectors of virus diseases may increase, and infection, contracted by the tops during the current season, is more likely to have reached the tubers in late- than in early-harvested stock. Healthy plants harvested early show a lower percentage of virus diseases than do healthy plants harvested late in the season. Early harvesting of seed plots or foundation seed is now a common practice in some potato seed producing areas.

Hand pulling was one of the first methods employed to destroy potato vines in an effort to produce better disease-free seed. It soon became apparent that the method was impractical because of the great cost and the high labor requirement.

Flame burning destroyed the leaves but left stems standing, from which new growth was produced in late-maturing varieties. A similar situation occurred when the foliage was mascerated with a rotobeater machine. The use of chemicals to kill the vines has become a common practice in many of the potato seed producing

areas. It helps reduce the spread of virus diseases, prevent infection of tubers by the late blight fungus (*Phytophthora infestans*), complete harvest before freezing weather, regulate the size of seed tubers, and reduce skinning and bruising of tubers. Late-maturing varieties have been found to be more difficult to kill than early-maturing ones. Vascular discoloration of the tuber frequently occurs from the use of chemicals to kill vines.

More work needs to be done to determine the factors that cause the discoloration.

Because some weather conditions mask symptoms of some tuber-transmitted virus diseases, detection is sometimes difficult in the northern areas. The diseases can be detected when the plants are grown under field conditions in winter in some of the Southern States and California. Thus it is now mandatory to test all foundation seed (and much of the certified seed) in winter test plots. Through this means some northern growers of foundation seed have been able to maintain relatively disease-free stocks. The winter tests of samples from fields of potatoes grown for certification are completed in time so that the data may be used by certification officials of the seed-producing States. The information also helps growers of certified seed to keep from planting inferior stock.

It is generally agreed that very little progress would have been made in controlling mosaic and other tuber-transmitted virus diseases if winter tests had not been established for guidance in the program of production of good foundation and certified seed.

The production of the good, new, resistant varieties of potatoes is largely due to the accomplishments of the National Potato Breeding Program, which began in 1929. It is a Nation-wide program in which State agricultural experiment stations and the Department of Agriculture cooperate. The Katahdin variety was the first distributed under this program. It has resistance to mild mosaic and some resistance to leaf roll. It is immune to net necrosis. Nearly 13 million bushels of certified Katahdin seed were grown in the United States in 1952. In 1952 it represented more than 30 percent of all certified seed potatoes and led all other varieties. Since then, 42 additional varieties have been introduced, some of which have replaced older varieties to a significant extent. Not all are resistant to any of the major potato diseases but were released because of their reported superior horticultural characters.

POTATO seed certification dates from 1914 and the work of Professor J. G. Milward of the University of Wisconsin. It was the object of the work then, as now, to put upon the market the best seed that could be produced. Certification is recognized as a constructive preventive measure in tuber-borne diseases. The industry has expanded greatly. The average production of certified seed potatoes in the United States, for the years between 1949 and 1952, was 44.7 million bushels.

The enforcement of certification standards is the responsibility of the colleges of agriculture and State departments of agriculture in most States. In Nebraska, Utah, and South Dakota, the work has been conducted by growers' organizations.

Certified potato seed is grown under a system of inspection. The plants are inspected twice in the field during the growing season. The tubers are inspected in the bin after they are dug. The first field inspection is usually made early so as to identify and rogue the diseased plants. The second inspection is made in the period between the time of blossoming and just before the vines mature. For each inspection a maximum percentage of affected plants or tubers for each disease is allowed. This disease tolerance varies for disease and by certifying States but is usually between 1 and 5 percent.

Each State has jurisdiction over its own certification work and sets the tolerances permitted for various diseases. For example, the tolerances allowed for various diseases and varietal mixtures by Maine are (the figures are percentages allowed in first inspection and second inspection, respectively): Leaf roll, 2 and 1; mosaic, 3 and 2; spindle tuber, 2 and 2; yellow dwarf, 0.5 and 0.5; total virus diseases, 5 and 3; blackleg, 2 and 1; wilt, 2 and 1; bacterial ring rot, 0 and 0; total for all diseases, 6 and 4; giant hills, 1 (second inspection); varietal mixtures, 1 and 0.25.

The production of certified seed potatoes depends upon the quality of foundation seed stocks from which they are grown. All plantings produced for certification must be grown from foundation stock of the best quality and should be thoroughly rogued. Improvement of foundation seed stock through field roguing permits the removal of diseased, weak, off-type, or varietal-mixture plants during the growing season. In order to insure freedom from virus diseases, the foundation seed is produced in areas isolated from other potatoes and free from disease-transmission insects. A comparatively small number of tubers indexed one year and planted in the field the next spring will give a sizable increase in seed stock for the following year. After one season's increase, a sufficient quantity would then be produced so that the grower could replace his old stock entirely with disease-free potatoes for the production of certified seed.

The most recent development is the operation of seed-source farms by the certifying agencies. The farms (in Maine and some other States) are operated to produce seed stocks for growers of foundation seed. Seed is carefully grown in isolated areas and is tested in winter field test plots. Seed thus produced is released to selected growers for the production of foundation seed. The varieties grown on the farms are planted by tuber-unit methods and carefully rogued by representatives of the certification agencies.

VEGETABLE SEED PRODUCTION areas have been shifted to areas where the weather is less favorable to the development of plant diseases. Such a shift is possible with crop-seed production because the total acreage of a particular crop is usually relatively small in proportion to the crop for which the seed is used.

Anthracnose (*Colletotrichum lindemuthianum*) and the bacterial blights (*Xanthomonas phaseoli* and *Pseudomonas phaseolicola*) are three major diseases of beans in the United States. They are wet-weather diseases, and their spread and development depend to a great degree on the presence of high moisture and suitable temperatures.

Before 1925, the production of bean seed was largely limited to the New England-New York area and Michigan. In those regions the weather conditions are generally favorable for the development of the three diseases. Between 1916 and 1919, losses in some of these localities were as much as 25 percent. For many subsequent years the diseases were widespread and destructive wherever beans were grown.

Since the causal organisms of the diseases are disseminated chiefly with the seed and it is imperative to have clean seed for planting, attention was centered on seed production in the West, where weather is unfavorable to the development of the diseases. Such areas were found in Idaho and California. Those centers of certified seed production have elevations of 2,000 to 3,000 feet, exceptionally low humidity, few showers, and little hail during the growing season. As a consequence of producing certified bean seed there, the three diseases have ceased to be the limiting factors in the production of the crop.

At one time pea seed for gardens and canning was grown chiefly in the Northeastern States. Since 1925 or so, the center of production has shifted to the irrigated and more arid parts of some of the Western States. Pea seed for these purposes is now produced in the Snake River Valley and the Twin Falls areas of Idaho, near Bozeman, Mont., the Palouse section of northern Idaho, and eastern Washington. This shift was made in order to produce seed free of bacterial blight (*Pseudomonas pisi*) and leaf and pod spot (*Ascochyta* species).

The growing of seed stocks of cabbage, turnip, rutabaga, and cauliflower used to be limited to the Midwest and East. More recently the ravages of blackleg (*Phoma lingam*) and black rot (*Xanthomonas campestris*) have caused the shifting of the seed-producing areas for these crops to localities along the Pacific coast. Because of the low rainfall in those areas during the time the seedling plants are growing in seedbeds, the two diseases do not become established. Hence a crop of disease-free seed can be produced from the seedlings, which are subsequently transplanted to clean fields.

Most of the cauliflower seed produced in the United States is grown in the coastal valleys of California.

In those areas, the seed has been relatively free from both blackleg and black rot.

THE USE OF RESISTANT VARIETIES, if available, is the most effective way of controlling the seed-borne organisms. That subject is discussed in the section that begins on page 165.

ERWIN L. LECLERG *is a research coordinator in the office of the Administrator of the Agricultural Research Administration. He is charged with coordinating parts of the research program of the Department that have to do with sugar crops, dry beans and peas, seeds, weeds, forage crops, pastures and ranges, pesticides and insecticides and related equipment. He holds degrees from Colorado Agricultural and Mechanical College, Iowa State College, and the University of Minnesota. He joined the Department in 1930.*

How Nurseries Get Virus-free Fruit Stock

L. C. Cochran, Earle C. Blodgett, J. Duain Moore, K. G. Parker

More than 40 virus diseases affect stone fruits. Others attack pome, citrus, avocado, fig, and other fruits. No major fruit crop is free from virus diseases. Some virus diseases have caused the destruction of orchards throughout communities and others have ruined orchards in large areas. Some, more insidious, do not kill trees but take an annual toll by reducing the yield and quality of the crops. Still others produce only mild effects and are important chiefly because they complicate the question of control.

Part of the geographic occurrence of most of the virus diseases affecting stone fruit is traceable to distribution in infected nursery stock. Most fruit trees now are grown from nursery stock produced by budding or grafting the desired variety onto seedlings or rootstocks propagated vegetatively from cuttings. If the variety or the rootstock is infected with a virus, the resulting nursery trees usually will be infected. If the nursery is located near infected trees, viruses may spread naturally into nursery stock during the growing season. When diseased nursery stock is planted in a district where the disease was not previously present, spread may take place to other trees and the disease soon becomes established.

The question of nursery improvement is complex. The many factors that are involved vary among areas because different diseases are present, different varieties of fruit are grown, and different conditions exist in each. It seems impossible to devise a program with provisions that would be entirely applicable to all areas, although some general procedures can be formulated.

Because some virus diseases of stone fruits are known to have been carried in the nursery stock, a logical starting point for improvement is the use of procedures to eliminate them from scion and budwood sources and from rootstock seed sources. Growers of such sources then could be issued certificates indicating the standards that have been met. Certification has value only when it refers to specified definite standards.

Any plan for the production of certified fruit tree nursery stock could well make use of the same principles and procedures developed for certified seed potatoes: Establishing disease-free foundation stocks true to variety; increasing the stocks in the field under rigid inspection and roguing; passing the stocks for certification if the number of diseased or off-type plants is maintained at or below a standard, which has been determined by practice to be necessary to insure high yields and good quality; and supervising sales to maintain the identity of the certified stock.

Considerable progress has been made toward nursery improvement in the more important fruit-growing States. The program has been mostly voluntary. The approach has been from different angles. Unknown and variable factors have prevented the formulation of any uniform procedure usable in all States.

In most of the States, the first step has been to inspect the orchard trees desired as a source of budwood and the trees adjacent to them. If no symptoms of virus or viruslike diseases are found, the nurseryman who gets buds from them may obtain a certificate that his trees were propagated from sources that had been inspected and found visibly free of virus diseases. The procedure has helped reduce the prevalence of such virus diseases as the peach yellows group, peach wart, and certain cherry diseases, which are generally expressed on all the horticultural varieties of the affected host. It has also helped in the elimination of cherry diseases like mottle leaf, twisted leaf, rusty mottle, the necrotic rusty mottle; apricot ring pox; the psorosis of citrus; and other diseases that damage some fruit varieties but are only meagerly expressed on others. Orchard inspection has also materially helped in the elimination of certain viruslike nontransmissible but bud-perpetuated disorders, such as sweet cherry crinkle leaf, sweet cherry deep suture, almond bud failure, and Italian Prune leaf spot and sparse leaf, and has assisted in the selection of fruitful types true to variety.

The usual procedure has been for the nurseryman to apply for the service by a given date to the State department of agriculture in his State. The trees then are inspected in the proper season and given some sort of identifying designation. Standards have to be set, such as minimum age of the trees to be used and the distance from the nearest diseased trees. Because most of the diseases spread in orchards, any certificate based on orchard inspection is good only for the year in which the inspection is made and new inspections must be made each year.

Orchard inspection alone is not enough to determine the presence of all the viruses that affect fruit trees. Some viruses that are destructive to one variety may exist in another without symptoms. Buds from such infected but symptomless trees produce similar infected nursery trees, which carry the virus to orchard locations where the trees are planted. The mottle leaf virus ruins the Napoleon (Royal Ann) and Bing varieties of cherries, but may cause few symptoms or none on Lambert.

Environment, such as high or low temperatures, influences the expression of symptoms of some diseases. Symptoms of leaf yellowing of the sour cherry yellows disease are expressed on sour cherry trees and damage is accentuated in areas where temperatures following petal fall are relatively low, but no leaf symptoms occur in areas where the temperatures are higher. Nursery stock propagated in warmer climates from vigorous-appearing trees can very innocently carry the sour cherry yellows virus and result in serious losses if planted in such areas as those near the Great Lakes, where summer growing temperatures are low.

The western X-disease virus, conversely, may not produce symptoms, especially on sweet cherries growing on mazzard rootstock in areas of high elevation where temperatures are low. Some virus diseases have long incubation periods; hence, if buds are cut from orchard trees in the early stages of infection before symptoms appear, they may carry the virus to nursery stock. The ring spot virus produces symptoms only during the acute or initial stages of infection on many fruit tree hosts, yet buds taken from trees in the chronic stages and showing no symptoms carry the virus.

The presence of viruses in symptomless trees is determined by indexing them on varieties that express symptoms. That commonly is done by budding healthy nursery trees of a susceptible symptom-expressing variety with buds from the suspect trees. Certain varieties and species are known to produce consistent and characteristic symptoms when infected with particular viruses. By use of a combination of such hosts in index procedures, a fruit tree can be tested for the presence of any of the known viruses. In order to keep the number of necessary hosts to a minimum, hosts that will express and differentiate a large number of the viruses may be used. Here is a list of index hosts and the diseases which each may serve to diagnose:

Peach. *Elberta:* Peach yellows, little peach, red suture, peach rosette, rosette mosaic, phony, peach mosaic, X-disease, western X-disease, yellow bud mosaic, wart, peach mottle, peach necrotic leaf spot, asteroid spot, golden-net, peach calico, peach blotch.

Peach. *J. H. Hale:* Ring spot, willow twig.

Peach. *Muir:* Muir peach dwarf.

Peach. *Seedlings* (open-pollinated seedlings of Lovell and Halehaven have been used): Necrotic ring spot, sour cherry yellows.

Sour cherry. *Montmorency:* Sour cherry yellows, green ring mottle, necrotic ring spot, pink fruit, peach mottle.

Sour cherry. *On mahaleb:* Western X-disease wilt and decline.

Sweet cherry. *Bing:* Buckskin, albino, mottle leaf, rusty mottle, mild rusty mottle, rasp leaf, twisted leaf, tatter leaf, small bitter cherry, western X little cherry, peach mottle.

Sweet cherry. *Royal Ann:* Black canker, cherry rugose mosaic, pinto leaf.

Sweet cherry. *Lambert:* Necrotic rusty mottle, little cherry, small bitter cherry, Lambert mottle, Utah Dixie rusty mottle.

Prunus serrulata vars. *Shirofugen:* Ring spot.

Prunus serrulata vars. *Kwanzan:* Other latents, rough bark.

Plum. *Italian Prune:* Prune dwarf.

Plum. *Shiro:* Line pattern.

Plum. *French Prune:* Prune diamond canker.

Plum. *Standard prune:* Standard prune constricting mosaic.

Plum. *Santa Rosa:* Plum white spot.

Apricot. *Tilton:* Ring pox.

Almond. *Nonpareil:* Drake almond bud failure.

It may not be necessary to index budwood sources in all areas on all of those hosts. For example, our evidence indicates that some of the cherry viruses are not present in peaches in some sections where only peaches are grown. Also, most peach virus diseases (or at least most of those that seriously damage peaches) affect all varieties of peaches similarly, and their presence generally is determined easily by orchard inspection. But cherries appear to be more commonly affected by viruses than peaches. Some viruses are ruinous on one variety of cherry but may infect another with only meager or no symptoms; index procedure to find virus-free trees therefore is needed for cherries more than for peaches.

The question of how much indexing should be done depends on what diseases are present in the area, the destination of the nursery stock, and the variety of the host.

Stone-fruit clones completely free of all viruses are difficult to achieve for a number of reasons. The complete host range of many of the stone-fruit viruses has not yet been determined. Completely satisfactory index hosts for all of the stone fruits have not been determined, particularly because of the variability of reaction caused by different forms of certain viruses. Some stone fruits are nearly universally infected, particularly with some of the latent viruses. Certain viruses (sour cherry yellows and ring spot) are transmitted through seeds. As insect vectors are known for only a few of the diseases, it is not known what measures are necessary to protect healthy stock from outside infection.

The problem of obtaining virus-free stocks by indexing procedure is complex. Index hosts have to be found that will serve with certainty to indicate the presence of a given virus in all its forms. The search for such hosts has been complicated by the fact that stocks of certain of those used were already infected. Orchard trees being indexed often are infected by more than one virus and therefore give confusing results. The long incubation period of some virus diseases, such as diamond canker of French Prune and willow twig of peach, makes the procedure slow and costly.

Some of the difficulties are exemplified by the efforts to get sour cherries free of the sour cherry yellows virus. The climate around the Great Lakes appears to be well suited to sour cherries, and most of the sour cherry orchards on the United States are there.

The climate also favors development of the sour cherry yellows disease, the cause of serious losses. Infected trees or nursery stocks grown in warmer climates may not be seriously affected and may not show leaf symptoms. A simple procedure for testing the sour cherry orchard trees for the presence of the sour cherry yellows virus or freedom from it would be to grow progenies located in an area where, if the virus were present in the progenies, symptoms would be sure to develop on them. Trees of other species could be correspondingly tested by placing buds from them into healthy sour cherry nursery trees. The chief objection to this procedure is that the nursery trees propagated from diseased trees, or healthy nursery trees infected by inoculation from diseased trees, sometimes take 2 years to develop symptoms; thus it takes a long time to get results. Some difficulty has been experienced in obtaining and maintaining disease-free indicator trees. Also, sour cherry does not express symptoms of many of the other viruses which may be present, thus necessitating further indexing on other hosts.

A high percentage of sour cherry trees is infected with the ring spot virus. Build-up of this virus has taken place over the years by indiscriminate propagation from infected trees, in which the virus had become latent; by propagation on infected seedling rootstocks, infected by passage of the virus through seeds; and by orchard spread.

Ring spot is much more prevalent than sour cherry yellows; in fact, all cultures of sour cherry yellows appear to contain the ring spot virus.

The universal occurrence of ring spot with yellows might indicate that yellows is the expression of the combined effect of two or more viruses, of which ring spot is one. Ring spot is known to exist without yellows and may be due to a single virus that is generally a contaminant of yellows. Any index procedure for sour cherry yellows would necessarily have to take ring spot into account.

In Michigan, index procedure for sour cherries has been developed with peach seedlings as indicator plants. Halehaven peach seedlings grown during the current season are budded with cherry buds in late August. If ring spot alone is present in the sour cherry trees from which the peach seedlings were budded, growth of the seedlings the following spring is retarded, buds die on many of the branches, and sometimes the branches die. Subsequent new peach growth from surviving buds assumes a normal appearance.

If sour cherry yellows is present in the cherry trees, the inoculated peach trees will show the retarding and dieback characteristic of and caused by the ring spot virus but in addition subsequent peach growth from surviving buds produces shoots with short internodes and abnormally green leaves crowded into loose rosettes. If neither ring spot nor sour cherry yellows was present in the cherries, the peach seedlings grow normally and should compare with uninoculated checks.

The peach seedling technique is quick and inexpensive. It can be done on a large scale in many areas in the open field. Its shortcomings are that peach does not react well in the greenhouse and cannot be used out-of-doors in regions where peaches are subject to winter injury. In some instances, possibly because of virus forms or individual seedling differences, peach does not give clear-cut reactions. The possibility exists that the dwarfing reaction attributed to yellows is due to a third virus, which is a contaminant commonly associated with sour cherry yellows.

In Wisconsin, indexing procedure has been developed by making use of the fact that ring spot is usually associated with sour cherry yellows. Indexing is done in one of two ways. Scions from the trees are grafted on potted disease-free Montmorency cherry trees in the greenhouse and held at 70° F. for 3 to 4 weeks; if the orchard tree has ring spot, ring spot symptoms will develop on the leaves of the potted tree. The second way is to cut scions from the orchard tree and hold them in cold storage. The tree is inoculated with a known culture of ring spot and observed for symptoms. If no symptoms develop, the tree is assumed to have had ring spot before the inoculation and the scions in storage are discarded. If the tree develops ring spot symptoms, it is assumed that it was not previously infected and the scion wood in storage is used for propagation. By eliminating ring spot, it is reasoned that sour cherry yellows also is eliminated. Our experience thus far has supported this conclusion.

Use has been made in Oregon of two varieties of *Prunus serrulata*, Kwanzan and Shirofugen, for indexing for the presence of ring spot and possibly other latent viruses. When buds carrying ring spot are inserted into arms of Shirofugen, the buds die without uniting, and gumming lesions are formed around the bud insertion points. The virus apparently moves very slowly, because if the branch is severed below the gumming lesion the virus is removed. By spacing index buds at intervals of 6 inches or less along a branch, a single Shirofugen tree can be used to index a large number of orchard trees. Trees that test negative on Shirofugen are then tested on Kwanzan, because in a few instances a virus has been found that will not affect Shirofugen but will cause a reaction on Kwanzan. Viruses usually spread rapidly through Kwanzan. A Kwanzan tree therefore can be used only for one test.

Prunus tomentosa, Manchu cherry, has been used in Iowa and is reported to be a more sensitive host for ring spot than Lovell peach seedlings. Manchu cherry was found unsatisfactory in California because of variability among seedlings and its failure to give a reaction with forms of the ring spot virus which reacted on Hale peach. Results of tests in Washington indicate that Shirofugen is a much more sensitive test plant than Manchu cherry.

More information is needed before the different index hosts can be evaluated. Where sour cherries are maintained as clones and do not show any symptoms of sour cherry yellows under growing conditions favorable for yellows, it can be presumed with reasonable certainty that they are free of yellows. Peach, sour cherry, and the Shirofugen and Kwanzan varieties of oriental flowering cherry all appear to be of value in indexing for ring spot. Shirofugen can be grown in climates with insufficient chilling requirements for sour cherries and appears to be as sensitive to the ring spot virus as sour cherry or peach.

Programs have been started in some States to develop certified foundation stocks. In some instances nurserymen were furnished budwood direct from orchard trees that had been determined by index methods to be free of virus. Tree performance was determined by observations directly on the orchard tree. In other instances progenies have been grown from indexed orchard trees and budwood has been supplied to the nurserymen from the progenies. In a few instances enough budwood for direct propagation of nursery stock has been supplied from progeny trees, but mostly nurserymen have increased their own foundation stocks to supply budwood sufficient for their needs.

Peach budwood heated at 122° F. for 5 minutes was used in Michigan on a sufficiently large scale to show that such treatment was practical for nursery procedure. Experiments earlier had shown that the treatment would eliminate viruses of the peach yellows group and X-disease. Certification on the basis of inspection of orchard trees has been used satisfactorily in Michigan for avoiding the yellows group of diseases in nursery stock; the heat treatment adds assurance against any of these diseases getting through.

A project has been undertaken in Washington by the State Department of Agriculture to assemble commercial stone-fruit varieties free of the known virus and viruslike diseases and to grow them at an isolation station near Moxee. The station is about 8 air miles from the closest commercial orchards. The water supply is such that the development of orchards nearby is unlikely. Wild species of *Prunus* are not present in the locality. Cooperating in the project are research divisions of the United States Department of Agriculture and the Washington State Agricultural Experiment Station. The plan is to establish foundation stocks, true to variety and free from diseases, that can be supplied to nurserymen for increase. Nurserymen are encouraged to use the budwood they obtain from Moxee to establish their own blocks of mother trees, from which they can get buds for nursery propagation.

The foundation stock-mother block procedure has several advantages over use of approved trees in orchards. Mother-block trees properly isolated can be maintained with less risk of becoming infected by natural spread. Pedigreed stocks, centrally located, can be given proper care and can more easily be checked for off-types or diseases. Centralization also makes for simplification of record keeping, especially as regards progeny performance and tracing troubles which may arise.

It also has limitations. Standards may be hard to determine. It has not been established that certain viruses, especially certain of the latent ones, are sufficiently harmful to warrant exclusion. New diseases are continually being found, and it may be difficult to prevent some of these from getting into stocks. There will be a continuing demand for the new varieties and new strains of varieties, which will pose a continuous problem of what should be stocked.

If the isolation station procedure is generally adopted, much expense can be saved by putting it on a regional basis. In the same way, procedure for interstate shipment of nursery stock could be simplified by interstate agreement on the requirements for certification.

The most serious virus diseases of citrus and pome fruits in most instances can be detected and avoided by orchard inspection. The psorosis disease of citrus occurs in all of the citrus-growing areas of the world. It was distributed in infected budwood before people knew it was caused by a virus. Infected trees do not commonly develop the spectacular scaling lesions and decline symptoms until they are 12 to 16 years old, yet the buds taken from them before the symptoms appear carry the virus. Exocortis, a disease that affects trifoliate orange rootstock, resulting in dwarfing the trees growing on it, can be carried by the top variety without symptoms if it is grown on other rootstocks. Stubborn disease, a third virus disease that reduces the vigor and fruitfulness of sweet orange, also requires several years for recognizable symptoms to develop in infected nursery stock.

All these diseases can be avoided by selecting budwood from vigorous, healthy-appearing orchard trees old enough to show symptoms. For freedom from the exocortis virus, budwood must be taken from trees growing on trifoliate orange rootstock. The discovery that psorosis could be diagnosed on the basis of symptoms in young leaves has greatly simplified certification procedure. Sweet orange seedlings can be used to index any species of citrus on which the presence of psorosis cannot be determined by orchard inspection.

None of the three citrus viruses we mentioned appears to have any means of natural spread in North America except by occasional natural root grafts between trees. Production of virus-free nursery stock is therefore an important and efficient way to control them.

The contagious nature of the quick decline disease of citrus, the lack of distinctive symptoms, and the wide occurrence of the causal virus in sweet orange on rootstocks other than sour orange make production of nursery stock free of the quick decline virus impractical as a control procedure within infected areas.

Several virus diseases affect pome fruits, but only one, stony pit of pear, has caused sufficient damage to merit selection of disease-free scion wood. Fruits of the Bosc variety on diseased trees are variously misshapen and pitted. Tissue at the base of the pits and around the core becomes hard and stony, making the fruit worthless. The disease can readily be recognized in the orchard just before harvest on fruits of the Bosc variety. Other varieties can be indexed by grafting healthy Bosc on one arm.

One rather serious virus disease of avocado, sun blotch, is the cause of unfruitfulness and misshapen fruits. The expression of the disease is erratic and no good indicator variety is known. The best method of avoiding the disease seems to be by the use of propagation material from trees shown by progeny performance to be free of sun blotch. The disease appears to have been spread chiefly in diseased nursery stock and is the cause of enough damage to warrant efforts to avoid it.

Elimination of viruses and viruslike disorders from nursery stock must precede measures applied in the orchard for effective control. To do this, several general steps are necessary. Viruses and viruslike disorders, which cause obvious symptoms, can be avoided by use of budwood from orchard trees that show no symptoms, are fruitful, and true to type. Such trees preferably should not be in plantings where contagious virus diseases are present and should not in any case be adjacent to virus-infected trees. Screening by index procedure is necessary to avoid viruses that may be latent in orchard trees. When desirable trees are once determined free of virus, they should be propagated on virus-free rootstocks and grown under isolation where they can be maintained under observation

and periodic testing to assure virus freedom and desirability of type. Such trees can serve as foundation material from which propagating materials can be supplied to nurserymen for establishing mother tree blocks, which in turn supply budwood for nursery propagation.

It is equally important that orchards producing seeds for growing rootstocks be virus-free and of desirable type.

Specifications for indexing and isolation would necessarily vary with districts, depending on the diseases present and the fruits grown, but effort should be made to devise provisions with enough uniformity to allow for interstate shipment. Growers should demand virus-free trees. Nurserymen need the cooperation and assistance of research, regulatory, and extension men, and growers. Nursery improvement programs are under development in several States and there is reason for optimism.

L. C. COCHRAN *is in charge of investigations of virus diseases of deciduous fruits in the Bureau of Plant Industry, Soils, and Agricultural Engineering.*

EARLE C. BLODGETT *is located at the Irrigation Experiment Station, Prosser, Wash., and holds a joint position of plant pathologist with the Washington State Department of Agriculture and the Washington Agricultural Experiment Station. He is responsible for developing fruit tree foundation stocks and nursery improvement procedures.*

J. DUAIN MOORE *is associate professor of plant pathology in the University of Wisconsin and is engaged in investigations of diseases of tree fruits, with particular interest in virus diseases of sour cherries. He is a native of Lancaster County, Pa., and holds degrees from Pennsylvania State College and the University of Wisconsin.*

K. G. PARKER *is professor of plant pathology at Cornell University. He has been investigating diseases of trees since 1928, and has been in charge of investigations of virus diseases of tree fruits since 1946. He is a native of Indiana and holds degrees from DePauw and Cornell.*

The Inspection of Imported Plants

Donald P. Limber, Paul R. Frink

Federal plant quarantines have been in effect in the United States since 1912. They do not prevent the importations of large numbers of plants each year. The plants offered for introduction must be examined to determine that they are free from plant pests that are not present in our country or are not widely established here. This first examination at the ports of entry searches out all plant pests—insects, fungi, virus diseases, and nematodes.

The Bureau of Entomology and Plant Quarantine is responsible for the pest-risk problem in the importation of plants. Two States, California and Florida, collaborate with the Federal Government at the ports within their borders. All States cooperate in the follow-up inspections that are given certain genera of plants when they are grown in the field under postentry quarantine.

The inspector's basic tools are a hand lens and a microscope. He examines the imported plant material to see if any plant diseases are present and identify the ones he finds. On the identification depends the decision as to whether those plants should be rejected, treated, or released. If he cannot identify the disease, the inspector holds the shipment and refers a specimen to the Washington office for determination by specialists.

The very nature of plant diseases makes it hard to enforce plant quarantines. Bacteria and the spores of the higher fungi that spread the diseases are so minute that they are usually invisible without magnification unless massed in large numbers. Even when the spores have germinated and invaded the tissues of the plant, evidence of the developing disease ordinarily does not appear at once. Leaves inoculated with *Colletotrichum cypripedii* show the first symptoms in 15 or 16 days. That is about the normal period for the incubation of many other diseases, but some may appear in as few as 4 days and others only after a month or longer.

Few fungus diseases can be eradicated when they are present in living plants. Therefore the plants on which a new disease is found usually are rejected. There are some exceptions. Hot-water treatments for nematode diseases and a few fungi (such as the leaf smut of rice, *Entyloma oryzae*, and the mint rust, *Puccinia menthae*) under favorable conditions may eliminate the parasites. Another example: The citrus seeds may carry the bacteria *Xanthomonas citri*, which cause the citrus canker. Citrus seeds immersed in a solution of 1 part peroxide of hydrogen to 2 parts of water for 10 minutes are completely cleansed of viable citrus canker bacteria.

THE PLANT QUARANTINE INSPECTOR at Houston, Tex., made his customary examination of the stores of a cargo vessel from Japan. The fruits and vegetables in ship's stores, though for use on the ship, may be a serious risk. The crew members may attempt to smuggle fruit ashore. Peelings and spoiled stores may be thrown into harbors and washed ashore.

In the stores the inspector found five citrus fruits on whose rinds were numerous small, round, corky spots. The fruits were confiscated and destroyed, as citrus from Japan is prohibited entry into the United States. Samples of the rind bearing the spots were sent to a Bureau mycologist at Hoboken, N. J. All five fruits were infected with citrus canker, *Xantho-*

monas citri, a highly destructive disease of citrus and one that is believed to have been completely eradicated from the United States after long and expensive effort.

Citrus canker was found in passengers' baggage and ships' stores on 10 occasions in a single month at the port of San Francisco—an illustration of the need for continuous vigilance.

AT THE OLD inspection house in Washington, D. C., which stood on the corner of Constitution Avenue at Twelfth Street, an inspector was examining some orchids from the wilds of Brazil. Some small patches of dusty, yellow material on a leaf caught his eye.

It seemed harmless at first glance and resembled amorphous materials sometimes found on orchid leaves. Upon turning the leaf over, however, he saw that there was a yellowing of the tissue extending through the leaf. Other leaves with more numerous spots were found. Some of the leaves were dead.

When sections were made, the dusty material proved to be the uredospores of the rust, *Hemileia oncidii.* All the infected leaves were removed and destroyed. The plants were then disinfected by a dip in bordeaux mixture. *Hemileia oncidii* and other rusts of orchids, which have also been intercepted many times, are not known to be established in the United States.

A LARGE SHIPMENT of lily-of-the-valley pips (*Convallaria majalis*) arrived on the docks at New York in 1950. The pips originated near Hamburg, Germany. The inspectors at the port gave them the usual thorough examination on the pier, as these plants are a known host of the stem and bulb nematode (*Ditylenchus dipsaci*).

No *Ditylenchus* was found, but the roots carried some sandy soil. Soil is a serious hazard in quarantine enforcement. It may carry insects, particularly the larvae and pupal stages, various soil-borne fungi, and plant nematodes. Imported plant material therefore must come with clean roots. The pips were ordered to be sent to the Hoboken Inspection House for cleaning. At Hoboken the washings from the roots were examined carefully for plant pests, and finally processed to recover any nematode cysts that might be present.

The plant pathologist, looking down through the microscope at the debris floating in the dish beneath the lens, observed a smooth, dark-red, spherical body with a short neck, floating around with the debris. The whole object was less than 1 millimeter in diameter. Here was a truly dangerous immigrant—the cyst of the golden nematode (*Heterodera rostochiensis*) filled with living eggs.

Further search revealed that it was not a lone cyst, but that the whole shipment of pips was heavily contaminated with golden nematode cysts, by hundreds at least, and possibly by thousands. Each cyst contained 10 to 400 eggs. It is quite probable that this one shipment of lily-of-the-valley, after being distributed by sale to florists for growing, might have established the nematode in not one but many new areas. Its introduction into our remaining potato-growing areas would be a disaster as it has proved to be on Long Island and in some parts of Europe.

The interception of the golden nematode on these *Convallaria* was not the first interception of this pest nor by any means the last. The cysts are found frequently not only in soil with plants, but they have also been intercepted adhering to straw and burlap bagging. The menace they present is heightened by the longevity of the eggs within the cysts. *H. rostochiensis* eggs have been known to hatch after 8 years.

Part of the *Convallaria* shipment was treated with hot water. The pips were immersed in hot water at 118° F. for 30 minutes, then removed and cooled with water after draining for 5 minutes. The treatment must be given with care as the margin between a complete kill of the nematodes and serious injury to the plants is very small. The plants not treated were forced in postentry quarantine in isolated greenhouses. After the flowers were harvested the plants were destroyed, and the soil and the benches then sterilized with steam.

Our three examples illustrate the varied nature of the inspector's problem. The virus diseases are especially difficult to detect in dormant plants, the condition in which most nursery stock is imported. It was largely to overcome this difficulty that postentry quarantine was devised.

POSTENTRY QUARANTINE is the requirement that some genera of plants be grown under observation of State and Federal inspectors, usually for two growing seasons, before they are released for sale or distribution. The plants subjected to this treatment are the ones known to be the hosts of some serious plant disease that does not occur here or is restricted in distribution in the United States. In most instances the plants are prohibited from the countries in which the disease is known to occur. The postentry provision then applies only to other countries in which it might be present but unreported.

Rose wilt virus (*Marmor flaccumfaciens*) occurs in Italy, Australia, and New Zealand. Rose plants or cuttings are prohibited from those countries. If a nurseryman wishes to import the material from any other foreign country he will be required to make a legal agreement that he will grow the material at a designated place, accessible to the State nursery inspector and the Federal plant quarantine inspector until it is released. In each of the following two growing seasons the State nursery inspector will inspect the plants several times. Sometimes he will be accompanied by an inspector from the postentry section of the division of plant quarantines. The plants will be examined particularly for any evidence of rose wilt virus, but also

for other foreign diseases or insects which may have accompanied them.

Postentry inspectors also must gather from the published records information on the foreign plant diseases which we are attempting to exclude. Summaries of the information are then distributed to the State inspection services. In that way the State inspectors can know the proper time to inspect roses, hops, or other postentry plants in their areas, and something of the appearance of the foreign diseases.

Daphne mosaic virus was found in 1950 in a lot of 250 *Daphne mezereum* plants from Holland. Then the disease was known only in Australia and New Zealand. It was the basis for the inclusion of daphne in the postentry list. The plants were promptly destroyed under the supervision of the State nursery inspector.

At the end of the second growing season those postentry plants which have remained free of diseases and insects new to the United States are released from quarantine.

The postentry inspection makes it possible to examine the plants when they are in leaf and at times favorable for detection of the particular diseases for which they are quarantined. In 1953 there were 50 genera of plants that must be grown in postentry quarantine when imported from certain parts of the world. Besides them, a blanket provision includes fruit and nut plants.

DONALD P. LIMBER *has been employed as a plant pathologist in the Department of Agriculture's plant quarantine work since 1924. He is now plant pathologist of the postentry section of the Bureau of Entomology and Plant Quarantine stationed at Hoboken, N. J.*

PAUL R. FRINK, *a native of Nebraska, received his graduate training in plant pathology at the University of Nebraska. He has worked with several Government agencies since 1931 and with the division of plant quarantines since 1942. He is employed as a plant quarantine inspector at the San Francisco Inspection Station.*

Protection Through Quarantines

Horace S. Dean

Modern transportation in the air age brings us close in time to lands far distant in point of miles. Travel for business, recreation, and cultural purposes stimulates interest in exotic plants, fruits, and other plant products. Modern commerce and world economy are conducive to an international flow of plants and plant products—together with the plant diseases which these materials may carry—across international boundaries, including our own.

Were there no barriers to plant disease entry, the United States could readily become the habitat for a host of plant diseases which are not now known in this country and which, if introduced and established here, could become the cause of untold additional annual losses in field crop, fruit, horticultural, floricultural, and forest production.

We take comfort, however, in the provisions of the Plant Quarantine Act of 1912, as amended, by which many safeguards are erected against entry and establishment of foreign plant diseases as well as against the domestic spread of introduced diseases. The safeguards consist of embargo and regulatory provisions in both foreign and domestic commerce. The following remarks relate only to the provisions of the Act concerning plant diseases.

In order to prevent the introduction of any plant disease that is not known in this country or that is not widely prevalent or distributed in the United States, the Act empowers the Secretary of Agriculture to issue a quarantine prohibiting the importation of the host materials of that disease and prescribes certain legal requirements which must precede the issuance of that quarantine. They include a determination of the necessity for the action, and a public hearing on the subject. The quarantine notice must specify the host materials to be excluded and name the countries where the disease occurs. Thereafter, and until the quarantine is withdrawn, the importation of the named host materials from the specified countries is prohibited regardless of the use for which the materials are intended.

All nursery stock not excluded by such embargo action may enter this country only when a permit has been issued by the Secretary of Agriculture for the importation. If the plants are to come from a country with an official phytosanitary inspection system, the shipment is to be accompanied by a certificate of the proper official of the country of origin that the nursery stock has been thoroughly inspected and is believed to be free from injurious plant diseases and insect pests. In the case of importations from countries without official systems of inspection, the shipment shall meet such conditions as the Secretary of Agriculture may prescribe.

Any plants, fruits, vegetables, roots, bulbs, seeds, or other plant products not defined as nursery stock in the Act may be brought under regulated entry comparable to that for nursery stock by action of the Secretary. To do so he must determine that the unrestricted importation of any such plant materials may result in the entry of injurious plant diseases. Other requirements are similar to those necessary to promulgate a prohibitory quarantine.

AN AMENDMENT to the Act that was approved July 31, 1947, improves the protection against foreign plant disease entry by making provision for growing nursery stock under postentry quarantine by, or under the supervision of, the Department of Agriculture, for the purpose of determining whether it may be infested with plant pests not discernible by port-of-entry inspection methods. Should there be such infection, the Secretary is authorized to prescribe remedial measures to prevent the spread. This feature is particularly useful in the instance of virus diseases.

THE VARIOUS QUARANTINES and orders issued under authority of the Act and now in force cover practically the entire field of foreign host materials—plants and plant parts, including fruits, vegetables, seeds, several fibers, and cut flowers—likely to carry injurious plant diseases into this country. Several of the quarantines and orders are issued under authority of both the prohibitory and regulatory parts of the Act.

A number of the foreign quarantines contain provisions complementing domestic plant disease control programs. For example, a feature of Nursery Stock, Plant, and Seed Quarantine No. 37 regulates the entry of barberry seeds and plants in harmony with the provisions of Federal domestic Stem Rust Quarantine No. 38. Another feature of Quarantine No. 37 prohibits the entry of citrus seeds into Florida, where there is a comparable State quarantine against citrus propagating materials from other States.

The quarantines and orders are enforced by plant quarantine inspectors at the principal ports of entry. The inspectors are assisted through cooperative relations by their associates in the Customs, Immigration, Public Health, and Postal Services, and the Bureau of Animal Industry and by collaborating State plant quarantine services. The total effort of those services and the foreign inspection and certification of plants before shipment provide an effective program for the enforcement of the quarantines and prevention of the entry of plant diseases. Carriers and cargoes, mail, and baggage from for-

eign countries are examined for unauthorized plant material.

The plant material that is permitted entry into the United States is inspected for the presence of plant pests. The more hazardous of the plant propagating materials that are permitted entry are routed, upon arrival, for intensive inspection at specified locations where specialized facilities are available, both for inspection and for whatever treatment is required. These facilities are maintained at Hoboken, N. J. (in the Port of New York); Miami, Fla.; Laredo, Tex.; San Francisco and San Pedro, Calif.; Seattle, Wash.; Honolulu, T. H.; and San Juan, P. R. Certain designated kinds of plants are then released only for growing by the importer pending further observation for plant pests—particularly virus diseases—not detectible at the time of entry.

Not all importations are inspected with equal thoroughness because that would be too costly and, according to experience, unnecessary. The Department therefore places greater emphasis on the inspection of some classes of plants and plant products than on others (according to known or potential risk of entry of plant diseases) in order to afford the maximum degree of protection possible with the facilities available. The State plant quarantine agencies support the Department in connection with the postentry quarantine work by assuming the primary responsibility for the growing-season surveillance of imported plants held under postentry quarantine conditions. Certain States contribute materially to the entry control program at ports of arrival.

The Department itself makes numerous importations in connection with its program for improving field and vegetable crops, the horticulture, floriculture, and forestry of the country, and for kindred experimental and scientific reasons. These introductions, which may legally include material prohibited entry, are subjected to even more rigid control and safeguards on entry than are introductions by the public.

As to domestic commerce, the Act in some respects is more adaptable to the needs of a program for prevention of the spread of plant diseases because it gives the Secretary authority to embargo or regulate the movement of "stone or quarry products, or any other article of any character whatsoever, capable of carrying any dangerous plant disease," as well as authority to embargo or regulate the movement of nursery stock and other plants and plant products.

In a manner similar to the procedure prescribed in the field of foreign commerce, the Secretary may quarantine any State, Territory, or District of the United States, or part thereof, whenever he determines it is necessary to do so in order to prevent the spread of a new or not yet widely prevalent or distributed dangerous plant disease. He is directed, when public interest will permit, to provide by regulation for the inspection, treatment, and certification of the regulated materials in order to govern their movement from the quarantine area.

Unless the Secretary has issued a quarantine to prevent the domestic spread of a dangerous plant disease, the Act specifically provides that a State, Territory, or District may enforce a measure for the same purpose. The Secretary has discretionary authority also to cooperate with States to carry out their quarantine measures.

The quarantines and regulations governing the domestic movement of plant materials may be divided roughly into two classes—those governing interstate movement on the mainland of the United States and those governing movement between the off-shore territories and possessions and the mainland, or other off-shore territories and possessions. These domestic quarantines on the mainland are usually associated with disease control projects of the Department.

The States help materially in carrying out these projects, including enforcement of related intrastate quarantines. Further assistance in the domestic quarantine enforcement is derived from the inspection by Federal inspectors of shipments of quarantined materials moving interstate through traffic centers. Although the Act provides for such protection, practical enforcement problems resulted in lifting the only quarantine of the mainland for the protection of an off-shore area. Only three quarantines of off-shore areas exist which are designed for plant disease reasons to protect the continental United States; namely the quarantine (No. 16) of Hawaii and Puerto Rico on account of sugarcane diseases, and the quarantines of Hawaii on account of citrus canker (Nos. 13 and 75).

THE ACT also makes especial provision with respect to the District of Columbia in order that it may have a plant quarantine inspection service similar to that of the States and Territories. The Secretary of Agriculture is authorized to make regulations to govern the movement of plants and plant products into and out of the District "in order further to control and eradicate and to prevent the dissemination of dangerous plant diseases." This part of the Act also confers authority to compel an owner to take sanitary action in case of a nuisance situation to prevent the dissemination of plant disease.

HORACE S. DEAN, *a graduate of the University of Tennessee, entered the employment of the Federal Horticultural Board in Washington, D. C., as a plant quarantine inspector in 1923. Except for a brief period as a plant pathologist in Central America, he has worked continuously in the field of Federal plant quarantine, with special emphasis in later years on program administration. He is now assistant division leader of the division of plant quarantines, Bureau of Entomology and Plant Quarantine.*

growing

healthier plants

The Nature of Resistance to Disease

S. A. Wingard

We can get a double economic gain if we can introduce into our agriculture crops that are naturally immune to diseases and thereby avoid both the loss from disease and the cost of sprays and other ways of combatting disease.

To do that—as W. A. Orton pointed out in 1908—one has to know the problems of heredity, the nature of a disease, its governing factors, and the type of resistance involved in order to adopt the most promising lines of approach in breeding.

Disease resistance in plants is not an easy subject to understand. It involves the intricate relations between the plant—the host—that is being attacked and the fungus or bacterial organism—the parasite—that is doing the attacking.

The terms "disease resistance" and "immunity" can be used to denote different degrees of the same thing. Various degrees of disease resistance are possible. Immunity means complete resistance to disease; immune means not subject to attack by a pathogenic organism or virus.

We might consider other definitions here at the start: A pathogen is a parasitic organism or virus whose activity causes disease in the host. The host is a living organism that harbors another organism or virus that depends on it for existence. Pathogenic, the adjective, means having the ability to induce disease. A parasite is an organism or virus that lives on the tissues of another living organism. To inoculate is to introduce a micro-organism or virus or a material containing either into an organism, a culture medium, soil, or something like them. To infect is to invade an organism and to bring about infection. A suscept is an organism that is affected or can be affected by a given disease. Resistance is the ability of a plant to withstand, oppose, lessen, or overcome the attack of a pathogen. Susceptibility is the inability of a plant to defend itself against an organism or to overcome the effects of invasion by a pathogenic organism or virus.

Immunity is absolute. Resistance and susceptibility are relative: A plant is either immune or not immune to a pathogen, but it may be more or less susceptible or resistant. A plant may be "slightly susceptible," "moderately resistant," or "extremely susceptible"— but not "moderately immune" or "highly immune."

The ability of a susceptible plant to avoid infection because it possesses some quality (such as earliness of maturity) that prevents successful inoculation is called escape, or klendusity. Escape must be clearly distinguished from resistance. Tolerance is the ability of a plant to endure the invasion of a pathogen without showing many symptoms or much damage. A degree of resistance great enough so that no serious economic loss results (although there might be considerable invasion by the pathogen) is termed "practical resistance." Certain varieties of wheat, for example, for practical purposes are resistant to leaf rust— the rust causes little loss although the plants may become heavily rusted as they approach maturity.

We use the term hypersensitiveness to denote such a violent reaction of a plant to an attack by an obligate parasite (a pathogen that depends on living tissue for its nutrition) that the invaded tissues of the host are quickly killed, so that there is no further spread of infection. In essence, hypersensitiveness is extreme susceptibility, but its prac-

tical effect, as far as crop loss is concerned, amounts to extreme resistance. This type of reaction is common in cases of infection of many plants by rust fungi and some of the viruses.

The definitions help us avoid some wrong ideas about the nature of resistance and help us understand what can and cannot be done in plant breeding. For instance, a variety that escapes a particular disease is not necessarily a resistant variety.

William A. Orton long ago pointed out the differences between what he termed disease-escaping, disease-enduring, disease-resisting, and immune varieties.

He said: "Disease endurance sometimes results from the ability of the plant to grow in spite of an attack, either through exceptional vigor or through a hardier structure, as in the case of certain melons which better survive the attacks of leaf-blight because the leaves do not dry out as quickly as do those of the ordinary melons. Drought-resistant plants are often disease-enduring. Watermelons from semiarid Russia were for this reason the last to succumb to the wilt disease when planted in our Southern States.

"Finally, we have disease-escaping varieties. Such, for example, are the extra early cowpeas which mature before the season for wilt and root-knot to develop. These varieties which escape disease through earliness or lateness are often really very susceptible. The Early Ohio and other early potatoes, which commonly mature before the appearance of the late blight disease, are among the first to succumb to this disease if planted so late as to be still immature when the moist weather of the late summer or early fall enables late blight to spread."

E. M. Freeman, a professor in the University of Minnesota and one of the pioneers in this subject, pointed out that little difference exists in the real resistance powers of oat varieties to the common oat rusts, and when a grower is told that an oat variety is resistant because it usually escapes the rust through earliness of ripening, he is led into a serious mistake. The essential character of true resistance lies in a protoplasmic activity and is independent of inoculation accidents.

A variety may escape a disease through certain peculiarities of the host. To prove that, Dr. Freeman grew a variety of barley in different soils, which varied from the normal garden soil to those containing about 2 percent of alkaline salts. Plants in the different soils, inoculated by sprays in the greenhouse, showed different amounts of rust. Those in the stronger alkaline soils generally showed less rust. The latter, however, when attacked outside the greenhouse, exhibited large and vigorous growths of the rust. That was undoubtedly due to the greater development of "bloom" on the barley foliage when it was grown in the strong alkali; the bloom caused the drops of water to roll off and the inoculating material to be lost. The bluish color of the plants in the alkaline soils and the greater tendency of the water drops to run off were quite pronounced. There seems to be no reason for assuming that there was any difference in real resistance to rust.

The economic importance of disease-enduring varieties ought not to be overlooked by pathologists and plant breeders. Effective work in selection and breeding may be accomplished in the production of disease-enduring plants. Some of the best varieties of the hard spring wheats commonly used in the North Central States, for example, come under this class in regard to stem rust, since they do not possess any appreciable amount of resistance. They can endure moderate attacks of rust, but all go down in a heavy epidemic of rust. No sharp distinction may exist between disease-enduring and disease-resistant varieties, but for practical purposes well-marked resistance can be detected readily under proper experimental conditions.

Immune varieties have perfect resistance. Their production will probably always remain rare in comparison with those possessing only a partial resistance or high powers of endurance.

E. J. Butler of India in 1918 emphasized the importance of distinguishing between disease resistance and disease escape, between avoidance of disease and endurance of disease, between true immunity and resistance. He gave several instances of the way in which plants may avoid a disease to which they are not truly resistant. They may be grown in areas with a climate that the parasite cannot stand. (Many of our most important cultivated plants have a wider range than their parasites.) Or the date of sowing may be changed to a period when the temperature or humidity is unsuitable for germination of the spores of the parasite. Varieties may be grown that mature quickly before the parasite can do them much damage. Instances of successful endurance of plants to attacks of parasites involve mostly the vigor of the plants and can be modified by different methods of cultivation and manuring.

True resistance to disease is different from those instances in that it depends on some structural or physiological characters of the plant that prevent successful invasion of the parasite.

C. Brick of Germany in 1919 pointed out that susceptibility of plants to disease is not due to degeneration, old age, and such causes, but usually is the result of certain differences in the structures of the host itself. He believed that a higher content of acid, sugar, and tannin also has a bearing on the resistance of a variety to parasites. He said that some plants escape disease because their season of blossoming or maturing does not coincide with the development of the parasite.

DIFFERENT TYPES of disease resistance exist in plants.

To quote Orton again: "The typical form of disease resistance involves a specific reaction on the part of the host cell against a true parasite, a character developed in nature in the evolution of the species and strengthened in cultivated plants through the work of the breeder.

"Less important from the breeder's standpoint are plants resistant through (a) structural differences, (b) disease endurance, and (c) disease avoidance. The evidence indicates that the resistance is due to a specific protective reaction of the host cell against the parasite. So in plants the evidence leads us to believe that more is involved than the acidity of the cell sap or the chemotactic effect of sugars or other food substances.

"The first group is the most important, relating as it does to diseases due to the most highly developed parasites, such as the rusts, mildews, and other injurious fungi. The evidence indicates that the resistance is due to a specific protective reaction of the host cell against the parasite."

Orton was not sure that the reaction between host cell and fungus parasite in plants was the same as that described for some forms of immunity in man and the higher animals, in which substances in the blood serum neutralize the toxin excreted by the invading bacteria and assist in the destruction of the latter. He stated, however, that the evidence in plants leads us to believe that more is involved than the acidity of the cell sap or the chemotactic effect of sugars or other substances.

He said: "The delicacy of the reaction may be better understood if we recall the fact that it is adjusted to repel specific invaders. A plant resistant to one disease may be quite susceptible to another. General hardiness is also another matter. A plant may be resistant to cold and yet extremely susceptible to the attack of some parasite.

"Structural differences do not seem to play much part in enabling plants to resist the true parasite. Satis-factory demonstrations of cases where resistance to highly adapted parasites is due to thickened epidermis, development of hairs, etc., are lacking. It has, on the other hand, been shown . . . that germinating spores of fungi often penetrate the epidermis of plants they can not parasitize, and are killed forthwith by the cells they attack. It is hard to understand why a thick cell wall should protect from infection a leaf which has many thousand openings as breathing pores through which a fungus might enter. . . .

"Resistance due to structural causes does occur in troubles due to wound parasites, a fruit or a tuber with a thick rind being thereby less liable to bruising; as there may be an indirect connection, a plant of more open habit of growth being thereby less subject to attack by fungi which require moisture for their development."

Observations by other early scientists showed that mechanical immunity may have some significance in certain instances but cannot be accepted as a universal phenomenon; natural immunity does not depend on the anatomical peculiarities of plants, but on properties of their cytoplasmic cell contents and on active resistance of host plant cells, usually accompanied by a complicated physiological reaction in response to penetration by the parasite.

Other workers just as strongly contend that resistance or immunity in plants is due to morphological factors. Still others have confused the "disease-enduring" and "disease-escaping" varieties with resistant or immune varieties.

THE CAUSES FOR APPARENT RESISTANCE or immunity to a disease and tolerance to a disease are rather easily explained. But when we consider the causes for true immunity and resistance, we find ourselves involved in a maze of anatomical, physiological, biochemical, and ecological evidence and

1eories, which have been offered, 2me to explain specific cases of re-istance and the others to explain the roblem in general.

Before entering into a discussion of 1em, we should have in mind the 1ct that what we commonly think of s infection consists of two stages. The rst is the entrance of the parasite 1to the tissues of the plants. The 2cond is the establishment of para-itic relationship with the host. Some 1ngi, such as the rusts, enter many lants from which they cannot obtain ourishment and therefore perish be-ause they cannot accomplish the 2cond stage of infection.

One realizes, then, that immunity nd resistance may be due to the lant's morphological and anatomical haracters that prevent the first stage f infection or entrance of the para-ite into the tissues; or to biochemical roperties or anatomical characters f the tissues of the host, which prevent he second stage of infection or the stablishment of parasitic relationship vith the tissues of the plant.

Cases of immunity or resistance due 2 the anatomical characters of the ost preventing entrance by the para-ite are frequent.

Coffee leaf disease usually starts on he under surface of the leaf because here are few stomata—pores or open-1gs—on the upper surface.

Young beet leaves are practically nmune to attacks by *Cercospora beticola* ecause their stomata are so small as 2 be incapable of opening widely nough to allow for the entrance of he germ tube of the spores of the ungus which can only enter the host hrough the mature stomata.

Some varieties of plums resist brown ot caused by *Sclerotinia cinerea* because he stomata soon become plugged vith masses of small parenchymatous ells. The toughness of the skin, the irmness of the flesh, and high fiber ontent also are characteristics that nake varieties of plums resistant to rown rot. As ripening progresses, the exture of the resistant varieties re-mains firm, while that of the suscep-tible becomes softer.

The stomata of Kanred wheat, which is resistant to certain strains of *Puccinia graminis tritici*, are said to be of such a nature as to shut out most of the fungi. Wheat has a tendency to keep many of its stomata closed.

It may be that a secretion of the rust fungus makes the mechanism of the stomata inoperative and they re-main closed, thus excluding the fun-gus. In the Kanred wheat, which has smaller stomata, those peculiarities might be more effective in excluding fungi than in varieties of wheat with larger stomata.

The resistance of *Citrus nobilus* to citrus canker is due to a broad ridge over-arching the outer chamber of the stomata, which practically excludes water from them, thus preventing the entrance of the canker bacteria.

The resistance of some carnations to rust may be due to the type of stomata that make it impossible for the rust hyphae to penetrate the leaves.

The resistance of some varieties of barley to rust is due to the bloom—waxy coating—on the leaves, which keeps drops of water from adhering to them. Consequently the rust spores cannot germinate on them. The more waxy varieties of raspberries and grapes are less damaged than others by cane blight.

Mr. B. F. Lutman, of the Vermont Agricultural Experiment Station, after investigating the resistance of potato tubers to scab (*Actinomyces scabies*), re-ported that at the head of the resist-ant class stand the potatoes of the russet type and that thickness of skin determines resistance of tubers to scab.

The hairs on the leaves may in-fluence resistance of plants. Varieties of potatoes with small, hairy leaves and open habit of growth dry quickly after wetting and are less liable to infection by late blight than other kinds, but perhaps the open habit of growth (and not the abundant hairs) is the chief factor with such varieties. Some technicians believe that hairs seem to save the under surface of the apple leaves from infection with the apple scab fungus (*Venturia inaequalis*), while *Venturia pyrina* readily attacks the smooth under surface of the pear leaves. That belief, however, does not agree entirely with other observations in regard to the scab on apple. Frequently most, if not all, primary infection by apple scab is on the lower surface of the leaves. It is also a matter of common observation that the young fruits, while still covered with down, are very susceptible to scab.

The very hairy common mullein (*Verbascum thapsus*) is attacked by six leaf-inhabiting parasitic fungi, but only three are reported as occurring on the moth mullein (*V. blattaria*), which is free of hairs.

Variations of form or structure in certain varieties may influence susceptibility. As an example: Varieties of pears with an open channel from calyx to core are most susceptible to *Fusarium petrefaciens*, a fruit-rotting organism. The immunity to loose smut in barley has been attributed to the closed flowers found in the resistant varieties. In closed flowers the stigmas are not exposed to infection. The rare occurrence of ergot on wheat is said to be due to the brief and irregular openings of the glumes at maturity.

LET US NEXT CONSIDER cases of immunity due to incompatibility of the invading organism with the tissues of the plant—the failure of the organism to accomplish the second stage of infection, which is the establishment of parasitic relationship with the host.

The prevention of this second stage of infection sometimes is due to the anatomical characters of the host tissue. More often it is due to biochemical properties of the cells.

Examples of structural characters influencing resistance have been observed in plums attacked by brown rot (*Sclerotinia cinera*) and potatoes infected by tuber rot (*Pythium debaryanum*). Some varieties of plums be-

come more susceptible to rot when they begin to ripen. That is due to a softening of the middle lamellae between the cells, which allows the fungus to force its way through the tissues more rapidly.

In making a physiological study of the parasitism of *Pythium debaryanum* on the potato tuber, Lena Hawkins and R. B. Harvey, of the Department of Agriculture, found that the fungus secretes a toxin that kills the cells and an enzyme that breaks down the middle lamellae but does not affect the secondary thickenings to any extent.

They observed that White McCormick, a potato very resistant to *Pythium debaryanum*, has a higher crude fiber content than that of susceptible varieties. The higher fiber content they attributed to more secondary thickenings in the cell walls. Resistance to infection is apparently due to the resistance of the cell wall to mechanical puncture by the invading hyphae.

When we come to consider cases of immunity due to biochemical properties of the cells, we are confronted with many complicated theories and speculations, all of which support the theory that such immunity is due to a chemical interaction between the host and the parasite.

E. C. Stakman, of the University of Minnesota, in 1919 showed that resistance of some plants to rust is due to the dying of the cells surrounding the point of infection and the consequent starving of the obligate parasite. That is called supersensitivity, or hypersensitiveness. The cause has not been determined, but it might be of biochemical origin.

J. G. Leach, then of the University of Minnesota, stated that in a variety of bean highly resistant to anthracnose seldom more than one or two cells are attacked and that resistance seems to be due to the inability of the fungus to obtain nourishment from the living protoplasm of the bean.

Tannin, often found in vegetable cells, generally is toxic to fungi.

M. T. Cook and J. J. Taubenhaus,

of the Delaware Agricultural Experiment Station, pointed out that beans are more susceptible to anthracnose *Colletotrichum lindemuthianum*) during the stages of their growth when the enzyme that acts on gallic acid in the cells to form tannin is least abundant. In apples, pears, and persimmons, and other fruits, the enzyme is less abundant when the fruits are ripe than when they are green. That explains the lower resistance to rots in the ripe fruits.

Cook found also that tannin affects differently the various species of the *Endothia* fungus. It inhibits *E. radicalis* and *E. gyrose*. *E. parasitica*, the cause of chestnut blight, is retarded at first but later is able to feed on the tannin.

Acidity of the cell sap evidently plays some part in resistance of grapes to black rot (*Guignardia bidwellii*). Varieties that contain less tartaric acid in their cell sap show greater resistance to the rot than those containing greater amounts. *Botrytis cinerea*, a parasitic fungus, is repelled by certain acids in plant cells. The resistance of grapes to powdery mildew (*Uncinula necator*) also has been correlated with the acidity of the cell sap. The resistant varieties contain more tartaric acid than do the less resistant kinds.

O. Comes, an Italian investigator, has drawn attention to the fact that Rieti, a variety of wheat strongly resistant to rust in Italy, has a more acid sap than that of any of the other less resistant kinds he tested. The loss of resistance in Rieti when it is grown in warmer localities than its native area is correlated with reduced acidity of the sap.

M. Popp, a German scientist who investigated the hydrogen-ion concentration and natural immunity of plants, found that infections of pathogenic bacteria cause the plants to respond with variations of the hydrogen-ion concentration. Immediately after infection the acidity decreases. At the end of the incubation period the acidity rises. If the plant can withstand the infection, the acidity then falls back to normal. If the plant cannot withstand the infection, hydrogen-ion concentration rises to a high level and then falls, usually below normal.

Other cell contents seem to account for some types of resistance.

Biologic species of parasitic fungi are sensitive to minute differences in the amounts of albumin in host plants. Maybe that explains why some varieties are resistant to certain biologic strains and not to others.

J. C. Walker, of the University of Wisconsin, observed that the smudge fungus, *Colletotrichum circinans*, normally attacks only white onions and not those with red or yellow papery scales. But if he removed the colored scales, the colored onions then became susceptible to the smudge disease. Acting on the hunch that the pigments were associated with the resistance of the colored onions, he extracted the pigments with water and found that in the extracts the spores of the smudge fungus would not germinate normally. Nor would the fungus grow, although it developed normally in similar extracts of white-scaled onions.

The extracts of red and yellow pigments were analyzed later by K. P. Link and H. R. Angell, Dr. Walker's associates. They found the toxic substances to be protocatechuic acid and catechol. They discovered that the substances also protect the colored onions from certain other diseases.

H. N. Kargopolova discovered in Russia that the cell sap of wheat varieties immune or highly resistant to the leaf rust fungus *Puccinia triticina* was characterized by a high content of phenols similar to protocatechuic acid, while that of susceptible varieties was low or completely devoid of these compounds.

J. Dufrenoy of France has shown that in resistant plants the vacuolar sap of cells adjacent to those killed by the invading pathogen become rich in phenolic compounds. He suggested that such elaboration of toxic materials is an important factor in the resistance of the plant.

W. N. Ezekiel and J. F. Fudge, of
the Texas Agricultural Experiment
Station, explained that the general immunity of monocot plants to root rot
(*Phymatotrichum omnivorum*) is due at
least in part to the presence in the roots
of these plants of minute quantities of
acids, ether-soluble substances, and
possibly organic acids or esters. G. A.
Greathouse and his associates of the
Texas station have shown that the
resistance of several species of plants to
phymatotrichum root rot can be accounted for on the basis of their alkaloid content.

L. I. Miller, of the Virginia Agricultural Experiment Station, noted a
close correlation between the riboflavin content of the leaves of peanut
varieties and the resistance of the
varieties to peanut leaf spot (*Cercospora
arachidicola*). The lower the riboflavin
content, the greater the susceptibility
to leaf spot. No apparent relationship
existed between leaf spot resistance and
the amount of protein, ether extract,
ash, crude fiber, and nitrogen-free
extract of the peanut leaves.

Chemical disease resistance in plants
offers the biochemist a fertile field for
research, and in that field we should
search for the causes of disease resistance in plants.

WE MUST NOT REGARD the different
degrees of disease resistance displayed
by plants as fixed and absolute. Environmental factors modify them profoundly. In fact, growers often believe
that unfavorable rainfall and temperature are the direct and only reasons for the trouble. Temperature,
moisture, fertility, and reaction of the
soil markedly affect disease development. Light and the temperature and
humidity of the air also may be
important.

Other factors, such as the age and
maturity of the plant, may affect disease resistance. Thus the observed degree of susceptibility or resistance in
any case is a product of many inter-
acting factors of which the inherent
susceptibility of the host is only one.

The degree of virulence of the pathogen, the age and condition of the plant,
and the environment with its many
effects on both host and pathogen, all
must be suitable before maximum susceptibility can be expressed.

K. Starr Chester, of the Oklahoma
Agricultural Experiment Station, has
compared infection with the operation
of a complicated lock, every tooth and
tumbler of which must be in proper
alinement before the lock will open,
as the failure of a single correspondence
between lock and key will prevent the
act of unlocking, just so the failure of
any of the many factors required for
disease expression may entirely inhibit
the infection.

WE HAVE SEEN THAT PLANTS have
many types and grades of resistance to
disease. In certain types the resistance
is due to a reaction of the cells or tissues of the host to invasion by the
parasite.

It is natural, therefore, for us to ask
whether there is in plants a type of induced or acquired immunity, such as
is so important a factor in animal and
human pathology. A patient, for instance, recovers from scarlet fever; his
blood contains antibodies that destroy
the pathogen; he has acquired an immunity from scarlet fever and he will
not again take the disease. Also, his
blood serum may be used to prevent
or cure scarlet fever in other patients.
Once a child is vaccinated with the
virus of cowpox, a mild form of smallpox, he suffers a mild attack of cowpox,
and as a consequence he acquires immunity from the more virulent smallpox disease.

Do plants have the same ability as
animals and human beings to recover
from one attack of disease and thereby
acquire an immunity against subsequent attacks of the same disease? If
not, why not? Much thought has been
given to those questions. With the exception of some of the virus diseases,
however, we have little or no clear evidence of the development of acquired
immunity in plants. There appears to

be no good evidence of the existence of antibodies elsewhere than in the immediate vicinity of the site of infection by fungus and bacterial parasites. Because infection by the organisms is usually localized, only local immunization is apt to occur.

The organization of plants is much simpler than that of animals in the sense that each component part is less closely linked with the well-being of all the other parts and is less dependent for its functioning on them. There is no central nervous system and no blood or lymph streams. Every living part has or may have within it the capacity to regenerate the whole plant. Therefore we should not draw analogies between what occurs in animal disease (where any local disturbances or localized injury may have rapid repercussions on other parts) and disease in a plant (where an organ, such as a leaf or branch, may be lost with little or no effect on the rest of the plant).

The only cases in which it has been fully demonstrated that infection can lead in plants, as in animals, to immunity from subsequent reinfection occur in the most completely systemic plant diseases that are known—the ones that are caused by viruses.

The virus diseases of plants are much like the diseases of animals in that the virus can spread through the entire plant and infect all its cells. In several virus diseases a previous inoculation, or "vaccination," will confer immunity against a later attack, even when the second inoculation is with a much more virulent strain of the virus.

Tobacco ring spot is an example. Its virus produces many dead lesions on the leaves of young tobacco plants. If the diseased plants are protected and allowed to continue growth, however, the severe phase of the disease passes, and the new leaves show less and less evidence of disease. Finally leaves are produced that are entirely normal in appearance. If the leaves are inoculated with the ring spot virus, no disease will develop; the plant has thus acquired immunity from ring

spot. Cuttings may be taken from the recovered parts of such plants and from the cuttings new plants may be produced. The plants appear entirely normal and they are immune, as they cannot again be made to show symptoms of ring spot by inoculation with the virus.

These "recovered" plants, however, still contain the virus. If juice from one of them is inoculated into a normal plant, the latter will develop typical ring spot symptoms. This type of immunity, as in animal medicine, is specific. The recovered ring spot plant is immune to ring spot but not to other virus diseases, just as the person who has recovered from smallpox or has been vaccinated against it is immune to that disease but not to any other disease.

S. A. WINGARD *is head of the department of plant pathology and physiology of the Virginia Polytechnic Institute and plant pathologist of the Virginia Agricultural Experiment Station and Extension Service, Blacksburg, Va. He has devoted most of his time to research on the diseases of tobacco, beans, and tree fruits and for many years has been especially interested in the nature of disease resistance in plants. Dr. Wingard holds degrees from the Alabama Polytechnic Institute and Columbia University.*

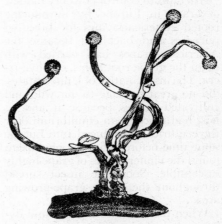

Ergot sclerotia producing sexual spore stage.

201500°—53——13

Breeding for Resistance to Disease

George H. Coons

In the botanical garden of the National School of Agriculture at Montpellier, France, stands a statue dedicated to Professor G. Foex, commemorating his success in saving the grape industry of France by resistant varieties from America. It symbolizes the spirit and aim behind man's effort to breed healthier plants.

The figure of the weak, old man in the statue represents the grape industry of southern France, about to die. Supporting and sustaining the man is a sturdy, young woman, America.

The statue commemorates the modern application of disease resistance as a control measure that began about 1870. The story of it has great meaning for us today.

Attempts to control powdery mildew of grape in Europe by introducing rooted American vines for breeding purposes had backfired because the American grapes had carried with them the grape root aphis, or phylloxera. The insect, native of United States, did no great damage to our wild and cultivated grapes because it and its host had reached an equilibrium over the centuries. Introduced into Europe some time before 1860, the phylloxera found the vinifera types of grape highly susceptible. Soon the insect spread throughout the entire grape-growing area.

When the vines were first found dying under attacks of the root aphis, the American varieties were remarkable in escaping injury. Attempts were then made to substitute the best American varieties to replace the dead vines. That was not satisfactory. Next, the old French vinifera varieties were grafted to the American varieties that had maintained vigorous growth despite the phylloxera. That procedure was more successful. It saved the grape industry until hybrids between the resistant or nearly immune American sorts and the French varieties could be bred to furnish better adapted, resistant stocks on which to graft the vinifera scions.

Powdery mildew, phylloxera, and downy mildew, introductions from the United States, revolutionized methods of grape culture in Europe. Some of the resistant stocks that were developed to meet the crisis still are being used wherever vinifera types are grown.

All that the statue at Montpellier tells. And more: It underscores the international aspects of the research program that seeks to control plant diseases by developing disease-resistant varieties.

That program has many facets.

Men the world over have searched within all species of crop plants subject to serious diseases and their cousins for breeding materials that carry the hereditary factors for resistance.

They have made worldwide collections of germ plasm and comprehensive assemblages of varieties and strains of crop plants and their related species.

The crop specialists have sought the wild forebears of the cultivated sorts at the places where the species presumably originated. They have combed the countries where the particular diseases are endemic in the search for strains and individuals which, through operation of natural selection, might have come to bear factors for disease resistance.

For experiments and tests of resistance, they have chosen sites where incidence of disease may be expected to be extremely high, the exposure severe and uniform, and other conditions conducive to efficient research.

All in all, then, breeding healthier plants is a long-time program whose many phases require diversified yet balanced, strong, consistent, and thoroughly coordinated efforts.

The research has to be international and national. It must also be regional in scope: Seasons have to be telescoped; tests of breeders' strains and selections under a range of disease exposures have to be conducted in many areas at the same time. Delays in producing seed and multiplying clones of desirable stocks must be avoided. Increases of seed for commercial purposes have to go forward promptly and efficiently.

Breeding for disease resistance has constituted for many years a major part of the Department of Agriculture's plant pathological program, in which the Bureau of Plant Industry, Soils, and Agricultural Engineering works in cooperation with State agricultural experiment stations, the seed growers, and farmers.

Outstanding results have come from the research. Among them are fundamental biological discoveries that apply not alone to plants and their reactions but shed light and afford new techniques for solution of problems of human and animal disease. They have added to our knowledge, especially to the concepts concerning man and his relations to his environment. They have had immediate practical significance. The disease-resistant varieties that have been developed and introduced have added greatly to our own wealth and to the wealth of nations.

An attempt was made in 1936 to appraise the contribution of disease-resistant varieties to American agriculture. The crop statistics and the dollar values of the 8-year average, 1928–1935, that were compiled then of course do not apply to today's farm production and values. But at that time the contribution to farm value for 17 leading farm and vegetable crops was placed at 10 percent.

In the years since 1935, the degree of disease resistance in the new varieties has been greatly increased, and many other disease problems have been put in line for solution by the introduction of superior types. The acreage of many crops has increased, and on the expanded acreage the disease-resistant varieties have gained wider and wider acceptance among growers. Almost revolutionary changes have occurred as old varieties have been replaced by new productions whose chief superiority derives from disease resistance. The acreage occupied by varieties for which it is proper to apply the term "disease-resistant" has moved from approximately 25 percent in 1935 to more than 50 percent. No small part of the increase derives from the almost total swing in many States to varieties of hybrid corn and to the popularity of newer kinds of wheat, oats, and potatoes. Very generally in the areas of greatest production the higher yielding, better adapted, and more disease-resistant sorts have replaced the old varieties.

If we want to put the benefit from disease resistance in terms of dollars, we may use the early, conservative estimate of 10 percent, which allows for seasons with lessened disease outbreak. But we must take into account the greater utilization of the superior sorts. We assume that about one-half of the acreage is concerned. Our total farm value of crops ranges from about 12 to 15 billion dollars annually. So we get a figure of 600 to 750 million dollars as the annual benefit that comes from the use of resistant varieties.

But the returns must not be based alone on the farm value of the crops, because that omits the marketing phase. In a farming area, if the farmers lose their crop or have a reduced production, those engaged in the processing, handling, sale, and transportation have their means of livelihood curtailed. With most crops, we are not far wrong in placing the contribution to the processing, packaging, marketing, and transportation industries as equivalent to that of the farm value—so that 1.2 to 1.5 billion dollars is the annual contribution to agriculture of disease-resistant varieties.

One more aspect: The utilization of disease resistance is not merely the stopping of leaks here and there in an otherwise profitable agriculture. The disease situation with our crops very frequently is serious and, almost without exception, control measures add to farming costs. The farmer, as he pays for fungicides and their application and as he employs other disease-control measures—such as sterilization of seed and soil—pays a heavy impost to the plant pathogens. Control of disease by use of a disease-resistant variety has been described as the "painless method" that does not levy on the farmer's pocketbook except as he has to pay for the care and harvest of a larger crop. As increasing crop production costs tend to make more and more crops marginal, the lessened expense for disease control may mean the difference between profit and loss from the farming business.

With some crops, notably the sugar plants, cereals, and potatoes, disease-resistant varieties may spell the difference between success and failure. Without the kinds resistant to curly top, western United States would have abandoned the culture of sugar beets, and this keystone crop would have been lost to irrigation agriculture. Without resistance to mosaic and root rot, sugarcane culture would have disappeared in the Sugar Belt of the South. The citrus industry must depend on trees reworked on resistant stocks if tristeza should develop in the United States at all comparably to its advance in Argentina, Brazil, and other countries. Wheat production has been threatened by a new race of the black stem rust, 15B, and new resistant varieties are imperatively needed.

The contribution of a disease-resistant variety includes other things. Improvement in yield and quality usually has accompanied the resistant variety as a result of better and more nearly normal growth or as intrinsic

improvement, irrespective of the factors of resistance. The farmer gives better culture to a crop that shows promise. Certainly the varieties that have gained ready acceptance and have moved into position of standards in our agriculture—such as Washington asparagus; Wisconsin yellows-resistant cabbage; the numerous wheat varieties; Bond, Victoria, and other disease-resistant oats; Michigan golden celery; the Robust bean; mosaic and root rot resistant C. P. sugarcane; U. S. 22/3 sugar beet, which is resistant to curly top; U. S. 215 x 216/3 and U. S. 216 x 226, the varieties of sugar beet that are resistant to leaf spot; Katahdin and Chippewa potatoes; and mildew-resistant cantaloups (to cite only a few)—all have had improved commercial quality and high capacities for yield, along with disease resistance. With the resistant varieties, even if the crop is somewhat reduced under epidemic conditions, there is certainly something to harvest which offsets labor costs of production—a striking contrast to crops of some of the old varieties that were not worth harvesting at all. Those intangible contributions—stability in rotation systems, permanence in the agricultural program of an area, and the increased security that comes from lessening of hazards in crop production—permit the farmer to plan with greater confidence.

ALMOST ALL of our cultivated plants trace back to primitive man. During the ages, as people wrested the plants from nature and conserved them, they must have improved them whenever disease outbreak retarded or eliminated the less resistant ones.

The early experiences in which resistant host plants were found in regions where a given disease or insect pest is endemic have shaped our thinking and forced recognition of the first and fundamental principle in breeding for disease resistance, namely, that where host and parasite are long associated, then in the evolutionary procss resistant forms are developed by natural selection.

Conversely, when an introduced parasite enters a new environment and finds new host plants, conditions may be conducive to its growth and spread; above all, the pathogen may find a host plant in which no resistance has ever been developed. Such plants are attacked with great virulence. Many of our serious outbreaks of plant disease trace to the introduction of parasites to which our nonresistant crop plants immediately succumb. Faced with such emergencies, it is almost axiomatic to apply this basic concept about host and parasite relations that came to light 75 years ago when grape culture in Europe was threatened with extinction.

WILLIAM A. ORTON inaugurated in the Department of Agriculture breeding for disease resistance as an effective and practical means of disease control. His investigations met the specific disease-control problems and gave the guiding principles to this branch of plant pathology. When Erwin F. Smith, famed plant pathologist and bacteriologist of the Department, had completed his studies on the pathology of the fusarium wilts of cotton, watermelon, and cowpea, he assigned to young Orton—fresh from the University of Vermont—the job of developing control measures. Each disease problem was solved by the application of disease resistance, but each crop required a different approach. To combat the wilt of cowpea, Orton utilized the natural resistance of an existing variety after his comparative tests on infested soil had shown the 'Iron" cowpea not only resistant to wilt but nearly immune to the root knot nematode.

Against cotton wilt, Orton employed methods that are operative today in all attempts to improve cotton varieties—the selection within desirable strains of individuals that survive under conditions of drastic exposure and the proving of the selections by

subsequent tests of the progeny. Cooperating closely with growers and a practical cotton breeder—E. L. Rivers, who had started some selections in 1895 at Centerville, S. C.—Orton centered his attention on fields of highest infestation with the fusarium wilt fungus. He subjected to further tests the progenies from the individual plants that were selected, because he soon learned that mass selection alone was not effective. In less than 10 years he produced many highly resistant varieties—Rivers, Centerville, Dillon, and Dixie varieties, each, in its day, a successful introduction that grew well where ordinary types failed and each a contributor of germ plasm for the use of cotton breeders to improve their varieties further.

In developing wilt-resistant watermelons, Orton had to go beyond just selection and progeny testing. Failing to find resistance in edible varieties of watermelon, he turned to the highly resistant citron melon, used only for feeding livestock, and incorporated genes for resistance from it into the "Eden" watermelon. Thus he synthesized a disease-resistant variety by hybridization. Those investigations antedated the rediscovery of Mendel's law, whose disciplines would have been extremely useful to the young scientist as he selected for desirable characteristics from the segregates in the F_2 generation. By further selection, Orton obtained the wilt-resistant watermelon, Conqueror, capable of giving good crops despite disease. In repeated tests in later years, Conqueror retained its qualities, and the problem apparently was solved, except, as Orton quaintly said, "styles in watermelons changed." Market demand for long melons of the Tom Watson type made the round type of melon unwanted. But the scientific contribution was there, and the genes from Conqueror still are used in research.

H. L. Bolley, another pioneer in plant pathological research, shares with Orton the distinction of bringing to the fore the possibility of meeting serious disease problems by resistance breeding. Bolley discovered in 1900 that flax wilt, most serious of all flax diseases, was caused by a soil-infesting fungus, *Fusarium lini*. Bolley added a new concept to plant pathology, namely, that of flax-sick soil—that is, soil infested with *Fusarium lini*. Bolley extended this concept of soil infestation to apply to other crops. He pointed out that greatly reduced yields below those of virgin soils and the so-called "running out of soil" might have a biological explanation. He used experimental plots, notably famed Plot 30, that were highly infested with *Fusarium lini* to develop resistant flax varieties: North Dakota Resistant 52, North Dakota Resistant 114, and Buda, and later, with O. A. Heggeness, produced the variety Bison, which is still in wide commercial use.

The investigations of Lewis R. Jones and his students, J. C. Gilman, J. C. Walker, and W. B. Tisdale, at the Wisconsin Agricultural Experiment Station, in breeding yellows-resistant cabbage firmly established disease-resistance breeding as a control measure. This wilt disease, caused by *Fusarium conglutinans*, had practically ruined cabbage production in the rich bottom lands near Racine, Wis.

Building on the work of Orton and Bolley, the Wisconsin investigators selected in 1910 some individual plants from fields sustaining an almost complete loss. Only a few of the remaining plants produced heads. The plants to serve as seed bearers were critically selected from them and brought to seed. Then the individual progenies were tested on highly infested soil. By this technique, yellows-resistant strains of Hollander type were obtained. Later, Walker and his associates produced yellows-resistant strains of other standard cabbage varieties. The results with the resistant cabbages were dramatic. The new strains gave almost a full crop where the commercial type failed. Before the work was concluded, resistant types, equivalent in quality and productiveness to any nonresistant

types previously grown, were made available to growers. This important vegetable crop was saved not alone for Wisconsin but for many other States where the disease had been introduced.

The work in Wisconsin stressed the influence of environment upon the parasitism of *Fusarium*. Soil temperature particularly was found to be highly significant in determining the ability of the fungus to attack and of the host to withstand the parasite. Here we have the beginning of the concept that disease resistance needs to be defined not alone in terms of the organism-host relation, but as well in terms that include the environmental conditions as they influence both host and parasite.

The work of W. H. Tisdale at the Wisconsin Agricultural Experiment Station with flax wilt developed that idea further. He showed why some varieties of flax resisted *Fusarium lini* only under certain conditions. Temperature relations determined the infecting powers of the fungus. Wilt-susceptible flax grown with soil temperatures below 60° F. escaped disease; grown at 68° F., it was completely susceptible.

By his experiments, conducted on a field that had grown flax continuously for a decade, H. D. Barker at the Minnesota Agricultural Experiment Station clarified a confused situation with respect to disease resistance by showing that resistance depends on the genotype and is not something acquired by mere association of host and parasite. The high incidence of infection in an experimental field at St. Paul, Minn., augmented by inoculation of the soil with pure cultures of the flax wilt *Fusarium*, allowed him to obtain clear-cut reactions with the resistant varieties then available. He showed that lines may be selected that breed true for resistance and that some lines are heterozygous. In his work we find the first research that indicated that the flax fungus itself breaks up into strains.

With the work on flax, cabbage,

omato, and other plants, the concept of strains within the pathogens analogous to what was known for the rusts became established. The success n breeding strains resistant to the soil-infesting vascular parasites of the genera *Fusarium* and *Verticillium* is impressive. Resistant varieties have been obtained for numerous plants, including aster, banana, cabbage, carnation, celery, chrysanthemum, cotton, flax, muskmelon, pea, spinach, sweetpotato, tobacco, tomato, and watermelon.

A basic thing in Orton's work with the wilt diseases was that he centered attention on fields with the highest disease incidence. With the watermelon wilt, Orton insisted on producing practically 100 percent infection in the test field. That he did by locating the tests in fields whose soil was known to harbor the fungus and by placing manure infested with the causal organism in the melon hills. He thereby subjected the plants to the severest of both natural and artificial exposures. In breeding techniques, disease exposures are of paramount importance.

ALTHOUGH in the breeding of rust-resistant varieties of cereal, the significance of biological races that exist within the rust species was given prominence from almost the beginning of the research, that concept, as we have seen, was rather slow in being recognized in the disease-resistance breeding programs with vegetables and certain other crops. The occasional failure of resistant types to meet disease situations eventually forced attention to the problem.

From the investigations of the cereal rusts and smuts, we have the most complete delineation of the problem to be faced in breeding for disease resistance—namely, the play of forces within the pathogen and the host, both living entities with inherent capacities for variation.

Writing in 1924, William B. Brierley, a British scientist, took note of the growing evidence of existence of biotypes within common species of parasitic fungi and pointed out that the true relation is between "host-strain" and "parasite-strain." That biotypes exist within our species of pathogens is now commonly accepted. Comparison of isolates on the basis of physiological reactions reveals the species to be composed of many subgroups that fall within the limits of the species, but differ among themselves; notably, this also is the situation with respect to pathogenicity. By means of the host plant and its varieties and segregates, it has been possible to demonstrate existence of a wide range of biotypes. The complexity of the disease producers, therefore, parallels that of the crop plant. We are thus concerned with the genetic make-up of the host and the parasite.

In seeking to explain the rather broad adaptation of resistant varieties as they were developed, some of them many decades ago, and their continued value in agriculture, we are led to another principle in disease-resistance breeding.

The first successes were obtained with a group of soil-infesting species. All had the characteristics of producing such severe disease exposures that only those plants survived that were truly resistant. Progeny tests conducted on the same soil eliminated the "escapes" and concentrated attention on truly resistant portions of the population. But in addition to those characteristics of the early experiments, the research was conducted in the field and against the full range of organisms that would be likely to accumulate in years of intensive agriculture. Thus we may suppose that a fairly large array of biotypes was included in the pathogenic material. A relatively high degree of resistance was sought and, as such, it would be likely to manifest itself similarly against most biotypes of the organism. Too often in subsequent research, similar breadth of exposures has not been sought, nor have criteria for resistance been high enough.

FROM THIS BACKGROUND and with such diverse plants as grape, cotton, watermelon, flax, tomato, and the cereals, a system of breeding has evolved. We have learned that wherever a serious disease has occurred in nature, plants carrying factors for resistance may be found, because without such qualities there would have been no survival.

From the research with *Fusarium*, we are taught to concentrate on fields having nearly total and uniform exposure to a given disease complex. The successful outcome may largely be attributed to the characteristics of the *Fusaria* to produce almost complete infestation. Thus the parasite cooperated by pointing out the plants to select and safeguarded against mistake. Should factors for resistance be lacking in the cultivated varieties, then we have learned to seek the genes in related resistant species and to incorporate them into the genotype. Already a body of knowledge has been built up concerning the inheritance of the factors for resistance.

Some form of inoculation procedure has commonly been found necessary as insurance that the work will not receive discouragement and setback by selection of individual plants that are mere "disease-escapes"—a bugbear in all such breeding. Here the plant pathologist, by learning how to create a localized epidemic in the experimental field, may make a highly significant contribution. Other logical steps along the course set by the pioneer research are the location of test fields at places where environmental factors are conducive to epidemic outbreak, the manipulation of cultural operations to increase disease exposure, the maintenance over the years of plots to insure heavy soil infestation, and other similar measures to insure maximum exposure to diseases.

We have learned the significance of the existence within both host and parasite of species of biotypes that differ with respect to their physiological reactions—using this term in its broadest sense. I cannot overstress the importance of this.

If the breeding is to succeed, if it is to have wide applicability and meet more than some restricted situation, and if it is to avoid disappointments, then there must be a utilization of the widest possible array of genotypes of both host and pathogen. The former could provide a broad base for selection and could provide genes for high resistance, and the latter could give as broad a base of exposure as possible.

How a crop plant may be tailored to fit a disease complex created by the multiplicity of biotypes within a pathogen is shown by research on wheat and oat diseases, as discussed in another chapter, page 35. Even though the parasites are on the move, and a once-prized variety may pass out of the picture because of a disease, a defeatist attitude is not warranted. Nevertheless, the facts are patent that unless the exposure encompasses about the ordinary range of virulence exhibited by the gamut of biotypes of the pathogen likely to be encountered, the resistant type as developed may be very restricted as to its area of adaptation and short-lived as an agricultural variety.

THE SUCCESS of these classic researches lead to the application of the principles and techniques with those diseases with which it was possible to produce high incidence of infection. The successful results of the investigations that stemmed from the early research constitute highlights of accomplishment. Subsequent sections of this Yearbook give, by crops, the results in detail. There has been extensive application of the techniques of disease-resistance breeding. My familiarity with the sugar-plant investigations leads me to draw upon them to show how it has been possible to broaden the scope of this method of disease control. These extensions fall into three groups: Breeding for resistance to virus infection, breeding for resistance to necrotic diseases, and the combining in one variety of resistance against several diseases.

CONTROL OF VIRUS DISEASES by breeding resistant varieties is well exemplified by sugarcane mosaic. When that disease was first definitely identified as the cause of decline of sugarcane production in the subtropical cane-growing districts of the Western Hemisphere probably no recent plant disease aroused more public attention. The early work of identification and clarification of the etiology among a welter of speculations and the discovery by E. W. Brandes at the Department of Agriculture that a plant-louse, *Aphis maidis*, is the vector are dealt with in another section. These discoveries came shortly after H. A. Allard's fundamental studies on tobacco mosaic had shown that insects can transmit virus infections. The first control of sugarcane mosaic was by introduction of mosaic-tolerant P. O. J. varieties from Java, where the disease had long been endemic. The P. O. J. varieties were introduced into Louisiana in 1926, when the sugarcane industry was about to fail. They stemmed the tide of bankruptcy and saved the industry.

Then began extensive breeding for the control of sugarcane disease in which lessons learned from experience in Java, where mosaic was endemic, were applied to the American problems. The research centered on hybridizing Java and Indian sugarcanes that derived their resistance from wild sugarcane, *Saccharum spontaneum*, with *Saccharum officinarum*, the noble cane. It was necessary to find a place in the United States where the sugarcane varieties would flower in order to make the hybrids and backcrosses. Canal Point, Fla., on Lake Okeechobee, was chosen for the experimental work. Then countless seeds had to be grown and progenies selected in the fields on the basis of agronomic characteristics. After this screening to obtain economic types, the seedlings that remained were subjected to a further winnowing process under severe exposure to sugarcane mosaic. Of the thousands of seedlings started in the first 10 years of work, only three—C. P. 807, C. P. 28/11, and C. P. 28/19—were introduced as economic varieties. These three and two importations—Co. 281 and Co. 290—became standard canes and were great advances over old varieties formerly cultivated.

The early breeding work at Canal Point was dominated by the need to find immediate replacements for D 74 and Louisiana Purple, old varieties that had failed because they were susceptible to mosaic, root rot, and red rot. The research was somewhat hit-and-miss. Beginning in 1928, a program of purposeful crossing, backcrossing, and selfing, accompanied by selection, was instituted. The plan sought to combine the favorable factors from two or more varieties of proved value into a single variety. The most important hybridizations have been those that sought to nobilize the interspecies crosses between *S. officinarum* and *S. spontaneum*, as well as *S. barberi*. These crosses have given rise to disease-resistant varieties that increased the unit yield several fold and are adapted to many soils and climatic conditions.

The success of the breeding program, which in essence has been the progressive nobilization of the resistant wild plant by application of genetic techniques while retaining its characteristics for disease resistance, is evidenced by the stream of disease-resistant, highly productive, and high-quality canes that have been introduced. Bearing in mind that the designation "C. P." denotes a selected sugarcane coming from the Canal Point breeding station, and that no cane could succeed under Louisiana conditions if it were not resistant to mosaic and other diseases, the census of varieties in use in Louisiana in 1951 showed that about 90 percent of the acreage was planted with disease-resistant C. P. varieties.

EQUALLY DRAMATIC in portraying the control of a virus disease is the breeding for the control of sugar beet curly top. With the sugar beet, it was not necessary to go to wild species of *Beta* for the genes for resistance because the commercial sugar beet as produced by European breeding was open-pollinated and extremely heterozygous. In the fields where curly top appeared early, every plant was affected. All but a very few resistant ones were rendered worthless, being curled and stunted. In those fields the complete and uniform exposure functioned to guide selections. Eubanks Carsner, Dean A. Pack, and others selected resistant individuals and by simple mass selection produced the first curly top resistant variety, U. S. 1. The variety was only moderately resistant; only about one-fourth of the plants in the population were resistant and the others were susceptible. In comparison with almost complete failure of commercial strains, however, it was outstanding. It offered hope to an industry about to quit and may be said to have held the line until more resistant strains could be bred by continued mass selection. The curly top resistant varieties scored a spectacular success and saved the sugar beet crop for western United States. It presents a second example of control of a virus disease by breeding for resistance to disease.

The early successes in obtaining resistant plants were confined mostly to the diseases in which the reaction between the host and pathogen was, as Orton phrased it, "very delicate." Such a highly specialized relationship would exist with diseases produced by the most highly developed parasites or with pathogens whose activities were intracellular. The rust fungi, together with the powdery mildews, and possibly the viruses, usually are considered as exhibiting the highest forms of parasitism. With them, therefore, we could expect that breeding investigations whose objective is to upset the relation of pathogen strain to host strain would be likely to be fruitful. The success in breeding varieties resistant to fusarium

wilt was with organisms belonging in the subsection of this genus in which the parasite invades the water-conducting vessels of the stem and induces systemic poisoning—a specialized form of parasitism. No cases have been reported in which resistance has been obtained against the Fusaria that cause necrosis of roots, stems, or leaves.

It is therefore of interest to consider diseases of the necrotic type to find if they offer possibilities for control by breeding. As I indicated, it has been more or less accepted that the general run of organisms such as *Sclerotinia libertiana, Sclerotium rolfsii, Phymatotrichum omnivorum, Fusarium solani* and its allies, *Botrytis* species, *Penicillium* species, *Rhizopus*, and others occur widely in nature as saprophytes; their invasion of plant tissue seems to be almost a function of the environmental conditions, irrespective of the host genotype.

The breeding work with sugarcane may be cited as contributing evidence that it is possible to make selections and obtain sugarcane types resistant to root rot and red rot, both necrotic diseases. As part of the regular screening procedure in selection of sugarcane seedlings, the plants are inoculated with red rot and are planted in fields where root rot is serious. Only resistant plants are considered for retention. In the newer sugarcane introductions, it is difficult to differentiate between resistance to red rot, root rot, and mosaic in their respective contributions to the success of the variety.

Investigations by John O. Gaskill of the Department of Agriculture indicate that resistance to rotting of sugar beet roots by species of *Botrytis* and by strains of *Phoma betae* may be found among sugar beet genotypes. In this study, Gaskill inoculated sectors taken from individual sugar beet roots, representative of various lines of breeding, with pure cultures of the fungi. The inoculated pieces were held in storage for more than 2 months under high temperature and humidity, which favor rotting of beet tissue. It was demonstrated that the sugar beet varieties differ in their resistance to decay organisms and that individuals within varieties also differ significantly among themselves. In the inoculation tests only a portion of the root was used for indexing for keeping quality of the mother root. The remaining portion was thus available for planting out if its record warranted its use as a seed bearer. Progenies of roots selected for superior keeping quality have been compared for keeping quality with parent strains, commercial varieties, and with progenies from roots that were very subject to decay. Replicated tests have shown that significant advance has been made by the selections.

Additional evidence that resistance against necrotic diseases may be obtained by breeding is given by the investigations with sugar beet leaf spot (*Cercospora beticola*). This disease has been controlled by disease-resistance breeding so that the U. S. varieties now introduced into districts subject to the disease do not blight despite epidemics of leaf spot. With the disease, however, resistance manifests itself chiefly with the younger and maturing leaves, but not so strikingly with the older and mature foliage. In comparison with susceptible varieties, the resistant plants show fewer spots on a leaf—often only flecks are produced—and the spots tend to be small and not confluent. Leaves of susceptible varieties become densely spotted, however, and shortly the leaves turn yellow and die. A plot of resistant plants next to a susceptible variety will be a green strip flanked by one that is dry and brown. The loss caused by leaf spot comes from the death of the leaves and the drain on the stored substance in the root brought about by the constant leaf replacement; resistant varieties retain their foliage to add to root substance, not to waste it.

Mass-selection methods, so effective in breeding varieties resistant to curly top, were not adapted for breeding for resistance to leaf spot. Even under epidemic conditions and with inspections throughout the season, resistant individuals within a variety were not readily recognized. No immune plants were to be found—only degrees of disease involvement—and the individual plants were hard to classify. Inbred strains of sugar beets, from earlier breeding work of the Department, were studied and of these a few (14 out of 250) were outstanding in resistance as compared with the others. The pedigrees of the outstanding strains revealed that they had been subjected to several selfings as against mass selection operative with less resistant lines. Accordingly, the entire leaf spot breeding program centered on inbreeding as the technique to segregate genotypes with leaf spot resistance. Inbreds, as they were obtained, were subjected to localized epidemics of leaf spot in the test fields, and selections among inbreds were made under conditions of drastic exposure.

After many years of inbreeding and intensive selection, inbreds highly resistant to leaf spot have been obtained. A few of them have enough vigor to be desirable as breeding stock. Continued inbreeding was found necessary to segregate the plants with adequate resistance, but vigor was lost in the process. The finding that hybrids made between certain inbred lines tended to regain productivity was exceedingly important. Although it is relatively easy to find hybrids that exceed in yield the mean of the parents, hybrids that exceed an open-pollinated variety in yield are hard to find. Very vigorous inbreds, when mated, give best possibilities for high productivity. Once highly resistant inbreds are found, the job resolves itself into production of a series of hybrids to determine the inbreds that give the best interactions.

As a result of the breeding for resistance to leaf spot, a number of varieties—U. S. 217, U. S. 200 x 215, U. S. 215 x 216, and U. S. 216 x 226—have been introduced. They and the varieties produced by research conducted by beet sugar companies now occupy essentially all the sugar beet districts subject to leaf spot and have accomplished such control that spraying or dusting against the disease is not necessary. The U. S. varieties in general are grown in Michigan, Ohio, Indiana, Illinois, Wisconsin, and in eastern Canada. Varieties of the beet sugar companies occupy the districts of Colorado, Nebraska, Wyoming, Iowa, and Minnesota. An outstanding inbred from this research is U. S. 216, a high-sugar type. It is a component of nearly all recent U. S. hybrids. In the production of sugar beet hybrids, male sterility introduced into one strain is used as a device to enforce the hybridization with the other strain that supplies the pollen. The beet breeder, to produce male-sterile plants, uses a special breeding technique to incorporate the genetic factor that makes a plant fail to produce pollen.

A HIGHLY IMPORTANT DEVELOPMENT in the breeding research with the sugar plants is the demonstration that it is possible to combine many desirable characteristics in one variety. In a way that had been foreshadowed when yielding capacity, high sucrose quality, and disease resistance were incorporated in one variety. It has already been noted that sugarcane varieties resistant to mosaic also could be bred for resistance to root rot and red rot. In the production of such strains, the job resolves itself to sorting out from the genotype complex those entities that manifest the desired qualities. Because of the polyploid nature of the sugarcane material, great diversity in biotypes resulted from the hybrids and the backcrosses so that there were many combinations from which to choose.

With the sugar beet, the possibility of finding within one variety factors for resistance against several diseases was first demonstrated with U. S. 15, a variety selected in experiments for curly top resistance in New Mexico. It was not so resistant to curly top as U. S. 22, but it had moderate resistance. It also had a high resistance to beet rust, *Uromyces betae*, and to beet

downy mildew, *Peronospora schachtii*. Futhermore, when planted in winter plantings in California it was nonbolting—that is, it did not go to seed the first, or vegetative, year—in strong contrast to other resistant varieties that tended to bolt in high percentage. The nonbolting character and the resistance to rust and downy mildew, coupled with enough resistance to curly top to meet needs with early-planted sorts, made U. S. 15 outyield others with which it was compared.

DEVELOPMENT of the sugar beet industry in the Imperial Valley of California is to be credited to U. S. 15. There the sugar beets are planted in the fall, the crop is grown during the winter months, and the harvest is in the spring. Under such conditions ordinary sugar beet varieties bolt. U. S. 33 and U. S. 34 proved to be entirely unsuitable. The nonbolting character of U. S. 15 made it especially adapted to the winter plantings. Its moderate resistance to curly top was adequate for the exposures to curly top that usually are encountered. In the San Joaquin Valley and coastal valleys of California it was possible to plant U. S. 15 in the winter, its nonbolting character again giving it advantage over other varieties. Winter plantings in coastal valleys are not usually subjected to curly top, but rust and downy mildew are serious. For those conditions, the resistance of U. S. 15 to both diseases was highly important.

Studies have been continued in California to combine resistance to many diseases and the nonbolting character in one variety. Already U. S. 56, a variety with more resistance to curly top than U. S. 15, has been released to replace the older variety.

More recently, U. S. varieties resistant to leaf spot have been intercrossed with U. S. strains resistant to curly top and then backcrossed. By repeated selections when leaf spot or curly top occurs, depending on the nature of recurrent parent in backcross, resistance to both diseases—essentially equivalent to that of the parents—has been combined in one variety.

The same general principle of combining in a variety resistance to more than one disease has also been applied to control of sugar beet black root in Michigan, Ohio, and Minnesota in sugar beet districts where both leaf spot resistance and black root resistance are requisites in a successful sugar beet variety. Since U. S. 216, an inbred resistant to leaf spot, had shown a considerable degree of resistance to black root, it was possible to use leaf-spot-resistant synthetic varieties and hybrids, in which U. S. 216 is a component, as source varieties. In fields where black root is extremely severe, these varieties were planted. In the series of selections from such stocks, adequate leaf spot resistance has been retained and at the same time advance has been registered in resistance to black root.

It has not been possible as yet to achieve immunity or near-immunity to disease in the breeding of sugar beets as with tobacco. Immunity from disease must ultimately be obtained if losses, which are considerable even with highly resistant varieties, are to be avoided. Growers in their enthusiasm when they see the contrast between a disease-resistant variety and the old susceptible type may minimize or overlook the loss that disease still causes. Probably the varieties resistant to curly top are as outstanding in their advantages over susceptible types as any that could be found, short of immune types; nevertheless, with the best resistant varieties, if exposures are severe, the reduction in yield may be as much as 25 percent of the potential were it possible to remove curly top as a factor. Similarly, varieties resistant to leaf spot make a profitable crop secure from crop failure, but the loss is still great over what could come from immunity.

Certain wild species of Beta—notably Beta patellaris, B. procumbens, and B. webbiana—are immune to both leaf spot and curly top. They produce F_1 seeds with Beta vulgaris that are viable, but the seedlings only grow a few inches tall and then die. By application of various techniques in breeding, and especially by use of a far wider range of biotypes of both the wild and cultivated species, it may be possible to introduce into the sugar beet the genes for immunity to two of the most serious beet diseases.

I have cited the sugar plants as examples of the extension of disease-resistance techniques for control of serious diseases. The investigations have required interspecies crosses when factors for resistance were not found in the cultivated species. Mass selection was effective with curly top, but to obtain resistance to leaf spot we had to inbreed repeatedly to intensify the factors for resistance, and then utilize hybrid vigor to get productive varieties. Male sterility has been used as a genetic tool to enforce hybridizations. Because of the breadth of its applicability, the demonstration that resistance to many diseases may be combined in one variety is exceedingly important. Sugarcane, representing polyploids, and sugar beets, representing heterozygous material, have been tailored to meet important disease conditions. Immunity to certain diseases now known for certain wild species of Beta offers possibilities for incorporation of those factors into cultivated beets. Those are goals for future work.

So FAR we have considered breeding for disease resistance from the point of view of its contributions, the techniques employed in obtaining disease-resistant varieties, and the more recent developments that have broadened the scope of this method of disease control. These manipulations of plant material have been made with only meager understanding of the cellular mechanisms and the reactions involved. It is not, however, a new thing in science for great basic forces to be manipulated with only imperfect knowledge of their nature or even of the basic principles involved. In the play of biological forces, we are often even more in the dark than with purely physical or chemical phenomena.

Our approach to the problems of disease resistance has had to be by trial and error because of the wide gaps in our knowledge of the physiology of both host and pathogen. But it may be of some value to summarize what we know of the causes of disease and to record the hypotheses that have been advanced as to the nature of disease resistance.

MANY PLANT DISEASES are caused by fungi that are known chiefly in their asexual stage. It has often been possible to find the sexual stage for a particular asexual stage, thus permitting classification of the pathogen as an Ascomycete or Basidiomycete. It is common for the fungus to be a pathogen in its asexual stage and for fruiting to take place on dead tissue in what has been termed the "saprogenic phase." Certain groups of fungi follow a common pattern of behavior. Thus the rust fungi, all obligate parasites, evoke a definite train of symptoms and frequently show the phenomenon of heteroecism, that is, two botanically unrelated hosts are involved in the complete life cycle of the rust. Some forms of smuts, after a period of semi-commensalism—eating together, as it were—within the developing hosts, may then completely occupy the inflorescence. Many smuts, however, show localized invasion and local tissue occupation. Among the plant pathogens the host-parasite relations range from a living together, through obligate parasitism, to rather simple necrotic processes. A classification which places obligate parasitism with conservation of the host as of high order and predatism as of low order seems generally accepted.

Plant pathogens may produce typical effects of underdevelopment. Others, such as the Exoascaceae, cause definite overdevelopment. The most common effects produced are necrotic lesions, the plant as a whole respond-

ing in various ways, depending on the physiological disturbance that may ensue. There is also generalized decay, which results from attack by bacteria or fungi on fleshy plant parts.

Sometimes an invading fungus may exert pressure in its penetration of the plant body and in its advance from cell to cell. A common histological picture is that of a cell wall pierced by a strongly constricted hypha, which enlarges when the cell wall is passed. Many organisms form an attachment organ, called an appressorium. As invasion takes place, a peglike structure passes into the plant. Through this structure the contents of the fungus cell flow; the penetrating thread enlarges to normal size or produces haustorial, or absorbing, apparatus within the cell. The cytological picture as the host cells are invaded is a movement of the nucleus toward the invading thread, followed by discoloration, dissolution of the cell contents, and eventual death of the cell. Certain specialized organisms occupy the vascular tissues and cause wilting and death by production of toxic substances.

The entrance of fungi into plants may be direct—through the unbroken epidermis or at points along the lines of juncture of epidermal cells. The entrance also may be through plant organs such as the stomata and floral parts. In lower types of parasitism the entrance is through wounds. There is also evidence that certain organisms kill in advance of penetration and move into the disintegrating cells.

The great German mycologist, Anton de Bary, showed in 1885 that *Sclerotinia libertiana*, the cause of a soft rot of vegetables, invades plants by means of a softening enzyme. L. R. Jones, in his studies at the Universities of Michigan and Vermont, greatly extended our knowledge on how parasites attack. He showed that *Erwinia carotovora*, the cause of bacterial soft rot of carrots, cabbage, and other vegetables, produces an enzyme that dissolves the cementing layer between cells, causing tissues to lose their form and structure. He called the enzyme pectinase and distinguished it from those that dissolve cellulose. Mancel T. Munn, in his investigations at the Michigan Agricultural Experiment Station, resolved the products of the onion neck rot fungus, *Botrytis allii*, into a pectinaselike enzyme and a toxic substance that worked together in rotting the onion. Such combination effects of an enzyme that dissolves the pectinlike substances in cell walls and a plant poison have been found to occur commonly with necrotic diseases.

Blackleg of potato, a bacterial disease caused by *Erwinia atroseptica*, has been considered by some to be a form of the *E. carotovora* soft rot. John E. Kotila and I in our work at the Michigan Agricultural Experiment Station in 1925 showed that the blackleg organism not only softens potato tissues but turns the cells black ahead of the softening. *E. carotovora* causes only a limited amount of softening and no blackening. Potatoes were grown in water culture and their uninjured roots were exposed to sterile filtrates from the blackleg bacillus cultures. The potato plants promptly turned canary yellow, matching the disease response frequently seen in diseased plants in the field. *E. carotovora* did not produce these effects. The two bacterial organisms therefore are alike in producing a softening enzyme, but only the blackleg organism produces the substance toxic to potato.

It is probable that effects characteristic of certain plant diseases on analysis will be found to come from the joint action of enzymes and toxic substances produced by the pathogens.

Death of cells is commonly attributed to toxic substances excreted by the invading organism, rather than to general effects such as plasmolysis or desiccation. Stimulation and other types of host response have been considered comparable to effects produced by minimal doses of plant poisons. The term "toxin" is avoided in referring to

these substances in order that analogy to toxins as recognized in animal pathology may not be implied. Some of the toxic substances are simple metabolic byproducts. L. J. Krakover, at the Michigan Agricultural Experiment Station, working with *Stemphylium sarciniforme*—cause of clover leaf spot—produced lesions on red clover leaves similar to those obtained by inoculations with the fungus, by pricking in filtrates from cultures of the organism. He obtained the same effects with ammonia solutions comparable in strength, as shown by Nessler reagent tests, to the filtrates. Erwin F. Smith, of the Department of Agriculture, in seeking an explanation of the mechanism of crown gall formation, attributed the effects produced by *Agrobacterium tumefaciens* to acetic acid and other chemicals arising from the growth of the bacterium. Smith suggested that they incite excessive cell division or remove natural inhibitors to growth of cells, which, in the normal plant, maintain a balance in cell division. He supported his hypothesis by experimental production of plant tumors by comparable chemical treatments in absence of the organism.

The vascular diseases caused by the Fusaria have received a great deal of study. It is characteristic of these diseases that the shoots of affected plants wilt. At first it was assumed that wilting came from plugging of the water-conducting vessels, comparable to what Erwin F. Smith had demonstrated with the bacterial wilt of cucurbits. R. W. Goss, at the Michigan Agricultural Experiment Station, demonstrated that if cut ends of potato shoots were immersed in filtrates of *Fusarium oxysporum*, the shoots promptly wilted. E. W. Brandes at Cornell University demonstrated the same thing for *Fusarium cubense* with buckwheat, bean, and banana leaves. That wilting comes from mechanical blocking was thus brought into question. Filtrates of ordinary saprophytes were shown to produce wilting. But the association of wilting with a specific *Fu-*

sarium is significant, because it enters the plant and there produces its toxic substances. More recently, Ernst Gäumann in Switzerland has extensively developed this field of research and attempted to relate it to antibiosis.

Plant pathologists, without excluding the possibility of complex organic compounds being involved, incline toward the point of view that the more simple compounds which are byproducts of fungus metabolism should first be explored in the study of toxic effects of fungi on host cells. Blocks in the respiration cycle are receiving attention as probable factors in disease production.

The defense mechanisms, if they may be so called, that are invoked in plants by infectious organisms appear to be relatively simple; the invader may in some cases stimulate the formation of corky tissues or may produce other growth effects. Automatic walling-off of the parasite occurs with hypersensitive varieties, in which invasion of the fungus is accompanied by prompt collapse of tissue. Thus the paradoxical situation exists in which hypersensitivity limits fungus extension to a mere flecking, and the most susceptible plants are the most resistant.

IT MIGHT SEEM simplest to explain disease resistance as an antagonism of the juices of the host cell to the parasitic invader. But antagonistic chemicals of host plants have mostly remained undiscovered—except for the catechol and protocatechuic acid in the red- and brown-skinned onions resistant to *Colletotrichum circinans* and *Botrytis allii*, as found by K. P. Link and J. C. Walker in their investigations at the University of Wisconsin in 1933. These chemicals are not found in the susceptible white-skinned types. But the chemical antagonism found by Link and Walker did not extend to all fungi, since *Aspergillus niger* could grow in extracts from the pigmented onions.

Plants, depending on how they are grown, vary in their resistance and in their chemical make-up. Furthermore, it is difficult to determine biochemical compounds, and so far there are no leads to relate any compound or class of compounds to disease resistance. Because of such obstacles, this field of research has remained almost unexplored. In the two decades since the discovery of resistance in pigmented onions, and the determination of the chemicals responsible, no additional information of parallel exactness has been obtained.

There is no accepted evidence of the production of antibodies in plants as a result of invasion by fungi. Localization in fungus attack, absence in plants of any circulating medium comparable to the blood stream, and the apparently simple chemical reactions involved in many of the lethal effects of fungi upon plant cells may explain why infected plants do not produce protective substances comparable to those known in animals.

Even with the bacterial organism, *A. tumefaciens*, which (on the basis of the type of cell division, presence of tumor strands, and the profound disturbances in cell morphogenesis) Erwin F. Smith considered as producing a plant cancer, it was not possible to demonstrate antibody formation. In Smith's tests, repeated inoculations of an individual plant did not bring about lessening of reaction.

The virus disease curly top furnishes some evidence of the production of protective substances as a result of infection. This effect differs from saturation phenomena known for tobacco ring spot and interference as known to take place between viruses. J. M. Wallace, working with curly top in the Department of Agriculture in 1944, inoculated tobacco and tomato plants by means of beet leafhoppers, *Circulifera tenellus*, which had fed on infected plants. The inoculated plants soon showed severe symptoms of curly top. Tomato plants did not recover, but many tobacco plants did. The leaves from such plants showed only mild symptoms in a few weeks. If healthy shoots of tobacco or tomato were grafted onto the tobacco plants that showed recovery, only mild symptoms were produced on the scions. The virus in the recovered plants was demonstrated to be highly virulent by insect transmission tests, but the symptoms produced were mild. When cuttings were taken from recovered plants of tobacco, or from tomato plants protected by the scion grafts from recovered tobacco plants, and these in turn were grafted onto tomato plants, the disease produced on the tomato was mild. Wallace attributed these results to protective substances against curly top developed in the respective tobacco and tomato plants in the course of infection. Once a tomato plant is protected, serial grafts give only a succession of mild curly top reactions, the scions taken from such plants serving as donors of the protective substance. If protective substances were to be sought, it would be logical to look for them with a systemic disease such as curly top.

We have considered so far entrance of fungi into plants, the mechanism of disease production, and the responses provoked. For the higher grades of parasitism, certain other essential requirements in disease production, namely, conditions for establishment of the organism within the host, are important. Suggestions have been made as to osmotic differentials which must prevail in host-parasite relationships. According to this, the concentration of the cell sap of the parasite must be higher than that of the crop plant, if the parasite is to take water from the host. No regularity in this respect has been found. To explain resistance of *Zea* to *Puccinia sorghi*, the hypothesis was advanced that susceptibility is determined by the presence of a relatively large quantity of a nutritive substance that attracts the fungus after penetration and makes possible abundant development of the rust. In resistant host plants, this hypothetical substance is present only in very small quantity; hence the fungus dies of starvation,

and that, in turn, leads to necrosis of the host tissue. It has been suggested that the slower development of the pathogen in a resistant host, as compared with abundant growth in a susceptible host, may be ascribed to a more favorable nutritive substance ratio in the latter.

In some investigations at the Michigan Agricultural Experiment Station, conducted with L. J. Klotz, I studied selectivity for host plants of certain species of *Cercospora*. *Cercospora apii* causes lesions only on celery and closely related umbellifers. It does not attack plants from other families. Diseased celery leaves gave strong nitrite tests, as compared with absence of nitrite in healthy leaves, indicating that breakdown of proteins and other nitrogenous compounds occurred. Now any of the species of *Cercospora* will grow readily and indiscriminately on cooked plant tissue, but with respect to living tissue they are very choicy. Furthermore, the pathogenic limits apparently tend to disappear as leaf tissue matures and cells are about to die. It does not seem that a parasite such as *Cercospora*, once it invades the cells, should have difficulty in appropriating water necessary for its growth. It seems probable also that the carbohydrates, such as sucrose, dextrose, or other sugars, and water-soluble substances exist in plants in much the same available state as in synthetic or cooked media. As a result of our investigations, we suggested that the nitrogen phase of fungus nutrition was particularly important and that the protein-dissolving enzymes that a given fungus has may determine its capacity for attacking a given plant species. •

THE OTHER SIDE of the picture also demands attention. How may the nutrition of the host influence susceptibility to disease? The factors that predispose a plant to disease have long been considered in phytopathology, but there has been more speculation than actual research. A well-nourished plant might well be expected to withstand disease better than one that is undernourished. But heavily fertilized plots frequently show more disease than untreated plots. A plausible explanation is that with heavier plant growth the conditions favor infection and the disease situation is aggravated. The literature is replete with experiences that seem to operate in reverse of anticipated results. For a number of virus diseases it has been shown recently that the predominating effect of added nutrients is to increase susceptibility.

Investigations in 1937 by F. G. Larmer, of the Department of Agriculture, on the phoma root rot of sugar beets gave some interesting results. *Phoma betae*, the causal organism, occurs rather generally in sugar beet tissue. The fungus is apparently seed-borne, and young plants may be killed by severe attack. Under ordinary conditions it appears to live in the beet plant without provoking any visible symptoms. If the sugar beet lags in its growth because of drought or lack of soil nutrients, the fungus may produce extensive and conspicuous decay of tissue. In the fall the fungus causes serious rotting of sugar beets in storage piles. Larmer found that well-nourished sugar beets, grown with adequate water supply, kept better in storage than sugar beets from the check plots that suffered from drought and poor soil conditions. The effects of plant food elements, especially phosphorus, were decisive. Sugar beets, grown with adequate phosphate, showed minimal decay as compared with serious decay in the sugar beets not receiving additional phosphorus. Inoculation tests were made with *Phoma betae* and showed that the plants grown with adequate phosphate definitely resisted invasion by the fungus, whereas the sugar beet roots grown with limited phosphate decayed. The practical applications of the experiments are obvious and afford an accessory advantage, besides crop increase, to be derived from appropriate applications of fertilizer. But the point to be stressed is that it seems definitely to be shown that plants whose nutrition was adequate, especially with respect to phosphate, were more resistant to *Phoma betae*. In recent experiments, adequate nitrogen nutrition has given improved keeping quality to sugar beets.

Black root of sugar beet has been found to be a disease complex, consisting of an acute form caused by the ordinary damping-off organisms and a chronic form caused by *Aphanomyces cochlioides*. Black root is most serious on soils of low available phosphate. Poor stands that result from attack of the soil organisms may be prevented by proper phosphate fertilization. A plausible explanation of the better stands that accompany liberal applications of P_2O_5 fertilizer is that phosphate makes the young sugar beet plants more resistant to the pathogens. The effect must be upon the beet, because abundant trial has failed to indicate any effects upon the fungi from comparable phosphate feeding. Black root control now is based on two things: First, the production of varieties that combine resistance to black root and to leaf spot; second, proper fertilization of the resistant variety with P_2O_5 and other necessary food elements. A favorable environment for the sugar beet increases the advantages that come from disease resistance.

The associative effects of nutrition and disease are not unique in phytopathology. Pronounced fungus invasion occurs with certain deficiency diseases—for example, the fungus rots or severe outbreaks of mildew that occur on plants short of boron. Existence of fungus disease does not of itself indicate malnutrition, but the association of disease and poor plant feeding is frequent. Sugar beet plants growing with scant phosphate show severe leaf injury following spotting of the leaves by *Cercospora beticola*, not because the leaf spot fungus is more aggressive but because weak parasites such as *Alternaria* can now invade and greatly enlarge the cercospora spots. The secondary attacks following leaf spot of this type do not occur with well-nourished plants. With many important plant diseases, the host-parasite relationships are very delicately balanced, and proper feeding of the crop plant may be highly important.

The nature of disease causation and of plant response may at first glance seem to contribute little to the practical problems of disease-resistance breeding. These seem to be moving along, with little reference to the theory. It is not unusual for practical applications to go far beyond the scientific explanation of phenomena—just as a driver may run a machine without understanding the mechanism or the source of power. But always in science the theoretical basis is the fruitful source of new concepts and new approaches.

We are concerned with the ways and means of the pathogen's attack and of the host plant's defense. With hundreds of thousands of pathogens, each composed of numerous biotypes, we cannot expect a single pattern of disease production or to find some specific substance that confers resistance. Thus, the theory is important in teaching what not to search for. The theory is important also in its teachings with regard to plant reactions. As I have brought out, disease exposure must be maximum, and knowledge of plant pathology must be put into service to initiate infection, produce disease, and finally to classify affected plants. The theory teaches also the specificity and delicateness of the interactions that exist between host and parasite, and the play of environmental factors as they influence these reactions. Thus light, temperature, length of day, nutrition, and the entire range of physiological forces are concerned. Plant response when subject to the parasite is the sum total of these effects. The goal of breeding for disease resistance is to manipulate host and parasite and the factors playing upon them in such a way that for a given environment disease-safe varieties may be provided.

The fungi, bacteria, and the viruses, each in its own specific manner, establish a food and water relation with the host plant. The invader may be tolerated; it may dwarf the plant or cause overgrowths or decay; it may kill the host. The tools the invader uses are enzymes and toxic substances; in considerable part, mere occupancy of the cells, appropriation of food, and the effects of the metabolic byproducts from the growth of the pathogen may be sufficient to explain the disease signs and symptoms.

Disease resistance as considered here is that which is of protoplasmic origin, as opposed to mechanical walling-off, escape, or other reactions than purely vital ones. We do not know at all what makes one plant less susceptible than another, nor do we know the basis of fungus specificity that makes one species, genus, or family of plants completely immune from a given parasite. Of the two hypotheses commonly advanced, antagonism (presumably chemical) and the so-called starvation hypothesis, the latter seems most tenable, with nitrogen nutrition appearing to be a significant phase.

Despite the common question posed by farmers, we do not know how to feed plants so as to make them more disease-resistant. Until recently, research along this line has been neglected. There are also strong indications that disease-resistant varieties may be made to do better by proper nutrition. The next decade may see important developments as the nutrition of our crop plants is studied from the point of view of plant disease control.

GEORGE H. COONS *was loaned in 1924 and in 1925 to the Bureau of Plant Industry, Soils, and Agricultural Engineering by the Michigan State College, where he was professor of botany, to initiate the research program of breeding varieties of sugar beet resistant to curly top and to leaf spot. After his return to the College, he continued as plant pathologist on a half-time basis with the Bureau until 1929, when he left Mich-*

igan State College to become principal pathologist in charge of sugar beet research projects in the division of sugar plant investigations. He received his undergraduate training at the University of Illinois, his master's training at the University of Nebraska, and his doctorate at the University of Michigan. After directing the sugar beet project of the Bureau for 23 years, he left administrative work to conduct research, particularly on virus yellows.

For further reading:
Breeding disease resistant varieties:
W. A. Orton: The Development of Farm Crops Resistant to Disease, U. S. D. A. Yearbook for 1908, pages 453–464.
L. R. Jones, J. C. Walker, and W. B. Tisdale: Fusarium Resistant Cabbage, Wisconsin Agricultural Experiment Station Research Bulletin 48, 34 pages, 1920.
H. L. Bolley: Flax Wilt and Flax-sick Soil, North Dakota Agricultural Experiment Station Bulletin 50, 58 pages, 1901.
G. H. Coons: Some Aspects of the Fusarium Problem in Plant Pathology and Physiology in Relation to Man, Mayo Foundation Lectures of 1926–27, pages 43–92, W. B. Saunders Company, Philadelphia, 1928.
Variability of fungi:
E. C. Stakman: Plant Pathologists' Merry-Go-Round, Journal of Heredity, volume 37, pages 259–265, 1946.
W. B. Brierley: The Relation of Plant Pathology to Genetics, Report of Imperial Botanical Congress (London) for 1924, pages 111–124, University Press, Cambridge.
Nature of disease resistance:
K. P. Link and J. C. Walker: The Isolation of Catechol from Pigmented Onion Scales and Its Significance in Relation to Disease Resistance in Onions, Journal of Biological Chemistry, volume 100, pages 379–383, 1933.
A. J. Riker: The Relation of Some Chemical and Physiochemical Factors to the Initiation of Pathological Plant Growth, Growth IV (Supplement), pages 105–117, 1942.
E. C. Stakman: Relation Between Puccinia graminis and Plants Highly Resistant to Its Attack, Journal of Agricultural Research, volume 4, pages 193–200, 1915.
J. M. Wallace: Acquired Immunity from Curly Top in Tobacco and Tomato, Journal of Agricultural Research, volume 69, pages 187–214, 1944.
Nutritional aspects:
F. C. Bawden and B. Kassanis: Some Effects of Host Nutrition on the Susceptibility of Plants to Infection by Certain Viruses, Annals of Applied Biology, volume 37, pages 46–47, 1950.
F. G. Larmer: Keeping Quality of Sugar Beets as Influenced by Growth and Nutritional Factors, Journal of Agricultural Research, volume 54, pages 185–198, 1937.

Some Sources of Resistance in Crop Plants

Frederick J. Stevenson, Henry A. Jones

We give in this chapter a list of crop plants and the diseases to which resistance has been found. Listed in order are the name of the crop, the disease (with the causative organism), the original source of resistance (O. S. R.), the present source of resistance (P. S. R.), and the mode of inheritance.

The abbreviation C. I. stands for Cereal Investigations—an accession number that, like a name, is assigned to a new variety of cereal grain.

In many instances the inheritance is reported as unknown or undetermined. Often the breeding behavior of the character for resistance is known, but the exact number of genes involved has not been determined. Some of the factors that make it hard to give a definite genetic explanation are multiple genes, polyploidy, physiologic races of causative organisms, and the effects of environment.

Write to your State agricultural experiment station for information concerning the sources of plant materials listed in this chapter.

For many diseases of crop plants there is still no known source of resistance. The search, however, is going forward steadily. If crop failures are to be avoided, new sources and higher levels of resistance to many destructive diseases have to be located. Undoubtedly many new sources of resistance will be uncovered in wild and cultivated species to be added to this already imposing list.

CEREALS: barley, corn, oats, rice, wheat.

BARLEY

COVERED SMUT, *Ustilago hordei*. O. S. R.: Jet C. I. 967, Ogalitsu C. I. 7152, Anoidium C. I. 7269, Kura C. I. 4306, Suchow C. I. 5091, Apsheron C. I. 5557, Hokudo C. I. 5176, C. I. 4308–2, and others in the barley world collection. P. S. R.: Same as preceding. Inheritance: Undetermined. Inheritance studies are difficult because it is hard to get consistently high levels of infection.

LEAF RUST, *Puccinia hordei*. O. S. R.: Bolivia C. I. 1257 and 100 to 200 additional varieties in the barley world collection. P. S. R.: Commercial varieties having leaf rust resistance often derived this resistance from the sources in O. S. R. Inheritance: Monogenic dominant in most crosses; an additional gene may be present in some varieties.

LOOSE SMUT, *Ustilago nigra*. O. S. R.: Pannier C. I. 1330, Jet C. I. 967, Anoidium C. I. 7269, Ogalitsu C. I. 7152, Kura C. I. 4306, Suchow C. I. 5091, Hokudo C. I. 5176, Apsheron C. I. 5557, C. I. Nos. 4308–2, 4326–1, 4327, 4329, 4967, and others in the world collection. P. S. R.: Same as preceding. Inheritance: Undetermined. Inheritance studies are difficult because it is hard to get consistently high levels of infection.

LOOSE SMUT, *Ustilago nuda*. O. S. R.: Jet C. I. 967, Trebi C. I. 936, Valentine C. I. 7242, Ogalitsu C. I. 7152, Anoidium C. I. 7269, Abyssinian C. I. 668, Bifarb C. I. 3951–3, Kitchin C. I. 1296, Afghanistan C. I. 4173, Suchow C. I. 5091, C. I. 4966, a number of hooded winter barley selections from Tennessee Beardless and Missouri Early Beardless, and other varieties in the world collection. P. S. R.: Resistant genes from some of these varieties now have been transferred to commercial varieties; for example, Velvon, Titan, Tregal, etc. Inheritance: Four resistant genes have been identified so far, two of which are

dominant and two are intermediate in effect. The smut gene in Valentine is closely linked with the gene for stem rust resistance.

NET BLOTCH, *Pyrenophora teres*. O. S. R.: Canadian Lake Shore C. I. 2750, Tifang C. I. 4407–1, Manchu C. I. 4795, Ming C. I. 4797, Harbin C. I. 4929, Velvet 26–95, C. I. 5084, and about 70 additional varieties in the barley world collection. P. S. R.: Partial protection to this disease now is present in some commercial varieties, which derived their germ plasm from barleys coming from Manchuria. Inheritance: Undetermined.

POWDERY MILDEW, *Erysiphe graminis*. O. S. R.: Duplex C. I. 2433, Hanna C. I. 906, Goldfoil C. I. 928, Arlington Awnless C. I. 702, Chinerme C. I. 1079, Algerian C. I. 1179, Kwan C. I. 1016, Psaknon C. I. 6305, Monte Cristo C. I. 1017, West China C. I. 7556, and many other varieties in the barley world collection. P. S. R.: Resistance to this disease is now found in several commercial varieties; for example, Atlas 46 and Erie. Inheritance: Nine dominant or incompletely dominant and three recessive genes for reaction to race 3 have been located.

SCAB, *Gibberella zeae*. O. S. R.: Chevron C. I. 1111, Himalaya C. I. 2448, Korsbyg C. I. 918, Cross C. I. Nos. 1613 and 2492, Peatland C. I. 5267, Svansota C. I. 1907, and Golden Pheasant C. I. 2488. P. S. R.: Same as preceding. Inheritance: Undetermined.

SCALD, *Rhynchosporium secalis*. O. S. R.: Turk C. I. 5611–2, La Mesita C. I. 7565, Modoc C. I. 7566, Trebi C. I. 936, and a number of additional varieties in the barley world collection. P. S. R.: Resistance to scald is present in Atlas 46, which was derived from the variety Turk.

SPOT BLOTCH, *Helminthosporium sativum*. O. S. R.: Oderbrucker C. I. 4666, Peatland C. I. 5267, Chevron C. I. 1111, Jet C. I. 967, OAC 21 C. I. 1470, Persicum C. I. 6531, Brachytic C. I. 6572, and others in the barley world collection. P. S. R.: The resistance in Moore is an example of the transfer of resistance from Chevron/Olli.

STEM RUST, *Puccinia graminis*. O. S. R.: Chevron C. I. 1111, Peatland C. I. 5267, Hietpas 5 C. I. 7124, Kindred C. I. 6969, and about 50 additional varieties in the barley world collection. P. S. R.: Several commercial varieties; for example, Mars, Moore, Kindred Feebar, and Plains. Inheritance: Monogenic dominant; an additional gene may be present in some varieties.

STRIPE, *Helminthosporium gramineum*. O. S. R.: Hannchen C. I. 531, Trebi C. I. 936, Club Mariout C. I. 261, Persicum C. I. 6531, Brachytic C. I. 6572, Lion 923, and others in the barley world collection. P. S. R.: Same as preceding. Inheritance: Six or more separate genes are involved and various degrees of dominance have been encountered.

CORN

BROWN SPOT, *Physoderma zeae-maydis*. O. S. R.: L87 and L87–2. P. S. R.: Same as preceding. Inheritance: Unknown; probably polygenic.

DIPLODIA EAR ROT, *Diplodia zeae*. O. S. R.: R4, C. I. 540, Ill. 90, P. S. R.: Same as preceding. Inheritance: Unknown; probably polygenic.

DIPLODIA STALK ROT, *Diplodia zeae*. O. S. R.: B14, B15, I159, L1, K166, K201, C103. P. S. R.: Same as preceding. Inheritance: Unknown; probably polygenic.

GIBBERELLA STALK ROT, *Gibberella zeae*. O. S. R.: C. I. 21E, K201, T8. P. S. R.: Same as preceding. Inheritance: Unknown; probably polygenic.

HELMINTHOSPORIUM LEAF SPOT, *Helminthosporium carbonum*, race 1. O. S. R.: Most inbred lines are resistant. Susceptible inbred lines are: Pr, K61, Mo. 21A, K44. P. S. R.: Same as preceding. Inheritance: Monogenic dominant.

NORTHERN CORN LEAF BLIGHT, *Helminthosporium turcicum*. O. S. R.: Mo. 21A, NC34, L97, Ky. 114, T13, C. I. 23, C103, Ky. 36-11, K175, K148,

and R39. P. S. R.: Same as preceding. Inheritance: Polygenic.

RUST, *Puccinia polysora*. O. S. R.: Little critical information available but in a greenhouse test inoculated when 6 weeks old, the following lines were resistant to infection: Hy, W22, 461-3, 38-11, Ohio 07, K148, T14, and C. I. 15. P. S. R.: Same as preceding. Inheritance: Unknown; probably polygenic.

RUST, *Puccinia sorghi*. O. S. R.: Little critical information available but inbred lines WF9, B2, C. I. 540, I. T. E. 701, and Ill. 90 have shown some resistance under field conditions. P. S. R.: Same as preceding. Inheritance: Probable polygenic; resistance to physiologic form 3, a monogenic dominant.

SEEDLING BLIGHT, *Pythium* species. O. S. R.: W23. P. S. R.: Same as preceding. Inheritance: Unknown; probably polygenic.

SEEDLING BLIGHT, *Penicillium oxalicum*. O. S. R.: Ill. 90, W22, Ohio 41, 38–11, W24, A375. P. S. R.: Same as preceding. Inheritance: Unknown; probably polygenic.

SMUT, *Ustilago maydis*. O. S. R.: Ind. 33–16, A321, and A. P. S. R.: Same as preceding. Inheritance: Polygenic.

SOUTHERN CORN LEAF BLIGHT, *Helminthosporium maydis*. O. S. R.: C103, Tr, G, M14, 0426, and W20. P. S. R.: Same as preceding. Inheritance: Unknown; probably polygenic.

STEWART'S WILT (late infection or leaf-blight phase), *Bacterium stewartii*. O. S. R.: K4, Ky. 27, C103, Ohio 28. P. S. R.: Same as preceding. Inheritance: Not fully known. Systemic phase apparently controlled by two major and one minor gene.

OATS

ANTHRACNOSE, *Colletotrichum graminicola*. P. S. R.: Early Red Rustproof, Red Rustproof, Saia, and Victoria. Inheritance: Unknown.

BACTERIAL STRIPE BLIGHT, *Pseudomonas striafaciens*. P. S. R.: Aurora, Coastblack, Colbert, Culberson, Fulghum, Navarro, Red Rustproof, Ruakura, Swedish Select, and Winter Turf. Inheritance: Unknown.

BLACK LOOSE SMUT, *Ustilago avenae.* P. S. R.: Black Mesdag, Bond, Landhafer, Markton, Navarro, Victoria, and many derivatives of preceding. Inheritance: Monogenic to polygenic.

COVERED SMUT, *Ustilago kolleri.* P. S. R.: Black Mesdag, Bond, Landhafer, Markton, Navarro, Victoria, and many derivatives of preceding. Inheritance: Monogenic to polygenic.

CROWN RUST, *Puccinia coronata avenae.* P. S. R.: Arkansas 674, Bond, Bondvic, Landhafer, Santa Fe, Trispernia, Ukraine, Victoria, and many derivatives of preceding. Inheritance: Monogenic to polygenic.

HALO BLIGHT, *Pseudomonas coronafaciens.* P. S. R.: Buck 212, Clinton, Coastblack, La Estanzuela, La Prevision, Navarro, Quincy Red, and Victoria. Inheritance: Unknown.

HELMINTHOSPORIUM LEAF BLOTCH, *Pyrenophora avenae, Helminthosporium avenae.* P. S. R.: Coker's B1–47–67, Coker's B1–47–79, and Wis. X279–1. Inheritance: Unknown.

MOSAIC, *Marmor terrestre* var. *typicum.* P. S. R.: Fulghum and Red Rustproof. Inheritance: Unknown.

OAT BLAST (not parasitic). P. S. R.: Alaska, Eagle, Fulghum, Hatchett, Kanota, and Lasalle. Inheritance: Unknown.

POWDERY MILDEW, *Erysiphe graminis avenae.* P. S. R.: Missouri 0–205, Missouri 04015, Neosho x Landhafer, Red Rustproof x Victoria Richland C. I. 4386, Sandhafer, and White Mildew Resistant. Inheritance: Trigenic.

PYTHIUM ROOT NECROSIS, *Pythium debaryanum.* P. S. R.: Black Algerian, Coastblack, Early Red Rustproof, Flughafer, Red Algerian, and Ruakura. Inheritance: Unknown.

RED LEAF (YELLOW DWARF), virus, no scientific name. P. S. R.: Anthony-Bond x Boone (C. I. 5220), Anthony-Bond x Boone (C. I. 5218), Anthony-Bond x Boone (C. I. 5224), Arkwin, Arlington, Atlantic, Bondvic (C. I. 5401), Fulghum 708, Fulwin, and Mustang. Inheritance: Unknown.

SEPTORIA LEAF SPOT AND BLACK STEM, *Leptosphaeria avenaria.* P. S. R.: Anthony-Bond x Boone, Ajax, Beaver, Branch, Clintafe, Clinton, Shelby, Spooner. Inheritance: Unknown.

STEM RUST, *Puccinia graminis avenae.* P. S. R.: Canuck (Hajira x Joanette), Clinton x Ukraine (C. I. 5871), Joanette strain, Richland, Victoria x (Hajira x Banner), White Tartar, and many derivatives of preceding. Inheritance: Monogenic.

VICTORIA BLIGHT, *Helminthosporium victoriae.* P. S. R.: Most varieties, except crown-rust-resistant Victoria derivatives. Inheritance: Monogenic.

RICE

BLAST, *Piricularia oryzae.* O. S. R.: Collections by the United States Department of Agriculture P. E. I. 13056 (C. I. 1344) from Formosa in 1905; P. E. I. 31169 (C. I. 1779) from the Philippines in 1911; and selections from commercial variety in the United States. P. S. R.: Available now as Zenith and Rexoro. Inheritance: Monogenic dominant (Sasaki).

BROWN LEAF SPOT, *Helminthosporium oryzae.* O. S. R.: Collection of United States Department of Agriculture C. I. 5309 from China in 1918 and local selection. P. S. R.: Available now as commercial types being developed. Inheritance: Polygenic.

NARROW BROWN LEAF SPOT, *Cercospora oryzae.* O. S. R.: Collection by United States Department of Agriculture C. I. 461 and C. I. 654 from 1904 exhibit of Philippine Islands at St. Louis, Mo. P. S. R.: Kamrose and Asahi. Inheritance: Monogenic dominant (Ryker, Jodon).

WHEAT

BLACK CHAFF, *Xanthomonas translucens undulosum.* O. S. R.: Unknown. P. S. R.: Thatcher and Marquis. Inheritance: Unknown.

BUNT, *Tilletia* spp. O. S. R.: Unknown. P. S. R.: Common bunt: Brevor, Elmar, Hope, Hussar, Martin, Newthatch, Oro-Turkey-Florence, Rex-Rio, and White Federation 38. Dwarf bunt: Brevor, Elmar, Hussar, Martin, Wasatch. Inheritance: Monogenic to polygenic.

FLAG SMUT, *Urocystis tritici*. O. S. R.: Unknown. P. S. R.: Golden. Inheritance: Unknown.

LEAF RUST, *Puccinia rubigo-vera tritici*. O. S. R.: Unknown. P. S. R.: Common wheat: Exchange, Frontana from Brazil (Ill. 1 x Chinese)[2]—Timopheevi (Wis. 245), Klein Titan, La Prevision 25 (P. E. I. 168732 from Argentina), No. 43 (P. E. I. 159106 from Union of South Africa), Rio Negro (P. E. I. 168687 from Brazil), Supremo, and Timstein. Durum wheat: Beladi (P. E. I. 57662–5 from Portugal), Golden Ball-Iumillo-Mindum, RL 1714, Tremez Molle (P. E. I. 56258–1 from Portugal), Tremez Rijo (P. E. I. 56257–1 from Portugal). Inheritance: Monogenic to polygenic.

LOOSE SMUT, *Ustilago tritici*. O. S. R.: Unknown. P. S. R.: Hope, Kawvale, Leap, Pawnee, and Trumbull. Inheritance: Trigenic and unknown.

POWDERY MILDEW, *Erysiphe graminis*. O. S. R.: Unknown. P. S. R.: Asosan (P. E. I. 155256 from Japan), Indian, Michigan Amber selection, Picardie (P. E. I. 168670 from France), Progress, Sturgeon, Suwon 92 (P. E. I. 157603 from Korea), Trumbull-Red Wonder-Steintim, C. I. 12559. Inheritance: Unknown.

SPECKLED LEAF SPOT, *Septoria tritici*. O. S. R.: Unknown. P. S. R.: Gladden, Nabob, and Nured. Inheritance: Unknown.

STEM RUST, *Puccinia graminis tritici*. O. S. R.: Unknown. P. S. R.: Common wheat: Egypt Na–95 (P. E. I. 153780), Hope, Kentana, Kenya 58, Kenya 117A, McMurachy, No. 43 (P. E. I. 159106 from Union of South Africa), Red Egyptian, Thatcher, Timstein. Durum wheat: Beladi (P. E. I. 57662–5 from Portugal), Golden Ball-Iumillo-Mindum, RL 1714, Tremez Molle (P. E. I. 56258–1 from Portugal), Tremez Rijo (P. E. I. 56257–1 from Portugal). Emmer:

Khapli. Inheritance: Monogenic to polygenic.

MOSAIC, *Marmor tritici*. O. S. R.: Unknown. P. S. R.: Butler, Chancellor, Royal, Thorne, Vigo. Inheritance: Unknown.

FIBER CROPS: cotton, fiber flax.

COTTON

WILT, *Verticillium albo-atrum*. O. S. R.: *Gossypium barbadense, G. hopii* (Lewton), and *G. hirsutum*. P. S. R.: *G. barbadense*, Tanguis from Peru, 1936, and American-Egyptian varieties; *G. hopii*, Moencopi, and Sacaton aboriginal; and Acala x Hopi x Acala crosses 1–9 and 6–1–26; *G. hirsutum*, Delfos 4–19, Acala 10–13, Acala 23–21, Acala 29–16, and Acala 4–42. Inheritance: Polygenic.

DAMPING-OFF, *Rhizoctonia solani*. O. S. R.: Acala 29–16. P. S. R.: Now available as Acala 29–16, line 64. Inheritance: Unknown.

ROOT KNOT, *Meloidogyne* sp. O. S. R.: Hopi, Moencopi, and Sacaton aboriginal strains, particularly the latter. P. S. R.: Acala x Hopi x Acala 1–9–56. Inheritance: Polygenic.

FIBER FLAX

RUST, *Melampsora lini*. O. S. R.: Variety Ottawa 770B. P. S. R.: Cascade, released in 1945, and Tallmune. Inheritance: Resistance is a monogenic dominant.

WILT, *Fusarium lini*. O. S. R.: Variety Ottawa 770B. P. S. R.: Varieties Cascade and Tallmune. Inheritance: Multiple factor.

ASTEROCYSTIS, *Asterocystis radicis*. O. S. R.: Variety Hercules, an introduction from Lincoln, New Zealand.

FORAGE CROPS: alfalfa, clover, cowpeas, southern legumes, soybeans.

ALFALFA

WILT, *Corynebacterium insidiosum*. O. S. R.: United States Department of Agriculture collections from Turkistan in 1898 (Turkistan) and north India in 1910 (Ladak). P. S. R.: Commercial varieties Ranger and Buffalo. Inheritance: Resistance is partially dominant, polygenic.

BLACK STEM, *Ascochyta imperfecta*. O. S. R.: Selected from commercial seed. P. S. R.: Clones in several breeding nurseries in Kansas. Inheritance: Several factors.

CROWN ROT, *Fusarium* sp. O. S. R.: Plant differences within strains. P. S. R.: Same as preceding. Inheritance: Unknown.

CROWN AND STEM ROT, *Sclerotinia trifoliorum*. O. S. R.: No clear strain or varietal difference. P. S. R.: Same as preceding. Inheritance: Unknown.

DOWNY MILDEW, *Peronospora trifoliorum*. O. S. R.: Plant and strain differences. P. S. R.: Same as preceding. Inheritance: Unknown.

LEAF SPOT, *Pseudopeziza medicaginis*. O. S. R.: Regionally adapted varieties. P. S. R.: Varieties Williamsburg, Narragansett, and Atlantic. Inheritance: Resistance is dominant.

ROOT ROT, *Rhizoctonia* sp. O. S. R.: Plant and varietal differences. P. S. R.: Same as preceding. Inheritance is unknown.

RUST, *Uromyces striatus*. O. S. R.: Mixed commercial seed stocks and varieties (Ladak). P. S. R.: Clones in several breeding nurseries in Nebraska. Inheritance: Multiple factors.

STEM BLIGHT and CROWN ROT, *Colletotrichum* sp. O. S. R.: Strain and varietal differences. P. S. R.: Same as preceding. Inheritance: Unknown.

YELLOW LEAF BLOTCH, *Pseudopeziza jonesii*. O. S. R.: Plant differences exist. P. S. R.: None.

DWARF. O. S. R.: Plant differences in commercial varieties. P. S. R.: California Common No. 49. Inheritance: Unknown.

YELLOW VIRUS. O. S. R.: Plant differences exist. P. S. R.: Same as preceding. Inheritance: Unknown.

PEA APHID. O. S. R.: Selections. P. S. R.: Selected inbred and hybrid plants are being tested. None available commercially. Inheritance: Unknown.

CLOVER

Several species of *Trifolium* are resistant to crown rot, *Sclerotinia trifoliorum*, and powdery mildew, *Erysiphe polygoni*, as reported in "Sclerotinia trifoliorum, a Pathogen of Ladino Clover" by K. W. Kreitlow, *Phytopathology*, volume 39, pages 158–166, 1949, and "Susceptibility of Some Species of *Trifolium*, and *Melilotus* to *Erysiphe polygoni*" by K. W. Kreitlow, *Plant Disease Reporter*, volume 32, pages 292–294, respectively.

LARGE HOP CLOVER

POWDERY MILDEW, *Erysiphe polygoni*. O. S. R.: Individual plant from a farm seed lot. P. S. R.: Resistant line in breeding material, North Florida Agricultural Experiment Station. Inheritance: Unknown.

RED CLOVER

CROWN ROT, *Sclerotinia trifoliorum*. O. S. R.: Slight resistance in some farm strains grown where the organism is prevalent. P. S. R.: Slight resistance in Kenland, Kentucky Agricultural Experiment Station; in Stevens, Maryland Agricultural Experiment Station; and in Pennscott, Pennsylvania Agricultural Experiment Station. Abridged list, Sanford, Virginia Agricultural Experiment Station. Inheritance: Unknown.

NORTHERN ANTHRACNOSE, *Kabatiella caulivora*. O. S. R.: Slight resistance in some farm strains grown where the organism is prevalent. P. S. R.: Highly resistant lines in breeding material, Wisconsin Agricultural Experiment Station; moderate resistance in Dollard, McDonald College, Quebec, Canada; some resistance in variety Ottawa, Dominion Experiment Farm, Ontario, Canada; abridged list, Purdue, Indiana Agricultural Experiment Station; and Midland, composite of selected farm strains. Inheritance: Unknown.

POWDERY MILDEW, *Erysiphe polygoni*. O. S. R.: Occasional plants of farm strains have moderate resistance. P. S. R.: High resistance in Wisconsin Mildew Resistant, Wisconsin Agricultural Experiment Station. Inheritance: Unknown.

SNOW MOLD (unidentified low-temperature basidiomycete). O. S. R.: Siberian red clover (source not known). P. S. R.: Siberian Red, Alberta, Canada. Inheritance: Unknown.

SOUTHERN ANTHRACNOSE, *Colletotrichum trifolii*. O. S. R.: Some resistance in most of the farm strains grown where the organism is prevalent. P. S. R.: High resistance in Kenland, Kentucky Agricultural Experiment Station; in Tennessee Purple Seeded, Tennessee Agricultural Experiment Station. Some resistance in Tennessee Anthracnose Resistant, Tennessee Agricultural Experiment Station; in Kentucky 215, Kentucky. Abridged list, Sanford, Virginia; Pennscott, Pennsylvania; Stevens, Maryland; and Cumberland, composite of selected strains. Inheritance: Unknown.

SUB CLOVER

POWDERY MILDEW, *Erysiphe polygoni*. O. S. R.: Unknown. P. S. R.: Seed originating in Australia. Inheritance: Unknown.

WHITE CLOVER

CROWN ROT, *Sclerotinia trifoliorum*. O. S. R.: Some resistance in some common white and Ladino stocks grown where the organism is prevalent. P. S. R.: Moderate resistance in lines of Ladino, United States Regional Pasture Research Laboratory, Pennsylvania. Inheritance: Unknown.

WHITE SWEETCLOVER

BLACK STEM, *Mycosphaerella lethalis*. O. S. R.: Some resistance in plant introductions from Turkey. P. S. R.: Moderate resistance in lines of breeding material, Wisconsin Agricultural Experiment Station. Inheritance: Unknown.

CROWN ROT, *Sclerotinia trifoliorum*. O. S. R.: Slight resistance in some seed lots that are grown where the organism is prevalent. P. S. R.: Willamette, Oregon Agricultural Experiment Station. Inheritance: Unknown.

GOOSENECK or STEM CANKER, *Ascochyta caulicola*. O. S. R.: Some resistance in seed lots. P. S. R.: High resistance in lines of breeding material, Wisconsin Agricultural Experiment Station. Inheritance: Polygenic.

LEAF SPOT, *Cercospora davisii*. O. S. R.: Some resistance in seed lot from Turkey. P. S. R.: Some resistance in lines of breeding material, Wisconsin Agricultural Experiment Station. Inheritance: Unknown.

ROOT ROT, *Phytophthora cactorum*. O. S. R.: Some resistance in some common seed stocks grown where the organism is prevalent. P. S. R.: Highly resistant lines in breeding material, Wisconsin Agricultural Experiment Station and Illinois Agricultural Experiment Station. Inheritance: Probably polygenic dominant.

SOUTHERN ANTHRACNOSE, *Colletotrichum trifolii*. O. S. R.: Some resistance in domestic seed lots. P. S. R.: High resistance in N-1, Nebraska Agricultural Experiment Station and in lines of breeding material, Wisconsin Agricultural Experiment Station. Inheritance: Unknown.

COWPEAS

BACTERIAL CANKER, *Xanthomonas vignicola*. O. S. R.: Brabham (Iron x Whippoorwill), Buff, Iron, Six-Weeks-Ala., Suwannee, and Victor (Groit x Brabham); *V. sinensis*, P. E. I. Nos. 152199 from Paraguay, 167284 from Turkey, and 186456 from Nigeria; *Vigna* spp. P. E. I. Nos. 158831 from Paraguay, 171985 from Dominican Republic, 182025 from Liberia, 124606 from India, 181584 from Union of South Africa, and 159210 from Union of South Africa. P. S. R.: Brabham, Buff, Iron, Suwannee, and Victor; P. E. I. Nos. 152199 from Paraguay, 167284 from Turkey, and 186456 from

Nigeria; and selections from Chinese Red x Iron and Blackeye x Iron hybrids available from the Division of Plant Exploration and Introduction, United States Department of Agriculture. Inheritance: Resistance is a monogenic dominant.

FUSARIUM WILT, *Fusarium oxysporum* f. *tracheiphilum*. O. S. R.: Iron, Clay, and Virginia Blackeye. P. S. R.: Iron, Clay, Calhoun Crowder (from Clay x Large Speckled Crowder), and Calva Blackeye (from California x Virginia Blackeye). Inheritance: Resistance is a monogenic dominant.

POWDERY MILDEW, *Erysiphe polygoni*. O. S. R.: *Vigna sesquipedalis* (Asparagus bean, Yardlong bean). P. S. R.: Selection from Yardlong x "Azul Grande" (New Era x Sugar Crowder selection) developed at Turrialba, Costa Rica. Inheritance: Multiple factor with resistance recessive. There are conflicting reports in the literature on mode of inheritance, which suggests the possibility of distinct races of the pathogen.

ROOT KNOT, *Meloidogyne* sp. O. S. R.: Iron, Clay, and Crowder. P. S. R.: Iron, Clay, Crowder (from Clay x Large Speckled Crowder), and Calva Blackeye (from Calif. x Virginia Blackeye). Inheritance: Unknown.

SOUTHERN LEGUMES

BLUE LUPINE (*Lupinus angustifolium*)

ANTHRACNOSE, *Glomerella cingulata*. O. S. R.: P. E. I. Nos. 167938, 167943, 168529, 168535 from Portugal. P. S. R.: Commercial types that are being developed. Inheritance: Unknown.

LESPEDEZA STIPULACEA

POWDERY MILDEW, *Microsphaera diffusa*. O. S. R.: Old fields of lespedeza. P. S. R.: Commercial variety Rowan is being released. Inheritance: Conditioned by at least two genes. One or more of these genes are linked with certain genes associated with flower color.

WINTER FIELD PEA (*Pisum arvense*)

ROOT ROT, *Aphanomyces euteiches*. O. S. R.: An imported pea from Puerto Rico. P. S. R.: Romack, a resistant variety available in limited quantities. Inheritance: Unknown.

SOYBEANS

BACTERIAL BLIGHT, *Pseudomonas glycinea*. O. S. R.: High resistance in P. E. I. 68521 from Manchuria, P. E. I. 68554–1 from Manchuria, and P. E. I. 153213 from Belgium; moderate resistance in Hawkeye. P. S. R.: High resistance in P. E. I. 68521 from Manchuria, P. E. I. 153213 from Belgium, P. E. I. 68554–1 from Manchuria, and N48–4860 (Haberlandt x Ogden); moderate resistance in Hawkeye. Inheritance: Multiple factor.

BACTERIAL PUSTULE, *Xanthomonas phaseoli* var. *sojensis*. O. S. R.: CNS (selection from Clemson, P. E. I. 71659 from China), FC 31592. P. S. R.: Lines from hybrid populations with CNS as one parent: N46–2566, N47–309, N48–1574, N49–2560, D49–772, D49–2524, D49–2477, S1–199, L9–4091, L9–4196, L9–4197. Inheritance: Resistance is a monogenic recessive.

WILDFIRE, *Pseudomonas tabaci*. O. S. R.: CNS (selection from Clemson, P. E. I. 71659 from China) and FC 31592. P. S. R.: Lines from hybrid populations with CNS as one parent: N46–2566, N47–309, N48–1574, N49–2560, D49–772, D49–2524, D49–2477, S1–199, L9–4091, L9–4196, L9–4197. Inheritance: Field resistance conditioned by resistance to bacterial pustule.

DOWNY MILDEW, *Peronospora manshurica* (3 physiologic races known). O. S. R.: Races 1 and 3 and moderate resistance to race 2: Chief, Dunfield, Manchu 3, Mukden, T 117; races unknown: Acadian and Ogden. P. S. R.: Races 1 and 3 and moderate resistance to race 2: Chief, Dunfield, Manchu 3, Mukden, T 117; races unknown: Acadian and Ogden. Inheritance: Resistance to each of races 1, 2, and 3 is monogenic dominant. Resistance to race 3 of Richland is conditioned by two genes.

FROGEYE, *Cercospora sojina*. O. S. R.: Adams, Lincoln, Anderson, Wabash, Roanoke, and FC 31592. P. S. R.: Adams, Lincoln, Anderson, Wabash, Roanoke, FC 31592, D49–772, D49–1633; Lincoln x (Lincoln x Richland), selections A6K–1011, A6K–1801, A7–6102, A7–6103, A7–6402, A7–6520, C 739, C 745, C 764, H 6150, L6–1152, L6–1503, L5–1656, L6–2132, L6–8179; Lincoln x (Richland x Earlyana), selections C 981, C 976; Earlyana x (Lincoln x Richland), selections C 996, C 997; Lincoln x Ogden selection C 985; Lincoln x (Lincoln x C 171) selections L8–10755 and L8–10780. Inheritance: Resistance is a monogenic dominant.

PURPLE SEED STAIN, *Cercospora kikuchii*. O. S. R.: CNS. P. S. R.: N46–2566 (S100 x CNS), N49–2560 (S100 x CNS), CNS. Inheritance: Undetermined.

STEM CANKER, *Diaporthe phaseolorum* var. *batatatis*. O. S. R.: Unknown. P. S. R.: Partially resistant: 6K–1521, 8T–812, 8T–1522, 87–1605. Inheritance: Unknown.

TARGET SPOT, *Corynespora cassiicola*. O. S. R.: Ogden, Palmetto, Tarheel Black. P. S. R.: Ogden, Palmetto, Tarheel Black, N47–3479, D49–772, and D49–2573. Inheritance: Undetermined.

ROOT KNOT, *Meloidogyne* spp. (soybeans attacked by five species). O. S. R.: Resistant to some species of nematodes: Palmetto, S100, and Laredo. P. S. R.: Resistant to some species of nematodes: Palmetto, S100, N45–3799 (Palmetto x Ogden), N46–2566 (S100 x CNS), N46–2652 (Volstate x Palmetto), and Laredo. Inheritance: Undetermined.

FORESTRY: American chestnut, American elm, European field elm, mimosa, white pine.

AMERICAN CHESTNUT

CHESTNUT BLIGHT, *Endothia parasitica*. O. S. R.: Asiatic chestnut trees, particularly the Chinese chestnut and the Japanese chestnut. P. S. R.: Outstanding strains are being selected from introductions by the United States Department of Agriculture from the Orient made between 1927 and 1932. Resistant hybrids between the Asiatic chestnuts and the native American chestnuts are being developed. Chinese chestnut trees, for nut production and ornamental use, are for sale by commercial nurserymen. Inheritance: Unknown.

AMERICAN ELM

PHLOEM NECROSIS (virus). O. S. R.: Field selections of American elm trees growing in central Kentucky. P. S. R.: Approximately one-half of the seedlings produced by the selected trees are resistant to the disease. Inheritance: Unknown.

EUROPEAN FIELD ELM

DUTCH ELM DISEASE, *Ceratostomella ulmi*. O. S. R.: European field elm, *Ulmus carpinifolia*, and variety, Christine Buisman, selected by Dutch pathologists. Imported from England in 1939 and released by the United States Department of Agriculture to nurserymen. P. S. R.: Christine Buisman. *Ulmus pumila*, the Siberian elm, is generally resistant. Inheritance: Unknown.

MIMOSA

MIMOSA WILT, *Fusarium oxysporum* f. *perniciosum*. O. S. R.: Seedling selections of *Albizzia julibrissin*. P. S. R.: Two clones released to nurserymen by the United States Department of Agriculture for propagation in 1951 as Tryon and U. S. No. 64. Inheritance: Unknown.

WHITE PINE

WHITE PINE BLISTER RUST, *Cronartium ribicola*. O. S. R.: Resistant strains of the white pine. P. S. R.: Resistant selections of white pine have been obtained and are being propagated

egetatively by rooted cuttings. In-
eritance: Unknown.

FRUITS: Apple, apricot, black-
erry, blueberry, cranberry, grapes,
uscadine grapes, peach, pear, rasp-
erry, strawberry.

APPLE

FIRE BLIGHT, *Erwina amylovora*. O. S.
.: Immunity has not been satisfac-
orily demonstrated. Somewhat resist-
nt commercial varieties include Deli-
ious, Arkansas Black, and Winesap.
nheritance: Polygenic; resistance par-
ally dominant.

APPLE SCAB, *Venturia inaequalis*. O. S.
.: *Malus atrosanguinea* (804), *M.
oribunda* (821), *M. micromalus* (245–
8), *M. prunifolia* (19651), *M. pumila
R No.* 12740–7A), *M. zumi calocarpa*,
ntonovka, and others. P. S. R.: Ca-
hay, Elk River, Kola, Red Tip, S. D.
onsib, Tipi, Zapata, and commercial
ypes now being developed. Inherit-
nce: Monogenic dominant in *M.
oribunda* (821); two dominant genes
M. micromalus* (245–38); three domi-
ant genes in *M. pumila* (R No. 12740–
A); probably one major dominant
ene in *M. atrosanguinea* (804), *M.
runifolia* (19651), and *M. zumi calo-
rpa*. Polygenic in Antonovka. All
ones listed are heterozygous for the
sistant genes as listed.

CEDAR-APPLE RUST, *Gymnosporan-
ium juniperi-virginianae*. O. S. R.:
rkansas Black, Delicious, McIntosh,
lacoun, Winesap, and Wolf River.
. S. R.: Same as preceding. Inherit-
nce: Monogenic dominant. Arkansas
lack and McIntosh are homozygous,
hereas others listed are heterozygous
sistant.

APRICOT

BROWN ROT, *Monilinia laxa*. O. S. R.:
ilton, Wenatchee Moorpark, Hems-
rke, and Hersey Moorpark are mod-
ately resistant. Moorpark and Peach
re most resistant. P. S. R.: Preceding
rieties and related seedlings. Inher-
ance: Unknown.

BLACKBERRY

DOUBLE BLOSSOM, *Cercosporella rubi*.
O. S. R.: Varieties Himalaya and
Rogers. P. S. R.: Varieties Brainerd
and Himalaya. Inheritance: Unknown.

LEAF SPOT, *Mycosphaerella rubi*. O. S.
R.: Varieties Evergreen and Himalaya. P. S. R.: Preceding varieties and
also selections from breeding work
of the United States Department of
Agriculture and the Oregon Agricultural Experiment Station. Inheritance:
Multiple factor with resistance partially dominant.

ORANGE RUST, *Gymnoconia intersti-
tialis*. O. S. R.: Varieties Evergreen,
Eldorado, Snyder, and Lucretia. P. S.
R.: Preceding varieties, as well as
Young and Boysen. Inheritance: Un-
known.

VERTICILLIUM WILT, *Verticillium albo-
atrum*. O. S. R.: The varieties Evergreen and Himalaya and clones of
Rubus ursinus. P. S. R.: Varieties Evergreen, Himalaya, Logan, Mammoth,
Cory, Thornless, and Burbank Thornless. Inheritance: Unknown.

BLUEBERRY

STEM CANKER, *Physalospora corticis*.
O. S. R.: Crabbe 6 selected from wild
type in North Carolina and selections
from commercial varieties. P. S. R.:
Varieties Wolcott, Murphy, Angola,
Crabbe 6, Adams, Scammell, Jersey,
Rubel, Harding, and all rabbiteye
varieties selected from wild. Inheritance: Resistance probably dominant.

STUNT VIRUS. O. S. R.: Unknown.
P. S. R.: Rancocas, in commercial use.
Inheritance: Unknown.

CRANBERRY

FALSE BLOSSOM, *Chlorogenus vaccinii*.
O. S. R.: Various selections from wild
cranberries in the eastern United
States, including the commercial varieties McFarlin, Early Black, and
Shaw's Success. P. S. R.: The preceding varieties and the recently introduced Wilcox variety. Hybrid selec-

tions are now under test by the United States Department of Agriculture and cooperating agencies. Inheritance: Resistance is actually klendusity, or escape, because the insect vectors do not feed on the plants. Klendusity is controlled by multiple factors.

Grapes

Downy mildew, *Plasmopara viticola.* O. S. R.: Black Monukka; Jaeger 70; certain selections of *Vitis rupestris*, such as Rupestris Martin and Rupestris Mission; *V. lincecumii;* several selections of *V. cinerea* Nos. 23, 24, 27, 45, 47, 48, and 54; *V. cordifolia* Nos. 15 and 29; and *V. riparia* Nos. 13 and 50. P. S. R.: S. V. 12–375, 12–303, 12–309, 12–401, 23–18, 23–657, S. 6768, 5813, 14664, 15062, and 12 named varieties are reported highly resistant. Inheritance: Multiple factor.

Powdery mildew, *Uncinula necator.* O. S. R.: Selections Nos. 23, 24, 27, 45, 47, 53 of *Vitis cinerea;* No. 15 of *V. cordifolia;* and varieties Rupestris Martin and Rupestris Le Reux of *V. rupestris.* P. S. R.: S. 6468, 14664, 9110, 11803, 15062, S. V. 12–303, 5–276, 12–375, 23–18, 23–410. Inheritance: Probably multiple factor.

Anthracnose, *Sphaceloma ampelinum.* O. S. R.: Selections of *Vitis cinerea* Nos. 23, 24, 27, 45, 47, and 54; *V. cordifolia* No. 15; and *V. riparia* Nos. 13 and 50. P. S. R.: S. 5455, S. V. 12–413, and 23–501. Inheritance: Resistance recessive, multiple factor.

Black rot, *Guignardia bidwellii.* O. S. R.: Selections from several wild species of *Vitis*, principally *V. cinerea*, *V. cordifolia*, and *V. rupestris;* selections of *V. cinerea* Nos. 23, 24, 27, 45, 47, 48, and 54; and *V. cordifolia* Nos. 15 and 29 have thus far been free of the black rot. Rupestris Martin, a rootstock variety, and Seibel 1,000, a French hybrid wine type, have shown no infection. In the literature Conderc Nos. 28–112, 175–38, 3304, and 162–97 are reported as immune, and 30 varieties are reported as highly resistant. P. S. R.: Preceding varieties and commer-

cial types now being developed. Inheritance: Unpublished data on several thousand vines artificially inoculated with the organism indicate that the resistance is apparently multiple factor with the very high resistance of *V. cinerea* strongly dominant in most crosses.

Muscadine grape

Black rot, *Guignardia bidwellii* f muscadinii. O. S. R.: Breeding selection of the United States Department of Agriculture. P. S. R.: Varieties Tarheel and Topsail. Inheritance: Multiple factor.

Peach

Bacterial spot, *Xanthomonas pruni.* O. S. R.: Unknown. P. S. R.: Varieties such as Hiley Ranger and Belle of Georgia. Inheritance: Multiple factor.

Powdery mildew, *Sphaerotheca pannosa.* O. S. R.: Unknown. P. S. R.: Eglandular type varieties. Inheritance Monogenic.

Root knot, *Meloidogyne* spp. O. S. R.: Mostly United States Department of Agriculture collections from India, China, and Turkestan. P. S. R.: Shalil, Yunnan, Bokhara, S–37, and some seedlings. Inheritance: Resistance is dominant; probably multiple factor.

Peach mosaic, *Marmor persicae.* O. S. R. (Here we are dealing with tolerance and not resistance). Many varieties of clingstone, such as Paloro Peak, Phillips, and Sims, and a few varieties of freestone peaches, such as Erly-Red-Fre, Fisher, and Valiant are highly tolerant. Most of the freestones become severely damaged. P. S. R.: Commercial varieties, mostly of the clingstone type, are tolerant. Symptom development is complicated by many strains of the virus. Inheritance: Unknown.

Pear

Stony pit, virus. O. S. R.: Bartlett pears are symptomless carriers, but the virus remains in the tree. Of the important varieties Bosc is one of the most seriously affected. The Waite variety is susceptible, and since this is probably a cross between Bartlett and another variety, it appears the symptomless characters are not dominant.

FIRE BLIGHT, *Erwinia amylovora.* P. S. R.: Immune, Richard Peters; highly resistant, Orient, Hood, and Pineapple; fairly resistant, Baldwin, Waite, and Ewart; slightly resistant, Kieffer.

RASPBERRY

ANTHRACNOSE, *Elsinoë veneta.* O. S. R.: *Rubus coreanus, R. biflorus, R. parifolius, R. kuntzeanus, R. albescens.* P. S. R.: Selections from breeding material of the North Carolina Agricultural Experiment Station. Inheritance: Multiple factor.

LATE RASPBERRY RUST, *Pucciniastrum americanum.* O. S. R.: *Rubus coreanus, R. biflorus, R. kuntzeanus, R. mirifolius, R. parvifolius, R. innominatus, R. lambertanus,* and *R. tephroides.* P. S. R.: Selections from breeding material of North Carolina Agricultural Experiment Station. Inheritance: Multiple factor.

LEAF SPOT, *Septoria rubi.* O. S. R.: *Rubus coreanus, R. biflorus, R. parvifolius, R. morifolius, R. wrightii, R. albescens,* and *R. innominatus.* P. S. R.: The varieties Dixie and Van Fleet, and selections from breeding material of the North Carolina Agricultural Experiment Station. Inheritance: Multiple factor.

RASPBERRY MOSAIC ESCAPING (resistant to aphid vector in United States). O. S. R.: Varieties Lloyd George, Herbert, Newburgh, and Newman. P. S. R.: Many commercial varieties including Washington, Milton, and September. Inheritance: Multiple factor with tendusity partially dominant.

STRAWBERRY

LEAF SCORCH, *Diplocarpon earliana.* O. S. R.: *Fragaria virginiana.* P. S. R.: Many commercial varieties, including Catskill, Midland, Fairfax, Howard 17, Blakemore, and Southland. Inheritance: Unknown.

LEAF SPOT, *Mycosphaerella fragariae.* O. S. R.: *Fragaria chiloensis.* P. S. R.: Many commercial varieties, including Fairfax, Massey, Midland, Southland, Howard 17, and Klonmore. Inheritance: Unknown.

RED STELE, *Phytophthora fragariae* (two races). O. S. R.: The variety Aberdeen in the United States, a chance seedling that originated in New Jersey, and Scotland No. 52 of the West of Scotland Agricultural Experiment Station. P. S. R.: The varieties Temple, Fairland, Sparkle, Redcrop, Pathfinder, and Vermilion, and the Scottish variety Climax. Selections from the breeding work of the United States Department of Agriculture and the Maryland and Oregon Agricultural Experiment Stations. Inheritance: Multiple factor with resistance partially dominant but complicated by several physiologic races.

VERTICILLIUM WILT, *Verticillium albo-atrum.* O. S. R.: *Fragaria chiloensis.* P. S. R.: The variety Sierra and selections from the breeding work of the California Agricultural Experiment Station and the California Strawberry Institute. Inheritance: Unknown.

GRASSES: Bahiagrass, Bermuda-grass, smooth brome, mountain brome, orchardgrass, slender wheatgrass, Sudangrass, tall fescue, meadow fescue, tall oatgrass, timothy, western wheatgrass, sand bluestem, side-oats grama blue grama, buffalograss.

BAHIAGRASS (*Paspalum notatum*)

Helminthosporium sativum. O. S. R.: Collection of United States Department of Agriculture, P. E. I. 148966, which was collected in Argentina. P. S. R.: Argentina Bahia. Inheritance: Unknown.

BERMUDA-GRASS (*Cynodon dactylon*)

Helminthosporium cynodontis. O. S. R.: Collection of United States Department of Agriculture, which was collected in South Africa, P. E. I. 105933 and 105935. P. S. R.: Coastal Bermuda. Inheritance: Probably multiple factor.

SMOOTH BROME (*Bromus inermis*)

BROWN SPOT, *Pyrenophora bromi*. O. S. R.: Plant selected from Nebraska 39–3400. P. S. R.: Has not been increased. Inheritance: Unknown.

MOUNTAIN BROME (*Bromus marginatus*)

HEAD SMUT, *Ustilago bullata*. O. S. R.: Seed collections at Pullman, Wash. P. S. R.: Bromar Mountain bromegrass. Inheritance: Unknown.

ORCHARDGRASS (*Dactylis glomerata*)

LEAF STREAK, *Scolecotrichum graminis*. O. S. R.: One plant selected in old field near Taneytown, Md., and one plant from S. C. S. 7060. P. S. R.: Preceding selections have not been increased. Inheritance: Unknown.

SLENDER WHEATGRASS (*Agropyron trachycaulum*)

HEAD SMUT, *Ustilago bullata*. O. S. R.: Canadian collection from Alberta. P. S. R.: Commercial variety Fyra. Inheritance: Unknown.
LEAF RUST, *Puccinia rubigo-vera*. O. S. R.: Forest Service collection near Beebe, Mont., in 1933. P. S. R.: Commercial variety Primar. Inheritance: Unknown.
STRIPE RUST, *Puccinia glumarum*. O. S. R.: Single plant collection in Saskatchewan, Canada, in 1923. P. S. R.: Commercial variety Mecca. Inheritance: Unknown.
STEM RUST, *Puccinia graminis*. O. S. R.: Canadian collection in Alberta. P. S. R.: Commercial variety Fyra. Inheritance: Unknown.

SUDANGRASS (*Sorghum vulgare* var. *sudanense*)

Pseudomonas andropogoni. O. S. R.: Leoti sorghum. P. S. R.: Tift Sudan.

Inheritance: Probably multiple factor
ANTHRACNOSE (*Colletotrichum graminicola*). O. S. R.: Leoti and other varieties of sorghum of similar resistance P. S. R.: Varieties Sweet, Piper, and Tift. Inheritance: Probably multiple factor.
Gloeocercospora sorghi. O. S. R.: Leoti sorghum. P. S. R.: Tift Sudan. Inheritance: Probably multiple factor.
LEAF BLIGHT, *Helminthosporium turcicum*. O. S. R.: Leoti and other varieties of sorghum of similar resistance. P. S. R.: Varieties Sweet, Piper and Tift. Inheritance: Probably multiple factor.

TALL FESCUE (*Festuca arundinacea*)

CROWN RUST, *Puccinia coronata*. O. S R.: Plant selection in 4-year-old planting of tall fescue at Corvallis Oreg. P. S. R.: Alta fescue. Inheritance: Unknown.

MEADOW FESCUE (*Festuca elatior*)

CROWN RUST, *Puccinia coronata*. O. S R.: Two plants selected from old field in Maine. P. S. R.: Selections have not been increased. Inheritance: Multiple factors.

TALL OATGRASS (*Arrhenatherum elatius*)

LEAF SMUT, *Puccinia rubigo-vera*. O. S R.: Varieties Tualatin and S. C. S. nonshattering. P. S. R.: Tualatin and S. C. S. nonshattering have not been increased. Inheritance: Unknown.

TIMOTHY (*Phleum pratense*)

STEM RUST, *Puccinia graminis*. O. S R.: Minnesota 79 and 81, Svalov 523 Cornell 1676, and F. C. 12468 Ohio P. S. R.: Varieties Milton and Manetta. Inheritance: Monogenic dominant.

WESTERN WHEATGRASS (*Agropyron smithii*)

RUST, *Puccinia rubigo-vera*. O. S. R. Some selected individuals appear to be resistant. P. S. R.: Same as preceding. Inheritance: Unknown.

SAND BLUESTEM (*Andropogon hallii*)

RUST, *Puccinia* sp. O. S. R.: Selected native strains. P. S. R.: Strain W2 contains many resistant plants in the population. Inheritance: Unknown.

SIDE-OATS GRAMA (*Bouteloua curtipendula*)

RUST, *Puccinia vexans*. O. S. R.: Individual plants in sexual populations. Most of the apomictic strains have some resistance also. P. S. R.: Tucson variety released; Hope and Encinoso, not released. Inheritance: Probably one or two factors in sexual types. Inheritance in apomicts unknown.

BLUE GRAMA (*Bouteloua gracilis*)

RUST, *Puccinia vexans*. O. S. R.: Individual plants in segregating populations. P. S. R.: Commercial types are being developed. Inheritance: Probably multiple factor.

BUFFALOGRASS (*Buchloë dactyloides*)

LEAF SPOT, *Helminthosporium inconspicuum*. O. S. R.: Individual plants in selected populations. P. S. R.: In breeding stock. Inheritance: Unknown.
RUST, *Puccinia kansensis*. O. S. R.: Individual plants in segregating populations. P. S. R.: In breeding stock. Inheritance: Unknown.

HOPS

DOWNY MILDEW, *Pseudoperonospora humuli*. O. S. R.: Chance seedling obtained in flower garden, Horsmonden, Kent, England, in 1861. P. S. R.: Fuggles and a number of related seedlings. Inheritance: Undetermined.

NUTS: Chinese chestnut, filbert, pecan, Persian (English) walnut, eastern black walnut.

CHINESE CHESTNUT

CHESTNUT BLIGHT, *Endothia parasitica*. O. S. R.: Most varieties and seedlings are highly resistant. P. S. R.: Varieties and seedlings.
PHYTOPHTHORA ROOT DISEASE, *Phytophthora cinnamomi*. O. S. R.: Most varieties and seedlings are highly resistant. P. S. R.: Most varieties and seedlings.
TWIG CANKER, *Cryptodiaporthe castanea*. O. S. R.: All varieties and seedlings are resistant when grown on proper sites. P. S. R.: All varieties and seedlings.
TWIG CANKER, *Botryosphaeria ribis chromogena*. O. S. R.: All varieties and seedlings are resistant when grown on proper sites. P. S. R.: All varieties and seedlings.

FILBERT

FILBERT BACTERIAL BLIGHT, *Xanthomonas corylina*. O. S. R.: No immunity. Daviana and Bolwyller are most resistant in the Pacific Northwest. These came from seedlings from a mixed population. P. S. R.: Preceding varieties. Inheritance: Unknown.
LABRELLA LEAF SPOT, *Labrella coryli*. O. S. R.: Variety Potomac shows some resistance. P. S. R.: Potomac.

PECAN

SCAB, *Cladosporium effusum*. O. S. R.: Varieties Stuart and Curtis are highly resistant. P. S. R.: Stuart and Curtis varieties.
BUNCH DISEASE, or WITCHES'-BROOM, virus. O. S. R.: Great difference in varieties; Schley and Mahan most susceptible. Stuart resistant or symptomless carrier. P. S. R.: Stuart.
DOWNY SPOT, *Mycosphaerella caryigena*. O. S. R.: Schley and a few other varieties are highly resistant. P. S. R.: Schley and a few other varieties.

PERSIAN (ENGLISH) WALNUT

WALNUT BACTERIAL BLIGHT, *Xanthomonas juglandis*. O. S. R.: Immunity not known. Eureka, San Jose, and Ehrhardt show some degree of resistance. Some seedling trees are seldom badly infected. In Oregon the Parisienne variety is somewhat resistant. Resistant varieties came originally from seedlings from a mixed population. P. S. R.: Eureka, San Jose, and Ehrhardt. Inheritance: Unknown.

BRANCH WILT, *Hendersonula toruloidea*. O. S. R.: Meylan, Eureka, Blackmer, Payne, and Concord are somewhat resistant. Concord is the most resistant of all. Varieties originally came from seedlings from a mixed population. P. S. R.: Preceding varieties. Inheritance: Unknown.

CROWN ROT, *Phytophthora cactorum*. O. S. R.: All Persian varieties are susceptible. Paradox hybrids (Persian x *J. hindsii*) show some resistance. P. S. R.: Commercial Paradox hybrids.

ROOT LESION, nematode injury, *Paratylenchus vulnus* and *Cacopaurus pestis*. O. S. R.: All Persian varieties are susceptible; Paradox hybrids (Persian x *J. hindsii*) show some resistance. P. S. R.: Commercial Paradox hybrids. Inheritance: Unknown.

EASTERN BLACK WALNUT

ANTHRACNOSE, *Marssonina juglandis*. O. S. R.:Varieties Ohio and Thomas are somewhat resistant. P. S. R.: Ohio and Thomas. Inheritance: Unknown.

OIL PLANTS: grain flax, safflower, peppermint, spearmint.

GRAIN FLAX

RUST, *Melampsora lini*. O. S. R.: Varieties Ottawa 770B, Buda, J. W. S., Pale Blue Crimped, Kenya, Williston Golden, Morye, Rio, Minn. 25–107, Newland, Bolley Golden, Billings, Pale Verbena, Victory A, Bombay, Akmolinsk, Abyssinian, Leona, and Tammes' Pale Blue. P. S. R.: Original and selections of original. Inheritance: Resistance is a monogenic dominant.

WILT, *Fusarium lini*. O. S. R.: Varieties North Dakota Resistant No. 114,

Bombay, Morye, Redwing, Buda, Ottawa 770B, Bison, and Pinnacle. P. S. R.: Preceding varieties and selections and hybrids of these. Inheritance: Multiple factor.

SAFFLOWER

RUST, *Puccinia carthami*. O. S. R. Introductions by Nebraska Agricultural Experiment Station from Rumania, Turkey, India, Egypt, and France. Resistant lines have been purified by the Nebraska Agricultural Experiment Station; others are being developed by the United States Department of Agriculture. Inheritance: Resistance is monogenic dominant.

ROOT ROT, *Phytophthora dreschleri*. O. S. R.: Introductions by the Nebraska Agricultural Experiment Station from Egypt and other introductions presumed to have originated in Russia. P. S. R.: Various degrees of root rot resistance in commercial varieties N–2, N–4, N–6, and N–8, developed by Nebraska Agricultural Experiment Station. Root rot resistant varieties are in process of development by the United States Department of Agriculture. Inheritance: Unknown.

PEPPERMINT

VERTICILLIUM WILT, *Verticillium albo-atrum* var. *menthae*. O. S. R.: *Mentha crispa* from unknown European source. P. S. R.: Clonal line maintained at Michigan State in regional mint nursery, East Lansing, Mich. Commercial types are in process of development at Michigan State College, Purdue University, United States Department of Agriculture, and A. M. Todd Co Kalamazoo, Mich. Inheritance: Polygenic; not completely understood.

SPEARMINT

SPEARMINT RUST, *Puccinia menthae*. O. S. R.: *Mentha crispa* from unknown European source. P. S. R.: Clonal line maintained at Michigan State College in regional mint nursery, East Lan ing, Mich. Commercial types in process of development at Michigan State College, Purdue University, United States Department of Agriculture, and A. M. Todd Company, Kalamazoo, Mich. Inheritance: Polygenic but not completely understood.

SNAPDRAGON

RUST, *Puccinia antirrhini*. O. S. R.: *Antirrhinum majus* strains from Dr. E. B. Mains. P. S. R.: The varieties Aristic, Campfire, Loveliness, Red Cross, Snow Giant, Yellow Giant, Rosalie, Alaska, Apple Blossom, Canary Bird, Copper King, Crimson, and other commercial types now being developed nheritance: Monogenic dominant.

SUGAR CROPS: sorgo, sugar beet, sugarcane.

SORGO

LEAF ANTHRACNOSE AND STALK RED ROT, *Colletotrichum graminicola*. O. S. R.: Collections made in Africa in 1945 by the United States Department of Agriculture. P. S. R.: Sart and noncommercial types. Inheritance: Resistance is inherited as monogenic dominant.

SUGAR BEET

BLACK ROOT, *Aphanomyces cochlioides*. O. S. R.: U. S. 216 and other U. S. varieties developed in leaf-spot resistance breeding project. P. S. R.: Seed increase of S. P. I. 48B3-00, now released as U. S. 1177, and related varieties; also varieties developed by beet sugar industry. Inheritance: Resistance is dominant in F_1, resistant x susceptible. Evidently disease reaction is conditioned by more than one pair of genes.

CERCOSPORA LEAF SPOT, *Cercospora beticola*. O. S. R.: Inbred lines established from European open-pollinated varieties. P. S. R.: U. S. 216, U. S. 225, U. S. 226, and hybrid combinations of these; also in varieties developed by the beet sugar industry. Inheritance: Disease reaction of the F_1, resistant x

susceptible, is intermediate. Segregation in F_2 indicates that disease reaction is conditioned by more than a single pair of genes.

DOWNY MILDEW, *Peronospora schachtii*. O. S. R.: U. S. 15 and other selections from commercial and U. S. sugar beet varieties. P. S. R.: Tolerant commercial varieties and highly resistant inbreds. Inheritance: Unknown.

CURLY TOP, *Ruga verrucosans*. O. S. R.: Selection out of heterogeneous commercial beet population released as U. S. No. 1 in 1933. P. S. R.: U. S. 22/3. Inheritance: Probably one major gene for resistance with modifiers.

SUGARCANE

RED ROT, *Physalospora tucumanensis*. O. S. R.: Some forms of *Saccharum spontaneum* and probably of *S. barberi*. P. S. R.: Commercial and unreleased clones that are interspecific hybrids with *S. spontaneum* or *S. barberi* inheritance, such as CO 281, CP 28/11, CP 36/105, and CP 44/101. Inheritance: Undetermined.

ROOT ROT, *Pythium arrhenomanes*. O. S. R.: Various forms of *Saccharum spontaneum* and *S. sinense*. P. S. R.: Some commercial and unreleased clones that are interspecific hybrids with inheritance from these species, such as CO 290, CP 28/11, CP 807, CP 33/409, and Kassoer. Inheritance: Undetermined.

MOSAIC, *Marmor sacchari*. O. S. R.: All known forms of *Saccharum spontaneum* except those from Turkestan. P. S. R.: Numerous commercial and unreleased clones that are interspecific hybrids, usually with *S. spontaneum* inheritance. Inheritance: Undetermined.

TOBACCO

BACTERIAL WILT, *Pseudomonas solanacearum*. O. S. R.: T. I. 448A, a selection out of a collection made in Colombia, South America, 1942. P. S. R.: Oxford 26 and Dixie Bright 101. Inheritance: Polygenic.

WILDFIRE, *Pseudomonas tabaci.* O. S. R.: *Nicotiana longiflora* immunity transferred to tobacco, 1947. P. S. R.: Commercial wildfire immune varieties will be available soon. Inheritance: Monogenic dominant.

BLACK ROOT ROT, *Thielaviopsis basicola.* O. S. R.: Isolated naturally occurring strains of Havana and Burley types. P. S. R.: Havana 142, Burley 1, and other commercial varieties. Inheritance: Polygenic.

BLACK SHANK, *Phytophthora parasitica* var. *nicotianae.* O. S. R.: Florida 301, obtained by crossing and selection within *Nicotiana tabacum* in 1931. P. S. R.: RG, Oxford 1, Vesta 33, Dixie Bright 101, and other commercial varieties. Inheritance: Polygenic.

TOBACCO MOSAIC. O. S. R.: *Nicotiana glutinosa* immunity transferred to tobacco 1938. P. S. R.: Kentucky 56, Vamorr 50, and other commercial varieties. Inheritance: Monogenic dominant.

VEGETABLES: asparagus, bean, celery, crucifers, cucumber, lettuce, lima bean, muskmelons, onion, pea, peanut, peppers, potatoes, spinach, sweetpotato, tomato, watermelon.

ASPARAGUS

ASPARAGUS RUST, *Puccinia asparagi.* O. S. R.: Martha Washington and Mary Washington developed by J. B. Norton from a male plant of unknown origin named Washington and female plants named Martha and Mary, selected from Reading Giant. P. S. R.: Above-named varieties and No. 500, developed by the California Agricultural Experiment Station. Inheritance: Probably polygenic.

BEAN

HALO BACTERIAL BLIGHT, *Pseudomonas phaseolicola.* O. S. R.: Most field bean varieties: Pinto, Great Northern, Michelite, and Red Mexican. P. S. R.: Preceding varieties; Pinto, University of Idaho Nos. 72, 78, and 111; Great Northern, University of Idaho Nos. 16, 31, and 123; Michelite and Red Mexican, University of Idaho Nos. and 34; and Fullgreen. Inheritance: One or two recessive factors depending on the resistant and susceptible parent used.

ANTHRACNOSE, *Colletotrichum lindemuthianum.* O. S. R.: Alpha race: Well Red Kidney, Cranberry, and Emmerson 847. Beta race: Michelite, Pinto Perry Marrow, and Emmerson 84 Gamma race: Robust, Perry Marrow and California Small White. P. S. R. Red Kidney and the preceding varieties. No commercial varieties are resistant to the three races. Inheritance: Single dominant factor pair for each race. When two or three races are involved resistance is governed by two or three dominant factor pair differences, respectively.

BEAN RUST, *Uromyces phaseoli typica.* O. S. R.: No strain is resistant to all physiologic races. A number are resistant to most of the races: No. 780 a White Kentucky Wonder type; No. 765, a Kentucky Wonder Wax type and No. 814, a brown-seeded Kentucky Wonder Wax type. P. S. R. U. S. Pinto Nos. 5 and 14 and Golden Gate Wax. Inheritance: Single dominant factor pair for each race thus far investigated.

POWDERY MILDEW, *Erysiphe polygoni.* O. S. R.: No strain or variety is resistant to all races. Pinto, U. S. Refugee, and Ideal Market are resistant to a number of races. P. S. R. Available in the preceding varieties and in others, such as Topcrop, Logan and Contender. Inheritance: Single dominant factor pair.

COMMON BEAN MOSAIC, *Marmor phaseoli.* O. S. R.: Corbett Refugee and Great Northern No. 1. P. S. R.: Many commercial varieties and Idaho Refugee, U. S. 5 Refugee, Sensation Refugee Nos. 1066 and 1071, Riva and Topcrop. Inheritance: There are two types of inheritance depending on resistant variety used. Corbett Refugee type, single dominant factor Great Northern or Robust type, single recessive factor.

CURLY TOP, *Ruga verrucosans*. O. S. R.: Varieties Pioneer, California Pink, Burtner's Blightless, and Red Mexican. P. S. R.: Red Mexican, University of Idaho Nos. 3 and 34; Great Northern, University of Idaho Nos. 16 and 31; and Pinto, University of Idaho Nos. 72, 78, and 111. Inheritance: Resistance is probably controlled by two genes, one of which is dominant to its allele, the other recessive to its allele. In a progeny segregating for both, the gene that is dominant to its allele is epistatic to the gene that is recessive to its allele.

NEW YORK 15 MOSAIC. O. S. R.: Great Northern No. 1 and No. 123. P. S. R.: Topcrop, Rival, Idaho Refugee, Great Northern, University of Idaho Nos. 123 and 16. Inheritance: Unknown.

POD MOTTLE VIRUS, *Marmor valvolorum*. O. S. R.: All local lesion susceptible varieties are considered commercially resistant: Great Northern, Pinto, Topcrop, Rival, U. S. 5 Refugee, and others. P. S. R.: Available in preceding varieties. Inheritance: Single factor with local lesion infection dominant.

SOUTHERN BEAN MOSAIC, *Marmor laesiofaciens*. O. S. R.: All local lesion susceptible varieties are considered commercially resistant: Pinto, Great Northern, Blue Lake, Ideal Market, Kentucky Wonder, and others. P. S. R.: Available in preceding varieties. Inheritance: Single factor with local lesion infection dominant.

CELERY

EARLY BLIGHT, *Cercospora apii*. O. S. R.: Danish celery received for trial by Eastern States Farmers' Exchange and P. E. I. 115557 and 120875 obtained from Turkey. P. S. R.: Emerson Pascal has moderate resistance and breeding lines not yet commercial have as high resistance as the original sources and improved. Inheritance: Multiple factor.

LATE BLIGHT, *Septoria apii-graveolentis*. O. S. R.: Danish celery received for trial by Eastern States Farmers' Exchange; P. E. I. 176869 from Turkey may have a little higher resistance; and P. E. I. 115557 and P. E. I. 120875 from Turkey. P. S. R.: Emerson Pascal, Giant Pascal, and White Plume have moderate resistance. Breeding lines with high resistance are available but they are far from commercial type. Inheritance: Multiple factor.

YELLOWS, *Fusarium apii* and *F. apii* var. *pallidum*. O. S. R.: Occasional plants in self-blanching varieties and most plants in most green varieties. P. S. R.: Michigan Golden, Cornell 19, and numerous green varieties. Inheritance: Information not definite, but a single dominant gene is probably responsible for most of the resistance.

CRUCIFERS

CABBAGE YELLOWS, *Fusarium oxysporum* f. *conglutinans*. O. S. R.: Commercial varieties of cabbage Wisconsin Ballhead and Wisconsin Hollander and selections from a susceptible variety Danish Ballhead. P. S. R.: Preceding varieties and numerous commercial cabbage varieties now in use. Nine varieties resistant to type A have been released. Inheritance: Type A, found in Wisconsin Ballhead, is monogenic dominant; type B, found in Wisconsin Hollander, is polygenic and becomes unstable when the soil temperature is unusually high.

CLUBROOT, *Plasmodiophora brassicae*. O. S. R.: Commercial varieties of turnip. P. S. R.: Resistant varieties of stock turnip are Bruce, May, and Dale's Hybrid; resistant varieties of rutabaga are Wilhelmsburger, Resistant Baugholm, and Immuna II. Inheritance: Polygenic.

MOSAIC, virus. O. S. R.: Commercial varieties of cabbage. P. S. R.: Improved All Seasons cabbage. Inheritance: Resistance to the mottle phase is incompletely dominant polygenic, but controlled by relatively few genes. Resistance to the chlorosis symptom, incited by the B virus, also is incompletely dominant and appears to be inherited quantitatively. Resistance to mottling seems to be independent of resistance to the chlorosis symptom.

CUCUMBER

BACTERIAL WILT, *Erwinia tracheiphila.* O. S. R.: Tokyo Long Green (wilt tolerance only). P. S. R.: Tokyo Long Green. No variety has been introduced. Inheritance: Not determined.
DOWNY MILDEW, *Pseudoperonospora cubensis.* O. S. R.: Chinese Long, which is used in South Carolina and Puerto Rico, and Bangalore, an Indian variety that is used in Louisiana. P. S. R.: Puerto Rico Nos. 39 and 40, Palmetto, Santee, and Surecrop. Inheritance: Not definite. There is some segregation for resistance in the F_2 but no definite ratio. Resistant plants are tolerant but show some infection late in season. They will produce a crop where susceptible varieties fail.
SCAB, *Cladosporium cucumerinum.* O. S. R.: Late-maturing slicing varieties Longfellow and Windermoor Wonder. P. S. R.: Maine No. 2 and an improved slicing variety Highmoor. A scab-resistant National Pickling type may be released soon. Inheritance: Monogenic dominant. Plants have very high resistance.
CUCUMBER MOSAIC, *Marmor cucumeris.* O. S. R.: Chinese Long and Tokyo Long Green have tolerance only. P. S. R.: Pickling varieties Ohio 31, Ohio MR–17, Yorkstate Pickling and slicing varieties Niagara, Surecrop, Burpee Hybrid, Puerto Rico 10, and Puerto Rico 17. Inheritance: Shifriss *et al.* state that three complementary genes apparently control the appearance or nonappearance of mottling in the cotyledon stage, the genetic ratio in the F_2 being 27 nonchlorotic to 37 chlorotic. The ratio of 27 : 37 is constantly changing in the true leaf stage. They state: "At this point several gene modifiers also take part in the genetical control of virus symptoms. Thus, the frequency of symptomless plants is very low."

LETTUCE

DOWNY MILDEW, *Bremia lactucae.* O. S. R.: There are several commercial varieties each resistant to single biotypes of the fungus but none resistant to all biotypes. P. S. R.: Some of the Imperial varieties. Inheritance: Resistance is a monogenic dominant.
POWDERY MILDEW, *Erysiphe cichoracearum.* O. S. R.: Most cultivated varieties. P. S. R.: Bell May (Mass.), Imperial varieties, Great Lakes, etc. Inheritance: Resistance is a monogenic dominant.
BROWN BLIGHT, cause undetermined. O. S. R.: Big Boston, White Chavigne, individual plants within variety, and New York. P. S. R.: Imperial varieties and Great Lakes. Inheritance: Unknown.
TIPBURN (physiological breakdown). O. S. R.: Slobolt x Great Lakes segregate (U. S. D. A.). P. S. R.: Varieties are being developed. Inheritance: Unknown.
MOSAIC. O. S. R.: P. E. I. 120965. P. S. R.: Parris Island (cos type). Inheritance: Unknown.

LIMA BEAN

DOWNY MILDEW, *Phytophthora phaseoli.* O. S. R.: P. E. I. 164155 from India and 163580 from Guatemala. P. S. R.: Same as preceding but not available in any commercial variety as yet. Inheritance: Single dominant factor pair.
LIMA BEAN MOSAIC, *Marmor cucumeris* var. *phaseoli.* O. S. R.: Fordhook types. P. S. R.: Concentrated Fordhook, Fordhook 242, and Regular Fordhook. Inheritance: Two dominant complementary factors.

MUSKMELONS

ALTERNARIA LEAF BLIGHT, *Alternaria cucumerina.* O. S. R.: MWR 3915 (Indiana). P. S. R.: Purdue 44. Inheritance: Unknown.
DOWNY MILDEW, *Pseudoperonospora cubensis.* U. S. D. A. melon-breeding Accession No. 29554 and P. E. I.

124112 from India and Cuban Castillian. P. S. R.: Commercial types in process of development and Georgia 47, Rio Sweet, and Weslaco H and F. Inheritance: Unknown.

FUSARIUM WILT, *Fusarium oxysporum*. O. S. R.: Certain plants in Honey Dew. P. S. R.: Golden Gopher and Iroquois. Inheritance: Probably one or two dominant factors.

MARSSONINA BLIGHT, *Marssonina melonis*. O. S. R.: Freeman cucumber. P. S. R.: Lines are being developed at Cornell University. Inheritance: Unknown.

POWDERY MILDEW, *Erysiphe cichoracearum*. O. S. R.: Varieties from India, California Accession No. 525, U. S. D. A. melon-breeding Accession No. 29554, and P. E. I. 79376. P. S. R.: PMR Cantaloupe No. 45, resistant to Race 1, and PMR Cantaloupes Nos. 5 and 6, resistant to all known races, and Georgia 47. Inheritance: Probably dependent upon a dominant single factor with several modifiers.

MOSAIC, *Marmor cucumeris*. O. S. R.: Freeman cucumber (*C. melo* var. *conoman*). P. S. R.: Lines with mosaic resistance and improved type are being developed at Cornell University. Inheritance: Unknown.

ONION

BLACK MOLD, *Aspergillus niger*. P. S. R.: White varieties, such as Southport White Globe and White Portugal, are resistant. Inheritance: Resistance is perfectly correlated with dry scale color. See statement under smudge regarding inheritance of dry scale color.

DOWNY MILDEW, *Peronospora destructor*. O. S. R.: Italian Red 13–53, self-sterile cross-fertile, propagated by top sets. P. S. R.: Preceding and Calred. Inheritance: Resistance of scapes is conditioned by two duplicate recessive genes. There is no association between foliage and scape resistance.

PINK ROOT, *Pyrenochaeta terrestris*. O. S. R.: *Allium fistulosum* and individual plants in Crystal Wax and Yellow Bermuda. P. S. R.: Preceding varieties and Yellow Bermuda prr and L 365. Inheritance: In *A. cepa* F_1 crosses resistance is incompletely dominant. Number of genes undetermined.

PURPLE BLOTCH, *Alternaria porri*. P. S. R.: Varieties, such as Yellow Globe Danvers and Red Creole, that have a covering of wax or "bloom" on the foliage are more resistant than varieties with a somewhat glossy foliage such as Sweet Spanish. Inheritance: Resistance is correlated with waxy (nonglossy) foliage. Waxy type of foliage dominant; probably monogenic.

SMUDGE, *Colletotrichum circinans*. P. S. R.: Red, yellow, and brown varieties, such as Southport Red Globe, Yellow Globe Danvers, and Australian Brown, are highly resistant. Inheritance: Resistance is perfectly correlated with dry scale color. Three pairs of genes are involved in the development of red, yellow, and white bulb color: C-c, a basic color factor, the dominant C gene being necessary for the development of any pigment, consequently all cc plants produce white bulbs; R-r, in the presence of C, the dominant R gene is responsible for the production of red pigment—its allele r is responsible for yellow; I-i, an inhibiting factor I is partially dominant over i—all II plants produce white bulbs.

SMUT, *Urocystis cepulae*. P. S. R.: *Allium fistulosum*. Inheritance: In species crosses between *A. fistulosum* and *A. cepa* the F_1 is intermediate in resistance but sterile. A fertile amphidiploid, Beltsville Bunching, has considerable resistance.

YELLOW DWARF, *Marmor cepae*. P. S. R.: *Allium fistulosum*. Nebuka and Beltsville Bunching are immune from all strains of yellow dwarf tested. Lines immune from the common strains of yellow dwarf are Burrell's Sweet Spanish, Colorado No. 6, Utah Sweet Spanish, White Sweet Spanish, Yellow Sweet Spanish, Crystal Grano, Early Grano, Early Yellow Babosa, White Babosa, Crystal Wax, Lord Howe Island, San Joaquin, and Yellow Bermuda. Inheritance: Undetermined.

PEA

POWDERY MILDEW, *Erysiphe polygoni.* O. S. R.: Stratagem variety. P. S. R.: Stratagem variety. Inheritance: Resistance is monogenic recessive.

SEPTORIA BLOTCH, *Septoria pisi.* O. S. R.: One strain of Perfection and an introduction from Puerto Rico. P. S. R.: Perfection, if strain is still available. Inheritance: Not known.

WILT, *Fusarium oxysporum* f. *pisi* race 1. O. S. R.: Commercial varieties Alcross, Wisconsin Early Sweet, Wisconsin Perfection, and many others. P. S. R.: Wilt-resistant Alaska, wilt-resistant Early Perfection, wilt-resistant Perfection, and many others. Inheritance: Monogenic dominant.

NEAR WILT, *Fusarium oxysporum* f. *pisi* race 2. O. S. R.: Progeny in E. J. Delwiche nursery. P. S. R.: Delwiche Commando variety. Inheritance: Monogenic dominant.

YELLOW BEAN MOSAIC, bean virus 2. O. S. R.: Wisconsin Perfection. P. S. R.: Wisconsin Perfection. Inheritance: Unknown.

PEANUT

LEAF SPOT, *Cercospora arachidicola* and *C. personata.* O. S. R.: No significant resistance in any cultivated variety examined. *Arachis marginata* and certain other wild species appear to be immune, but crosses with varieties of *A. hypogaea* have not been obtained. P. S. R.: None. Inheritance: Not known.

PEPPERS (*Capsicum annuum*)

BACTERIAL SPOT, *Xanthomonas vesicatoria.* O. S. R.: Commercial varieties Waltham Beauty, Oshkosh, Sunnybrook, Squash, Harris Early Giant (some strains only), Wonder (some strains only), Harris Earliest (some strains only), Cayenne (selections), Santaka (selections). P. S. R.: Those listed under O. S. R. Inheritance: Both monofactorial dominant resistance gene and multiple factors are suggested. There are no clear-cut data.

BACTERIAL WILT, *Pseudomonas solanacearum.* O. S. R.: Ornamental variety grown locally on island of Oahu Hawaii, is highly resistant but no immune. P. S. R.: Ornamental variety only. Inheritance: Undetermined.

ROOT ROT, *Phytophthora capsici.* O. S. R.: Oakview Wonder is reported resistant under field conditions. P. S. R.: Oakview Wonder. Inheritance Unknown.

SOUTHERN BLIGHT, *Sclerotium rolfsii* O. S. R.: *Capsicum frutescens* var Tabasco is highly resistant; *C. annuum* var. Santaka is moderately resistant P. S. R.: Varieties Tabasco and Santaka. Resistance is being incorporated into commercial varieties, primarily Bell and Pimiento types. Inheritance Undetermined.

TOBACCO ETCH VIRUS, *Marmor erodens.* O. S. R.: Selections from Elephant Trunk x World Beater; Red Cherry tolerant; P. E. I. 159241 highly resistant, possibly immune. P. S. R. Varieties listed above, and resistance is being incorporated into commercial varieties, mainly Bell and Pimiento types. Inheritance: Undetermined.

WILT, *Fusarium annuum.* O. S. R.: A local variety in New Mexico and Mexican and Peruvian varieties. P. S. R. Chili No. 9 and College No. 6 were developed by the New Mexico Agricultural Experiment Station, and the varieties Cristal, Nora de Murcia, and Cacho de Cabra were developed in Peru. Inheritance: Undetermined.

ROOT KNOT, *Meloidogyne* spp. O. S. R.: Varieties Anaheim Chili, Italian Pickling, Santaka, Cayenne (selections). P. S. R.: Varieties under O. S. R. Inheritance: Unknown.

HAWAIIAN PEPPER VIRUS (identity unknown; distinct from tobacco mosaic). O. S. R.: Hawaiian variety Waialau highly resistant; Red Chili Small Chili, and Tabasco are tolerant P. S. R.: Varieties listed under O. S. R. Inheritance: Unknown; probably mulitple factor.

PUERTO RICO MOSAIC VIRUS (identity uncertain; possibly related to potato mild mosaic, distinct from tobacco mosaic). O. S. R.: Native pepper of Puerto Rico and Cuaresmeño variety from Mexico. P. S. R.: California Wonder types. Inheritance: Resistance is monogenic.

TOBACCO MOSAIC, *Marmor tabaci*. O. S. R.: *Capsicum annuum* and varieties World Beater No. 13, Elephant Trunk, Hungarian Paprika, Fresno Chili, *Capsicum frutescens*, and Tabasco. P. S. R.: Commercial types of most varieties are being developed. Inheritance: Single dominant gene for necrotic flecking and leaf abscission.

POTATOES

BLACKLEG, *Erwinia phytophthora*. O. S. R.: Weak resistance in Europe exists in varieties Flava, Prisca, Robusta, and Starkeragis. P. S. R.: Original source and related seedlings. Inheritance: Unknown.

BROWN ROT or SOUTHERN BACTERIAL WILT, *Pseudomonas solanacearum*. O. S. R.: Weak resistance exists in Katahdin and Sebago. P. S. R.: Original sources. Inheritance: Unknown.

RING ROT, *Corynebacterium sepedonicum*. O. S. R.: President, Friso, Teton, and United States Department of Agriculture seedlings 46952 and 055. P. S. R.: President, Furore, Teton, Saranac, Seedling 46952, and a number of seedling varieties related to these. Inheritance: Unknown. Five resistant varieties selfed; 55.4 to 85.0 percent of seedlings resistant.

COMMON SCAB, *Streptomyces scabies*. O. S. R.: European varieties, Jubel, Arnica, Hindenburg, Rheingold, Ackersegen, and Ostragis. P. S. R.: Preceding varieties and American varieties, Ontario, Menominee, Seneca, Cayuga, Yampa, Cherokee, and related seedling varieties; also wild species *Solanum commersonii*, *S. chacoense*, *S. caldasii* var. *glabrescens* and *S. jamesii*. Inheritance: Tetrasomic. There is one gene difference in some crosses; apparently more than one in others. Degree of resistance depends on dosage of resistance genes.

LATE BLIGHT, *Phytophthora infestans*.

O. S. R.: *Solanum demissum* immune from all known races. *S. andreanum*, *S. ajuscoense*, *S. henryi*, *S. antipovichi*, *S. milani*, *S. polyadenium*, *S. vallis-mexici*, *S. verrucosum* probably immune. *W* varieties from Germany, probably related to *S. demissum*, are resistant to field races. P. S. R.: Original sources. There is immunity from certain races in Essex, Ashworth, Placid, and seedling varieties related to *Solanum demissum* and Kennebec, Cherokee, and other named and numbered varieties descended from German *W* varieties. Inheritance: Tetrasomic polygenic, immunity dominant. Three, four, or more genes combined to produce immunity to all known races. Number of genes is determined by the reaction of different seedlings to different physiologic races of the organism; mode of inheritance of individual genes determined by ratios found in selfed lines.

VERTICILLIUM WILT, *Verticillium albo-atrum*. O. S. R.: Menominee, Sequoia, Saranac, United States Department of Agriculture seedling varieties 41956, 792–88, X 528–170, B986–8, B595–76, and European varieties Libertas, Voran, Furore, Aquila, Friso, Iduna, and Populair. P. S. R.: Original sources and related seedling varieties. Inheritance: Unknown.

WART, *Synchytrium endobioticum*. O. S. R.: Snowdrop, Great Scott, Jubel, Hindenburg, and other European varieties, and the American varieties Green Mountain, Irish Cobbler, Triumph, Spaulding Rose, and Burbank. P. S. R.: In at least 80 European varieties and in Green Mountain, Irish Cobbler, Triumph, Spaulding Rose, Burbank, Katahdin, Sequoia, Pawnee, Ontario, Kennebec, Calrose, Mohawk, Chisago, Mesaba, and a number of seedling varieties. Inheritance: Tetrasomic. One gene difference in some crosses and more than one in others. Dominant gene X giving immunity even in simplex. Genes Y and Z complementary conditioning immunity when both present even in simplex.

APHID INJURY. O. S. R.: Segregates

of a cross between Houma and United States Department of Agriculture seedling variety 96–56. P. S. R: Same as original. Inheritance: Unknown.

HOPPERBURN. O. S. R.: *Solanum polyadenium*, *S. macolae*, *S. commersonii*, *S. chacoense*, *S. caldasii*, Rural, Sequoia, Hindenburg, Jubel, Katahdin, and Sebago. P. S. R.: Original species and varieties and seedling selections related to the original varieties. Inheritance: Unknown.

LEAF ROLL. O. S. R.: Degree of resistance exists in Houma, Katahdin, Triumf, Jubel, Flava, Imperia, Kepplestone Kidney, and Aquila. No varieties are immune. Immunity probably in *Solanum chacoense* and *S. andigenum;* tolerance in *S. polyadenium.* P. S. R.: Preceding varieties and species and in the United States Department of Agriculture seedlings X 927–3, X 1276–185, B 24–58, B 579–3, and other related seedlings. Some are more resistant than original varieties. Inheritance: Tetrasomic. Probably several genes. Katahdin and Houma probably simplex for one gene; X 1276–185 probably duplex.

NET NECROSIS, current-season infection by leaf roll virus. O. S. R.: Immunity in Katahdin, Chippewa, and several other varieties. P. S. R.: Preceding varieties and related seedling varieties. Inheritance: Unknown.

VIRUS A (A+X=mild mosaic). O. S. R.: United States Department of Agriculture seedling 24642, Irish Cobbler, and Spaulding Rose. P. S. R.: Seedling 24642, Irish Cobbler, Katahdin, Chippewa, Sebago, Kennebec, Earlaine, and many related seedling varieties. Irish Cobbler and Earlaine show hypersensitivity. Inheritance: Tetrasomic. Single dominant gene for field immunity. Katahdin probably duplex.

VIRUS X (latent mosaic). O. S. R.: United States Department of Agriculture seedling 41956. P. S. R.: Seedling 41956 and seedling varieties related to seedling 41956 and *Solanum acaule*.: Inheritance: Tetrasomic. Two comple-

mentary genes, immunity dominant. Seedling 41956 heterozygous; some plants of *S. acaule* probably homozygous; others heterozygous.

VIRUS Y, vein banding or vein clearing, (X+Y=rugose mosaic). O. S. R. Hypersensitivity in *Solanum simplici folium*, *S. salamanii*, *S. demissum*, *S rybinii*, and accession Nos. 25941 and 25942. Immunity in *S. chacoense*, *S cordobense*, *S. garciae*, *S. macolae*, *S ajuscoense*, *S. antipovichi*, *S. polyadenium* and probably *S. commersonii* and *S chaucha*. Field immunity in accessio Nos. 25830 and 25832. Weak resistanc in Katahdin and Chippewa. P. S. R. In original sources and in seedlin varieties related to them. Inheritance Tetrasomic. Hypersensitive reactio depends on one or more recessiv genes. Tolerance to virus is dominant

YELLOW DWARF. O. S. R.: Sebago Russet Burbank, and Irish Cobbler ar resistant but not immune. P. S. R. Sebago, Russet Burbank, Iris. Cobbler. Inheritance: Unknown.

SPINACH

BLUE MOLD, *Peronospora effusa.* O. S R.: United States Department c Agriculture collection, P. E. I. 140467 made in Iran in 1940. P. S. R.: Com mercial types are now being developec Inheritance: Resistance is a monogeni dominant.

FUSARIUM WILT, *Fusarium oxysporur spinaciae.* O. S. R.: Commercial Vir ginia Savoy. P. S. R.: Resistant selec tion of Virginia Savoy was develope by the Virginia Truck Experimen Station. Inheritance: Not determined

BLIGHT, cucumber virus 1. O. S. R. Wilt plant of *Spinacia oleracea*, collecte near Liaoyang in North Manchuria i 1918. P. S. R.: Commercial varietie Virginia Savoy and Old Dominior Inheritance: Resistance is monogeni dominant.

SWEETPOTATO

STEM ROT (WILT), *Fusarium hyperoxy sporum* and *F. oxysporum* f. *batatas* O. S. R.: Selections from open pollinated seedlings of Cuban variety Americano; P. E. I. 153655, introduced from Tinian Island in 1946; Triumph, a white-flesh American variety; and Japanese white-flesh varieties Norin No. 2, Norin No. 3, Taihaku Saitama No. 1. P. S. R.: Goldrush and numerous seedling selections now being developed. Inheritance: Multiple factor.

Tomato

Bacterial canker, *Corynebacterium michiganense*. O. S. R.: Some collections of *Lycopersicon pimpinellifolium*. P. S. R.: *L. pimpinellifolium*. No commercial varieties. Inheritance: Unknown.

Bacterial wilt, *Pseudomonas solanacearum*. P. S. R.: Puerto Rico pear and some *L. pimpinellifolium*. P. S. R.: Preceding varieties and commercial types now being developed. Inheritance: Unknown.

Collar rot, *Alternaria solani*. O. S. R.: Devon Surprize and some other European forcing varieties. P. S. R.: Southland, Urbana, and other commercial types under development. Inheritance: Monogenic; fluctuating dominance.

Early blight, *Alternaria solani*. O. S. R.: Devon Surprize and some other European forcing varieties. P. S. R.: Preceding varieties and commercial types now being developed. Inheritance: Probably two factors or more.

Fusarium wilt, *Fusarium bulbigenum* var. *lycopersici*. O. S. R.: P. E. I. 79532 from Peru and other collections of *L. pimpinellifolium*. P. S. R.: Pan America, Sunray, Southland, Fortune, Jefferson, Golden Sphere, and Manahill. Inheritance: Monogenic; near-immunity partially dominant.

Gray leaf spot, *Stemphylium solani*. O. S. R.: *L. pimpinellifolium*. P. S. R.: *L. pimpinellifolium* and commercial types now being developed. Inheritance: Monogenic; resistance dominant, linked with wilt immunity.

Late blight, *Phytophthora infestans*. O. S. R.: Low-level resistance in several wilt types of *L. esculentum*, i. e.,

P. E. I. 134208 from India. P. S. R.: Low-level resistance in Garden State and Southland. Inheritance: Two small-fruited tomato types used as ornamentals and designated as P_1 and P_3 were observed to have a high degree of resistance in southern Florida. Inheritance segregation ratios in crosses made with cultivated varieties indicated that resistance was due to one main factor and one or more modifying factors. F_3 stocks uniformly resistant at Homestead, Fla., were not resistant in the high valleys of North Carolina or at Huttonsville, W. Va. The reason for the difference has not been determined.

Leaf mold, *Cladosporium fulvum*. O. S. R.: *L. pimpinellifolium* and *L. hirsutum*. P. S. R.: Vetomold, Improved Bay State, Quebec 5, and Globelle. Inheritance: Polygenic dominance incomplete. Multiple strains of causative organism.

Septoria leaf spot, *Septoria lycopersici*. O. S. R.: *L. hirsutum*, P. E. I. 127827 from Peru, and T6–02–M6. P. S. R.: Preceding varieties and commercial types now being developed. Inheritance: Resistance partially dominant.

Verticillium wilt, *Verticillium alboatrum*. O. S. R.: Peru wilt, *L. pimpinellifolium*, and Utah accession No. 665. P. S. R.: Riverside, Essar, Simi, VR 4, and VR 11. Inheritance: Resistance is monogenic dominant.

Curly top, *Ruga verrucosans*. O. S. R.: *L. peruvianum* var. *dentatum;* P. E. I. 128660, collected in Tacna, Peru, 1938; *L. chilense; L. pissisi;* P. E. I. 127829, collected between San Juan and Magdalena, Peru, 1938; *L. glandulosum;* P. E. I. 126440, collected between Yangos and Canta, Peru, 1938; and Red Peach. P. S. R.: Original introductions and commercial types now being developed. Inheritance: Not determined.

Mosaic, *Marmor tabaci*. O. S. R.: *L. hirsutum*. P. S. R.: *L. hirsutum;* no commercial varieties. Inheritance: Unknown.

Root knot, *Meloidogyne incognita*.

O. S. R.: *L. peruvianum.* P. S. R.: *L. peru-vianum* and commercial types being developed. Inheritance: Resistance partially dominant, apparently due to one or two major dominant genes; modifiers or additive action genes possible.

SPOTTED WILT, 3 viruses. O. S. R.: *L. pimpinellifolium, L. peruvianum,* and California BC 10. P. S. R.: Pearl Harbor, Manzana, German Sugar, Oahu, Lanai, Hawaii, Maui, Molokai, Kaudi, and Nuhau. The last 7 of these varieties probably inherited their resistance from German Sugar and *L. peruvianum.* Inheritance: Resistance from Pearl Harbor to Hawaii strain of spotted wilt is a monogenic dominant.

WATERMELON

ANTHRACNOSE, *Colletotrichum lagenarium.* O. S. R.: Native African melons. P. S. R.: Congo. Inheritance: Monogenic, partially dominant.

DOWNY MILDEW, *Pseudoperonospora cubensis.* O. S. R.: Santo Domingo melons. P. S. R.: None. Inheritance: Unknown.

WILT, *Fusarium niveum.* O. S. R.: Probably citron P. S. R.: Hawkesbury, Leesburg, Blacklee, Klondike R7, etc. Inheritance: Unknown; probably polygenic.

FREDERICK J. STEVENSON *has been employed since 1930 as a geneticist in charge of the national potato-breeding program of the Department of Agriculture. From 1919 to 1925, at the State College of Washington, he worked with breeding for resistance to bunt in wheat and smut in oats. From 1925 to 1930, at the University of Minnesota, he cooperated with others in breeding for resistance to rusts in wheat and oats and Helminthosporium in barley.*

HENRY A. JONES *has been with the Department of Agriculture since 1936. Previously he was head of the division of truck crops at the University of California. His chief investigations have had to do with the development of hybrid onions and disease resistance in onions. He is a graduate of the University of Nebraska and the University of Chicago, and in 1952 received an honor-ary degree of doctor of science from the University of Nebraska.*

Many persons, who are among the leaders in the efforts to breed disease-resistant plants, gave them the information regarding the crops with which they work. They are:

Alfalfa, O. S. Aamodt; Apples, J. R. Shay, Apricots, C. O. Hesse; Asparagus, G. C. Hanna Barley, G. A. Wiebe; Beans and Lima Beans R. D. Thomas, R. E. Wester, and W. J. Zaumeyer; Celery, H. M. Munger; Clovers, E. A Hollowell; Corn, M. T. Jenkins; Cotton, G. J Harrison; Cowpeas, Helen Sherwin; Cranberry A. C. Goheen; Crucifers, J. C. Walker; Cucumber, S. P. Doolittle; Flax, fiber, D. W. Fishler, Flax, grain, H. H. Flor; Flowers, snapdragons S. L. Emsweller; Forestry, Lee M. Hutchins Grapes, H. C. Barrett, N. H. Loomis, H. P Olmo, and C. F. Williams; Grasses, J. R. Harlan M. A. Hein, W. R. Kneebone, and K. W. Kreit low; Hops, K. R. Keller; Lettuce, R. C. Thomp son and T. W. Whitaker; Muskmelons, H. M Munger and T. W. Whitaker; Nut crops, J. W McKay; Oats, H. C. Murphy; Onions, H. A Jones; Pea, J. C. Walker and W. J. Zaumeyer Peach, J. H. Weinberger; Peanut, B. B. Higgins Pear, J. R. Kienholz; Peppers, P. G. Smith Peppermint, M. J. Murray; Potatoes, F. J. Stev enson; Rice, J. W. Jones; Safflower, C. E. Claas sen; Sorgo, O. H. Coleman; Small fruits, G. M Darrow and D. H. Scott; Southern legumes P. R. Henson; Soybeans, M. G. Weiss; Spear mint, M. J. Murray; Spinach, G. S. Pound; Ston fruits, L. C. Cochran; Sugar beets, Eubanks Cars ner, F. V. Owen, J. S. McFarlane, and Dewe Stewart; Sugarcane, E. V. Abbott; Sweetpotatoes C. E. Steinbauer; Tobacco, E. E. Clayton; To mato, C. F. Andrus, O. S. Cannon, W. A. Frazier J. W. Lesley, and J. T. Middleton; Wheat E. R. Ausemus, B. B. Bayles, and E. C. Stak man; and Watermelon, C. F. Andrus.

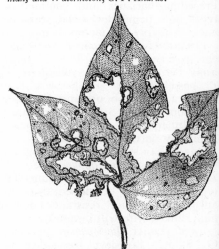

Rhizoctonia leaf spot on cotton.

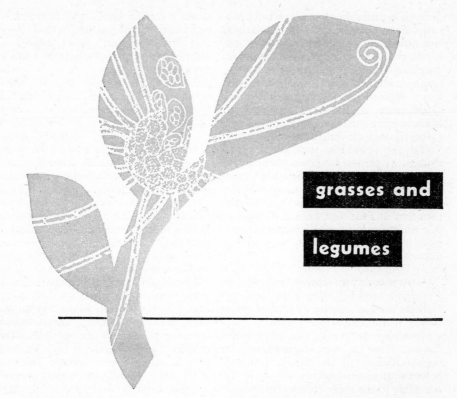

The Many Ailments of Clover

Earle W. Hanson, Kermit W. Kreitlow

There are some 250 described species of true clovers (*Trifolium*) but only four species—red, alsike, white (including Ladino), and the crimson—are widely grown and of great importance.

The sweetclovers (*Melilotus*) are not true clovers. Twenty-two species of sweetclover are recognized. Three species—white, yellow, and sour clover—are of importance in agriculture.

All clovers are subject to injury from diseases. All parts of the plant are attacked and sometimes destroyed—the roots, crowns, stems, leaves, and inflorescences. Fungi, bacteria, and the viruses all can damage the clovers.

Some of the pathogens infect only specific organs of the plant, such as the leaves or roots. Others attack several or all parts of a plant. The pathogens differ also in parasitism. Some infect only certain species of clover. Others have a broad range of hosts and can attack nearly all clovers and many other hosts as well.

AN IMPORTANT PROBLEM in producing clovers, the establishment and maintenance of stand, involves several factors. One is the root and crown disease complex, which includes the seedling blights, root rots, and crown rots.

Those diseases probably are the most important of all clover diseases. They occur wherever clovers are grown. They are caused by a complex of soil inhabiting fungi. The fungi may

217

be widely distributed or occur only locally. Some are virulent pathogens that can attack vigorous plants. Others are weak pathogens that cause damage only after the plants have been weakened by winter injury, nematodes, insects, drought, unfavorable soil conditions, or improper management. Some are primarily seedling pathogens. Others attack clover plants of any age. Some are primarily root pathogens. Others are primarily crown pathogens. Several organisms may attack a plant simultaneously, or one may follow another in sequence. Thus the difficult problem of root and crown disease is one that must receive greater attention if productive stands are to be maintained.

CROWN WART of clover, caused by *Urophlyctis trifolii*, occurs in central Europe on red clover (*Trifolium pratense*), white clover (*T. repens*), and some others. In the United States the disease is of minor importance. It occurs mainly in the South Central States and on excessively wet soils. It is similar to the more important crown wart of alfalfa. Its characteristic symptom is the formation of irregularly shaped galls around the crown of the plant, at and just below the soil level. The galls first become noticeable in late spring and increase in size as summer advances. Infected plants wilt in hot weather. Leaves of white clover are sometimes distorted.

Sclerotinia crown and stem rot is caused by *Sclerotinia trifoliorum*, and is widely distributed, especially in the regions of mild winters or heavy snow cover. It has long been recognized as one of the most destructive diseases of clover in northern Europe. It occurs also in the Soviet Union and Canada. In the United States it is of considerable economic importance in the southern and central clover belts and causes extensive damage in the Pacific Northwest and in the Northeast. Rarely does it occur in the north central part of the northern clover belt. The disease spreads and develops most

rapidly during cool—55° to 65° F.—wet weather, but the fungus that causes it can grow and infect plants at temperatures ranging from below freezing to 75°.

Sclerotinia trifoliorum has a broad range of hosts, which include all important true clovers and the sweetclovers, alfalfa (*Medicago sativa*), black medic (*M. lupulina*), birdsfoot trefoil (*Lotus corniculatus*), sainfoin (*Onobrychis viciaefolia*), and many other legumes and nonlegumes, including numerous weeds. Red clover, crimson clover (*Trifolium incarnatum*), and alsike clover (*T. hybridum*) are all very susceptible. White clover is generally considered to be less susceptible but not immune. Some other species of *Sclerotinia* may also occasionally infect clovers.

The disease is commonly referred to as a crown and stem rot, but it can attack all parts of the plant. Symptoms first appear in the fall as small, brown spots on the leaves and petioles. The heavily infected leaves turn grayish brown, wither, and become overrun with white mycelium, which spreads to the crowns and roots. By late winter or early spring the crowns and basal parts of the young stems show a brown, soft rot, which extends downward into the roots. Consequently part or all of the new growth of the infected plants wilts and dies. Stolons of Ladino clover may become soft and flaccid over their entire length or only small areas may be affected.

As the stems and petioles are killed, a mass of white mycelium grows over them. Some of the masses of mycelium then change into small, hard, black, cartilaginous bodies—the sclerotia. They are attached to the surface of (or imbedded in) the dead stems, crowns, and roots or in the soil near the roots. Some are as small as a clover seed. Some are larger than a pea seed.

When the affected plant parts decay, the sclerotia remain in the soil as a future source of infection. Sclerotia are the chief means by which the fungus survives from year to year.

They can remain viable in soil for several years. In the fall, if conditions are right, the sclerotia germinate and produce one or more small, disk-shaped, pinkish-buff, mushroomlike fruiting bodies called apothecia, which are borne individually on slender stalks. The apothecia are one-sixteenth to one-fourth of an inch in diameter. They produce millions of spores, which spread to the leaves and petioles of nearby plants, causing infection and repeating the cycle.

The greatest reduction in stands occurs in late winter and early spring. The damage therefore is sometimes confused with winter killing. The disease usually occurs in patches throughout a field, but when conditions are very favorable the patches may become so numerous as to merge and cause extensive damage to a stand. In the South a few days of warm weather sometimes checks the disease, and the plants recover.

Control is difficult. Clean cultivation, deep plowing to bury the sclerotia beyond their capacity to send up apothecia, and long rotations are helpful. Care should be taken not to distribute the sclerotia with clover seed. Grazing or clipping in late fall sometimes removes infected leaves and reduces the amount of foliage that may become infected and mat down on the crowns during the winter. Adapted varieties are more resistant than nonadapted strains. The most promising method of control appears to be the breeding of resistant strains.

Common root rot is a group of root diseases caused by species of *Fusarium* and several other soil fungi that produce similar symptoms and frequently attack plants simultaneously. The relative prevalence and importance of the fungi vary with the locality, kind of clover, age of plant, season of the year, soil type, and management practices. Mostly they are weak pathogens and cause damage after the plants have been weakened or injured. Most of them are widely distributed and cause damage wherever clovers are grown.

Scientists have learned a lot about the problem, but relatively little is understood concerning many of its phases. The field symptoms of common root rot of red clover are well known, for example, but attempts to reproduce them under controlled conditions often are unsuccessful. Research men have demonstrated that some isolates of the fungi can attack clover seedlings.

Species of *Fusarium* have been most frequently reported as causing root rot.

Symptoms of the disease are a localized or general rotting of any part of the root system. Taproot, secondary roots, and even the crown may be attacked. The color of the diseased areas ranges from light brown to black. The rotting may be limited to the cortical areas around the exterior of the root, the vascular core may be discolored, or the entire root may be affected. Secondary roots are constantly pruned away by the rots and new secondary roots are formed to compensate, but the replacement process is usually the slower, so that by the end of the second year most plants have left only a few short secondary roots. The lower part of the taproot often is destroyed completely. Such destruction causes wilting and a gradual dying of the plant.

Common root rot kills plants in all stages of development. Effects on stand are most conspicuous during the second year, but losses up to 45 percent during the first year are not uncommon. Stand losses occasionally occur in the spring when the plants are weak because of low food reserves or winter injury. Diseased stands frequently produce a fair first crop of hay but fail to recover and to produce a second crop. Most clovers and sweetclovers are susceptible to root rot.

Besides *Fusarium*, *Rhizoctonia*, *Phoma*, and other organisms may be associated with root rots. *Plenodomus meliloti* and *Cylindrocarpon ehrenbergi* are of primary importance following the winter dormancy period on sweetclover in Alberta, Canada.

Control is difficult, but any practice

that improves the general vigor of the plant is helpful. Proper liming, fertilization, and crop rotation are important. Only adapted varieties should be grown. No varieties available in 1953 had high resistance when conditions favor the disease. Plant breeders have under way a project to develop resistant strains of red clover.

Phytophthora root rot, caused by *Phytophthora cactorum*, is a widespread disease of sweetclover in North America, notably Ohio, Indiana, Illinois, and Missouri. It occurs in Alberta and Ontario. The fungus attacks individual plants or small groups of plants in fields or along roadsides. It is most abundant in low, wet parts of fields, where in seasons of heavy spring rainfall and cool temperatures it may kill most of the plants.

Its presence is first noted in the spring, when infected plants wilt, die, or are generally unthrifty. When their roots are examined, the upper portions usually are found to be rotted. The decay generally is limited to the upper 3 or 4 inches but may extend as much as 8 inches below the crown. The decayed places usually are soft and watery. The color changes but little at first. Later they may become discolored and shrunken.

Crop rotation and the use of well-drained fields are helpful control measures. It should also be possible to develop resistant varieties because resistant plants are known to exist.

Seedling blights, caused by *Pythium*, *Rhizoctonia*, and other fungi, are the most destructive seedling diseases. They occur wherever clovers are grown. Sometimes they seriously reduce the stands. Three types of injury occur. Preemergence killing starts shortly after the seed is sown and develops rapidly, so that the seedlings are destroyed before they emerge from the soil. In postemergence damping-off, infection commonly occurs before emergence, although the rate of disease development is slower and the seedlings emerge only to be killed soon thereafter. Root and hypocotyl rotting

causes varying degrees of stunting, in which plants survive the early seedling stages, after which some recover and some die.

Seedling blights are caused by a complex of fungi, including several species of *Pythium, Rhizoctonia, Fusarium, Gliocladium, Phoma*, and others. One of the most virulent is *Pythium debaryanum*. It would seem that seed treatment might help control this group of diseases, but the results of field tests have given limited encouragement for this method of control.

THE STEM diseases attack the supporting and conducting systems of the plant. Often they cause serious losses. Usual symptoms are stem discoloration, withering and dying of attached leaves and petioles, and general wilting and stunting of the plant. Frequently stems break off or crack open at the site of infection. Several of the major diseases of clover are included in this group.

Northern anthracnose, caused by *Kabatiella caulivora*, is a major disease of red clover in the cooler areas of North America, Europe, and Asia. It develops best at 68° to 77° F. and is checked by continuous hot dry weather. In the United States it is important only in the northern clover regions but there it frequently causes damage—occasionally exceeding 50 percent of the crop in some fields. Losses as high as 50 to 60 percent have been reported in Germany. Complete crop failures have been observed in the Netherlands. Seed production and hay yield and quality are greatly reduced in badly infected fields.

The disease is serious only on red clover. It may occur on alsike, white, crimson, and Persian (*Trifolium resupinatum*) clovers and possibly others. It has never been found on alfalfa, but has been reported on black medic and on sainfoin in the Netherlands. The species of fungus inciting the disease consists of a large number of physiologic races, which differ in their capacity to infect different species of clover and different strains of a particular species. No red clover strain yet developed is immune to the disease, but wide differences in resistance exist among European and American strains. Varieties developed in the southern part of the United States are more susceptible than those developed in the northern clover areas.

Symptoms are confined mostly to the petioles and stems. Infection also occurs on the petiolules—small stalks connecting the leaflets to the petiole—and occasionally on the leaflets themselves. The first symptoms noticed in the field are usually dark-brown or black spots on the petioles. The spots soon cut off translocation to the parts above them—the upper part of the petiole and the leaf—causing them to wilt, turn grayish brown, and die. The petiole bends downward at the site of the lesion to form the familiar "shepherd's crook." Stem lesions are most characteristic. They develop first as small, dark spots, which soon lengthen to form lesions with dark margins and light-colored centers. As the stem grows, a crack often appears in the center of the lesion. Stems finally may be girdled and killed. Plants in a badly infected field look as if they were scorched with fire, because of the abundance of blackened and broken stems, withered petioles, and brown, dead leaves. The name scorch has been aptly used in Britain to denote the disease.

Southern anthracnose, caused by *Colletotrichum trifolii*, is a major disease of red clover in the southern clover belt of the United States. It has been recorded as far north as southern Canada, but is primarily a high-temperature disease that flourishes at about 82° F. It is of little economic importance in the northern clover areas. It is confined mostly to North America, although it has been reported on alfalfa in South Africa and in Europe. It occurs occasionally on crimson clover, sub clover (*Trifolium subterraneum*), bur-clover (*Medicago hispida*), and white sweetclover (*Melilotus alba*). It has not been observed on white clover. Alsike clover is practically immune.

Southern anthracnose has been regarded as the most destructive disease of red clover in the Southern States. It reduces yields of hay and seed and can destroy stands of clover. A resistant variety, Kenland, is available. Most European and American strains developed in regions where the disease does not occur are susceptible; hence it is important to grow only locally adapted strains or strains known to be resistant.

Symptoms resemble those of northern anthracnose; in fact, a positive identification in the field is frequently difficult and sometimes impossible. Dark tufts of setae in the older lesions indicate that the disease is southern anthracnose. But there are other distinguishing features. Southern anthracnose commonly attacks the upper part of the taproot; that has not been observed for northern anthracnose. Southern anthracnose usually produces more spotting of the leaves, but that is not an infallible characteristic because of the frequent presence of similar leaf spots incited by other pathogens. Like northern anthracnose, it may occur on plants at any stage of development. It most commonly develops on the young, succulent parts of stems and petioles but is not limited to them.

The disease occurs on the leaves as dark-brown spots of irregular shape, which vary from pin-point lesions to a general infection over most of the surface. Petioles are very susceptible. They become dark brown, and the attached leaflets droop. First symptoms on the stems and petioles are small, water-soaked spots, which usually lengthen to form long, depressed, dark-brown or black lesions, many of which develop gray or light-brown centers. Lesions near the base of a stem often cause death and browning of the entire stem.

The most destructive effect of southern anthracnose is on the taproot and crown. Dark lesions develop on the upper part of the taproot, gradually girdle it, and cause the plant to wilt and die. This crown rot is closely associated with taproot decay and may result from spread of the fungus upward from the roots or downward from the stems and petioles. Diseased crowns become brittle so that the stems are readily broken off at the soil level. Crown and root rot caused by southern anthracnose kills some plants and weakens others so that they cannot survive long drought, adverse winter conditions, and attacks of other diseases.

Black stem, caused by *Phoma, Mycosphaerella,* and *Ascochyta,* is a major disease of clovers. It is widely distributed and may cause extensive damage during cool, wet weather in the fall, late winter, and spring. It causes the familiar stem blackening and repeated defoliation, which weakens and sometimes destroys stands. The disease was so severe in Kentucky in 1933 on some of the unadapted red clovers that plots that had had perfect stands the previous December were bare by April.

Among the fungi that cause black stem of clovers are *Ascochyta imperfecta,* which occurs mostly on alfalfa but sometimes on clovers; *Phoma trifolii,* the organism most frequently attacking red clover; and *Mycosphaerella lethalis,* the cause of black stem of sweetclover. Little is known about the host range of these pathogens except that each of them can infect alfalfa, red clover, and sweetclover and each is primarily the cause of the disease on its own crop. During midsummer and fall, another pathogen, *Cercospora,* also causes black stem.

The most conspicuous symptom is stem blackening, which may involve all or any part of the stem. Blackening increases when clover is not cut at the proper time or when the crop is left for seed. Frequently young shoots or petioles are girdled and killed. This, as well as leaf infection, may result in severe defoliation.

On red clover the disease produces small, dark-brown or black spots, which increase slowly in size and eventually kill the affected parts. Infection occurs the first summer on spring-sown clover but becomes more destructive the following late winter and spring. On unadapted clovers, new leaves may be killed as rapidly as they are formed. On sweetclover the disease appears most commonly in the spring of the second year. The spots at first are dark. As they enlarge they change to light brown. Leaf spotting is increased by frost injury, which seems to provide an avenue of entrance for the fungus. Heavy stands may be greatly injured. The disease is more severe on plants that have been clipped or grazed.

Crop rotation and burning of dead leaves and stems before new growth develops in the spring are helpful control measures. Breeding for resistance has been started.

Stem canker, or gooseneck, is caused by *Ascochyta caulicola.* It was first reported in Germany in 1903 as a new disease of sweetclover. It is now known to occur in most areas of the world where sweetclover is grown. It has not been observed on other legumes.

It produces silvery-white cankers on the stems, petioles, and occasionally the midribs of the leaves. The cankers vary in size. They are stippled with numerous tiny black dots and have brown margins. On the lower parts of the stems the cankers may be so large and numerous as to girdle the stems. On the upper parts they are less abundant, smaller, and more isolated. Heavily infected stems often appear swollen, are retarded in development, and have fewer and smaller leaves. They also tend to twist and bend at the top.

LEAF DISEASES usually do not kill plants, but they interfere with the normal functions of the leaf. Sometimes they cause defoliation, which reduces yield, quality, and palatability of the forage. If the defoliation is extensive and continuous, the plants lose vigor, are less able to survive unfavorable

onditions, and are more readily at-
acked by pathogens that cause root
ots.

Pseudopeziza leaf spot, caused by
Pseudopeziza trifolii, is widespread in the
ooler, humid clover regions of the
United States and Europe. It has been
eported also from Canada and Russia.
t usually is of minor importance, but
occasionally severe local outbreaks
ause extensive defoliation. Serious
outbreaks have occurred in northern
ndiana, Ohio, and the Northeastern
States. It has been called the most serious leaf disease of red clover in New
York.

It resembles the pseudopeziza leaf
pot of alfalfa, but it does not attack
lfalfa and the disease of alfalfa does
ot attack the clovers. It occurs on red,
lsike, white, crimson, zigzag (*Trifol-
um medium*), and strawberry (*T. fragi-
erum*) clovers and several others. A
imilar disease of sweetclover is caused
oy *P. meliloti*.

Dark spots that may be olive to red-
lish brown, purple, or black develop
on either leaf surface. The spots are
iny, angular, or round and commonly
ave dendritic margins. A minute, am-
er, jellylike globule occurs in the cen-
er of the older spots. The globules, or
ruiting bodies, more frequently are
ound on the lower side of the leaf but
ccasionally occur on both sides. They
re most abundant in wet weather.
ater they dry up, shrink, become almost black, and are not readily de-
ected. Positive diagnosis of the disease
n its early stages in the field is difficult
ecause at first the minute pin-point
sions are not markedly different from
hose of other leaf spots. The disease is
lmost entirely limited to the leaves,
ut has been reported to produce small,
ong, dark streaks on the petioles.

Stemphylium leaf spot, or target spot,
s caused by *Stemphylium sarciniforme*. It
s common on red clover in the United
tates and Europe. It is not considered
major disease of red clover, but its
mportance may have been underesti-
nated. It can cause serious defoliation
nd losses of 15 to 40 percent of the

crop in individual fields. It is known to
occur in nature only on red clover.
L. J. Krakover, working at the Michigan Agricultural Experiment Station
at East Lansing, inoculated sweetclover, alsike, white, and crimson clovers,
as well as alfalfa, vetch, and several
other legumes, but he was not able to
infect them. James G. Horsfall, at the
New York Agricultural Experiment
Station at Ithaca, however, reported
infection from artificial inoculations on
alsike and white clovers, sweetclover,
and alfalfa. That difference in ability
of the isolates to cause disease suggests
that the fungus may have more than
one race.

Symptoms are limited almost exclusively to the leaflets. Minute, light-
brown spots, similar to the early symptoms of some of the other leaf spot
diseases, appear first. Fully developed
spots are mostly oval or round and
about one-fifth inch across. They may
be larger when only a few occur on a
leaf. The most characteristic symptom
is the occurrence of concentric rings
within the lesion, suggesting the name
target spot. The center of a typical
spot is dark and distinct. It is surrounded by alternately light and dark
rings. The darker rings are sepia to
dark brown. The lighter ones are
ocher to light brown. The darker
rings near the center of the lesion are
narrow and ridged. The color contrast between the two outermost rings
is very sharp. Spots are most abundant
near the margin of a leaf but may
occur anywhere. Frequently they coalesce, killing large areas of the leaf
and causing defoliation. Symptoms on
the stems and petioles are uncommon
but when they do occur they appear as
dark-brown to black linear streaks.

A related fungus, *S. botryosum*, attacks alfalfa and sometimes occurs on
red clover.

Blackpatch, caused by an unidentified fungus, was first recognized in
Kentucky as a disease of red and white
clovers. It has also been reported from
Wisconsin, West Virginia, and Georgia. It has generally been considered

of little economic importance but occasionally causes losses in local areas. In heavily infected fields of red clover the seed yield may be reduced at least 50 percent.

In addition to red and white clovers, the disease has been found on soybean (*Glycine max*), cowpea (*Vigna sinensis*), kudzu (*Pueraria thunbergiana*), and blue lupine (*Lupinus angustifolius*). It has not yet been reported as occurring in nature on alsike clover, crimson clover, alfalfa, and the sweetclovers, but all of those crops have been infected by artificial inoculation.

Blackpatch attacks the leaves, stems, flowers, and seeds. Under normal conditions it occurs in patches. Otherwise it appears only on scattered plants. Leaf lesions are similar in size and color to those caused by *Stemphylium sarciniforme*. They vary from brown to grayish black and usually have concentric rings. Large areas of a leaf may be affected. Sometimes all the lower leaves are killed. Greatest damage results from the girdling of the stems beneath the flower head or from direct infection of the flowers before the seeds are fully developed. The fungus is seed-transmitted. It also causes seedling blight. Examination of diseased plant parts with a hand lens usually reveals the presence of coarse, dark, aerial mycelium, a characteristic that helps in diagnosing the disease.

Treating the seed with a fungicide should aid in preventing initial infection. In hayfields, losses can be reduced by early harvesting. Crop rotation and sanitation should also be helpful.

Curvularia leaf spot is caused by *Curvularia trifolii*. It sometimes causes considerable wilting and premature dying of leaves of Ladino clover in the eastern United States. It was first discovered in 1919, when it caused minor damage to white clover near Washington, D. C. Since 1940 it has occurred more frequently, presumably because of the widespread use of Ladino clover along the Atlantic seaboard. Up to 25 percent of the leaves may be attacked and damaged. Ladino

clover may be more susceptible tha common white clover. It is possible t infect other species of clover in th laboratory, but the disease has no been found attacking them in th field. Infected leaves usually have large yellowed area, which soon turn watery gray and translucent, the light brown. A yellowish band usuall outlines the advancing edge of th infected part of a leaf. Diseased area that originate at a leaf tip sometime become V-shaped. Infected leaves wil then shrivel and die. Sometimes th dead V-shaped part of a leaf curl The fungus can invade the entir leaflet and grow down the petiol causing complete wilting of the lea Apparently it does not attack stolon The disease develops most rapidl during warm, wet weather. A tempe: ature of 75°–80° F. is most favorabl

Cercospora leaf and stem spot, als called summer black stem, is widel distributed in the United States an Europe. It is commonly found o most of the true clovers, including rec alsike, white, crimson, zigzag, ho] (*Trifolium agrarium*), and many other A similar disease occurs on alfalfa sweetclover, black medic, and relate species. *Cercospora zebrina* is the mo important pathogen on all of thos hosts except sweetclover. *C. davisii* the most important (or the only species infecting sweetclover. Damag varies from year to year, depending o weather conditions, but the disease always present and frequently cause excessive premature defoliation.

Symptoms vary somewhat on th different host plants. Leaves, stem petioles, petiolules, and seeds may b attacked. Leaf lesions are usuall angular and more or less confined b the veins. The size and shape of th lesions vary from rather small, linea spots on red clover to large, almos circular ones on sweetclover. Appa ently atmospheric conditions and th kind of tissue influence the size an shape of the lesions. Color of the spo also varies considerably. On the tru clovers the general tone is reddish c smoky brown. On sweetclover it is ashy gray. When conditions favor sporulation of the pathogens, a silvery-gray down develops on mature lesions. Lesions on the stems and petioles are somewhat sunken but with colors like those of the leaf spots. Stem infections are serious as they cause the distal parts to wilt and die. Seeds may also be infected. The disease may be distributed on the seed.

Infection may occur at any time during the growing season on plants of any age, but the disease is usually most abundant in late summer and autumn. On sweetclover the disease is most conspicuous on second-year plants after they have started to bloom and is more severe on plants that have been cut or grazed.

Little is known concerning the control of this leaf and stem spot. Removing old crop residues and crop rotation help reduce damage. Infected seed should be treated with a fungicide to reduce seedling infection. The development of resistant varieties of legumes seems to hold out the most hope for controlling it.

Pseudoplea leaf spot, or pepper spot, is due to *Pseudoplea trifolii*, a fungus that attacks the true clovers and less commonly alfalfa. It occurs throughout the United States, Canada, Europe, and Asia. The disease has not been reported on sweetclover. It is important on Ladino and white clover in Northeastern and Southern States, where severe infection frequently causes premature yellowing and defoliation of lower leaves. It occurs throughout the growing season but develops most abundantly in cool, wet weather.

Tiny, sunken black flecks develop on both surfaces of leaves and on petioles. The flecks rarely reach a diameter of more than a few millimeters but frequently are very numerous—hence the name pepper spot. Later they turn gray with a dark, reddish-brown margin. Heavily infected leaves and petioles become yellow, wither, turn brown, and

collapse as a dead mass. Flower stalks and floral parts may also become infected and be killed.

Infection occurs from spores that develop on dead, overwintered leaves and petioles. Spots can usually be found on the first new leaves that emerge in the spring.

No practical control measures are known, but plants differ in susceptibility, and breeding for resistance is possible.

Bacterial leaf spot, caused by *Pseudomonas syringae*, does not usually cause serious damage, although it is widespread in the United States and has been reported in Italy and England. Wet weather favors its rapid spread and development. Hot, dry weather checks it.

The disease may appear at any time during the growing season. It is most conspicuous on the leaflets. It also affects the stems, petioles, petiolules, stipules, and flower pedicels. First symptoms are tiny, translucent dots on the lower leaf surface. The spots enlarge and fill the angles between the veins. They are tiny and black except for the margins, which retain a water-soaked appearance. In wet weather a milky-white bacterial exudate may develop as a thin film or as droplets. On drying, the exudate becomes a thin, incrusting film, which glistens in the light. Tissues surrounding the spots are yellowish green. Infection may be so abundant that whole sections of a leaflet are killed. Mature leaves are often perforated and frayed because of the drying and shattering of parts of the diseased tissues. Lesions on the petioles and stems are dark, elongated, and slightly sunken.

Several clovers, including red, alsike, white, crimson, zigzag, and Berseem (*Trifolium alexandrinum*), are known hosts of this pathogen. Isolates from different areas differ in pathogenicity.

Several other bacterial diseases have been found on clovers, but none of them is important in America.

Sooty blotch, caused by *Cymadothea*

trifolii, is one of the most conspicuous and easily identified leaf spots of clover. It is prevalent throughout North America, particularly in the southern part of the United States, and in Europe. It is most common in alsike, red, and white clovers. Frequently it reaches epidemic proportions on crimson clover. It also has been reported as occurring on some 24 other true clovers.

In the Southern States the disease appears in the spring. In Northern States it is more prevalent in late summer and fall. The earliest symptom is the development of minute, olive-green dots mostly on the lower leaf surface. The dots enlarge and become thicker and darker until they acquire the appearance of velvety black, angular, elevated patches or warts. In the fall the warts are replaced by other black areas, which have a shiny surface. Chlorotic and later necrotic spots appear on the upper surface of the leaf immediately above the warts. When spots are abundant the entire leaf may turn brown, die, and fall off. Sooty blotch is of considerable economic importance on crimson clover, causing reduction in seed yield.

Powdery mildew, caused by *Erysiphe polygoni*, is a common and widespread disease of clovers. It probably occurs wherever they are grown. It can cause reductions in the yield and quality of hay. Ordinarily it is of little consequence on the first hay crop but is more abundant on the second. It can attack plants at any stage of maturity but develops best during the cool nights and warm days of the latter half of summer and fall. Long spells of dry weather favor its development.

The pathogen has been recorded on some 359 species belonging to 154 genera. It consists of a number of physiologic races, which differ in their ability to attack different genera and species of hosts and different varieties of a species. European varieties of red clover have been reported generally to be more resistant than American varieties, but American strains are now available that are highly resistant. Wisconsin Mildew Resistant is one of them. Most varieties contain a few resistant plants.

At first barely perceptible patches of fine, white, cobwebby mycelium develop on the upper surface of the leaves. The patches enlarge and merge, the fungus sporulates, and the leaf surface appears as if it had been dusted with white flour. Symptoms may also occur on the lower surface of leaves. Severe attacks can make whole fields appear white.

RUSTS OF CLOVERS are widely distributed in the humid and subhumid areas of the world. Damage is difficult to assess because heavy infection usually does not occur until late in the summer. Occasionally heavy infection occurs, and severe loss results when a grower attempts to produce two seed crops in a season and leaves the accumulated rust-infected old growth to infect the new growth.

Three common varieties of rust attack clovers. They cannot be distinguished on the basis of symptoms but can be differentiated by differences in their capacity to infect the various clovers. For example, the variety of rust on alsike clover (*Uromyces trifolii hybridi*) infects only alsike, while the rust on red clover (*U. trifolii fallens*) infects red, zigzag, crimson, Berseem, and several other clovers. The rust on white clover (*U. trifolii trifolii-repentis*) does not infect red or zigzag clovers but does infect crimson and Berseem, besides white clover. These rust fungi differ from those causing the cereal rusts in that they can complete their entire life cycle on a clover species and do not require an alternate host.

The most conspicuous symptom of clover rust is the uredial, or brown rust, stage, in which round or irregular, pale-brown pustules, surrounded by the torn epidermis, appear on the lower surface of leaves and on the petioles and the stems. Sometimes in winter in the South and early spring in the North, small swollen whitish-to-yellow clusters of tiny cuplike structures occur on the stems, petioles, and large veins of the leaves. These are called the aecia and may cause distortion of the affected leaves and petioles. Rust fungi in the telial, or black spore, stage overwinter on the debris of diseased plants.

Fungicides such as sulfur can be used to control the clover rusts, but rarely is it practical to use them. Resistant plants exist in present varieties and resistant strains can be developed if the importance of the disease warrants it.

ALL COMMON CLOVERS are susceptible to several viruses, some of which are widely distributed. Most of the legume viruses have a wide range of hosts—so that clover viruses infect not only clovers but also other legumes, and viruses of other legumes attack clovers. Some viruses from nonlegume hosts such as tobacco, gladiolus, potato, and some weeds can readily infect clovers. That means that many of the virus diseases spread from one crop to another. The extent of the spread and amount of infection usually depend on the kinds and numbers of insects present. Aphids are probably the most important carriers.

Symptoms vary with the virus and host. Most of the clover viruses are systemic—that is, they are present in all parts of the plant. The most conspicuous symptoms are usually found in the leaves. They include vein chlorosis, mild to severe mottling, chlorotic patches between the veins, and other abnormal combinations. Sometimes the leaves are curled, puckered, or ruffled. Some viruses cause a reduction in vigor as indicated by a general stunting of the plant. Others have no apparent effect on vigor. Viruses that have little effect on one clover may kill another. Symptoms of most clover virus diseases are conspicuous during the cooler periods of the growing season and sometimes disappear temporarily or are masked during hot weather. Weaken-

ing caused by virus disease may predispose plants to attack by other pathogens (especially those that cause root rots) or prevent them from surviving severe winters or prolonged droughts.

The virus diseases reported to occur on the more important clovers are:

Red clover: Red clover vein-mosaic, common pea mosaic, yellow bean mosaic, potato yellow dwarf, American pea streak, New Zealand pea streak, Wisconsin pea streak, pea mottle, pea wilt, alfalfa mosaic, sub clover mosaic, ring spot, broadbean common mosaic, broadbean mild mosaic, and cucumber mosaic.

Alsike clover: Alsike clover mosaic, red clover vein-mosaic, sub clover mosaic, common pea mosaic, pea mottle, pea wilt, and New Zealand pea streak.

White clover: Alfalfa mosaic, red clover vein-mosaic, yellow bean mosaic, pea mottle, pea wilt, American pea streak, New Zealand pea streak, and broadbean mild mosaic.

Crimson clover: Alfalfa mosaic, red clover vein-mosaic, sub clover mosaic, alsike clover mosaic, common pea mosaic, yellow bean mosaic, pea mottle, pea wilt, American pea streak, potato yellow dwarf, and broadbean common mosaic.

Sub clover: Sub clover mosaic and yellow bean mosaic.

Sweetclovers: Alfalfa mosaic, alsike clover mosaic, red clover vein-mosaic, sub clover mosaic, common pea mosaic yellow bean mosaic, pea mottle, pea wilt, American pea streak, tobacco streak, tobacco ring spot, and broadbean mild mosaic.

Little has been done to control the virus diseases of clovers. Some of the newer insecticides kill the insect vectors. When possible, clover should not be grown close to other legumes, particularly peas or beans. The ultimate solution is to develop varieties of clovers resistant to the most prevalent and injurious virus diseases. That remains to be done.

SEVERAL PATHOGENS can attack the floral parts of the clovers under some conditions. They are of importance only when they interfere with seed production.

Anther mold (*Botrytis anthophila*) was first reported from Russia in 1914 and has since been found to be widely distributed in Europe. In the United States it has been found to a limited extent in Oregon. It has no apparent effect on the plants until flowering time, when it destroys the normally yellow pollen grains, replacing them with the gray spores of the fungus. If abundant it can reduce seed setting.

EARLE W. HANSON, *a native of Minnesota, joined the Department of Agriculture in 1937. From 1937 to 1946 he was employed by the division of cereal crops and diseases of the Bureau of Plant Industry, Soils, and Agricultural Engineering doing research at the Minnesota Agricultural Experiment Station on the diseases of hard red spring wheats and the development of disease-resistant varieties of wheat. Since 1946 he has been employed jointly by the division of forage crops and diseases of the Bureau and the University of Wisconsin.*

KERMIT W. KREITLOW *is also a member of the division of forage crops and diseases and is stationed at Beltsville, Md. He is a graduate of the University of Minnesota and Louisiana State University. Dr. Kreitlow has been engaged in work on forage crop diseases since 1941.*

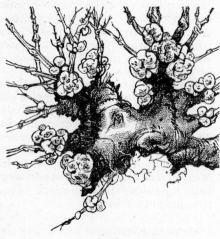

Crown wart of alfalfa.

Sources of Healthier Alfalfa

Fred R. Jones, Oliver F. Smith

Alfalfa as a forage crop in the United States is recognized as consisting of strains of *Medicago sativa* and of hybrids of that species with *Medicago falcata*. *M. sativa* occupies the southern and central alfalfa regions. The apparent hybrids appear to use the superior hardiness of the *M. falcata* parent to give them longevity in the severe climate of the northern part of the range of the crop. Thus two species, which vary greatly within themselves, produce in their combined resources a crop that in the hands of progressive agriculturists has spread across a wide range of climate.

As often happens in such wide and intensive culture, serious diseases have appeared. Many have reduced the quantity and quality of alfalfa forage. To overcome the loss, breeding for resistance has been undertaken. Already those efforts have demonstrated that the qualities of two variable species can be utilized to develop resistance to many of the diseases.

The evaluation of the resistant characters is one of the major tasks that face pathologists and breeders. Therefore in this discussion of diseases of alfalfa, we emphasize sources of resistance.

OF THE NONPARASITIC DISEASES, winter injury is often the cause of weak growth in the spring and the subsequent unthrifty condition of many plants. Besides, injured tissues often become the avenues of entrance for parasitic micro-organisms that weaken and kill the plants. In the northern alfalfa regions, effects of winter injury can be modified by using hardy or adapted varieties. Also, if snow is expected to be a factor in winter protection, fall growth should be left to hold the snow. If a field is damaged, but is to be saved, one should avoid early cutting or grazing the following spring.

Occasionally some white spots occur around the margins of upper leaves on scattered plants. Sometimes the spotting seems to be an inherited character, which develops in plants several years old when the crown begins to decay. Sometimes it develops after winter injury. It has been produced experimentally in young plants grown in soil deficient in potash. Thus at times its occurrence is taken as an indication of potash deficiency. White spot also develops extensively in response to moisture change in irrigation, although the spotting then may develop over the entire leaf instead of only at the margins.

Yellowing and dwarfing of alfalfa is often widespread from feeding of the potato leafhopper. Yellowing may also be an indication of boron deficiency.

OF THE VIRUS DISEASES, alfalfa dwarf comes first. It is known to occur only in California. It was first reported in 1931 when it was localized in Riverside and adjacent counties south of the Tehachapi Mountains. In 1952 the disease occurred over much of the San Joaquin Valley and caused a rapid thinning of second- and third-year stands in about a third of the alfalfa acreage of California.

Alfalfa dwarf is due to a virus that leafhoppers and spittlebugs carry from plant to plant. Fourteen species of leafhoppers and four species of spittlebugs can carry it. Two species of leafhoppers (*Craeculacephala minerva* and *Corneocephala fulgida*) are the most important vectors in the field. When the leafhoppers feed upon dwarf-diseased plants, they take the virus into their bodies and retain it for several months, during which time they may spread

the virus to healthy plants when they feed. Only leafhoppers can spread the disease from field to field.

The virus that causes alfalfa dwarf is the same virus which causes Pierce's disease of grapevines.

Alfalfa plants infected with the dwarf virus gradually lose vigor for several months. Stems are short and spindly. The leaves get smaller and often seem darker in color than leaves of healthy plants. Internally, gum forms in the water-conducting elements and the woody portion of the roots and crown becomes yellow or brown. Susceptible plants usually die 6 to 8 months after infection.

Tests conducted at the University of California indicate that no available variety of alfalfa carries any degree of resistance greater than that shown by California Common. Many varieties are much more susceptible. In fields of California Common, four or more years old, practically all plants were dead or infected with the virus; about one plant in each 2,000 square feet made a normal growth even though root symptoms showed that the plants had been diseased 1 or 2 years. Several such plants were selected and self-pollinated to produce seed. Progenies from most of the selected plants were quite tolerant to the virus and maintained normal growth two to three times as long as unselected California Common. The plants were used to develop a variety—California Common 49—highly tolerant to the dwarf virus.

WITCHES'-BROOM OF ALFALFA was first recognized in the United States in 1925. It also occurs in Canada and Australia. Except in a few localities where outbreaks were severe, it has been considered of minor importance.

The first outbreak occurred in Salt Lake County, Utah, in 1925. In some fields 60 to 65 percent of the plants were infected. Farmers used short crop rotations to combat the disease effectively.

An outbreak occurred in Methow

Valley and Yakima Valley of Washington in the 1930's. When first reported, infection ranged from 25 to 60 percent. Later surveys showed that infection reached 80 percent. A similar outbreak and build-up of the disease occurred in the Nicola Valley, British Columbia, in 1943.

Some of the alfalfa seed fields in the Uintah Basin, Utah, have shown a marked increase in the occurrence of witches'-broom since 1950. In some fields 15 to 20 percent of the plants have been infected. In 1943 witches'-broom could scarcely be found on the Yuma Mesa in Arizona; 8 years later some of the fields had 20 to 30 percent infection.

Witches'-broom slowly modifies the appearance of affected plants in several ways. Plants that show symptoms for the first time have many more stems, an erect habit of growth, and slight marginal chlorosis of the younger leaves. In the advanced stage of infection the plants are severely dwarfed and bunchy because of excessive numbers of short, spindly shoots from the crown and axillary buds along the stems. Leaflets of affected plants are smaller and usually lack the notches at the apex. The plants usually have a yellowish cast. In advanced stages, the plants may develop a prostrate type of growth.

The virus that causes witches'-broom in alfalfa is transmitted from diseased to healthy plants by the leafhoppers *Soaphytopius (Cloanthanus) dubius* and *Orosius argentatus*. We have no evidence that the virus is transmitted in seed, but production of seed is almost prevented in diseased plants because flowers are sparse.

The possibility of resistance to the witches'-broom virus is almost entirely unexplored. We have some evidence that some degree of tolerance does exist in alfalfa. J. D. Menzies made observations on the length of life of infected plants and found that almost half of them died the first winter but 10 percent survived three winters. Some plants are more tolerant to infection than others; if greater numbers were tested, perhaps individual plants could be found with a high degree of tolerance.

Alfalfa also often carries alfalfa mosaic, or *Medicago* virus 1. It usually is more conspicuous as a mottling of the foliage in spring or autumn. Its symptoms disappear in midsummer. It may not be of economic importance on alfalfa, but alfalfa sometimes is an overwintering host from which aphids carry the virus to annual legumes in spring.

Two other viruses, pea mottle virus and alsike clover mosaic virus, may also be infectious to alfalfa.

AMONG THE SYSTEMIC PARASITIC DISEASES is bacterial wilt (caused by *Corynebacterium insidiosum*), one of the most destructive diseases of alfalfa in the United States. It was first recognized about 1925. That the disease occurs in Turkistan and was presumably introduced into the United States with seed is based on the identification by staining in the host and by bacterial cultures obtained from a single root collected November 1, 1929, by H. L. Westover and W. E. Whitehouse, north of Bokhara, Turkistan. Most of the alfalfa grown in that region is highly resistant to the disease; consequently few specimens were found. When fully recognized in 1925, the disease was scattered from Colorado to the Great Lakes. It is now known in most of our well-established alfalfa-growing regions. It is most serious in central and northern areas of abundant rainfall or irrigation and frequent winter injury. It diminishes in importance with low rainfall and with long growing season in the Southern States. Because the disease does not usually become destructive until the third crop year, it is of small importance where alfalfa is grown in short rotations.

This bacterial disease is called a wilt because it develops in a characteristic manner that causes a wilting in more succulent plants. Wilting may occur in alfalfa, but the more common symptom is a yellowing and dwarfing of stems and leaves. Sometimes in very vigorous plants the bacteria that enter the crown near the soil surface cause a decay of the crown with but slow spread downward into the taproot. Thus the disease is sometimes more fully designated a wilt and crown rot. Bacterial wilt is most readily distinguished from other wilts and crown rots by the appearance of the taproot. Because the bacteria develop in and discolor only the newest growth, a yellow ring is found just beneath the bark. This discoloration may extend all the way to the bark and far down the root by the time the stems and leaves are conspicuously dwarfed. Considerable yellowing may be found in the root before the foliage shows any indication of disease.

Four resistant varieties have been produced. Men at the Nebraska Agricultural Experiment Station, in cooperation with the United States Department of Agriculture, produced Ranger, which is hardy enough for the northern part of the United States. At the Kansas Agricultural Experiment Station, Buffalo was produced; it is adapted to the region where Kansas Common is grown and perhaps a little northward. Ranger is a synthetic variety from selections originating in the varieties Cossack, Turkistan, and Ladak. Buffalo is from an old line of Kansas Common.

Resistance to wilt in Ranger and Buffalo is determined first by inoculation of populations of seedlings either in the greenhouse or field. Such inoculation gives earlier results than in inoculated field plots and higher percentages of infection. Thus field tests are used to determine how much resistance in terms of artificial inoculation is needed to protect against crop loss. In greenhouse trials of the two varieties, about 25 percent of the seedlings escape infection. Presumably a large part of the rest are but slightly infected, although figures are not given. Field trials of these varieties rarely record the appearance of wilt in them, and thus adequate protection appears to be insured. However, at Madison, Wis., in a 3-year-old stand after an unusually favorable season for infection, an estimated 30 percent of infected plants was recorded.

The third resistant variety, Caliverdi, was produced at the California Agricultural Experiment Station. It is essentially California Common, but it carries as much resistance to bacterial wilt as Ranger and is resistant to pseudopeziza leaf spot and downy mildew. In breeding it, a single dominant factor for wilt resistance from Turkistan alfalfa was transferred to California Common by the backcross method of breeding. It may be the first instance in which wilt resistance has been transferred to a favorite variety in which it was not found, although such a procedure is practicable.

The fourth variety, Vernal, was announced from the Wisconsin Agricultural Experiment Station, February 3, 1953. It has hardiness for northern use. Certified seed may be available in 1956 or later.

Bacterial stem blight, caused by *Pseudomonas medicaginis*, has occurred on alfalfa for many years in the Western States. It appears on the first crop during cool, wet weather following temperatures low enough to injure top growth of the plants. Ordinarily it is of minor importance, but it may cause considerable loss of the first crop.

Lesions occur on the stems, petioles, and leaves and may extend into the crowns and roots. In the early stages of development, the lesions have light-brown, linear areas with droplets of bacterial exudate. They look as though they were soaked with water. Stem and petiole lesions, several weeks old, normally become dark brown or nearly black. Secondary invaders intensify the color.

Severity of infection is closely correlated with frost injury.

Resistance in strains that had been grown for some time in Colorado was noted by W. G. Sackett, who described the disease. It appeared to be largely resistance to cracking of the stems. B. L. Richards, in Utah, has also noted great differences in resistance of varieties to the disease, Ladak being the most resistant in his trials. The disease, destructive as it is at times, however, does not appear to have given rise to any program of breeding for resistance.

Fusarium wilt of alfalfa (caused by *Fusarium oxysporum* f. *medicaginis*) was first described by J. L. Weimer in Mississippi in 1927. It has been found since as far north as Virginia. The disease is so similar to bacterial wilt that the two have been confused. The tops turn yellow and wilt much as with the bacterial disease. The discoloration extends down the taproot in much the same manner, except that it is usually darker brown and less uniformly distributed about the circumference of the root. It occurs in scattered plants. It does not destroy plants in patches as wilt does. Several reports have mentioned the spread of the disease in Southern States, but its economic importance has been questioned.

THE STEM AND LEAF DISEASES include crown wart. It is caused by a fungus, *Urophlyctis alfalfae*, that enters scales and leaf tissue of developing buds about the crowns of well-established plants and causes them to expand into rough galls often of remarkable size. The young galls are white, but they turn brown and disintegrate as the fungus spores mature within them. Infection and gall development seem to require a long wet and cool spell in early spring and a supply of germinating spores from the previous year. Thus there are few localities—in Western and Southern States—where the disease appears sporadically. The damage to infected plants appears largely from loss of shoots in the spring and from crown necrosis following decay of the galls.

Downy mildew (caused by *Peronospora trifoliorum*) occurs widely in temperate regions. It is one of the less important foliage diseases, however mainly because only about a fourth of the plants of common varieties are susceptible to it. In the most susceptible plants the disease may become systemic, especially in seedlings and in entire branches of large plants. In them the foliage becomes distorted and yellowed. Sometimes the growing end is killed, although vigorous shoots may outgrow the fungus. Spores are produced in succession from the under sides of the leaves. If the fungus is outgrown in the main shoot, it may persist in the nodes and enter side branches that are produced later in moist weather, thus continuing the distribution of the fungus. Usually only single leaves are infected without spread of the fungus back through the petiole into the main stem. In highly susceptible plants, grown buds, infected in late fall, may carry the fungus over winter in systemic invasion of the shoots developing from them. Probably these shoots are the first source of infection in the spring for, while oospores are formed in great numbers in infected leaves, they have not been germinated.

No biological races of the fungus on alfalfa have been distinguished. Susceptibility appears to behave approximately as a dominant character in inheritance. In strains that have a high percentage of susceptible plants, the disease attacks seedlings grown under a cover crop in wet weather and damages or destroys them somewhat as blue mold, a similar disease, destroys tobacco seedlings in the tobacco seed beds. Because susceptible plants sometimes appear to be the most vigorous and succulent in a population, it is easy to introduce them into breeding stocks. The control of the disease in new varieties therefore lies in the hands of the plant breeder.

Spring black stem of alfalfa (caused by *Ascochyta imperfecta*) could properly be placed at the head of a class of diseases designated as being due to poor sanitation. The fungus, which is almost always present in alfalfa fields, fruits on dead stems. Therefore dead stems and foliage-carrying fruiting structures of pathogenic fungi should not be allowed to remain in a field where new growth is starting. One should not let weeds become densely matted around plants, especially in mild winters when plants can make but feeble growth and may be frosted from time to time. A high stubble should not be left in fields. Abundant moisture in each of those situations favors the growth of the fungi and the infection of the alfalfa shoots when they can make but little growth.

Sometimes unsanitary conditions cannot be avoided. Leaving considerable growth in the field over winter may be justified to protect from freezing injury, but the debris, which is not easily removed in the spring, may furnish abundant spores of several fungi that were established in the leaves and stems the previous fall.

Black stem is a well-established name for the injury caused by *Ascochyta imperfecta*. It is an unfortunate name, however, because the fungus may attack any part of the plant from seed to roots and because other fungi cause blackening of stems. In appearance it is one of the least distinctive of the alfalfa diseases. It is often found by isolation in roots with other fungi that presumably are the more aggressive parasites.

As the fungus does not persist in a field more than 2 years after a crop of alfalfa is plowed, it is not commonly abundant in new seedlings unless introduced with seed or from nearby plantings. Once established, it may cause a great deal of curling of leaves and dwarfing of young shoots in cold, wet springs. In vigorous stems the fungus is sometimes discovered by isolation long before any discoloration has become visible. Thus the disease becomes important in northern regions especially when the first growth is left for seed and some of the stems and leaves are dead and producing spores by the time the seed is set.

Differences in susceptibility to black stem in strains of alfalfa have been recorded. Differences between plants within strains have been indicated by M. L. Peterson and his associates in Kansas. The character of the resistance has not been explored. The first selection for resistance consisted of discarding plants that showed an unusual amount of blackening of stems from any cause.

Summer black stem (caused by *Cercospora zebrina*) is sporadic in occurrence and of less importance than spring black stem. Its fungus, usually known as producing only an unimportant leaf spot, however, does produce considerable blackening of stems, especially in late summer. It differs from the spring black stem in that it attacks chiefly the upper parts of stems—not stem bases. The associated leaf spot symptom also is usually present. The leaf spots are rounded and dark brown or black at the center. In moist weather the spots and blackened stems may have a whitish sheen from the spores that develop on the surface. Observations in nurseries indicate that occasional plants are quite susceptible to stem blackening but that most plants are relatively resistant.

Common leaf spot, one of the best known of the foliage diseases of alfalfa, was once thought to be the most destructive of all. The fungus that causes it, *Pseudopeziza medicaginis*, is one of a small group occurring on species of *Medicago* and *Trifolium*.

Spots produced on the hosts are round and 3 to 4 millimeters in diameter when fully developed. The edge of the spot is toothed, a feature that distinguishes it from all other leaf spots. At the center of the spot is a tiny apothecium, which is flesh-colored when it is open under moist conditions and from which great numbers of spores are discharged. The airborne fungus is soon found on alfalfa no matter how far away from old fields.

The fungus lives over winter in one of two ways: In apothecia fully formed in the fall on leaves that escape complete decay during the winter or in newly infected immature leaves that survive the winter. Thus the fungus is rarely abundant in early spring in northern regions and depends on moisture for development and spread. The injury caused by spots is local, but the spots, when they are abundant, cause yellowing of foliage and dropping of leaflets.

We have known about plants resistant to leaf spot only a few years. Only a few individuals in common varieties are highly resistant. Du Puits, a strain of alfalfa from France, has a higher percentage of resistant plants than observed elsewhere, possibly 10 in 100.

Resistance in its highest level is almost the same as immunity in young foliage. If old leaves persist, however, spots may develop slowly in them, although only rarely does the fungus develop to the fruiting stage. Spots rarely become abundant enough in old leaves to cause much loss of foliage. The only variety in which resistance had been reported to be incorporated in 1953 was Caliverdi.

Yellow leaf blotch (caused by *Pseudopeziza jonesii*) is one of the most common of the alfalfa leaf spots. It is most destructive in somewhat dry climates. It begins less conspicuously than most and is commonly found along leaf margins or along veins. Infection in vigorous leaves may produce fruiting structures with sterile spores before tissue is notably discolored. The first discoloration is a slight yellowing in streaks at the edges of leaves. The streaks usually cause the injury to the leaf more by their number than by the size of those formed at the initial infection. The small, sclerotial hyphal masses that produce apothecia—several in a single blotch—develop while most of the leaf is still alive, but the apothecia rarely mature until the entire leaf is dead. In contrast to most leaf diseases, killed leaves have a marked tendency to remain attached to the stems. Killing of foliage by this fungus thus becomes conspicuous chiefly in stands that have remained uncut for an unusually long

time. In fact, so slowly does the fungus develop that when common leaf spot and other more rapidly developing leaf diseases also are present the leaves usually fall before yellow leaf blotch can develop extensively.

Plants resistant to yellow leaf blotch seem to be even more rare than plants resistant to common leaf spot. Progress in testing plants for resistance is slow because the fungus has not been induced to fruit abundantly in culture and artificial inoculation with naturally infected leaves is difficult. Plants resistant to both the yellow leaf blotch and leaf spot have been found, however; it should be possible therefore to develop strains resistant to both diseases.

Of the many minor leaf diseases, one of the most common is caused by *Pseudoplea trifolii*. On occasion it may become conspicuous in humid weather in the South in spring and in the North in autumn. The irregular brown spots developing in persistent moist weather may destroy a large part of the leaf.

A similar leaf spot occurring in warmer weather is caused by *Pleospora herbarum* (*Stemphylium botryosum*).

Likewise in warm weather, a rounded black spot is caused by *Cercospora zebrina*. This fungus is also a cause of blackening of stems.

Leaf rust, *Uromyces striatus medicaginis*, causes reddish pustules on leaves of alfalfa during warm moist weather. The pustules usually are single but are sometimes arranged in circles around a single pustule. Differences between plants in susceptibility to rust have been observed. Plants differ considerably in resistance to the *Pleospora*, *Cercospora*, and rust.

AMONG THE CROWN AND ROOT ROTS of alfalfa, several occur in western Canada, but had not been reported in the United States in 1953.

A low-temperature basidiomycete causes extensive killing of alfalfa in Alberta each year about the time of the first spring thaw. It has been reported as the most virulent fungus yet isolated from crown and root tissues of alfalfa in Alberta.

The basidiomycete behaves mainly as a crown-rotting fungus, but the dark-brown lesions it causes sometimes extend into the root. Under field conditions, plants are killed in irregular patches, which get larger year to year. Damage to alfalfa fields in central and northern Alberta may be as much as 50 percent of the plants.

Canadian workers have obtained resistance to the low-temperature basidiomycete. They have found that *Medicago falcata* and varieties having *M. falcata* in their parentage offer the best sources of resistance.

Resistance has been concentrated in progenies by selfing and intercrossing plants that survive in soil heavily infested with the basidiomycete. Because of the predominence of *M. falcata* types among surviving plants, they have been out-crossed with plants having desirable seed and forage characters. A high correlation exists between survival of inbred and outcrossed progenies. Survival of some intercrossed and inbred progenies has been as high as 50 percent and 70 percent, respectively, in tests that almost completely eliminated Grimm alfalfa. Fortunately the pathogen does not survive to any extent for longer than from 2 to 3 years in the absence of a susceptible host.

In the United States a widely dispersed crown rot of old plants is caused by *Leptosphaeria pratensis*, a fungus long known as causing a rather rare leaf spot. In crowns it probably enters through buds that are first destroyed and then passes to the center of the root through the wood rays, which become discolored. Such discoloration resembles winter injury in the wood; indeed, it is likely that the progress of the fungus is facilitated by such injury. The presence of the fungus can be determined by isolation or by the Gram stain, as used in bacteriology to identify Gram-positive bacteria. Such procedure is troublesome, however, and the disease is usually recognized only from careful surveys.

In the Southeastern States, *Sclerotinia trifoliorum* has been known for many years as causing a destructive crown and root rot of alfalfa. It is identified by the small, black, tough sclerotia about the size of wheat kernels formed by the fungus in decayed plants.

A similar summer decay of stems and crown is produced in the Southeast by the widespread fungus *Sclerotium rolfsii*, which attacks many crop plants. The small, brown, seedlike bodies produced by the fungus in dead plants serve to identify the disease.

Often more than one agency known to be capable of causing decay of crowns can be found in a single plant. Such decay is sometimes called the root rot complex. One of the fungi that attack roots and one often found with other parasites is a stem-blackening fungus *Ascochyta imperfecta*. Because it rarely fruits on roots, its presence is seldom detected.

Colletotrichum trifolii, the cause of southern anthracnose of clover, is also found on alfalfa and contributes to crown rot. It usually causes a black or blue-black discoloration of invaded crowns. Fruiting occurs only on stems. In the nursery it attacks some selected lines far more severely than others; therefore it seems that resistance to it can be found in alfalfa as in clover.

Two species of *Rhizoctonia* are pathogenic on alfalfa, *R. solani* and *R. crocorum*. *R. crocorum* is primarily responsible for root rot. *R. solani* causes foliage blight, crown rot, and root canker, but different strains of the fungus apparently are involved in producing disease symptoms on the different parts of the plant.

As a foliage blight, *R. solani* is worst during prolonged wet and hot periods. Leaves and petioles become infected and water-soaked areas appear. Soon the entire leaflet, leaf, or branch collapses. The fungus advances from plant to plant wherever leaf parts touch. Areas many feet in diameter often become blighted.

When the fungus invades the crowns it causes a crown rot. New buds and shoots are destroyed. The plants are so weakened that they are readily invaded by saprophytic or weakly parasitic soil fungi, which accelerate disintegration of the crown tissues.

In the warmer areas of the Southwestern States, *Rhizoctonia solani* causes a root canker of alfalfa. The disease is characterized by dark, sunken areas, which sometimes have a brownish border. The diseased areas are usually circular, but sometimes they are oblong and extend part way around the root. Lesions generally occur where young roots emerge from larger ones. They often develop inwardly to the central region of the root, but the root usually is not completely rotted off.

The disease is seasonal in its development and closely correlated with warm temperatures. Lesions develop mainly in June, July, August, and September, when soil temperature, at 3 inches below the soil surface, varies from about 70° to 95° F., whereas there is practically no disease development during the winter months when soil temperature at 3 inches below the soil surface may be as low as 41° to 50°. Under controlled conditions lesions develop abundantly on roots grown in soil at a temperature of 77° to 86°, whereas they develop very little, if at all, on roots grown at soil temperature of 61° to 64°.

The economic importance of the disease is not well defined. In regions where it is known to occur, alfalfa stands are of short duration. Plant mortality is highest during the summer when the disease is most prevalent. It causes the death of many small roots and some large ones.

As *R. solani* is soil-borne and has a wide host range, development of resistant varieties offers the best means of control. Technicians have found little resistance in the many varieties of alfalfa that they have studied, but there is need for a more thorough search among varieties.

Rhizoctonia crocorum causes a root rot of alfalfa. Usually the fungus spread in all directions through the soil, killing the plants as it progresses. Top growth of infected plants turns yellow, wilts, and eventually dies. Infected roots have a mat of reddish-brown or violet fungus threads on the outside of the bark. The threads penetrate the roots. Later the roots begin to decay and the bark sloughs off. The disease is more prevalent in poorly drained fields. Since no resistance to the causal fungus is known to occur in alfalfa crop rotation and drainage are the most practical ways to control it.

LET US NOW CONSIDER the diseases caused by nematodes.

The stem nematode (*Ditylenchus dipsaci*) occurs on alfalfa in Canada Europe, South America, and the United States. It is destructive only in rather restricted areas where high moisture and especially flood irrigation favor its development.

The extent of damage by this eelworm varies from year to year. Its development is favored by cool, moist conditions in fall and spring. Sometimes it kills a stand of alfalfa in 2 or 3 years after seeding.

The stem nematode may infect alfalfa at any age of the plant. In very young seedlings it infects the plant at the cotyledonary node, causing it to become greatly swollen. Unifoliolate and trifoliolate leaves produced by the plant have short petioles, which are somewhat swollen and distorted. Seedling plants are dwarfed and seldom recover from infection.

On established plants, injury is mainly in the crown, and young buds and stem bases are affected. Infected buds become thickened and deformed and usually do not elongate into stems. As spring advances, they turn dark and rot off. A condition best described as a crown rot is produced. As infected buds usually do not elongate, infected plants have a reduced number of stems. Later in the season, stems often become infected at the base, become dark brown or black, and break off easily. The interior is decayed. Occasionally colonies of nematodes become established a foot or more above the ground and cause swollen areas on the stems.

The causal organism is a slender, nearly colorless eellike worm, which is about one-twentieth of an inch long. Those that first enter the plant are usually the preadult form. After feeding for a few days they mature, mate, and begin producing eggs. The eggs hatch soon after being laid. The young begin feeding, and the colony soon contains nematodes in all stages of development. Several generations occur in a single season. They pass the winter in an inactive state in infected buds and in soil and rubbish about the crowns of plants.

The alfalfa stem nematode does not adapt itself readily to many host plants in the United States. It is known to occur naturally on alfalfa, sweetclover, and white clover. Two biologic races are known to occur on alfalfa.

Resistance in alfalfa plants was first noted in some that were introduced from Turkistan. Now known as Nemastan, at least 85 percent of these plants are highly resistant or immune to the stem nematode. More recently, two strains were introduced from Iran; about 90 percent are highly resistant or immune. Other searches for resistant material have disclosed occasional resistant plants in some of the varieties commonly grown for hay in the United States. The introductions from Turkistan and Iran have a high degree of resistance to the stem nematode, but they are not high in seed and forage production and are extremely susceptible to some of the foliage diseases. They have been used in Nevada as a source of resistance in developing a variety which will be high in forage and seed production and maintain its high degree of resistance to the stem nematode.

The root knot nematode (*Meloidogyne* species) has characteristic root galls, which are sometimes found upon alfalfa in the region where this nematode is abundant upon other crops. It is not reported as causing serious disease.

The meadow nematode (*Pratylenchus pratensis*) is known to occur on roots of alfalfa and other legumes in Kentucky. Presumably it is widespread.

FRED R. JONES *has been engaged in research on diseases of forage crops since 1917, for 33 years with the Department of Agriculture in cooperation with the Wisconsin Agricultural Experiment Station and later as associate in research in the University of Wisconsin.*

OLIVER F. SMITH *has been engaged in research on forage legumes since 1934—from 1934 to 1940 with the Department of Agriculture in cooperation with the Wisconsin Agricultural Experiment Station and since 1940 with the Department of Agriculture in cooperation with the Nevada Agricultural Experiment Station.*

Leaf scald of tall fescue.

Bacteria, Fungi, and Viruses on Soybeans

Howard W. Johnson,
Donald W. Chamberlain

Twenty-five parasitic diseases are common on soybeans in the United States. They are a constant menace to the crop. Three are caused by bacteria, nineteen by fungi, and three by viruses.

THE BACTERIAL diseases are bacterial blight (caused by *Pseudomonas glycinea*); bacterial pustule (*Xanthomonas phaseoli*); and wildfire (*Pseudomonas tabaci*).

The fungus diseases and the fungi that cause them are alternaria leaf spot (species of *Alternaria*), brown stem rot (*Cephalosporium gregatum*), frogeye (*Cercospora sojina*), purple seed stain (*Cercospora kikuchii*), two kinds of anthracnose (*Colletotrichum truncatum* and *Glomerella glycines*), target spot (*Corynespora cassiicola*), stem canker (*Diaporthe phaseolorum* var. *batatatis*), pod and stem blight (*Diaporthe phaseolorum* var. *sojae*), fusarium blight or wilt (*Fusarium oxysporum* f. *tracheiphilum*), charcoal rot (*Macrophomina phaseoli*), yeast spot (*Nematospora coryli*), downy mildew (*Peronospora manshurica*), phyllosticta leaf spot (*Phyllosticta sojicola*), pythium root rot (*Pythium ultimum*), rhizoctonia root rot and blight (*Rhizoctonia solani*), stem rot (*Sclerotinia sclerotiorum*), sclerotial blight (*Sclerotium rolfsii*), and brown spot (*Septoria glycines*).

The virus diseases are soybean mosaic (caused by *Soja* virus 1), yellow bean mosaic (caused by *Phaseolus* virus 2), and bud blight (caused by the tobacco ring spot virus).

BACTERIAL BLIGHT is one of our most widespread diseases of soybeans. It can affect the stems and pods, but is most common and conspicuous on the leaves. The first symptoms on the leaves are small, angular, yellow spots, frequently water-soaked at the center and sometimes surrounded by a small yellowish-green halo. Later the spots become brown or black as the tissue die, with marginal water soaking around the dead central part and yellowing of the surrounding area. Many small infections sometimes run together, causing large dead areas on the leaf. Under certain conditions the infection travels along the tissues next to the veins. At times this may result in badly shredded leaves, especially during periods of wind and rain. Heavy infection may cause defoliation. Bacterial blight is likely to be most serious during periods of cool weather and frequent rain. The bacteria are seed-borne and can survive also on dead leaves from one growing season to the next. Susceptibility varies with the varieties. Flambeau and Hawkeye, for example, appear to be less susceptible than most northern varieties, but are not immune.

Bacterial pustule is found to some extent over most of our soybean areas. In the Northern States its prevalence and severity seem to vary considerably with the season, but in the South it is more uniformly severe. Although the pods may become infected, it is most common on the leaves. The symptoms are much like those of bacterial blight. At first they appear as small, yellowish green spots with reddish-brown centers, more conspicuous on the upper surface of the leaf. A small, raised pustule usually develops at the center of the lesion, especially on the lower leaf surface. This is the stage at which the disease is most readily distinguished from bacterial blight. The pustule and the absence of water soaking serve to distinguish bacterial pustule from blight. The latter shows water soaking at the center or at the margin of the dead area in the early stages of infection.

ion. In bacterial pustule, small infections may run together and cause large, irregular brown areas surrounded by a yellow margin. Parts of the brown dead area may break out, giving the leaf a ragged appearance. The bacteria overwinter in diseased leaves and also are seed-borne. Although most commercial varieties are susceptible to bacterial pustule, the soybean variety CNS is highly resistant. Ogden also has some resistance.

Wildfire was first recognized as a disease of soybeans in 1943. It was reported in most of the North and South Central States in 1944. Generally it is more serious in the Southern States than in the Midwest. The symptoms are distinctive. Light-brown necrotic spots of variable size, surrounded by broad yellow halos, appear on the leaves. At times the necrotic spot is dark brown or black with an indistinct halo. In damp weather the lesions enlarge and run together, forming large dead areas on the leaf. Such severe infection may cause considerable loss of leaves. Several investigators have noted that wildfire infection is most prevalent when bacterial pustule is common. The presence of pustules at the center of wildfire lesions has led to the belief that wildfire infection takes place most readily when the leaves are already infected with pustule. Experimental evidence obtained at the North Carolina and Illinois Agricultural Experiment Stations indicates that most wildfire infection takes place through the bacterial pustule lesions and that bacterial blight lesions may also serve the same purpose. Attempts to infect soybeans with the wildfire disease in the absence of other bacterial diseases have been largely unsuccessful. Further, the variety CNS, which is highly resistant to bacterial pustule, has remained generally free of wildfire infection in the field. Tests at the North Carolina station show that the organism is seed-borne and that it can live for 3 to 4 months in infected leaves on the ground. In buried leaves, the organism lived less than 4 months. Seed stored for 18 months produced plants free of wildfire. It appears that fall plowing might give some control of infection that is carried over in diseased leaves.

OF THE DISEASES CAUSED BY FUNGI, we discuss only the more important and representative ones.

Brown stem rot is rather limited in distribution. It was first discovered in central Illinois in 1944, and has become one of the most serious diseases of soybeans in the State. It has been confined largely to the Midwest—notably Illinois, Indiana, Ohio, and Iowa. It occurs also in parts of Missouri, Minnesota, Kentucky, and Canada. The fungus enters the plant through the roots and lower stem. The first symptoms appear in late July or early August. No outward signs of the disease appear then, but when infected stems are split open, a brown discoloration can be seen inside the lower part of the stem. Cool weather in August favors the progress of the disease. Eventually the browning becomes continuous throughout the stem. Sustained high temperatures in July and August suppress the disease. Leaf symptoms appear in late August or early September. A sudden blighting and drying of the leaves takes place so rapidly that the grower often suspects frost damage. The leaf tissues between the veins turn brown; those near the veins remain green for several days. Soon the entire leaf withers. Seen from a distance, a badly infected field has a brownish appearance; a normally maturing field is yellow green. Considerable lodging occurs in diseased fields. The size of the seeds may be reduced. One of the peculiarities of brown stem rot is that leaf symptoms do not always occur. In some seasons the disease may escape notice entirely unless the stems are split open for examination. Observations indicate that leaf symptoms occur during a warm, dry period following a week or two of cool weather in August. Brown stem rot is soil-borne. We have no evidence that it is carried on the seed. The only control measure we know is a rotation wherein soybeans are grown in a field only once in 3 or 4 years.

Pod and stem blight kills the plants in the later stages of development. It can be identified by the numerous, small, black fruiting bodies (pycnidia) that appear on the stems and pods of infected plants. On the pods, the pycnidia are scattered; on the stems they usually are arranged in rows. The disease occurs over most of the United States. High humidity and rain favor the production and spread of the spores from the pycnidia. Wet seasons are likely to show more damage from pod and stem blight than dry ones. The disease is seed-borne. The fungus can also overwinter on diseased stems in the field. Sanitation, the use of disease-free seed, and crop rotation are recommended as control measures.

Stem canker and pod and stem blight were considered one disease for many years. A. W. Welch and J. C. Gilman at the Iowa Agricultural Experiment Station discovered in 1947 that two separate diseases were involved. They found that pod and stem blight attacks older plants nearing maturity. Stem canker kills plants earlier in the season. Stem canker appears to be more common in the Midwest, especially in Illinois, Indiana, and Iowa, than in other regions. It usually appears after mid-July. Dead plants, with the dried leaves still attached, may be the first indication of its presence. A brown, slightly sunken type of lesion girdles the stem, usually at the base of a branch or leaf petiole. The stem canker fungus does not produce pycnidia on the infected plant, but sexual fruiting bodies (perithecia) develop on dead stems in the field during the winter. The spores (ascospores) produced in them serve to spread the disease during the following season. Stem canker, like pod and stem blight, is seed-borne. Since diseased stubble in the field is a source of infection in both diseases, the same control measures are recommended as for pod and stem

blight. We have no variety that is r sistant to stem canker. Hawkeye seer to be very susceptible.

Anthracnose of soybeans is caused two species of fungi. Each produc similar lesions on the petioles, sten and pods of plants nearing maturi The diseased areas have a dark, stu ble-bearded appearance because of t dark spines (setae) that emerge fro the numerous black, fungus fruiti: bodies (acervuli) that develop. *Glo erella glycines* was first reported as t causal agent of the disease in t United States. More recently *Colle trichum truncatum*, which causes ste anthracnose of lima bean, has be proved capable of attacking soybea The latter is probably the fungus m commonly associated with soybe: anthracnose. When soybean seeds i fected with either of these fungi a planted, many of the germinati: seeds are killed in the ground. T seedlings from such seed that emer from the soil often have brown, sunk cankers on the cotyledons. The fung may grow from them into the you stem. Those preemergence and po emergence seedling losses are probak more serious phases of soybean a thracnose than are the more evide symptoms on older plants. Seed tre: ment prevents some of the loss seedlings, and thus improves the sta obtained from anthracnose-infect seed. It does not eliminate the disea: however, because both fungi can ove winter also in diseased stems left the field. Fall plowing and rotatie should be practiced to avoid outbrea of the disease that may arise from ove wintered, diseased stems.

The first report of the frogeye disea of soybeans in the United States w from North Carolina in 1926. It primarily a foliage disease and characterized by an "eyespot" cor posed of a gray or tan center and narrow, reddish-brown border. The is no chlorotic tissue around the spo The reddish-brown color merges a ruptly with the green of the norm leaf. Heavily spotted leaves usual fall prematurely, thus causing a loss to the hay and seed crops. Stem infections are less numerous and somewhat less conspicuous than those on the leaves. They appear in the field in large numbers only in late fall when the plants are maturing seed. Stem lesions are elongated and have some shade of red when young. They become brown, then smoke gray, or almost black with age. Pod infections also occur late in the season. The fungus frequently grows through the pod wall and infects the seed. The causal fungus overwinters on diseased leaves and stems and apparently is introduced into new fields and communities through the planting of infected seed. Seed treatment has failed to give satisfactory control of the disease in field tests. Crop rotation should aid in holding it in check. When frogeye is abundant in a field soybeans should not be planted on the land the following year. The disease has been increasing in prevalence in some areas. Experimental tests of susceptibility of varieties and strains have been conducted at the Indiana Agricultural Experiment Station.

Target spot affects primarily the soybean leaves. The fungus also causes spotting of the petioles, stems, pods, and seeds. On the leaves, the spots are reddish brown, circular or irregular in shape. They vary from pin-point size when immature to one-half inch or more in diameter. The larger spots are sometimes distinctly zonate, and the common name target spot was suggested by such zonation. The spots of dead tissue are frequently surrounded by a dull-green or yellow-green halo, thus resembling wildfire. They may be told from the latter by their reddish-brown color and by the zonation, if any. Narrow, elongated spots are sometimes observed along the veins on the upper leaf surface. On petioles and stems, the spots are dark brown and vary from mere specks to elongated, spindle-shaped lesions. Pod spots are generally circular, about one-sixteenth inch in diameter, with slightly depressed purple-black centers and brown margins. The fungus penetrates the pod wall in some cases and causes a small blackish-brown spot on the seed.

The disease was first reported in the United States in 1945. It quickly became prevalent on soybeans grown in the alluvial soil area near the Mississippi River in Louisiana, Mississippi, and Arkansas. It is known to occur also on the Coastal Plain in North Carolina, South Carolina, Georgia, Florida, Alabama, and Mississippi and in the hill section of Mississippi. It possesses the potentiality of becoming a serious disease of soybeans in the southern producing areas. It had not been reported in the Corn Belt States in 1953. Ogden, the variety grown most commonly in the South, has moderate resistance. Soybean breeders and pathologists are on the alert to prevent the release of new soybean varieties more susceptible to this disease than Ogden. The fungus attacks cowpeas as well as soybeans, and growing those two crops close together or in sequence probably should be avoided. Rotation and plowing under of crop refuse in the fall should be of aid in controlling target spot.

A spotting of soybean leaves caused by one or more species of *Phyllosticta* has been known to occur in the United States since 1927. In some years the disease has caused appreciable premature defoliation in localized areas, such as the Eastern Shore of Maryland and Southeast Missouri. The leaf spots are round to oval, light or dark brown in color, and approximately one-quarter inch in diameter. Spots near the margin of the leaf blade frequently coalesce to give the leaf margin a fired appearance. The small, black, fruiting dots of the fungus are found abundantly on the leaf spots. Severely attacked leaves fall from the plants prematurely. The fungus also causes lesions on the petioles and stems, which add to the total injury. Lesions on the soybean pods have been reported from Germany and were observed in the United States for the first time in 1951.

An ascospore-producing stage of the causal fungus has been reported from the Orient but has not been observed in the United States. Plowing under the crop refuse in the fall should aid in controlling the disease by destroying much of the overwintering inoculum.

Downy mildew of soybeans is characterized in its early stages by indefinite yellowish-green areas on the upper surface of the leaves. In severe outbreaks, entire leaflets are thus discolored. As the disease progresses, those areas become grayish brown or dark brown and have yellowish-green margins. Severely infected leaves fall prematurely. A grayish and moldlike growth develops on the under surface of the lesions. The spores produced on the growth spread the disease from plant to plant. Besides these externally borne summer spores, the thick-walled resting spores develop within the leaf tissues. They overwinter in the fallen leaves and probably provide inoculum for infecting the next season's crop. The causal fungus also grows within the pods and covers part of the seeds with a white crust composed largely of the thick-walled resting spores. When such seeds are planted, a small percentage of the seedlings have the fungus growing within them. The first leaves to unfold on such seedlings usually are covered with mildew growth and thus provide centers of infection in the new season's crop. Downy mildew occurs throughout the soybean-growing areas of the United States. In some years it is one of the most prevalent soybean diseases. Severe epidemics have not been observed. The loss appears to be restricted to more or less premature defoliation, depending on seasonal conditions. The existence of races of the downy mildew fungus was proved by work conducted at the Wisconsin Agricultural Experiment Station. Differences in susceptibility have been observed in soybean strains and varieties. Should the disease become more severe, breeding resistant varieties would therefore appear to be possible.

Purple seed stain was first found on soybeans in the United States in 1926, when a report from the Indiana Agricultural Experiment Station directed attention to the objectionable nature of the discoloration from the standpoint of the producer of pure seed. The disease has since been observed in most other States where soybeans are grown. Weather conditions prevailing as the seed mature apparently have a pronounced influence on the percentage of discolored seeds that develop, since this varies widely from year to year with a given variety. Under some conditions, 50 to 100 percent of the seeds of certain varieties may be discolored. The symptoms of purple stain are most evident on the seeds, but the causal fungus also attacks the leaves, stems, and pods. On the seed, the discoloration varies from pink or light purple to dark purple and ranges from a small spot to the entire area of the seed coat. Cracks often occur in the discolored areas, giving the seed coat a rough, dull appearance. When diseased seed are planted, the fungus grows from the seed coats into the seedling leaves (cotyledons) and from them into the seedling stem (hypocotyl) of a small percentage of the seedlings. The fungus produces spores abundantly on the diseased seedlings and the wind-blown and rain-splashed spores lodge on the leaves of nearby plants. The leaf spots caused by the spores soon produce a secondary crop of spores, which cause infections on other leaves, stems, and pods. The fungus probably survives the winter in diseased leaves and stems as well as in infected seed. Varietal differences in susceptibility have been observed, and breeding for resistance to purple stain appears to be possible. Seed treatment aids in preventing loss of seedlings, but will not assure freedom from purple stain in the seed crop. Dusting with copper dusts during the growing season has given partial but inadequate control of purple seed stain in tests conducted at the North Carolina Experiment Station.

Charcoal rot attacks the roots and he base of the stem of the soybean lant. When the bark is peeled from hose parts, small black specks (the clerotia or propagating bodies of the ausal fungus) may be seen. The specks requently are abundant enough to mpart a grayish-black color, like char-oal, to the tissues beneath the bark. Occasionally the fungus produces porebearing structures (pycnidia) on esions on the soybean stem. The fun-us appears to be a rather weak para-ite of soybeans and attacks young lants only when their growth is re-arded by hot, dry weather, poor soil, r some other unfavorable condition. The fungus is widely distributed in oils in the warmer sections of the Jnited States, and attacks other culti-ated plants and weeds, as well as oybeans.

Sclerotial blight, like charcoal rot, is haracterized by a rot at the base of he plant stem, but it differs from the atter in that the fungus sclerotia are arger, rounder, and brown instead of lack. Further, they are produced on cottony, mycelial growth on the out-ide of the stem, rather than under the ark. Attacked plants die prematurely, ometimes before the seed has formed. The disease is found in the sandy soil reas of the South where high summer emperatures occur, and the common ame "southern blight" is sometimes pplied to this disease. Losses may be s high as 25 to 30 percent of the plants, ut it is more common to see small cattered areas of killed plants among he healthy ones. Under favorable con-litions, the disease can cause a spotting f the soybean leaves as well as the asal stem rot. The fungus attacks a vide variety of plants, including prac-ically all the summer legumes adapted o the South. Attempts to select soy-ean plants resistant to sclerotial blight ave been made at the Georgia Agri-ultural Experiment Station without uccess.

Fusarium blight or wilt occurs on andy soils in the Southern States but as never caused as extensive losses as have the similar wilts of cotton, cow-pea, and watermelon. Wilting is not a prominent symptom on soybeans. In-stead, the leaves of attacked plants yel-low and fall off prematurely and the plants then die. When the stem base and taproot of an attacked plant are split longitudinally, a brown or black discoloration of the vascular tissues is evident, as in the case of other diseases of this type caused by species of *Fusa-rium*. Work reported from the South Carolina Agricultural Experiment Sta-tion in 1950 showed that one or more races of *Fusarium oxysporum* f. *trachei-philum* can cause such symptoms on soybeans. In 1951, the workers in South Carolina reported that the cro-talaria wilt fungus, *Fusarium udum* f. *crotalariae*, also can infect certain varie-ties of soybeans and cause wilt. Most varieties of soybeans grown in the South appear to be resistant to fusa-rium wilt. The disease therefore should not become one of major importance unless newly released varieties prove susceptible or more virulent races of the causal fungus develop. A root rot of soybeans caused by a species of *Fusarium* has been observed in Illinois and Wisconsin—probably not the same species as those reported on soybeans in the South.

Rhizoctonia root rot of soybeans occurs in the Midwest as an early-season disease. It attacks young plants where the soil is unusually wet. The fungus causes a reddish-brown decay of the cortical or outer layer of the main root and basal stem. It destroys much of the secondary root system. The plants wilt and die. Dead plants typically appear in areas 4 to 10 feet in diameter, usually distributed at irregular intervals over the field. The disease is of importance only in wet seasons. In 1950 and 1951, for ex-ample, when unusually frequent rains fell through July, rhizoctonia root and basal stem rot was found up to mid-August through the Midwest. As the soil dried out, such plants died or showed wilting at midday. When pulled and examined, the basal portion of the taproot, with its secondary roots, was found to be completely destroyed. Such plants frequently had developed new roots just below the soil line and partially recovered from the injury. As the upper layer of soil dried out, the plants could no longer obtain sufficient water. Twelve soybean strains with a high degree of resistance to rhizoctonia root rot have been selected at the Minnesota Agricultural Experiment Station. The development of varieties resistant to this disease appears possible. Seed treatment in Minnesota has given some promise of controlling damping-off and root rot due to *Rhizoctonia*, especially when the fungicide is pelleted on the seed. The fungus sometimes attacks the aerial portions of the soybean plants in the South and causes a spotting or blighting of the leaf blades. The blighted areas are irregular in shape and light buff to almost white in color. This phase of the disease has been observed in soybean fields in the eastern part of North Carolina and in Louisiana.

THE THREE VIRUS DISEASES are mosiac, yellow mosaic, and bud blight.

G. P. Clinton reported mosaic in Connecticut in 1916 under the name of chlorosis, or crinkling. M. W. Gardner and J. B. Kendrick of the Indiana Agricultural Experiment Station in 1921 established the virus nature of the disease and the fact that it is seed-transmitted. K. Heinze and E. Kohler, working in Germany, demonstrated in 1940 that aphids transmit the virus. R. A. Conover at the Illinois Agricultural Experiment Station in 1948 found that soybean mosaic actually consists of two diseases, mosaic and yellow mosaic. The third virus disease, bud blight, was first reported in 1941 in Indiana. Since that time it has appeared throughout the Midwest and in Canada.

Soybean mosaic is commonly found over all the soybean areas of the United States. Symptoms appear as a distortion of the leaves, which may be narrower than normal, with margi turning downward. Some of the vari ties (especially some of the vegetab varieties, such as Bansei) may show severe ruffling along the margins of t main veins and stunting of the plar In oil-type varieties, temperature h a marked effect on leaf sympton Plants that have leaf distortion ear in the season show progressively le evidence of the disease with the ons of high summer temperatures. Son of the vegetable varieties, howeve continue to develop leaf distortion r gardless of temperature. Plants a fected by mosaic produce misshap pods and fewer seed than normal plan Mosaic is seed-borne. Therefore, i fected plants should be rogued fro fields where soybeans are grown f seed. Leaf symptoms strongly resex bling those of mosaic are frequent caused by the application of 2,4– The widespread use of the chemical weed control has led to many fa reports of mosaic in fields near the s of application. Especially on win days, spraying with 2,4–D may resu in injury to soybeans several hundr feet away. Most of the injury seems be temporary, with only 3 or 4 leav showing distortion, and the affect plants then recover. Whether this h any effect on yield is not known.

Dr. Conover established in 1948 th yellow mosaic of soybeans was caus by *Phaseolus* virus 2, the virus causi the yellow mosaic of garden bean. T leaves of infected plants are not d torted as in common mosaic. T younger leaves show a yellow mottlir scattered in random spots over t leaflet, or sometimes an indefin yellow band along the major ve Rusty necrotic spots develop in t yellowed areas as the leaves matu Infected plants are not noticeal stunted. We have no evidence that t disease is seed-borne. Its effect yield is not serious. The disease widely distributed in the Midwest, b infection thus far has not exceeded percent in any field. Apparently it not common in the South.

Bud blight, the most serious of the three virus diseases, occurs throughout the soybean areas of the Midwestern States and in Ontario. It occurs rarely in the South. Losses up to 100 percent occurred in some midwestern fields between 1943 and 1947. Bud blight has decreased considerably, both in severity and prevalence since then. The symptomatology of bud blight is varied. When young plants are infected before blossoming, the tip bud turns brown, curves markedly, and becomes dry and brittle. Often the leaf immediately below the tip bud shows a rusty flecking. The plant is dwarfed and produces no seed. There is sometimes a browning of the pith inside the stem in the region of the nodes below the blighted terminal bud. If infection takes place about blossoming time, the plant may produce small, undeveloped pods, or no pods at all. Later infection may result in the formation of poorly filled pods or pods that show a conspicuous purple blotching. Many of these drop prematurely. Plants infected with bud blight remain green after normal plants have matured and are thus easily found in the fall. Bud blight is caused by the tobacco ring spot virus. There is no definite evidence that it is seed-borne. The disease usually appears first at the border of a field, progressing inward. That suggests an insect carrier, but such an insect has never been found. In Nebraska in 1951, H. J. Walters demonstrated that grasshoppers can carry this virus from tobacco to tobacco. Whether that holds true for soybeans we do not know. There is no known resistance to bud blight in any soybean variety and no effective control. Because of its direct effect on yield, it is potentially one of the most serious diseases of soybeans.

THE USE OF DISEASE-RESISTANT varieties is the most effective and economical measure of control for diseases of field crops. In the older established crops, such as wheat, oats, corn, and cotton, such varieties have been in use for many years. The soybean, being a relatively new major crop in the United States, is still in its infancy with respect to disease resistance. Consequently one of the major problems has been to find resistant types for use in the soybean-breeding programs.

Since 1943 the Department of Agriculture, in cooperation with several State agricultural experiment stations, has conducted a search for disease resistance in soybeans. Varieties grown in 1953 seem to have little resistance to some of our most serious diseases. An intensive effort has therefore been under way to test varieties and strains developed in this country and introductions brought in from other countries, especially the Orient.

A notable instance of progress was the discovery at the North Carolina Agricultural Experiment Station in 1943 that the variety CNS is highly resistant to bacterial pustule. The variety lacks some of the better agronomic characters, but its resistance to pustule makes it a valuable parent for hybridization with other varieties. Lines derived from hybridizing it with superior varieties, such as Roanoke and Ogden, at the North Carolina Station have yielded strains having the same high type of resistance as CNS. The same has been done at the Illinois Station, using Lincoln in the cross with CNS. Those strains give excellent promise of future varieties that combine the pustule resistance of CNS with more desirable agronomic characters, such as a high content of oil, resistance to lodging, and high yields.

About 1,100 plant introductions of soybeans were tested for resistance to bacterial blight at the Illinois Agricultural Experiment Station in 1947. Two that had high resistance to the disease were selected and used in crosses with locally adapted strains. Even in the preliminary stages of testing, strains resulting from the matings showed a high degree of resistance to bacterial blight. The hope was to develop from them varieties that have blight resistance plus high yield and oil content. None of the varieties used in the Midwest in 1953 is highly resistant to bacterial blight, but there is considerable varietal difference in susceptibility. Illini, Lincoln, Blackhawk, and Monroe are highly susceptible. Richland and Hawkeye are intermediate. Flambeau and Patoka appear to have some resistance, but develop the disease to some extent.

Workers in the Wisconsin Agricultural Experiment Station reported in 1946 that Mandarin 7, Ottawa Mandarin, Habaro, Dunfield, Mukden, Flambeau, Kabott, Pridesoy, and several Manchu selections were resistant to downy mildew and that Richland and Illini were highly susceptible. Further work at the station, reported in 1950, showed that there were three physiologic races of the causal fungus. The variety Illini was found to be highly susceptible to all three races; Richland susceptible to two; while Chief, Manchu 3, Mukden, and Dunfield were resistant to all three races.

Most, if not all, of the existing varieties are susceptible to rhizoctonia root rot. Work at the Minnesota Agricultural Experiment Station, however, points to the development of future varieties incorporating resistance to this trouble. Reselection from Ottawa Mandarin, Flambeau, and the progenies of certain hybrids yielded 12 lines with a high degree of resistance to rhizoctonia root rot.

The severity of frogeye on certain varieties was observed in southern Indiana and studies of varietal resistance were undertaken at the Indiana Agricultural Experiment Station. The varieties Capital, Flambeau, Hokien, Mandarin (Ott.), Blackhawk, Earlyana, Habaro, Monroe, Richland, Harosoy, Cypress No. 1, Dunfield, Illini, Gibson, Patoka, Hawkeye, and Chief were found to be susceptible. Adams, Lincoln, Anderson, and Wabash were resistant.

Resistance is still unknown for some of our most serious diseases, such as brown stem rot, stem canker, and bud blight. At the Iowa Agricultural Ex-

periment Station, various strains, varieties, and selections have been tested for resistance to stem canker. At the Illinois station, similar tests with introductions, strains, and varieties have been under way for 5 years in a search for resistance to bud blight and brown stem rot. Nothing with high resistance had been found in 1953.

Until such disease-resistant varieties are available, the following practices are recommended to soybean growers as disease control measures: Crop rotation, plowing under of crop residues in the fall, the selection of seed for planting from fields relatively free from diseases, and seed treatment in some areas.

Tests of ways to treat the soybean seed have been conducted in various places since 1925. They have usually shown that the emergence of soybean seedlings can be increased 10 to 15 percent by treating the seed with a suitable chemical disinfectant before planting. Only a few reports, however, have said that an increased yield of soybeans resulted from the increased stand obtained by seed treatment. This failure to increase yields has been due apparently to the fact that the recommended seeding rate of 1 bushel or more to the acre provides sufficient plants for a maximum yield, even though 10 to 15 percent of the potential stand is lost through seed decay and damping-off of seedlings. Consequently treatment of soybean seed has not been recommended as a general practice in the major producing States of the Corn Belt.

In the southern areas, on the other hand, the combination of poorer seed and a cold, wet spring sometimes results in the loss of 20 to 25 percent of the potential stand if the seed is not treated before planting. Under such conditions, yield increases due to seed treatment can be demonstrated, and the practice has been recommended in the South as a disease control measure. A somewhat similar situation exists apparently as one approaches the northern limits of soybean cultivation.

Of the numerous seed-treating chemicals tested on soybeans, Arasan and Spergon dusts at the rate of 2 ounces to the bushel have consistently given good results. The slurry formulations of these materials are apparently just as satisfactory as the dusts and are somewhat more convenient to use. Tests conducted at the Delta Branch Experiment Station, Stoneville, Miss., show that the treatments may be applied in the fall or early winter and, when so applied, will aid in maintaining the germinability of the planting seed during its storage period.

Observations at many places are that seed treatment with those materials will have no serious effects on root nodulation in soils that have grown nodulated soybeans previously. When planting in such fields, therefore, a grower need have no apprehensions regarding the effect of seed treatment on nodulation.

When soybeans are being planted on land for the first time, the situation is somewhat different. Then the seed should always be inoculated with a culture of the root-nodule-forming bacteria just before planting. The presence of a seed-treating disinfectant on the soybean seed at the time of inoculation impairs the efficiency of the inoculation process to a greater or lesser extent, depending on the treatment used. For example, mercurial compounds are generally more injurious to the inoculation than are the nonmercurial seed treatments. For that reason seed treatment is not recommended for the first soybean crop on a field.

Should a grower wish to practice both seed treatment and seed inoculation, the procedures should be in that order. Treating can be done at any time before planting, even in the preceding fall. Inoculating should be done just before planting, whether the seed is treated or nontreated.

HOWARD W. JOHNSON, *a graduate of Ohio State University, obtained his doctorate in plant pathology at the University of Minnesota. He has been engaged in research on forage crop diseases since 1930. He is employed jointly by the division of forage crops and diseases of the Bureau of Plant Industry, Soils, and Agricultural Engineering and the Mississippi Agricultural Experiment Station, with headquarters at the Delta Branch Experiment Station, Stoneville, Miss.*

DONALD W. CHAMBERLAIN *is a graduate of St. Norbert College. He obtained his doctorate in plant pathology at the University of Wisconsin. He has been engaged in research on soybean diseases since 1946. He is employed by the division of forage crops and diseases, and is stationed at the United States Regional Soybean Laboratory Headquarters, Urbana, Ill.*

For further information on diseases of soybeans, the authors recommend: Soybean Diseases in Illinois, *by Dr. Chamberlain and Benjamin Koehler (University of Illinois Extension Service Circular 676, 1951);* Soybean Diseases and Their Control, *by Dr. Johnson and Benjamin Koehler (U. S. D. A. Farmers' Bulletin 1937, 1943); and* Bibliography of Soybean Diseases, *by Lee Ling (Plant Disease Reporter Supplement 204, pages 110–173, 1951).*

Frogeye, bacterial blight, and purple seed stain of soybean are illustrated in the section of color photographs.

Fungus fruiting body.

Legumes in the South

J. L. Weimer, J. Lewis Allison

The annual legumes grown in the Southeastern States are classified into two groups, winter and summer annuals, according to their adaptation. They are grown in rotations, for green manure, intermixed with a main crop but subsidiary to it, following a main crop, and for hay and pasture. Some are grown as seed crops. A few perennial legumes are also grown for soil improvement, erosion control, hay, and pasture.

The winter annuals are field pea (*Pisum arvense*), vetch (*Vicia* species), crimson clover (*Trifolium incarnatum*), lupine (*Lupinus* species), roughpea (*Lathyrus hirsutus*), and bur-clover (*Medicago* species).

The summer annuals are lespedeza (*Lespedeza* species), cowpea (*Vigna sinensis*), velvetbean (*Stizolobium* species), crotalaria (*Crotalaria* species), and alyceclover (*Alysicarpus vaginalis*).

The perennials are kudzu (*Pueraria thunbergiana*), sericea lespedeza (*Lespedeza cuneata*), and big trefoil (*Lotus uliginosus*).

None of them is native to the Southeast. All are susceptible to diseases, some of which are widespread and serious. The diseases are caused by bacteria, fungi, viruses, nematodes, and parasitic seed plants.

Root knot nematodes (*Meloidogyne* species) occur throughout the Southeastern States. They are usually more abundant in sandy soils than in heavy soils and cause greater damage to the roots of susceptible plants during the summer than in the winter, although they are active and do multiply to some extent on the roots of winter crops. All the legumes we named except species of *Crotalaria*, are susceptible to root knot nematodes; their culture in areas where nematodes are present tends to increase the nematode population in the soil and to increase the possible damage to susceptible crops that follow in rotations.

THE FIELD PEA (represented by the Austrian winter) is grown largely as a soil-improvement crop. It has lost favor with some growers because of competition from the blue lupine, its failure to produce seed well in the Southeast, and its susceptibility to diseases.

The most destructive of the diseases in most years is caused by the fungi *Ascochyta pinodella* and *Mycosphaerella pinodes*, which involve so much of the stem tissue and turn it dark brown or black that the name black stem is applied to the disease they produce. All above-ground parts of the plant are susceptible to it. Sometimes the plants are killed before they can produce seed. The disease may live over summer in the seed or soil. The best way to control it therefore is to plant disease-free seed and practice a rotation of 3 or 4 years.

Another common disease of pea is leaf blotch, caused by the fungus *Septoria pisi*. It usually is the first to appear on the seedlings in the autumn. Often it is present a month or so after planting time. It attacks the first leaves, causing the tissues to turn yellow and later brown. Gradually it kills them. Brown or black pycnidia soon appear in the diseased areas. In them are formed the spores, which spread the disease still further. A single blotch may involve the petiole and tendrils and run down these into the stem and girdle it. It usually does not involve as much of the stem above or below the node as does the black stem. The blotch disease continues to spread in winter, when it often is too cold for the black stem. Rotation is the only control method we know of.

Peas are commonly attacked in spring by powdery mildew, caused by the fungus *Erysiphe polygoni*. The mildew attacks the lower leaves first and gradually spreads toward the top. The mildew fungus gives the plant a whitish color as if it had been dusted with flour. Seriously affected plants eventually die. Because the disease does not appear until late spring, it usually is not very injurious if the crop is plowed under for green manure. This disease and the others we mentioned largely are responsible for the low yield of seed. No control method is known.

Root rot, caused by the fungus *Aphanomyces euteiches*, is a destructive disease of peas. In late winter or spring it gives a dwarfed appearance and pale yellow color to the affected plants. The affected roots and underground part of the stem are slightly darker in color than the healthy parts and have a moist rot, mostly on the outer layers. The discolored and dwarfed condition of the tops is brought about by the inefficient functioning of the diseased roots. Many of the plants die but others, although alive, make little growth and set little seed. The Romack variety of pea is resistant to the disease.

Winter peas are susceptible to root knot nematodes but usually are not seriously damaged by them, except in the southernmost part of the pea belt and in some of the soils of the Coastal Plain.

VETCHES are planted largely for soil improvement and winter pasture, but they have lost favor in areas in which lupines can be grown. Diseases also have been a factor.

One of the most common fungus diseases is anthracnose, caused by *Colletotrichum villosum*. On the leaves it produces small, round spots, which first are light green and later become light brown or gray, with a brown or red border. The stem lesions are linear and usually dark brown. On the pods the lesions are dark red, with a darker margin and lighter center. Severe defoliation and death of the entire plant may occur during wet weather. The disease can be controlled by rotation or by planting such resistant species as the bigflower vetch (*Vicia grandiflora*), monantha vetch (*V. articulata*), and Hungarian vetch (*V. pannonica*).

Some species are quite susceptible to a blight caused by the *Ascochyta* fungi that attack pea. The blight causes more or less circular spots on the leaves and long, reddish lesions, which later turn gray on the stems. The lesions usually have a reddish border surrounding the grayish center. Black pycnidia are scattered over the gray area. Pod lesions are like those on the stem. Leaves, stems, and pods may be killed. The disease can be controlled by rotation of crops.

Several species of vetch are rather severely attacked by a leaf spot caused by the fungus *Botrytis cinerea*. Small, dark-red spots are produced on the leaflets, stems, tendrils, and petioles of some species. The spots may be so numerous that they cause considerable defoliation and kill the stems. The disease is especially serious in wet weather. It can be controlled by rotation and by planting resistant species, such as hairy vetch (*Vicia villosa*) and purple vetch (*V. atropurpurea*).

Many vetches are quite susceptible to the aphanomyces root rot. Hairy vetch is resistant and should be used when that fungus is known to occur in the soil. Vetches are susceptible to root knot nematodes but usually are not seriously injured by them.

CRIMSON CLOVER is grown for soil improvement and pasture throughout the Southeastern States and in some places as a seed crop. The development of hard-seeded varieties, such as Dixie and Auburn, which are maintained by volunteer reseeding for several years, has increased its use for pasture.

Crimson clover is prey to several

diseases. Crown and stem rot, caused by the fungus *Sclerotinia trifoliorum*, is the most destructive. It develops and spreads rapidly in cool, wet weather. It can be recognized by the scalded, circular patches of dead and dying plants in affected fields.

The fungus produces small, black, tough bodies about the size of wheat kernels after it has destroyed the plants. The sclerotial bodies carry the fungus through hot weather, which is unfavorable for its growth. They germinate in fall when the weather is again cool and wet. Small, inconspicuous structures like toadstools, which develop from them, produce the spores or seeds of the fungus. These reinfect plants and start the disease off anew each year.

Rotations that use crops not susceptible to the disease are one way of holding it in check. The fungus dies in the soil when susceptible plants are absent. Deep plowing of land is another way of controlling it. The sclerotial bodies are buried deeply and cannot get their sporebearing structures to the soil surface. The normal life cycle of the fungus is broken and it soon dies.

Sooty blotch, caused by the fungus *Cymadothea trifolii*, appears as black, crusty blotches on the under sides of leaves and on petioles. It prefers wet, cool weather and causes the greatest damage in late fall while plants are still in the seedling stage. No control method is known.

Crimson clover is susceptible to root knot nematodes. Nematode injury stunts and yellows the plants.

THE BLUE LUPINE has largely replaced peas and vetches as a soil-improvement crop in places where it is adapted because it grows vigorously and yields abundant seed. The sweet strains of lupine also provide winter forage. Like the other winter legumes, however, the lupines are subject to a number of diseases.

Anthracnose, caused by the fungus *Glomerella cingulata*, is destructive in some areas. It attacks all above-ground parts of the plant. The first symptoms are dark-colored, circular spots on the cotyledons. From those lesions the disease usually spreads to the stem, where it causes black bands, which may eventually girdle the stem and kill the plant. Small, dark lesions, usually one-third to one-half as wide as the leaflet and having light centers and dark borders, may be found on the leaflets. Older stems and branches may have many long, brown lesions, often with concentric rings on the surface. Pod lesions are nearly black and circular or irregular; they may involve half or more of the pod, often killing it and destroying the seeds within. Anthracnose can be controlled by planting disease-free seed on land that has not grown lupines for at least 2 or 3 years. As the fungus in the seed dies in about 18 months, seed held over until the second planting time after harvest is free of disease.

Brown spot, caused by the fungus *Ceratophorum setosum*, appears as small, nearly black spots on leaves, petioles, stems, blossoms, and pods. When the spots are very abundant, severe defoliation results. The spots may be so abundant on the stems that they merge and form large, black cankers, which may girdle and kill the stem. The causal fungus may grow through the pod and enter the seed. The fungus in the seed remains alive for more than 2 years; hence, 2-year-old seed is not disease-free, as is that affected with the anthracnose fungus. Rotation is the only control method known.

All above-ground parts of the lupine plant are susceptible to powdery mildew. The disease appears too late in the spring, except possibly in the extreme southern part of the lupine belt, to do much harm to the part of the crop turned under for green manure, but it can cause defoliation and loss of the seed crop. No control method is known.

Southern blight, caused by the fungus *Sclerotium rolfsii*, may attack lupines. It rots the base of the stem and kills many plants. It usually can be identified by the presence of white mold on the surface of the decayed area. Often, especially in wet weather, small white or brown sclerotia are present on the base of the diseased plant or on the nearby soil. Seedlings and grown plants may be attacked if conditions are suitable. Generally the disease is confined to a plant here and there, but occasionally it kills large numbers of plants. No control method is known.

Lupines are susceptible but are seldom conspicuously injured by root knot nematodes. Occasionally swelling of the roots and dwarfing of the tops of affected plants are seen, especially in areas where the nematodes are abundant.

THE SO-CALLED ROUGHPEA, singletary pea, Caley-pea, or wild winter pea is grown in small areas in the Southeast for soil improvement and pasture. The plant is more resistant to diseases than are most legumes. It may be attacked by some of the diseases described for field peas, such as the Ascochytas, but it seldom is seriously injured by them. Roughpea is susceptible to root knot nematodes but is seldom seriously damaged by them.

SEVERAL SPECIES OF BUR-CLOVER are grown to some extent in the Southeast for soil improvement, forage, and seed. All are susceptible to anthracnose, caused by the fungus *Colletotrichum trifolii*, which also attacks other clovers. The disease may girdle the petioles, thereby killing the leaves and eventually the entire plant.

Another clover disease that sometimes causes considerable injury to burclover is cercospora leaf spot, caused by the fungus *Cercospora zebrina*, which produces dark, circular spots on leaves and linear lesions on the petioles. Many leaves are killed during wet periods. Rotation is the only control method known for the diseases.

Bur-clovers are also susceptible to the root knot nematodes, but, like most other winter annuals, are not seriously retarded by them.

LESPEDEZA is grown extensively in many of the Southeastern States as a summer annual. It is commonly grown intermixed with a main crop but subsidiary to it. Lespedeza is utilized as a hay, pasture, seed, and soil-improvement crop. It is host to several diseases.

Dodder (*Cuscuta arvensis*) is a parasitic seed plant that attacks lespedeza and frequently overruns entire fields in late summer. It retards normal plant growth. Once dodder is introduced into the soil it persists for many years. Rotation with crops that it does not attack is the only known method of control.

Southern blight, discussed earlier as a disease of lupines, also attacks lespedeza and destroys many plants in late summer. Hot, wet weather favors its development and spread. We know of no way to control it.

Powdery mildew, caused by *Microsphaera diffusa*, is also common on lespedeza. Resistance to powdery mildew has been incorporated into Rowan, a new variety.

Root knot nematodes attack lespedeza throughout its entire range and frequently cause severe stunting and yellowing of infested plants. During drought periods such plants die as their root systems are so completely knotted by the multiplying nematode population that they can no longer function properly. Rowan is resistant to root knot nematode and will likely replace susceptible varieties wherever it is adapted.

COWPEAS have been grown in most of the Southeast for many years. The many varieties are utilized for hay, soil improvement, and food. Diseases were recognized as a limiting factor in the production of cowpea at an early date, and some of the first selection for disease resistance was done with this crop.

Wilt, caused by *Fusarium oxysporum* f. *tracheiphilum*, probably is the most serious disease. It affects the vascular systems and causes the plants to wilt and die. Brabham, Buff, Iron, Victor, and Groit are resistant varieties.

Powdery mildew, described earlier as a fungus disease of winter pea and lupine, also attacks cowpeas. White spot, caused by *Aristastoma oeconomicum*, is another fungus disease very common on cowpeas. It often does severe damage to leaves. No control for either disease is known.

Bacterial blight, caused by *Xanthomonas vignicola*, a destructive disease of cowpeas in some areas, produces stem cankers, which blight and often kill infected plants. Brabham, Buff, and Iron are resistant varieties and should be grown in the areas where blight is known to occur.

Cowpeas are host to several viruses, about which little is known.

Root knot nematodes commonly attack cowpeas and retard their growth. The cowpea is a host on which the nematodes multiply rapidly.

VELVETBEANS are grown extensively in limited areas in the Gulf Coast States and are utilized primarily for pasture and soil improvement. Diseases have not been reported destructive on any of the many species that are grown, although several are known to attack velvetbeans. They are susceptible to the southern blight fungus, which has been mentioned as attacking other annual legumes. Two leaf spots, one caused by a bacterium, *Pseudomonas syringae*, and the second caused by a fungus, *Cercospora stizolobi*, are common diseases on velvetbeans. Root knot nematodes attack velvetbeans but are considered less severe than on many other legumes.

CROTALARIA is a summer annual grown on very sandy soils in limited areas in the Southeast. It is commonly planted following an early crop and is used quite extensively to improve soil in peach orchards. It is the only annual legume grown in the region that resists root knot nematodes. This resistance

accounts for its specialized use as a cover crop in orchards and with other perennial plantings that are susceptible to root knot.

Although resistant to root knot, crotalaria is susceptible to several fungus diseases. Stem canker, caused by *Rhizoctonia solani*, destroys many young plants in hot, dry weather. Leaf spot, caused by *Cercospora crotalariae*, is common on crotalaria wherever it is grown and frequently causes severe defoliation. No control methods are known.

ALYCECLOVER is a summer annual grown only in limited areas in the Gulf Coast States. It is utilized as a pasture, hay, and soil-improvement crop. It is very susceptible to root knot nematodes and is quickly killed by them. No other diseases are known to be destructive to alyceclover.

KUDZU, a perennial, is grown quite widely in the Southeast for the control of soil erosion and for pasture and hay. It is a vigorous grower and seldom is injured severely by disease. Small plants are sometimes killed by a root rot caused by the fungus *Rhizoctonia solani*. Leaflets are commonly affected with halo blight, caused by the bacterium *Pseudomonas phaseolicola*, a disease that also attacks the garden bean plant. On kudzu it produces a small, brown center, surrounded by a wide yellow band or halo. Sometimes the halo is several times as large as the brown center. Only when the spots are numerous does much defoliation occur. New leaves are produced so rapidly that the loss of a few of the older ones is of minor importance.

A disease more limited in its distribution but more destructive when it does occur is caused by the fungus *Mycosphaerella pueraricola*. Lesions are confined to the leaves and are dark brown and often have a yellowish margin. Lesions may coalesce over large areas of the leaf, and defoliation results. Leaves having many lesions gradually die and fall off. Kudzu is susceptible to root knot nematodes but seldom is damaged by them.

SERICEA LESPEDEZA is a perennial grown throughout the Southeast. It is widely utilized for hay, pasture, soil improvement, and erosion control. Many of the diseases that attack annual lespedeza also attack sericea. None is considered destructive, however, and on the whole sericea lespedeza is quite free from disease troubles. It is somewhat susceptible to root knot nematodes but is not seriously retarded by them.

BIG TREFOIL is a perennial legume. It is well adapted on the low, wet soils in the coastal areas of the entire region and it is planted with grasses for pasture purposes.

Trefoil is susceptible to a foliage blight caused by *Rhizoctonia solani*. Blight is most destructive during the hot, wet summer season on rank, dense growth. Proper management through grazing is the only means of checking extensive damage from the disease. That does not eliminate the fungus from the soil but does check its destructiveness as a foliage disease of trefoil.

Big trefoil is also susceptible to root knot nematodes. It does not suffer extensive damage from them, however, as it is grown on low, wet land; secondary drought effects frequently associated with root knot damage do not occur.

J. L. WEIMER *was a pathologist in the division of forage crops and disease, Bureau of Plant Industry, Soils, and Agricultural Engineering, until he retired in 1952. He was engaged in research on forage disease problems in the Southeastern United States for several years.*

J. LEWIS ALLISON *is a pathologist in the same division and research professor in North Carolina State College of Agriculture and Engineering. In 1952 he was on leave of absence in Iraq with the Food and Agriculture Organization of the United Nations.*

201500°—53——18

Leaf Diseases of Range Grasses

John R. Hardison

Of the troubles that beset forage grasses, the leaf diseases are the most numerous and often the most conspicuous. Although one or only a few of them may be serious on a specific grass and their individual effect on grasses may be relatively mild, their total damage can be serious.

Leaves killed by disease become weathered, low in food value, and less palatable for livestock. They cut the quantity and quality of hay and pasture. The weakened plants are less likely to withstand drought and severe winters. Even worse is the result in areas of low rainfall. There grasses may have only one chance to make their season's growth. Disease, by robbing plants of normal leaf growth, can impair the carrying capacity of a range or pasture and reduce the yields of seed to a point where self-propagation or artificial reseeding is retarded.

The more prevalent or striking types of leaf diseases are considered here. We discuss successively those of western grasses, southern grasses, and northern grasses.

WHEATGRASSES (species of *Agropyron*) are prey to at least 70 diseases. More than half are leaf troubles, notably rusts, leaf smuts, leaf blotches and spots, bacterial chocolate spot, scolecotrichum brown stripe, rhynchosporium scald, and powdery mildew.

Powdery mildew is caused by the fungus *Erysiphe graminis*. It occurs throughout the northern Great Plains and the Pacific Northwest. It usually is more severe in cool, humid, cloudy climates, although it needs little moisture for spore germination. Therefore the disease also survives in drier places and attacks most of the wheatgrasses there, too.

Powdery mildew occurs as white patches on the leaf blades, sheaths, and inflorescences. The fungus is conspicuous, because most of the mycelium and spores are on the surface. Small rootlike organs, haustoria, penetrate the leaf tissue and absorb nutrients at the expense of the plant. Infected leaves turn yellow and brown. The fungus may kill all the leaves in very susceptible grasses. The result is premature dormancy or unthrifty growth of the plant.

New infections start from windborne spores. Within a week new infections produce abundant spores, which spread to other plants. Thus a little powdery mildew rapidly can become an epidemic. The amount of loss it causes in yield of forage has not been determined, but comparable infection in barley has caused a reduction of 30 percent in yield of grain.

Chemical dusts and sprays control powdery mildew, but they are impractical except when grass is intensively grown for seed. The development of resistant varieties of many grasses is possible.

Strains of powdery mildew that infect wheatgrasses have been found on barley, wheat, wheatgrass, and wild-rye grasses. Other mildew strains that attack barley occur on quackgrass (*Agropyron repens*) and a wild-rye grass (*Elymus dahuricus*). Grasses, therefore, can serve as sources of infection of wheat and barley. Other strains of mildew attack only wheatgrasses and wild-rye grasses. The existence of several different mildew races complicates the problem of breeding mildew-resistant wheatgrasses.

Powdery mildew is also prevalent and sometimes destructive on bluegrasses in the Pacific Northwest and

northern Great Plains. A similar problem in breeding for resistance exists there, because a number of strains infect different species of bluegrass and strains within the species. Resistant plants in many species of bluegrass are known to exist, however.

Wheatgrasses in dry regions are often free from serious leaf diseases. Lack of moisture and coarse leaf texture may explain why few leaf diseases are important on those grasses.

MEADOW FOXTAIL (*Alopecurus pratensis*) is attacked by at least 15 diseases. The most serious leaf troubles are scolecotrichum brown leaf stripe and rhynchosporium scald.

Meadow foxtail grows throughout the northern Great Plains and Pacific Northwest where enough moisture is available. Growth begins in early spring and is best in cool, moist weather—which also favors maximum development of scald.

Scald, caused by *Rhynchosporium orthosporum*, makes blotches on the leaf blades and sheaths, which at first are water-soaked, ovate to irregular, and scaldlike. The color of the blotches changes from a solid, bluish green to zonated, scalded, and brown zones. Finally the centers become pale. West of the Cascade Mountains in Oregon and Washington the disease develops throughout winter and spring and usually causes much leaf killing. A related fungus, *Rhynchosporium secalis*, damages barley, wheatgrasses, wildrye grasses, western brome grasses, and sometimes reed canarygrass in the Northwest and the North Central States.

No variety of meadow foxtail is resistant to scald. Crop rotation and attention to sanitation are recommended. Careful spring burning of residues will reduce infection in some areas but would be difficult in regions where the grass grows during the wet winter and spring months.

BLUESTEM, or beardgrass (species of *Andropogon*) is attacked by a great

ariety of leaf disorders, including leaf
usts, black choke, anthracnose, cat-
ail, leaf spots, and tar spot.

Tar spot, incited by *Phyllachora luteo-
maculata*, is of striking appearance.
The fungus produces black, sunken,
glossy spots on the leaves. Spores
produced in organs immersed in these
black masses start new infections.
Many grasses are attacked by the tar
spot diseases caused by similar species
of this fungus. Control of tar spot has
not been reported. The disease does
not kill the grass, and the effect on
forage and yields of seed has not been
measured.

Septoria leaf spots occur from North
Dakota to New Mexico and are occasionally serious. Bluestem grasses
generally are subject to more injury
from disease in the southern, humid
part of their range.

Research to produce disease-resistant varieties of bluestem has been
started in Kansas. The Kaw strain of
big bluestem, *Andropogon gerardi* (*A.
furcatus*), released by the Kansas State
College in 1950, is relatively free from
disease.

GRAMA GRASSES (species of *Bouteloua*)
are subject to 30-odd diseases. In some
areas phyllachora tar spot and selenophoma eyespot are important leaf
diseases. Leaf rust is often serious.
Other leaf disorders include leaf spots,
choke, scald, and black ring.

Black ring disease gets its name from
the peculiar black organs of a fungus,
Balansia strangulans, which surround
grass culms with a tight collar that
strangles the stem and leaves above
the fungus body. The seed head is often
blighted or is unable to form.

Burning could possibly help control
it by destroying the fungus bodies outside the plant and thus eliminating
spores that otherwise would be disseminated. New spore organs will arise
from the mycelium inside the plant,
however.

Seed infection was a problem in the
1930's when efforts were made to reestablish stands of native grasses in
midwestern drought areas. Among the
native short-grass species used was
Fendler three-awn grass (*Aristida fendleriana*). W. W. Diehl, of the Department of Agriculture, inspected some
of the seed of that grass harvested in
New Mexico for the purpose and found
a high percentage of sterile florets infected by *Balansia hemicrypta*. It may
be necessary eventually to find disease-
free seed when other susceptible
grasses are wanted for regrassing
programs.

Efforts to breed improved, disease-
resistant strains of grama grasses
have been started at agricultural
experiment stations in Kansas and
Oklahoma.

MOUNTAIN BROME (*Bromus marginatus*) and related species are subject to
at least 25 diseases. Foliage troubles
include several leaf spots, anthracnose,
powdery mildew, snow mold, gray leaf
spot, tar spot, bacterial chocolate spot,
scald, leaf rot, char spot, leaf speckle,
brown blotch, brown stripe, rusts, and
bacterial blight. Ordinarily the important leaf diseases are scolecotrichum
leaf stripe, rhynchosporium scald, and
bacterial chocolate spot.

Rescuegrass, *Bromus catharticus*, is
subject to fewer and different diseases,
including bacterial leaf streak.

Chocolate leaf spot, or bacterial
blight, is caused by a bacterium,
Pseudomonas coronafaciens var. *atropurpurea*. The lesions, circular to elliptical
and water-soaked at first, later turn
brown and coalesce to form purplish-
brown areas on the leaf blade and
sheath. Bacterial slime is absent on the
surface of the leaf spots. Spots on the
panicles are smaller and restricted. In
severe attacks the upper nodes may be
killed by secondary infections of the
organism. In such plants the panicles
wither and die, as though injured by
frost.

The disease attacks many grasses. It
is important on wheatgrasses. We do
not know how to control it. The bacteria are believed to overwinter in the
lesions on dead grass. Careful burning

before spring growth should reduce the disease.

BUFFALOGRASS (*Buchloë dactyloides*) suffers from 11 diseases. One of them is a leaf and glume spot, frequently called false smut and caused by *Cercospora seminalis*.

The fungus forms a compact, olive-green mass held by the spines that enclose the seed spikelets. Fungus mycelium penetrates the seed and replaces it with a mass of spores. False smut occurs sporadically in dry areas, although it is abundant in wet years. The disease is especially troublesome when buffalograss is grown under irrigation for seed.

Because it reduces yields of seed, false smut has caused a shortage of seed of improved strains. Regrassing programs in which buffalograss is the chief grass used have therefore been retarded. No strains highly resistant to false smut are available, but we hope plant breeding work at several State and Federal stations in the southern Great Plains will develop some.

WILD-RYE GRASSES (species of *Elymus*) are heir to some 75 ills. Common leaf diseases are rusts, leaf smuts, powdery mildew, ascochyta leaf spot, fusarium head blight, phyllachora tar spot, scolecotrichum brown stripe, selenophoma stem speckle, bacterial chocolate spot, septogloeum tar spot, septoria leaf spots, stagonospora purple brown blotch, and epichloe choke or cattail disease.

Cattail disease is named for the whitish body of the fungus, *Epichloe typhina*, which surrounds grass stems with a tight sleeve like the heads of the cattail plant. It occurs sparingly on a large number of grasses in North America. It is sometimes abundant on bluegrasses in the North Central States. Patches of wild-rye sometimes are heavily infested in Northern and Central States. The disease is apparently restricted to sections that have cool seasons and mild winters or in places where the plants are pro-

tected by snow. It may severel[y] damage seed-producing stands. It i[s] much more important in Europe tha[n] in North America. It is relativel[y] common on prairie junegrass, *Koeler[a] cristata*, over our prairies and on blue[e] grasses and wheatgrasses in limite[d] regions.

The fungus produces a perennia[l] mycelium in the crown buds. In sum[-] mer the mycelium forms a white fe[lt] over the surface of late tillers and ofte[n] covers the seed heads as they emerg[e] from the sheath. The fungus bod[y] usually encloses all the seed spike [or] else parts of the panicle in this typ[e] of inflorescence. In late-flowerin[g] grasses, such as timothy, tillers ma[y] be trapped and delayed or destroye[d.] As the fungus increases in thickness, [it] becomes yellow, then orange, an[d] forms the collar around the leaf sheat[h] or stem.

The disease is transmitted in see[d] of red fescue, *Festuca rubra*, and possibl[y] in other grasses in which disease[d] plants produce seed.

The disease was introduced int[o] Pennsylvania in red fescue seeds fro[m] Hungary. Growers of grass seed shoul[d] look for cattail disease in grass-see[d] crops. With all the present traffic [of] grass seeds from domestic and foreig[n] sources, this and other diseases cou[ld] be introduced and become new prob[-] lems. No adequate control for catta[il] disease has been developed althoug[h] roguing is partly successful.

A fusarium head blight has cause[d] serious seed losses in Russian wild-ry[e,] *Elymus junceus*, in New Mexico. Bact[e-] rial leaf spots are common on the wil[d] rye grasses in the northern Grea[t] Plains. Powdery mildew is fairly ser[i-] ous on Russian wild-rye in Nort[h] Dakota.

CANARYGRASSES (*Phalaris* specie[s]) have nearly 30 diseases, but most [of] the leaf diseases are not serious.

Reed canarygrass, *Phalaris arund[i-] nacea*, is adapted throughout the Wes[t-] ern States, but it grows mainly i[n] locations with abundant moistur[e] such as swampy spots, lake shores, and stream banks. Even so, it generally is free of injurious leaf diseases.

A fungus, *Stagonospora foliicola*, causes a tawny spot on leaves. The lesions, which may be brown, wine-colored, tawny, or buff, sometimes cover the entire leaf blade. The disease has been prevalent in late summer at Mandan, N. Dak., in years of abundant precipitation. The trouble was found in plots and native stands in the Missouri River bottom lands and is common in marshes in Minnesota and South Dakota.

Distinct differences in susceptibility of reed canarygrass plants have been noted in upland plots at the Northern Great Plains Field Station—an indication that varieties resistant to the disease are possible.

FIFTY RECOGNIZED PARASITES occur on the western bluegrasses—mutton bluegrass (*Poa fendleriana*), alkali bluegrass (*P. juncifolia*), Nevada bluegrass (*P. nevadensis*), big bluegrass (*P. ampla*), and related species. Their more important leaf disorders are rusts, scolecotrichum leaf stripe, selenophoma leaf spot, septoria leaf spot, and powdery mildew. Control must be sought for by breeding disease-resistant strains of bluegrass.

FOXTAIL MILLET (*Setaria italica*) is subject to cercospora leaf spot, helminthosporium leaf spots, bacterial leaf spots, downy mildew, gray leaf spot, and 17 other diseases.

Gray leaf spot is common on foxtail millets in the United States; it is a minor, but sometimes destructive, leaf spot on many grasses. Severe spotting progresses to a blighting or blasting of the foliage. The causal fungus, *Piricularia grisea*, is like the fungus that causes the blast disease of rice. No control has been suggested for gray leaf spot. Because the grass is an annual plant, crop rotation should help reduce the disease.

Downy mildew, *Sclerospora graminicola*, is probably the most serious leaf disease on foxtail millet in the United States. Affected plants are dwarfed because elongation of culms is retarded. Excessive tillering from the crown and development of branches from the axillary buds along the culm are characteristic. Leaflike malformations of the floral bracts and failure of kernel development are other common symptoms. A downy mass of spores is common on infected plants in humid areas.

Leaf killing and browning are followed by splitting and shredding of the invaded leaf tissues, especially as plants approach maturity. Excessive proliferation of buds and seed heads combined with little or no kernel development causes a serious reduction in yield if infection is high.

Control of downy mildew is difficult in places where those crops are grown continually over large areas because of general soil infestation and windborne spores. It is difficult also when the crop is sown in areas where the wild *Setaria viridis* is infected.

Formaldehyde, sulfuric acid, and organic mercury compounds are the best seed treatments.

DROPSEEDS (*Sporobolus* species) are attacked by 36 organisms. Leaf diseases include leaf rust, stem rust, ascochyta leaf spot, bacterial leaf spot, powdery mildew, phyllachora tar spot, selenophoma speckle, cercospora leaf spot, septoria leaf spot, stagonospora leaf mold, and false smut.

False smut or head mold, caused by *Helminthosporium ravenelii*, has a striking appearance. The fungus grows over the seed heads and covers the affected parts with a velvety, brownish-olive mantle, which later becomes black and crusted. Head mold is so common on *Sporobolus indicus* and *S. poiretii* that they are called smutgrasses.

It would be a good thing to treat seed to prevent spread of false smut on infected seed, but that cannot control the disease in infested areas because of contamination by wind-borne spores. Burning might help. The use of resistant varieties seems to be the best solution in places where the disease does great damage.

NEEDLEGRASSES (*Stipa* species) suffer from 50 or more diseases. The more important are septoria leaf spots, selenophoma leaf and stem spots, stagonospora leaf blotch, and scolecotrichum brown stripe.

Brown stripe disease is caused by the fungus *Scolecotrichum graminis*. Young leaf infections show water-soaked, circular or oval lesions, which are olive gray in the morning when they are wet with dew and dull gray when they are dry. The spots become brownish purple to ocher with gray centers. They tend to form streaks as the leaves slowly die. The spore-bearing bodies of the fungus can be seen as prominent, black dots arranged in parallel rows.

Many grasses are affected with brown stripe. The fungus causes one of the most important leaf spot diseases of timothy, orchardgrass, bluegrasses, tall oatgrasses, redtop, and needlegrasses. Early maturity of timothy and some other grasses is often forced by loss of leaves killed by the fungus.

Careful burning of dead grass reduces the spores for infection of new leaves. The relationship of infected wild grasses as sources of infection of domestic grasses needs study. Varieties resistant to the disease are needed in the needlegrasses, tall oatgrass, orchardgrass, and many others.

IT IS HARD TO CONTROL leaf diseases of the range grasses. Extensive application of chemical dusts or sprays is out of the question because of the danger of poisoning livestock. Such materials generally are too expensive for use on forage plants even when land is used intensively for pastures. The cost of treating the many low-producing acres on ranges would be prohibitive.

Crop rotation, clipping, and deep plowing obviously are not feasible for range land. Early or late grazing might remove some infected leaves, but that is not wholly effective because animals avoid badly diseased and dead leaves.

Seed treatment may be helpful in preventing introduction of diseases carried on the seed to new areas in the initial reseeding of range land. Spores of many disease fungi are wind-carried into the new plantings from wild stands, however, and nullify much of the value of seed treatment.

Fire is an effective but dangerous means of destroying diseased leaves. By exercising extreme care and utilizing fire breaks and other precautions to prevent uncontrolled range fires, burning can be a cheap method of reducing initial infection by some diseases. There is, of course, a loss of organic matter and the risk of killing valuable perennial grasses, so that undesirable plants might take over the range lands.

All in all, then, the best way to control most range grass diseases is to use resistant plants. Development of disease-resistant grasses requires exact information on behavior of the disease-producing organisms so that tests for resistance can be performed and understood. Such information is not available for many of the leaf diseases.

A good start has been made, however. Research by many workers has shown which species can be grown in various sections of the country. The identity of the organisms causing many grass diseases has been determined. Disease problems are being further clarified. Prospects are good that more and more adapted, high-yielding, disease-resistant grasses will become available eventually to increase forage on range lands.

JOHN R. HARDISON, *a graduate of Washington State College, obtained his doctorate in plant pathology at the University of Michigan. He has been engaged in work on diseases of forage crops since 1942.*

References on leaf diseases of forage crops are given on pages 262 and 267.

Leaf Diseases of Grasses in the South

Howard W. Johnson

The more important perennial grasses that provide summer grazing in the Southern States are Bermuda-grass (*Cynodon dactylon*), carpetgrass (*Axonopus affinis*), and Dallisgrass (*Paspalum dilatatum*).

Bermuda-grass is attacked by two species of *Helminthosporium*. *H. giganteum* causes a zonate eyespot with tan center and brown margin. *H. cynodontis* causes a bleaching and withering, particularly of the leaf tips.

The leaves of carpetgrass are sometimes spotted by a species of *Helminthosporium*, and one species of *Curvularia* has also been reported from leaf spots on this grass.

Dallisgrass is attacked in some areas by anthracnose (*Colletotrichum graminicola*). In spring the leaves sometimes are spotted by *Stagonospora paspali*. Neither has been severe enough to warrant intensive work by plant pathologists.

Johnsongrass (*Sorghum halepense*) is another perennial warm-season grass that is grazed and cut for hay in some parts of the South. It is quite susceptible to the numerous leaf diseases that attack Sudangrass and frequently suffers severe leaf injury.

Tall fescue (*Festuca arundinacea*) is utilized commonly for cool-season grazing in the South. Three leaf diseases of some importance attack it. Leaf scald, caused by *Rhizoctonia solani*, has caused the most serious losses. It causes large, bleached, tan-colored areas on the leaves, especially noticeable in summer. A dark-brown, diffuse, netlike leaf discoloration (net blotch), caused by *Helminthosporium dictyoides*, sometimes becomes rather abundant on leaves of tall fescue during the cool months of fall, winter, and spring.

The leaf spot caused by *Cercospora festucae* has a gray center and a purplish border, which differentiate it from net blotch. Cercospora leaf spot is first evident in spring and becomes more severe as summer progresses. It was first observed on tall fescue in Kentucky in 1944. It became severe on tall fescue at College Station and Temple, Tex., in 1949, and appeared to be responsible for the death of both seedling and mature plants.

TEMPORARY WINTER GRAZING in the South is furnished largely by the early growth of winter cereals (oats, rye, barley, and wheat). The foliar diseases of these grasses are discussed in another section (page 344). Annual ryegrass (*Lolium multiflorum*) is also utilized throughout the South for winter grazing. Its chief foliar disease is crown rust, caused by *Puccinia coronata*. It is discussed on page 279.

Sudangrass (*Sorghum vulgare* var. *sudanense*) and pearlmillet (*Pennisetum glaucum*) are the grasses most widely grown for temporary summer grazing in the South.

Sudangrass is attacked by a number of bacterial and fungus diseases, which limit its usefulness. Pearlmillet is less widely grown and so far has been attacked by fewer parasites.

Bacterial stripe (*Pseudomonas andropogoni*) is probably the most common and destructive bacterial disease of Sudangrass. It occurs also on Johnsongrass and sorghums. It shows as stripes with blunt or jagged ends. The stripes are about one-fourth inch long when young and a foot or more when mature. The color, continuous throughout the lesion, ranges from purplish red to brown or tan, depending on the variety. Abundant bacterial exudate forms over the lesions and dries to form crusts or scales, especially on the lower leaf surface. The scales of exudate are the same color as the stripes.

Bacterial streak (*Xanthomonas holcicola*) is another widely distributed disease of Sudangrass, Johnsongrass, and sorghums. The young lesions are narrow, water-soaked streaks 1 to 6 inches long. They bear beadlike, light-yellow drops of exudate. Red or brown margins later develop, and irregular blotches of color appear in the streaks, breaking their continuity. The streaks may join to form irregular areas that cover much of the leaf blade. At that stage the exudate has dried to thin, white or cream-colored scales, which distinguish this disease from bacterial stripe, which has a darker exudate.

Bacterial spot (*Pseudomonas syringae*) is somewhat less common than the other two bacterial diseases, but some years it occurs abundantly on the leaves of Sudangrass, Johnsongrass, pearlmillet, foxtail millet, sorghums, and corn. The spots, circular to elliptical, vary from tiny dots to almost one-half inch circles in later stages. They appear water-soaked at first. Soon they become dry and light-colored in the center and develop a red or brown border. The spots may unite to form large diseased areas, but they do not elongate to form stripes or streaks. Exudate does not form on the lesions.

Leaf blight, caused by the fungus *Helminthosporium turcicum*, is probably the most destructive disease of Sudangrass in the Southern States. The disease occurs also on Johnsongrass, sorghums, and corn. The causal fungus is seed-borne and lives also on dead plant material on or in the soil. It may cause seed rot and seedling blight, which make it difficult to obtain a satisfactory stand. When the leaves of older plants are attacked, the fungus causes long, elliptical lesions one-eighth to one-half inch wide and several inches long. The lesions may

coalesce and kill large areas of the leaves, so that severely affected plant appear as though they had bee blighted by an early frost.

The center of the individual lesions i usually gray to straw-colored. Th border of the lesions varies fror reddish purple to tan. In warm humid weather, the lesions ar covered with a dark, moldlike growtl of fungus spores. Wind and rai scatter the spores and spread th disease.

Two other species of *Helminthosporiur* attack Sudangrass, but the folia diseases they cause are less damagin than leaf blight. Target spot, cause by the fungus *Helminthosporium sorgh cola*, the more serious, occurs o Johnsongrass and sorghums, as well a Sudangrass. It forms small, round o oval lesions. They consist of alternat light-tan and brown bands of tissues The tissues have a zonate or "targe spot" appearance on varieties such a Tift Sudan, which contain a ta pigment. On common Sudan, whic contains a darker pigment, the lesion are purplish black and are less zonate The disease may become more seriou in the South as the acreage planted t Tift Sudan increases, because while i resists leaf blight it appears to b quite susceptible to target spot.

The second species, *Helminthosporiur rostratum*, is primarily a parasite of cor and pearlmillet but can attack Sudan grass, Johnsongrass, and sorghum The leaf spots it causes are small an light brown in color when young Older lesions have straw-colored cen ters and may coalesce to form large necrotic areas. On sorghums an Sudangrasses having dark pigmen there is some purpling around th lesions.

Anthracnose, caused by the fungu *Colletotrichum graminicola*, occurs com monly on the leaves of Sudangrass Johnsongrass, and sorghums in th South. When young, the spots ar about one-sixteenth inch in diamete circular to elliptical, and reddis purple. Later the spots enlarge an the centers fade to tan or straw color. The border of the mature spots is reddish or brown. Dark-colored fungus bodies (acervuli) develop on the older spots. The spores produced in those structures are spread by wind and rain. Anthracnose lesions develop on the midrib of the leaf quite commonly and cause a rather striking discoloration. The fungus is seed-borne and over-winters also in dead plant refuse on, or in, the soil. Lesions appear on the leaves of seedling plants, but it is usually midsummer before the disease is abundant. It develops rapidly from that time until the plants are mature.

Zonate leaf spot (*Gloeocercospora sorghi*) is a conspicuous disease of Sudangrass, Johnsongrass, and sorghums. It has been reported also on sugarcane, corn, and pearlmillet. The mature spots are large and composed of alternating bands of reddish-purple and tan or straw-colored tissue, forming a zonate pattern. Spots near the leaf margin are semicircular. Those nearer the center of the leaf are nearly circular with irregular, wavy margins. Black sclerotia of the fungus develop within the tissues of the older leaf lesions and the fungus spores are borne in salmon-colored gelatinous masses (sporodochia) in and around the necrotic areas. In some seasons the disease is rather common in the lower Mississippi Valley.

Rough spot (*Ascochyta sorghina*) attacks Sudangrass, Johnsongrass, and sorghums. It has round or oval spots, which are yellowish brown or reddish purple and are covered with small black fruiting bodies. The bodies usually are so abundant that the affected areas feel rough when rubbed between the fingertips.

Gray leaf spot, caused by the fungus *Cercospora sorghi*, is found commonly on Sudangrass, Johnsongrass, and sorghums in the Gulf States. When small, the reddish-purple to tan spots are indistinguishable from other leaf spots, but as they elongate they become covered with a grayish-white fuzz, composed of fungus conidiophores and conidia. The conidia, spread by wind and rain, cause new infections.

Sooty stripe, caused by *Ramulispora sorghi*, occurs in the Southern States on Sudangrass, Johnsongrass, and sorghums. Mature lesions are elongate-elliptical, have a straw-colored center surrounded by a purple border, and usually are covered by numerous black sclerotia. In moist weather, fungus spores are produced in light-pink, gelatinous masses (sporodochia) on the lesions. The sclerotia function primarily in overwintering the fungus and the conidia produced by them are the chief source of infection in the spring.

Rust, caused by *Puccinia purpurea*, frequently attacks Sudangrass, Johnsongrass, and sorghums in the humid Gulf States. It causes the leaves to dry and break off, thus reducing the forage value. Rust pustules occur on both the upper and lower surfaces of the leaf. They are covered at first by a brownish coating. This soon breaks open and allows the chestnut-brown rust spores to escape. Purplish-red or tan areas develop around the rust pustules and the functional efficiency of large areas of leaf tissue is eventually destroyed.

Nonparasitic leaf discolorations caused by environmental conditions or hereditary factors also occur commonly on Sudangrass, Johnsongrass, and sorghums in the South. These lesions lack bacterial exudate and show no evidence of fungus fruiting structures, which serves to differentiate them from the parasitic disorders I have discussed.

SEED TREATMENT and crop rotation help check the diseases of Sudangrass, but the most feasible control measure is the development of disease-resistant varieties.

Tift Sudan, a variety resistant to leaf blight, anthracnose, bacterial stripe, and bacterial streak, was developed through cooperative work by the Department of Agriculture and the Georgia Coastal Plain Experiment Station.

The origin and early testing of this improved variety is described by Glenn W. Burton in Georgia Circular 11, published in April 1943.

Tift Sudan has become popular in the South because of its disease resistance. Plant breeders use it in attempts to improve Sudangrass still more.

Pearlmillet is susceptible to three of the diseases that attack Sudangrass—bacterial spot, zonate leaf spot, and the leaf spot caused by *Helminthosporium rostratum*. Eyespot, caused by *Helminthosporium sacchari*, also occurs on pearlmillet. The fungus infects and blackens the seed and causes a conspicuous leaf spot. Species of *Curvularia* have also been reported from leaf spots and seed of pearlmillet.

A more common leaf disease than any of those is caused by a species of *Cercospora*, which had not been named in 1953. That fungus causes a small, circular to elliptical spot with gray center and reddish-brown border. Both the improved variety Starr and commercial pearlmillet are susceptible to it. The disease usually develops rather late in the summer, however, and so the damage is not great during the pasturing season.

HOWARD W. JOHNSON *is a graduate of Ohio State University. He has a doctorate in plant pathology from the University of Minnesota. He has been engaged in work on diseases of forage crops since 1930. He is employed jointly by the division of forage crops and diseases and the Mississippi Agricultural Experiment Station with headquarters at the Delta Branch Experiment Station, Stoneville, Miss.*

For further reference (see also page 267):

G. W. Bruehl and J. G. Dickson: Anthracnose of Cereals and Grasses, U. S. D. A. Technical Bulletin 1005, 37 pages, 1950.

W. W. Diehl: Balansia and the Balansiae in America, U. S. D. A. Agriculture Monograph 4, 1950.

John R. Hardison: Specialization of Pathogenicity in Erysiphe graminis on Wild and Cultivated Grasses, Phytopathology, volume 34, pages 1–20, 1944; Specialization of Pathogenicity in Erysiphe graminis on Poa and its Relation to Bluegrass Improvement, Phytopathology, volume 35, pages 62–71, 1945.

The Northern Forage Grasses

Kermit W. Kreitlow

Many of the organisms that attack western and southern grasses occur on northern grasses. I mention them briefly and discuss in more detail the other serious diseases on northern grasses.

Redtop (*Agrostis alba*) is a perennial species that occurs most commonly in poorly drained areas but grows well on poor, acid soils. The most widespread and important disease of redtop, brown stripe, is discussed in the section on needlegrasses, page 258.

Redtop also is attacked by rust and smut. In the humid northeastern and north central sections, redtop is damaged by several species of *Helminthosporium*. The most common, *H. erythrospilum*, is termed red leaf spot. It also attacks other species of *Agrostis*.

Small spots, with round, water-soaked areas, develop on leaves. They turn straw-colored, with a reddish or brownish-red border. As the spots lengthen and merge, they form streaks and cause the leaves to wither and turn brown. Sometimes the leaves wither immediately without developing leaf spots. The injury then resembles the effect of drought.

Infection occurs from spores spread by wind and rain. Heavy infection follows periods of warm, wet weather. The fungus overwinters on old, dead leaves. Resistant plants exist within the species, and it should be possible to develop resistant varieties.

Tall oatgrass (*Arrhenatherum elatius*)

is not so widely grown as some species, but it is important in mixtures for hay or pasture in some regions. Brown stripe (*Scolecotrichum graminis*) is one of its most important foliar diseases. It is also susceptible to anthracnose (*Colletotrichum graminicola*), one of the common pathogens on a great many grasses. Anthracnose injures many cereals and grasses in the humid north central area in late summer or autumn as the plants approach maturity. If conditions are favorable for development of the disease, the fungus attacks seedlings, causing stunting and wilting. In older plants, the fungus attacks the culm or leaf sheath, but it may spread into the crown and roots of perennial grasses, frequently causing stands to die out in the second or third season, especially in infertile places. Early attacks cause a general reduction in vigor and premature ripening or dying. The disease is especially destructive to Sudangrass, which it attacks at the height of vegetative vigor in midsummer.

Lesions on leaf sheath or stem are usually light tan with a darker border of red or brown. The center of the lesion usually contains small, dark specks, the fruiting organs of the fungus. Sometimes stems are attacked early at the nodes. The result is premature ripening and shriveling of seed. Affected stems usually bleach and turn brown at the base. On leaves of large grasses like Sudangrass, the fungus forms small round or oval spots, straw-colored with a pigmented border or zonate. The spots eventually form long bleached streaks on which black fruiting organs are scattered.

The fungus is spread by spores and fungus threads (mycelium), which live saprophytically on crop residues. Spores of the fungus can germinate and penetrate uninjured leaves to establish infection. In some grasses the disease is seed-borne and infects seedling roots and crowns. The fungus thrives at 80° F.—the reason for its prevalence in midsummer.

General control measures include adequate soil fertility, crop rotation (but not a sequence of closely related species), complete coverage of old plant residues, and the use of resistant varieties.

Smooth brome (*Bromus inermis*) and related species are severely damaged at times by several diseases. One, brown spot, caused by *Helminthosporium bromi*, is common. It appears as small, dark-brown, oblong spots on the first leaves to develop in spring. The spots later merge and form large, yellowed areas on leaves. Older spots are generally dark purple to brown, surrounded by a yellow border or halo. Affected leaves turn brown from tip to base, then wither and die. Fruiting bodies (perithecia) of the fungus form in diseased leaves in summer and carry the fungus through the winter.

In early spring when adequate moisture is present, ascospores are discharged from the fruiting bodies developed in old leaves the previous summer and are carried by wind and rain to initiate infection on new leaves. All perithecia do not discharge spores at one time, and a continuous supply of inoculum is provided throughout spring and early summer by successive liberation of spores from the fruiting bodies. The disease also may be seed-borne.

Brown spot develops best during cool, wet weather. In the Northern States it reaches its peak about the first week in June. It spreads very little during hot, dry periods of midsummer. It becomes prevalent again in the fall.

Improved varieties of smooth brome resistant to brown leaf spot are being developed at several agricultural experiment stations. They should help reduce losses.

Another disease of smooth brome is leaf scald, caused by *Rhynchosporium secalis*. That fungus also attacks barley, rye, and many other grasses. A different species, *Rhynchosporium orthosporum*, parasitizes orchardgrass and a few other grasses. Leaf scald is widespread in the cooler humid sections of North and South America, Europe, and Asia. It occurs primarily on leaf blades and less extensively on the sheaths. It is most destructive in spring and autumn.

The symptoms, similar on the different hosts, consist first of small, water-soaked, bluish-gray, ovate spots that enlarge to form irregular, light-gray, conspicuous scaldlike blotches. The blotches usually have darker brown margins. Symptoms may develop on the first green leaves. If conditions are favorable, the disease becomes progressively more destructive as the season advances. Scalded leaves are often killed, and almost complete defoliation results. The hot, dry weather of midsummer retards the disease, but it develops again in the fall.

The leaf scald fungus overwinters on dead leaves in old crowns and (in milder climates) in lesions on perennial grasses. Abundant spores are produced in old lesions. Wind carries them to infect new leaves during cool, wet periods. The best temperature for infection lies between 60° and 70° F., but the spores can germinate over a range of 40° to 80°.

A number of specialized races of the fungus must be considered in developing resistant varieties. Resistant lines of smooth brome exist, and new varieties are being developed that contain resistance to the pathogen. Crop rotation, elimination of old plant residues, and spring burning help control the disease.

Leaf spot (*Selenophoma bromigena*), although destructive, is more restricted in its range. It occurs primarily in the Central and Western States, Canada, and parts of Europe. The fungus can attack other species of *Bromus*. It has started to become increasingly prevalent on mountain brome (*Bromus marginatus*) in the West.

The first lesions appear as small, brown flecks on leaves early in spring. The lesions usually remain localized, but if conditions are good they may enlarge and merge. The spots generally are gray and round or irregular. They

have narrow brown borders. Infection often spreads to the stem and seed heads. Infected leaves turn yellow and die; defoliation, stunting, and death result. Tiny fruiting bodies of the fungus develop in the discolored lesions; they frequently drop out of the tissue, leaving small holes in the lesions.

The spores inside the fruiting bodies can remain alive at least 18 months. Probably they overwinter there. Wind and rain carry the fruiting bodies to other plants. The fungus also is carried on the seed.

High humidity and temperature of 60° to 70° F. favor infection. Heavily infected leaves of smooth brome have been reported at St. Paul, Minn., as early as March 15. The disease develops rapidly in April, May, and early June but is relatively inactive in summer. It appears again in September and October.

Crop rotation and spring burning are the best temporary means for control. Resistant varieties may be developed eventually.

Smooth brome and other species of *Bromus* sometimes are seriously damaged by a bacterial disease (*Pseudomonas coronafaciens* var. *atropurpurea*), brown stripe (*Scolecotrichum graminis*), and septoria leaf spot (*Septoria bromi*).

Orchardgrass (*Dactylis glomerata*) harbors many diseases. Some, such as brown stripe (*Scolecotrichum graminis*), scald (*Rhynchosporium orthosporum*), and the rusts, are widespread. Others, such as the leaf spots caused by *Mastigosporium rubricosum* and *Stagonospora maculata*, are more prevalent and destructive in the Northwest and Northeast, respectively. The effects of brown stripe, scald, and rust are discussed on pages 258, 254, and 276; the leaf spot diseases caused by *Mastigosporium rubricosum* and *Stagonospora maculata* are dealt with here.

Mastigosporium rubricosum attacks several grasses besides orchardgrass. The leaf spot fungus is commonly found in spring and autumn in the more humid parts of the Northwest. Numerous dark-purple or brownish flecks form on the leaves and enlarge to elliptical spots with ashy-gray or fawn-colored centers. Later the spots become gray with red or purple borders. When lesions are numerous, leaves are killed, and the plants are largely defoliated.

Spores produced in old lesions spread the disease. The spores help the fungus survive the winter and summer. The fungus also can survive in a vegetative state in old leaves.

Infection develops most extensively during rainy, foggy weather and is largely checked during long periods of low humidity. Near the west coast, the disease is most evident during the winter and is largely checked in summer.

Very little has been done to control the disease. It may be possible to select resistant lines.

Stagonospora maculata is a fungus that causes effects similar to the mastigosporium leaf spot, but it occurs primarily in the Northeast. It attacks only orchardgrass but related species can attack many grasses.

It produces small, somewhat elongated, dark-brown or dark-purple lesions on leaves of orchardgrass. Leaves of some plants are so heavily spotted that they turn brown, wither, and die prematurely. Sometimes the brown area develops first at the tip of a leaf and gradually works back toward the base until the leaf is completely brown. On other leaves long, brown streaks develop along the margins.

Tiny sunken fruiting bodies develop in the dead parts of infected leaves. The spores overwinter inside the fruiting bodies, which remain embedded until the leaves shred or disintegrate. In the Northeast new infections occur early in the spring on the first green leaves. Spores emerge from the fruiting bodies throughout the growing season and new lesions can be found during the summer except in periods of prolonged hot, dry weather. The disease reaches its peak shortly before

plants head or at the time of heading and severely infected plants are almost completely defoliated. Infection is abundant in fall and new spots develop until snowfall. Agricultural experiment stations and the Department of Agriculture have cooperated in the Northeast to incorporate only the most resistant lines into new varieties of orchardgrass. Although no immune or highly resistant plants have been found, the level of resistance in new strains of orchardgrass is enough to help overcome some of the damaging effects of the disease.

Timothy (*Phleum pratense*) is harmed by a number of diseases of other species of grasses. Among them are stem rust, stripe smut, and Scolecotrichum brown stripe. Timothy also is attacked by eyespot and bacterial stripe.

Eyespot is caused by a fungus (*Heterosporium phlei*), which is widespread on timothy and related species. It occurs most abundantly in the East and Midwest and to a limited extent in the far West. It has also been reported in Europe and Japan.

The small, oval spots generally have light-colored centers with narrow, violet borders, which later fade to brown. Heavily infected leaves become yellow, then brown, and wither prematurely.

Despite the prevalence and sometimes damaging effects of the disease, we know little about its life history. The fungus produces relatively few spores in the field, so it probably overwinters on green leaves. Spots can be found at almost any season. The spores can germinate at temperatures as low as $40°$ and as high as $90°$.

Most of the newer varieties of timothy possess some resistance to leaf spot diseases. Continued selection and breeding for resistance should further reduce the prevalence of this disease.

Bacterial stripe is caused by a species of bacterium (*Xanthomonas translucens* var. *phlei-pratensis*) capable of attacking many grasses and cereals.

Bacterial stripe is most prevalent during wet seasons. Damage therefore fluctuates considerably from year to year. On leaf blades of young shoots, streaks indicative of infection vary from barely visible lesions to those more than an inch long. The streaks are at first small, water-soaked, translucent areas, which gradually elongate and turn yellowish, with only isolated translucent areas. Later they become brownish black, with small, golden areas. After periods of warm, humid weather, bacterial streaks may extend from the tip of the leaf to the base. Yellowish droplets of bacterial exudate may form on the streaks. When dry, the droplets form hard, resinous granules. Sometimes emerging heads are distorted, as the bacterial exudate occasionally makes the heads stick inside the spiral whorl. In the hay stage, streaking of blades and sheaths of flag leaves is noticeable. During cooler periods, especially in the fall, streaks are shorter and change rapidly from translucent to dry, brown areas.

The bacteria that cause stripe of grasses and cereals can overwinter in tissues of perennial grasses and in the soil. They can infect new leaves any time during warm, wet periods and are spread principally by wind and rain. Mowing and grazing can also spread bacterial diseases, particularly if the foliage is moist from rain or dew.

Resistant varieties need to be developed in order to control the disease.

Kentucky bluegrass (*Poa pratensis*) suffers from leaf spot, caused by the fungus *Helminthosporium vagans*. The disease is common in Europe and the United States, particularly the eastern and midwestern sections. The disease is most conspicuous as a leaf spot, but it also attacks the stems and crowns.

Leaf spot occurs as purple-black to reddish-brown spots, which may be only the size of a pinhead or may extend the width of a leaf blade. Older spots usually have a light-colored center surrounded by a red or brown margin. Sometimes paired, symmetrical lesions occur on opposite halves of a leaf blade—usually an indication that infection occurred while the leaf was tightly folded and the infection area was separated into two halves as the leaf unfolded. When the leaf sheath is infected, the flower heads inside are also frequently attacked. If infection occurs at the base of a culm, it frequently spreads to the crown and causes a browning of the tissues, so that the plant is weakened or killed. Seedlings are quickly killed by stem infection. Diseased leaves generally wither from the tip and die.

Infection throughout the growing season occurs from spores produced on older lesions. The spores are disseminated by wind and rain to healthy leaves. The fungus overwinters in lesions on living leaves and stems and by spores on dead leaves. There is also evidence the disease is seed-borne.

Cool, wet weather of spring and fall favors maximum development of the disease. Pure thick stands of Kentucky bluegrass also are more seriously affected than are mixed stands of grasses. Damage from the disease is accelerated by frequent close clipping, as the succulent new growth is more susceptible. Application of nitrogenous fertilizers in summer stimulates formation of new growth, which in turn favors development of the disease. Damage is also severe when a heavy mat of clippings or hay is left on the grass during moist weather.

Except on lawns or park areas, chemical dusts or sprays are impractical. There may be some merit in seed treatment. Resistant lines of Kentucky bluegrass have been found. A new variety, Merion, is considerably more resistant than ordinary commercial varieties.

Many species of *Septoria* occur on grasses and cereals in the temperate and subtropical zones. At least two species (*S. macropoda* var. *septulata* and *S. oudemansii*) commonly attack Kentucky bluegrass in the Northern States. Strains of the two organisms also attack other species of *Poa*.

Symptoms of septoria leaf blotch vary somewhat on different grasses, but generally they resemble those caused by the Septorias on Kentucky bluegrass. Usually the leaf tip dies or gray to brown spots develop along the leaf blade. The spots may be bordered by red to yellow bands. The spots fade to a straw color, and the dark-brown or black fruiting bodies can be seen scattered along the faded part of the spots. The disease develops during cool wet weather and may cause extensive defoliation.

The spores within the small fruiting bodies can persist for a long time, and old infected leaves can be blown around or scattered and become the source of new infections.

Control of septoria infection in annual grasses is aided by rotation with nonsusceptible crops and sanitation. Perennial grasses resistant to leaf blotch must be developed to effect control. Differences exist among strains of grasses and newer varieties should help reduce effects of the disease.

KERMIT W. KREITLOW *is employed by the division of forage crops and diseases with headquarters at the Plant Industry Station, Beltsville, Md. He has degrees from the University of Minnesota and Louisiana State University. Dr. Kreitlow has been engaged in work on the diseases of forage crops since 1941.*

For further reading on leaf diseases of forage grasses:

J. Lewis Allison: Some Diseases of Forage Grasses, *in* Grass, *Yearbook of Agriculture 1948, pages 261–266;* Distinguishing Characteristics of Some Forage-Grass Diseases Prevalent in the North Central States, *with Donald W. Chamberlain, U. S. D. A. Circular 747, 16 pages, 1946.*

Charles Drechsler: Some Graminicolous Species of Helminthosporium: I, *Journal of Agricultural Research, volume 24, pages 641–670, 1923.*

James G. Horsfall: A Study of Meadow-Crop Diseases in New York, *Cornell Agricultural Experiment Station Memoir 130, 193 pages, 1930.*

C. Orton: Graminicolous Species of Phyllachora in North America, *Mycologia, volume 36, pages 18–53, 1944.*

C. S. Reddy and James Godkin: A Bacterial Disease of Brome Grass, *Phytopathology, volume 13, pages 75–86, 1923.*

Roderick Sprague: Diseases of Cereals and Grasses in North America, *538 pages, Ronald Press Co., New York, 1950.*

See also page 262.

Root and Crown Rots of the Grasses

Roderick Sprague

Range and pasture grasses during various stages of their life are subject to attack by soil-borne parasitic fungi.

Some parasitic fungi can stand considerable drought, but most of the relatively delicate organisms need plenty of moisture. During the early life of the grass host, the fungi are well favored because the grass seeds germinate in moist soil, where the fungi are waiting. Later in its life grass may form mats of foliage, which help to keep the humidity high and therefore favor root and crown rots.

Root rots and crown rots are in total probably the most destructive group of parasites of the grass family. In parts of the Great Plains, for instance, they were one of the chief reasons why regrassing after the drought years was so difficult. Losses up to 100 percent from seedling blight, for instance, were general.

Most of the soil-borne fungus parasites of grasses develop fine filamentous mycelium without producing any conspicuous fruiting bodies. A few develop small, hard, black sclerotia, which later give rise to small fruiting bodies about one-third inch high. A number of them produce colored or obscure masses of spores on diseased parts. Others form microscopic or nearly microscopic fruiting bodies in diseased parts.

The identification of the various root rots and crown rots must depend to some extent on microscopic examination of the diseased tissue and frequently only after isolation of pure cultures. Certain symptoms, however, aid in distinguishing some of the diseases without great difficulty.

SOME OF THE FUNGI in the soil can survive alone and are called soil inhabiting. Most of them, however, depend on humus in the soil to survive during part of their life. Such fungi can grow through the soil for some distances away from the nearest particle of humus, but they must retain a life line of mycelium with the piece of humus from which they started. Such fungi are called soil invading.

Most of the root rot fungi are soil invading and can therefore be starved out by prolonged fallowing. They need nitrogen, phosphorus, and other chemicals to grow, the same as plants do. They tend to accumulate in the area next to the roots in the soil—the rhizosphere. The region teems with activity from fungi, bacteria, and the plant roots. As the available supply of soil nutrients may become depleted, the fungi sometimes invade living cells in the roots of the grasses in search of food.

If they maintain a mild form of parasitism with mutual exchange of nutrients, both host and fungus may benefit. Actually these mycorhizal fungi serve as root hairs. They grow out into the soil, seeking nutrients which they carry through their mycelial filaments into the cells of the plant. The mycorhizal fungi take from the plant but give food from the soil in exchange. If the parasitism is favorable to both fungus and plant it is called symbiosis.

Usually in grasses, however, when fungi invade the roots they are destructively parasitic. In young plants death may quickly follow. In older ones the process may be prolonged as a slow necrosis and "going-out" of old stands. All soil fungi are not parasitic. Some cannot attack living plant tissue. They are called saprophytes. Some are weakly parasitic or are starved into invading living tissue. Sometimes some of the *Pythium* species appear to act in this way. Other fungi prefer the parasitic life. They are especially to be feared.

Species of grasses differ in their resistance to root rots and crown rots. Sometimes the resistance may be due to some mechanical feature of the plant, such as stout cell walls, but more likely the resistance lies in some chemical antagonism within the cytoplasm of the cell itself. We also have some instances of strain differences in grass species in their tolerance to certain fungi, but in relation to root rots these instances are all too few.

The adaptability of the host to the environment greatly influences it ability to withstand attacks by soil fungi. If the grass, for instance, is a warm-temperature-loving grass from the southern plains, it will often be wiped out by relatively weak soil borne parasites if sown in cold, wet soil in the northern Great Plains. If the grass prefers a particular soil acidity it may die from root rots if grown in a place where the acidity is not favorable for the growth of the grass. A desert grass such as Indian ricegrass will soon damp-off or decay if grown in areas of high humidity and frequent rain. Also, grasses that are not hardy are sometimes so weakened that they are more subject to common root rot than are vigorous ones. Winter injury however, is not a great factor in the ecology of root rot. Much of the injury is to young spring-seeded plants. Injury to older plants is sometimes associated with winter-injured plants or with plants growing in infertile soil. These cases are usually associated with weak parasites, such as certain species of *Fusarium*, *Curvularia*, and *Gloeosporium bolleyi*. Some strains of those fungi however, are strongly parasitic, so that their presence does not necessarily mean that the root rot injury is on weakened plants.

THE SYMPTOMS the various fungi cause on the host are more interesting o the general reader than the exact dentity of the organisms. We can lassify the many rots into a few general groups on the basis of symptoms vith a minimum of reference to the ausal organism. It is important, however, to know something about the various species and genera of the fungi hat cause the rots.

The same organism may cause more han one type of decay. For instance: *Helminthosporium sativum* may cause a eed rot or seedling blight if it occurs on moldy, untreated seed; several ears later it may be involved in a crown rot of older plants.

1. *Preemergence rots.* The plant or seed s killed as the seed starts to germinate or just before it emerges from the soil. The rootlets are often rotted to short tubs or collapse in a soft decay. Seed ot in the soil is most frequent in early pring or late fall in cold, wet soil or ater in the year if the seed is planted ust before a heavy, beating rain. Warm-temperature grasses or grasses vith small seeds are especially subject o preemergence rot. The loss of seed rom this cause alone averages well above 25 percent of all seed planted. Much of the loss is so common as to be taken for granted.

The most common causes of seed rot are certain species of bacteria and some fungi, including *Pythium debaryanum, P. ultimum, Fusarium culmorum,* and *Rhizoctonia solani.*

Control of preemergence decay includes the judicious selection of appropriate seeding dates in well-drained oil; the use of viable, clean seed of ecent harvest; and seed free from ced-borne molds. The seed should be reated with some seed-treatment material such as Arasan or Ceresan M.

2. *Root necrosis, common root rots, and damping-off.* Sometimes the plants that scape preemergence rots will develop a rapid soft rot and fall over soon after emergence. That is damping-off. Such fungi as *Rhizoctonia solani* and *Pythium debaryanum* are usually the ause of damping-off. Damping-off s common in ornamental and vege-table seedlings but less common in grasses. Sometimes one will encounter damping-off in prolonged rainy periods in thick stands that had emerged earlier during weather that was more favorable.

Grass roots are more likely to suffer from a slower decay, or necrosis. Necrosis due to *Pythium debaryanum* is likely in poorly drained soil or soil saturated by prolonged rains. The roots are often stubbed back by a slow and complete decay. Plants affected with pythium necrosis tend to recover rapidly when good growing conditions return.

The common root rot of maturing cereal plants has its counterpart in grasses. The grass roots are slowly killed by the action of *Fusarium culmorum* or *Helminthosporium sativum* and associated molds, sometimes alone, often competing in the roots of the same host. The *Fusarium* may cause pink or rosy colors on the dead roots, especially at the ground line, where masses of spores form.

Head scab of cereals and sometimes of grasses is caused by *Fusarium* (part of the *F. roseum* complex). This organism or group of organisms can also cause a seedling blight.

The associated fungus *Helminthosporium sativum* causes a brown blotch and root decay of wheatgrasses and, in fact, on many range and pasture grasses. Some seedling blight may result from it. It can also cause preemergence rot when its spores are borne on the seed of grasses raised in areas with high rainfall in summer. Such seed should be treated before seeding. Grass seed grown in the drier western regions, however, are usually free of seed-borne parasitic molds.

3. *Root browning and seedling blights.* In root browning, the root decay is represented by a firm, brown rot, usually of young rootlets. Its action is slow but often deadly. The diseased seedlings gradually fail to keep pace with healthy ones; about 6 weeks after seeding in the spring, they shrivel and die. They soon disappear in the winds

that sweep across the plains and are replaced by weeds.

The main cause of seedling blight in grasses in the Great Plains and far West is another species of *Pythium* (*P. graminicola*). Its action differs from that of root necrosis caused by *P. debaryanum* in that the plants fail to recover when good weather returns. In fact, the damage often occurs during relatively favorable growing conditions. Some conditions favor its prevalence. It seems to be especially active in grass planted on old plowed sod. It outlasts the bacteria in summer fallow and can only be starved out by several years of continuous fallow. It is possibly less serious on ground that has last grown a crop of corn, oats, or potatoes.

Damage from the root browning fungus is sometimes lessened by the use of a balanced fertilizer that supplies nitrogen and phosphorus to the host and probably to the fungus. The same organism destroys the roots of mature plants in old stands, especially when the stands are sod-bound and have too little nitrogen.

Fall seeding, where practical, is helpful in checking loss from seedling blight. By the following June the plants have passed their most susceptible stage.

Seed treatment does little to check root browning. The sphere of control that seed-borne chemicals can effect is in a small zone close to the seed. Seed treatment helps control seed rot, but it is useless in controlling decay that originates on the rootlets just beyond the old seed.

In South Dakota long search for strains of grasses resistant to seedling blight has resulted in a few strains of grass said to have some tolerance to *Pythium graminicola*.

Other fungi besides *P. graminicola* cause seedling blights, but they are considerably less widespread and less often reach the devastating proportions that this disease assumes. The common root rot *Fusaria*, *Helminthosporium*, *Curvularia*, and *Rhizoctonia* sometimes kill seedlings.

4. *Crown rots, eyespots, and maturity necrosis.* The soil fungi are carried by rain or winds to adjacent crown and stem parts. Sometimes elliptical lesions are formed at the base of the stem. The brown-bordered lesions, pointed at the top and bottom, are called eyespots. The eyespot lesions often form only on the leaf sheath at the base of the stem. *Rhizoctonia solani* sometimes causes eyespots in grasses. In the Columbia Basin of Oregon, Washington, and Idaho, another eyespot fungus, *Cercosporella herpotrichoides*, sometimes spreads from wheat to nearby grasses. Both fungi can work their way through the grass stem and cause a foot rot condition. If the stems break over at this point, the condition is called strawbreaker.

Rhizoctonia solani, one of the causes of eyespot, can produce other symptoms. In closely planted turf its cobwebby mycelium spreads radially, rotting the leaves and forming brown patch areas. We sometimes find brown patch in pastures. Occasionally it also causes some stunting by attacking the roots themselves; then it is often associated with common root rot fungi, and the symptoms are blended in one complex. *R. solani* has at least four races that can be distinguished more or less by their capacity to attack a number of grass, cereal, and leguminous and vegetable crops. One race in western Oregon and Washington is especially virulent on the basal parts of the stems of cereals and some grasses but is scarcely parasitic on legumes. Other races in the Midwest and eastern seaboard are actively parasitic on both grasses and legumes.

Crop rotation to control *Rhizoctonia* is difficult because of its adaptability to numerous hosts and because of the complexity of its races.

CROWN ROTS usually develop on older plants. The interior of the crowns show brown, dry rot. Such plants are probably affected with common rot, the same as occurs in cereals. An abundance of pink *Fusarium* spores may be present. Sometimes the less conspicuous brown ones of *Helminthosporium* are found.

On Kentucky bluegrass a crown or foot rot occurs. It is caused by a distinct fungus (*Helminthosporium vagans*), which usually attacks the leaves and causes a dark spot.

The roots of plants suffering from crown rots usually are decayed and serve as poor anchors for the plants, which are readily removed from the ground. Old, sod-bound stands especially are subject to crown rots. They also may suffer from root browning, caused by the same fungus that causes seedling blight in young plants (*Pythium graminicola*). Root browning and crown rots often work together in the old stands. Sometimes the plants may be kept producing for a few more years by use of fertilizer to balance the activity of the *Pythium*.

5. *Snow molds.* Some soil-borne fungi attack all above-ground parts of grasses as they lie under the snow in late winter. For many years field workers confused these diseases with winter injury, which is due to low temperature. It has been shown, however, that the elimination of the parasitic mold permitted the plants to survive without injury despite the winter weather. In other words, the parasitic snow mold fungi prefer to live at a temperature approximating that of melting snow.

THERE ARE two common groups of snow mold—the pink snow mold, caused by *Fusarium nivale*, and the speckled snow mold, caused by species of *Typhula*.

Pink snow mold attacks field and turf grasses in late winter, either under the snow or during raw winter weather. The leaves in the prostrate winter rosette stage are killed and formed into pink or straw-colored mats, which later dry to papery films. Sometimes plants recover from the disease if the crowns are not deeply injured. The color of the dead leaves is due partly to the masses of pink

spores that are formed. The spores sometimes cause a secondary leaf spot in early spring if cold, wet weather follows melting of the snow.

Pink snow mold is especially common in the Pacific Northwest on cheatgrass brome (*Bromus tectorum*), which serves as one of its carriers.

SPECKLED snow mold, more restricted than pink snow mold, is a true snow mold in that it cannot thrive without the semirefrigeration of melting snow. It causes a slimy, gray rot of grass and cereal leaves under the snow in midwinter or late winter. The gray mold soon forms many tiny, black, hard sclerotia, which dot the white dried leaves after the snow has gone—hence the name speckled snow mold. The sclerotia, which form on the leaves in March to April in the Pacific Northwest, germinate the following November. They produce small, fragile, club-shaped fruiting bodies. The bodies shoot off spores into the air.

Speckled snow mold is controlled by fall applications of mercurials and several organic chemicals, such as PMAS. Chemical control is not at all practical on grasses because of cost, except on greens and other turfs of relatively high value.

HERE is a list of some groups of grasses, their more important diseases, and their general geographic distribution:
Bermuda-grass (*Cynodon dactylon*): Rhizoctonia rot (Southern States).
Bluestems (*Andropogon*): Seedling blight (Great Plains); seed rots (Great Plains).
Brome grasses (*Bromus*): Seedling blight (Great Plains); seed rots (general); snow molds (Northwest and Northeast); rhizoctonia rot (general); common root rot (general).
Dropseeds (*Sporobolus*): Seedling blight (Western States); common root rot (Western States).
Foxtail millet (*Setaria italica*): Seedling blight (general); seed rots (general, North); root necrosis (general).
Grama and buffalo grasses: Seed

rots (Great Plains); seedling blight (Great Plains).

Indian ricegrass (*Oryzopsis hymenoides*): Seedling blight (far West); common root rot and crown rot (far West); rhizoctonia rot (scattered); snow molds (Pacific Northwest); seed rots (general); root necrosis and crown rots (far West).

Kentucky bluegrass (*Poa pratensis*): Dollar spot (Northeast); brown patch (general); foot rot, *Helminthosporium* (general).

Lovegrass (*Eragrostis*): Sometimes seedling blight and common root rot (Southwest and Plains).

Orchardgrass (*Dactylis*): Root necrosis (general); seed rot (general); seedling blight (scattered).

Panicum grasses: Seedling blight (Great Plains); root necrosis (Plains and South).

Redtop and bents (*Agrostis*): Seed rots (general); rhizoctonia rot (general); damping-off (coastal areas).

Ryegrasses (*Lolium*): Common root rot (general); root necrosis (general); rhizoctonia rots (general); seed rots (general).

Timothy (*Phleum pratense*): Seedling blight (general); seed rots (general); root necrosis (general).

Wheatgrasses (*Agropyron*): Seedling blight (Western States); common root rot and crown rot (Western States).

Wild-rye grasses (*Elymus*): Seedling blight (general); common root rot and crown rot (general).

Stipa grasses: Seedling blight (Plains and far West); common root rot and crown rot (Western States).

RODERICK SPRAGUE, *a pathologist at the Tree Fruit Experiment Station, Wenatchee, Wash., has been investigating soil-borne fungi in the Western States since 1929. He was with the Bureau of Plant Industry, Soils, and Agricultural Engineering until 1947, when he returned to Washington State College. He holds degrees from that institution and from the University of Cincinnati. He has written many technical articles and a reference manual on diseases of the grass family.*

Seed Disorders of Forage Plants

John R. Hardison

Seed diseases of forage plants are relatively few, if we do not count the smuts. The four seed disorders I discuss here are different from the seed-borne diseases, in which the causative agents primarily infect leaves, stems, or roots, but also may attack seeds.

Seed diseases are particularly important when they reduce the supply of seed needed to plant forage crops, lawns, or turf. In two diseases—ergot and grass seed nematode disease—the grass seeds are replaced by the sclerotia and galls, which are poisonous to animals.

BLIND SEED DISEASE of perennial ryegrass, *Lolium perenne*, apparently became established in the United States about 1940, although it has been a seed production problem in New Zealand since 1932. Poor germination of seed of domestic perennial ryegrass alarmed growers in Oregon in 1943 and led to positive identification of the disease. But three-fourths of the Oregon crop by then had become infested, and more than one-third of the 1943 seed could not be certified.

The causal fungus, *Phialea temulenta*, was identified in France on cereal rye in 1892, and was identified on perennial ryegrass in New Zealand in 1942. Since then the pathogen has been recognized on perennial ryegrass in England, Ireland, and Scotland; probably it can be found on the grass wherever climate permits infection.

Heavily diseased crops have many seeds that fail to germinate. Such dead seeds were referred to as blind seeds in New Zealand, and the malady was named blind seed disease.

It is hard to tell infected seeds from healthy ones unless the lemma and palea are removed. Then one can see the shriveled, soft, pasty appearance of diseased seeds. Healthy seeds have hard, plump, purple endosperms.

Diseased seeds reach the soil by pre-harvest shattering of the crop, planting diseased seed, feeding infested seed or screenings, harvesting operations, and, in unharvested areas, by the natural dispersal of seed.

The blind seeds remain dormant during the winter. In spring, when perennial ryegrass flowers, the small-stalked, cup-shaped spore-producing organs (apothecia) arise from the overwintered blind seeds and forcibly discharge the primary spores (asco-spores). The ascospores are showered on the ryegrass flowers and infect the developing seeds. Asexual spores are produced in a slimy matrix surround-ing infected seeds. These secondary spores can infect other developing seeds when rain and insects spread them from head to head. Badly in-fected seeds that overwinter at or near the surface of the soil produce spore cups the following spring and repeat the cycle. The entire life cycle is con-fined to the seed. Infected seeds are not toxic to livestock. The disease is important only when the grass is grown for seed.

To provide a basis for control, each sample of cleaned seed of perennial ryegrass entered for certification in Oregon is examined for disease. Growers then are advised through their county agents of the amount of disease in all fields. Plowing before May 1 is recommended for fields that appear too badly infested to produce a profitable crop of seed. The procedure makes it possible for each seed grower in Oregon to know how much disease is in his field and what to do each year. He can avoid unprofitable crops and

use the land for spring grain or leave it fallow to reduce weeds. Thorough burning of the straw and stubble after harvest gives good control for a year.

Disease-free seed is selected after harvest and approved for planting in new seed-production fields. The blind seed fungus dies after 24 months in dry storage; aged seed therefore is also safe to plant. The planting of any seed more than one-half inch deep, with complete soil coverage, prevents emer-gence of the apothecia.

Much heavily infected seed is spread on the field with the straw during com-bine harvesting, as such seed is lighter in weight than healthy seed. Because the disease is perpetuated primarily by infected seed that is left on the soil, precautions should be taken during harvest so that light as well as heavy seed is removed from the field.

It is helpful also to destroy infested perennial ryegrass screenings, prevent heading in pastures until after July, plow clean to bury infected seeds deeply, have good soil drainage, and plow all ryegrass on a farm at the same time to prevent spread of disease from old fields to new plantings nearby.

ANTHER MOLD was first discovered in Ladino clover in 1947. A seed blight of white clover had been seen in Scotland before 1928, but the identity of the causal fungus was unclear until Mary Noble, of the University of Edinburgh, named it in 1948. By comparing data with Dr. Noble, we found that the seed blight of white clover in Scotland and the anther mold in Ladino clover in Oregon are different stages of the same disease.

Anther mold is caused by *Sclerotinia spermophila*, a fungus that can live in-side the clover stems and leaves. In-fected plants look the same as healthy plants. The disease is evident only in the flowers and seeds. Infected flowers bear gray, fuzzy anthers, on which the fungus produces spores that largely replace the pollen—hence the name anther mold. Bees carry the fungus spores to healthy flowers. Infection of young seeds in the flower is the only known way the fungus can enter the plant.

Infected seeds are shriveled and have a dull-brown or gray-pink color. Healthy seeds are plump and bright yellow or reddish brown. Most infected seeds will not germinate. The fungus therefore appears to be largely self-eliminating, and the disease has not been economically important. If a less lethal strain of the fungus would appear by mutation or other genetic change, however, more diseased seeds could grow and produce infected plants, which could furnish inoculum for infecting healthy seeds. The disease might then rapidly become a serious problem in the production of seed of white and Ladino clover.

The disease seems not to affect the vegetative growth of infected plants. Its dissemination has been retarded by the use of modern seed-cleaning machinery, which removes the lighter infected seed.

GRASS SEED NEMATODE DISEASE, caused by *Anguina agrostis*, is a main disorder of chewings fescue and Astoria and Seaside bents west of the Cascade Mountains in the Pacific Northwest, where those grasses are grown for seed. A similar nematode infests seeds of buffalograss in the Great Plains. Other related nematode species infest seeds sporadically in species of *Calamagrostis*, *Danthonia*, *Elymus*, *Holcus*, *Sporobolus*, and *Stipa* throughout the United States. I found a few heads of orchardgrass infested with a seed nematode in Oregon in 1947.

The life history of the grass seed nematodes is like that of *Anguina tritici*, which causes the eelworm disease of wheat and rye in Southeastern States. Only the seed is infested, so that utilization of a grass for lawn and turf purposes is not affected by the presence of the grass seed nematode.

Striking symptoms occur in bentgrass. The seeds are transformed into purple to black galls that may be much longer than the healthy seed. In orchardgrass the seed panicles are greatly malformed. In chewings fescue the symptoms are less easily seen.

Each gall contains many nematodes which leave the galls after fall rain and migrate to grass leaves. Eventually they work their way between the folded leaves near the growing points. When the grass panicles develop, the microscopic roundworm penetrate the ovaries and stimulate the plant to produce the galls, within which many eggs are laid. Thus the cycle is repeated.

Satisfactory methods have been devised for control of the grass seed nematode in chewings fescue in the Pacific Northwest. Clean seed for planting seed-production fields can be had from dry-land districts or by disinfesting seed with a specific gravity separator, using air flotation. Chewings fescue seed weighing 21 pounds per bushel from such seed-cleaning machinery contained no nematode galls. Burning fescue fields after seed harvest is effective because it destroys many of the nematode galls in the grass stubble or in the straw. Vacuum machines, which were developed to pick up seeds on bare soil, could be helpful in removing the lightweight nematode galls from a grass field if they are adapted to work in the thick stubble. Crop rotations that use crops other than susceptible grasses effectively starve out the grass seed nematode.

Many cases of fatal poisoning of sheep, cattle, and hogs have occurred in western Oregon from feeding chewings fescue screenings that contained nematode galls. When heavily infested screenings of chewings fescue were fed to sheep and rats in controlled experiments at the Oregon Agricultural Experiment Station, the animals were killed. Nervous phenomena in sheep and gangrenous developments in rats similar to ergotism, also appeared. The poisonous principle is not known.

SEVERAL SPECIES OF ERGOT fungi attack grasses in the United States.

Claviceps cinerea infects curly-mesquite (*Hilaria belangeri*) and tobosa grass (*H. mutica*) in the Southwest. *Claviceps tripsaci* occurs on eastern gamagrass, *Tripsacum dactyloides*, in the Southeast. *Claviceps paspali* is restricted to members of the genus *Paspalum*. The most common and important species, *Claviceps purpurea*, causes the ergot disease in about 150 different grasses throughout the United States.

Ergot has retarded seed production of grass desirable for regrassing programs. Seed production of big bluegrass, *Poa ampla*, was discontinued in Union County, Oreg., because of such heavy infestations that harvesting and cleaning were difficult. Production of seed of some grasses in the Great Plains is often a failure because of sterility due to ergot. Most of the seed often is blighted, although only a few sclerotia may develop.

Ergot poisons livestock that graze heavily diseased grass inflorescences and feed on contaminated seed screenings. Substances in the ergot sclerotia cause abortion, nervous disorders, blindness, and paralysis. In gangrenous ergotism there is a sloughing of the hoofs, tips of ears, and tail; shedding of teeth and hair; and death.

Ergotism in man is no less severe. The disease is contracted usually by eating rye bread made from contaminated flour. Epidemics in humans were common in the Middle Ages.

Modern methods of grain cleaning permit the removal of ergot to within the tolerance of 0.3 percent by weight set by the Federal grades and pure food laws. This has almost eliminated the disease in man, although local epidemics occurred in France and India in 1951.

The ergot fungus attacks only the developing seeds of grasses. It has economic importance when the susceptible grasses are grown for seed or are allowed to flower and seed before grazing or cutting for hay. Ergot is of no importance in seed for planting lawns or other clipped turf.

The first sign of ergot infection appears at flowering time when a sweet exudate, "honeydew," is noticeable. Infested heads feel sticky when drawn through the hand. The exudate, which contains the asexual spores (conidia) of the fungus, attracts flies and other insects. Conidia carried by such insects to healthy heads or spread by rain in the same head start new infections. As the infection progresses, purple or blue-black horny bodies (sclerotia) develop in place of seeds. These sclerotia may fall to the ground or be harvested with the seed. When planted or left on the soil they produce specialized sporebearing organs that eject spores into the air. The spores are then carried by wind to grass flowers and infect the young seeds, thereby repeating the disease cycle the following spring.

Many grasses are susceptible to ergot, *Claviceps purpurea*, and wild grass may serve as sources of infection for grass seed or grain crops.

Control of ergot involves avoidance of the airborne primary spores or the secondary spores spread by rain and insects. This can be accomplished by planting nonsusceptible crops, deep plowing to bury the sclerotia too deeply for emergence of the spore organs, clipping grass before seed heads bloom, and eradication or preventing the heading of grasses in fence rows or other adjacent waste areas. Deep planting, permissible with the larger grass seeds, will prevent emergence of the sporebearing organs from the ergot sclerotia. However, selection of ergot-free seed, removal of ergot sclerotia by seed cleaning with specific gravity separators, or aging the seed for 2 years would be preferable.

Some grasses, such as the bents, produce their flowers in midsummer when the soil is too dry in many areas for development of spore organs from sclerotia. Under such conditions, infection depends entirely on spores carried by insects that have visited the spore slime on grasses infected earlier; control of the offending insect carriers could prevent ergot infection.

Ergot in perennial ryegrass has been materially reduced in western Oregon by burning the fields after the seed harvest. The fire destroys many of the ergot sclerotia in the straw and stubble and also prevents regrowth head formation in the late summer and fall. Such late-formed spikes are usually abundantly infected even in the years that are dry.

ALTHOUGH infection starts in the spring on the early-flowering grasses, the heaviest ergot infestations occur in the fall in many areas. The phenomenon is due to recurrent heading of many grasses, which become infected by insect-carried spores. This is important, because of the increase in sclerotia that furnish inoculum for infection of grass-seed crops the following spring. Such heavy infestation in late-grass heads is especially dangerous to livestock, because leaf growth is at a low ebb and grazing is heavy on the infected inflorescences.

JOHN R. HARDISON, *a graduate of Washington State College, obtained his doctorate in plant pathology at the University of Michigan. He has been engaged in work on forage-crop diseases since 1942. He is employed jointly by the division of forage crops and diseases of the Bureau of Plant Industry, Soils, and Agricultural Engineering and the Oregon Agricultural Experiment Station with headquarters at Corvallis.*

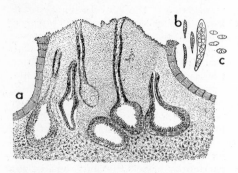

Endothia parasitica : a, Cross-section of a fungus mass (stroma) showing perithecia; b, saclike membranes (asci), in which ascospores, c, are produced.

Some of the 125 Rusts of Grasses

George W. Fischer

About 125 different species of rusts attack grasses in the United States. Nearly 400 species of grasses are among the hosts of the rusts.

Some of the rusts attack only one or a few grasses. Others can attack a great many. Stem rust, *Puccinia graminis*, for example, has been recorded on nearly 200 species of grasses in the United States. Among the rusts, which have such large numbers of hosts, we find innumerable strains or races, which look alike, even under the microscope, but differ in their comparative ability to attack species or varieties of grasses.

Some of the rusts of grasses are often destructive on the cereals. Most of the so-called cereal rusts have numerous grass hosts; probably the cereal rusts originally were grass rusts that found susceptible hosts among the cereals during the centuries they have been cultivated by man. However, since the cereals—wheat, oats, barley—are really only grasses whose seeds are large enough and nutritious enough to warrant intensive cultivation as food, it is only to be expected that there would be a great deal of similarity between the rusts that attack grasses and those that attack cereals.

THE RUSTS are microscopic fungi and are strictly parasites. They are among that parasitic classification known as obligate parasites; that is, they can grow only on a living plant. Indeed, many of the rust fungi require not only a certain species of grass or cereal but frequently a definite strain or variety of that species—a phenomenon known as host specialization, host specificity, or physiologic specialization. It has an important part in breeding crop plants for resistance to rust.

Because the rust fungi are parasites, their development on a host plant is at the expense of that plant and the nutriments they take would otherwise go into seed, forage, or both.

A light infestation of rust is not likely to cause noticeable effects on yield of seed or forage, but a heavy infestation definitely will. In grasses grown for seed, a heavy infestation will result in low test weight of the seed because of the direct effect of parasitism in sapping nutrients from the host and because of water loss through the numerous open rust pustules on the leaves and stems. Rust likewise affects the production of grasses for forage, chiefly in lower yields as a result of reduced vigor. That, however, is partly offset by the somewhat higher protein content of rust-infested grass over rust-free grass.

Secondary or indirect adverse effects should not be overlooked. Heavy attacks of rusts on grasses will make them more likely to succumb to other factors that are always more severe on the already weakened plant—drought, winter injury, root rot, snow mold, and perhaps other diseases.

Reproduction and dissemination in the rust fungi, as in fungi generally, is by microscopic cells or groups of cells known as spores. Many of the rusts produce several kinds of spores during their life cycle. Very common are the familiar red uredospores, whose mass appearance accounts for the name rust. Those spores are borne throughout the summer and spread the disease rapidly during the growing season. As the plants mature, however, the red pustules gradually change to a black type. The black spores (teliospores) usually cannot germinate until the following spring; thus they insure survival of the rust fungus through fall, winter, and early spring.

IN MANY of the rusts, especially the grass and cereal rusts, the black spores cannot infect any grass or cereal host but only some entirely different kind of plant, as the examples given later will show. Such a plant is known as the alternate host and usually is infected in the spring or early summer. The spores produced on the alternate host cannot reinfect that host; instead, they give rise to the initial red spore stage again on grasses or cereals, and thus the life cycle is completed.

Few of the 125-odd species of rust fungi that attack grasses in the United States are of economic importance: Many of the rusts are so limited geographically that they have not presented any general problem. Many are specialized to a few grasses, frequently of limited distribution and importance in the over-all range and forage picture. Another circumstance: In many wild grasses, especially of the bunch type, individual plants of a species often are separated by many other types of vegetation and by resistant grasses of other species. Susceptible individuals of one species have to be close by before rusts and leaf diseases in general can develop into an epidemic. That has been demonstrated countless times and often with disastrous results in cultivated fields of cereals and grasses.

Nevertheless, several rusts often reach economic proportions in important forage grasses and merit specific mention here. They are stem rust, leaf rust, stripe rust, crown rust, and bluegrass rust.

STEM RUST OF GRASSES (*Puccinia graminis*) is better known as a destructive disease of small-grain cereals than as an important disease of numerous grasses. It is evident primarily as small red pustules, chiefly on the stems, but sometimes also on the leaves, particularly on young grass plants. As the summer draws to a close and the plants mature, the red pustules gradually are replaced by black ones.

The six varieties of the stem rust fungus in the United States are differentiated mostly by the cereals and grasses they can attack. Thus the wheat variety of stem rust (*Puccinia graminis tritici*) attacks wheat, barley, rye, and many grasses. The oats variety (*P. graminis avenae*) attacks oats and various grasses. The rye variety (*P. graminis secalis*) parasitizes not only rye but also certain grasses. The redtop variety (*P. graminis agrostidis*) occurs on redtop and related grasses. The bluegrass variety (*P. graminis poae*) is on Kentucky bluegrass and many other bluegrasses. The timothy variety (*P. graminis phlei-pratensis*) attacks timothy and a few other grasses.

The wheat variety of stem rust has been found on many of the wheatgrasses (*Agropyron* species), orchardgrass, wild-rye grasses (*Elymus* species), barley grasses (*Hordeum* species), and a few less important grasses. The stem rust of oats occurs on tall oatgrass, sweet vernalgrass, some brome grasses, orchardgrass, a few fescues, canarygrass, timothy, a few bluegrasses, and some others of less importance. Stem rust of rye attacks many of the wheatgrasses, a few bromes, many of the wild-rye grasses, and barley grasses. The redtop variety is practically restricted to redtop and related grasses (*Agrostis* species). Stem rust of bluegrasses likewise is restricted to Kentucky bluegrass and a few other of the bluegrasses. The timothy variety is virulent on tall oatgrass, orchardgrass, meadow fescue, and tall fescue. So it is apparent that three of the varieties of stem rust attack both cereals and grasses and that the other three are restricted to grasses only.

In the Southern States and other places of mild winters, stem rust usually overwinters in the red stage on grasses and on volunteer or fall-sown grain. In regions of colder winters, such overwintering is exceptional, and the rust fungus depends on the black spore stage for survival during fall and winter and for reestablishmen in the following early summer. Reestablishment is impossible withou intervention of a spring stage of sten rust on an entirely unrelated plant the common barberry (species o *Berberis*), the alternate host. The resulting infections on barberry bushe: produce spores that set up the initia red spore stage on cereals and grasse, in early summer. It is this stage tha builds up in epidemic form by repeated generations during summer of frequent rains or prolonged dew.

LEAF RUST (*Puccinia rubigo-vera*) oc curs mainly on the leaves of cereal and grasses, although stem infection are encountered sometimes. Host spe cialization occurs, similar to tha described for stem rust, so that we have six varieties, as follows:

One variety of leaf rust, *Puccini. rubigo-vera agropyri*, common in th Rocky Mountain region, infects man of the wheatgrasses, various bromes and several of the wild-rye grasses It has many alternate hosts, all in th buttercup family (clematis, buttercup columbine, larkspur, and others).

Another rust variety, *P. rubigo-ver apocrypta*, also occurs on a few wheat grasses and wild-rye grasses but ha alternate hosts in the waterleaf famil (e. g. *Hydrophyllum*) and the borag family (e. g. *Mertensia*).

A third variety, *P. rubigo-vera im patientis*, attacks redtop and relate grasses and several of the wild-ry grasses and barley grasses. The alter nate host of the fungus is the commo touch-me-not.

Another of the wheatgrass varietie of leaf rust (*P. rubigo-vera agropyrina* is like the first one I described, bu it occurs outside of the mountainou areas. Besides wheatgrasses, it attack bromes, meadow foxtail, alkali-gras: mannagrass, the wild-ryes, and man others. The numerous alternate hos: are all in the buttercup family.

The wheat variety of leaf rust (*F rubigo-vera tritici*) is restricted to variou: wheats and apparently will not infec grasses. The alternate host is meadow-ue.

The sixth variety, the leaf rust of rye *P. rubigo-vera secalis*), is restricted to ye. Its alternate host is the wild forget-ne-not or bugloss (*Lycopsis*).

Leaf rust frequently is as destructive as stem rust. Occasionally infection is o heavy that the infected plants are iterally dusty red with rust and may even be killed by it. As a species, leaf rust is widespread from coast to coast, although some of the varieties are imited by geography or climate.

STRIPE RUST (*Puccinia glumarum*) is quite different in appearance from tem rust and leaf rust. The individual pustules, instead of being orange red, are yellow and arranged in long rows or stripes. A cool-weather rust, it makes its best progress in the spring and early summer before hot weather ets in. It is restricted to the Rocky Mountain States and westward.

Stripe rust is found commonly on he various wheatgrasses, wild-ryes, bromes, and barley grasses, besides wheat, barley, and rye. Some grasses, uch as crested wheatgrass and blue wild-rye, frequently are infected to the extent that plants are killed outright or are rendered easy prey to drought and other diseases.

The alternate host of stripe rust is unknown. Being a cool-weather rust, it overwinters easily without an alternate host.

CROWN RUST (*Puccinia coronata*) is really a leaf rust and to the unaided eye looks just like true leaf rust. The difference between the two lies in the black spore stage and in its alternate hosts. Under the microscope its black pores (teliospores) are seen to bear a crown of long projections at the top hence the name crown rust); these are acking in the leaf rust spores. Also, it has only a few alternate hosts—cascara buckthorn (chittum bark) and related species of buckthorn (*Rhamnus*).

Crown rust occurs on oats, wild oats, and many grasses—velvetgrass, Eng-lish ryegrass, Italian ryegrass, meadow fescue, tall fescue, orchardgrass, and some of the bentgrasses, among them. It is of economic significance more in the Mississippi Valley than east or west.

BLUEGRASS LEAF RUST (*Puccinia poae-sudeticae*) is common only on grasses. It does not occur on any of the cereals.

As the name indicates, the chief grasses affected are the bluegrasses, but occasionally others (such as mead-ow fescue and alpine timothy) are in-fected. It occurs chiefly in the leaves and produces numerous, minute, or-ange-red pustules, but frequently stem infections occur. Of the bluegrasses, Kentucky bluegrass is by far the most commonly infected. It rarely develops in epidemic proportion in lawns and pastures, however, probably because of too frequent mowing or grazing, but in nurseries or other undisturbed stands heavy developments often oc-cur. Several other valuable bluegrasses are commonly infected, sometimes very badly. Bluegrass leaf rust does not have a known alternate host. It over-winters easily and effectively in the red spore stage.

STEM RUST is controlled by eradicat-ing the alternate host, the common barberry (*Berberis vulgaris*). In the interests of controlling stem rust on wheat, oats, barley, and rye, an active barberry eradication campaign has been in force in 18 States. The cam-paign also is in the interests of suscepti-ble forage grasses. For example, in eastern Washington, before that State joined the eradication campaign in 1944, stem rust could be found on numerous grasses and sometimes in epidemic quantity. By 1951, with the barberry all but eliminated (except for numerous small seedlings), it was unusual to find stem rust in anything more than trace amounts.

In the States where crown rust is a problem, its alternate host, buckthorn, has been eradicated along with the common barberry. Those are the only rusts of importance on grasses that can thus be controlled to any practical degree. Elimination of the alternate host has another advantage: It is on that host that hybridization between strains of rust takes place, often with the result of new and more virulent strains capable of attacking varieties of grasses and cereals that previously were resistant.

The development or selection of grasses resistant to rust has lagged behind such projects in the cereals. Strains have been noted in timothy, orchardgrass, crested wheatgrass, blue bunchgrass, big bluegrass, and others that are resistant to their particular rusts. It is usually true, however, that those resistant strains are valid only in restricted regions and are not generally resistant to the various and numerous races or strains of rusts in all localities. The individual State colleges can best give advice on such local problems.

The fact remains that genetic resistance does exist in strains of most of our forage grasses and can be used in breeding work when necessary or desirable.

GEORGE W. FISCHER, *a native of Indiana, has degrees from Butler University, Northwestern University, and the University of Michigan. From 1936 to 1945 he was plant pathologist with the division of forage crops and diseases, Bureau of Plant Industry, Soils, and Agricultural Engineering. In 1945 he became chairman of the department of plant pathology at the State College of Washington.*

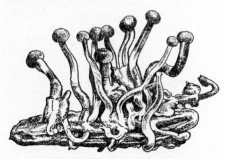

Germinating ergot sclerotia.

Smuts That Parasitize Grasses

George W. Fischer

Nearly 140 different species of smuts attack approximately 300 species of grasses in the United States.

The common name smut derives from words meaning to besmirch or smudge and refers to the presence of sooty, dirty, black, or brownish masses on the affected plants.

All the smuts are plant parasites. Most of them occur on grasses and cereals. As with the rusts, the average person is much more familiar with the destruction wrought by smuts on cereals than on grasses. Familiar examples of destructive cereal smuts are bunt or stinking smut of wheat, oat smuts, barley smuts, sorghum smut, and boil smut on corn. In everyday practice, the name smut is used to designate the disease as well as the fungus responsible for the disease, although the latter is more correctly spoken of as the smut fungus.

The smut fungi have much less complicated life histories than do the rust fungi and generally are easier to control. The familiar dusty black smut masses are made up mostly of millions of tiny cells or groups of cells—spores, which serve the same purpose to the smut fungi as seeds do to the seed-bearing plants, namely, for reproduction and dissemination.

Some smuts destroy the flowering structure. Others are restricted only to certain parts of it. Some are confined almost exclusively to the stems of grasses. Others produce galls or tumorlike structures in various parts of their host plants.

As with the rust fungi, many smut fungi exhibit a remarkable degree of specialization not only to certain species of plants but also to certain varieties or strains within those host species. Likewise, there are often strains or races of the smut fungi to contend with. The common stinking smut, for example, has nearly 30 known strains or races, each capable of attacking different varieties of wheat and different strains or varieties of wheatgrasses and related grasses.

The smut fungi are not entirely obligate parasites as are the rust fungi. In fact, some smuts can easily complete their entire life cycle on an artificial medium if it contains the nutrients essential for growth. Some smuts apparently persist indefinitely in the soil or in old manure piles. They are fully capable, however, of attacking their host plants when the plants are available under the requisite conditions for infection.

The smut fungi have a more adverse effect directly (and perhaps indirectly) on their hosts than do the rust fungi. The smuts that attack all or parts of the flowering structures generally destroy the seeds entirely. The leaf smuts and the stem smuts, while only occasionally involving the flowering structures, do nevertheless generally suppress these structures and likewise result in a more or less complete loss of seed on affected plants. The smuts that attack the vegetative structures (that is, the leaf smuts and stem smuts) have a decidedly weakening effect on their host plants and make them more susceptible to other sinister factors in their environment.

Many of the grass smuts are seed-borne. The wind carries millions of smut spores, which become lodged in or on the developing seeds of healthy plants. When the seeds germinate, the smut spores also germinate and infect the young seedlings. Then the plants that arise from the seedlings are smutted.

Some of the smut fungi are not limited to seedling infection. Apparently they can infect any succulent or rapidly growing part of their host plants and thereby make them smutty in time. The time between infection and the appearance of smut varies rather widely. In the stripe smut of grasses, for example, seedlings often show smut within 6 weeks of the time the smut-contaminated seed is planted. Other smuts are not evident until their hosts head out. One of the stem smuts, to be described later, requires 2 to 4 years after infection before smut actually appears.

Spores of the smut fungi generally are much more durable than are those of the rust fungi. It is hard to maintain viability of rust spores for more than a year; usually it is much less than that. In the case of the smut fungi, it is unusual for viability to be maintained for less than a year. For most smuts viability is maintained for two to several years, especially if humidity is low. Some smuts have been known to retain at least some viability for 25 years.

The cultivation of grasses seems to have much to do with the development of smut in them: Often cultivation practices, including harvesting and threshing, disperse the smut and contribute toward an increase in the amount of smut in succeeding crops. Any of the grass smuts therefore is a potential threat to the welfare of its grass host if the grass comes under cultivation.

Some of the grass smuts are the same as those that are destructive parasites of our cereal crops.

SEED SMUTS or bunt (*Tilletia* species) are terms used here to designate the smuts of grasses in which the normal seeds are replaced by smut "balls." The balls retain somewhat the shape of the normal seed and are even encased by the seed wall; actually, though, the inside of the seed is a solid mass of spores.

About 25 of these grass seed smuts

YEARBOOK OF AGRICULTURE 1953

occur in the United States. Several have actual or potential importance in cultivated grasses. One of the potentially most important is the one that on wheat is commonly called stinking smut or bunt. Three species of fungi are involved in it, including what is commonly known as dwarf smut. These smuts are well known on wheat because of the very extensive losses they have caused for a long time the world over. Besides wheat, tall oatgrass and several of the wheatgrasses are known to be susceptible, including crested wheatgrass, slender wheatgrass, and intermediate wheatgrass. Care has to be taken to keep those grasses from falling prey to the cereal smuts.

The dwarf bunt is soil-borne. It has thus far presented a knotty problem of control except when resistant varieties are used. The other two species, being mostly seed-borne, may be controlled by seed treatment and the use of resistant varieties.

Some of the bentgrasses are susceptible to another of the seed smuts, especially on the east and west coasts where considerable smut infestation is sometimes encountered in harvested seed crops. The life history of this smut is not known.

Various other groups of grasses, for example the bromes, fescues, wildryes, hairgrasses, velvetgrass, and others, are prey to similar seed smuts.

HEAD SMUT (species of *Sorosporium*, *Sphacelotheca*, and *Ustilago*) applies loosely to a variety of rather conspicuous smuts that occupy all or part of the flowering structures but do not replace the seeds themselves as do the seed smuts I mentioned. By virtue of prevalence, severity, wide distribution, and their very numbers, this group of smuts probably comprises the most economically important group of the several here discussed. Familiar examples are loose smut of wheat and barley, loose smut of oats, covered smut of barley and oats, and kernel smut and loose smut of sorghum. Many similar types of smuts occur on many

of the grasses, but only a few pose an economic problem, probably because grasses have been cultivated only to a limited extent.

One of the most common of the head smuts of grasses is caused by *Ustilago bullata*. It complicates the cultivation and production of several of our best forage grasses. More than 60 species of grasses have been reported as hosts to it, among them wheatgrasses, bromes, fescues, wild ryes, and barley grasses. In 1946 it was thought that head smut in mountain brome, one of our most valuable forage grasses, was under control through the release of a new variety, Bromar, which was developed jointly by the Department of Agriculture and the Washington Agricultural Experiment Station. In repeated tests the new strain had remained resistant to the various races of the head smut fungus. In 1950, however, an entirely new and very virulent strain of head smut made its appearance and caused some very badly smutted fields of Bromar mountain brome. There are 12 known races or strains of the head smut fungus, each of which is specialized to different species of the wheatgrasses, bromes, wild-ryes, and barley grasses. None of the cereals is susceptible to it.

Several dozen other head smuts of grasses constitute a potential problem among economically important forage or range grasses. Practically nothing is known concerning the life history and methods of controlling most of them.

LEAF SMUTS are of two types: The spot or blister smuts (*Entyloma* species) and the stripe smuts (*Urocystis* and *Ustilago* species).

The spot or blister smuts appear as flat or slightly raised, blackish, round or oval spots in the leaves. Although rather widely distributed, they seldom cause great losses. Once in a while spot smut develops in a bluegrass lawn to such an extent as to cause premature yellowing and death of the leaves. With the stripe smuts, however, it is quite a different matter.

The stripe smuts are evident in the leaves as black stripes, which contain the smut spores. The spores are shed and dispersed into the wind. Afterwards the affected leaves take on a shredded and curled appearance and soon wither. Affected plants quite frequently are dwarfed and contorted and produce abnormal, sterile heads, if any at all. Seedlings of grasses affected with stripe smut are predisposed to drought injury and root rot. Mature plants often are so weakened that they cannot survive severe winters.

Most of the stripe smuts of grasses cannot be told apart by the unaided eye, but they are different enough under a microscope. One of the most common and most virulent is known as flag smut. Many grasses and cultivated wheat are its hosts. Flag smut has several strains, each capable of attacking different groups of grasses.

Another of the common and destructive stripe smuts is the one that has long gone under the name of stripe smut or leaf smut. It has the same effect on its grass hosts as does flag smut and affects many of the same grasses, including some of our best forage grasses—the wheatgrasses, bromes, wild-ryes, fescues, and barley grasses. None of the cereals is known to be susceptible to it. Stripe smut is carried on the seed and can be controlled by seed treatment.

Still another type of leaf smut is the "sausage" smut of the grama grasses. It produces small but conspicuous blisterlike (often sausage-shaped) black pustules on the leaves of the grama grasses, which make up a valuable component of our western ranges. It is restricted to the grama grasses, but often is widespread and undoubtedly results in reduced forage. Its life history is not known. Methods of control therefore have not been developed.

STEM SMUTS (*Ustilago* species) are represented by several species that develop in significant abundance on economic grasses. All are marked by the development of conspicuous, dusty, brown or black layers of smut around the internodes of the stems. Sometimes nearly all the internodes seem to be smutty. Sometimes only the top one or two seem so. At first the smut is hidden by the leaf sheath that envelopes the stem, but as the stem elongates, the smut is exposed.

The stem smuts occur on some of our most valuable forage grasses—the wheatgrasses, wild-ryes, some of the bluegrasses, the needlegrasses, Indian ricegrass, and a few of the fescues.

Quackgrass is commonly infected. It might indeed furnish a supply of smut for the infection of more desirable grasses such as crested wheatgrass, big bluegrass, and blue wild-rye. A peculiar feature about the quackgrass stem smut is that an incubation period of 2 or 3 years is required after infection before the smut appears. The smut is perennial in the plant once it becomes infected. After the incubation period, the plant will produce a crop of smutty stems each year as long as it lives. Infection takes place in the vegetative tissues and thus spreads from plant to plant in a field.

THE CONTROL OF GRASS SMUTS is accomplished mainly in two ways: Chemical treatment of the seed in the case of seed-borne smuts and through the use of resistant varieties or strains.

Not all of the grass smuts can be controlled by seed treatment, but most of the head smuts and the stripe smuts can be. Among the grasses that could be expected to respond favorably to seed treatment for the control of smut are the various wheatgrasses, mountain brome, rescuegrass and related bromes, tall oatgrass, Canada wild-rye and other wild-rye grasses, big bluegrass and perhaps other of the bluegrasses, and the barley grasses. Such seed treatment for the control of smut will also help protect the seed and seedlings from seed decay and damping-off.

The procedure of treating grass seed with chemicals for the control of smut is much the same as that employed with cereal seeds and thus consists in principle of thoroughly applying a certain amount of a seed-treatment chemical to a certain weight of the seed and thoroughly mixing the two. However, comparatively little is known of the effectiveness of such control for many of the grass smuts. This is probably because intensive grass cultivation is relatively recent and the need for such knowledge has not been strongly felt.

The organic mercury dusts and some of the organic sulfur dusts generally are effective in the control of some of the grass smuts. New Improved Ceresan and Ceresan M, 1 ounce to a bushel, have given excellent control. Overdosage, however, hurts the seed and reduces the stands.

The organic sulfur dusts, Arasan, Arasan SFX, and Tersan, at 3 to 4 ounces to a bushel, likewise have given good control but not so consistently as organic mercury materials. They have an advantage, however, in that danger of overdosage is less. In fact, these three fungicidal dusts can be applied at maximum dosage (that is, all that can be retained by the dry seed) with little or no seed injury. This tolerance of grass seed to maximum dosage of certain of the fungicides is an advantage if small lots of seed are to be treated. Then it is not practical to attempt to weigh out minute quantities of fungicide, as needed on an ounce-per-bushel basis. Therefore, it is convenient to be able to apply an excess of the fungicide to the seed and, after mixing thoroughly, shake off the excess fungicide and not have to worry about overdosage. Others of the newer fungicides appear promising and eventually testing may show them to be as reliable as the ones here mentioned or possibly even superior.

Better results are had if the seed is stored in the treated condition for a few days. As much as 8 weeks will do no harm. It is possible therefore to treat the seed well ahead of the rush of planting time.

Comparatively little progress has been made toward the control of grass smuts through the use of resistant varieties. In the various studies that have been made of head smut, stripe smut, stinking smut, and others, and in nursery row observations, it has been noticed repeatedly that resistant lines or strains do exist, but very few attempts have been made to combine that resistance with superior agronomic qualities by the process of hybridization and selection. It is a neglected field of endeavor that merits attention, especially with regard to certain smut-susceptible species of forage grasses.

Certain it is that the smut diseases of grasses are going to come more and more into prominence as our grassland agriculture is extended. We should not delay, therefore, to make studies of the life histories of the grass smuts for which this information is lacking, because only on such a basis can intelligent control measures be devised.

GEORGE W. FISCHER *is chairman of the department of plant pathology in the State College of Washington.*

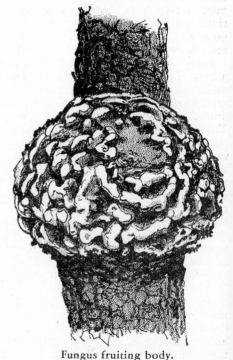

Fungus fruiting body.

How To Keep Turf Grass Healthy

C. L. Lefebvre, F. L. Howard,
Fred V. Grau

The 20 million acres of turf and 20 million lawns in the United States are prey to 100 different disease-producing organisms. Large sums are spent each year to establish good grass on golf courses, lawns, parks, and playgrounds, but the results are often disappointing. The main reason lies in the fact that the grasses that compose turf are subjected to unnatural conditions. When man first mowed grasses closely to produce turf for specific purposes, the possibilities of disease incidence were multiplied.

Turf is so commonplace that little attention has been given to its proper maintenance. However, cutting the grass blades wounds the plant and reduces its ability to manufacture food. The lessened supply of food and repeated injury make the plant more susceptible to attack by pathogenic micro-organisms. The grass that grows normally may be attacked by the same diseases, but it is better able to recover because it has a full leaf system. (An exception is the bentgrasses, the mowing of which makes for a healthier and better turf, while longer cutting causes matting, more disease, and actual smothering of the plants.)

Natural selection, operating over a long time among the closely mowed mixed grasses, has given us types or species of turf grasses that are better able to survive diseases and to recover from injuries with greater vigor.

201500°—53——20

Many of the common pasture grasses, which grow more normally, never have been called on to survive repeated clipping. Sometimes a turf grass and a pasture grass may be the same, yet disease control measures applicable to lawns and golf greens are not feasible on pasture grasses that are grazed continually.

Diseases of turf are parasitic or nonparasitic.

Fungi cause the main parasitic diseases. Fungi usually are more destructive to grass plants that produce what is considered a good, dense turf. At their leaf tips, the rapidly growing plants secrete drops of water of guttation, which encourage the quick development of the fungi. Moreover, the densely growing plants shade each other and tend to hold moisture longer, as there is less chance for evaporation of the surface moisture. Because water is essential for germination and growth of the spores and other reproductive structures of fungi, conditions that favor air circulation and the removal of water films from the grass blades also help to control disease.

Temperature may markedly affect the development of both the grass plant and the fungus parasite. The bluegrasses and fescues grow best in the cooler temperatures of early spring and fall, for example, and grasses like Bermuda-grass and *Zoysia* species thrive best at summer temperatures. Similarly, the fungus that causes the destructive dollar spot disease thrives at temperatures below 80° F., but the brown patch fungus is much more injurious at temperatures above 80°.

The nonparasitic, or physiological, ailments injure a plant through unfavorable nutrition, moisture, light, temperature, soil reaction, or some chemical that has been added to the soil. For normal growth, plants must have the essential nutrients in proper balance. Acidity or alkalinity of the soil must be adjusted to suit the requirements of the grasses. Frequently in alkaline (or "sweet") soil, iron is not absorbed sufficiently, so that an application of iron sulfate gives a better green color. Heavy applications of fertilizer, especially when the grass blades are wet, often causes burning of the turf. The use of chemicals to control weeds frequently reduces the vigor of desirable turf grasses and provides a suitable medium for fungi. An oversupply of water in the soil excludes oxygen, which the roots need. Too much water also promotes the development of pathogenic fungi that attack the grass roots weakened by lack of oxygen.

PROPER MANAGEMENT, based on knowledge of the physiology of grasses and their cultural requirements, can do much to reduce the severity of diseases. Even if the recommended practices do not cure a disease, they may curb it so that chemical controls can be more effective.

Because the fungi need moisture, proper drainage of turf areas to prevent excessive accumulation of moisture helps to control diseases.

Aerification of compacted soils helps water and air to reach the roots of grasses. Aerifying the soil also releases trapped air, removes excess surface water, and seems to free certain nutrients by changing the degree of acidity and alkalinity. Any practice that encourages vigor is good, for a rapidly growing, vigorous plant often is better able to withstand a disease or to recover more speedily.

Lime and fertilizers at the proper time and rate may alleviate the effects of the diseases. Technicians at the Georgia Agricultural Experiment Station learned that 2 pounds of nitrogen to 1,000 square feet, applied a month before seeding or at seeding time, reduced the occurrence of dollar spot in ryegrass. Research at Pennsylvania State College disclosed a striking inverse relationship between the application of nitrogen and the prevalence of dollar spot.

Practices that provide for good seedbed preparation, proper rate of seeding, adequate air and drainage, and the height of cut recommended for a particular species or strain of grass are other management practices that will retard disease. For example, in 1951 the workers in Georgia found that injury from diseases was much greater when ryegrass was sown at 100 pounds than at 40 pounds to 1,000 square feet.

IT'S A GOOD THING to grow grasses that are resistant to disease. That is easier said than done, though, for it is hard to find and develop grasses that have high disease resistance and the required agronomic characteristics. Newly developed strains of grasses may retain resistance for only a short time, because new strains of fungi may develop.

Washington, Cohansey, and Arlington bents are much more resistant to brown patch than is Metropolitan. Seaside bent is moderately susceptible. Colonial is very susceptible. Washington bent, however, is very susceptible to dollar spot, as is the Toronto strain. Elk 16, Arlington, Congressional, Highland, Seaside, and velvet bents appear to have resistance to the dollar spot fungus. Congressional bent has shown resistance to snow mold.

The leading vegetative selections of creeping bentgrasses in use in the United States in 1953 included these strains, arranged in approximate order of their resistance to the more common diseases: Dahlgren (C–115, according to the numbering system used by the Green Section to designate creeping bents); Arlington (C–1); Congressional (C–19); Old Orchard (C–15); Cohansey (C–7); and Toronto (C–15).

An outstanding advance was the development of Merion bluegrass by the United States Golf Association Green Section in cooperation with the Department of Agriculture. It is resistant to the fungus, *Helminthosporium vagans*, that causes a destructive leaf spot, but it does seem susceptible to pink patch and anthracnose at the Rhode Island Agricultural Experiment Station. It may also be injured by the brown patch fungus during periods of high temperature and humidity. It will, however, withstand close mowing (one-half inch) under good management, which includes proper fertilization, aeration, and irrigation.

Merion bluegrass originated from a single plant that developed from one of countless millions of bluegrass seeds sown over the years on the Merion Golf Club, Ardmore, Pa. That plant thrived and spread on the seventeenth tee until it formed a pure solid turf, which caught the eye of the golf course superintendent. A patch of the turf was sent to Arlington Farm, Va., in 1936. It was later transferred to Beltsville, Md., where it was extensively tested until 1950, when it was made available.

The consistent failure of common Kentucky bluegrass to form good turf under close mowing is an example of how mowing weakens a grass and causes a condition favorable to disease attack. The leaf spot fungus weakens and kills so many of the common bluegrass plants that open areas are produced, which afford favorable situations for crabgrass seedlings to develop rapidly.

H. vagans, the fungus that is destructive to the common Kentucky bluegrass, likes cool, wet weather; it is therefore more active in spring and fall. When hot weather (which is unfavorable for bluegrass) follows, the weakened turf cannot compete with weed invasion, especially crabgrass. Thus a fungus disease played an important part in producing conditions that made it necessary for researchers to initiate and develop a crabgrass control program with chemicals. Merion bluegrass turf, which is resistant to leaf spot, consistently contains less crabgrass than turf of common bluegrass grown under identical conditions. Since it is resistant to weed invasion, it produces a more attractive turf of better quality. The new bluegrass produces more vigorous rhizomes than the common bluegrass, and it can therefore spread faster. Merion bluegrass is more tolerant to heat and drought than were the other strains.

The seed of Merion bluegrass is shorter and plumper and lacks the usual brown color found at the base of the common bluegrass seed. Seed experts are thus able to distinguish it from seed of other bluegrasses. Merion is not a "miracle grass" but it does give the home owner a better opportunity to have a lawn free of weeds, one that requires less irrigation and fewer mowings.

Since Merion bluegrass is not a heavy seed producer, it is taking somewhat longer than usual to increase the seed. It is expected that seed supplies will be ample within a few years and the prices will be much lower. Even at present prices, however, it costs very little more to establish a Merion bluegrass lawn as the recommended rate of seeding is much less than for common Kentucky bluegrass. The American Society of Agronomy's 1951 Turf Committee has recommended 1 pound of seed to 1,000 square feet or 44 pounds an acre as the maximum rate of seeding for Merion bluegrass.

The development of Tifton 57 Bermuda-grass by the Georgia Agricultural Experiment Station, the Department of Agriculture, and the United States Golf Association Green Section is another step toward better turf. It is a narrow-leaved strain and is resistant to a severe leaf spot and crown rot caused by a species of *Helminthosporium*.

U–3 Bermuda-grass is another improved selection. It is a fine-bladed, cold-hardy strain, which although discovered in Savannah, Ga., has found favor within the northern limits of the southern grass-growing areas where Bermuda is not expected to survive. It is finding increasing use in such sections as New Jersey, Maryland, Virginia, Missouri, Kansas, Oklahoma, and California. It requires close, frequent mowing and generous fertilization, but very little irrigation.

Meyer (Z–52) Zoysia is another promising disease-resistant grass that has shown up well under tests. It is an improved warm-season grass. It was developed by the United States Golf Association Green Section and cooperating agencies and named in memory of Frank N. Meyer, a Department plant explorer.

Meyer Zoysia is drought-tolerant. It needs less irrigation than do most grasses. It will grow on almost any soil. It is easy to mow when cut regularly and requires less mowing than many other grasses. It can be cut at heights of one-half inch to 4 inches without loss of vigor. It produces a firm, resilient turf which is very resistant to wear. It also does well in association with Merion bluegrass. Meyer Zoysia is a warm-season grass so it will be more useful for planting in the southern half of the United States, although it has lived in plots as far north as Massachusetts and Michigan. It has some undesirable characteristics. Like Bermuda-grass, Meyer Zoysia loses its green color in late fall after the first or second killing frost, but regains it in the spring about the time the weather is warm enough for people to begin using their lawns.

No seed of Meyer Zoysia is available, so vegetative planting by plugs of sod or sprigging must be done. Plugging or sprigging is done in the spring or late summer, the preferred time of planting.

BROWN PATCH, caused by the fungus *Pellicularia filamentosa* (*Rhizoctonia solani*), may attack susceptible turf wherever high temperatures and humidity prevail. It makes roundish areas that are 1 inch to 3 feet across or may extend over an entire putting green or large portions of lawns. The grass first turns dark and the leaves wilt. Gradually the area becomes light brown as the leaves die. When the fungus is growing actively, it produces grayish or black mycelium among the grass blades like a smoke ring. If the climatic conditions remain favorable and affected areas are not treated, the fungus will kill the grass

to the point where reseeding may be necessary.

Brown patch has been controlled by a combination of mercury chlorides— 1 part corrosive sublimate to 2 parts calomel. Phenyl mercury acetate and lactate at dilutions of 1¼ ounce (10 percent active ingredient) to 5 gallons of water per 1,000 square feet applied as sprays are partly effective. A wettable thiram known as Tersan has been widely used.

Dollar spot, once known as small brown patch, is caused by the fungus *Sclerotinia homoeocarpa*. The injured spots are dark and water-soaked at first. Then they turn brown. Later they become straw-colored and are about 2 inches in diameter. The spots are usually regular in size and shape, but in cool, humid weather they may be so close together that they may merge into large, irregular areas of dead turf. When the fungus is actively growing in turf, a fine, white cobwebby mycelium may be observed in the early morning when the dew is still on the grass blades. In mild attacks of the fungus, only the uppermost grass blades may be injured. If the disease spread is checked then, the turf will recover quickly. When, however, the fungus is permitted to develop until all the leaf blades in an affected spot are destroyed, it may take many weeks for new grass to fill in the dead areas sufficiently to cover the scars of the disease.

The mercury chlorides, calomel and corrosive sublimate, are old stand-bys. The newer cadmium-containing fungicides, Cadminate, Puraturf 177, and Crag 531, are now recommended. Monthly applications of the cadmium compounds during the growing season are usually sufficient because of their good residual protection. The phenyl mercurials, Puraturf and PMAS, are effective but are apt to cause injury unless carefully applied.

Spot blight (grease spot or pythium blight) causes injury that appears in early morning as a circular spot surrounded by blackened grass blades, which are intertwined with mycelial threads of the causal fungus. The dark grass blades are water-soaked but soon wither, becoming reddish brown, especially if the weather is sunny and windy. The spots, usually not more than 2 inches in diameter, generally occur in groups. They tend to form streaks—apparently the fungus is spread by the mower or because of water in poorly drained low places. The disease can be very destructive in periods of high temperature and humidity, especially on poorly drained turf areas. Spot blight is usually more injurious to newly established turf, but if all conditions are favorable it will attack turf of any age. A sudden drop in temperature and a dry atmosphere checks its spread.

No satisfactory control measure has been developed for spot blight. Corrosive sublimate applied as a spray helps somewhat in checking it. One pound of iron sulfate in 30 gallons of water, applied to 5,000 square feet, may be worth trying. Copper sulfate at 3 ounces to 1,000 square feet gives partial control.

Copper spot makes coppery or orange areas, which usually are 1 to 3 inches in diameter. Close examination of the affected grass blades with a magnifying glass will reveal characteristic salmon-pink spore masses of the causal fungus, *Gloeocercospora sorghi*. The fungus seems to be active on grasses when the acidity of the soil is between pH 4.5 to 5.5.

The cadmium compounds are satisfactory in checking copper spot. The phenyl mercury formulations also are effective.

Snow mold is caused by several fungi, among them *Typhula itoana* and *Calonectria nivalis* (*Fusarium nivale*). They grow and spread beneath the snow cover, as the snow melts, or during winter rains. The first symptom is a dense, cottony growth of mycelium that covers patches of turf. The patches are 1 to 12 inches or more in diameter. Although it occurs as far

south as Virginia, the disease is more prevalent in the northern part of the United States. Snow mold is usually more severe on greens located in low places or pockets and in places that have a deep covering of snow for long periods. The borders of greens are most often severely injured. Seaside and Highland bents are very susceptible.

Applications of mercury chlorides at the rate of 2 to 4 ounces to 1,000 square feet before the first snow is forecast, and again during a midwinter thaw, have given satisfactory control.

Bluegrass leaf spot first shows small, brown, round to elliptical specks. The cause is the fungus *Helminthosporium vagans*. The spots enlarge and may extend the width of the infected leaf. The tissue in the center of the lesion dies and turns a straw color. A purplish-brown border may surround the straw-colored center. If the weather is cool and humid, spores are produced on the lesions and spread to other plants. Under favorable conditions, the lesions enlarge and may coalesce, involving most of the tissue of the leaf blade. The fungus may then spread to the leaf sheaths and to the crown of the plant, causing a crown and foot rot. The latter stage of the disease kills the grass plant, thins the turf, and leaves a bare spot for weeds to get started. Bluegrass leaf spot occurs wherever bluegrass grows. It is most severe in the spring and fall on grass that is closely clipped.

Merion bluegrass, which is resistant to leaf spot, offers a means of control. Fertilizing the bluegrass to stimulate new growth and raising the mower blades to allow longer leaves to develop will help overcome the disease.

Zonate eyespot first makes small spots on grass leaves like those produced on bluegrass by the leaf spot fungus. Here also the lesion has a bleached center, usually surrounded by a brown border. In the presence of dew, the daily growth of the fungus, *Helminthosporium giganteum*, into new areas of the leaf gives rise to a zonation that characterizes this lesion and distinguishes it from the lesions of the other leaf spot. The fungus may spread over the whole area of a leaf blade. In severe cases much of the plant may be defoliated. The causal fungus attacks many grasses, but it is most severe on Bermuda-grass and some of the bents. Warm, wet seasons favor it.

Fertilizing the grass to stimulate rapid growth and raising the mower to permit a higher cut help the plants to withstand attacks of the disease. Metropolitan, velvet, and some of the other bentgrasses seem less injured by the disease.

Pink patch is characterized by reddish bundles of mycelial threads of the fungus, *Corticium fuciforme*, that mat the grass leaves together. The attacked leaves are at first water-soaked and then lose their green color as the tissues dry. Turf is killed in distinct, isolated patches 2 to 15 inches in diameter. Pink, gelatinous branched strands (or horns) of the fungus develop during moist weather and tend to mat or bind the leaves and stems together. The fungus bodies shrink on drying, become bright coral red, taper irregularly, and are one-eighth to 2 inches long. The brittle fragments break and spread the pathogen. The fungus attacks grasses within a wide range of temperatures, but high humidity is most conducive to its development.

The cadmium and mercury compounds seem to give satisfactory control, especially when applied as a preventive before the disease is observed. The colonial and creeping bents appear to suffer less than the velvet bents from attacks of this fungus.

Fading out: Lawns and putting greens from June to October sometimes show an off-color that has often been attributed to drought, iron deficiency, or low fertility. Later an indefinite yellow and green dappled color pattern develops. When the disease is severe and not controlled, the turf fades out, leaving irregular patches, seldom more than 2 to 3 inches in diameter, of dead plants. Observations at the Rhode Island Agricultural Experiment Station have shown that species of the fungus *Curvularia* are always associated with grasses showing these symptoms. The disease has been found in several strains of velvet bent, piper bent, creeping bent, and annual bluegrass. Samples of infected grasses have been received from Connecticut, Massachusetts, Missouri, New Jersey, and New York.

The phenyl mercurials (PMAS, Puratized Agricultural Spray, Puraturf, Tag) when used at the equivalent of 1¼ ounce of 10 percent of the active ingredient per 1,000 square feet, were effective in tests in 1949 and 1952 at the Rhode Island station.

Fairy ring: Many kinds of mushrooms or puffballs are known to make fairy rings in fairways, rough, and lawns. On greens where the turf is usually well fertilized and treated with fungicides to prevent diseases, fairy rings are seldom seen. People once believed that fairies danced in circles and caused mushrooms to grow. Actually the ring is caused by the growth of a fungus spreading from a central point. The mycelium of the fungus grows profusely among the grass roots at the perimeter of the ring. The grass close to the fungus is often stimulated as if fertilized, producing an obvious unevenness of the turf. The soil thus invaded takes up water less rapidly than surrounding areas. In dry periods the grasses may wilt and die where the fungus has permeated the soil. Under favorable conditions the fungus produces the fruiting bodies that emerge from the soil in a ring.

There is no proved remedy for fairy rings. Organic cadium fungicides seem to have some inhibiting effect. Weak solutions of corrosive sublimate or other mercury compounds give some degree of control. On greens it may be necessary to dig up the turf and soil

Commercial Fungicides for Use Against Turf Diseases

Disease	Fungicide	Amount for 1,000 square feet [1]	Active Ingredient
Brown patch.....	Caloclor	2.0 ounces	Mercurous chloride (2 parts) Mercuric bichloride (1 part)
	Calocure	2.0 ounces	Mercury chlorides
	Puratized	.1 pint	Phenyl mercury acetate
	Tersan 75	3.0 ounces	Tetramethyl thiuram-disulfide
	Cadminate	.5 ounce	Cadmium succinate
	Crag 531	3.0 ounces	Cadmium, zinc, copper, chromium complex.
Dollar spot, pink patch, copper spot, fading out.	Puraturf 177	1.6 ounces	Organic cadmium complex
	Actidione	. . . .	Antifungal antibiotic
	Caloclor	2.0 ounces	. . . .
	PMAS	.1 pint	Phenyl mercury acetate
	Puraturf	.2 pint	Phenyl mercury triethanol ammonium lactate.
Snow mold.......	Caloclor	2 to 4 ounces	. . . .
Pythium blight...	Caloclor	2.0 ounces	. . . .

[1] The amount shown is usually diluted with 5 to 10 gallons of water, or enough to make sure that the chemical is applied evenly.

to a depth of 6 to 8 inches and to replace it with new soil and turf. Aeration, good fertilization, and liberal watering have helped to relieve the trouble.

FUNGICIDES can be applied to turf in a dry form or as a liquid, depending on the user's preference and the equipment available. In general, the method to use is the one that gives the most uniform distribution in the shortest time and at the least cost.

Many of the fungicides will cause yellowing of the grass if used carelessly and in excessive amounts, particularly at temperatures above 80° F. The manufacturer's directions on the container should be followed. The amount of fungicide usually applied to a given area is very small.

In order to apply dry chemicals evenly, one usually dilutes them with sand, compost, or dry fertilizers. Fungicides applied in a liquid form are diluted with water so that about 5 to 10 gallons of the solution are used to 1,000 square feet of turf. To assure even distribution, some operators start along one side of the area to be treated and walk back and forth in parallel lines so that the applications will not overlap, then back and forth at right angles to the direction of the first treatment. The preventive treatments should be applied after mowing.

Poisonous chemicals should be handled cautiously and in such a way that they will not become mixed with the food of animals or human beings. Labels on containers should be read carefully.

The table lists the fungicides that are effective against turf diseases.

C. L. LEFEBVRE *is an experiment station administrator in the Office of Experiment Stations of the Department of Agriculture. He has degrees from the University of Minnesota and Harvard University. He joined the Department in 1937 and has worked successively on projects having to do with diseases of forage crops. From 1932 to 1937 he taught in Kansas State College.*

F. L. HOWARD *is head of the department of plant pathology-entomology in the Rhode Island Agricultural Experiment Station. He received his training at four universities and has been interested in the development of fungicidal chemicals and plant chemotherapeutants since 1940.*

FRED V. GRAU, *director of the United States Golf Association Green Section from 1945 to 1953, is chairman of the turf committee of the American Society of Agronomy and a consultant on golf course turf problems.*

cotton

Fusarium and Nematodes on Cotton

Albert L. Smith

Wilt of cotton resembles the wilt disease of tomato, cowpeas, watermelons, cabbage, and several other crops. It is primarily a disease of the water-conducting vessels of the woody or stem part of the plant and is caused by a fungus that inhabits the soil.

The disease is complicated by nematodes, the eellike microscopic worms that also inhabit the soil and provide the openings through which the wilt fungus enters cotton roots. Nematodes reduce the root growth and increase the susceptibility of cotton plants to fusarium wilt. Thus the disease is considered a wilt-nematode complex.

Some nematodes enter the tip end of young roots. Others enter and feed on the root tissue some distance back from the tip. The root knot nematode makes galls, or knots, on roots, which later decay and leave the ends of the water-conducting vessels open and exposed to soil-borne organisms. The meadow nematode, feeding some distance from the root tips, may cause a pruning off of the small rootlets.

THE WOUNDS made by those and other species of nematode provide numerous openings for the wilt fungus, *Fusarium oxysporum* f. *vasinfectum*. Once the wilt pathogen gets into the vascular system, which conducts water to all parts of the plant, it can grow and spread throughout the woody portion. In the vascular ducts it may be found in pure culture, and appears especially adapted to grow in this tissue while most other organisms from the soil are excluded.

The wilt disease of cotton is distributed throughout the world wherever American cottons are grown in acid alluvial sandy soils. Pathologists believe the disease originated in Mexico or Central America in the same locality as upland cotton. The wilt fungus is carried inside cotton seeds and has been transported by the seed to new cotton-growing areas. In the United States the disease occurs in all States from Virginia to eastern Oklahoma and Texas. It is limited in those States by low rainfall and alkaline soils. Greatest losses occur in Coastal Plain soils of the Carolinas, Georgia, and Alabama. Wilt is also an important disease in Arkansas, Louisiana, Mississippi, and southeastern Texas. Although the disease is more severe in the sandy soils, it occurs in the lighter soils scattered throughout some of the heavier soils series of the Piedmont and Mississippi Delta regions.

Losses to the cotton crop from the wilt-nematode disease complex have been greater than those caused by any other disease except possibly Texas root rot. Losses in yields result from reduced stands, stunted plants, small bolls, and poor-quality lint. Before the development, distribution, and general use of wilt-resistant varieties, losses to individual growers often amounted to 75 to 90 percent of the crop. The growing of sea-island cotton had ceased on many acres before 1902, when Rivers, a resistant variety, became available. The first wilt-resistant upland variety, Dillon, was released in 1905. Estimates of crop losses beginning in 1920 indicate wilt losses from 1 to 5 percent for the different States. Additional losses from the root knot nematode ranged from a trace to 3 percent. Between 1940 and 1950 the release of improved wilt-resistant varieties brought further reductions in wilt losses. Now the losses from nematodes and wilt together probably do not exceed 3 or 4 percent in any State.

SYMPTOMS OF WILT may appear on cotton plants at any stage of development. The earliest symptoms to be seen on seedlings and small plants are the yellowing and browning of cotyledons and leaves. The affected parts ultimately die and fall off. The bare stem soon blackens and dies. The first symptom in older plants may be stunting, followed by yellowing, wilting, and dropping of most of the leaves. Leaf discoloration first appears near the margin of the blade near a vein. The affected areas enlarge, and an abscission layer may form at the base of the petiole, causing the leaf to drop.

An outstanding symptom is the browning and blackening of the woody tissue. When a stem or branch is cut crosswise, the discoloration is usually found in a ring just beneath the bark. Sometimes the discoloration is dispersed through the woody cylinder. In advanced cases, discoloration may extend throughout the plant from the roots through the stem, branches, leaf petioles, and peduncles and into the bolls.

Wilting mostly occurs gradually, but after a rain, following a dry period, plants may wilt suddenly and in large numbers. Wilted plants may produce some bolls, which usually are smaller and open prematurely. Plants may die one at a time until the stand is reduced or largely eliminated, depending on the susceptibility of the variety and the amount of infestation.

The wilt fungus survives in the soil on organic matter. It grows as a threadlike mycelium and produces two kinds of spores. One type, known as conidia, is relatively short-lived. The second type, chlamydospores, is a resting stage, which may live longer. Both types give rise to a mycelium that infects the roots of the host plants.

Dissemination by spores probably accounts for the rapid spread of the disease to all parts of a field once the disease is introduced by cotton seed. Spores may be washed about in the field or blown about by the wind or transported by many other means. The wilt fungus lives in the soil indefinitely once it is introduced even though cotton and other susceptible plants are not grown. Fields not planted to cotton for as long as 25 years have shown severe wilting the first year after cotton planting was resumed. No method of eradicating the organism economically from fields is known.

Many laboratory experiments indicate that with large amounts of inoculum the fungus enters healthy cotton roots in the absence of openings made by nematodes. Field experiments show that the openings caused by nematodes largely account for the infections occurring naturally. In experiments at the Alabama Agricultural Experiment Station, I found that wilt is readily controlled with soil fumigants, which reduce or eliminate nematodes before planting.

After entering the small roots, the fungus inhabits the water-conducting vessels and spreads by growth of the mycelium and by movement of spores upward in the water stream. The vascular tubes become browned and later blackened by the formation of gum-like substances and by growth of tyloses. Plugging or partial plugging of the vessels lowers the flow of water and uptake of salts from the soil and stunts the plant or causes wilting. Toxic products, which injure the host cells, are also produced by the fungus. Browning, drying, and killing follow; the ultimate falling of most leaves is a symptom largely produced by toxic materials. When bolls are present, the mycelium may grow through the peduncle into the seed. After the plant dies, the organism invades all its tissues; if enough moisture is present, spores are produced, which may be spread to all parts of fields.

THE ROOT KNOT NEMATODE is the most common of the nematodes that affect cotton roots. It occurs on cotton roots in all lighter soils of the Cotton Belt. The immature larvae infest cotton plants by invasion through the soft root tips. After entering the tip, the larvae push their way between the cells. Then they become stationary and feed by puncturing all the cell walls within reach with a spearlike stylet and sucking out the juices from inside the cell. The affected cells grow much larger and proliferate to form knots, or galls. With susceptible varieties and the feeding of large numbers of nematodes, the knotlike enlargements may become a half-inch in diameter. Tissues in the galls are quite soft and are likely to decay and leave the ends of vascular bundles exposed to the wilt fungus. The enlarged worms are filled with eggs, which hatch and release numerous young nematodes. They, in turn, feed on any new cotton rootlets in the vicinity. Some cotton plants become infected by wilt when quite young; perhaps the mycelium enters the root tissue with the young larvae as well as later when the galls decompose.

If nematodes have made many points of entry for the fungus, multiple infections gradually envelop the root system, even in fusarium-resistant plants of upland cotton.

The meadow or root rot nematode (*Pratylenchus pratensis*) multiplies rapidly on corn, crabgrass, and other fibrous rooted crops, following which it might become the predominant species on cotton. The meadow nematode is also found abundantly in some soils too heavy in texture to support the root knot nematode. It may enter the soft cortical root tissue at any point near the growing zone. In feeding, the female moves about, destroying cells and depositing eggs throughout a short segment of the root. The young larvae intensify the destruction of the cortical tissues so that usually the rootlet is cut off. Many openings are thus left for the wilt organism to enter directly into the vascular tubes.

The sting nematode or coarse root nematode (*Belonolaimus gracilis*) is a third type that provides openings for the wilt fungus. The sting nematode does not enter roots but feeds on cortical root cells from the outside. It is one of a group of ectoparasites, or free-living nematodes, which complete their life cycle outside the root, entirely in the soil. The fine roots are pruned off leaving many openings accessible to the wilt fungus.

Direct losses in yield from nematodes alone may be of greater importance in some soils than losses resulting from the wilt-nematode complex. Serious losses occur in some irrigated soils where fusarium wilt is unknown. Losses occur throughout the lighter soils of the rain belt but often go unnoticed by growers.

The main effect of nematodes is a reduced rate of growth, which means smaller plants and lower yields. Growers are inclined to attribute them to other causes. The effect of nematodes on yield can best be demonstrated by using soil fumigants: Often they double yields in severely infested fields in both the western irrigated and eastern rain belt soils. Nematode-reducing rotations also demonstrate how great are the losses caused by nematodes. In some western soils the root knot nematode becomes the limiting factor to profitable cotton production and rotation or soil fumigation becomes necessary.

The host range of the cotton wilt fungus is limited. It may enter the roots of a number of different crops, but it produces wilt symptoms only on cotton, okra, coffeeweed (*Cassia tora*), and some varieties of burley tobacco. The host range of the root knot nematode is extensive. It attacks and reproduces in the roots of more than 1,200 different species of plants.

Studies made by V. H. Young and W. H. Tharp at the Arkansas Agricultural Experiment Station show that the maximum growth rate of the fungus and maximum disease development require relatively high soil temperature and moisture. Soil temperatures between 80° and 90° F. were favorable for maximum disease development. Although some wilt occurs in seedlings

and small plants in the field in April and May, maximum appearance of symptoms is in late June or July and August when soil temperatures are highest. In greenhouse studies, maximum wilt development was obtained at 80 to 90 percent of the water-holding capacity of the soil.

High soil temperatures also are favorable for nematode development. The soil moisture conditions that are favorable for plant growth usually are favorable for nematodes. Field observations indicate that maximum wilt development occurs during years of highest soil temperatures, which also favor maximum nematode development. High soil moisture tends to lower soil temperatures. Alternate dry, hot periods of rather long duration followed by rains provide conditions favorable for maximum wilt development.

Measures to control wilt consist of practices directed at both the wilt organism and nematodes. Resistant varieties and the use of balanced fertilizers to produce healthy plants help control *Fusarium*. The planting of varieties resistant to root knot, the use of root knot reducing crops in rotation with cotton, and the application of soil fumigants are important in the control of nematodes.

The early history of the wilt disease illustrates the early participation of the Department of Agriculture in the study and control of a disease threatening a major farm crop. Cotton wilt was first described by George F. Atkinson at the Alabama Agricultural Experiment Station in 1892. Atkinson also clarified the effects of wilt, which farmers confused with rust or potash deficiency. Atkinson also described the root knot nematode on cotton and found that it provided openings through which the wilt fungus entered cotton roots. The Department of Agriculture was requested to help on the wilt problem in 1895, when the disease became serious on the sea-island plantations off the coast of South Carolina. Erwin F. Smith visited the area at that time and began his studies on the wilt diseases of cotton, watermelon, and cowpeas. E. L. Rivers, a sea-island plantation operator, in 1895 began the selection work that ultimately led to the production of the wilt-resistant sea-island variety that bears his name.

W. A. Orton, of the Department of Agriculture, entered the work in South Carolina in 1899. He cooperated in the later breeding phases and distribution of the Rivers variety. Orton also initiated a successful breeding program with upland cottons in 1899. The early breeding work of Rivers and Orton was the forerunner of the breeding programs that ultimately led to the practical control of cotton wilt and the wilts of other crops.

The importance of wilt-resistant varieties was demonstrated by the release of Rivers. It saved the industry that centered on the islands off the South Carolina coast and extended along the coast.

The early work by Rivers and Orton also established the plant-to-row selection method essentially as it is used by modern breeders. They picked out individual plants that had survived on severely infested soils. The following year the seed from each plant was planted in a single row. The rows that combined the best resistance and agronomic characters were then increased to establish the variety. Orton extended this method to include hybridization to improve upland varieties in work that he and associates initiated in 1899. The method was adopted by other workers in breeding flax, peas, and watermelons resistant to fusarium wilt.

The inheritance of fusarium resistance in sea-island cotton later was found to be determined by two dominant pairs of factors. The resistance in sea-island, when pure, approaches immunity. Such high resistance greatly simplified the problem of selecting for resistance; it was fortunate that the earliest breeding work was done with sea-island. Upland cotton does not possess factors for the same high degree of resistance and has not yet been bred

to compare with the resistance of Rivers sea-island.

From the breeding of wilt-resistant upland varieties initiated by Orton and his associates came Dillon, which was developed from a wilt-resistant selection of Jackson's Limbless in South Carolina and released in 1905. They developed a second variety, Dixie, in Alabama. A cross between Dixie and Triumph yielded a third variety, Dixie-Triumph, which was widely grown and used extensively in later selection and crossing. Beginning in 1913 the Alabama Agricultural Experiment Station made available to growers Cook 307 and other related varieties, which were developed by H. B. Tisdale. Additional varieties released before 1940 were Cleveland, Miller, Express, Lightning Express, Super Seven, Clevewilt, Toole, and Lewis 63. Most of them matured rather late and yielded less than the best nonresistant kinds.

The long effort of breeders to produce agronomically superior wilt-resistant varieties was climaxed in 1942 with the introduction of Coker 100 wilt. It was as productive as nonresistant varieties and had other desirable characteristics such as a medium staple length, earliness, and adaptability to a wide range of growing conditions. It quickly became popular in southeastern and south central regions where wilt is a factor. Other superior wilt-resistant varieties, Empire, Stonewilt, Pandora, White Gold, and Plains, were introduced in 1940–1950.

Breeders have started efforts to transfer the greater resistance of sea-island to upland. Greater resistance is also available in the wild, or 13-chromosome, cottons of Asia and the Americas. Geneticists doubled the chromosome numbers of wild species and were then able to cross them with upland varieties. Attempts are being made to improve the wilt resistance of modern varieties by using crosses with the wild, or 13-chromosome, cottons.

A moderate amount of root knot resistance is associated with fusarium esistance in varieties developed in the southeast and selected on wilt- and nematode-infested soils. In the process of selecting for fusarium resistance and high yield in segregating progenies, moderate resistance to root knot is obtained without specific effort on the part of the breeder. This resistance contributes to the fusarium resistance and to the yield of such lines. High resistance to root knot is not present in any upland varieties. However, there are considerable differences between the most susceptible and the most resistant ones. Varieties combining both fusarium resistance and moderate root knot resistance are Stonewilt, Coker 100 wilt, and Plains. Several varieties considered susceptible to root knot are Rowden, Miller, Deltapine, Bobshaw, Stoneville, Empire, and Pandora.

A SEARCH for high resistance to root knot was made at the Alabama Agricultural Experiment Station in 1951. A number of the world cotton species and many types and varieties were planted, and the roots were later examined for size and abundance of galls. Several sources of resistance were found, the most promising of which were *Gossypium barbadense* var. *darwinii* and two wild cottons from Mexico. The latter two introductions from Mexico are much like upland (*G. hirsutum*) but are not productive. These three were crossed and backcrossed to productive upland varieties. The segregating progenies will be selected for root knot resistance and further backcrossed. Eventually high root knot resistance in combination with desirable agronomic characters will be obtained. Improved root knot resistance will increase the yields of varieties grown on infested soils and should also improve the resistance to fusarium wilt.

THE USE OF BALANCED FERTILIZERS to maintain a vigorous growth of cotton plants is an important cultural practice to prevent losses from cotton wilt. Potash tends to reduce wilt losses.

Nitrogen and phosphorus tend to increase wilt within certain limits. The proper balance of nitrogen, phosphorus, and potash gives the maximum yields and best control of wilt when no one of the three elements is deficient. Cotton rust, or potash deficiency, was early confused with cotton wilt. George F. Atkinson discovered that ample application of potash prevented the occurrence of rust. Rust on cotton continued to cause serious losses and increased the losses from wilt until 1926, when American sources of potash were developed, which provided ample supplies at a reasonable cost.

NEMATOCIDES can control fusarium wilt and nematodes and thereby can double yields of resistant varieties and triple and quadruple the yields of susceptible varieties grown on soils heavily infested by both pathogens. In experiments in Alabama in 1947, I learned that wilt is controlled indirectly by destroying the nematodes. The yields are increased as a result of control of both the wilt and nematodes. On treated plots better stands are maintained, the plants grow off more rapidly, grow larger, and produce greater yields.

Most economical control is obtained by applying the material in the row at the rate of 6 to 8 gallons an acre a few days before planting. Materials giving satisfactory control are ethylene dibromide and a mixture of dichloropropene and dichloropropane. Their trade names are Dowfume W–40 and D–D. Row application gives control of nematodes in a zone near the young plants. Once the plants are established and growing rapidly, later nematode infections do little damage to the crop. Annual applications are necessary if only the row application is made.

ROTATING COTTON with crops that reduce the amount of root knot is a cultural practice of value in reducing wilt losses and increasing yields. Crops that reduce root knot nematodes are grasses, sorghum, small grains, corn, peanuts, crotalaria, velvetbeans, alfalfa, and nematode-resistant cowpeas.

Several crops that are particularly susceptible to root knot tend to intensify wilt and nematode losses. Among them are cowpeas susceptible to root knot, annual lespedezas, sweetpotatoes, and tobacco.

Crops grown during mild winters for green manure sometimes increase populations of root knot to the extent of causing increased losses in the cotton crop that follows them. Blue lupine, Austrian winter peas, and vetch are examples. On the contrary, increased organic matter is beneficial in improving yields and reducing wilt losses.

Rotations help to control other diseases of cotton. An example is ascochyta blight of young plants, which sometimes becomes epidemic. Rotation is likewise of value against bacterial blight infections in the Southwest and irrigated valleys, where plant refuse is not decayed over winter.

The rotation of cotton with other crops has not become a widely used practice. Farmers are reluctant to follow some other crops with cotton, particularly peanuts and hay crops, which exhaust the soils of some minerals to the extent that yields of cotton may be reduced. Other reasons may have to do with the accessibility of the land to the house, weeds, and the tendency to select the most productive land for cotton.

ALBERT L. SMITH *is a graduate of Oklahoma Agricultural and Mechanical College and the University of Wisconsin. He joined the Department of Agriculture as a pathologist in 1936 to work on cotton diseases and breeding for disease resistance. Most of his time has been devoted to studies on fusarium wilt and nematode disease of cotton. Plains, a wilt-resistant variety of cotton was developed by him and released in 1949. He is stationed at the Alabama Polytechnic Institute in Auburn.*

The Rot That Attacks 2,000 Species

Lester M. Blank

Cotton root rot, caused by the soil-inhabiting fungus *Phymatotrichum omnivorum*, flourishes on more than 2,000 species of wild and cultivated plants. Cotton grows in most of the area where the fungus is present, and the disease is usually designated as cotton root rot, although it also attacks the roots of trees, shrubs, fruits, and vegetables. The monocots—grasses, corn, sorghum, and such—are considered immune to it.

The fungus occurs naturally in the alkaline soils of the southwestern United States and northern Mexico. It has not been found in other parts of the world. The disease is serious in parts of Texas, Oklahoma, New Mexico, Arizona, and northern Mexico. It has been reported in California, Nevada, Utah, Arkansas, and Louisiana. It is particularly damaging in the blackland prairie of central Texas.

It has been alarmingly destructive. In Arizona, the average yearly loss between 1924 and 1929 was 10.3 percent. Losses in Texas were estimated at 130,000 bales in 1918, 314,000 in 1919, 630,000 in 1920, 444,000 in 1928, 300,000 in 1937, and 191,000 in 1939. Those were reductions in yields of 5 to 15 percent.

The losses fluctuate from year to year according to acreage in cotton and the moisture conditions under which the crop is grown. High temperature and high soil moisture favor the development of the disease.

Symptoms of infection are sometimes evident 6 to 8 weeks after planting, but ordinarily are most apparent during the period of squaring and fruiting. At first only an occasional plant may display symptoms, but within days or weeks the surrounding plants succumb. By midseason and later, irregular or circular spots or patches of brown, dead plants present a characteristic symptom of the presence of the disease. Such spots shade off abruptly from the dead, browned plants through a narrow zone of wilted plants into normal green plants.

The first above-ground symptom on a plant is a slight yellowing or bronzing of the leaves. There is an increase in leaf temperature, which one can feel. Wilting of the leaves occurs in a day or two and is rapidly followed by drying and browning of the foliage. The browned leaves stay on the plant for some time.

Roots of infected cotton plants show various symptoms, depending on the length of time the root has been subjected to the action of the parasite. Roots of apparently healthy plants that are near plants showing early symptoms sometimes reveal the fungus in the first stages of its action. Whitish or tan threads of the fungus mycelium overrun the roots and break down the outer cells of the root, producing lightly discolored, depressed areas or lesions. Development of the lesions destroys the cortical tissues, and the organism penetrates into the woody central cylinder. The mycelium assumes a tan or buff color. Individual threads join together to form fuzzy strands. In more advanced stages, the cortical tissues completely disintegrate, and the infected part of the central cylinder becomes red or brown, quite different from the white to cream color of the adjacent healthy tissues.

This fungus has several forms, or stages. The vegetative stage consists of individual threads—filaments, or hyphae—of the fungus, or the threads may fuse to form mycelial strands. Filaments and strands may push through the soil until they reach another plant whose healthy roots they envelop and penetrate; failing that, they grow until their food supply is exhausted. Young filaments and strands are light-colored. Later they become cream to buff to brown.

A second stage is the spore mat, or fruiting, phase, which arises from the vegetative strands. One sometimes sees spore mats in cotton fields but more often in alfalfa fields. In warm weather when the soil is damp, the irregular or circular mats appear on the surface of the soil. If conditions are to their liking, they may become a foot or more in diameter. The mats develop rapidly. They appear first as a fluffy white fungal growth on the surface. They become creamy white or tan or buff in a few days. The mature mats are composed almost entirely of minute pores. Attempts to germinate the spores so far have been unsuccessful. The function of the spores is unknown.

A third phase is the sclerotial, or resting, stage. Mature sclerotia are light brown to dark brown and as tiny as mustard seed. In shape they are irregularly round. They are produced singly or in chains or clusters. Sclerotia develop on the mycelium or strands of the fungus, appearing first as slight, spindle-shaped swellings. They attain full size in 4 or 5 days and mature in 10 to 14 days. The fungus produces them apparently in response to an abundant food supply. They have been found in quantities to a depth of 8 feet in the Texas blacklands. The greatest concentration occurs at a depth of 1 to 2 feet. If moisture and temperature are right, the sclerotia germinate readily, and produce the typical *Phymatotrichum* mycelium and strands. Sclerotia may remain viable in the soil for at least 12 years, and upon germination can reinfect the roots of susceptible plants.

The fungus spreads mainly by the growth of the mycelial strands from root to root of the host plants or by free growth through the soil. There seems to be little spread by ordinary tillage practices or on farm equipment. A danger exists, however, of spread in the movement of nursery plants from an infested area, either as mycelium on the roots or as sclerotia in the ball of soil. Irrigation water or movement of surface water after moderate rains apparently does not spread the fungus, but heavy rains and gullying of the soil could possibly move sclerotia and set up new areas of infections.

EXPERIMENTS with a number of field crops have established that rotations in which cotton is grown in alternate years are of little value in reducing losses from root rot. Rotations in which nonsusceptible crops occupy the land for 2 of 3 years give moderate protection. Marked and consistent control is obtained in rotations with nonsusceptible crops in which cotton is grown 1 year in 4. Because many of the tap-rooted weeds are susceptible to the fungus, a rigid weed-control program is necessary during the rotation.

Other practices have value, although in themselves they are not considered to be economical or adequate control measures. Clean fallow for 2 years does not give consistently effective control in the cotton crop following the fallow period. After 8 years of clean fallow, the disease appears on the first crop of cotton and becomes increasingly severe on successive crops. Deep tillage has given some evidence of control the next year, but the effect does not consistently persist beyond 1 year. Early-fall plowing of infested fields reduces somewhat the amount of disease in the following crop, but it is not cumulative in effect.

A slightly better control is obtained by the combination of nitrogen fertilizer and early-fall plowing. Inorganic fertilizers alone, particularly those high in nitrogen and phosphorus, increase the yield of cotton on infested soils, but their economic value has not been proved. Many soil disinfectants

or fungicides have been tested against root rot, but the cost of materials or application precludes their use under ordinary field conditions.

The search for varieties of cotton resistant to the disease has yielded negative results. Early-maturing varieties of upland cotton, however, will set a partial crop of bolls before the period of greatest mortality, and their use is recommended on infested soils.

Practical control of root rot in the irrigated Southwest has been obtained by the incorporation of large amounts of corral or other organic material into trenches or furrows. The furrows are then covered over, beds are prepared above them, and the land is irrigated well before planting time. Yearly treatment of experimental areas in that way has reduced the disease greatly, although complete eradication is not attained. In nonirrigated places in the central blacklands of Texas, that principle has been applied successfully through the growing and turning under of legume crops in rotation with cotton. Sweetclovers, such as Hubam and sourclover (*Melilotus indica*) as winter and winter-summer crops increase the nitrogen and organic content of the soils, reduce the amount of root rot, and increase the yield of cotton.

In both irrigated and nonirrigated areas, control through the application of organic materials to the soil appears to be linked with the increased microbiological activity incidental to the decomposition of the organic matter.

Under laboratory conditions, both sclerotia and mycelium of the fungus are largely eliminated in organic-amended soils. In field experiments that used organic amendments (barnyard manure or sorghum fodder) and October plowing, the incidence of root rot was much less on the following crop of cotton, and no sclerotia were found in the upper 12 inches of soil. In adjacent plots that received only normal bedding operations, root rot was severe, and sclerotia occurred abundantly at the 6-inch to 12-inch level.

The importance of microbial action in the elimination of sclerotia and mycelium from organic-amended soils is strongly suggested by those data, but we cannot overlook the importance of the increased nitrogen content and the improved physical condition of the amended soils.

In summary: The greatest promise of practical control of root rot appears to lie in the use of organic manure, particularly in the form of legumes. Legumes may be used as winter green-manure crops and followed immediately by cotton, or they may be grown to maturity and the residues turned under during the summer. The use of organic manures, plus rotations, early-fall plowing, and early-maturing varieties, should provide satisfactory control of root rot.

LESTER M. BLANK *is in charge of the cotton disease investigations for the Bureau of Plant Industry, Soils, and Agricultural Engineering at the New Mexico Agricultural Experiment Station, located at State College, N. Mex. He received degrees from Washburn University and the University of Wisconsin. He joined the Department of Agriculture in 1929. His investigations have been concerned primarily with phymatotrichum root rot, bacterial blight, and verticillium wilt.*

For a review of the literature before 1937 pertaining to root rot, Dr. Blank suggests R. B. Streets' Phymatotrichum (Cotton or Texas) Root Rot in Arizona, *University of Arizona Technical Bulletin 71, 1937. More recent publications include:*

L. M. Blank: Effect of Nitrogen and Phosphorus on the Yield and Root Rot Responses of Early and Late Varieties of Cotton, *Journal of the American Society of Agronomy, volume 36, pages 875–888, 1944.*

F. E. Clark: Experiments Toward the Control of the Take All Disease of Wheat and the Phymatotrichum Root Rot of Cotton, *U. S. D. A. Technical Bulletin 835, 1942.*

H. V. Jordan, J. E. Adams, D. R. Hooton, D. D. Porter, L. M. Blank, E. W. Lyle, and C. H. Rogers: Cultural Practices as Related to Incidence of Cotton Root Rot in Texas, *U. S. D. A. Technical Bulletin 948, 1947.*

E. W. Lyle, A. A. Dunlap, H. O. Hill, and B. D. Hargrove: Control of Cotton Root Rot by Sweetclover in Rotation, *Texas Agricultural Experiment Station Bulletin 699, 1948.*

Verticillium Wilt of Cotton

J. T. Presley

Verticillium wilt of cotton is caused by a soil-borne fungus. The disease occurs across the entire Cotton Belt from South Carolina to California. It is of major importance in the lower Mississippi Valley and the irrigated areas of the Southwest. Losses in yield from it may reach 50 percent. Average losses of 10 to 15 percent over large areas are not uncommon. Cool, wet weather favors the disease and plants may be attacked at any stage of development. The fiber from wilted plants is often damaged to the extent that the number of neps and manufacturing waste are increased, and the yarns are inferior in grade and looks.

The cotyledons of infected cotton plants become yellowish and quickly dry out. Young plants with three to five true leaves suffer considerable stunting. The leaves appear darker green than those of a normal plant and become somewhat crinkled between the veins. The amount of stunting apparently depends on the stage of development of the plant when it becomes infected. The outstanding symptom is the chlorotic areas on the leaf margins and between the principal veins, which make it look mottled.

In older plants the symptoms usually occur in the lower leaves first. They spread to the middle and upper leaves of the plant later in the season. The chlorotic areas gradually become larger and paler. Severely affected plants shed all the leaves and most of the bolls. Older plants may nevertheless survive the entire season and sometimes send up sprouts from the base of the plant.

Sometimes it is hard to tell verticillium wilt from fusarium wilt. In the early stages of verticillium wilt the vascular discoloration appears to be more evenly distributed through the stele of the plant at the ground line and to be lighter brown than the discoloration produced by fusarium wilt. In fusarium-affected plants, one or more leaves near the crown may wilt suddenly and die, while the other leaves remain apparently healthy. That condition has never been found in verticillium wilt.

In hop plantings in England, wilt appeared to spread in the direction of cultivation, since the spread of the disease was more rapid in cross-cultivated fields than in those cultivated in only one direction. Technicians at Shafter, Calif., found that the fungus spread more rapidly in the heavier soils. The spread usually was against the flow of irrigation water. In Mississippi, where the spread of the fungus was carefully studied, the fungus moved approximately 3 feet a year and spread out from centers of infection.

Diseased cotton stalks and leaf and stem trash from diseased stalks can carry the fungus over from one season to the next and spread the disease into new parts of a field.

MOST OF THE COMMERCIAL VARIETIES of upland cotton (*Gossypium hirsutum*) appear to be susceptible to verticillium wilt. Varieties of Egyptian, Pima, sea-island, and some South American cottons (*G. barbadense*) have a high degree of resistance or tolerance. Numerous observations in the field indicate that the nutrition of the host has a pronounced effect on the development of verticillium wilt. Workers have found that it is particularly severe on soils high in organic matter and also that the disease is favored by heavy application of organic matter to the soil. Efforts were made at Shafter to control the disease by applications of chemicals and soil amendments, but none of the practices appeared promising.

Despite the extreme susceptibility of most commercial upland varieties some progress has been made through selection and breeding toward a high degree of tolerance or resistance George J. Harrison at the United States Cotton Field Station, Shafter, has produced Acala 4-42, which has some tolerance to the disease. Further selections have been made that are even more tolerant.

A. R. Leding at the United States Cotton Field Station, State College, N. Mex., selected a wilt-tolerant variety Acala 1517 W. R. from Acala 1517. It was made available to growers in 1949 Of the cottons adapted to the Southeastern States, none has a high degree of tolerance to verticillium wilt. The fusarium-resistant varieties, such as Coker 100 wilt, Coker 4-in-1, Empire, and Plains, however, have consistently yielded better than wilt-susceptible varieties when grown on soil infested with verticillium wilt.

At the Mississippi Agricultural Experiment Station, Hartsville was found to be highly resistant to verticillium wilt, but the variety was agronomically undesirable. Workers at several State agricultural experiment stations have used Hartsville in a selection and breeding program designed to develop an agronomically acceptable variety that tolerates the wilt.

A grower should choose the most tolerant variety adapted to his particular location to be planted in fields infested with verticillium wilt. Any cultural practice that produces and maintains a higher soil temperature tends to reduce the amount of wilt. Mr. Harrison at Shafter, by carefully controlling soil moisture after the first of July reduced the incidence and severity of wilt. His method is based upon frequent light irrigations which permit more rapid warming of the soil following each irrigation.

L. M. Blank and P. J. Leyendecker, at the New Mexico Agricultural Experiment Station, found that by planting cotton on high ridges a certain degree of control was obtained due to increased soil temperature. They also found that dry fallow for one year and a rotation with barley or barley-Hubam mixture reduced the percentage of infected plants in the first cotton crop.

Alfalfa is also used in rotation with cotton on wilt soil and the first crop following the alfalfa generally has less wilt. Succeeding cotton crops, however, are often more severely attacked than on land where no alfalfa has been grown.

J. T. PRESLEY *is project leader for plant pathology in the division of cotton and other fiber crops and diseases of the Bureau of Plant Industry, Soils, and Agricultural Engineering. He received degrees from the University of Maryland and the University of Minnesota. Since 1935 he has devoted the major part of his time to investigations of cotton diseases, primarily phymatotrichum root rot and verticillium wilt.*

Septoria leaf spot on tomato.

Anthracnose and Some Blights

Albert L. Smith

Cotton anthracnose, caused by *Glomerella gossypii*, is the primary cause of seedling blight, boll rot, and fiber deterioration in the more humid cotton-growing States of the South and Southeast.

The boll rot phase was first discovered in Louisiana in 1890. The seedling blight and other phases of the disease were described in 1892 by George F. Atkinson at the Alabama Agricultural Experiment Station.

From that time until about 1920 the pink boll rot phase of the disease was extremely destructive. Anthracnose boll rot losses diminished with the coming of the boll weevil and the change to earlier, smaller, less vegetative varietal types.

The well-known sore shin of cotton seedlings is caused mostly by anthracnose. The fungus is mainly a secondary invader, entering through wounds, and is adapted to a semisaprophytic existence on injured or dead parts of the cotton plant. It is apparently universally present in all fields throughout the area of its distribution. Anthracnose and ascochyta blight have many features in common although caused by different pathogens.

Anthracnose exists in all humid cotton-growing areas. It has been distributed on seeds to all cotton-producing countries. In the United States it is widespread from Virginia to Texas and Oklahoma. It is delimited by the 40-inch rainfall line.

The line extends north and south through eastern Texas and Oklahoma. West of that line, low rainfall and low humidity are unfavorable for the fungus. The disease reaches its maximum intensity along the Atlantic and Gulf coasts and tapers off toward the inland areas in the Southeast, where somewhat lower humidity prevails. The fungus may be recovered in the laboratory from a high percentage of healthy-appearing leaves, stems, and bracts of most plants selected at random in fields from April to October—particularly during periods of continued wet weather. Consequently the fungus is apparently present most of the time even on healthy-looking plant parts. No other disease of cotton is more widely prevalent.

Anthracnose seedling blight losses were serious for many years before 1935–1945, when seed-treatment disinfectants came into general use. A 4-year (1938–1941) survey of seedling diseases indicated that anthracnose was the predominant cause of seedling blights. The causal organism was recovered from 81.2 percent of the diseased seedling samples. In many fields the characteristic blight lesions could be seen on the below-ground stems of all seedlings. Stand reductions are brought about by preemergence and postemergence blighting-off.

Skippy stands reduce yields. Where planting-over becomes necessary, there are additional costs for seed, labor, and reduced yields caused by lateness and greater weevil damage. Cotton planted over may yield only 60 to 80 percent of the first planting.

Losses from anthracnose boll rot were serious for many years after discovery of the disease in 1890. Commonly, damage was estimated from 10 to 70 percent of the crop. Losses were much less after coming of the boll weevil and are now estimated at from 0.5 to 3 percent, depending on weather conditions.

The anthracnose fungus is often associated with *Alternaria*, *Fusarium*, other fungi, and bacteria in boll rot lesions. A 4-year survey made by Paul R. Miller and Richard Weindling of the Department of Agriculture showed that the anthracnose fungus was present in 67.8 percent of diseased boll samples. They considered it to be the major boll rot disease. Losses are caused by a direct invasion of the unopened bolls with destruction of the seed and lint, by invasion of the partially open bolls causing hard locks, and by weakening and staining of the fiber.

Symptoms on cotyledons are usually diseased areas on margins or small reddish or light-colored spots. Diseased seedlings show reddish-brown lesions below ground. The lesions may be on one side of the stem, or they may surround it and extend down on the root.

Many seedlings are killed before or after they emerge. Others survive with the change to more favorable growing conditions. With the falling of diseased cotyledons, anthracnose symptoms disappear over summer until lesions appear on bolls.

ON THE BOLLS the disease appears as small, round, water-soaked spots, which enlarge and become sunken and brownish in color. A sticky mass of spores comes over the surface of lesions on bolls. The lesions may occur near the tip or at any other point. Often they are associated with wounds made by boll weevils. The bacterial blight pathogen often may be the primary invader, with anthracnose following in the same wound and often associated with other fungi. The lint and seed are rapidly invaded once the disease gets through the husk of the boll. P. B. Marsh and his associates, in studies in 1950 at the Pee Dee Agricultural Experiment Station, described "tight lock," caused by anthracnose and other fungi. Invasion of the lint and seed after cracking of the bur in wet weather produced a hardened, discolored lock. Long periods of rainy weather retard drying and fluffing of the lint and provide favorable condiions for development of fungi on the seed and lint.

Planting seed of cotton are almost always infested with the anthracnose fungus. H. W. Barre in studies at the South Carolina Agricultural Experiment Station found the fungus growing through the seed coat into the embryo. Seed fully invaded failed to germinate. Those that were partly invaded produced diseased seedlings.

C. W. Edgerton, in studies at the Louisiana Agricultural Experiment Station, found—by washing the seeds and counting the spores—that as many as 3,000 spores were carried by each seed.

Paul R. Miller, in studies at the Clemson Agricultural Experiment Station, made other studies on spore load. Samples of cottonseed collected at random from gins in South Carolina in 1941 showed as many as 80,000 spores to a seed, although the average was much lower. Germination tests from the same lots of seed indicated that most of the seedlings had anthracnose infections even though few surface-borne spores were present. The small amount of boll infections in many fields was not enough to account for the heavy spore loads carried by seed. Mr. Miller found that some of the spores came from the trash brought to the gin with the seed cotton. He also determined that clean cotton lots became contaminated with anthracnose conidia when ginned after infested lots. Thus the gin caused thorough contamination of all seed in an individual lot and served to contaminate several lots of clean seed ginned immediately following the ginning of infested cotton.

The disease overwinters on the old rotten bolls and other crop refuse in the field as well as on the seed. The lesions on cotyledons and young stems along with the inoculum on the overwintering crop refuse furnish an abundance of spores for initiating secondary infections. The spores of anthracnose have a sticky covering and are spread mainly by rain. The spores are spread by run-off water over the soil surface.

Rain drops splash spores from the soil onto the plants, from leaf to leaf, and from plant to plant. Infection is favored by moderate temperature and high moisture. The fungi become more easily established in tissues affected by some kind of injury. There are no obvious symptoms of anthracnose infection in summer.

Essentially, the organism exists as a saprophyte in injured tissues. It may also live on honeydew on leaf surfaces. During dry periods it remains dormant and survives for long periods as mycelium in tissues or appressoria attached to the surface. With the return of wet periods it builds up to epidemic proportions and becomes destructive on the bolls.

Infections on the boll gain entrance through the corolla, through bacterial blight lesions or insect wounds, through the sutures separating the loculi, or directly through the uninjured surface. The lint and seed of bolls beginning to open are invaded directly to produce tight lock without invasion going through the boll wall.

Anthracnose seedling blight can be readily controlled by seed-treatment disinfectants. Beginning in 1936 uniform seed-treatment tests were conducted across the Cotton Belt by members of the cotton disease council of the southern section of the American Phytopathological Society. An average increase of 30 percent in emerged seedlings was obtained from application of dust disinfectants. After testing a large number of materials, the committee recommended the use of organic mercury compounds (5 percent Ceresan and Ceresan M) and zinc pentachlorophenate (Dow 9–B). Those two volatile materials largely eliminate surface-borne anthracnose spores and give some protection to the young seedling in the soil. The council has also recommended the use of slurry treaters to replace the dust applicators. The slurry application largely eliminates the obnoxious dusts and reduces the danger to workers handling seed in processing plants.

Anthracnose boll rot, tight lock, and fiber deterioration still are serious problems. Losses are greatest in the Coastal Plain where cotton opens earlier and during the September storm period.

Earlier recommendations for control of anthracnose boll rot included 1-year rotations to eliminate winter carryover of the organism on crop refuse and the selection of planting seed from healthy bolls or from noninfested fields. It was found that the seed-borne fungus died out or was greatly reduced if the seed were stored for 18 months. Thus 2- or 3-year-old planting seed were recommended. Fall plowing was found beneficial for destruction of the stalks and other crop refuse before spring planting where rotations were not possible. Those measures, while effective, were not generally practical or widely adopted by growers.

Defoliation can be the most effective method of reducing boll rot losses from anthracnose and other rots.

Good defoliation is obtained when calcium cyanamide is applied as a dust at the rate of 30 pounds an acre. Removal of the leaves permits rapid drying of the bolls and lint after rains and dews and reduces boll and fiber losses. Other practices of value in reducing boll damage are the planting of varieties with smaller leaves and open-type growth, limiting vegetative growth of the cotton plant by reducing nitrogen applications, controlling insects that damage bolls, and controlling grass and weeds that hinder air circulation.

Varieties have different degrees of resistance to the pink boll rot phase of anthracnose. Somewhat resistant varieties are Toole, Dixie, Dillon, Express, Rowden, Cleveland, and Deltapine. Other varieties considered susceptible are Cook, Half and Half, Hi-Bred, Lone Star, Wilds, Triumph, Trice, and Stoneville. The lack of recent severe infestations of anthracnose boll rot has prevented a classification for resistance of newly introduced varieties. The diminution in anthracnose boll rot may be attributed partly

to the discontinued production of many of the older susceptible types in favor of the newer, less vegetative, earlier resistant ones.

Resistance to anthracnose seedling blight has not been investigated thoroughly. As considerable success has been achieved in controlling seedling blights with dust disinfectants, an intensive effort has not been made to obtain resistant varieties. It is generally agreed that all commercial varieties are quite susceptible in the seedling stage.

ASCOCHYTA BLIGHT, commonly called wet-weather blight or wet-weather canker, is the most sporadic of all cotton diseases. The causal organism is *Ascochyta gossypii*.

The distribution of ascochyta blight parallels the distribution of anthracnose. It occurs in all cotton States from Virginia westward to the 40-inch rainfall line in eastern Texas and Oklahoma. In 1950, a relatively wet year, it was reported prevalent in central Texas and as far west as Lubbock. The most serious occurrences of the disease have been in the Piedmont areas of the Carolinas and Georgia and in the northern parts of Alabama, Mississippi, and central Arkansas.

Losses from the blight result primarily from reduction or loss of stand in the young plant stage. These losses were generally not recognized by pathologists until 1947. From 1947 through 1950, a 4-year period of relatively heavier rainfall years, losses were common and serious in areas involving the northern parts of the Carolinas, Georgia, Alabama, and Mississippi. Serious losses occur during periods unfavorable for plant growth brought about by moist, cool weather. Plants 3 to 8 weeks old are particularly susceptible. The more spectacular but less damaging stem canker has occurred sporadically at infrequent intervals since 1914. Additional but minor losses are caused by leaf blighting and partial defoliation of older plants and boll rotting.

The earliest infections are produced primarily from spores that overwinter on the old plant refuse in the field and are splashed by rain or blown to the leaf surfaces. The spores also overwinter on planting seed that is not treated with a disinfectant.

Earliest symptoms are small, circular white spots on cotyledons and leaves. The lesions enlarge, often coalesce, become brown and roughened, and often fall out, leaving a ragged appearance. Cotyledons and leaves often are defoliated and the young stems are left bare. Additional infections girdle the stems and kill the terminal buds and adjacent stem tissues; the result is loss of stands. From June to August, conspicuous stem cankers occur at the branch axils and center about the stipules. Cankers are from one-half inch to an inch long, dark brown, and ragged at the edges. Sometimes the stems or branches are killed by cankers, but usually stem cankers cause minor damage.

Stem cankers occur only during periods of several consecutive days of cloudy, wet weather. With the return of dry, hot weather, the disease is checked and canker symptoms are quickly obscured by new growth. During wet weather in July and August, older leaves frequently become infected. The lesions may spread quickly and consume most of the leaf area, so that there is extensive defoliation, particularly of the lower leaves. Boll rot lesions are rough, circular, and brownish. Invasion of the seed and lint complete destruction of the boll.

Excellent control of ascochyta seedling blight is had by seed treatment and crop rotation. Primary infections originating from seed-borne spores are largely eliminated by seed treatment with disinfectants. Rotation eliminates the overwintering inoculum that originates in the cotton plant refuse from the previous crop, and excellent control of seedling disease phases is obtained. Partial, but generally satisfactory, control is obtained by plowing old stalks and leaves under deeply in the fall and planting flat to leave such material buried. Other practices that reduce the amount of old plant refuse left on the surface of the soil at planting time may be beneficial.

We have little information on resistance in varieties. Studies made at the Georgia Agricultural Experiment Station in 1947 indicate Empire, Deltapine 15, and Stoneville 2B have slightly more resistance to stem canker in older plants than several other commercial varieties. No varieties have enough resistance to withstand the seedling blight attacks, which are the most destructive phase of the disease.

BACTERIAL BLIGHT of cotton was first described in 1892 by George F. Atkinson in studies conducted at the Alabama Agricultural Experiment Station. He named the disease angular leaf spot and found a bacterium to be the causal agent. The thin-walled parenchyma cells of leaves, stems, and bolls are attacked. The stems may be girdled and show the "black arm" symptoms. Spread of the bacteria along the leaf veins is commonly called vein blight. Lesions on bolls are commonly called boll rot or boll blight. The common name bacterial blight has been adopted to include all those symptoms. The causal organism is *Xanthomonas malvacearum*.

Bacterial blight is prevalent in all cotton-producing areas. It may have originated in India, the center of origin of Old World cottons. It apparently has been associated with cotton in the United States from the beginning of cotton culture. The disease is worst in the subhumid and semiarid areas of the Cotton Belt where the rainfall varies from 10 to 30 inches. Epidemics occur almost every year in the High Plains of west Texas, in the Pecos and Rio Grande Valleys of New Mexico and Texas, and in Arizona and Oklahoma. The disease has been of minor importance in California. In the mid-South and Southeastern States the occurrence is universal, but damage is less serious and more sporadic. Winds of cyclonic intensity accompanied by rain sometimes cause epidemics of the disease over large areas in the Southeast.

Losses result from reduction in stand, defoliation of leaves, stem blighting, shedding of small bolls, boll rotting, and reduction in grade from lint staining. The American-Egyptian irrigated varieties of the Southwest may become complete crop failures during serious outbreaks. In 1949 the yield reduction was estimated at 35 to 50 percent on 40,000 acres in New Mexico. For upland varieties in the United States as a whole the damage is from 1 to 2 percent of the crop. The southwestern upland crop, from Oklahoma westward to Arizona, is consistently affected to the extent that bacterial blight is considered the major disease problem. Besides lower yields largely due to leaf defoliation, the yellow bacterial slime stains the fibers and lowers the grade and price received by the grower. In the South and Southeastern States the blight bacteria provide primary lesions on bolls through which the boll-rotting *Diplodia*, *Alternaria*, *Glomerella*, *Fusarium*, and other fungi gain entrance and rot the seed and fiber.

The first symptoms are small, circular, water-soaked spots on the cotyledons. Leaf spots are translucent, water-soaked, and angular. Later they become browned and blackened. The angular spots are bordered by the veins and vary in size from one-eighth to one-fourth inch in diameter. Multiple infections may merge to involve solid areas of the blade. Many infections often cause leaves to fall prematurely. The bacteria may invade the petiole of the cotyledons or leaves, blackening the tissue as they move into the stem. When young plant stems become infected at the base of a petiole, a curved type of stem growth may follow. Such stems are then often broken off by wind. Stand reduction or complete losses follow early infections.

Branches may be cankered or girdled and turn black. This symptom is known as black arm. It occurs commonly in the more susceptible American-Egyptian varieties. Occasionally the Acala upland varieties also show black arm symptoms. Spread of the organism along the midrib and major veins produces the commonly known vein blight. Younger leaves are more susceptible to vein blighting than are fully mature and older leaves.

Infections originating in the corolla may spread to the young boll and cause extensive shedding. On older bolls the lesions are circular and shiny and later become sunken and browned and blackened. Penetration of the blight organism through the husk wall permits staining of the fiber and invasion of the seed. Infected bolls become deformed and open prematurely.

Most of the infections of seedlings in spring are caused by bacteria carried over the winter on seed. The bacteria may be attached to the seed coat or seed fuzz or inside the seed coat. Seed harvested from heavily infested fields may produce seedlings with 25 percent infection.

Such early and heavy infestations often produce blight epidemics by the end of the growing season. The blight organism may also overwinter on plant refuse left in the field in arid areas. Volunteer seedlings from diseased bolls or old plants which survive the winter may carry the disease over and infect the new crop. Bacteria on infested seed are washed to the germinating embryo and initiate the new infections. The primary lesions produce inoculum, which is splashed to the lower leaves to initiate secondary infections. The disease is carried through several generations on the leaves until the bolls are formed. Greatest damage by the disease is caused by boll infections. High temperatures and high humidity are favorable for maximum infection. The infrequent rains accompanied by strong winds of the High Plains area of the Southwest are most favorable for epidemic spread. Relative scarcity of the disease in California is attributed to the higher elevation and average lower temperatures and scarcity of rainfall.

Blight bacteria gain entrance to the host tissue through stomata and wounds. Entrance to leaf tissue is generally on the lower surface, where the stomatal openings are more abundant. Bacteria are transported by water to the stomatal cavity. The organism characteristically invades the parenchymatous tissue, made up of the thin-walled cells. Less frequently they enter the xylem, or water-conducting vessels, of the leaf petiole, stem, or leaf vein. Once inside the stomata, the bacteria multiply and crush adjacent cells and continue to utilize and multiply on the destroyed cell contents. A bacterial exudate is produced and accumulates on the surface of the wound or drops off to other leaves or to the soil. The exudate dries as a thin, yellowish, translucent film. This material is readily dispersed in rain water and serves as inoculum to further spread the disease. Water congestion of the leaf tissue caused by hard, blowing rains facilitates infection. Wounds made by insects also facilitate infections. Hailstorms which injure all parts of the plant may be followed by blight epiphytotics. The incubation period on bolls and leaves is 8 to 10 days, from time of inoculation to earliest appearance of symptoms.

The world-wide distribution of bacterial blight is attributed to the seed-borne bacteria. Spread in the field is largely attributed to wind-blown rain water and splashing from plant to plant and leaf to leaf by falling water. Bacteria are also carried by flowing of surface water. In irrigated fields the spread of the disease may be traced in the direction of the water flow. Experimentally, dissemination of the disease in fields can be correlated with the direction and velocity of the wind during periods of rainfall. The spread of bacteria by dust storms has been observed in Arizona. The wind-blown rains characteristic of the High Plains of Texas and the irrigated valleys of New Mexico and western Texas are more effective in spreading the disease than the rainfalls of the mid-South and Southeast. The movement of fallen diseased leaves by strong winds also spreads the disease.

CONTROL MEASURES for the bacterial blight disease have been directed toward eliminating the overwintering sources of inoculum on the seed and in the field. When F. M. Rolfs found blight bacteria adhering to the seed fuzz and seed coat he demonstrated the possibility of removing them with sulfuric acid in experiments at the South Carolina Agricultural Experiment Station in 1915. With concentrated sulfuric acid all fibers are removed from the seed. Any adhering bacteria on the seed coat are also removed. Washing the acid off of the seed may remove any lightweight seed or floaters and give a high-grade planting seed.

Beginning about 1930, organic mercurial dust disinfectants became available for seed treatment, which also largely controlled seed-borne bacteria. A combination of delinting and dust treatment became widely used in areas where serious bacterial blight losses occurred. As an outgrowth of delinting efforts to control blight, commercial processing plants are now operating across the Cotton Belt and delinted seed of all major varieties is available. Many growers prefer the delinted seed for more precise planting with tractors.

Other practices for blight control are the selection of seed grown in disease-free fields and the destruction in early fall of the previous crop refuse by deep, clean plowing. Any volunteer seedlings are also destroyed in spring before planting.

Although a fair degree of success in controlling blight by sanitation, delinting, and seed treatment is obtained, the results are not always satisfactory. Internally borne infections often survive the treatments and initiate disease centers. Because all growers sometimes do not cooperate in the blight-control program, the spread of infection from an adjoining farm may cause losses. Pathologists believe therefore that the only fully satisfactory possibility for control is the development of blight-resistant varieties.

THE SEVERE LOSSES from bacterial blight in the Gezira of the Sudan caused British workers to make an intensive search for resistance to bacterial blight. The work was done by R. L. Knight and associates in studies conducted at the Agricultural Research Institute, Khartoum, Sudan. An upland-type cotton, Ugandi B31, was found to have a high degree of resistance. It has been used in breeding programs.

A blight-resistant upland, Stoneville 20, was discovered in 1939 by D. M. Simpson and Richard Weindling in breeding plots at the Tennessee Agricultural Experiment Station. Stoneville 20 is not a desirable commercial type, but it has no bad characteristics and is valuable as a source of resistance. In 1953 it was being used as a source of resistance in several breeding programs in the Cotton Belt.

A satisfactory technique for artificial inoculation had to be developed before progress could be made in selecting resistant plants in the breeding program. Mr. Knight at Khartoum learned that he could get uniform infections by soaking 10 pounds of diseased leaves in 40 gallons of water and using the liquid as a spray. The technique was improved by Richard Weindling in research work he did at the South Carolina Agricultural Experiment Station. He found that a single potato-dextrose agar culture grown in a petri plate and diluted with $2\frac{1}{2}$ gallons of water provided a more satisfactory source of inoculum. He also discovered the best time to spray was from midmorning until noon on sunny days when the stomata were wider open. The lower leaf surface due to the larger number of stomata also gave more infections than the upper

surface. Additional improvements in the inoculation technique now indicate that by using an orchard sprayer, with 400 pounds pressure to the square inch, and forcing the bacterial suspension into the stomata very satisfactory infections are obtained on a field scale.

A technique for infecting greenhouse seedlings has also proved useful in the search for blight resistance within established varieties. The seed are first soaked in a bacterial suspension, planted in a greenhouse bench, and examined on emergence for size of bacterial lesions. The lesions are nonexistent, or very small, on resistant plants. Resistance to leaf blight, black arm, and boll blight were all found to be positively correlated, and therefore the leaf symptoms alone could be used as an index to resistance within the individual plant in breeding work.

The inheritance of resistance to blight has been studied by Mr. Knight. In a survey of all cotton species and a large number of species types and varieties, he found five factors for resistance, B_1 to B_5. The factors varied in the amount of resistance they contributed and were generally additive or accumulative in contributing to the resistance of the plant. In segregating populations the resistance factors segregated as dominants or partial dominants.

The resistance in Stoneville 20 is largely determined by a single gene. Resistance is recessive and susceptibility is dominant. In addition to the major gene in Stoneville 20, several minor genes contribute to the resistance with additive effects. The minor genes account for varying amounts of blight tolerance in commercial upland varieties. Deltapine has a high level of minor genes, Stoneville 2B somewhat less, and Acala a very low level. Resistance can be established in American uplands by the accumulation of several minor genes centered about a major gene, as found in Stoneville 20.

The breeding of blight-resistant varieties adapted to all sections of the Cotton Belt is an extensive project and was well under way in 1953. L. S. Bird and L. M. Blank demonstrated the possibilities in breeding for resistance and outlined a backcross method in studies conducted at the Texas Agricultural Experiment Station. Four varieties—Stoneville 2B, Deltapine, Empire, and Coker 100 wilt—were each crossed with Stoneville 20. Using the backcross method and the inoculation technique developed by Weindling, they were able to obtain satisfactory blight-resistant commercial types within 5 years. A search was started for naturally occurring resistant individual plants within a number of additional varieties. The work is done by growing several thousand plants in a field planting and inoculating them with a power sprayer. Promising plants have been found in several varieties. Pathologists are confident that all commercial varieties will sometime be bred resistant to bacterial blight.

ALBERT L. SMITH *is a graduate of Oklahoma Agricultural and Mechanical College and the University of Wisconsin. He joined the Department of Agriculture as a pathologist in 1936 to work on cotton diseases and breeding for disease resistance. He is currently conducting studies on the use of fungicides for the control of ascochyta blight. Most of his time has been devoted to studies on fusarium wilt and nematode disease of cotton. He is stationed at the Alabama Polytechnic Institute in Auburn.*

For further reading on ascochyta blight of cotton, Dr. Smith suggests his article, Ascochyta Seedling Blight of Cotton in Alabama in 1950, *in the Plant Disease Reporter, volume 34, pages 233–235, 1950; and John A. Elliott's* A New Ascochyta Disease of Cotton, *Arkansas Agricultural Experiment Station Bulletin 178, 1922.*
Suggested references for bacterial blight:
L. S. Bird and L. M. Blank: Breeding Strains of Cotton Resistant to Bacterial Blight, *Texas Agricultural Experiment Station Bulletin 736, 1951.*
R. L. Knight: The Genetics of Blackarm Resistance. VIII, *Journal of Genetics, volume 50, pages 67–76, 1950.*
Richard Weindling: Bacterial Blight of Cotton Under Conditions of Artificial Inoculation, *U. S. D. A. Technical Bulletin 956, 1948.*

Bacteria and Fungi on Seedlings

David C. Neal

Cotton seedlings are subject to attack by several fungus and bacterial diseases, especially when soil temperatures are low and wet weather prevails in the spring following planting.

Some of the diseases are caused by strong pathogens, which deplete the stand to such an extent that replanting becomes necessary. The additional expense for more seed and labor for replanting and a reduction in yield (which ranges as high as 15 percent) because of late planting are considerable.

Many species of fungi, bacteria, and nematodes have been encountered by pathologists in studies of seedling diseases of cotton, but little is known regarding the pathogenicity of some of them. I limit this report mainly to the pathogens whose distribution over the Cotton Belt and effects on seedlings are well known.

The name sore shin apparently was first used to describe the symptoms produced by damping-off of cotton seedlings in Alabama by George F. Atkinson in 1892. The disease is caused by the soil-inhabiting fungus, *Rhizoctonia solani.* It occurs throughout the Cotton Belt and is considered to be the most serious seedling disease of cotton in Oklahoma, Texas, and the Western States. It is also frequently prevalent and destructive in the Mississippi terrace and delta soils of Arkansas, Louisiana, Mississippi, and western Tennessee and in other heavier soils of the middle South. It attacks cotton seedlings only under conditions favorable to the fungus and unfavorable to the plant, such as cold, moist weather. The disease is also more severe when seedlings are damaged by thrips.

When seedlings are attacked by the sore shin fungus, usually within 5 or 10 days after planting, dark- to reddish-brown cankers develop on the stems near the soil line. In severe attacks, the cankers encircle the stems or penetrate so deeply that the plants fall over and die. The attack usually occurs in early-planted cotton before the formation of true leaves, but the fungus may persist and continue to restrict root development and top growth until the plants begin to flower. Infection also occurs on the leaves late in the season in some States. Some defoliation results, but that is of little economic importance.

Tests have been made of various chemical and fungicidal materials for possible control of sore shin of cotton, but we had no satisfactory control measure in 1953. Certain practices will reduce losses.

First is the thorough preparation of the seedbed so that rows are well pulverized at the surface, firm beneath, and slightly raised—4 to 6 inches—to give good drainage.

Second is the planting of seed that is certified as to viability and has been treated according to accepted practice for control of seed-borne diseases.

Third is to avoid planting too early. Early plantings usually are subjected to cool nights and moist weather which favor attack by the disease. With the newer and more effective insecticides now available for insect control, the planting date for cotton could be delayed with safety in many areas for 10 or 14 days or until the soil warms up.

Fourth is speeding up germination by using reginned or acid-delinted seed and liberal fertilization so as to give the seedlings a vigorous start.

Other soil-borne organisms that attack cotton seedlings are *Fusarium oxysporum*, *F. vasinfectum*, the wilt fungus; *Fusarium moniliforme* and other species of *Fusarium*, which cause rots and blights; *Thielaviopsis basicola*, the cause of root rot; species of *Pythium* that cause damping-off; *Sclerotium bataticola* and *S. rolfsii*, which cause rots; and the parasitic nematodes *Meloidogyne incognita* var. *acrita* (which causes root knot), *Pratylenchus leiocephalus* (the meadow nematode), species of *Trichodorus* (which cause stubby root), and other nematodes, such as *Helicotylenchus nannus* and *Rotylenchulus reniformis*, which affect cotton and are known to be associated with the incidence of fusarium wilt.

Most of those organisms are pathogenic on seedlings and cause damage in some areas, but, with the exception of the root knot nematode, which frequently reduces seedling stands of Egyptian cotton in Arizona and New Mexico, they are of minor importance in the complex of seedling diseases.

THE ANTHRACNOSE FUNGUS, *Glomerella gossypii*, is the main pathogen responsible for seedling blight and damping-off in all of the cotton-growing States east of the 40-inch rain belt of Oklahoma and Texas.

In a survey conducted from 1938 to 1941 by pathologists of the Department of Agriculture in 14 States, the anthracnose fungus was found to be the predominant organism affecting cotton seedlings throughout the Southwestern and Mississippi Valley States. Its distribution on seedlings also coincided with the area affected with anthracnose boll rot. It occurred in 81.2 percent of seedling samples, but in Texas and Oklahoma the occurrence of the fungus was limited to the eastern parts of the States. The absence of the disease in the western belt is apparently due to dry conditions and high temperatures that prevent the survival of the fungus during the interval between the seedling blight stage and the boll rot stage.

Seed become contaminated at the

gin with anthracnose spores, which are present in such trash as infected leaves, bracts, stems, and bolls. All such material may carry heavy loads of spores, which are mixed with the seed in ginning and adhere to the fuzz or linters.

In studying the relation of germination to contamination of cotton seed by the anthracnose fungus, Richard Weindling and P. R. Miller, of the Department of Agriculture, find no relation between the size of spore loads of *Glomerella gossypii* on a given sample of seed and the percentage of germination of the seed. They emphasize, however, that the size of the spore load seems to influence the amount of postemergence damping-off when the seeds are planted.

When anthracnose-infested seed are planted, the seed-borne spores become active and may attack the germinating seedling. Infected seedlings may be killed before emergence or after emergence or they may survive and overcome the disease. Affected seedlings have reddish or dark-brown lesions on the stems below the soil line and frequently on the roots. The cotyledons—the seed leaves—also may be attacked, the disease producing brownish spots that enlarge before the plant wilts and succumbs. If cool, moist weather prevails for several days after planting, infested seedlings continue to blight and damp-off to the extent that stands become skimpy and replanting is necessary.

Uniform, regional, seed-treatment experiments conducted between 1938 and 1948 in most of the cotton States by a committee of the Cotton Disease Council, composed of Federal and State research pathologists, gave good control of anthracnose of seedlings. In the tests the increases in emergence from seed treatment were usually larger in the early plantings (when emergence was often delayed by cool, rainy weather) than in later plantings (when weather conditions generally were more favorable for rapid seed emergence and growth).

Data from 63 tests conducted between 1946 and 1948 show the value of seed treatment. The mean increase in surviving seedlings was 33, 30, and 26 percent when fuzzy, reginned, and acid-delinted seed, respectively, were compared with untreated seed.

Of a large number of materials tested, higher percentages of emerged seedlings were obtained with the organic mercury dusts, ethyl mercury chloride, ethyl mercury phosphate, and ethyl mercury p-toluene sulfonanilide, which are sold under the trade names of 2 percent Ceresan, New Improved Ceresan 5 percent, and Ceresan M 7.7 percent, respectively. Another material recommended by the committee is zinc trichlorophenate, 50 percent, in a suitable diluent. It is marketed under the trade name Dow 9-B.

The materials are applied at the following rates: Fuzzy seed, 1½ ounces to a bushel; acid-delinted seed, 2 ounces to 100 pounds; and reginned seed, 3 ounces to 100 pounds. They also are wettable and may be applied by the slurry method, which has given emergence values of seedlings comparable to the dust treatment.

The slurry method involves the suspension of the disinfectant in water and its application to the seed in that form rather than as a dust or powder. The method eliminates flying dust during seed-treating operations, ventilation or dust exhaustion, and the use of masks by workmen. Another advantage of the slurry method over dusts is that it gives greater accuracy and uniformity of dosage.

Chemicals for treating seed may be applied as dusts or slurry in homemade rotary drums equipped with tight-fitting lids or in specially constructed motor-driven machines with treating capacities of 4 to 6 tons of seed an hour.

Reginning, or machine delinting of cotton seed, is done extensively in the Central and Southeastern States. The linters are removed in the process, so that planting is more uniform, hill dropping equipment can be used, and seed and chemical dusts are saved. Light reginning is preferable; close reginning may damage some seed. During certain years of the regional tests, reginned treated seed gave a higher emergence of seedlings than fuzzy treated seed, but in other years the differences were small.

In 1938, for instance, reginned, Ceresan-treated seed in 21 plantings gave a higher mean number of surviving seedlings than comparable fuzzy treated seed. In 1939 in 18 regional plantings, the increase in number of surviving seedlings from reginned seed treated with 5 percent Ceresan was much higher than fuzzy seed similarly treated. In other tests later, the number of surviving seedlings for reginned was highest in 1946, slightly higher for fuzzy in 1947, and practically the same for both seed sublots in 1948.

Acid delinting of cotton seed is used more extensively in the drier areas of Texas and Oklahoma and in the irrigated areas of the western cotton States. It is used to a lesser extent in the Mississippi Valley and the Southeastern States. Either sulfuric acid or hydrochloric acid gas is used for delinting.

With the sulfuric acid method, the seed is mixed with the acid in delinting machines, which do the work rapidly and efficiently. After the linters are dissolved, the seed is thoroughly washed in large vats to remove the acid. The lighter seeds, or floaters, are removed during washing. The heavier seeds, or sinkers, are given a final rinsing, usually in dilute limewater, dried, and retained for planting.

With hydrochloric gas, the linters are removed by the gas from the heated acid. It has the advantage over the sulfuric acid method in that the seed is kept dry throughout the treatment. The lighter seeds are removed with fans.

Acid-delinted seed usually give a higher emergence of seedlings than reginned or fuzzy seed if weather conditions are favorable. But we have instances in which seed so treated gave only poor to fair germination during cool, wet weather. In 13 regional plantings in 1946, the surviving seedlings at final count (as percentage of seeds planted) were 73.0 for delinted, 61.7 for reginned, and 60.0 for fuzzy seed of the same lot. While acid-delinted seed gives good stands and requires less seed to the acre, especially if hill-dropped, the method is more expensive than machine delinting.

BACTERIAL BLIGHT causes death of seedlings and loss of young plants because infected stems are weakened by blight and break during wind storms. The disease occurs throughout the Cotton Belt. It is most destructive in the Southwestern States.

First, small, round, water-soaked lesions develop on the cotyledons as they emerge from the seed coat. The lesions furnish inoculum for the developing true leaves, the bacteria later infecting the terminal bud and main stem.

Delinting cotton seed with sulfuric acid plus fungicidal treatment eliminates blight bacteria from the seed.

DAVID C. NEAL, *a pathologist in the Department of Agriculture since 1928, has been engaged in research on cotton diseases in the Southern States since 1917. His contributions include physiological studies of fusarium wilt, techniques for studying varietal resistance, and the effects of nutrition upon the incidence of this disease. He has also investigated the morphology and life history of phymatotrichum root rot, seed treatment for stand improvement, and crinkle leaf found to be caused by manganese toxicity. While working on phymatotrichum root rot of cotton in Texas in 1929, Dr. Neal discovered the sclerotium stage of that fungus in nature and thereby established its importance in the persistence and overwintering of the disease in the soil. He is a native of Mississippi, a graduate of Mississippi State College, and postgraduate of Washington University, St. Louis, Mo.*

The Leaf Spots of Cotton Plants

Lester M. Blank

One or more of the leaf spots of cotton occur in practically every cotton-field when the crop is growing.

Some have to do with maturity of the plant and have no great effect on its growth or yield. Others develop on seedlings or young plants and damage the normal growth and fruiting processes. The leaf spot organisms commonly cause shedding of the affected leaves, but some may injure the branches and bolls.

This article deals mostly with the effect of some of the leaf-spotting organisms on the foliage of the plant.

The leaf spot caused by *Alternaria tenuis* probably is one of the most common. We have known about it since 1918, when investigators learned that it was often linked with angular leaf spot, or bacterial blight, and that it was found on leaves throughout the growing season. Often it was found overgrowing old angular leaf spot lesions or in places where spider mites were doing harm. We have learned that it can infect undamaged leaves and may be considered as a weak parasite. Sometimes *Alternaria* may cause severe shedding of leaves.

In the early stages, the spots on the leaves have a pale-green area with an indefinite and irregular margin. As the area enlarges, the color of the older part becomes straw yellow and then rusty brown. By then the spot contains a number of irregular concentric zones in the roughly circular lesions and the fungal spores may be found on the surface of the lesions.

We do not know exactly which environmental conditions favor the development of this leaf spot, but it has been reported on plants suffering from low vigor because of drought or deficiency of potash. Experiments indicate that plants can be inoculated most easily if humidity is high. Although the alternaria leaf spot is common, it is considered of less importance than other leaf-spotting organisms. Little therefore has been done on control measures.

ASCOCHYTA LEAF SPOT, canker or blight, wet-weather canker, and wet-weather blight are names commonly given to the disease caused by the fungus *Ascochyta gossypii*. As the names indicate, the disease may manifest itself as a seedling blight, a leaf spot, a stem or petiole canker, and as a boll spot. Ordinarily several phases of the disease may be seen on a plant.

The first symptoms are small, round, white, purple-ringed spots on the cotyledons and lower leaves. The spots become somewhat elongated and raised on the upper surface. Later they change to a light brown, the purple ring around the outside disappears, and the diseased tissue often falls out. If infections are numerous, irregular diseased areas result and are followed by drying and shedding of infected cotyledons and lower leaves. Pycnidia—fruiting bodies—of the fungus are produced irregularly or in concentric rings and are visible on the upper surface of the lesion. Growth of the plant is stunted. The upper small leaves, petioles, and buds are often infected, and the plant dies. The almost bare stems, with a few small leaves at the tip, are characteristic of the disease in the later stages.

Outbreaks have been associated with long periods of rain and cool weather. Ascochyta may be seed-borne, but the carry-over of diseased stalks and branches from the preceding year's crop may be of greater importance in setting up new infections. The disease can be spread in infected plant debris; local spread appears to be mainly by the flow of surface water from contaminated fields to lower places.

Rotation with other crops helps control it by eliminating the carry-over of the fungus from one season to another. If rotation is not practicable, old cotton stalks should be plowed as soon as possible after harvest to obtain maximum decay or deep-plowed in the spring to reduce the amount of infected plant material on the surface at time of planting. Seed treatment reduces the amount of carry-over on the seed and improves the initial stand but does not give protection beyond the early seedling stage.

THE BACTERIAL BLIGHT disease, caused by *Xanthomonas malvacearum*, can affect all above-ground parts of the cotton plant. It occurs in all cotton areas. In the United States it is particularly severe in the Southwest.

It shows up on the leaves as angular, water-soaked lesions, which turn brown or black when dry. On the bolls, it appears as round water-soaked lesions, which are sunken and black when dry. On the stems and fruiting branches, it produces black, elongated lesions. Therefore the disease is commonly known as angular leaf spot, boll blight, and black arm.

On upland varieties it may cause a blight of seedlings, defoliation of plants, or shedding and rotting of the bolls. Upland varieties in the Cotton Belt are affected by the black arm phase, but it is more common on the American, Egyptian, and the sea-island varieties, which often show almost complete destruction of bolls and branches. Severe leaf infection in all varieties means extreme defoli-ation; slight to severe losses in yield of seed cotton may follow.

The bacteria that cause the disease may overwinter on the surface of the seed, within the seed coat, and on diseased cotton stalks and bolls from the previous crop. Volunteer seedlings from infected bolls can be responsible for early appearance and spread of the disease, particularly when splashing rain or irrigation water aid in the movement of the bacteria.

The first evidence of the disease is seen on the under surface of the coty-ledons as water-soaked spots, circular or irregular but without the marked angular appearance noted on the true leaves. Such lesions are first evident along the margins of the cotyledons and then spread inwardly. Later the part near the original site of infection becomes brown and dry, frequently distorting the shape of the cotyledon. The bacteria may move along the petiole of the cotyledon and into the stem of the young seedling, producing the typical water-soaked appearance of the tissues. Continued movement of the bacteria into the terminal bud region results in tissue collapse and death of the young plant.

On the true leaves the external symptoms appear as water-soaked lesions, first on the under surface and later on the upper surface. The lesions are bounded by small veinlets of the leaf—hence their characteristic angular appearance. If the young leaves are held toward the light, the spots appear translucent. As the lesions become older, large amounts of bac-terial slime are exuded and form a dry film on the discolored lesions, usually on the under side of the leaf. The infected area of the leaves finally becomes dry and sunken and turns reddish brown or black; often the nearby healthy areas become yel-lowish. At times the blight lesions along the veins of the leaf produce a symptom known as vein blight.

The bacteria are spread from older to newly formed leaves and eventually to the bolls by wind-driven and splashing rain. Dry, hot weather checks the progress of the disease.

Control measures have centered around the use of disease-free seed, attained through acid-delinting and the application of a chemical disinfect-ant. That practice has been successful particularly in the rain-belt part of the production area. In drier parts of the Southwest, however, there may be more overwintering of the organism in undecomposed, infected plant material, and the use of acid-delinted and dust-treated seed has not been uniformly successful. In order to reduce the carry-over of the blight organism in plant debris, we recommend rotation with other crops or the early and complete turning under of infected material, followed by irrigation to promote decomposition.

But the use of resistant varieties is the only adequate control throughout the entire period of plant development. D. M. Simpson, at the Cotton Field Station, Knoxville, Tenn., found a high degree of resistance in one of his breeding strains of cotton. It was released to other breeders as Stoneville 20 and has been used widely as the resistant parent in crosses with a number of desirable, but susceptible, commercial varieties. The qualities of the commercial parent are then regained through a series of back-crosses to this parent, accompanied by selection for the resistance and for good fiber properties and high yield. Field tests in 1950, 1951, and 1952 in Texas and New Mexico confirmed the practicability of combining blight resistance with the desired fiber and yield properties of the recurrent commercial varieties.

LEAF SPOT DUE TO THE ATTACK of the Cercospora fungus (*Cercospora gossypina*) is common in almost every cotton field toward the end of the season. The spots it causes are rarely more than one-fourth of an inch in diameter and are roundish or irregular. The lesions have purple borders and white centers, which finally fall out and leave a riddled appearance. The fungus may attack uninjured tissues, but it seldom causes much defoliation and is of minor economic importance.

RAMULARIA LEAF SPOT, also called areolate mildew and frosty blight, was first discovered in 1889 on leaves collected near Auburn, Ala. It has been found since in many Southeastern States and abroad. The disease usually occurs toward the end of the growing season. It may cause some leaf shedding, but it is not of great economic importance.

A typical symptom is the whitish growth of the fungus on the under side of leaves, which produces a frosty or mildew appearance. The spots are angular and bordered by the veinlets of the leaf. Viewed from above, the lesions are bright green to yellowish green, and only occasionally show the white coating so typical on the under surface of the infected leaves. Similar lesions may form on the bracts surrounding the bolls.

THE FUNGUS that causes sore shin and damping-off of cotton seedlings, *Rhizoctonia solani*, has been reported also as a leaf-spotting fungus in Louisiana.

In the early stage, light-brown, irregular spots of varying size appear between the veins and are bordered by dark, purplish rings. As the fungus advances, it causes the tissue immediately surrounding the spots to become chlorotic and the dead tissue in the center of the old spot cracks or falls out. On the lower surface of the leaves the smaller spots may be covered by light- to yellowish-brown growth of the fungus. It might affect considerable leaf area, but it is not of serious economic importance as a leaf-spotting organism.

LESTER M. BLANK, *a graduate of Washburn University and the University of Wisconsin, is in charge of the cotton disease investigations for the Bureau of Plant Industry, Soils, and Agricultural Engineering at the New Mexico Agricultural Experiment Station, State College, N. Mex. He joined the Department of Agriculture in 1929. His investigations have been concerned primarily with phymatotrichum root rot, bacterial blight, and verticillium wilt.*

Nonparasitic Disorders of Cotton

W. Hardy Tharp

Potash hunger of cotton was known as rust or black rust before 1892, when George F. Atkinson demonstrated that it could be controlled by additions of potash to the soil. He called the disease yellow leaf blight, but the name rust has remained in common usage.

Scientists frequently use the term "rust or potash hunger" because it describes both the symptoms and the cause.

Rust occurs commonly on the lighter soils of the Coastal Plain areas of the Cotton Belt and in many other soils of several mid-South States, including Alabama, Arkansas, Louisiana, and Mississippi. W. W. Gilbert estimated the average damage for the entire Cotton Belt at 4 or 5 percent in 1920, but greater use of balanced fertilizers in the affected areas undoubtedly has reduced the loss in recent years.

Affected plants are usually stunted and fail to develop a normal green color. The lower or older leaves are first to show the typical mottled appearance; the areas between the veins turn yellow. Toward midseason the symptoms are visible over the entire plant. The yellowish spots on the leaves enlarge and become reddish brown or bronzed. Later the entire leaf may become blackened, curled downward, and ragged. Brown or black circular or irregular spots are often produced on many affected leaves by the growth of *Alternaria* and perhaps other secondary invaders. Leaves usually are shed prematurely and often the stalk is left bare. The number and the size of bolls are reduced. Yields are severely lowered. Affected bolls do not flare open properly, and so the cotton is hard to pick. Lint and seed from affected plants are inferior.

The primary cause of rust is insufficient potash to meet the nutritional requirements of the plant. The condition usually is found on potash-deficient soils, but not necessarily so. Excessive applications of nitrogen or phosphorus, or both, often may accentuate severity. Overliming or a scarcity of sodium, which substitutes to some extent for potash, likewise tend to increase rust. Lack of humus in the soil and improper drainage have also been listed as conditions responsible for or contributing to severity of the disease.

The application of fertilizers that contain ample potash to furnish the needs of the plant throughout the season is considered the standard method of control. The exact amount needed to correct the condition depends on the supply of other soil nutrients. A common practice on lighter soils, where early rains can easily leach out some of the available potash supplied before planting, is to apply some potash along with nitrogen as a side dressing after the plants are established.

Potash hunger should not be confused with the true rust of cotton, which is caused by attack of the parasitic fungus *Puccinia stakmanii*, and occurs in limited areas of the Western States. Fusarium wilt and root knot nematodes also are often prevalent in the soils where potash hunger is common. It is not always easy to determine the exact degree of damage associated with each cause in this complex.

THE CRAZY TOP disorder of cotton was first recognized by C. J. King and H. F. Loomis in a field of Pima cotton near Scottsdale, Ariz., in 1919. Three years later it was observed in a field of upland cotton near Casa Grande, Ariz. By 1924 the disorder had become common in Arizona and by 1936 it was still considered one of the most important problems of cotton production in certain districts of the State. Mild stages of the disease were also known to have appeared in the San Joaquin and Imperial Valleys of California between 1926 and 1933.

O. F. Cook was first to present an accurate description of the disorder. He named the disease acromania, but the term crazy top, which is descriptive of the abnormal branching and fruiting in the upper part of affected plants, has remained the one in common use. The first symptom is an abrupt change in the type of new growth made in the top of the cotton plants. Fruiting branches frequently are replaced by vegetative branches, which have regrown in an upright position and are developing an abnormal or crazy appearance in the tops of the plants. Typical features of the abnormality include reductions and distortions of leaves, internodes, bracts, and floral parts. The leaves are small, rounded, cupped, and thickened. Flowers are small and distorted. Sterility is common and may be expressed either as complete suppression of floral buds or as profuse shedding of flowers. The few bolls that develop are usually small and malformed and contain a reduced number of seed.

The disease occurs only on calcareous soils and has been found almost entirely related to irrigation practice. It is associated with the checking of growth from water shortages and the resumption of growth when abundant moisture is restored. The disease is controlled easily by applying irrigation water frequently enough to prohibit a checking of plant growth during the summer months. Water shortage may not be the only factor involved in bringing about the abnormalities—maintaining organic matter at higher levels by rotation with alfalfa is beneficial.

CRINKLE LEAF is the name given by D. C. Neal in 1937 to a peculiar disorder of cotton plants occurring in Lintonia and Oliver silt loam soils of Louisiana and Arkansas. The typical symptoms are a puckering, mottling, partial chlorosis, and distortion of the leaves. The branches are often fasciated and the floral buds, flowers, and bolls are distorted. The fiber from affected bolls is often so weak as to be considered worthless.

Dr. Neal and H. C. Lovett demonstrated by experiments they conducted in Louisiana in 1937 and 1938 that the disease was associated with high soil acidity, calcium deficiency, and manganese toxicity. The typical symptoms were readily produced by adding increasing amounts of manganese sulfate to pot cultures of cotton. But it was easy to control the disease in the field by adding limestone. At the higher pH produced by treating the soil with limestone, or with other material containing basic carbonates, the manganese apparently is precipitated, and so the plants remain healthy.

THRIPS INJURY is not strictly a nonparasitic disease of cotton, but I include a brief description because its symptoms are not unlike those of certain stages of crinkle leaf and crazy top.

Infestation by thrips frequently causes serious injury to cotton plants. Reduced stands or reduced yields result from stunting and delayed fruiting of the plants. Damage is severe only in the early-season development of the plants and is usually restricted to mutilation of seedling leaves as they unfold from the bud. Often, however, the terminal bud is destroyed, so that the plant gets a stunted appearance. Until it outgrows the disorder around midseason, the branching is bunched or fasciated. The leaves may appear torn, perforated, cupped, and distorted. Usually there will be little if any change from normal green color.

A serious aspect of the disease is that the injury and decreased vigor tend to make plants more susceptible to the sore shin disease of cotton seedlings caused by *Rhizoctonia solani*—a fact demonstrated in experiments conducted by Neal and L. D. Newsome in Louisiana in 1950.

Considerable variation in susceptibility among commercial varieties of cotton was observed by W. W. Ballard in Georgia. He pointed out that dense pubescence of juvenile terminal leaves appeared to be associated with resistance to thrips in some cases. He noted also that the degree of injury was usually correlated with the amount of aborted terminal buds, although a few varieties exhibited a degree of injury independent of the proportion of terminal buds aborted.

2,4-D (2,4-dichlorophenoxyacetic acid), a hormone-type herbicide commonly used to kill broadleaf pests in lawns, is extremely toxic to cotton plants. The minute quantities that light on cotton plants when the drift from adjacent applications is not controlled can cause severe injury. The danger has been thoroughly recognized since this weed killer was first introduced commercially in 1946 but, despite adequate and repeated warnings, cotton may be found injured occasionally from drift, from accidental contamination of other chemicals used on cotton, or from improperly cleaned machinery and containers that have been used with 2,4-D.

The symptoms on cotton are characteristic and specific formative effects, except where the dosage is sufficiently high to kill the plants or plant parts outright. The effects are first noted near the growing points and the characteristic symptoms are usually the result of an abnormal stimulation of growth of the affected parts. Leaves are greatly modified. They become narrow, closely and conspicuously veined, and deeply lobed. Affected flowers are modified in a manner similar to the leaf—elongated and narrow. Bracts are modified. They become deeply lobed and elongated and they fail to separate; they grow as a sheath around the developing boll.

When enough material is absorbed to kill or inhibit the terminal bud, the plant may become branched and fasciated, with slender and malformed leaves, branches, buds, and flowers. Affected bolls and squares may turn yellow and then drop, although some malformed and partially fertile mature bolls have been observed. Often, however, the squares or bolls die without shedding. Excessive shedding of leaves as a result of 2,4-D injury has not been reported. If the tops of plants are damaged, they may send out strong laterals, which produce apparently normal branches. The fully grown leaves, branches, or bolls seldom show much injury from the low dosages.

The formative effects in cotton continue to develop for some weeks following application of 2,4-D but the persistence of the stimulus depends on the stage of plant development and the concentration applied. If young bolls are present, the seed may be injured. The likelihood of damage is greater for seed developing from plants treated at the time of flowering and, normally, no effects on the seed will be noted if parent plants are treated before the young square stage of growth.

Some instances have been reported where applications of organic insecticides have been associated with injury to cotton plants similar to that produced by 2,4-D. Many are undoubtedly cases of contamination, but with the use of certain of the organic phosphates it may be the insecticide itself causing the injury. Wayne J. McIlrath has shown a striking similarity of symptoms produced by treating comparable plants with 2,4-D and with commercial HETP (hexaethyl tetraphosphate), and to some extent with TEPP (tetraethyl pyrophosphate).

W. HARDY THARP *is a project leader for plant physiology in the Department of Agriculture. He was graduated from Montana State College. He received his advanced training at the University of Wisconsin and Cornell University. He joined the Department in 1934.*

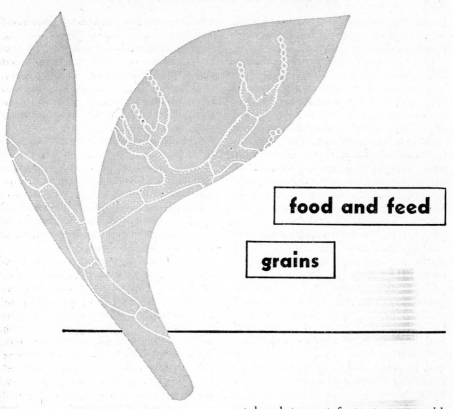

Root Rots of Wheat, Oats, Rye, Barley

J. J. Christensen

The root rots of wheat, oats, barley, and rye are among the least conspicuous diseases of cereals, but they are among the most destructive.

They are caused by many species of fungi, which are widespread and live on or in seed, soil, and dead plant refuse. They attack a large number of hosts and thrive under a wide range of conditions.

To the many types of root rots in cereal crops many names have been given—seedling blight, take-all, root rot, basal stem rot, foot rot, snow mold, Victoria blight, the helminthosporium blight, stem break. I use the term root rot here to include all diseases that affect roots and basal portions of the culms, although occasionally I refer to special types of root rot.

Root rots of cereals were prevalent in the United States many years ago, but they did not attract attention until about 1900. H. L. Bolley in North Dakota in 1909 emphasized the importance of root rots on cereals in the United States. He proved that the root rots of wheat were caused by several fungi that accumulated in the soil, particularly if crop rotation was not practiced. He attributed the unproductiveness of certain wheat lands in the Northwest to root rots, instead of depleted soil fertility or to toxins. The discovery of wheat rosette (a virus disease) in Illinois in 1919, originally attributed to root rot fungi, and the severe outbreak of root rots in the rust nursery at St. Paul, Minn., in 1919 and 1920 stimulated further investigations.

In the United States the prevalence and severity of root diseases depends largely on the particular kinds of crop and varieties. In general, take-all is the most important root disease in winter wheat areas, cercosporella root rot is prevalent only in the Columbia Basin of the Pacific Northwest, and helminthosporium and fusarium root rots are usually more destructive in the spring wheat region. The diseases are not restricted to any region, however. For instance, root rot of oats, caused by *Helminthosporium victoriae*, has been destructive in all districts where varieties from Victoria crosses are grown.

Root rots probably are present every year in all fields of cereals in the United States. Sometimes they cause enormous losses to wheat, oats, and barley. In some places they are the limiting factor in crop production and prevent the growing of certain varieties of cereals in a region, such as barley varieties susceptible to common root rot in Minnesota and oat varieties susceptible to helminthosporium blight in the United States.

The amount of damage they cause varies greatly from season to season and from one field to another and often is difficult to determine because of the nature of the diseases.

Root rots usually are not conspicuous, like the rusts and smuts. Infected plants commonly reach maturity, although various organisms may injure their roots. Unless damage is severe and plants are actually killed in definite places, as frequently happens in fields infected by the take-all and snow mold organisms, damage caused by root rots frequently is overlooked. Infected plants yield less. Their seeds are fewer, smaller, sometimes shriveled, and of poorer quality than those from healthy plants.

Take-all is a major disease of wheat in Australia. Losses may be as much as 60 percent. Heavy losses also have been reported in the United States and Europe.

Two destructive epidemics of root rots of barley occurred in 1943–1944 in the upper Mississippi Valley. Barley production in Minnesota dropped from about 50 million bushels to less than 13 million. Yields dropped more than 30 percent.

Helminthosporium blight of oats was first observed in Iowa in 1944. By 1946 it was prevalent in every important oats-growing State, and ruined many millions of bushels of oats. In Iowa and Illinois it caused an estimated loss of at least 20 percent of the potential oats crop—more than 20 million bushels in Iowa alone. The disease was so destructive in 1947 that the growing of varieties such as Vicland and Tama that were released to growers because of their resistance to crown and stem rusts actually had to be discontinued.

THE SYMPTOMS of some root rots, such as typhula and take-all, can be diagnosed readily. But it is nearly impossible to distinguish the symptoms of root rots caused by some organisms, and one must use laboratory procedures to identify the cause. The difficulty arises because the symptoms caused by different pathogens often overlap. They may be almost identical under some conditions. Two or more pathogens may be associated on a given host. Saprophytes may be present and may modify the symptoms.

Root rots generally are characterized by seedling blight, stunting of plants, yellowing and bleaching of foliage, discoloration of roots and bases of the stems, and premature killing of adult plants. The same root-rotting organisms also may attack the upper part of the plants and cause head and seed blight, foliage lesions, and rotting of nodes.

Take-all, caused by *Ophiobolus graminis*, is a common root rot of wheat. It also attacks rye, barley, and oats. The diseased plants frequently are stunted, ripen prematurely, and occur in patches, which stand out among the normal plants. The black lesions of the rotted tissue, sometimes with conspicuous mycelium at the base of culms, are easy to spot.

The root rot that is caused by *Cercosporella herpotrichoides* is called foot rot or stem break. It makes eyespot lesions at the base of culms. Infected plants have a tendency to fall over as the heads fill and make patches of lodged and tangled plants. The pathogen attacks wheat, barley, and rye, but not oats. It may be the same as *Leptosphaeria herpotrichoides*, the cause of the destructive stem break of winter wheat in northern Europe.

The root rot symptoms caused by species of *Pythium* vary and are influenced largely by the crop and the organism: In Japan they are associated with certain types of snow mold on wheat; in Canada the disease is called "browning" because of the brown color that follows the gradual dying of foliage; in the United States *Pythium* causes root rot of mature plants and seedling blight of wheat, oats, and barley. The symptoms produced by *Pythium* may be confused with other types of root rot. The leaves of infected plants, particularly the lower ones, tend to lose their green color. Infected roots develop reddish-brown lesions.

Snow mold is common in winter cereals in northern Europe. It is caused by several fungi, among them *Calonectria graminicola*, *Typhula itoana*, and *Pythium* species. The outstanding symptom is a conspicuous mycelial growth, which covers the affected seedling as the snow disappears in spring.

The root rot caused by *Colletotrichum graminicola* is an important disease on oats. The fungus produces a distinct black stromatic formation (cushion-like) at the base of the stem near the surface of the soil.

The so-called common root rot fungi on wheat, oats, barley, and rye produce few distinguishing symptoms. They generally attack all underground parts of the plant and cause varying degrees of rots on roots, crown, and basal parts of stems. The diseased tissue often has large light-brown to black areas. Common root rot may kill plants at any time from germination until maturity. They may or may not be stunted. Seedling blight commonly occurs. Symptoms usually are not apparent on adult plants unless their bases are examined. Common root rot is caused by many species of fungi. *Helminthosporium sativum*, *H. victoriae*, *H. avenae*, *Fusarium graminearum*, *F. culmorum*, *F. nivale*, and *Rhizoctonia solani* are the more common ones.

ROOT-ROTTING FUNGI usually cause most damage when conditions are unfavorable for the development of the host plants. Temperature, moisture, the amount of inoculum, and mechanical injuries of the host, such as insect damage, have a bearing on the severity of root rots. Rusts and foliage diseases may predispose plants to root rots. Sometimes that effect is indirect— severe rust in the fall on winter grain may make plants more subject to winter injury, which, in turn, predisposes the plants to root rot.

Soil temperature affects both host and pathogen, but its effect apparently is more important on the host. High temperatures, which are detrimental for normal development of wheat, oats, barley, and rye, favor the growth of many of the root-rotting fungi. Seedling blights and root rots generally are most severe at relatively high temperatures. Early seeding of spring-sown grain therefore reduces the incidence of root rot and increases yield. The organisms associated with snow mold, however, are most destructive at relatively cool temperatures and cause the greatest damage while the hosts are covered with snow. Winter injury to fall-sown grain may predispose plants to root rots.

Root rots generally are most destructive in dry soil, but pythium and cercosporella root rots usually are more severe in moist soil. In the Pacific coast region, the greater the amount of precipitation the greater the amount of cercosporella root rot. Likewise, the greater the amount of snow and the longer it persists, the greater the damage from snow mold.

Diseased seeds often are a source of primary root infection and are important in relation to seedling blight. Cereal seeds grown in the more humid parts of the United States are commonly attacked by a large group of fungi and bacteria. Fungi of more than 25 genera and several kinds of bacteria have been isolated from wheat and barley kernels. Many are saprophytic or weakly pathogenic. Species of *Alternaria*, which usually are nonpathogenic, are the most common organisms associated with kernels of grain, but *Helminthosporium* species and *Fusarium* species are the most common virulent root-rotting pathogens prevalent in the seed. Preemergence killing, seedling blight, root rot, basal stem rot, and lowered yields frequently result when such seed is sown.

Striking differences exist in the prevalence of seed-borne parasitic fungi, especially *Helminthosporium* and *Fusarium*, not only in different seasons but in different localities in the same year. Seed of wheat, oats, and barley with 10 to 25 percent infection with *Fusarium* and *Helminthosporium* are fairly common some seasons. Seed lots with more than 50 percent infection are not infrequent. The percentage of seed infected with *Helminthosporium* species and *Fusarium* species is closely associated with the percentage of germination, stand, amount of seedling blight, and the number of stunted and deformed plants.

Various kinds of mechanical injuries, such as cracking and chipping of the seed coat during threshing, may be the indirect cause of poor stands from seeds that are relatively free from root-rotting organisms. The injuries may not be enough to reduce germination in laboratory tests. Sometimes the cracks are so small that they can be seen only through a magnifying glass. When such seed is planted, especially under conditions unfavorable for germination, however, soil-inhabiting fungi may enter through the breaks and rot the seed before it can germinate. Treatment with a suitable disinfectant places a layer of protective fungicide over the openings and prevents the entrance of root-rotting organisms. The more extensive the seed-coat injuries, however, the greater the need for seed treatment and the greater the benefits from it.

MANY SPECIES OF INSECTS and nematodes attack the roots and basal portion of the stems of cereals and grasses. The bluegrass billbug, *Calendra parvula*, has received the greatest attention of technicians. It attacks the roots, crown, and lower internodes of the stem, often weakening the plants and providing avenues of entrance for rot-inducing fungi and bacteria.

As the external symptoms of insect injury are seldom conspicuous, the relationship of insects to the rot is apt to be overlooked. Decay usually starts around the wounds the insect makes when it feeds and deposits its eggs. It is most common on wheat, but it also attacks barley, rye, and many grasses. In 1939 the amount of infested wheat plants in the hard red spring wheat region ranged from a trace to 96 percent. In southern Minnesota and eastern South Dakota, fields with 25 to 50 percent infestation were not uncommon.

Studies made in the north central region of the United States by Earle W. Hanson, of the Department of Agriculture in cooperation with the Minnesota Agricultural Experiment Station, indicate that the greater the infestation of billbugs the greater the amount of root rot. Obviously symptoms of root rot do not necessarily indicate insect infestation, since root rots may develop in the absence of insects, but invariably the insect-infested plants are more severely rotted than the noninfested plants. Furthermore, varieties somewhat resistant to root rots may develop severe infection when injured by insects.

Some of the root-rotting organisms are relatively weak parasites. They can cause damage only when the plants are weakened or when entrance to the plant is provided through wounds, such as those caused by insects, nematodes, and mechanical injuries. The frass deposit within insect tunnels in the base of the plant makes a good medium for growth and multiplication of many fungi. The movement of the insect inside the plant helps to distribute the fungus organisms within the host.

The injured tissues are readily attacked even by semiweak parasites. Therefore rots that follow insect injuries usually involve much more tissue than that destroyed by the insect. Insect injuries, in a sense, predispose plants to root rot and also greatly complicate the development of varieties of cereals resistant to root rots.

PHYSIOLOGIC SPECIALIZATION is a common phenomenon among parasitic fungi, including those that cause root rots of cereals. Not only are the root rots of cereals caused by many distinct species of fungi but most of the species comprise many parasitic races. For example, *Helminthosporium sativum* consists of many distinct cultural and parasitic races. The races vary greatly in their parasitic capabilities on cereals and grasses. Some races of *H. sativum* are very virulent on wheat, barley, and rye. Others are moderately virulent. Still others are only weakly virulent. They also differ in host range. Some attack wheat, barley, rye, and oats. Others do not attack oats. Some attack corn readily. Others are nonvirulent on corn.

Similar genetic variation in parasitism has been reported in other root-rotting fungi—*Calonectria graminicola, Fusarium culmorum, F. graminearum, Ophiobolus graminis,* and *Rhizoctonia solani.*

Root-rotting fungi are not static. New races may arise by means of hybridization between races or by mutation. Differences in virulence of races are of great importance because they complicate the study of inheritance of resistance to root rots and the selection of varieties resistant to root rots.

New varieties may be resistant in one locality in North America, but susceptible in another because of the prevalence of different pathogens and the existence of different races of the pathogens in different regions. Moreover, root rot problems are continually changing because new pathogens are introduced or new virulent races of old pathogens are developed or introduced from the other regions or countries. Sometimes problems change because relatively minor root diseases become major diseases. Changes in cropping systems and the introduction of new varieties also may create new conditions. All new varieties therefore should be tested for resistance to root rot before they are made available to the growers.

One of the best means of selecting varieties resistant to root rots is to test them in pathological nurseries—disease gardens—in the regions in which they will be grown. Disease gardens were established in Minnesota in 1919 for testing the varietal reaction of wheat to diseases. The procedure is now common for testing different crops against root rot.

A disease garden is a "sick" plot of land in which varieties of the same crop are grown in successive years and subjected to the most severe disease tests that can be devised. The soil in the disease gardens is inoculated with all available physiologic races of seed-borne and soil-inhabiting pathogens and potentially important root-rotting pathogens that occur in the region in which the varieties are to be grown. The gardens actually are the critical testing grounds for the selection of varieties and hybrids resistant to rot.

Different species of fungi or different physiologic races of some fungi may be widespread in some seasons but not others. If one wants to be certain of resistance, he must test the variety in the disease garden for several years.

The production of new disease-resistant varieties takes at least 10 years,
usually much longer. Root rot tests
should be continued during that
period.

THE USE OF RESISTANT varieties and
good farming practices that promote
strong plants are the best ways to
reduce damage caused by root rots.
Control measures generally do not
eliminate the disease but tend to
reduce the amount of infection. Specific control measures, therefore, are
restricted at best to localities. To
control or limit root rots one should
plant sound seed; treat the seed with
suitable fungicides; plant early, shallow, and at recommended rates; use
good cultural methods; practice sanitation and good cropping sequence; and
grow resistant varieties.

Seeds used to be treated with
fungicides primarily to control smuts.
Since 1949 many varieties of cereals
have been developed that are resistant
to smuts, so that treatment of their
seed appears to be unnecessary. Nevertheless, seed treatment of the new
smut-resistant varieties makes for increases in yield, chiefly because the
newer fungicides are effective in preventing seed decay and the seedling
blight.

Seedling blight can be controlled or
reduced by treating seed with fungicides and growing the seed in relatively
disease-free soil. The treatments retard
primary seed-borne infection and thus
reduce the amount of root rot inoculum early in the season. The early
protection of the seedlings affords an
easy way to increase crop yields.
Seed treatments do not reduce the
amount of secondary infection, as
plants grown in infested soil may become infected any time between
germination of seed and maturity.

Increases in yield of wheat, oats, and
barley of 5 to 10 percent or more are
common. H. Murphy, of the Department of Agriculture, obtained increases up to 60 percent in yields of
oats when he treated seed heavily

infected with *H. victoriae* with New
Improved Ceresan and sowed it in
experimental plots at Ames, Iowa.

Deep-planted seeds of cereals are
more subject to seedling blight than
shallow-sown seeds. That is especially
true if seed lots are not disease-free, if
the seedbed is not well prepared, and
if weather conditions become unfavorable for normal germination. The
deeper the seeds are planted, the
longer the succulent tissues are exposed
to attack by seed and soil-borne
organisms. Field and greenhouse tests
indicate that deep seeding increases
root rot and lowers stand and yield.
Specific depth of seeding cannot be
given, as the recommended depth of
seeding varies with the crop, soil type,
precipitation, and region in which the
crop is grown. As a general rule, seed
should be sown just deep enough to
provide sufficient moisture for good
germination.

Fertilizers apparently have little
effect on the development of most root
rots unless the fertility level is so low
that the hosts do not grow well. Most
attempts to control common rots by
application of commercial fertilizers
have been unsuccessful. On the other
hand, H. R. Rosen and J. A. Elliott in
Arkansas were able to control take-all
by using commercial fertilizers. S. D.
Garrett in England recommended acid
phosphates for the control of the
disease. T. C. Vanterpool, in Alberta,
Canada, found that an unbalanced
phosphorus-nitrate relationship predisposes wheat seedlings to attack by
Pythium.

Take-all is usually most injurious on
nonacid soils. According to Mr.
Garrett, antibiotic organisms are more
active in acid soil than in alkaline soil.
Probably that is why differences occur
in the severity of root rots. Root rots
are intensified when the plants are
grown in soil containing soluble alkali
salts, especially when they are
deposited near the soil surface. Plants
also may be predisposed to root rot
by an excess of toxic material, like
boron.

Crop rotation and summer fallow often reduce damages from root rots, because many of the pathogens survive in the soil, on refuse of crops, and on wild and cultivated grasses. They also develop on plant remains in and on the surface of the soil. Some, such as species of *Fusarium*, attack crops other than cereals. Proper crop sequence is important therefore in fighting root rot.

Root rot is usually more prevalent in soils that have been cropped continuously to a given crop than those in which rotation has been practiced. A rotation that includes immune or highly resistant crops suppresses the pathogens and consequently reduces root rot. Take-all, for example, can be reduced materially if the crop sequence includes such nonsusceptible crops as alfalfa, sweetclover, flax, and corn. In regions where the race of the take-all fungus that attacks oats is not prevalent wheat can follow oats.

Summer fallow is also an effective control measure against take-all and to some extent against other types of root rots, with the exception of browning. In fact, summer fallow tends to increase the severity of this disease in wheat.

ANTIBIOSIS is the association of two kinds of organisms in which one inhibits the growth of the other. Antibiosis is important in the control of root rots. Agricultural soil is teeming with microscopic organisms—algae, fungi, bacteria, protozoa, and nematodes. Some have no apparent effect on plant growth. Some are beneficial. Some, especially the root-rotting fungi, are destructive. As organisms grow and multiply rapidly in the soil and on plant refuse, they struggle constantly for survival. If it were not for this constant "biological warfare" the soil-borne organisms that cause root rots would multiply so fast that the arable land would become "sick" and then be unsuitable for grain crops.

Many factors other than the prevalence of micro-organisms in the soil determine how long a soil-borne pathogen can persist in the soil—temperature, moisture, acidity, type of soil. Nevertheless, soil-borne pathogens cannot compete in the soil with their enemies, the saprophytic organisms. Indeed, many pathogens that cannot survive in normal soil actually grow well in sterilized soil. Some of them can survive in the soil for a short time. Others may live in the soil for years. Those that persist are more tolerant to antibiotic substances and therefore are more difficult to control by cultural methods.

The biological control of soil-borne disease is promising, but we still do not know the extent to which the method can be applied. Adding large amounts of specific antibiotic organisms or their extracts to the soil will control or greatly reduce some soil-borne diseases. Seedling blight of wheat, barley, and rye caused by *Helminthosporium* species can be controlled by applying cultures of antibiotic organisms to the soil at the time of planting. That practice may not be feasible on a large scale; cultural practices must then be resorted to. We have some evidence that antibiotic substances may be used as seed disinfectants for controlling soil-borne diseases. The application of manure and plant refuse to the soil and cropping sequences of cultivated crops have a pronounced influence on the number of micro-organisms in the soil. Take-all has been controlled by applying manure to the soil. More studies are needed on control of soil-borne diseases by means of antibiosis, especially in relation to crop sequence.

VARIETAL RESISTANCE is perhaps the most promising key to the control of root rot diseases, even though resistance is only relative. The degree of susceptibility of a given variety is influenced tremendously by ecological conditions and cultural practices. Nevertheless, varieties differ greatly in susceptibility to specific organisms when grown under uniform tests. Most varieties of wheat are susceptible to root rots. Apex, Thatcher, and Marquis are among the more resistant spring wheats to the common root rots. Kota, Kubanka, and McMurachy Selection are moderately resistant to take-all.

All varieties of oats that have Victoria as one parent, such as Vicland, Tama, and Boone, are very susceptible to helminthosporium root rot. Many commercial varieties, such as Clinton, Benton, and Bonda, are highly resistant.

A variety may be resistant to one type of rot but susceptible to another. Kubanka wheat is moderately resistant to take-all, but is susceptible to the common root rots. Victoria oats is fairly resistant to root rot caused by *Fusarium culmorum* but extremely susceptible to *H. victoriae*. Peatland barley is moderately resistant to helminthosporium root rot but very susceptible to pythium root rot.

Resistance must be bred into the adapted commercial varieties that do not have it. That was done by scientists in Minnesota, who developed varieties of wheat, barley, and oats that are resistant to helminthosporium root rot.

The disease gardens have been of practical help in eliminating inferior varieties and hybrid lines. The idea could well be expanded: Growing a world collection of wheat, oats, and barley in nurseries in different regions of the United States and maybe in other countries would give us a wonderful opportunity for selecting disease-resistant varieties and desirable parental materials.

IN CONCLUSION: Root rots are among the most destructive diseases of cereals in the United States. They are debilitating, insidious, and usually inconspicuous, but sometimes they become epidemic. Their importance varies greatly with season, locality, and the crop. Host plants are subject to attack from the time the seeds are sown until the crops are mature. The pathogens are of diverse types and attack all underground parts of the plants and induce root decay, seedling blight, and premature death of older plants.

Root-rotting pathogens live in the soil and tend to increase in the soils when susceptible crops are grown year after year. Soil is not just soil; it is actually teeming with microscopic life—protozoa, bacteria, and fungi. Those organisms are carrying on a biological war, struggling for the survival of the fittest. They destroy many of the root-rotting organisms and hence help to prevent the development of root rot. Their relative prevalence in the soil can be greatly modified by cropping sequences and cultural methods.

Although root rots cannot be completely prevented where cereals are grown intensely, they can be greatly reduced by good agricultural practices. Sound seed of recommended varieties should be treated with a fungicide to eliminate the pathogens from the seed and to give the young seedlings protection against soil-borne organisms. Also, the seed should be sown only deep enough to provide adequate moisture for germination.

A good cropping sequence must be followed. The seed beds should be well prepared, and appropriate fertilizer applied if there is a deficiency of essential elements. Varieties differ in susceptibility and only the recommended varieties should be grown. In general, good farming is the most feasible method of controlling root rots of cereals.

J. J. CHRISTENSEN *is professor of plant pathology in the University of Minnesota, where he obtained his doctor's degree. He has made extensive studies of cereal diseases and the genetics of plant pathogens in relation to breeding for resistance and has participated in cereal breeding programs. In addition to work at Minnesota, Dr. Christensen has studied genetics of plant pathogens in Europe, has been adviser to SCAP on plant diseases in Japan, and has traveled extensively in South America on a study of cereal diseases.*

The Rusts of Wheat, Oats, Barley, Rye

John H. Martin, S. C. Salmon

Wheat, oats, barley, and rye may be attacked by eight distinct species or subspecies of rust fungi.

Wheat is subject to stem rust (*Puccinia graminis tritici*), leaf rust (*P. rubigo-vera*), and stripe rust (*P. glumarum*).

Oats are attacked by a stem rust (*P. graminis avenae*) and by crown rust (*P. coronata avenae*).

Barley may fall prey to the same stem rust (*P. graminis tritici*) that attacks wheat and a leaf rust (*P. hordei*).

A stem rust (*P. graminis secalis*) and a leaf rust (*P. rubigo-vera*) attack rye.

Each of the eight rusts is made up of several or many different races, which may attack certain varieties of a particular cereal crop but not others.

Stem rust of wheat causes the most spectacular and perhaps the greatest losses. Leaf rust of wheat and crown rust of oats occur more frequently, usually affect larger acreages, and so may cause greater average losses year in and year out. Before the extensive use of resistant varieties, stem rust was most destructive in spring wheat in the northern Great Plains. Severe losses sometimes occur in the southern Plains, many Eastern States, California, and occasionally in localities in the Pacific Northwest and Intermountain States.

Leaf rust of wheat and crown rust of oats occur wherever wheat and oats are grown. They cause little damage west of the Rocky Mountains or in the drier parts of the Great Plains. Some damage occurs in the eastern half of the United States nearly every year. Reductions in acre yields are especially great in the Southern and Southeastern States although neither wheat nor oats is grown extensively in much of that area.

Most varieties of barley, some of oats, and all varieties of rye escape considerable damage because of their early maturity as compared with wheat. Stem rust sometimes injures barley seriously. Leaf rust is not usually serious but is sometimes locally destructive on spring barley. The stem and leaf rusts do not cause serious losses in rye. Stripe rust occurs most commonly on wheat but only in special situations in the United States has it caused serious losses.

WHEAT STEM RUST is characterized by pustules that develop and break through the surface of the stems, leaves, and sheaths and often the chaff and beards of the wheat plant. Myriads of brick-red spores escape from the pustules and are carried by the wind to other wheat plants.

The crop is damaged by the growth of the rust fungus on the wheat stems and leaves and by the developing spores, both of which use up the water and nutrient materials needed for developing the wheat kernels. The water requirement in rusted wheat is much higher than in healthy wheat.

As a result, the kernels are badly shriveled, many of them being so light and chaffy that they are blown out with the chaff in threshing. The remaining grains may be shrunken to one-half or two-thirds normal size. Losses range up to 85 or 90 percent; at that point the crop is not worth harvesting and is a total loss. The rusted straw turns brown, becomes dry and brittle, and soon breaks over.

Wheat stem rust also attacks barley and occasionally rye. It attacks many wild grasses, including wild barley or squirreltail grasses (*Hordeum* species); certain wheatgrasses (*Agropyron* species); wild-rye grasses (*Elymus* species); bottlebrush grasses (*Hystrix* species);

and some bromegrasses. It does not attack oats.

The rust lives over the summer on volunteer grains and wild grasses in the Southern States and in northern Mexico. These spores and those blown down from the north in late summer and early fall infect fall-sown wheat or barley. The rust lives over winter in the red rust stage in the southern part of the United States and in northern Mexico but not in the Northern States.

If weather conditions are favorable in the spring, the rust multiplies and the spores sweep northward with the advance of the crop season. Thus a heavy rust epidemic in Texas is a threat to the wheatfields of Oklahoma and Kansas, and the latter, in turn, are sources of inoculum for the grainfields in the North Central and Intermountain States.

The red rust spores that spread the disease are about one-thousandth of an inch long. They fall upon a wheat leaf and may germinate in an hour in warm, humid weather or in several hours at temperatures of 40° to 50° F. Germinating spores send out germ tubes, which grow along the surface of the leaf or stem of the plant until they reach a breathing pore (stoma), where they enter, send out branches that grow within the tissues of the plant, draw nourishment from them for a week or longer, and then produce the red pustules with another crop of spores. At low temperatures, or when there is but little sunlight, it may take 2 or 3 weeks from the time the germ tube first enters the plant until the spores form. In warm, moist weather, however, they may reach full development within a week.

Thus a new generation of rust spores may be produced every 10 to 14 days during the spring and summer, starting in Texas and advancing northward with the progressive development of the wheat crop at different latitudes. Since a single rust pustule may produce 350,000 spores, the rust can spread very rapidly. Rising air currents can lift the spores up to altitudes exceeding 10,000 feet and from such height winds can carry the spores many miles before they fall to the ground.

A heavy rust epidemic on the nearly 4 million acres of wheat in South Dakota could produce about 2 sextillion rust spores. If only one in 10,000 of the spores blew north into North Dakota, four spores would be provided for every wheat plant in the State. Spores carried northward reach young wheat plants that are in a succulent stage, in which they are easily infected with rust. Spores blown southward in early summer fall on ripening or ripe wheat, which is not readily infected with rust. Those blown southward in late summer can attack volunteer wheat, early-sown wheat, and certain grasses. These plants in turn serve as a source of inoculum for fall-sown wheat in the South, where the rust lives over winter.

An additional source of rust menaces the wheat in the northern half of the country—rust that develops on the barberry. The production of the brick-red uredospores ceases as wheat approaches maturity and black spores (teliospores) are produced in the same pustules. The latter stage is important only in the Northern States because the spores cannot survive the hot summers in the South.

The teliospores usually will not germinate immediately after they are formed but require a relatively long resting period, somewhat like the hard seeds of alfalfa and clover. They are not blown about by the wind, but remain on straw or stubble throughout the winter and germinate in the spring, especially in moist, cool weather. On germination, they produce small colorless spores (sporidia), which germinate and readily infect certain species of barberry.

The most important susceptible species is the common barberry (*Berberis vulgaris*), which was introduced from Europe as an ornamental shrub

Others are wild native species, *Berberis canadensis* in the eastern Allegheny region and *B. fendleri* in the Rocky Mountains. The Japanese barberry (*B. thunbergii*) and the ornamental evergreen barberries are not attacked. The winter spores themselves do not directly cause infection on grains; their sporidia cannot infect grains or grasses, but infect only the barberry. The sporidia germinate on barberry leaves and send out small germ tubes that penetrate the epidermis directly. Only young parts of the plant therefore can be infected, for the germ tubes cannot penetrate the older, tougher parts.

Within a week or 10 days after germ tubes of the sporidia have entered the barberry, small yellowish or honey-colored spots appear on the infected parts, especially the young leaves. The yellow spots comprise the spermagonia, which contain the spermatia. Spermatia function in connection with the sexual reproduction of the rust by means of pycniospores, which may develop new races of the rust as a result of new combinations formed during sexual reproduction. Within a short time the cluster cups (aecia) are produced, commonly on the under surface of the infected leaf. The small cup-shaped structures contain long chains of cluster-cup spores (aeciospores), which are shot forcibly from their cups, especially during moist weather, are blown about by the wind, and initiate the red, or summer, stage of the rust on grains or grasses.

The typical life history of stem rust where barberries become infected is, then, as follows: The rust overwinters in the black, or teliospore, stage; the teliospores germinate in the spring and produce sporidia, which cannot infect grains and grasses but do infect certain kinds of barberries, on which the aecial stage subsequently develops. The aeciospores cannot infect the barberry but, falling upon grains and grasses, germinate and induce the uredial stage. This stage may persist and produce successive crops of uredospores until growing conditions become unfavorable, when the teliospores are produced. While the stem rust fungus actually produces five kinds of spores, only the uredospores and aeciospores can infect grains and grasses. The teliospores, by means of which the rust usually survives the winter, are harmless unless there are barberries nearby.

Usually the rust is spreading from barberries to the grainfields some 2 or 3 weeks before the general rust spread arrives from the South. Because of this early start they may cause severe damage to grains growing near infected barberry bushes. The spread from barberries usually can be traced only short distances or up to a few miles; so the damage is largely local. However, they supply additional inoculum to hasten the spread of general epidemics. As many as 70 billion aeciospores may be produced on one large barberry bush.

About 240 parasitic strains or physiologic races of stem rust of wheat have been discovered, but not more than a dozen are widely prevalent or are important in any one year. Even fewer recognized races are of common occurrence in South America. These races differ in their ability to attack certain varieties of wheat. For example, some attack Marquis but not Pawnee; others attack Pawnee but not Marquis.

The Little Club variety is attacked by all races. Race 15B attacks all wheat varieties grown on farms in the United States, but does not attack certain varieties from Kenya, Africa.

The same parasitic strains are not always present in a given region in different years, and there may be different strains in several regions in the same year. For that reason a variety may be susceptible to rust in one region and resistant in another; it may be susceptible in a given region in certain years and resistant in others. The development of stem rust on wheat, then, depends not only on the presence of numerous spores early in the growing season but also on the presence of spores of the particular parasitic strains that normally can attack the variety of wheat grown in that region. Conversely, the particular races that occur in any region depend in part on the variety or varieties of wheat that are grown.

THE LEAF RUST (*Puccinia rubigo-vera tritici*) of wheat usually attacks the leaf blades and sheaths, although it may sometimes occur on the stem proper, especially just below the heads. Sometimes it occurs also on the chaff and awns or beards. The rust pustules are smaller than those of stem rust, are more nearly round, and are less likely to unite. Usually they appear only on the upper side of the leaf. The color of the summer (uredial) stage is orange to orange brown, being brighter than that of pustules of stem rust.

The pustules of the black, or winter, stage (telia) are of about the same size as those of the red stage, but they seldom break through the epidermis of the plant, and the color, therefore, is likely to be lead gray. Leaf rust of wheat is found in nearly every place that wheat is grown. In the United States it is most abundant and destructive in the Southeastern States and in the Ohio and Mississippi Valleys, where weather conditions usually are most favorable for its development. It is less destructive in the hard red winter and the hard red spring wheat areas, although it is usually present to some extent and in favorable seasons may cause considerable damage to certain varieties. It usually is present in the irrigated areas of the West and on the Pacific coast but seldom does extensive damage, although sometimes it may be of importance locally.

Leaf rust may cause much damage to certain varieties of wheat in certain regions, although the damage usually is less conspicuous than that caused by stem rust. Leaf rust seldom shrivels the kernels, but it does reduce their size and number and the quality of the grain. Furthermore, when plants become heavily rusted while still young, the entire plant may be weakened and somewhat dwarfed, and under such circumstances, the yield may be reduced as much as 90 percent.

This rust may occasionally attack barley to a slight extent, but for practical purposes it may be considered as attacking only wheat and a few species of goatgrasses (*Aegilops* species). The cluster-cup, or aecial, stage of leaf rust occurs on certain species of meadowrue (*Thalictrum*), but this is of no practical importance in the United States, as the species that are native here do not get infected under natural conditions.

The many parasitic strains of the leaf rust of wheat differ in their ability to attack different varieties. More than 140 of these strains are known and 85 have been identified in the United States. New ones are occasionally encountered. The exact manner in which they originate, however, is not known.

Leaf rust of wheat, like all other rusts, is caused by a very small parasitic fungus that enters the wheat plant through its breathing pores. The red, or summer, stage continues as long as the wheat plants are green and growing. The orange-colored pustules that develop on the wheat contain thousands of summer spores (uredospores), which are easily blown about by the wind and are capable of causing rust on other wheat plants. During warm, moist weather, this red stage may recur every week; therefore the rust can increase and spread rapidly. When conditions become unfavorable for the growth of the wheat and for the development of the red stage, the black, or telial, stage appears.

The red stage is capable of surviving the winter in most of the wheat-growing regions of the United States. It can be found at all times of the year in the Southern States and in some years in the Northern States. If weather conditions in late summer and early fall favor rust development—that is, if there is considerable moisture—the red stage attacks volunteer wheat plants and fall-sown wheat, where it may remain and even increase somewhat during the winter.

In the spring it increases rapidly if weather conditions are favorable. The spores then may be carried long distances by the wind and infect wheat plants in regions where the rust may not have survived the winter. The destructiveness of the epidemic will depend on the earliness with which plants are attacked in the spring.

When there is abundant rainfall or heavy dews in the spring and early summer, following a winter that has favored the survival of the red stage of the rust, abundant early infection may occur. If the weather continues warm and moist, there is danger of a destructive epidemic. As in the case of stem rust, warm, moist weather is most favorable for the development of leaf rust, but this rust seems able to develop under a wider range of conditions than does stem rust.

STRIPE RUST, *Puccinia glumarum*, has been commonly known as yellow rust because of the yellow or orange-yellow pustules of the summer stage. Stripe rust seems a better name, however, because one of its main features is the arrangement of the pustules in rows of various lengths, giving the appearance of fairly narrow yellow stripes.

Stripe rust attacks wheat, barley, rye, spelt, emmer, and more than 60 species of wild and cultivated grasses. In the United States it is most prevalent on wheat and certain wild grasses. It is seldom found on barley and rarely on rye. It is especially common on some of the wild barleys and bromegrasses and on a species of goatgrass.

Stripe rust develops most abundantly on the glumes or chaff, on the leaves, and on the leaf sheaths, but it may also attack the stems and the kernels. On seedling plants, and sometimes on older plants, the stripes are not distinct, but the yellow color distinguishes the rust from other cereal rusts.

If the attack of stripe rust is heavy, especially on the necks and glumes, considerable damage is likely to result, particularly if plants have become rusted during the milk stage or earlier.

Under such conditions the kernels may be shriveled and the yields considerably reduced. Often, however, stripe rust is most abundant in seasons that are so favorable to wheat that high yields are obtained despite the damage from the disease.

The black stage of the rust is formed after the red, or summer, stage but may develop at any time during the growing season and at any stage in the development of the host. The black pustules (telia) also are produced more or less in rows that look like long, narrow, dark-brown, or black stripes. They may appear on all above-ground parts of the plant, including even the kernels.

Stripe rust is the commonest and most destructive grain rust in many regions of Europe. It occurs also in Africa, South America, Japan, China, and India. Stripe rust has been in the United States at least since 1892 but was not recognized until 1915. It occurs sporadically over the western half of the United States and at corresponding longitudes in Canada and Mexico.

The several physiologic races of stripe rust differ in their ability to attack certain varieties of wheat and other grass species. A special race attacks only a wild barley (*Hordeum murinum*). Both the summer, or yellow-spore, stage and the black stage of stripe rust are produced in the United States. An alternate host and therefore the cluster-cup (aecial) stage are unknown. The exact conditions under which the yellow stage overwinters most abundantly are not known, although it persists throughout the winter under a variety of climatic conditions.

Epidemics of stripe rust are most likely to occur when there has been abundant infection in late summer and fall of the previous year, when a large number of summer spores and abundant mycelium have survived the winter, and when spring and summer conditions, such as cool nights, warm days, heavy dews, and abundant sunshine, prevail during the growing season. Unlike some of the other cereal rusts, stripe rust seems to thrive best at low temperatures; in fact, its development is likely to be checked by hot weather.

While stripe rust is extremely destructive in some foreign countries, it has caused relatively little damage in the United States, except in limited areas where susceptible varieties are grown and where weather conditions are very favorable.

Stripe rust has not become established in the principal grain-growing regions of the Mississippi Valley. Experience in other countries, however, indicates that it might be destructive to some varieties of wheat under favorable weather conditions.

When the upper part of the stems, chaff, and kernels become rusted during the milk or early dough stage of kernel development, the grain may be considerably shriveled. Yields then are smaller and the wheat is of inferior quality. Badly rusted grain may germinate poorly, but infection is not transmitted to plants grown from such diseased seed.

STEM RUST ON OATS (*Puccinia graminis avenae*) looks like the stem rust on wheat. Stem rust is darker in color than crown rust and usually produces longer pustules and is more abundant on the necks of the plants. The color of the summer stage of stem rust usually is brick red; that of crown rust is a bright yellow or yellow orange. This disease attacks oats, a number of the wild grasses, orchardgrass, some of the fescues, meadow foxtail, and bluejoint. Normally it does not attack wheat, barley, or rye. Its life history and methods of spread are like those of the stem rust of wheat.

CROWN RUST OF OATS (*Puccinia coronata*), often known also as leaf rust or orange leaf rust of oats, occurs principally on the leaves, although it is frequently present also on the leaf sheaths and sometimes on the stems

and panicles. The most destructive disease of oats, it often cuts the yields 20 to 50 percent. Crown rust is particularly destructive in the South and in the North Central States. More than 80 species of grasses may be attacked by one or another of several varieties of crown rust. Among them are quackgrass, reedgrass, redtop, meadow fescue, ryegrass, and bluegrass. The variety of crown rust most prevalent on oats also attacks several grasses and a number of different kinds of buckthorn. The oats variety of crown rust comprises in turn a number of distinct parasitic strains, which differ in their ability to attack different varieties of oats. More than 100 physiologic races of crown rust have been identified in the United States.

The pustules of the red, or summer, stage of crown rust are usually more or less circular. They rupture the epidermis and release uredospores. Later in the season the black, or winter, stage appears. The black pustules usually do not rupture the epidermis. The cluster-cup stage of crown rust develops on a number of species of buckthorn (*Rhamnus*). The first stage (spermagonium stage) appears on the upper surfaces of the leaves or on young twigs as small bright-yellow or orange spots. Opposite these spots, usually on the under surface of the leaf, the cluster-cup stage appears.

The life history of crown rust is similar to that of stem rust except that the cluster-cup stage develops on buckthorns instead of on barberries. The summer spores overwinter in the South and are spread to other plants and fields in the spring. In the Northern States the red, or summer, stage does not overwinter commonly, and epidemics result from summer spores that may be blown in from the South or from the development of the cluster-cup stage on buckthorns.

Warm, moist weather is most favorable for the rapid development and spread of crown rust. Moisture from dews or rains is likely to be held longer in dense stands of oats; that favors the development of rust. Epidemics are most likely to develop when there are many spores in the spring and when weather conditions favor the development of the rust. In the fields of winter oats in the South, where the summer spores survive the winter, the rust gets an early start in the spring. The amount that overwinters depends on the amount of infection in the previous season and on weather conditions; mild winters are particularly favorable for the survival of the rust. In the Northern States the amount of infection on buckthorn bushes determines how early and how good a start the rust gets. If the weather in the early spring has been favorable for abundant infection on the buckthorns, there may be considerable crown rust if the subsequent weather conditions are also favorable. Summer spores blown into the Northern States from the South may also cause widespread epidemics. All buckthorn bushes in the northern oat-growing States should be destroyed because inoculum from them causes severe losses to oats in the vicinity and provides inoculum for an early spread of crown rust.

Barley is attacked by both the wheat and rye strains of stem rust and the development and spread of the disease on barley is the same as for those crops.

LEAF RUST OF BARLEY is seldom of economic importance in areas where spring barley is grown but is sometimes destructive locally to winter barley. At times it is so abundant as to prevent the proper heading of infected plants and may sometimes reduce the yields and the quality of the grain.

The pustules of the summer stage of leaf rust of barley appear on the leaf blades and sheaths of the barley plant. They are yellow or yellowish brown, small, and round. The black stage follows the red stage and produces lead-gray pustules, which do not rupture the epidermis of the plant.

Leaf rust attacks cultivated varieties of barley, although under some conditions it may develop weakly on some of the other cereals and on several wild grasses.

The life history of leaf rust of barley is similar to that of the leaf rust of wheat. The rust survives the winters in the red, or summer, stage, particularly in the winter regions. The spring, or cluster-cup, stage, when it is produced, develops on the star-of-Bethlehem (*Ornithogalum umbellatum*), and a closely related species (*O. narbonense*). Although those plants are fairly common in certain parts of the United States, they rarely become rusted.

STEM RUST OF RYE (*Puccinia graminis secalis*) has a life history similar to that of wheat rust. However, stem rust of rye attacks barley but does not develop on the wheat and oats, except under specially favorable experimental conditions. In addition, it attacks many of the same grasses as does wheat stem rust from wheat but particularly quackgrass, which is not commonly attacked by wheat stem rust. Because of the early maturity of rye and the fact that it is grown but little in the South, severe attacks of stem rust on rye are rare except where there are barberry bushes. The eradication of barberry is the only control measure needed.

LEAF RUST OF RYE (*Puccinia rubigovera*) is similar to the leaf rust of wheat; so similar, in fact, that it is considered as belonging to the same species. It may occur wherever rye is grown. In the South, where rye is sometimes used for winter pasturage, it may become so abundant as to kill the plants during the winter. It may also cause considerable losses in the northern rye-growing regions. It attacks *Secale montanum*, a wild species of rye. Some wild grasses may occasionally become infected if the conditions are favorable, but the rust generally is restricted to rye.

It usually attacks the leaf blades and sheaths. It may occur also on the necks and glumes of severely rusted plants. The pustules of the red stage are scattered more or less irregularly and are orange brown to cinnamon brown. They are usually small but may unite to form fairly large pustules. The pustules of the black stage are gray to black and remain covered by the epidermis until it decays or falls away. The rust persists during the winter in the red, or summer (uredial), stage. The spring, or cluster-cup, stage can develop on some plants of the borage family, but it is seldom found in nature in the United States and is therefore of no importance in the life history of the rust.

The development of epidemics occurs under conditions similar to those that promote epidemics of leaf rust of wheat. The degree to which the summer stage persists during the winter depends on weather conditions. In the spring, new infections occur; if the weather is warm and humid, the rust may become epidemic.

Rainy weather or cool, dewy nights and warm, humid days are most favorable for the development of the rust. No variety of rye is uniformly highly resistant to leaf rust. Rye is cross-pollinated and no varieties are uniformly pure. Certain pure inbred self-fertile strains are highly resistant to leaf rust but are not vigorous and are therefore useful only as resistant breeding stocks.

THREE METHODS OF CONTROLLING leaf and stem rusts of wheat, rye, oats, and barley have been suggested— the use of resistant varieties, eradication of the alternate host, and dusting with fungicides. Early varieties and such cultural practices as early seeding and use of phosphate fertilizers that hasten ripening may help to escape rust but do not prevent damage in bad years. Their effect is indirect rather than direct. In general the recommended control measures are much the same for both leaf and stem rust and for all small grains with some modifications, depending on the particular crop or alternate host.

Late seeding, especially of spring grains, delays ripening and is likely to increase the damage because it provides a longer period for the development of the rust organism. Farmers generally recognize the advantages of early seeding and usually do their seeding as early as possible. Phosphorus often hastens ripening and thereby reduces rust damage. Heavy applications of barnyard manure or of nitrogen, on the other hand, may delay ripening and also may produce a heavy vegetative growth that retains moisture and favors the development of rust.

Extensive trials have shown that stem and leaf rusts of wheat and presumably those of other cereals can be prevented by dusting with sulfur or other suitable fungicides. Usually three or more treatments during the season are necessary. More are needed if the fungicide is washed off by frequent rains. Dusting should begin before rust damage appears, but that is wasted effort in seasons in which rust development is light and the cost generally is too great to be practical in the United States. Some of the newer fungicides may be more effective than sulfur.

Eradication of the common barberry (the alternate host of stem rust of wheat, rye, oats, and barley) and of buckthorn (the alternate host of crown rust of oats) has been widely practiced.

Damage from stem rust has been greatly reduced since eradication of the barberry was started. At the same time an aggressive breeding program has sought to produce resistant varieties, especially of wheat. In the more humid sections of the northern Great Plains where stem rust has been most destructive, practically no varieties of wheat susceptible to the ordinary races of stem rust (other than race 15B) have been grown since about 1938. It is certain that eradication of the barberries did not prevent the widespread distribution of race 15B in 1950 and again in 1952 nor infection of susceptible varieties in experimental plots at several locations in recent years.

The reason doubtless is that wind-blown spores from rust overwintering in Mexico and southern Texas were carried to northern wheatfields in the late spring and early summer. Eradication of the barberries in some years has delayed the onset of rust infection and thereby reduced damage in local areas below what it otherwise would have been.

The discovery that rust may hybridize on barberry bushes and thus produce new races is an additional reason for continuing the eradication campaign. Varieties formerly considered to be resistant, including Ceres, Vernal emmer, and Iumillo durum, were attacked later by races of rust believed to have originated on the barberry. Despite this menace from new races, Iumillo durum retained its resistance to rust in the field in the United States for nearly 50 years and Vernal emmer probably for 75 years, and both for an unknown period elsewhere before finally succumbing to race 15B. We have evidence also that new rust races may be produced by mutations in the absence of barberry bushes. Whatever the answer may be, the past losses and future potential losses are so great that no promising method of control should be neglected. Eradicating the common barberry and breeding resistant varieties both fall in this category.

BREEDING RESISTANT VARIETIES is certainly one of the most promising methods for controlling all rusts of small grains. It takes a long time, however, and often is difficult. Since stem rust has been most destructive on wheat, most of the outstanding examples of successful breeding for resistance to this disease relate to wheat. Outstanding progress also was made in breeding oats resistant to crown rust.

Both stem and leaf rust of wheat were recognized as among the more important hazards in growing wheat in many sections of the United States before 1900. About 1890 B. T. Galloway of the Department of Agriculture conducted spraying experiments that showed that rust could be reduced by fungicides, but he concluded that resistant varieties, if available, would be a more practical method of control. No markedly resistant varieties were known at that time. M. A. Carleton, who was employed by the Department of Agriculture in 1894, sowed an extensive collection of wheats from many countries at Garrett Park, Md., that fall, in a search for resistant varieties. It was known then that soft winter varieties grown extensively in Texas, Kansas, and southern Nebraska were more susceptible than the hard winter wheats then being adopted in those States, but even the latter were severely damaged in years when rust was bad. Some of the durums were known to be resistant to leaf rust, but they had not been used to any material degree as parents in crosses.

By 1900 Mr. Carleton and others had introduced from Russia and other countries a number of varieties of durum wheat and emmer, which were widely grown in experimental plots throughout the Great Plains. In 1902 and again in 1904 at Brookings, S. Dak., John S. Cole observed that certain varieties, specifically Yaroslav emmer from Russia and Iumillo durum from Italy, were almost completely immune to attacks by stem rust.

They were not satisfactory commercial or bread-making wheats, but they provided rust-resistant parents for hybrids and thereby the basis for an effective breeding program. Their usefulness is attested by the fact that practically all varieties grown in 1953 in Minnesota, the Dakotas, Wisconsin, and Canada, many of those grown in California, and some of those grown in the Eastern States carry resistance genes from one or both of those two early introductions. The job has by no means been completed—as proved by the widespread invasion of race 15B, which attacks all commercial varieties.

Losses from rust have been greatly reduced; even more important perhaps are the lessons that have been learned and the confidence in ultimate success that has been generated as a result of this experience. Such progress as has been made is the result of more than 60 years of research. Many difficulties have been met and overcome. A brief account of some of the problems and the ways in which they have been solved may be of value.

Crosses between commercial varieties of common wheat and Iumillo durum and Yaroslav emmer were made by Mr. Cole at Brookings almost immediately after the resistance of the latter was discovered in 1904 or 1905. But the crosses were lost before anything useful was derived from them because of changes in personnel. Similar crosses were made at the University of Minnesota about 1907 and at other places in later years. Serious difficulties were at once encountered because of a high degree of sterility and of linkage of rust resistance with undesirable characteristics from the durum and emmer parents. As a result it was nearly 30 years before any really satisfactory variety was derived from such crosses. Other sources of resistance had been discovered in the meantime and used in crosses to produce some commercially desirable common wheats.

The first of the latter to become really important was Ceres, produced by L. R. Waldron of the North Dakota Agricultural Experiment Station and distributed to farmers in 1926. Ceres was derived from a cross between the famous Marquis variety from Canada and Kota, a rust-resistant common wheat found mixed in a durum wheat that had been introduced from Russia by H. L. Bolley in 1903. Ceres was resistant to the prevailing races of stem rust. It was also moderately early and resistant to drought. It was soon grown throughout the northern Great Plains until after 1935, the year in which it was severely damaged by race 56, to which it is susceptible and which first appeared in epidemic proportions in that year.

The second resistant common wheat to be developed from a cross was Hope. It was first distributed to farmers in 1927. It was never widely grown, largely because of its susceptibility to heat and drought and low relative yields in the absence of rust. It is of great interest, however, because it or its near relatives have entered into the parentage of most of the resistant varieties now generally grown (except Thatcher) and because of the somewhat unorthodox manner in which it was produced.

Hope was derived from a cross between Yaroslav emmer and Marquis wheat made in 1915 by E. S. McFadden, then employed by the South Dakota Agricultural Experiment Station as an undergraduate student assistant. Because of the high degree of sterility, only a few poorly developed seeds were secured from the cross. From them developed a single plant. The first of the subsequent generations consisted of nondescript, unpromising plants, which were grown in bulk at the Highmore Substation in order "to permit natural selection to eliminate some of the undesirable combinations. . . ." An important feature was the strict elimination of shrunken seed by screens and strong blasts of air in a fanning mill. Another was the relatively large population of plants which could be grown by this method.

Marquillo was the first commercially grown variety to be derived from crosses involving Iumillo. It was distributed by the Minnesota Agricultural Experiment Station in 1928. Like Hope, it was never extensively grown, mostly because of the yellow color of the flour produced from it. It and sister strains have been useful, however, as parents in other crosses.

The famous Thatcher variety, distributed by the Minnesota Station in 1934, was derived from a double cross involving a sister strain of Marquillo and a selection from a cross between Marquis and Kanred winter wheats. As Kanred is resistant to some races of stem rust, it is generally considered that the resistance of Thatcher is due to genes both from the Iumillo durum and from Kanred.

Thatcher was first grown by farmers in 1934. In the severe stem rust epidemic of 1935 it often outyielded Marquis and Ceres by 20 to 30 bushels an acre. In subsequent years its acreage increased as rapidly as seed supplies permitted. It was highly resistant to the prevailing races of stem rust, ripened early, had short, stiff straw, and produced grain of excellent quality. By 1939 it was the most important variety of spring wheat in the United States.

Thatcher, however, is very susceptible to leaf rust. It was severely damaged by that disease in 1938 and 1941. In the meantime, other new varieties resistant both to leaf and stem rust had been produced and distributed to farmers. The principal ones are Rival and Pilot, distributed in 1939; Regent, released in Canada in 1939; Newthatch, released in 1944; Mida, in 1944; Rushmore, in 1949; and Lee, in 1951.

The acreage of Thatcher began to decline after 1940 and since then has practically disappeared in the eastern half of the northern Plains of the United States, although it continued to be grown in the drier western sections and in Canada. All of the newer varieties, except Lee, derived most of their resistance from Hope or H–44, a sister selection of Hope.

Hope and its derivatives fortunately were resistant to the prevailing races of leaf rust as well as stem rust. About 1944 a new race of leaf rust that attacked most previously resistant varieties appeared generally in farmers' fields throughout the Great Plains. That meant that varieties resistant to the new race and to the older races were needed.

Lee was produced in Minnesota from a cross between Hope and Timstein. Timstein is a selection from a cross between *Triticum timopheevi*, a wheat relative, and Steinwedel, a common wheat, made by J. T. Pridham of Australia and brought to the United States by his associate, S. L. McIndoe. Lee is highly resistant to most prevailing races of leaf and stem rust except stem rust race 15B.

Interest in 1953 centered in the production of new varieties resistant to 15B as well as to other races of stem rust. The race now known as 15B was identified as early as 1939, and attention was at once directed to discovering new sources of resistance. Since the widespread onset of 15B in farmers' fields in 1950, these efforts have been greatly intensified. Much progress has been made and it is reasonably certain that new varieties will be produced that are resistant to all the prevalent races both of leaf and stem rust and which are satisfactory or superior in other respects.

Considerable control of stem and leaf rust in the southern Great Plains has come about indirectly, and to some extent perhaps unexpectedly, through the development of early maturing varieties. Many of the newer ones carry genes for resistance derived from various sources. Even more important has been the discovery that early ripening varieties are generally superior throughout much of the region even in the absence of rust. Unfortunately these early varieties are not so winter hardy as the old Turkey and others they largely replaced and hence are not suitable for the colder areas. Some notion of the importance of this development may be gained from the fact that early or moderately early varieties, including such important ones as Pawnee, Comanche, and Wichita, occupied more than 75 percent of the wheat acreage in Kansas in 1952.

Much progress has also been made in California in breeding new varieties resistant to the races of stem rust that prevail in that State. The California program is unique in that the backcrossing technique has been used exclusively in producing new varieties resistant not only to stem rust but also to bunt and hessian fly. This technique

insures that the new varieties are very
similar to the old varieties except for
the addition of the resistant genes.
Hence there is not the usual uncertainty regarding yield performance,
quality, and other characteristics of
the new varieties. Consequently less
extensive tests for yield and quality
are believed to be necessary. Out of
this breeding program have come such
varieties as Baart 38, Baart 46, White
Federation 38, Ramona 44, and Big
Club 48, which occupy some 85 percent of the wheat acreage of California.

Breeding for resistance to leaf rust
and in some cases also for resistance to
stem rust has been an important objective in several Eastern States—Indiana, Illinois, Kentucky, Georgia,
and North Carolina—and by the Department of Agriculture at Beltsville,
Md. Several new varieties resistant to
leaf rust and in some cases to stem rust
have been released to farmers. The
more important of these are Vigo in
Indiana; Saline in Illinois; Chancellor
in Georgia; Atlas 50 and Atlas 66 in
North Carolina; Anderson in South
Carolina and North Carolina; and
Coastal in South Carolina.

The history of breeding for rust resistance in the durum wheats is similar
to that for the hard spring, but is less
involved. Most of the introduced durums at the time of their release were
moderately or highly resistant to the
prevailing races of both rusts. New or
previously unimportant races, especially stem rust races 17 and 21, to
which they are susceptible, soon appeared, however.

Among the earliest attempts to obtain resistant varieties were crosses
made in Minnesota between durums
of good quality and the poor but highly
resistant red durum, Pentad. No suitable progenies came from the cross,
and attention was then concentrated
on Vernal emmer as a source of resistance. Stewart and Carleton, produced in North Dakota from a Mindum x Vernal emmer cross and
distributed in 1943, are resistant to
these and older races. Stewart has

since become the leading variety of
durum wheat. Vernum and Nugget,
also produced in North Dakota, were
released to farmers in 1947 and 1951,
respectively. None of these newer varieties nor the old ones is resistant to
15B. Resistance to 15B has been found
in certain poor-quality durums from
Portugal and Spain, and they have
been crossed with the leading commercial varieties. Promising selections are being increased.

All commercially grown varieties
of durum are even more susceptible
to 15B than are the common wheats.
Moreover, the durums generally ripen
later and hence favor the development of this race of stem rust to an
unusual degree. Although the immediate outlook is rather unfavorable,
we believe that satisfactory resistant
varieties will be developed.

The experience since 1900 helps to
explain why the creation of new
varieties is often a slow and uncertain process. Sterility and linkage
are always a problem in dealing with
intergeneric crosses, but plant breeders
know better how to deal with them
than they did a generation ago.

IN OATS more than in any other
major crop, there has been a parade of
new varieties and frequent and complete changes in varieties in the past 50
years. Breeders have been successful
in producing high-yielding, rust-resistant varieties widely grown by farmers.
As new or previously unimportant
races of the rust organisms have
appeared, still other varieties resistant
to them have been developed. The
introduction and creation of early
maturing varieties that escape much
rust damage have also been important
factors.

At the beginning of the century
only late or medium-early varieties
and only rust-susceptible varieties
(with a few exceptions) were available.
The main exceptions were the late
or comparatively late White Russian
and Green Russian varieties, which
were resistant to stem rust but highly

susceptible to leaf rust, and Red Rustproof and Burt, in the Southern States. It is now known that the Red Rustproof types are better designated as late rusters rather than as rustproof, since they are not resistant.

The first important step in avoiding damage from oat rusts in general consisted of the introduction of the Kherson and Sixty Day varieties from Russia, the first by the Nebraska Agricultural Experiment Station in 1896 and the second by the Department of Agriculture in 1901. Neither is resistant to stem or crown rust, but they matured early and escaped much damage that otherwise would have occurred. Widely adapted throughout the central United States from the Atlantic almost to the Pacific coast, they soon became the dominant varieties, especially in the Corn Belt.

Another important introduction was Swedish Select, brought to the United States from Russia in 1899. It also is not resistant to either stem or crown rust but matured somewhat earlier than many of the varieties it replaced in the northern United States. Burt, an early-maturing crown-rust-escaping selection from Red Rustproof, made in 1878, has been widely grown throughout the South and sparingly in the southern part of the Corn Belt. Another important early but rust-susceptible variety was Fulghum, selected about 1900 from Red Rustproof by a farmer, J. A. Fulghum of Warrenton, Ga. Kanota, often regarded as a synonym of Fulghum, was distributed in 1919 by the Kansas Agricultural Experiment Station. Because of its early maturity, it did much to reduce crown rust damage in Kansas and nearby States.

The importance of breeding for resistance to stem rust apparently was first recognized about 1918 when White Russian was crossed with Victory in Minnesota. From it the resistant variety Anthony was produced. Anthony was distributed to farmers in 1929. Richland and Iogold were selected at the Iowa Agricultural Ex-

periment Station from Kherson in 1906 and distributed to farmers in 1914 and 1926, respectively. Rainbow, highly resistant to stem rust and moderately resistant to crown rust, was selected at the North Dakota Agricultural Experiment Station in 1925 and distributed to farmers in 1930.

One of the first definite attempts to produce varieties resistant to crown rust was made in 1928 when Rainbow, resistant to stem rust and moderately resistant to crown rust, was crossed with Markton at Aberdeen, Idaho. Selections later were grown at Ames, Iowa, and Arlington Farm, Va., where they were tested for resistance to rust, for yield, and for other characteristics. One of them, Marion, was distributed to farmers in 1941.

Several severe epidemics of crown rust and the discovery of the high degree of resistance of two varieties to the disease centered the attention of oat breeders on crown rust resistance as an important objective. One, Victoria, had been introduced from Uruguay in 1927. The other, Bond, came from New South Wales in 1929. Neither was satisfactory for growing on United States farms but appeared to be just what the oat breeders wanted as parent material.

Victoria was crossed with Richland in 1930. In subsequent years 30 varieties were selected from it and other Victoria crosses and distributed to farmers. They were soon the dominant varieties in all Corn Belt States and were important also in the Northeast and South. They were grown on approximately 30 million acres—about two-thirds of our oats acreage—in 1946. They produced high average yields, had short, stiff straw, and did not easily lodge, a characteristic almost unique among varieties adapted to the Corn Belt and highly prized by farmers who use combines.

Helminthosporium blight, a previously unimportant disease, caught up with the oats crop in 1946. Victoria and selections from crosses in which Victoria was a parent were especially susceptible and were seriously damaged. Fortunately Bond was resistant; in the meantime it had been used extensively as a parent and a number of selections were then in the yield-testing stage. Seed supplies of a few of them had been increased to be distributed if and when their superiority should be demonstrated. The widespread damage from helminthosporium blight emphasized their potential value and stimulated more extensive tests for yield and other characteristics. Out of this work have come such outstanding varieties as Clinton, Bonda, Andrew, Benton, and Mindo, now widely grown in the Corn Belt; and Camellia, Taggart, and Delair, which are grown to some extent in the Southern States. These new varieties, derived from crosses in which Bond was one parent, are resistant to the helminthosporium blight and generally to crown rust and are fully equal to the Victoria-derived varieties in yield, stiffness of straw, and quality.

Those achievements do not, however, justify complacency. Crown rust races 45 and 57 attack Bond and most of its derivatives. More recently crown rust race 101 has been discovered; it attacks both Victoria and Bond and their derivatives.

Two otherwise poorly adapted varieties, Landhafer and Santa Fe, which are resistant to those races and also to helminthosporium blight, have been crossed with Bond and Victoria derivatives to produce varieties with the necessary resistance to both diseases. Two such varieties, one produced at the Iowa Agricultural Experiment Station and the other at the Indiana Station, were to be made available for general growing in 1954. Floriland, a new variety that is resistant to crown rust race 101, was distributed in Florida in 1953. Other varieties resistant to one or more of these races and used as parents in crosses are Ukraine, Trispernia, and Klein.

Stem rust came again into the picture with races 6, 7, and 8, to which most of the new varieties are suscepti-ble. Race 8 is widespread and abundant. Race 7 appears to be rapidly increasing. A new, more virulent biotype, 7A, has been reported from Canada. Race 6 occurs infrequently.

Segregates from crosses designed to combine resistance to those races with resistance to other races of stem rust, crown rust, and the helminthosporium blight were in the yield-testing stage in 1953.

RUSTS OF BARLEY were not generally considered important enough to justify intensive breeding for resistance to them until about 1935, when many fields in the North Central States and western prairie regions were severely damaged by stem rust. It is now generally recognized that leaf rust may do damage generally in all humid barley-growing areas but principally on winter barley in the Eastern and Southeastern States. Resistance to both rusts has been an important objective in most barley-breeding programs in those areas.

The most important commercial variety resistant to stem rust was found by a farmer, S. T. Lykkens of Kindred, N. Dak. In 1935 he decided to plow up his field of Wisconsin Pedigree 37 because of severe damage by stem rust. He observed a single plant that was free of rust, saved the seed, planted it in his garden the next spring, and in subsequent years sold seed to his neighbors. By 1942 it was a recognized commercial variety. Its resistance has since been verified by others. It has been included in numerous yield trials and tests of quality. Although it has some defects, such as weak straw, it has compared favorably with other varieties in most important respects. It has been named Kindred and is now grown more extensively for use in malting than any other variety in the principal barley-producing area of the United States.

Other commercially grown varieties resistant to stem rust are Peatland, Mars, Plains, Feebar, and Moore.

Fifty or more other varieties, most of them from the world collection of barley from various foreign countries and as selections from farmers' fields known to be resistant to stem rust, are valuable sources of resistance for use by plant breeders, even though they are not grown commercially. Progress has been made also in breeding varieties resistant to leaf rust, but only one, Goliad, had been released in 1953. Goliad is also resistant to stem rust.

THE LARGE NUMBER of physiologic races (240 or more of stem rust of wheat, for example) has sometimes seemed an insurmountable obstacle to the successful breeding of resistant varieties. Nevertheless a great deal of progress has been made. From the years of experience has come a better understanding of their relation to breeding programs.

Our concept of a large number of races stems mostly from the manner in which they are identified. Because of technical difficulties, it is not generally feasible to determine the ability of each of a large number of collections of rust spores to infect each of a large number of varieties in an advanced stage of growth in the field. Yet this is the information that is needed. The nearest approach to this so far devised for identifying races is to infect young plants, usually seedlings, growing in a greenhouse. Only a few varieties, often not more than a dozen, are included in the tests, and they are usually the same year after year. They are known as host testers. It is hardly to be expected that results from the tests could be applied directly to breeding without due consideration of the conditions under which they are obtained.

One important fact is that resistance or susceptibility in the seedling stage in the greenhouse does not necessarily mean resistance or susceptibility when a plant is in an advanced stage of development in the field. A physiologic race that infects a given variety in the seedling stage but not when the plants are approaching maturity is not likely to be a serious menace to that variety, but it may add to the number of physiologic races.

Another fact that makes breeding for resistance to all prevalent races less formidable than it may seem to be is that many varieties are resistant to several races. It is known, for example, that Kanred in the seedling stage is resistant to 11 races of stem rust. Hope is resistant to at least 17 races, Red Egyptian to 26, Kenya-Gular to 30, and certain other Kenya derivatives to at least 35. They may be and probably are resistant to a larger number in advanced stages of growth in the field, although, as we indicated, the exact situation would be hard to determine.

Somewhat the same applies to leaf rust of wheat and to the rusts of oats and barley. In most cases it is possible on the basis of known information to choose a small number of varieties of each crop that collectively are resistant to all known races of a given rust. If this resistance were to be concentrated in a single variety, and no new races appeared, the job of producing resistant varieties would be finished except as there might be need for resistant varieties for other areas or for other reasons. And this, of course, is what cereal breeders for rust resistance have been trying to do for some 75 years with considerable success.

From this point of view, the appearance of a new physiologic race does not mean defeat. Rather, it should be regarded as a warning of danger: A highway sign is designed not to frighten but to be respected.

JOHN H. MARTIN *is an agronomist in charge of sorghum investigations in the division of cereal crops and diseases at the Plant Industry Station, Beltsville, Md. He has written many bulletins, circulars, and other publications on cereal culture.*

S. C. SALMON *is an agronomist in charge of investigations of wheat in the same division. Before he joined the Department of Agriculture in 1930 he was on the staff of Kansas State College.*

Leaf and Head Blights of Cereals

James G. Dickson

Leaf blights reduce the green leaf surface that a plant needs to produce its carbohydrates. If that happens early in the life of a cereal plant, it has fewer numbers of heads and kernels in a head. Later leaf blighting reduces the size and weight of kernels.

Head blights kill the head or many of the young kernels when the attack occurs early. When the attack occurs after the kernels are partly developed, the grain is shriveled and may be lost in threshing. Blight late in the season may cause discolored and shrunken grain. Kernels blighted by scab disease will sicken hogs. The fungus bodies (sclerotia) produced on crops blighted by ergot are poisonous. The presence of blighted grains also increases the cost of cleaning and processing grain.

Often one organism or a similar one may incite the same or a similar disease on several of the grain crops. So I group the leaf blights and head blights according to the micro-organism that incites the disease: Bacterial leaf and head blights; fusarium head blights, or scab; ergot of grains and grasses; helminthosporium leaf blights and kernel blights; septoria leaf and culm blights; and rhynchosporium leaf and head blights.

Many of the bacterial leaf and kernel blights occur on cereals and grasses but are generally unimportant. They produce water-soaked stripes or halo-surrounded spots on the leaves. Leaf lesions frequently are abundant for short periods during the growing season, but they cause only minor damage unless they persist into the heading period. Then the bacterial blights produce a sticky mass of bacteria around the spike. The result is a poor set of seed.

Blasted heads are common when moist weather and bacterial blight occur during heading. Later kernel infection is marked by black or brown areas on the chaff and brown, sunken lesions near the germ end of the kernel. The bacteria also may be carried on the kernels without external evidence of their presence.

The bacteria that cause these diseases are minute, short, rod-shaped cells of various species and races. Some species are restricted to a single cereal or grass. Others comprise races, each of which may attack a given grain crop and its closely related grasses.

Seed-borne bacteria are controlled by the use of organic mercury, but the bacteria that spread to grainfields from crop residues and grasses are not affected by seed treatments. Most of the adapted varieties of wheat, oats, and barley are not damaged greatly by bacterial blights. Very susceptible varieties, however, are unsuited to humid areas.

FUSARIUM HEAD BLIGHT, or scab, a disease of wheat, barley, rye, and some grasses, sometimes causes extensive losses. It also damages corn and sorghum. Heavy losses are most frequent in the eastern and central Corn Belt and in similar humid or subhumid areas in this and other countries.

The head blight develops during warm, humid weather at any stage from kernal formation to ripening of the grain. Infection occurs in the flowers and then spreads up and down the spike. The diseased part of the head soon turns a straw color in wheat and rye and light brown in barley. Frequently pink mold growth develops around the base of the flower and cements the chaff to the grain. The kernels of wheat and rye are shriveled, white or gray, and show a rough, scabby surface. In barley the kernels are light in weight and grayish brown; with the hulls removed, they look like scabbed kernels of wheat and rye.

The fungus grows into the kernels and makes the starch floury, discolored, and partly changed to sugars. The proteins are partly broken down into soluble nitrogen compounds. Some of the fats become rancid because of the formation of fatty acids. New compounds are produced that cause acute vomiting in dogs, pigs, and man, but do not affect sheep, cattle, or mature poultry. Grain containing 5 percent or more of badly scabbed kernels, fed to pigs, causes vomiting, loss of appetite, and arrested growth. Scabbed kernels in grain therefore should not be processed into human food or used to feed swine. Scabbed kernels can be separated readily from the sound wheat, rye, or corn. Because it is hard to separate scabbed from healthy barley grain, scabby barley should be fed to cattle, sheep, or poultry.

Several species of *Fusarium* incite the disease on cereals and grasses. The most common species, *F. graminearum*, produces the sexual stage (perithecia) on old corn stalks and straw.

The sexual stage is known as *Gibberella zeae*. The minute, blue-black spore cases (perithecia) of this stage are abundant on the surface of stalks and straw from April through June. The spores that incite head blight or ear rot are carried to the young heads of the small grains and to corn silks by the wind. Two other species, *F. culmorum* and *F. avenaceum*, are common north of the Corn Belt and in Canada. All of them also cause seedling blight and root and stalk rot in the cereals.

These pathogens are carried over on crop residues. Spores are not produced or dispersed if all crop residues are covered by a thin layer of soil. All straw and stalks should be plowed under and left below the soil surface to control the diseases. Surface mulching with straw and stalks invites head blight in small grains where wet, warm weather occurs after small grains are headed.

No highly resistant varieties of wheat, rye, or barley have been produced, but some varieties are more susceptible than others. All known varieties will be scabbed if spores are present and the weather is favorable from the heading period to maturity. Two barleys, Chevron (C. I. 1111) and Peatland (C. I. 5267), and three wheats, Haynes Bluestem (C. I. 2874), Progress (C. I. 6902), and Rival (C. I. 11708), are among the least susceptible varieties. Investigations at the Minnesota and Wisconsin Agricultural Experiment Stations indicate that the inheritance of resistance is complicated.

Seed treatment of well-cleaned grain with organic mercury compounds will control the seed-borne infections.

ERGOT OF GRAINS and grasses is not strictly a head blight, although loss in yield from sterility is always associated with the disease. Resting bodies (sclerotia) of the fungus replace some of the kernels, and the adjacent kernels do not develop. The disease is common and destructive on grasses, rye, barley, durum wheat, and some varieties of hard spring wheat. The damage from it occurs in the humid sections and extends into the subhumid regions, notably in the spring grain areas of Nebraska, the Dakotas, and Montana.

The disease is recognized first by the sticky fluid (honeydew stage) on parts of the spikes soon after heading and later by the purplish-black sclerotia in the ripening heads. The honeydew attracts flies and other insects to the diseased heads. The sclerotia are shaped somewhat like a rye kernel. They usually are longer than a grain and thus protrude from the chaff. The sclerotia thresh out with the grain. The presence of ergot in flour or other grain products can be determined by standard color tests.

The ergot sclerotia contain several chemical compounds, some of which cause acute injury to animals and man. One group of similar compounds has special medicinal value. Bright, hard ergot sclerotia free from molds command a high price for medicinal use. Ergot sclerotia invaded by *Fusarium* contain compounds affecting the respiratory and other automatic muscular action. Because most of the ergot sclerotia produced in the humid, central area are attacked by *Fusarium* and are unsuitable for medical extracts, supplies usually are obtained from the drier west central areas or imported. Ergot samples are tested before they are purchased by pharmaceutical companies. The ergot sclerotia contain compounds that cause contraction of the fine blood vessels. Investigations at the Montana Agricultural Experiment Station have confirmed early reports that milk flow in livestock is reduced greatly by continuous feeding of small quantities of ergot sclerotia. Relatively small quantities of ergot may cause serious losses among animals.

Any grain containing more than 0.3 percent ergot sclerotia by weight is graded as ergoty and is discounted on the markets. The ergot content of milled products is limited by law. Although most of the sclerotia can be removed with modern cleaning machinery, it is difficult and expensive to bring the percentage down to the content permitted.

The life cycle of the fungus, *Claviceps purpurea*, is well synchronized with that of the grain or grass host. The sclerotia falling on the soil or planted with the seed germinate when the grains and grasses are flowering.

The sexual spores are wind-borne to the flowers of the grain or grass, where they invade the young kernel and replace it with fungus growth. The first fungus growth forms a folded mat, which bears millions of spores in a sticky, sweet, honeydew-like mass. The minute spores are carried by insects or are spattered by rain to infect numerous other kernels. The sclerotia develop following this spreading stage.

Some grasses are infected regularly from sclerotia dropped from the previous year's growth. The ergot spreads from the grasses to cereal crops, which are related to them botanically. Therefore, neither crop rotation nor ergot-free seed controls the disease.

Destroying grasses in the grainfields, particularly quackgrass, bromegrass, and wheatgrasses, and mowing grasses near grainfields before they head helps in control. Heavy pasturing, or mowing of grass pastures before heading, also reduces the danger of ergot poisoning of livestock.

No varieties of barley, rye, or wheat resistant to ergot have been found. The Mississippi Agricultural Experiment Station has produced a paspalum grass resistant to the ergot that is common and destructive on this southern pasture grass.

HELMINTHOSPORIUM LEAF BLIGHTS and kernel blights on cereals and grasses are caused by several species of *Helminthosporium*. Some of the diseases have been so damaging as to necessitate changes in varieties to maintain profitable grain production. Helminthosporium blight, for example, forced much of the susceptible Wisconsin Barbless (Wis. 38) barley out of production in the North Central States not long ago. Another helminthosporium blight forced oats growers to drop varieties with Victoria parentage from production in the Central States. Such diseases are devastating when susceptible varieties are used throughout large areas.

This group of disease-producing fungi attacks seedlings, roots, crowns, leaves, and kernels.

Spores, however, spread from the diseased seedlings to the leaves of healthy plants and from diseased kernels cause blighted seedlings. The spores, produced abundantly on crop residues, further spread the disease to the leaves and heads of growing grain. Seed treatment with organic mercury compounds, crop rotation, plowing under crop residues, and the use of resistant varieties are generally applicable control measures for this large group of cereal diseases.

The fungi inciting these leaf and kernel blights are all *Helminthosporium* species. In their sexual stage they fall into two groups, *Pyrenophora* species and *Cochliobolus* species. Specific characteristics in both the sexual and asexual stages differentiate the two groups.

Net blotch and kernel blight incited by *Pyrenophora teres* (*Helminthosporium teres*) occur on barley only. The characteristic symptoms are netted blotches or irregular stripes on the leaves, brown discoloration on the culm, and light brown, indistinct blotches on the kernels. The size of kernels is reduced, but badly shriveled grain is uncommon. The sexual stage of the fungus is produced abundantly on the old stubble and straw.

At least two distinct races of the pathogen have been identified. They react differently on the two general groups of barley. C. W. Schaller, of the California Agricultural Experiment Station, and R. G. Shands, of the Department of Agriculture and the Wisconsin Agricultural Experiment Station, found that resistance to the western race is concentrated in the Manchurian-Oderbrucker group of barleys, including Peatland (C. I. 5267), whereas resistance to the eastern race is concentrated in the North African and Abyssinian barleys. Only a few in the Manchurian-Oderbrucker group are resistant.

Stripe disease incited by *Helminthosporium gramineum* occurs on barley only. The sexual stage of this fungus is not found in nature and the life cycle differs from that of other species. Seedling infection results in fungus invasion of all plant parts, and spores are produced during the period of barley flowering. Seed infection occurs from wind-borne spores.

All leaves of a diseased plant generally are affected. Chlorotic stripes appear on the young leaves as they unfold. The stripes turn brown and spread to the leaf sheath also when the leaves reach full development.

All spikes of affected plants are blighted and brown in susceptible barleys of the Manchurian type. Diseased plants of the Coast barleys in California frequently develop some seed. Spores are abundant on the striped plants during and after flowering. Kernels infected from wind-borne spores do not show the disease in the dormant seed.

Several physiologic races of the pathogen occur, but practical resistance to the known races has been obtained and incorporated into commercial varieties. Inheritance of resistance is conditioned by two or more factor pairs with resistance dominant or partially dominant. Several genes for resistance are reported. Those used most extensively for breeding are from Lion (C. I. 923), Peatland (C. I. 5267), Chevron (C. I. 1111), Brachytic (C. I. 6572), and Persicum (C. I. 6531).

Leaf blotch and kernel blight incited by *Pyrenophora avenae* (*Helminthosporium avenae*) occurs on oats and several related grasses. The disease and its pathogen resemble those of net blotch of barley. Small, brown spots or irregular blotches, which may spread over the entire leaf blade, are the characteristic symptoms. Defoliation occurs in winter oats in the Southern States and on very susceptible spring oats in North Central States. Kernel infection is not conspicuous. Yields are reduced when the leaf blighting is severe.

Crop rotation, plowing under crop residues, seed treatment with organic mercury compounds, and using resistant varieties are the recommended control measures.

Most of the commercial oat varieties are moderately resistant to the disease.

Yellow leaf spot of wheat (*Helminthosporium tritici-vulgaris*) was reported first in Pennsylvania and Virginia, the eastern part of the region where soft red winter wheat is grown. It has since spread westward into the hard red winter wheat area of Kansas and Nebraska. It is of minor importance.

Leaf spot and blight of rye incited by *Pyrenophora secalis* (*Helminthosporium secalis*) first shows as a small brown spot, which spreads until the leaf blade is yellow and dry. Sexual spore cases are abundant on old rye straw. The disease is of minor importance if crop rotation and seed treatment are practiced. The first general occurrence of the disease was in North Central States in 1940.

Leaf spot (culm blight and kernel blight of barley, wheat, and grasses) is caused by *Cochliobolus sativus* (*Helminthosporium sativum*). The damaging seedling blight and root rot caused by the fungus is described on page 321. The brown leaf spot phase is common on barley. The spots spread to cause yellowing and the death of the leaves. Diseased kernels of barley and wheat are dark brown or almost black, especially near the germ end of the kernel. That condition sometimes is called black point. Kernels infected early are shriveled and light in weight. The sexual stage of the fungus has been produced readily in culture through mating of compatable lines of the fungus by two Canadian scientists, R. D. Tinline and P. M. Simmonds.

The disease is controlled by maintaining good fertility of the soil, crop rotation, seed treatment with organic mercury compounds, and the use of resistant varieties.

D. C. Arny, of the Wisconsin Agricultural Experiment Station, found resistance in barley to be controlled by a single factor pair when using Lion (C. I. 923) as the susceptible parent and races of the pathogen found in the North Central States. The more resistant barleys are in the Manchurian group including Peatland and Chevron. Mars (C. I. 7015) and Moore (C. I. 7251) are resistant commercial varieties.

Victoria blight of oats, incited by *Helminthosporium victoriae*, a relatively new disease, has nearly eliminated several high-yielding, rust- and smut-resistant varieties that had been obtained from crosses with Victoria. It is primarily a seedling and culm disease. Leaves show a reddish-brown striping or spotting. The straw breaks over as the crop is heading. The grain is shriveled and chaffy, largely because of infection at the base of the culm. The pathogen is carried over on the seed. The straw and stubble of susceptible varieties are darkened by the mass of conidia (asexual spores), which are produced at the nodes as the plants are killed and cover the surface of the straw in late fall and the following spring. Infected seed and crop residues spread the pathogen to the crop the following year.

Seed treatment with organic mercury compounds reduces seedling loss but does not control the later culm blight. Apparently only oats derived from Victoria hybrids are very susceptible to the disease. Investigations at the Iowa and Wisconsin Agricultural Experiment Stations and at the Dominion Rust Laboratory, Winnipeg, Canada, indicate that susceptibility to Victoria blight is not completely linked with the Victoria type of crown rust resistance and that a factor for resistance to crown rust can be used without bringing in susceptibility to Victoria blight.

SEPTORIA LEAF AND CULM blights are common on cereals and grasses. The leaf blotches and spots frequently are indefinite in color, shape, and margin. Usually the leaf and culm tissue surrounding the lesion bleaches slowly and turns straw color or brown, depending somewhat on the host. As the leaves bleach or as the diseased plants approach maturity, the small, regular spore cases (pycnidia) develop beneath the leaf surface of the diseased areas. These are globe-shaped, with a definite opening to the surface and light golden brown to brown in color. The abundant spores borne in these spore cases are slender to threadlike and colorless to light yellow. The different species are based largely on the length of the spores and on the hosts upon which they develop. The slender spores are wind-borne.

The damage they cause results largely from shriveled kernels and lodging. Shriveled kernels and reduced yields are common in susceptible varieties. The damage in susceptible varieties of wheat, barley, and oats is similar to that caused by stem rust.

Control is difficult as the spore cases are produced in abundance on the old straw and stubble. Crop rotation, plowing under old straw, and the use of resistant varieties offer the only means of control. Many of the older varieties are moderately resistant to the disease. Some of the newer varieties of wheat, oats, and barley are susceptible. Cereal breeders, in their search for better rust resistance, sometimes have used septoria-susceptible varieties as parents, but that has meant an increase in damage from this group of diseases.

The septoria blights of grains and grasses are incited by several different fungus species. Each is restricted to a particular grain crop and its closely related grasses. I list the common species on the grain crops.

Wheat: Two species are common on wheat, *Septoria tritici*, a long-spored species that attacks mainly leaves and is widely distributed; and *S. nodorum*, a very short-spored species that attacks leaves, culms, and heads.

Barley: *S. passerinii* has thin, medium-long spores and occurs on cultivated barley and some of its wild relatives. Varieties of the Manchuria-Oderbrucker type are susceptible or moderately susceptible. Dorsett (C. I. 4821), Valentine (C. I. 7242), and Jet (C. I. 967) used extensively in breeding are resistant. North African and Egyptian types often show considerable resistance. Atlas (C. I. 4118) and Atlas 46 (C. I. 7323) are resistant commercial varieties of the Coast type.

Oats: *S. avenae* has medium-narrow, short spores and produces the sexual stage abundantly on susceptible varieties. The varieties from Bond are relatively susceptible to culm rotting by this species, and perithecia develop on the old diseased straw. A relatively large number of grasses including wheat are attacked by this species and its varieties. Most of the commercial oat varieties other than those derived from Bond are relatively resistant.

Rye: *S. secalis* has slender, medium-short spores. This species and variety occur on rye and related grasses especially in the north central area.

RHYNCHOSPORIUM LEAF SCALD and kernel blight is primarily a leaf scald of barley, rye, and numerous grasses, although kernel blight is common in the southwestern barleys grown during the winter. The leaf scald appears as oval to irregular areas, which at first are water-soaked and gray green and later become zonated and yellow or brown and gray green. The pathogen produces a mat of tiny colorless asexual spores in the gray-green surface of the lesion. The spores are scattered by rain and wind. Spores are produced abundantly on crop residues especially during cool weather. The pathogen has specialized races, which are restricted closely to the different small grain and grass species. Experiments at the California Agricultural Experiment Station indicate losses in yield of barley up to 20 percent when leaf scald is severe. Early development of scald reduces the number of kernels; later infection reduces kernel weight. Atlas 46 (C. I. 7323), Trebi (C. I. 936) and some experimental varieties are highly resistant. Many of the Manchurian barleys are relatively resistant.

JAMES G. DICKSON *is professor of plant pathology in the University of Wisconsin and an agent of the division of cereal crops and diseases of the Bureau of Plant Industry, Soils, and Agricultural Engineering. He has been engaged in investigations of field crops and their diseases since 1915.*

Virus Diseases of Cereal Crops

H. H. McKinney

Most of the plant viruses impair or destroy chlorophyll, the all-important food-synthesizing green pigment in crop plants. The plant struggles for its existence or dies if its chlorophyll has been impaired.

Some viruses stunt or otherwise deform or alter the growth of plants without seriously affecting the chlorophyll. Sometimes it seems that the chlorophyll even may be increased. Some plants may carry a virus but show no signs of disease.

Some viruses tend to impair or destroy the chlorophyll uniformly through the leaf. They cause chlorosis—a general yellowing or bleaching. In others the impairment or destruction occurs in patches, spots, or streaks in the leaf; there is a light-green or yellow or white mosaic mottling, spotting, or streaking. The chlorotic patterns in the leaves are strikingly similar for many of the virus diseases of the grasses, even though the viruses are quite different.

Among the cereal crops in the United States the greatest losses from the virus diseases are caused by the mosaics of winter wheat. Several viruses attack cereals. Some have been controlled through the use of resistant varieties, but for a destructive group of viruses in the area between Oklahoma to South Dakota no effective control is known.

We identify the viruses of cereals and other plants largely on the basis of symptom reactions of the infected plants when grown under proper environmental conditions; the host-range characteristics; the methods by which a virus can be transmitted from diseased to healthy plants; and the ability of a virus to live in extracted plant juice or in dried tissue under different temperatures, and other physical and chemical treatments for given lengths of time.

The method of perpetuating a virus is determined by the characteristics of the virus. If the virus can be transmitted only by tissue union or by insects, it is kept alive in the living plant or sometimes in the living insects. Many viruses that can be transmitted experimentally by manual methods of inoculation are kept alive for months or years in frozen juice or in dried tissues near freezing.

The wheat, barley, oat, and cucumber viruses that can be transmitted by manual methods of inoculation are kept in clipped leaf tissue that is dehydrated over calcium chloride, and stored over anhydrone at temperatures just above freezing. At intervals the stored viruses are increased in growing plants, and new dehydrated tissues are prepared and stored. The virus of brome mosaic and viruses of the *Agropyron* mosaic can be maintained in that way, but usually less work is involved when they are carried in their respective native host plants, and the new cultures are started by the division of the plant stools or from the rhizomes. The virus of barley stripe mosaic can be kept in infected seeds for at least 8 years.

SOIL-BORNE wheat mosaic viruses occur in Illinois, Indiana, Iowa, Kansas, Maryland, Missouri, Nebraska, North Carolina, Oklahoma, South Carolina, and Virginia. Infected fields have been found in nearly one-half of the counties in Illinois. Indiana also has many infected areas. In many places, particularly in Illinois, the viruses would curtail the production of wheat were it not for resistant wheats.

These viruses of wheat and its close

relatives also infect barley and rye, although they have shown relatively high resistance. Oats, corn, and plants outside of the grass family apparently are not susceptible to them. *Bromus commutatus*, a wild grass, is susceptible. The viruses are not carried in the seed from the diseased plants.

The virus of wheat mosaic-rosette (*Marmor tritici* var. *typicum*), is the first virus that we knew could be carried over in the soil from season to season. The rosette phase of the disease attracted attention in 1919, near Granite City, Ill., but its virus nature was not recognized until 1925. Previously it was suspected that insects (particularly the hessian fly), cold winter temperatures, and several species of fungi were causing the trouble. In 1920 it was learned that the causal agent is associated with soils and that it can be inactivated in the soil by steaming and treatment with formaldehyde.

Many varieties of wheat were found to be immune to rosette. From 1920 to 1923 I selected rosette-immune strains from the highly susceptible varieties Harvest Queen and Illini Chief. Years later, when Illinois 2 wheat was found to be highly susceptible to mosaic-rosette, O. T. Bonnett and his associates at the University of Illinois selected lines that were immune to rosette and highly resistant to mosaic and that had several of the desirable characteristics of Illinois 2. Those lines contributed to the development of Prairie and Royal varieties.

The evidence that the causal agent of rosette was associated with the soil actually delayed the discovery that a virus caused the disease. In 1920 workers generally considered that viruses did not overseason in the soil. Even today few viruses are known to be carried over in the soil. Fortunately the rosette symptoms occur in only a few varieties, such as Harvest Queen, Illini Chief, and Missouri Bluestem. Most varieties, however, develop mosaic mottling when they are grown in infested soils.

Along with the field experiments, microscopic studies that Sophia Eckerson, R. W. Webb, and I conducted at the University of Wisconsin revealed the presence of abnormal inclusion bodies in many of the cells of both rosetted and mosaic plants. These cell inclusions were so strikingly like those associated with some known virus diseases, and the mosaic symptoms were so evident in many of the varieties of wheat, that we strongly suspected the virus nature of rosette and the mosaics.

Inoculation methods commonly used to transmit mosaic viruses in plants like tobacco and cucumber failed to transmit the disease to healthy wheat seedlings. Neither rosette nor mosaic developed when I grew winter wheat out of its natural growing season. So I got the idea that cool temperatures favor infection and disease expression.

Tests by Dr. Webb demonstrated that soil temperatures near 60° F. and comparatively high soil moisture favored natural infection from the soil. When I inoculated healthy wheat seedlings with the juice from the diseased plants and then cultured them at cool temperatures, they developed the disease.

Mosaic symptoms are transmitted most successfully by growing the inoculated plants with ample sunlight, a daily photoperiod of 8 hours, and a temperature near 60°.

I observed that some of the wheat plants growing in the field developed light-green mosaic mottling. Others developed severe yellow mottling. In the inoculation tests with virus from mosaic spelt and wheat plants, I saw that some of the plants of Harvest Queen wheat developed light-green mosaic and rosette, while others developed yellow mosaic—somewhat like the situation that I had observed in the study of the mosaic viruses that infect tobacco. Virus-selection techniques soon enabled the isolation of two viruses. One induced mild light-green mosaic and rosette in Harvest Queen wheat. The other induced severe yellow mosaic in Harvest Queen, but no rosette.

I found that most varieties of wheat developed only mosaic when they were inoculated with the mosaic-rosette virus. Some varieties developed light-green mosaic. Others developed mild yellow mosaic.

Some of the severe yellow mosaic viruses that have been isolated from the soil-borne series differ somewhat in their ability to destroy chlorophyll and to stunt or otherwise deform the plant. None, however, has been observed to cause the excessive stooling or bud proliferation caused by the mosaic-rosette virus. To distinguish them from other viruses that cause yellow mosaic in wheat, they are referred to as the prairie wheat yellow mosaic viruses (*Marmor tritici* var. *fulvum*). Attempts to isolate a virus that induces rosette without the mild mosaic mottling have failed.

These yellow mosaic viruses are regarded as strains of the mosaic-rosette virus, but further study is needed to determine whether they are direct mutants or more distant relatives. I have not seen the strong unilateral interference, characteristic of the tobacco mosaic virus in combination with its yellow mosaic virus mutants, in the soil-borne viruses isolated thus far from wheat. It is therefore harder to demonstrate mutation in the wheat mosaic viruses than it is in the tobacco mosaic virus.

The soil-borne wheat mosaic viruses are relatively unstable in extracted plant juices and in tissues removed from the plant and kept at ordinary temperatures. The viruses are inactive when the leaves die on the plant. When fresh mosaic leaves are dried in the laboratory, the virus becomes inactive within 2 or 3 weeks. Furthermore, the viruses soon die when fresh mosaic leaves are allowed to decompose in moist soil. The thermal death point of the yellow mosaic viruses tested thus far is 140° to 149° F., with 10 minutes exposure when in the plant juice. Traces of yellow mosaic virus passed a Schott-Jena fritted glass filter having an average pore size of 880 milli-microns. The dilution end points for the rosette and the yellow mosaic viruses in distilled water are between 100 and 1,000 times.

Mosaic may occur in an infested field every year for at least 12 years, or it may fail to appear after the first year. Air-dried soil stored in the laboratory for 3 years remained infectious. Some lightly infested soils lost their infecting power when stored through one summer, however.

In a cropping test that covered 5 years on infested land, Benjamin Koehler, of the Illinois Agricultural Experiment Station, found that continuous cropping with a susceptible wheat greatly favored the occurrence of mosaic and rosette. Cropping for 4 years with an immune wheat, oats, soybeans, and corn greatly reduced or controlled completely the rosette and mosaic in the susceptible wheats grown on the land the fifth season. Four years of cropping with alfalfa also reduced the amount of disease, but less than other crops did. Under favorable conditions, which are not completely understood, Dr. Koehler found that a lightly infectious soil gradually became highly infectious after four successive croppings with susceptible wheats.

The effects of various chemicals and heat on infested soil have been tested by Koehler and me and also by Folke Johnson at Ohio State University. Infestation can be eliminated by the use of heat, formaldehyde, chloropicrin, dichloropropene-dichloropropane (D–D), napthalene, calcium cyanide, carbon disulfide, methyl bromide, rotenone, napthalene, and ethyl alcohol. Ethylene dichloride was less effective than the other chemicals. Ethyl chloride gave no control. Toluene gave no control in air-dried infested soil that was saturated with the chemical for 4 days, followed by complete evaporation of the chemical and seeding within 5 days to a susceptible wheat.

We do not know the exact relation

of these wheat viruses to the soil. Perhaps they live in some soil-inhabiting organism that carries the virus and introduces it into the underground parts of the young seedling in autumn.

Any such vector must be very small, because dried infested soil remains infectious after passage through a 250-mesh Tyler screen. Many organisms (especially nematodes) in the soil might serve as a carrier of virus, but no mosaic has been induced in wheat by the species of nema which have been used in tests conducted in collaboration with Jesse R. Christie, of the Department of Agriculture, and M. B. Linford, of the Illinois Agricultural Experiment Station.

THE PLAINS WHEAT MOSAIC viruses were collected by L. E. Melchers from a few scattered wheat plants growing in nurseries and fields near Manhattan, Kans., in 1931 and by me in 1941. Tests with the soil in which the mosaic plants were growing failed to indicate that the viruses are soil-borne. The viruses transmit by manual inoculation with some difficulty even at favorable temperatures of from 60° to 65°. They cannot be maintained in plants growing at summer temperatures at Beltsville.

We isolated green mosaic and yellow mosaic strains of virus. The green mosaic strain does not induce rosette in mosaic-rosette-susceptible Harvest Queen wheat. Unfortunately the viruses were lost in the summer of 1942, when no cool-temperature culture chambers were available.

Soil-borne viruses isolated recently from collections made in Kansas and Oklahoma are so similar to the plains wheat mosaic viruses that it is suspected that the viruses collected in 1931 and 1941 may have been soil-borne. The negative results obtained with the earlier collections of soil may have been due to a low level of infestation, and the plains wheat mosaic viruses may be strains of *Marmor tritici*.

SOIL-BORNE VIRUSES of oat mosaic occur in Alabama, Georgia, South Carolina, and North Carolina. The mosaics were observed first in the experiment station plots at Auburn, Ala. When they are abundant, they reduce the yields of grain and forage of susceptible oat varieties such as Bond, Camellia, Victoria, and Letoria. Growing resistant and tolerant varieties—Anderson, Atlantic, Appler, Arlington, Custis, Fulgrain, Fulwin, Lee, Lemont, Victorgrain, Winter Resistant—should prevent widespread losses from the mosaics. The mosaics have been observed in fields only in winter-grown oats and in oat relatives.

The viruses can be transmitted by manual methods of inoculation when the oat plants are grown at temperatures near 60° to 65° F. Two viruses have been isolated. One, *Marmor terrestre* var. *typicum*, causes apical mosaic, a light-green mosaic mottling that tends to be prominent toward the tip portion of the leaves of Letoria oats. The other, *M. terrestre* var. *oculatum*, causes eyespot mosaic, which in Letoria oats causes light-green or yellow, nearly elliptical spots, which have green centers. Some plants in certain oat strains that are grown in infested soil develop a typical rosette. A specific virus for oat rosette has not been isolated. The viruses of these mosaics are not carried in seed from diseased plants. In the soil they have shown much the same characteristics as the soil-borne wheat mosaic viruses.

WHEAT STREAK MOSAIC viruses were first collected at Salina, Kans., in 1932, but records of L. E. Melchers make it seem likely that similar mosaics may have been present in Kansas before 1930. In 1922 G. L. Peltier found a wheat mosaic in Nebraska that had characteristics of streak mosaic.

The disease has been worst in western Kansas, but it has caused damage in Nebraska, Colorado, and South Dakota. Some damage has been reported in Wyoming and western Iowa. The disease is known to occur in Oklahoma, the Salt River Valley in Arizona, California, and Canada. In Nebraska and South Dakota spring wheats as well as winter wheats are affected.

Streak mosaics gradually increased over the years. In 1949 they caused an estimated loss of 7 percent of the wheat crop in Kansas. That amounted to a loss of 30 million dollars. The loss in 1951 also was heavy. It is not uncommon to find entire fields and sometimes entire communities in which streak mosaic has wiped out the wheat crop. The destruction of the chlorophyll in the leaves frequently is so great that the plants are yellow. Growth is halted and the plants fail to set seed.

The viruses do not overseason in the soil. They are easily transmitted by manual inoculation at summer temperatures characteristic of Washington, D. C. Infection is erratic at high summer temperatures, such as those that prevail at Stillwater, Okla. They are not seed-borne. Maybe some insect carries them.

The strains of streak mosaic virus range from those that induce severe yellow spotting, streaking, and mottling (*Marmor virgatum* var. *typicum*), to those that cause mild, light-green or weak-yellow streaking and mottling (*M. virgatum* var. *viride*). With the strains of virus studied thus far, chlorophyll destruction or yellowing is favored by cool temperatures with the daily averages ranging from 60° to 70°. Wheat varieties differ in the degree of yellowing caused by a given strain of virus. Under certain conditions streak mosaics can be confused with the soil-borne virus mosaics.

The thermal death point of these viruses in plant juice is near 129.2°, with an exposure of 10 minutes. The survival time at room temperature in air-dried leaf tissue has not been more than 40 days. The dilution end point in water is near 5,000 times. The virus passed a Berkefeld "W" filter, pore size 3 to 4 microns.

Streak mosaic viruses occur in several wild grasses. They can infect corn, oats, barley, several species of winter annual bromegrasses, sand lovegrass, Canada bluegrass, some of the crabgrasses, and other range and pasture grasses.

In some oats, the virus favors reddening in association with the chlorotic patterns. In Golden Giant sweet corn, streak mosaic viruses induce a rather typical mosaic mottling, rings, dots, dashes, and short streaks, some of which are elliptic and have green centers. The symptoms generally resemble those induced in field corn by the sugarcane mosaic virus. The long, yellow, or bleached stripes associated with so many other viruses in corn are not characteristic of streak mosaic. The plants are never killed, and infection has never been obtained in all inoculated sweet corn plants. Some lines of sugarcane develop local lesions when the leaves of the true seedlings are inoculated with streak mosaic virus. The virus does not become systemic, though. Sorghum and the perennial smooth brome, *Bromus inermis*, are highly resistant or immune. Several of the susceptible forage and wild grass species may contain resistant varieties. Tests have failed to reveal any plant outside of the grass family that is susceptible to the streak mosaic viruses.

Because methods for inducing natural infection have not been worked out, the wheat variety test nurseries have to be inoculated by spraying. Varieties of wheat show some differences in the reaction to streak mosaic, but none has shown a safe degree of resistance to the severe yellow strains of the virus.

High resistance and immunity have been found in rye, several wheatgrasses (species of *Agropyron*), and some of the hybrids between wheat and the *Agropyron* species.

BARLEY STRIPE MOSAIC virus was identified with the barley false stripe disease in 1950, but the disease has been known since about 1910. It used to be thought to be of nonparasitic origin. False stripe was first noted in spring barley growing at the Wisconsin Agricultural Experiment Station at Madison. Pressed specimens of the diseased plants, prepared by A. G. Johnson on June 27, 1913, and still in existence, leave little doubt that the symptoms are the same as those induced by the virus. Perhaps it was the first virus disease on a grass species to be collected in the United States.

The disease occurs throughout the spring barley region in the United States, and it occurs in Canada. It has not been regarded as a menace to the crop. Pot tests out of doors prove, however, that it causes serious reduction in the yield of grain and forage in several varieties of spring barley.

The brown stripes often induced by the virus in some plant species and varieties tend to distinguish it from other viruses associated with grasses. The most common symptoms associated with the virus, however, are the unmistakable mosaic types of chlorotic mottling, spotting, and streaking. The chlorotic areas in the leaves frequently are ashy gray to white because of the complete or nearly complete destruction of the carotinoids, or yellow pigments, as well as the chlorophyll.

The virus is transmitted easily by manual methods of inoculation at summer temperatures at Beltsville. It infects wheat, sweet corn, field corn, smooth crabgrass, and occasional seedlings of smooth brome. It has induced only local lesions in inoculated leaves of rice and tobacco. In Michigan Amber wheat seedlings, the first one or two leaves that develop systemic signs usually become almost solid ivory color or white, denoting a marked, acute phase of the disease. The seedlings are not killed. The new leaves become much less chlorotic in the chronic phase. But when infection is through the seed, only the chronic symptoms appear, beginning with the first leaf of the wheat seedlings. In Golden Giant sweet corn and U. S. 13 field corn, the virus seldom kills the seedlings, but the plants become badly stunted and usually worthless. The long yellow or bleached stripes in the foliage are like those induced by the brome mosaic virus, the cucumber mosaic viruses, and by some leafhopper-transmitted viruses that infect corn. With the small grains, cool temperatures favor strong symptoms in the infected plants.

The thermal death point of the virus in plant juice is near 154.4° F., with 10 minutes exposure. The survival time in air-dried tissue at room temperature has not been more than 40 days. The dilution end point in water is slightly beyond 10,000 times. Traces of the virus have passed the Berkefeld "N" filter, but not the Berkefeld "W" filter.

Outstanding is the ability of the virus to enter some of the seeds of the diseased barley and wheat plants. Very few viruses are seed-borne; this was the first to be discovered in a grass species. Because infected barley seeds tend to be poorly filled, many probably go with the screenings during threshing and thus tend to keep down the occurrence of the disease. Tests have failed to show the virus to overseason in the soil.

WHEAT STRIATE MOSAIC was discovered in winter wheat in South Dakota in 1950 by John T. Slykhuis, who succeeded in transmitting the virus to healthy wheat plants and reproducing the disease by means of the leafhopper *Endria inimica*. Attempts to transmit the virus by manual methods of inoculation have failed. The disease occurs also in Kansas and Nebraska. The extent of the losses caused by striate mosaic is not known.

In Minter and Rushmore varieties, the disease shows up in fine, light-green or yellow lines in a streaked pattern. In the early stages, the lines are in the tissues directly over the veins. In Minter, brown necrotic spots may develop later. In Rushmore and other varieties, the streaks are followed by premature yellowing and death of the leaves. The diseased plants frequently are so stunted they produce little or no seed. In the advanced stages, striate mosaic is readily confused with other yellow mosaics of wheat. The host range of the virus is not known.

BARLEY YELLOW DWARF, another new virus disease of cereals, was widespread and destructive in California in 1951. John W. Oswald and Byron R. Houston found the virus to be transmitted by five widely distributed species of aphids, the corn aphid (*Rhopalosiphum maidis*), the apple grain aphid (*R. prunifoliae*), the English grain aphid (*Macrosiphum granarium*), the grass aphid (*M. dirhodum*), and the greenbug (*Toxoptera graminum*). Attempts to transmit this virus by manual methods of inoculation have failed.

Wheat and oats have been infected experimentally.

The chlorotic symptoms induced by the virus are similar to those caused by nonparasitic factors—an excess of soil water, drought, a shortage of nitrogen, and low-temperature injury to the chlorophyll system. The light-green or yellow mottling, the broken streaking, and the spotting that characterize the other virus diseases of the small grains are relatively temporary or absent in yellow dwarf. Leaves of infected plants rapidly turn light green and yellow, beginning at the tips. The chlorotic foliage tends to redden in oats, as when some of the nonparasitic factors are operating. Diagnosis therefore is difficult, except in fields where the nonparasitic factors and other diseases can be excluded from consideration. The most certain diagnosis is through transmission tests with one or more of the aphid vectors.

Plants become infected at all stages. Young plants are frequently killed. Stunting gradually decreases with advancing age of the plant. Only the flag leaf shows signs of yellowing or reddening when infection takes place in the late stages of development. As with other virus diseases, the yield of grain shows the greatest reduction when the plants are infected in their early growth.

The wheat variety Kanred has shown some tolerance to yellow dwarf, but inoculated plants were stunted.

AGROPYRON OR QUACKGRASS MOSAIC viruses were collected at Arlington Farm, Va. The green mosaic virus (*Marmor agropyri* var. *typicum*), was collected in 1934, and the yellow mosaic virus (*M. agropyri* var. *flavum*), was collected in 1936 in the same area from which the green mosaic virus was collected. Mosaic was found in 1950 in quackgrass in South Dakota by John Slykhuis and in Iowa by Vernon E. Wilson. In 1951 mosaic quackgrass was found on the Plant Industry Station grounds at Beltsville. At Arlington Farm, the green mosaic virus was isolated once from wheat growing near the patch of mosaic quackgrass.

The viruses collected at Arlington Farm transmit to quackgrass and to wheat by manual inoculation, but with some difficulty. Infection and symptoms are favored by temperatures ranging from 60° to 65°, but infection will take place at summer temperatures. At the higher temperatures, however, the green mosaic frequently becomes masked and the yellow mosaic becomes very mild. The viruses overseason in the rhizomes. Tests with soil in which the mosaic plants were growing in the field failed to indicate overseasoning in the soil.

All attempts to infect *Agropyron repens* with the soil-borne wheat mosaic viruses have failed.

CORN STUNT was found in 1945 in the San Joaquin Valley, Calif., by N. W. Frazier, and in the lower Rio Grande Valley, Tex., by George E. Alstatt. The studies of L. O. Kunkel showed that corn stunt virus is transmitted by the leafhopper *Dalbulus* (*Baldulus*) *maidus*. The virus infects many varieties of field corn, sweet corn, and teosinte, a close relative of corn. Attempts to infect the small grains, other grasses, and nongrass species have been unsuccessful. The virus cannot be transmitted from diseased to healthy plants by manual methods of inoculation, but Karl Maramorosch, of the Rockefeller Institute for Medical Research, succeeded in transmitting the virus to leafhoppers by manual means. The disease was reported from the Mesa Central, Mexico, by J. S. Niederhauser and J. Cervantes in 1950. They found another leafhopper, *Dalbulus* (*Baldulus*) *elimatus*, that transmits the virus.

In the early stages of corn stunt, the chlorotic spotting, streaking, and banding in the leaves resemble the markings associated with some of the mosaics. As the disease progresses, the signs resemble those associated with the corn streak disease. In the advanced stages the leaves may be completely yellow or bleached; the leaves and stalks also may show a tinge of red. Chlorotic markings appear in the sheaths and husks. The upper part of the stem may become chlorotic. The tassels may be deformed. Infected plants tend to have short internodes and extra shoots that originate from the axillary buds and from the ear branches, so that the plant is stunted and bushy. Husks tend to have unusually long tips. The ears produce few kernels. The roots and the brace roots sometimes branch profusely and are stunted.

The disease tends to be more extensive in late corn than in early corn, probably because the insect carriers are more abundant late in the season. The virus is not carried in the seed from diseased plants.

SUGARCANE MOSAIC is the first virus disease of grasses to be identified as such. The virus, *Marmor sacchari*, was introduced from the Tropics. Soon after its discovery, E. W. Brandes found out that the virus is transmitted by the corn aphid, and that the virus infects corn, sorghum, pearlmillet, and many other grasses in the Southern States where cane is grown. The virus apparently does not infect any of the small grains.

Several strains of the virus can be differentiated on sugarcane. At least four species of aphids transmit the virus.

In studies by Hugo Stoneberg, this mosaic had no apparent effect on the rate of growth or the total height of the corn plants, and tended to increase suckering and the number of ears slightly. Yields were reduced less than 10 percent, and the quality of the corn was reduced slightly by the disease.

THE SOUTHERN CELERY MOSAIC virus, a strain of cucumber mosaic virus (*Marmor cucumeris*), infects corn in several parts of Florida. Natural infection is by the melon aphid, *Aphis gossypii*. Infections have been induced in teosinte, field corn, sweet corn, kafir, sorgo, milo, wheat, and rye by means of the aphid in studies conducted by F. L. Wellman.

In my tests with this virus and related cucumber mosaic viruses, I was unable to infect wheat from manual inoculations, although infection could thus be induced in Golden Giant sweet corn. In it the yellow stripes in the leaves are like those induced in corn by the mosaic (stripe) virus occurring in Cuba, Trinidad, and Hawaii; by the barley stripe mosaic virus; and by the brome mosaic virus when the corn plants are inoculated after the seedling stage to avoid early death.

The cucumber mosaic viruses frequently kill sweet corn seedlings and young plants in greenhouse tests. Diseased plants that survive early infection are worthless for crop production.

THE BROME MOSAIC virus (*Marmor graminis*) has been collected in nature only on smooth brome (*Bromus inermis*) from three locations near Manhattan, Kans., and Lincoln, Nebr. No insect vector for it is known. The virus induces local or systemic signs in a wide range of grass species, including wheat, barley, oats, rye, corn, sorghum, and many wild grasses. Local lesions develop on the inoculated leaves of some breeding lines of sugarcane in the young seedling stage. It is one of the few viruses that can infect certain nongrass species, besides grass. Its range among the nongrass plants seems to be more limited than Pierce's disease virus of grape, southern celery mosaic virus, and certain other strains of the cucumber mosaic group, which also infect a few grass species.

Brome mosaic virus induces local lesions in the wiped leaves of Samsun Turkish tobacco, Early White Spine cucumber, Scotia beans, some varieties of sugar beet, garden beets, Swiss chard, and lambsquarters (*Chenopodium album*). In lambsquarters all inoculated plants give local lesions, and some of the plants in a population develop systemic chlorotic spotting.

In the small grains, the symptoms it induces can be confused with those of the wheat yellow streak mosaic virus. The virus kills young seedlings of Golden Giant sweet corn, although the seedlings gain resistance as they grow. When older plants become infected, their growing points are usually killed, and the foliage develops yellow stripes or streaks resembling those induced by the barley stripe mosaic virus, the cucumber mosaic viruses, and several of the leafhopper-transmitted viruses that infect corn.

Brome mosaic virus spreads easily at summer temperatures by manual methods of inoculation. Accidental infections from this virus must be guarded against more than with any other grass virus we know. There has been no evidence of transmission of this virus through the seeds from infected plants.

To determine the spread of brome mosaic in the field, close plantings in small plats of alternated healthy and mosaic smooth brome and orchardgrass plants were observed by C. L. Lefebvre and me. We started the test in the spring of 1946 and continued it through the 1947 crop season. During the period of the test, the plants were often walked on to simulate conditions in a pasture. At the end of the test, 12 out of the original 23 healthy bromegrass plants and 6 out of the original 27 healthy orchardgrass plants had become infected. The disease reduced the forage yield about 90 percent in the smooth brome and about 80 percent in the orchardgrass.

Of the viruses that have host ranges chiefly among the grasses, the brome mosaic virus has the highest thermal death point (172.4° to 174.2° F., for 10 minutes), the longest survival time in air-dried tissue at room temperatures (more than 20 months), and the highest dilution characteristic (100,000 to 300,000 times in water). The virus passed a Schott-Jena fritted glass filter having an average pore size of 780 millimicrons.

THE VIRUS OF PIERCE'S DISEASE of grape and of alfalfa dwarf (*Morsus suffodiens*), infects an exceedingly wide range of plant types, including grasses and a sedge. Eight species of grass are known to become infected in nature in California. One is wild oats. Fifteen species of grass have been tested experimentally, and 12, including barley, became infected with the virus. Other small grains were not tested.

An outstanding characteristic is the inability of the virus to induce apparent signs of disease in most of the plants it infects. None of the infected grasses has expressed symptoms, yet these hosts carry large amounts of the virus, and they are favored by the leafhoppers that transmit the virus. The association of the virus with the xylem tissue may account for the suppression of symptoms in most plant species. The fact that symptoms occur in grape and in certain legume species, however, suggests the possiblity that symptoms might be incited in other plants by providing suitable environmental conditions.

SEVERAL VIRUS DISEASES of cereals have not been found in the United

States. All of the known viruses infecting cereal species outside of continental United States and Canada, except the soil-borne wheat mosaic viruses in Japan, are transmitted by insects belonging to some one of the so-called hopper groups of the order Homoptera. None is transmitted by manual methods of inoculation.

CORN STREAK VIRUS and wheat stunt virus (*Fractilinea maidis*), cause serious diseases in corn and wheat in parts of Africa. The best control of corn streak obtains when there is a break in the succession of crops, as corn seems to be the best carry-over reservoir of the virus. Three species of leafhopper, *Cicadulina mbila*, *C. zeae*, and *C. nicholsi*, transmit the virus. The first symptoms in corn consist of small, almost circular, colorless spots. As the disease progresses, the new leaves develop narrow broken streaks, which are yellow and sometimes translucent. The "A-form" of the virus species causes the wheat stunt disease in South Africa. The disease is destructive in early sown spring varieties because the warm conditions favor the leafhopper vector, *C. mbila*. Resistant and immune wheats are known. The chlorotic spotting and streaking in the leaves suggests some of the yellow mosaics of wheat. The infected leaves tend to be curled. The bunchy, stunted plants resemble plants that have the wheat mosaic-rosette disease.

CORN MOSAIC of Hawaii and the corn stripe disease of Cuba are caused by the same virus, *Fractilinea zeae*. The virus has been reported also from Trinidad, Tanganyika, and Mauritius. It may occur in Puerto Rico. It has been found in sorghum. Transmission of the virus is by means of the leafhopper *Peregrinus maidis*. In corn, the chlorotic markings on the foliage resemble those associated with corn streak, as well as those associated with some of the mosaic viruses that can be transmitted by manual methods of inoculation.

CORN WALLABY-EAR VIRUS (*Galla zeae*), occurs in Queensland, Australia. It is transmitted by the leafhopper *Cicadula bimaculata*. In young corn plants the virus induces elongated swellings, or galls, on the secondary veins on the under side of the leaves. The leaves tend to roll inward, as under conditions of drought, and their green color is intensified. The plants are dwarfed. When older plants become infected, the reactions tend to be mild.

RUSSIAN WINTER WHEAT mosaic virus (*Fractilinea tritici*) is limited to Russia, as far as we know. It is transmitted by the leafhopper *Deltocephalus striatus*. The virus infects winter and spring wheats, rye, barley, and oats. It induces light-green or yellow mottling and streaking in the leaves. Infected plants may be dwarfed. Some varieties of winter wheat proliferate, causing rosette. Infected young plants are sometimes killed. The virus is not soil-borne.

PUPATION DISEASE VIRUS of oats (*Fractilinea avenae*) is also known as zakooklivanie and Siberian oat mosaic virus. It apparently occurs only in Siberia. The virus is transmitted by the leafhopper *Delphacodes* (*Delfax*) *striatella*. It infects oats, wheat, rye, barley, rice, corn, and several wild grasses. The symptoms in oats resemble those described for wheat mosaic caused by the virus *Fractilinea tritici*. The virus of rice stripe disease in Japan is also transmitted by *Delphacodes striatella*, suggesting that the virus *F. avenae* may be the causal agent of this rice disease.

RICE DWARF VIRUS (*Fractilinea oryzae*) occurs in Japan and the Philippines. The disease is also called rice stunt. The virus infects rice, wheat, rye, oats, and several wild grasses. It does not infect barley, corn, or sorghum. Infected rice plants are dwarfed. The young leaves have light-green or yellow spots along the veins. With the succession of new leaves, the markings

consist of chlorotic spots and streaks.
The virus is transmitted by at least two
species of leafhoppers, *Nephotettix
apicalis* (*bipunctatus*) var. *cincticeps* and
Deltocephalus dorsalis. Experiments with
N. apicalis have shown that the virus
passes through part of the eggs to the
next generation, for as many as seven
generations.

H. H. McKinney *holds degrees from
Michigan State College and the University
of Wisconsin. In 1919 he joined the staff of
the division of cereal crops and diseases of
the Bureau of Plant Industry, Soils, and
Agricultural Engineering, where he has
devoted most of his time in research on
viruses and virus diseases.*

For further reading:
H. H. McKinney: Evidence of Virus Mutation in the Common Mosaic of Tobacco,
*Journal of Agricultural Research, volume 51,
pages 951–981, 1935;* Mosaic Diseases of Wheat
and Related Cereals, *U. S. D. A. Circular 442,
1937;* Mosaic of Bromus inermis, *with H.
Fellows and C. O. Johnston, Phytopathology,
volume 32, page 331, 1942;* Genera of the Plant
Viruses, *Journal of the Washington Academy of
Sciences, volume 34, pages 139–154, 1944;* De-
scriptions and Revision of Several Species of
Viruses in the Genera Marmor, Fractilinea,
and Galla, *Journal of the Washington Academy
of Sciences, volume 34, pages 322–329, 1944;* Soil
Factors in Relation to Incidence and Symp-
tom Expression of Virus Diseases, *Soil Science,
volume 61, pages 93–100, 1946;* Mosaics of
Winter Oats Induced by Soil-borne Viruses,
Phytopathology, volume 36, pages 359–369, 1946;
Stability of Labile Viruses in Desiccated
Tissue, *Phytopathology, volume 37, pages 139–
142, 1947;* Wheats Immune From Soil-borne
Mosaic Viruses in the Field, Susceptible
When Inoculated Manually, *Phytopathology,
volume 38, pages 1003–1013, 1948;* Tests of
Varieties of Wheat, Barley, Oats, and Corn
for Reaction to Wheat Streak-Mosaic Viruses,
*Plant Disease Reporter, volume 33, pages 359–369,
1949;* Mosaics of Winter Oats and Their
Control in the Southeastern States, *with T. R.
Stanton, J. L. Seal, T. H. Rogers, W. R. Paden,
G. K. Middleton, and U. R. Gore, U. S. D. A.
Circular 809, 1949;* A Seed-borne Virus Caus-
ing False-Stripe Symptoms in Barley, *Plant
Disease Reporter, volume 35, page 48, 1951;* A
Method for Inoculating Varietal Test Nur-
series With the Wheat Streak-Mosaic Virus,
*with H. Fellows, Plant Disease Reporter, volume
35, pages 264–266, 1951;* Wild and Forage
Grasses Found To Be Susceptible to the Wheat
Streak-Mosaic Virus, *with H. Fellows, Plant
Disease Reporter, volume 35, pages 441–442, 1951.*

The Smuts of Wheat, Oats, Barley

C. S. Holton, V. F. Tapke

Many millions of dollars' worth of
grain are destroyed every year by
the smuts of wheat, oats, and barley.

For purposes of study and control,
we can consider the smuts as being
seedling-infecting or floral-infecting.

The seedling-infecting species come
in contact with the host plants as
follows: The microscopic spores from
smutted plants are carried by wind,
rain, insects, and other agencies to
the heads of healthy plants (as in
loose smut of oats). Or, smutted
heads are crushed in threshing and
spores are distributed to the clean
seed or blown to fields, where later
they come in contact with the host
at seeding time (as in the stinking
smuts of wheat). As the seed germinates and the seedling grows through
the soil to the surface of the ground,
the smut inoculum develops thin
threads, which penetrate the seedling
and initiate infection. The fungus
then grows internally in the plant
and eventually forms spores in the
young heads. That completes the
cycle and sets the stage for a new crop
of smut.

STINKING SMUT, or bunt, apparently
has been a plague of wheat since wheat
was first cultivated. It was prominent
among the diseases studied by the
earliest plant scientists. It has been
widely investigated, and certain control measures have long been known.
Nevertheless bunt is still an economic

threat to the production of wheat, especially winter wheat, in all important wheat regions of the world.

The average annual loss in the United States is estimated to be 1.3 percent of the crop, or about 25 million dollars. Its severity fluctuates from year to year and from region to region. The heaviest losses occur in the winter wheat regions of the Midwest and Pacific Northwest. Estimated annual losses in Kansas over 30 years range from less than 200,000 dollars to almost 20 million dollars; the average is almost 3 million dollars. In recent years the Pacific Northwest has suffered the most. The loss there was about 10 million dollars in 1950.

The main loss comes from the reduction in yield. The percentage of reduction in yield roughly equals the percentage of smutted heads in the field. Losses in quality result when market grain is discounted in price because of the dark color and the offensive odor of the smut spores that adhere to the kernels. Smut that is removed from the grain by cleaning and washing is assessed as dockage against smutty grain. Stinking smut increases the cost of processing. It also is a fire hazard to threshing equipment and storage bins.

Two KINDS OF BUNT occur on wheat. The common bunt is caused by *Tilletia caries* and *T. foetida*. Dwarf bunt is caused by *T. caries*.

Common bunt is more prevalent and better known than dwarf bunt.

Dwarf bunt stunts infected plants severely. It has been recognized as a distinct type only since 1925. Its prevalence and severity have increased steadily. Its principal region of distribution is the Pacific Northwest, but it also occurs in Wyoming, Colorado, and New York.

Wheat plants infected with bunt are recognized first by their reduced height. Common bunt shortens the plants a few inches or as much as half the height of healthy plants, depending on the physiologic race

of the bunt fungus, the host variety, and the conditions of growth. Plants with dwarf bunt are one-half to one-fourth the height of healthy plants. Because of intergrading types, identification solely on the basis of stunting is sometimes difficult.

The smutted wheat heads are bluish green when they emerge from the boot. The healthy heads are yellowish green. Smutted wheat heads tend to be long and lax and to ripen sooner than healthy ones. The smut balls protrude beyond the glumes as they enlarge. Dwarf bunt infected heads usually are more compact than those infected with common bunt, and the glumes are spread apart so that the smutted heads have a feathery look.

The smut balls vary considerably. The size depends on host variety, location in the spikelet, physiologic race, and climate. Common bunt balls are elongate or round. Dwarf bunt balls are always round. Common bunt balls are more fragile and absorb water less readily than those of dwarf bunt.

Dwarf bunt stimulates excessive tillering of infected plants. The effect is more pronounced in the Turkey variety than in others. Forty tillers on dwarf bunt infected plants are not uncommon.

Bunt-infected flowers have longer pistils and longer and broader ovaries than do healthy flowers. Diseased ovaries are green; healthy ones are white. Stamens in diseased flowers are reduced in length and breadth, and the anthers have a pale-yellow color instead of a pronounced green, as in healthy ones. The stamens in diseased heads fail to extrude at flowering time.

Bunted plants are more susceptible to seedling blights and to yellow stripe rust but more resistant to powdery mildew than are healthy plants. Winter injury is more pronounced in bunted plants. Increased sensitivity of infected plants to gravity has been reported.

The spores of *Tilletia caries* are uniformly globose and have "netted" spore walls. Spores of *T. foetida* are globose, elongate, or oval and have smooth walls. The bunt balls of *T. foetida* are larger and more elongate than those of *T. caries* on the same variety of wheat. In both, the ball shape tends to conform to the shape of the wheat kernel.

The spore balls are broken in threshing. The grain becomes contaminated with spores. If it is used for seed, the spores germinate and penetrate the young seedling in the course of its subterranean emergence from the seed to the surface of the soil and infection is established in the growing point. The growth of the parasite keeps pace with plant development; at maturity, bunt balls are formed in place of wheat kernels.

Wheat seedlings also may become infected by soil-borne spores. In less humid regions like the Pacific Northwest, airborne spores from the combine harvester settle on summer fallow land and remain dormant until moisture and temperature are favorable for germination in the fall. Usually that occurs at the time winter wheat is seeded, so that smut spores and wheat seeds germinate at the same time, thus exposing the seedlings to infection. Spores of common bunt perish in the soil in less than a year. Those of dwarf bunt may remain viable for 7 years. Even so, dwarf bunt does not attack spring wheat.

The greatest infection occurs at soil temperatures of 40° to 60° F., with moisture content ranging from 15 to 60 percent of field carrying capacity. Other factors affecting the development of bunt are soil fertility, depth of seeding, and length of day. The spore load is important. About 0.5 gram of spores to 100 grams of seed are necessary for maximum infection. The greater the concentration of spore load around the embryo, the higher the degree of infection.

Both species of the bunt fungus are highly specialized into distinct physiologic races. The races differ in their ability to attack different varieties, also in the size and shape of their smut balls and rate and mode of spore germination. In the dwarf bunt race infection comes primarily from soil-borne inoculum.

Pathogenic specialization in the bunt fungi was discovered in 1925 or so. Different races have been identified from various parts of the world. In the United States about 25 races are recognized by their reaction to a set of eight differential wheat varieties.

New or previously unrecognized races frequently appear, especially in places where varieties resistant to the recognized races have been introduced. The new races attack and spread with the new varieties. Every smut-resistant variety introduced in the Pacific Northwest eventually has become the distributor of one or more new races of bunt.

The two species as well as different races of the bunt fungus have been intercrossed artificially and new pathogenic lines were selected from the hybrid populations. The frequent occurrence of intermediate spore forms in field collections indicates that natural hybridization also occurs. Invariably the intermediate forms are found on highly susceptible varieties. These varieties, however, tend to perpetuate the old, established races, despite their susceptibility to the new races.

EFFECTIVE CONTROL OF BUNT depends on the use of clean seed of a smut-resistant variety properly treated with an appropriate fungicide. Also effective, when it is practical, is the seeding of wheat when soil temperatures are unfavorable to bunt development.

Those control measures seem so simple that they give no hint of the long and costly struggle of plant scientists to develop them. And the struggle continues today in an effort to keep pace with the ever-changing problem, brought on by shifts in wheat varieties and by the adaptive nature of the smut fungi.

The accidental discovery of seed treatment as a means of controlling wheat smut was made long before the parasitic nature of the disease was known.

Some wheat seed salvaged from a grounded sailing ship off the southern coast of England was sown by nearby farmers. The crop they got had less smut than that from local seed. That may have been the origin of the 100-year-old practice of brining the wheat seed.

A scientific approach to the problem of smut control by seed treatment began about 1800 with the discovery of spore germination and the harmful effect of copper sulfate on their germination. Fifty years later the parasitic nature of wheat smut was established, and the quest for more effective control by seed treatment was begun.

Scientists recognized at the outset that a good chemical for treating seed should be highly toxic to the smut spores but harmless to the seed. Copper sulfate did not always give good control and often injured the seed. Seed had to be soaked in the solution and dried afterwards. It left much to be desired as a suitable fungicide for seed treatment. It took almost 50 years of search to find a better treatment, but progress was faster thereafter.

The discovery of the value of formaldehyde about 1895 was hailed as the answer to smut control by seed treatment. After its adoption in the United States, formaldehyde rapidly replaced copper sulfate because of its several advantages. Even so, it still had the disadvantage of being a wet treatment and was likely to injure the seed unless used properly. The impelling need for a dry treatment led to the discovery of the value of copper carbonate dust in Australia. Copper carbonate was first tested in the United States about 1918. It gradually displaced formaldehyde for the control of wheat smut but was ineffective against oat and barley smuts, for which formaldehyde continued to be used.

We had organic mercury materials for treating seed before we had copper carbonate, but the organic mercury dust treatments for cereal smut control were not developed until several years later. They had some advantages over copper carbonate, which they gradually replaced after 1930.

Paradoxically, the elimination of the wet feature of the formaldehyde and copper sulfate introduced the dust hazard of the dry treatments. Many workers were made ill when they inhaled the dusts.

Efforts to eliminate this undesirable feature brought the development of the slurry treatment, by which the fungicide is applied in a concentrated water suspension or slurry in such small amounts that the seed is not wetted appreciably. It avoids the main disadvantages of both wet and dry treatments. It became the predominant method of treating seed wheat in the Pacific Northwest within 5 years.

The value of resistant varieties in the fight against wheat smut is illustrated by experience in the Pacific Northwest, where soil contamination occurs and where seed treatment is practiced universally. Between 1931 and 1942, when resistant varieties predominated, the incidence of wheat smut declined from more than 30 percent to less than 3 percent. In the succeeding years up to 1951, when susceptible varieties predominated, the incidence of smut again increased to 30 percent.

That different varieties of wheat reacted differently to smut was observed almost 200 years ago. Only 50 years ago did plant breeders begin to breed smut-resistant varieties systematically. At first they thought that complete control of bunt could be realized through the use of resistant varieties. They emphasized the development of varieties with smut resistance. The first of the new varieties carried the recommendation that they could be grown without seed treatment. Invariably, however, they became susceptible to new races of smut. Breeding for smut resistance consequently is recognized as a perpetual contest between the directed processes of man to produce resistant varieties of wheat and the processes of nature to develop new races of bunt.

The breeding of smut-resistant varieties has been facilitated by the systematic identification of different genetic factors for resistance. At least two major and numerous minor factors are recognized. Probably others exist. Thus far, however, the two major factors (Martin MM and Turkey TT) control the entire gamut of physiologic races now recognized, but this simple situation may not always remain. Consequently it is advisable to develop additional varieties with maximum resistance to smut while continuing to search for new sources of resistances.

The best temperature for bunt infection is 37° to 57° F. Seeding early (before the soil temperature drops that low) or late (after it has fallen below that point) tends to reduce the amount of smut. Both early and very late seeding, however, hurt the wheat crop. A reasonable delay in seeding should aid in control where soil contamination prevails, as in the Pacific Northwest.

Seeding practices have never been widely adopted as a means of smut control—they have obvious limitations, particularly that sowing must be done when the soil is moist enough to germinate the wheat.

FLAG SMUT occurs on wheat in most of the world's major wheat countries but has caused heavy losses only in Australia. Its presence in the United States was established first in 1919 in Illinois. It was found in Missouri and Kansas shortly thereafter. The source of infection was never discovered, but imports of wheat for feed from Australia were suspected.

Considerable apprehension followed the discovery of flag smut in the United States. Quarantines were established to prevent further importation of wheat from Australia and to prevent the spread of the smut outside the known infested area. Those measures—or natural factors—may have operated against the spread of the disease; flag smut was not found outside the original area of infestation until 1941, when i was reported in central Washington Up to 1953 it had not become widely prevalent or intensively severe in any locality, but its persistence in the major wheat areas posed a constan threat.

Infected plants usually are dwarfec and have twisted leaf blades anc sheaths marked with grayish-black stripes. The stems also may be invaded Infected plants rarely produce heads but smutted heads occasionally appear At maturity the diseased tissues dry uf and become shredded. The stripe: rupture and expose the black spore masses. Symptoms may appear on in fected plants at any time from the fourth leaf stage, or 1 month after germination, up to the heading stage One or all culms of a plant may be in fected. The oldest culms of partly smutted plants are smut-free. Partia smutting is more common in the green house than in the field and in some varieties more than in others. Infectec plants may die and dry prematurely thus obscuring much of the loss from the disease.

Flag smut of wheat is caused by the fungus *Urocystis tritici*. Its spores occur singly or in balls, which usually are covered by a layer of sterile cells and contain three spores. Individual spores are smooth, oval to spherical, dark brown, and 12 to 16 microns by 9 to 12 microns in size. Germinated spores have a short promycelium on which 2 to 6 sporidia are borne. The sporidia remain attached to the promycelium. fuse, and give rise to infecting mycelium.

Infection occurs in the seedling stage from spores carried on the seed or in the soil. Systemic development inside the plant follows. The cycle is complete with the production of spore masses in the diseased tissues.

The number of races of *U. tritici* is relatively small. Five races have been identified in China. Only two races are known in the United States. One occurs in the Midwest. The other, more widely virulent, is in the Pacific Northwest.

Germination of spores and infection take place in a wide range of temperature and humidity. Spores germinate best at temperatures of 40° to 80° F. Soil temperatures of 57° to 70° are favorable for infection. The highest infection occurs at 66° to 70°. Optimum moisture content apparently shifts with prevailing temperatures. With soil moisture at 40 percent, best infection occurs at 50° to 59°. At 60 percent soil-moisture infection is best at 50°. At temperatures above 59°, best infection occurs when soil moisture is below 40 percent. Spore viability is best retained at relative humidities of 50 to 75 percent.

Seed treatment with a suitable fungicide destroys spores carried on the seed. The use of resistant varieties prevents infection by soil-borne spores. Because the spores of flag smut may remain viable in the soil more than one season, crop rotation helps control the smut.

SMUTS ON OATS seem to be among the first cereal diseases to come under the scrutiny of early writers on plant diseases. Their prevalence and economic importance are world-wide. They destroy 40 to 50 million bushels of oats in the United States each year. Total losses aggregating more than 27 million bushels were reported in 1945 from Iowa, Minnesota, Illinois, and Wisconsin, the leaders in the production of oats. The heaviest infections occur in the South Atlantic region, where losses up to 35 percent have been reported in some States. The least damage occurs in the West.

The two kinds of smuts on oats destroy the panicles by producing masses of spores in place of oat kernels.

Loose smut, caused by *Ustilago avenae*, destroys the enveloping glumes as well. The spores, borne in a loose mass, are quickly disseminated by wind currents, leaving behind a denuded panicle skeleton.

Covered smut, caused by *U. kolleri*, produces spores in balls enclosed by the glumes. The branches are shortened, so that the panicle has a compact appearance. Covered smut panicles ripen prematurely, but the spore balls remain intact until broken up in harvesting. A buff-colored type of covered smut was collected from experimental material, but it has not been observed in commercial fields of oats.

Scientists in experiments have demonstrated hybridization between species and races of the smuts and the segregation and recombination of pathogenic and other characters to produce intergrading types. The occurrence of intergrading types in the field is evidence that hybridization occurs in nature. New types of smut are produced in that way.

Both oat smuts infect the seedlings, develop systemically in the host, and finally destroy the oat kernel.

Spores of loose smut are disseminated by wind immediately after the diseased panicle emerges from the leaf sheath. Infection thus is spread to flowers of healthy panicles in the same field or other fields. The spores germinate in the flowers and produce mycelium, which establishes itself between the developing kernel and the glumes or chaff. The mycelium becomes dormant as the kernel matures. The smut mycelium becomes active again when the oats germinate and the seedling is infected.

The covered smut, on the other hand, emerges from the host with the spores enclosed in the glumes. The spore balls remain intact until broken in harvesting and threshing. The spores are then distributed over the surface of the threshed seed. They remain dormant until the seed germinates, when they also germinate and infect the seedling.

The dissemination of the loose smut spores by wind makes it ten times more prevalent than covered smut, which spreads only by contact with infested seed.

Covered smut is rare in the South Atlantic region. Loose smut occurs least often in the western region.

The degree of infection by the smuts is determined chiefly by soil temperature and moisture when the seedlings emerge. Infection may occur at temperatures between 41° and 86° F., but usually it is highest between 59° and 68°. Infection may occur when soils have a moisture content between 5 percent and 60 percent, but chiefly at about 35 to 40 percent. Soil reaction near the neutral point or slightly acid seems to favor infection. Response to environmental factors is highly variable, possibly because the smuts have such a high degree of specialization.

About 25 races of the oat smut fungus species are recognized in the United States by the reaction of 10 host testers of the species *Avena sativa* and *A. byzantina*. All the major commercial varieties grown in 1953 were susceptible to one or more races of smut. The Victoria oat was highly smut-resistant for at least 15 years and was used as a source of smut resistance in breeding new varieties. Races of smut that attack varieties derived from Victoria are widely prevalent throughout the southern half of the United States. That experience with the formerly smut-resistant Victoria oat emphasizes the perpetual nature of the problem.

Smuts on oats can be controlled by growing resistant varieties and by seed treatment—positive measures that should eliminate most of the loss if they are applied diligently everywhere. But seed treatment is not universal, and smut continues to reduce the crop. New smut races that attack formerly resistant varieties appear at times.

THE COVERED SMUT OF BARLEY is found the world over. In the United States it destroys half a million to 4 million bushels annually.

The disease first becomes noticeable at heading time, when smutted heads emerge from the boot. The hard, black masses of smut along the axis of the affected heads are covered with a grayish membrane. Each smutted head contains millions of microscopic spores.

The membranes begin to split a few days after the smutted heads emerge. The spores scatter and inoculate developing seed in healthy heads. The spores may spread until the grain is threshed. Some that reach the seed lie dormant on the surface of the grain. Others are carried under the hulls or send infection hyphae beneath the hulls before or after threshing. The spores and mycelium beneath the hulls produce most of the infection.

In experimental cultures a good infection is obtained by inoculating the seed with a suspension of spores. The seed is washed and dried to loosen the hulls around the kernel, the suspension is mixed with the grain, and the moist inoculated seed is stored for 16 to 20 hours to promote spore germination and the spread of mycelium under the hull.

Higher infection has been obtained in plants kept under mild temperatures for 2 to 4 weeks after the seedlings emerged than when the plants were grown continuously under cool conditions like those of fall and winter. During the initial infection, between seed germination and the emergence of the seedling, the highest percentages of smutted plants are obtained at soil temperatures of 50° to 70° F.

The amounts of smut tend to be higher in plants grown in acid soil than in neutral or alkaline soil. Soil type, soil compaction, depth of seeding, and the rate of seedling growth also may affect development of smut.

Thirteen physiologic races of the barley covered smut fungus have been isolated by their reactions on eight varieties of spring barley. One prevails in the winter barley region, another in the Mississippi Valley, and a third race along the Pacific coast. Several varieties have shown high resistance to covered smut. Two varieties, Ogalitsu and Jet, are resistant to 13 races of covered smut, 9 races of nigra loose smut, and 6 races of nuda loose smut. Covered smut may be controlled by treating the seed with formaldehyde or organic mercury dusts.

NIGRA LOOSE SMUT of barley, *Ustilago nigra*, was first discovered in 1932 by V. F. Tapke, who separated it from ordinary loose smut. The two loose smuts, which often were mixed together in a field, previously had been regarded as a single type that infected barley only through the flowers. The two loose smuts look alike, but the nigra pathogen is a seedling-infecting smut and is controlled by treating the seed with surface disinfectants. When the two loose smuts occur together only partial control can be obtained by surface disinfection because the deep-borne loose smut is not affected by such treatment. The fungi causing barley covered smut and nigra loose smut have been hybridized artificially. Nigra loose smut causes an average annual loss of 1 million bushels of barley in the United States.

The disease usually first becomes noticeable at heading time, when dusty, smutted heads appear. Each contains millions of loosely held, dark-brown microscopic spores. Wind carries the spores. Spores that come in contact with the flowers and young developing seeds of healthy heads then behave like the spores of covered smut. They may lie dormant or germinate and form a subhull mycelium. Moisture, temperature, and other conditions affect germination of spores.

Temperatures of 60° to 70° and a relatively dry soil are most favorable to infection of the seedling during the period of emergence.

Immediately after the seedlings have emerged, temperatures of 60° to 70° for 10 to 30 days give higher percentages of smut than do constant low temperatures.

Nine distinct pathogenic strains or physiologic races of the nigra loose smut fungus from this country have been isolated by their reaction on eight varieties of spring barley. Four are rather widespread in the United States. At least four races that do not occur in the United States have been found in smutted barley from various parts of Israel.

At least four varieties of barley are highly resistant to all races of the pathogen thus far found in the United States. None is grown commercially, but all are useful in breeding productive resistant varieties.

ONLY TWO of the small grain smuts are floral-infecting. The smutted heads appear at heading time. They shed their spores during the bloom period of the normal heads. The loosely held spores are distributed by wind, rain, insects, or other agents. Initial infection rarely occurs after the fertilized ovary has attained one-third of its mature size. Spores that come in contact with healthy flowers germinate by forming infection threads, which grow down the pistil or through the ovary wall into the young, developing seeds. A deep infection of the seed follows, so that surface seed disinfectants do little good. The fungi also are unable to produce infection when spores are applied to the surface of ripe seed.

The two floral-infecting loose smuts, one of wheat and one of barley, are practically identical except that one attacks wheat but not barley and the other attacks barley but not wheat. Both are widely distributed in humid and subhumid areas but are less common in dry areas. Infection threads develop too slowly in dry air to penetrate the ovary during its brief period of susceptibility.

Wheat loose smut caused annual losses ranging from 3 million to 18 million bushels in the United States from 1917 to 1939. Loose smut in barley caused annual losses of 750,000 to 4.5 million bushels in those years.

High humidity favors infection by loose smut in wheat and barley, but the ranges of temperature and humidity most favorable to infection have not been determined exactly. Certain wheats that rarely develop loose smut when grown under the dry conditions of western United States are extremely susceptible when grown in humid climates.

The experiments in the Netherlands

368 YEARBOOK OF AGRICULTURE 1953

show that wheat loose smut spores may
be disseminated and cause infection up
to at least 100 yards from their point
of origin. Infection diminished regularly with distance from the source of
inoculum where high winds prevailed
during the flowering season; it was
spotty when air currents were irregular.

A warm soil when seedlings emerge
seems more conducive to smut than
does a cold soil. In Japan, for example,
early seedings of winter wheats and
barleys often show higher amounts of
loose smut than do later seedings.
Grains that follow rice show little
smut because seeding then is delayed
for at least 6 weeks.

Soil fertility seems to have little influence on infection. Wheat plants
grown from infected seed are more
susceptible to winterkilling, especially
under severe conditions, than are
similar healthy plants.

The deep-infecting loose smuts of
wheat and barley can be controlled by
hot-water seed treatment. The usual
method involves immersing the seed
4 to 12 hours in unheated water,
followed by a 10-minute dip in water
at 129° F. A single immersion in water
held at 120° for 95 minutes also is
effective in control. Such treatments
are so laborious that individual growers
rarely use them. The treated seed is
soft, swollen, and hard to dry before
seeding. The treatment often injures
germination. Occasionally central
treating plants, established where
steam or hot water are available, treat
the seed for local growers. Control also
has been obtained by soaking the seed
for 6 hours in water at room temperature followed by a soak of 40 hours in
a 0.2-percent solution of Spergon.

C. S. HOLTON *holds degrees from
Louisiana State University and the Uni-
versity of Minnesota. He is in charge of
the wheat smut program in the Northwest.*
V. F. TAPKE *has conducted research on
cereal diseases since joining the Bureau of
Plant Industry, Soils, and Agricultural
Engineering in 1918.*

Four Enemies
of Sorghum
Crops

R. W. Leukel, John H. Martin

The sorghum crops include grain
sorghum, sorgo (or sweet sorghum),
broomcorn, Sudangrass, and Johnsongrass.

Four general types of diseases attack
them: Those that rot the seed or kill
the seedlings; those that attack the
leaves and lower the value of the
plants for forage; those that attack
only the heads and so prevent the
normal formation of grain; and those
that cause root or stalk rots and prevent the normal development of the
plant.

Seed rot is most severe when the soil
is cold and wet after planting—a common condition in the North and in
other areas when seed is planted early.
Much of the seed then fails to germinate and rots because it is attacked by
various seed-borne and soil-inhabiting
fungi. To germinate promptly, sorghum seed requires a relatively warm
soil, above 70° F. Most seed-rotting
fungi thrive at lower temperatures
that retard the germination of the
seed and give the harmful fungi an
opportunity to attack it.

Some fungi (chiefly species of *Fusarium, Aspergillus, Rhizopus, Rhizoctonia,
Penicillium,* and *Helminthosporium*) invade and destroy the endosperm, the
starchy tissue of the seed, thus robbing
it of the food necessary to produce a
strong seedling. Cracks in the seed
coats of the kernels give the fungi
ready access to the interior and thus
aggravate the trouble.

FOUR ENEMIES OF SORGHUM CROPS

Some fungi, especially species of *Pythium*, attack the young sprout in its early stage and prevent its emergence.

These fungi also attack and rot the primary roots and thus keep the young seedlings from getting enough food materials from the soil to become well established.

Fusarium moniliforme, besides rotting the seed, frequently attacks sorghum seedlings at the surface of the soil soon after they have emerged and causes them to rot or damp-off and fall over. It also may destroy the primary roots of young seedlings. Some races of the fungus are more harmful than others.

Penicillium oxalicum attacks the endosperm and thus arrests germination. It may also kill the seedlings even after they have reached the third- or fourth-leaf stage.

Seed rot and seedling blight may be controlled pretty well by careful selection and treatment of seed and proper cultural practices. Seed should be well matured and properly dried. The seed coat should be as free as possible from cracks and nicks, such as those that are often caused by improper adjustment of the threshing machine. Before being planted, the seed should be treated with a good disinfectant that will protect it from seed-borne fungi and, to a great extent, from the harmful fungi in the soil. The seed should be planted after the soil is warm enough for prompt germination.

SORGHUM LEAF DISEASES may range in severity from small, unimportant spots or stripes on the leaves to diseased areas covering practically the entire leaf. High temperatures and humid weather generally favor the leaf diseases.

The diseased spots or stripes are usually discolored because of chemical substances or pigments that are produced in the plant cells whenever they are injured. In most varieties of sorghum and Sudangrass this pigment ranges from reddish or brownish purple to almost black. In most broomcorn, kaoliangs, and a few other sorghums, the spots or stripes on the leaves are red. In shallu, Ellis sorgo, and Tift and Sweet Sudangrass they are tan.

Certain environmental conditions or hereditary factors occasionally discolor leaves of sorghum and Sudangrass. Those spots often are confused with symptoms produced by fungus or bacterial diseases. A common condition in sorghum is the presence of intensely colored leaf spots or stripes without any other indication of disease.

Much of this nonparasitic spotting may be due to mechanical injuries from insect punctures, wind, or sand particles. When chlorate weed-killing chemicals or grasshopper bait containing arsenic fall on the leaves of sorghum, they cause a burning effect in irregular but characteristic spots, which resemble those caused by parasitic leaf diseases.

Often, however, the cause of this leaf spotting apparently is a physiological breakdown of the leaf tissues. Occasional plants have leaves so badly discolored that most of their leaf area is involved. The spots may be solid, or they may follow various concentric or irregular patterns. Some of the latter types are hereditary.

Leaf diseases may be caused by bacteria or fungi. Those caused by bacteria usually are characterized by the presence of drops or films of exudate that dry to thin, crustlike scales. Leaf spots caused by fungi have no exudate and usually are more or less roughened, because of the presence of fungal fruiting bodies.

BACTERIAL LEAF DISEASES occur in the United States wherever sorghum is grown. Like most leaf diseases, they are favored by warm (75° to 85° F.), moist weather. The causal organisms may be carried over from one season to another on the seed, on infected plant material in or on the soil, and occasionally on plants that overwinter. They may be spread from one leaf or plant to another by wind, splashing rain, and insects. Infection takes place through breathing pores of leaves.

The bacterial diseases usually do not cause serious losses, because they generally do not develop fully until the plants have reached their full size. During warm, moist seasons, however, they may spread rapidly from the lower to the upper leaves until one-half to two-thirds of the leaf surface is destroyed. The forage value of the crop is impaired and the kernels may not fill properly.

Three bacterial diseases of sorghum are known in the United States: Bacterial stripe, bacterial streak, and bacterial spot.

Bacterial stripe, caused by *Pseudomonas andropogoni,* the most serious and abundant, attacks grain, forage, and sweet sorghums, broomcorn, and Sudangrass.

Bacterial streak, caused by *Xanthomonas holcicola,* occurs on the leaves of sorghum and Johnsongrass as narrow, water-soaked, translucent streaks about one-eighth inch wide and 1 to 6 inches long.

Bacterial spot, caused by *Xanthomonas syringae,* attacks the leaves of sorghum, broomcorn, Sudangrass, Johnsongrass, pearl millet, foxtail millet, and corn. On sorghum the spots appear first on the lower leaves; infection gradually spreads to the upper leaves as the plants approach maturity. Frequently the spots are so numerous that they unite into large diseased areas and kill the whole leaf.

Recommended control measures are sanitation, seed treatment, and the use of resistant varieties. Disposing of old infected plant litter and infected plants that overwinter, along with crop rotation, will reduce the quantity of inoculum present in the fields the next season. Seed treatment before planting will keep the disease from being carried over on the seed. The sorgos as a class seem to be more susceptible to bacterial stripe than are grain sorghums and Sudangrass. The kafirs are resistant to bacterial streak.

EIGHT DISTINCT FUNGUS leaf diseases, caused by as many different fungi, are commonly found on sorghums in the United States: Rough spot, anthracnose, leaf blight, zonate leaf spot, gray leaf spot, target spot, sooty stripe, and rust.

The rough spot disease, caused by *Ascochyta sorghina* is widespread in Florida, Georgia, Alabama, South Carolina, North Carolina, Louisiana, and Mississippi.

It attacks sorghum, Sudangrass, and Johnsongrass. It is first observed as circular or oblong, light-colored spots. Then usually the red or tan pigment, depending on the variety, becomes apparent as the fungus spreads and injures the leaf tissue. Soon small black specks, the young fruiting bodies of the fungus, develop in the injured spots. The most striking characteristic of rough spot is the abundant development of these fruiting bodies (pycnidia), usually on the surface of the diseased discolored area, but occasionally on green, healthy-appearing parts of the leaf surface.

When the affected areas are rubbed between the fingertips, the sandpaper-like roughness, caused by the hard, raised fruiting bodies, can be detected readily. By the time the leaves die and become dry and papery, the fruiting bodies often are so abundant that they cover most of the leaf surface. Similar lesions occur on the leaf sheaths and occasionally on the stalks.

Sorghum or Sudangrass should not be grown on land where rough spot occurred the preceding season. Seed treatment and the use of available resistant varieties are advisable.

Anthracnose occurs commonly on the leaves of sorghum, Sudangrass, Johnsongrass, and other grasses grown in the humid areas of the South. Most varieties of broomcorn are especially susceptible.

The disease is caused by the fungus *Colletotrichum graminicola.* It may be carried on the seed and also may live on dead and decaying plant refuse on or in the soil. Infection often auses spots to develop on the leaves when the plants are still in the seeding stage. Later the disease may spread o other leaves as they appear. Usually, however, the leaves are not affected severely until about the middle of the growing season, when the plants have reached the jointing stage.

Infection first appears on the leaves as small, circular or elliptical spots, which later enlarge and may unite o involve large areas of the leaf. The leaf midrib, which is commonly nfected along with the leaf blade, is often strikingly discolored. Later the centers of the leaf spots fade to a grayish-tan color; examination with a hand lens reveals the presence of numerous pin-point black specks with short, stiff hairs. Those are the fruiting bodies of the fungus, which, under moist conditions, produce pinkish spore masses. The spores are spread by rain and wind to other leaves, where they start new areas of infection.

Defoliation due to anthracnose reduces the value of the plants for forage and may reduce the sugar content of the stalks in very susceptible varieties. It also may lower the ratio of sucrose to invert sugars.

Clean culture and rotation to avoid planting sorghum in fields cropped the previous year to Sudangrass, sorghum, or Johnsongrass should reduce the losses due to anthracnose. The principal means of control is growing resistant varieties.

Leaf blight, caused by *Helminthosporium turcicum*, is most prevalent in the warmer humid Atlantic and Gulf Coastal Plains of the Southern and Southeastern States, where it causes serious losses in sorghum and Sudangrass. It also attacks corn. It probably is the most destructive Sudangrass disease of this area.

The causal fungus is carried on the seed and also lives in the soil on dead or decaying plant material. It may cause seed rot and seedling blight, especially in cold and excessively moist soil. Seedlings then can become infected readily and many either die or develop into stunted plants. Small reddish-purple or yellowish-tan spots usually develop on the leaves of infected seedlings. The spots may merge sufficiently to kill large parts of the leaves, which then wither to the extent that badly affected plants look as if they had been frosted.

A greenish, moldlike growth of spores develops in the center of the leaf spots during warm, humid weather. The spores are scattered by wind or rain and infect other leaves. When the weather is favorable, the disease spreads rapidly and may cause serious damage by killing parts or all of the leaves before the plant has matured.

The chief hope of controlling leaf blight lies in the development of resistant varieties.

All commercial strains or lots of Sudangrass that have been tested are highly susceptible. Plant breeders are attempting to develop resistant strains of Sudangrass from crosses between Sudangrass and resistant varieties of sorghum. Tift Sudan shows some resistance but is not immune.

Rotation does not appear to be an effective method of control, because the fungus lives in the soil for several years.

Seed treatment may prevent some seedling infection and spread of the disease to new areas.

Zonate leaf spot, caused by *Gloeocercospora sorghi*, attacks sorghum, Sudangrass, Johnsongrass, and also sugarcane, corn, and cattail, or pearl, millet. It has been observed in eight Southeastern States. The disease is conspicuous on sorghum leaves as reddish-purple bands of tissue, alternating with tan or straw-colored areas and forming a zonate pattern.

Not much is known about the damage caused by this disease. When plants are so heavily infected that the leaves are killed prematurely, the forage value of the crop is undoubtedly reduced.

No fully proved control measures are known. The fungus has been found in the glumes and seed, which suggests that the planting of disease-free or adequately treated seed would help to prevent the spread of the disease. No highly resistant varieties are known.

Gray leaf spot, caused by *Cercospora sorghi*, occurs on sorghum, Sudangrass, Johnsongrass, and corn. It is not certain that the races that attack corn are the same as those that attack sorghum. The disease is of minor importance, but occasionally it causes considerable spotting of sorghum leaves in the more humid and warmer sections, particularly in the Gulf States. It is commonly found on Johnsongrass along highways and fences.

The development of resistant varieties appears to be the most feasible control measure. The reaction of sorghum varieties to this disease, however, is not yet known.

Target spot, caused by *Helminthosporium sorghicola*, occurs on sorghum, Sudangrass, and Johnsongrass. It has been found in five States. It produces small, well-defined spots, which are tan on Tift Sudangrass and certain other Leoti crosses and reddish purple on common Sudangrass and other varieties of sorghum. Older lesions have light centers surrounded by alternate dark and light bands; they look like a target. The fungus fruits sparsely under ordinary field conditions; hence its spread is not rapid. Spores form in abundance in a moist atmosphere.

The use of resistant varieties seems to offer the likeliest means of control, but none has yet been developed. As the disease may be seed-borne, effective seed treatment will prevent the spread of the disease to new areas in infected seed.

Sooty stripe, caused by the fungus *Ramulispora sorghi*, occurs on sorghum, Sudangrass, and Johnsongrass. It has been observed in 10 States and on many varieties of sorghum and Sudangrass and Johnsongrass. It attacks the leaves and sheaths. On the leaves, the spots begin as small, oblong, reddish-purple areas, with purplish borders and straw-colored dead centers. These

dead centers usually are more or less densely covered with small black bodies (sclerotia of the fungus), which may impart a sooty appearance to the lesions—hence the common name of the disease, sooty stripe.

In some varieties, particularly Leoti sorgo and Tift and Sweet Sudan grasses, the borders around the leaf stripes are tan instead of purple. In Johnsongrass the purple border usually is less pronounced than in most varieties of sorghum.

The use of resistant varieties offers the most promising means of control but none has yet been developed.

Sorghum rust, caused by *Puccinia purpurea*, attacks Sudangrass, Johnson grass, and most varieties of sorghum. It occurs frequently in the Gulf coast region and occasionally during wet seasons in States as far north as Nebraska and Indiana. Usually it does not become evident until the seed is well developed, so that it causes relatively slight losses to the grain sorghum crop except in certain seasons such as that of 1950. Abundant rust, however, causes the leaves to dry and break off so that the forage value of the crop may be lowered. The method by which sorghum rust is carried over winter is not known, but the abundance of Johnsongrass throughout the South suggests that it might serve as the principal overwintering host for the fungus.

Growing resistant varieties is the only feasible method for controlling sorghum rust.

THE SMUTS OF SORGHUM in the United States are covered kernel smut, loose kernel smut, and head smut.

Covered kernel smut is caused by a fungus (*Sphacelotheca sorghi*) that attacks all groups of sorghum, including Johnsongrass. It is practically the only disease in which injury to the plant is confined almost entirely to the head. It occurs wherever sorghum is grown, but it is most prevalent in the Kansas-Oklahoma-Texas area.

Usually all, but occasionally only a

art, of the kernels on a smutted plant are affected. In smutted heads, enlarged cylindrical or cone-shaped smut galls are formed instead of the kernels. At first the smut galls are covered with a light-gray or brown membrane that later may break and release the dark-brown spores. Threshing breaks up the galls and spreads the spores to the healthy seeds.

When smutted seed is planted, the spores germinate along with the seed. The growing fungus then invades the developing seedling and continues to grow undetected inside the plant until after heading, when the smut galls, which have formed in place of the kernels, become evident. Plants affected by covered kernel smut appear normal except for the smutted heads.

Covered kernel smut can be effectively controlled by properly treating the seed, planting only smut-free seed, or growing resistant varieties. Because it is not safe to assume that seed is entirely free from smut and because resistant varieties of all types of sorghum are not available, seed treatment is the most logical means of control.

Loose kernel smut, caused by the fungus *Sphacelotheca cruenta*, is much less common than covered kernel smut. It attacks all groups of sorghum, including Sudangrass and Johnsongrass, although certain varieties in some groups are immune or highly resistant.

The galls formed by loose kernel smut are long and pointed. The thin membrane over them usually breaks soon after the galls reach full size. Most of the dark-brown spores are soon blown away, leaving a long, dark, pointed, curved structure, called a columella, in the central part of what was the gall. As in covered kernel smut, the spores of the fungus are carried on the seed and germinate soon after the seed is planted, when the fungus invades the young sorghum plant. It continues to grow unobserved inside the plant until after heading, when the long pointed smut galls

appear in the heads in place of normal kernels. Unlike covered kernel smut, however, this disease stunts the infected plants and frequently induces the development of abundant side branches.

Loose kernel smut, besides being seed-borne and able to infect sorghum seedlings, may cause secondary infection—that is, the spores from a smutted head may infect and cause smut to develop in late heads on otherwise healthy plants.

The control measures for loose kernel smut are the same as those for covered kernel smut; namely, seed treatment and the use of smut-free seed and resistant varieties. The treatments that control covered kernel smut will also control loose kernel smut.

Johnsongrass frequently is infected in the Southwestern States with a peculiar type of loose kernel smut caused by *Sphacelotheca holci*, which differs in several respects from that commonly found on sorghum. This smut also attacks some varieties of sorghum. Several feteritas and feterita crosses are susceptible. The kafirs (Reed, Sharon, and Red) appear to be immune, although they are highly susceptible to the other kernel smuts.

Infected plants head early and are severely stunted. Often they get to be less than a foot high and sometimes die prematurely. The thin membrane covering the smut gall ruptures as soon as the gall appears, and the spores are spread at an early stage. The spores under ordinary conditions lose their viability within a few months. In Johnsongrass the smut is transmitted largely through the underground rhizomes and also by spores falling on freshly cut stubble. Second-growth sorghum also may be infected through the stubble.

The control of this smut on its natural host is not important because Johnsongrass mostly is a noxious weed. Because of its short-lived spores, this smut is not considered a menace to sorghum.

HEAD SMUT, caused by the fungus *Sphacelotheca reiliana*, attacks sorghum, Sudangrass, and, to some extent, corn. It is not common in the United States, but occasionally is somewhat damaging in individual fields of some varieties of sorghum. Although head smut has been known in this country since 1890, the total losses from it have been small.

Head smut is distinguishable from the kernel smuts because it destroys the entire head, transforming it into a large mass of dark-brown, powdery chlamydospores. The smut first becomes evident at heading time, when the large gall bulges out of the boot. The gall is covered at first with a whitish membrane, which soon breaks and allows the spores to be scattered by the wind and rain to the soil and to plant refuse, where they overwinter. The following spring and summer the spores germinate in the soil and produce sporidia, which, in turn, infect the sorghum plants. After invading a young sorghum plant, the fungus grows within it until the plant reaches the heading stage, when the smut gall becomes evident.

Because this smut fungus is carried in the soil, sorghum grown from clean seed planted on infested soil may be attacked. Some of the smut spores from the broken galls also may contaminate the seeds produced on nearby healthy plants. When such infested seeds are sown, head smut may be introduced into the soil of previously noninfested fields.

Sanitation is the chief means of controlling head smut. If seed that came from a field containing plants infected with head smut must be used for planting in an uninfested area, it should first be treated with a good fungicide to prevent spreading the smut to the soil in this area. If head smut is discovered in a field, the infected plants, or at least the galls, should be removed and burned before the spores are scattered. This is usually feasible in most fields in which the disease is found, as only a few of the plants are smutted. Prompt destruction of all smut galls usually rids a farm of head smut in a few years.

THE MOST SERIOUS root and stalk diseases of sorghum are periconia root rot (milo disease), weak neck, and stalk rot. Except for periconia root rot which under some conditions may appear at a relatively early stage, these diseases usually do not become evident until the plants are almost mature.

Periconia root rot (milo disease) is caused by the fungus *Periconia circinata* and has been especially destructive to milo. It was discovered in 1925 in Texas, and in Kansas on irrigated land that had been cropped to milo for several years. Since then the disease has been observed in Oklahoma, New Mexico, Nebraska, Arizona, and California.

THE DISEASE apparently does no damage sorghum on any land not cropped previously to susceptible varieties. It is the most serious disease known on milo, darso, and their hybrids and, until resistant varieties became available, was a limiting factor in the growing of these varieties in infested areas. Other sorghums, with few exceptions, are not affected.

In heavily infested soil, the disease may appear 3 to 4 weeks after planting when the plants are only 6 to 9 inches high. The first indication of the disease is a stunting of the plants and a slight rolling of the leaves; the older leaves turn light yellow at the tips and margins. This yellowing and drying progresses until all the leaves are affected and the plants die, usually without heading. They look as if they had been injured by excessive drought, alkali, or chinch bugs. In less heavily infested soil, the disease may not appear until the plants are about ready to head. Then it progresses less rapidly; the plants may grow weakly until late in the season and may form small, poorly filled heads.

The disease attacks the roots before the above-ground parts of the plant how any symptoms. When affected plants are only a few inches tall, examination reveals a water-soaked brown or reddish discoloration of the outer part of the roots. A soft rot later destroys most or all of the fine root system and the outer part of the larger roots, while the central part of the large roots turns dark red or brown. The tissue at the base of the crown also turns dark red, and this discoloration extends up into the base of the stalk.

After the disease appears in a field, it becomes more severe each year that susceptible varieties are grown. It may appear at first in a few isolated spots in which the plants are stunted or retarded or may have died prematurely. The following year these areas will be larger and the plants growing in them will be more severely affected. If a susceptible variety is grown a third year, the entire crop may be completely destroyed early in the season.

The disease may be spread by soil carried in run-off or irrigation water and by farm implements, wind-blown soil, or any agency that transports soil from infested fields. Although small areas of badly infested soil can be sterilized effectively by steam, formaldehyde, chloropicrin, or other agents, it is not economically feasible or practicable to do so in larger fields.

Effective control measures are limited to the planting of resistant varieties. Highly resistant strains of all desirable but hitherto susceptible varieties of milo have been developed. They have largely replaced the susceptible varieties. The combine-type grain sorghum varieties now widely grown are resistant to the disease.

CROP ROTATION offers small hope for controlling periconia root rot because the causal fungus persists in the soil for several years.

Weak neck has become a serious farm problem in some areas since the introduction of combine harvesting of grain sorghums. The principal and most objectionable feature of weak neck is the breaking over of the peduncles—the upper part of the stalks—so that the heads fall to the ground and are missed by the combine.

Weak neck is the result of over-ripeness accompanied by an inherent weakness of the tissues in the rachis (the center stem of the head) and the peduncle, especially of the main stalk, of certain dwarf varieties of sorghum.

Before we had the combine, grain sorghums usually were harvested soon after the grain was ripe and while the peduncle was still moist and rigid. Now, however, they often are combined long after the grain has matured or after a freeze, when the upper part of the stalk has lost its sap and the grain is dry enough for safe storage. Under those conditions some dwarf varieties frequently break over at the base of the peduncle, which by this time has become dry and spongy so that in wet weather it absorbs moisture readily, becomes limp, and is easily broken over by the wind and the weight of the head.

Since weak neck is largely a varietal characteristic, the remedy lies in developing and growing combine types of grain sorghum having peduncles like those of sorgo, which remain green for a considerable period after the grain is ripe. Two such varieties —Westland and Midland—are now widely grown. Another possibility of avoiding loss lies in the development of combine varieties that have a stalk with a stiff rind, which will support the head after the peduncle has dried out.

Stalk rot of sorghum has become increasingly important since it was first generally observed in 1938. Most of the stalk rot and lodging used to be attributed to the fungus causing charcoal rot, but now it seems that several other fungi may be involved. Some of them apparently invade the plant through openings caused by insects or by mechanical injuries. Bacteria also invade the stalk and thus help bring about a water-soaked, and later, a rotted condition.

The symptoms of stalk rot may vary

with the cause and location of the initial infection. Infections in the middle or lower part of the stalk, especially when they occur through wounds near the base of the stalk, usually are most destructive. External symptoms of such infections may at first consist of a water-soaked appearance of the stalk, with or without red or purple discoloration, or streaks on the surface of the stalk and in the veins of the sheaths and leaves. Later, one may see poorly developed kernels, premature ripening, and frequently a softening at the base of the stalk, followed by lodging. The inside of the stalk may show water-soaked or discolored pith, or both, and a streaking of the vascular bundles or fibers. The inside of the roots of affected plants likewise usually appears water-soaked and discolored, and frequently the tips of the diseased roots are dead.

There are four fungi to which stalk rot has been attributed. While no one of them is definitely known to be the sole cause, each may have a part. The diseases believed to be caused by them are known as charcoal rot, fusarium stalk rot, colletotrichum stalk rot, and rhizoctonia stalk rot.

Stalk rot may follow a period of drought, extreme heat, or other unfavorable conditions that weaken the plant. The disease is favored also by injuries to the stem, crown, or roots caused by cultivation implements, insects, wind, and hail, or any other agency that makes an opening for the entrance of destructive fungi and bacteria.

DEFINITE METHODS for control of the four stalk rots are not known, although resistant varieties offer the chief hope of reducing losses caused by them. Some varieties appear to be resistant to charcoal rot and to colletotrichum stalk rot, but none has been observed to be resistant to the other stalk rots. Rotation and other cultural practices may prove helpful, as will also the control of insects that attack the stalks of sorghum plants and leave

openings through which stalk ro fungi gain ready entrance.

Charcoal rot, caused by the fungu *Macrophomina phaseoli* (or *Sclerotiu bataticola*), is the most destructive c the stalk rots. It is unpredictable an more or less sporadic in its appearance It is associated with crop sequenc and soil and weather conditions tha subject the crop to extreme heat o drought at a critical stage in it development.

Usually injury is not apparent befor the plants approach maturity, whe many poorly filled heads are eviden along with lightweight kernels an premature ripening and drying c the stalks, many of which are lodged The diseased stalks may be soft an discolored at the base, the pith i disintegrated, and the separated vas cular fibers have a shredded appear ance. After a period of dry, warm weather, the fibers become covere with small black sclerotia formed b the fungus. When the roots and stubble decay in the field, the sclerotia become incorporated with the so where they may germinate later an infect the roots of any one of 30 o more different crops.

Another soil-borne fungus, *Rhizoc tonia solani*, which attacks cotton and several other crops, also may cause a stalk rot of sorghum. This stalk ro differs from charcoal rot in that i first attacks the pith, giving it a red dish color, while the vascular fiber remain white. Large brown sclerotia are formed on the outside of the stalk

The colletotrichum stalk rot, which is severe on broomcorn, is caused by the same organism, *Colletotrichum gra minicola*, that causes anthracnose on the leaves. The stalk rot phase usually is preceded by the anthracnose stage

The fungus enters the stalk directly through the rind and spreads rapidly throughout the conducting tubes and vessels of the plant. That interfere with the movement of water and food material and results in inferior head and seeds. Diseased stalks frequently break over at the base or at a point several joints above the ground, making harvesting difficult. That and the poor quality of broomcorn brush mean that many fields of broomcorn remain unharvested. Control measures are based on clean culture, crop rotation, and the use of resistant varieties.

TREATMENT OF SORGHUM SEED every year with an effective fungicide is a cheap form of crop insurance. Treatment of sufficient seed for most farms is economical with regard to chemicals and labor, because only 2 to 5 pounds is usually required to plant an acre. This quantity can be treated at a cost of a cent or less for material.

Fungi, which may rot the seed or kill the seedling, can be combatted to a great extent by treating the seed with an effective fungicide, of which there are several on the market. The fungicides also control the two kernel smuts and prevent the spread of head smut to the soil of other fields by means of spores on the seed. Although seed treatments cannot be depended upon to prevent bacterial and fungus leaf diseases, they may prevent their spread to new areas.

Methods and materials for treating seed are discussed on page 134.

R. W. LEUKEL *is a plant pathologist in the division of cereal crops and diseases at the Plant Industry Station, Beltsville, Md. He received his training at the University of Wisconsin and is a native of that State. He has been engaged in the study of the cause and control of cereal diseases since 1919 and is the author of more than 50 articles on that subject.*

JOHN H. MARTIN *is senior agronomist in charge of sorghum investigations in the division of cereal crops and diseases at Beltsville. He has written numerous bulletins, circulars, and other publications on cereal culture and is senior author of a widely used textbook,* Principles of Field Crop Production. *He, R. W. Leukel, and C. L. Lefebvre are authors of* Sorghum Diseases and Their Control, *Bulletin 1959 of the Department of Agriculture.*

Infections of Corn Seedlings

Paul E. Hoppe

The germination period is a critical one in the life of a corn plant. Corn seedlings normally are resistant to most parasitic diseases under the conditions that favor germination and early growth. But in cold, wet soils, a germinating corn kernel may be attacked by fungus parasites that cause the seed to decay and weaken the seedlings. The seedling diseases of corn are carried on the seed or in the soil.

Seed infection is less common in hybrid corn than in open-pollinated varieties partly because most of the hybrids involve inbred lines that were selected for resistance to ear and kernel rot diseases, caused by fungi that also attack seeds and seedlings. Also the prompt drying of hybrid seed corn checks the spread of initial infections.

Seed infection ordinarily can be detected only by germination or plating tests. Among the fungi concerned are *Diplodia zeae*, *Gibberella zeae*, *Fusarium moniliforme*, species of *Penicillium* and *Aspergillus*, and many others of lesser importance.

Their symptoms are generally similar. In cold soils the seed decay or seedlings die before they emerge. In warmer soils the seedlings usually emerge from the soil but they may be stunted because seminal and primary roots and the subcrown internode rot. The seedling dies when the fungus penetrates the central cylinder (stele) of the subcrown internode (mesocotyl), or invades the crown tissues before the roots arising in that region become established.

Diplodia, the most virulent and important of the seed-infecting fungi, causes severe disease, even in warm soils. In the United States it occurs most frequently in the warmer and more humid areas of the Corn Belt, and in Maryland, Delaware, southeastern Pennsylvania, and the Southern States.

Gibberella infection is prevalent in the cooler corn-growing areas, such as Minnesota, northern Iowa, and Wisconsin, particularly in seasons when wet weather occurs during the silking period. It also occurs commonly in Maryland and Delaware. Unlike *Diplodia*, the *Gibberella* fungus is short-lived and rarely can be found alive on old seed. Severe disease develops only in cold soils.

Infections with *Fusarium moniliforme* occur wherever corn is grown. Except for highly pathogenic strains reported in Florida, the fungus usually is weakly parasitic and is of only minor importance in the principal corn areas.

Infection with various species of *Penicillium, Aspergillus*, and many other fungi occurs most commonly when seed corn is stored with a high moisture content or under very humid conditions. *Aspergillus* infects seed corn also in relatively dry weather. Generally the storage rot fungi are only mildly pathogenic to germinating seeds. Wide differences in pathogenicity exist, however, among the various species and strains of *Penicillium* and *Aspergillus*. *Penicillium oxalicum* is unique in that it is most pathogenic in warm, dry soils.

SOIL-INHABITING FUNGI are the most common cause of seed rots and seedling diseases in corn. Their importance has increased because of the many kernel injuries that often occur in harvesting and processing the seed by modern machinery. Wounded kernels are particularly susceptible to attack by the soil fungi.

Many fungi attack a corn kernel that is lying dormant or is germinating slowly in cold soil. Among them are species of *Fusarium, Helminthosporium, Sclerotium, Rhizoctonia, Trichoderma*, and *Pythium*. Some are pathogenic only under unusual field conditions: *Trichoderma viride* attacks seed corn only at continuous temperatures exceeding 80° F., and *Sclerotium bataticola* is not pathogenic to seedlings in unsteamed or unsterilized soil.

Pythium species are the most common cause of seed decay and seedling disease in corn. *Pythium* was found in nearly all decayed corn kernels and diseased seedlings, following germination at low temperature, in a variety of Wisconsin soils. Nearly total seed decay occurred in untreated seed planted in Plainfield sand and peat soils.

The lowest amount of disease among the cropped soils was in seed planted in Superior red clay, where the seedlings generally emerged but were stunted. Differences in disease intensity in the various soils were attributed to the presence of different species of *Pythium*. The frequency that various species were isolated from Wisconsin soils, in descending order of their virulence or pathogenicity, was *P. irregulare*, 46; *P. debaryanum*, 5; *P. ultimum*, 67; *P. paroecandrum*, 2; *P. splendens*, 7; *P. rostratum;* 7; and *P. vexans*, 3.

Seed decay develops most rapidly in soils at temperatures of 48° to 50° F. That is too cold for corn, and untreated, susceptible seed is killed in 8 days or sooner by the more pathogenic species of *Pythium*. At a soil temperature of 40°, disease may be equally severe; because of slower growth of the fungus parasites at this low temperature, however, longer periods are required before disease actually affects the seed. Since cold, in itself, is not injurious to seed corn, kernels protected with an efficient fungicide will germinate and grow normally later when the soil warms up, even after having been exposed 3 weeks at 40° in wet soils.

Corn germinates rapidly in warm

soils, and sound seed is highly resistant to the soil-borne diseases. Kernels having crown wounds are attacked, however, by *Pythium* even in the warm soils, and the seedlings may become severely stunted.

Soil moisture has less influence than temperature on disease of seedlings. Disease is severe in cold soils over a wide range of soil moistures with marked reductions in level of disease only in soils that are extremely dry. In experiments in Wisconsin it was found that disease was heaviest in peat soil that had been wetted to 60 percent of its water-holding capacity.

Inbred lines of corn differ widely in their inherent resistance to seed rot diseases. In severe tests of Wisconsin inbreds, seedling stands have ranged from nothing to more than 70 percent when the highest quality of seed was used. Corn inbreds also differ in the extent of physical injuries sustained in rough handling of the seed. Resistance to breakage is important because injured kernels become so susceptible to attack by soil fungi.

The reaction in corn hybrids to seedling diseases is influenced by the inbred lines used in their combination. The female, or seed parent, sometimes exerts the stronger influence in resisting disease, but inherent resistance in either parent is important.

Inferior seed corn—inferior because of immaturity, frost injury, old age, improper curing or storing, or physical injury—is susceptible to attack by soil fungi.

Kernel injury is the most serious. Injured seeds have little chance of survival when they are planted in cold soils unless treated with an effective fungicide. Broken seed coats over or near the germ are the most damaging; next are chipped crowns and broken tip caps.

Kernel injuries occur during all the steps of mechanical harvesting and processing. Most damage comes during shelling. In some commercial lots of seed all kernels are injured. Reductions in field stands and ultimate yields usu-ally are nearly proportionate to the amount of injury to kernels.

COLD TESTS first were used by commercial companies to test seed lots to see if they would germinate in cold soil. They essentially are tests against soil-borne diseases. Improved testing methods enabled corn breeders to evaluate their stocks for resistance and pathologists to test fungicides.

The walk-in refrigerator method, older and widely used, requires large refrigeration equipment and a warm room or greenhouse. The corn kernels are planted in soil in flats or pans that are kept usually for 6 to 10 days in a large refrigerator maintained at about 50° F. Following the low-temperature incubation, the flats are moved to a warm place, where germination is completed. Data are recorded when seedlings have reached the three- to four-leaf stage of growth. A complete test requires about 3 weeks.

The paper doll method is easy and rapid and permits extensive testing without large refrigerators or greenhouse facilities. The kernels are placed on wet paper towels on which soil is spread thinly. The towels then are rolled into "rag dolls" and incubated in covered refrigerator pans in an ordinary electric refrigerator for the desired time, at 48° to 50°. Afterward the pans are stored at room temperature. Germination is recorded 2 or 3 days later. The paper doll technique permits the testing of fungicides in 9 days—6 days in refrigerator and 3 at room temperature.

SEEDLING DISEASES of corn are controlled by seed treatment, the use of good seed, and the use of resistant varieties.

Proper seed treatment is the most practical. Mercury-containing compounds have been replaced largely by organic nonmercurials, among them Arasan, Thiram, Phygon, and Orthocide. Properly applied as dusts or slurries, they give good protection under severe conditions. Proper application calls for adequate dosages and good materials.

Quality of seed is important. Seed corn should be mature and harvested before heavy freezes occur. Injury from frosts usually is correlated with the moisture content of the seed—the higher the moisture the greater the damage. Improved methods of harvesting and processing may reduce kernel wounds. Reducing the cylinder speed of shellers and the use of rubberized surfaces in processing machinery eliminates much injury to seed.

Care is necessary in curing and storing seed. Temperatures exceeding 110° F. during artificial drying are injurious. Seed should be stored where it is cool and dry.

PAUL E. HOPPE, *a native of Wisconsin, has been engaged in corn disease research since 1929, when he became affiliated with the division of cereal crops and diseases, Bureau of Plant Industry, Soils, and Agricultural Engineering. He has specialized on the diseases which occur in the more northern areas of the Corn Belt, particularly on seedling diseases.*

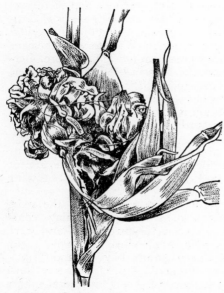

Common corn smut.

Some of the Leaf Blights of Corn

Alice L. Robert

Corn is subject to about 30 different leaf diseases in the United States. Fewer than one-third of them cause noticeable damage, even in rather small areas.

Most leaf diseases, or so-called leaf blights, produce spots or streaks on the leaves. The damage may be light to heavy and sporadic or persistent. The diseases injure or kill the leaf tissues and thereby reduce the area of green chlorophyll, which manufactures food for the plant. If considerable leaf areas are killed, the vigor and yield of the plant are reduced, stalks are weakened, and the grain is chaffy and light. The value of the plant for forage is reduced, and so many stalks may be broken that harvesting with machines is difficult.

The leaf diseases have characteristic marks that identify them. Some of them may infect the plants in the seedling stage and kill the entire plant at an early age. They usually enter all parts of the plant and thus are systemic diseases. When they appear later they usually attack only the leaves. Unbalanced supplies of available minerals in the soil may cause streaking, spotting, and discolorations in leaves that sometimes are confused with parasitic diseases. Hereditary factors and unfavorable environmental conditions occasionally produce leaf disorders or discolorations.

Parasitic leaf diseases generally are favored by high humidity and warm temperatures. Wind or insects spread them from one plant to another and from field to field. Fungi or bacteria cause parasitic leaf blights.

LEAF DISEASES caused by fungi occur throughout the corn-producing areas. Five of just more than 20 fungus leaf diseases of corn are serious in the United States. They are characterized by spots or lesions, which usually have fruiting bodies or spores of the causal fungus on the killed parts of the leaves. The lesions may be considerably darkened by the abundance of these spores. Some of the fungi remain in fields from one season to another in corn residues. They generally are spread by wind.

NORTHERN CORN LEAF BLIGHT is caused by the fungus *Helminthosporium turcicum.* It is found in most of the corn areas of the United States and attacks all types of corn. The disease was first identified in 1878 in this country. It is most generally noticeable in the southern part of the Corn Belt, eastward to the Atlantic coast, and southward into Florida. It has been found as far north as Wisconsin, Minnesota, and South Dakota. The most severe damage is in States that have heavy dews and abundant rainfall, which, with warm summer weather, make ideal conditions for its development and spread. Its occurrence is often sporadic but it may persist through several severe seasons in an area. Since 1942 it has been somewhat serious in some sections of the lower Corn Belt. Heavy infections occurred in Illinois and neighboring States in 1951 and 1952. Fields of sweet corn in Florida were seriously attacked by it in 1952 as the infections were established early on young plants.

Some fields may be severely affected, while others nearby may suffer little damage. Usually the plants become infected as they approach maturity. Losses may range from a trace to as much as 50 percent of the grain yield, depending on the severity of attack and the time the disease becomes established. Sometimes a heavy infection

may appear before tasseling and cause severe damage. In a less favorable season the plants may be almost free from disease until they near maturity; then only minor damage results. If much of the green leaf area is killed, starch formation is restricted and the kernels are chaffy. The blighted leaves are less suitable for fodder because of lowered nutritive value. Many of the dead leaves are lost in harvesting.

Heavy rainfall seems to encourage the development of northern corn leaf blight. Its severity might be predicted somewhat from rainfall and temperature records for an area. Heavily infected corn seems to be more susceptible to stalk rots. Early-maturing lines of corn generally are more susceptible than those that mature later.

The lower leaves of the corn plant usually are the first to be attacked by *Helminthosporium turcicum.* The disease progresses upward as severity increases. Small elliptical spots first appear as dark and grayish-green, water-soaked areas. Later they turn greenish tan. With age they get bigger and become a distinct spindle shape. Individual lesions usually are one-half to three-fourths inch wide and 2 to 3 inches long. They may be 2 inches wide and 6 inches long. Spores develop abundantly on both surfaces of the spots after rain or heavy dews and give a dark-green, velvety look to the lesions, more heavily in the center than near the margin. Several lesions may join and form large areas, that may kill entire leaves and in turn the plants. Heavily infected fields may appear dry and fired.

The fungus lives over winter inside the dried infected leaves of corn residue in the field, produces spores the following spring, and infects the growing corn. Once started, the infection is spread by the wind.

In 1942 no hybrids or inbred lines of corn were known to be resistant to northern corn leaf blight. Since that time plant pathologists and corn breeders have tested all of the important inbred lines of corn and evaluated them for resistance. The experiments were conducted by the Department of Agriculture at Beltsville, Md., and, in cooperation with the Purdue University Agricultural Experiment Station, at Lafayette, Ind.

A few highly resistant inbred lines were found. They are not used in commercial hybrids, but their resistance can be transferred to commercially important lines, thereby making them resistant to the disease. By 1952 some of the inbred lines commonly used in making hybrids for the Corn Belt had been converted and by 1958 they will be available for making hybrid seed for the farmer. Resistance is controlled by a large number of hereditary factors, or genes, that may be transferred from one inbred line to another.

Dry Parzate and Dithane sprays or dusts were used in 1951 and 1952 in Florida on large sweet corn fields and in dent corn seed-breeding fields of some Corn Belt hybrid seed companies. Six to eight applications were necessary for control.

The best control of northern corn leaf blight lies in the development and planting of resistant hybrids.

SOUTHERN CORN LEAF BLIGHT is caused by the fungus *Cochliobolus heterostrophus* (*Helminthosporium maydis*). It was first observed in the United States in 1923. Now it occurs throughout the corn areas of the Southern States and reaches northward into Illinois, Indiana, Missouri, and Ohio and eastward to the Atlantic coast. A warm, humid climate favors its development, but it thrives better at higher temperatures than does northern corn leaf blight.

It kills the green tissue of the leaves and reduces the effective leaf area. Yield may be reduced, stalks weakened and the fodder value of the plant damaged. Most of the damage is found in the Southern States, where temperatures and moisture conditions are ideal for its development.

The disease is seen as a grayish-tan to straw-colored spotting, which may extend over most of the leaf surface. The spots may be up to 1½ inches long and one-fourth inch wide. Their sides are more or less parallel, following along leaf veins. Several spots may unite to form large areas of killed tissue when the infection is heavy. Badly damaged fields may appear to be fired. Very susceptible hybrids or varieties have numerous spots even on the upper leaves.

Its fungus also produces microscopic vegetative spores, which are blown from plant to plant to spread the disease. The spores and consequently the spots are light in color, in contrast to the dark spores and spot surfaces of northern corn leaf blight. They are characteristically slender and curved. The perithecial or sexual stage is known, but its importance in epidemics of southern corn leaf blight is not definitely established. The fungus lives over in the vegetative or asexual stage in the dead leaf tissue in the fields, and, when wet, warm weather comes in the spring, vegetative spores are formed and spread to the growing corn. The fungus may live over in the field for at least 2 years. Wind carries the spores from plant to plant.

The only known means of controlling the disease is the use of resistant hybrids. The Department of Agriculture and the agricultural experiment stations in Indiana, North Carolina, and Georgia had discovered by 1950 several sources of resistance that scientists have used to improve inbred lines. Resistance to this disease appears to be inherited in a manner similar to that of northern corn leaf blight, but it is governed by an entirely different set of genes.

ANOTHER DISEASE, commonly called southern corn leaf spot and caused by *Helminthosporium carbonum*, was identified in 1938 in Indiana. The two known races of the fungus produce different symptoms, although the spores look alike. Neither has been of great economic importance between 1938 and 1953.

Race 1 of the fungus attacks only a few susceptible inbred lines of corn that are used mostly in the southern part of the Corn Belt. Race 2 occurs more commonly in the Southern States and frequently in Virginia and North Carolina. It is easily confused with southern corn leaf blight caused by *Helminthosporium maydis.* Because of this uncertainty its extent may be greater than has been reported.

Race 1 produces circular or oval spots up to 1 inch in diameter. At first they are yellowish green, but as they age they become reddish tan and profusely covered with dark spores, which give them a velvety appearance. Often the spores are arranged in concentric rings in the lesions. The fungus infects the sheaths, forming larger round areas that may become black with spores. Ears and husks are also attacked. Kernels become a carbon black. In some ears only a part of the kernels may be blackened; in others all are black. Race 1 affects all visible parts of the plant and causes it to die early. When plants are infected in the young or seedling stage, they may become completely covered with spots and die before tasseling. Young seedlings may become infected from the seed.

Race 2 produces leaf symptoms that are easily confused with southern corn leaf blight. Spots are tan or light brown and angular. They elongate slightly with the leaf and are one-eighth to one-fourth inch wide and up to 1 inch long. In heavy infection they coalesce to form large deadened areas, which often kill the lower leaves. This race also causes a blackening of the ears. The sporulation it causes on the spots is not heavy.

Losses from southern corn leaf spot can be controlled by the development of resistant strains. Susceptibility to race 1 is of a rather simple genetic nature, and resistance can be easily obtained. Several of the useful inbred

lines of corn have been converted from susceptible to nonsusceptible lines by cross-breeding. The mode of inheritance of reaction pertaining to race 2 is not known.

GRAY LEAF SPOT of corn occurs throughout the Southern States. In 1943 it was prevalent in Kentucky and Tennessee. Since that time heavy infections have been found in Georgia and Virginia. The disease may be caused by two fungi, *Cercospora sorghi* and *C. zeae-maydis,* which sometimes occur on the same leaf.

On hasty examination this spotting may be confused with that caused by southern corn leaf blight. The spots are narrower, however; some are less than one-sixteenth inch wide and are one-fourth to 1½ inches long. They begin as light-sepia spots, but as they age they bleach to an ashen gray with narrow light-sepia borders. The spores of the fungi are very light, and are long and narrow with several cross walls. The mode if inheritance of resistance to attack by these fungi is not known.

BACTERIAL LEAF DISEASES are found all over the United States. Like other leaf diseases, they are favored by humid, warm weather. They are spread by insects, wind, and contaminated material in the soil. Their severity may vary from year to year.

Three bacterial leaf diseases of corn are known in the United States. Only two, bacterial wilt and bacterial leaf blight, cause much concern.

BACTERIAL WILT, also known as Stewart's disease, is caused by *Bacterium stewartii* and is the most important of the bacterial leaf diseases of corn. It attacks sweet, dent, and pop corn. Generally it does more damage to sweet corn, particularly the early, yellow, sweeter varieties. It was first found in New York in 1895 and occurs to some extent each year in the Eastern States, throughout the Corn Belt, and in fields of sweet corn in the South.

Up to 1940 bacterial wilt caused extensive damage to sweet corn and heavy losses to canners. In the 1930's it appeared also in a somewhat different form in field corn as a leaf blight on dent corn in Indiana and Illinois. Losses as high as 20 percent were sustained in many dent corn fields in the Corn Belt. The introduction of sweet corn as a commercial green market crop in Florida also brought the menace of bacterial wilt.

Canners and green marketers turned to the use of late-maturing resistant white varieties as Country Gentleman and Stowell Evergreen. They have since replaced the susceptible corn with resistant hybrids, and losses have been reduced. One of the outstanding resistant hybrids and one of the first to be used is the yellow Golden Cross Bantam. A few of the others used in the United States are Aristogold, Hoosier Gold, Golden Harvest, Ioana, Marcross, Carmelcross, and Iochief. Their use offers substantial control in sweet corn. The disease is not so serious to field corn, but it may cause appreciable damage if conditions are favorable.

Stewart's disease is a typical vascular disease of sweet corn. It is caused by a nonmotile bacterium that grows into a small yellow colony on artificial culture media. In the corn plant, bacteria develop inside the vascular bundles, plug them full, and induce wilting as if the plant were suffering from lack of water. The whole young plant may wilt and die early even though plenty of water is in the soil. Those that do not die become stunted and do not produce normal ears. The leaves develop long, pale-green streaks with wavy margins, and they soon wilt and die. In a severely affected plant bacteria ooze out as tiny yellow droplets from the bundles in the stalk if it is cut across. Other infected parts also will ooze the bacteria. If cut across and placed in a drop of water, clouding will be seen. All parts of the plant may be infected.

Infection that takes place after the plant is firmly established comes about through wounds made by flea beetles as they feed on the leaves. Infection may spread through the bundles of the leaves into the other parts of the vascular system of the plant and cause severe damage.

Dent corn is generally more resistant than sweet corn to bacterial wilt. Rarely is the infection so severe that the plants die before they tassel, but that may occur in a few inbred lines. Large numbers of streaks may develop on the leaves as the corn approaches maturity. They usually develop from beetle feeding points, and, in susceptible lines, they increase to cause a severe leaf blight. Streaks are long and pale green with irregular or wavy margins. They turn lighter, die, and eventually kill large portions of the leaf in severe cases. Sometimes a heavily infected cornfield looks as if it had suffered from frost. Susceptibility to stalk rot is increased when a large area of leaf surface is destroyed.

Bacterial wilt may be carried over inside the seed. This is another source of infection for young plants. The bacteria also may live over winter in the soil, in manure, or in old cornstalks and leaves left in the field. Infection of a new crop seldom starts from these.

The bacteria must enter through a wound in the plant to cause disease and initial infections generally start from injuries caused by flea beetles in feeding. These tiny beetles carry bacteria within their bodies over winter, come out in April and May, start feeding on the young corn plants, and thus introduce the bacteria.

A correlation exists between the severity of winter and the amount of bacterial wilt the following spring. Mild winters tend to maintain large beetle populations, and wilt may reach epidemic proportions the following year. Bacterial wilt is less severe after a cold winter, apparently because fewer beetles survive. As new generations of beetles appear in the spring, they feed on infected corn leaves, harbor the bacterium in their bodies, and spread the disease to other plants throughout the growing season.

Sprays and dusts do not control the disease. Seed treatment is ineffective. Spraying of the young plants with DDT as the first beetles emerge in the spring has reduced the beetle population on experimental plots and thus lessened the bacterial wilt spread. The use of resistant hybrids is the recommended control.

BACTERIAL LEAF BLIGHT of corn, caused by *Pseudomonas alboprecipitans*, has occurred sporadically in several Central and Southern States since 1928. It was recognized first in Alabama and soon thereafter was found in Virginia, Georgia, Texas, Kansas, and Nebraska. Since then it has been found in other States.

The disease affects some varieties of dent, sweet, and pop corn. The same bacterium causes a disease on yellow bristlegrass (*Setaria lutescens*), a common weed in cornfields. It is not known if it spreads from yellow bristlegrass to the corn. There is no evidence that the disease is transmitted naturally by seeds. Temperatures between 85° and 95° F. favor infection.

The disease usually is seen in spots in the field as a leaf blight, that may cause stalks and tops to rot as it develops in the plant.

The lesions are scattered irregularly over the leaves. They appear as sharply delimited necrotic stripes from one-eighth to one-fourth inch wide and from 1 to 16 inches long.

The stripes at first are water-soaked and olive green. Later the color changes to a light buff, with delicate margins of sepia to cinnamon buff. They appear somewhat translucent. In rather heavy infections, the stripes may merge into extensive areas of dead tissue, sometimes over the entire width of the leaf. As the lesions become older they may break lengthwise and give a shredded appearance to leaves, especially if they are badly diseased and exposed to rainy and windy weather.

Small sections of the stripes cut and placed in a drop of water show a clouding, which is caused by a streaming out of the bacteria from the diseased tissues.

The stalk rot that sometimes accompanies this leaf blight is in the upper part of the plant, usually at or just above the node where the ear is produced. The outside of the stalk may show reddish-brown streaks and inside the stalk is a dark brown to black rot that decays the pith of nodes and internodes leaving the fibrous bundles as long loose shreds. As the rot progresses, the tops of the corn plants fade and die and often the tassels fail to appear. Many infected plants are dwarfed, show bleached tops, and produce sterile multiple ears.

The bacterium that causes this disease is a small motile one that develops on artificial culture media as a small white colony, sometimes surrounded by a definite clearing or halo.

BACTERIAL LEAF SPOT of corn is caused by *Pseudomonas syringae* (*Bacterium holci*) and sometimes results in the firing of the lower leaves of young plants. It was first observed in Iowa in 1916 but has never become serious. It is seen on the lower leaves of the corn plant as round, elliptical, or irregular, water-soaked lesions ranging from one-eighth to one-half inch in diameter. The spots at first are dark green and water-soaked, but later become light brown, with a darker brown or reddish-brown narrow border. A yellowish halo may be seen around some of the larger spots. In extremely rainy weather there may be an infection of the margins and tips of the lower leaves, which causes them to become brown and die.

ALICE L. ROBERT, *a native of Louisiana, has been a pathologist in the division of cereal crops and diseases, Bureau of Plant Industry, Soils, and Agricultural Engineering, since 1938. She is a graduate of Louisiana State University and conducts research in corn diseases at Beltsville, Md.*

Some Smuts
and Rusts
of Corn

Arnold J. Ullstrup

Corn is susceptible to two smuts. Common smut, or boil smut, is widely distributed. Head smut occurs in the far West and rarely east of the Great Plains. It is known to occur in eastern Europe, Asia, Africa, and Australia.

Common smut of corn was identified in Europe in 1754. It was first recorded in the United States in 1822. Since corn is native to the Western Hemisphere, it is probable that common smut has existed along with the culture of its host. Teosinte is the only other host susceptible to the disease.

The prevalence of common smut varies from year to year and from one area to another. In the Corn Belt estimates of loss due to the disease have ranged from a trace to 6 percent. It is doubtful if losses exceed 2 percent for field corn over very wide areas. In sweet corn local losses may be considerably higher and reductions in the yield of sweet corn up to 60 percent have been known.

The size, location, and number of galls on a plant determine the amount of damage. Large galls are more detrimental to a plant than small galls are. Galls above the ear are generally more destructive than those below the ear. Galls on young plants cause more damage than do those that develop later.

Common smut is perhaps the most conspicuous and easily recognized of all corn diseases. Galls or tumors ranging in size from beadlike structures to 6 inches or more in diameter are the distinguishing symptom. All aboveground parts of the plant are attacked—tassels, leaves, ears, stalks, and brace roots.

The galls are at first covered with a glistening, whitish-green membrane. As the gall enlarges, the membrane ruptures, exposing a powdery black mass of spores. Galls may occur wherever young, rapidly growing tissue is exposed to infection. Galls on leaves seldom develop beyond the size of a pea. They usually dry up and become hard and warty. Only a few spores are formed inside them. Ears are especially vulnerable to infection. The largest galls are formed in the ears because they have so much embryonic tissue.

Ustilago maydis is the fungus causing common smut of corn. The spores, called chlamydospores, are brownish black, thick-walled, heavily spined, and oval to spherical in shape. Chlamydospores, which are resistant to extremes of exposure, germinate in the presence of moisture, and within a temperature range of 46° to 97° F., to form small, single-celled, thin-walled, colorless spores, called sporidia. The sporidia germinate and may penetrate the host tissue, but infections arising from single sporidia are not typical; galls and chlamydospores usually are not formed and the life cycle of the fungus is not completed. Typical invasion of the corn plant, with subsequent formation of galls and chlamydospores, takes place following fusion of sporidia of opposite mating type. This fusion process is similar in many respects to the sexual process—fertilization—that precedes seed formation in higher plants. Each sporidium has a single nucleus and when fusion takes place, nuclei of the opposite types are associated in pairs in the infection hyphae and mycelium of the fungus. These paired nuclei in the mycelium eventually fuse after chlamydospore formation.

The mycelium develops between the host cells and stimulates them to increase in size and number until galls are formed. Galls continue growth until chlamydospores are again formed in the mycelium of the fungus. When the gall is mature it breaks open and releases chlamydospores which may be carried to other plants where they germinate and continue the disease cycle. Thus local infections may continue throughout the growing season because of successive generation of chlamydospores. Infection of young plants may result in infection throughout the plant; galls form as the host tissues develop during the growing season.

The factors determining the incidence of common smut are not fully understood. Dry weather in late spring and early summer seems to favor its spread and development. Corn grown on heavily manured soils often shows a lot of smut. Plants on such soils make a succulent growth, which probably provides for easy penetration of the infection hyphae of the fungus. Such soils may also provide a good medium for overwintering and germination of the chlamydospores. Hail damage and injuries from cultivating machinery increase the prevalence of smut by exposing the host tissue to infection by the smut fungus. Detasseling corn in seed fields often increases smut because the tissues are exposed at the break in the upper stalk where the tassels are removed. Failure of pollination, which sometimes occurs in seed fields, stimulates the plants to produce several small ear shoots, which are susceptible to smut infection.

Planting resistant hybrids is the most effective means of controlling the common smut. No hybrid is completely immune, but most of the popular hybrids are reasonably resistant. In selecting a hybrid, consideration must be given to desirable agronomic characters, resistance to other diseases, and resistance to smut. Most smut-susceptible inbred lines are usually discarded before they reach commercial production. Breeding for smut resistance has been somewhat complicated by the occurrence of physiologic races of the pathogen and by lack of a completely satisfactory method of artificial inoculation that could be used as a tool to distinguish resistant from susceptible plants. An inbred line may appear resistant in one location and susceptible in another because of the presence of different physiologic races of the smut fungus. Inheritance of resistance to common smut is determined by a relatively large number of genes.

Seed treatment is not effective in reducing the incidence of smut, but may kill smut spores carried on the outside of seed and thus prevent their introduction into places where the disease is not present.

Rotation and sanitation are ineffective in controlling smut where corn is extensively grown. In small garden plantings of sweet corn, destruction of smut galls before spores are produced may help reduce prevalence of the disease in following years.

Head smut of corn was first found in the United States in 1895. The disease is of minor importance in this country and only in localized areas of some of the Western States has it caused any appreciable damage. It is more common in Asia, Africa, Australia, and eastern Europe.

The first symptoms become evident when the tassels and ears appear. Those organs may be completely or partly converted into smut galls. Occasionally the tip of the stalk is involved. Smut galls are at first covered with a delicate membrane that soon breaks open and exposes a mass of reddish-brown to black chlamydospores and strands of conductive tissue. The strands, or fibers, in the galls help to distinguish this disease from common smut. Little or no stunting occurs in infected plants.

Sphacelotheca reiliana is the fungus that causes head smut of corn. Chlamydospores, produced in large numbers in the galls, are reddish brown to black, thick-walled, finely spined, and spherical or else slightly irregular in shape. Chlamydospores, which can withstand periods of unfavorable weather, live over from one growing season to the next in soil or on the seed. They germinate to form small, oval, secondary spores—the sporidia.

Penetration of young seedlings is effected by binucleate mycelium that arises following fusion of uninucleate sporidia of compatible mating types. The parasitic mycelium develops in the tissues of the young corn plant and chlamydospores are formed following gall development in the tassels and ears. In head smut, the parasitic fungus is entirely systemic (growing within the plant), and successive local infections do not occur throughout the growing season as in common smut. Sorghum is susceptible to head smut, but the physiologic races attacking it do not parasitize corn; those that attack corn cannot cause the disease in sorghum.

Little is known concerning the conditions influencing the prevalence of head smut. Infection may take place over a fairly wide range of temperature, but relatively dry soil seems to be more favorable for invasion of the host than wet soil. Because of the systemic nature of the disease, injuries to the host do not seem to increase incidence of head smut, as is the case with common smut.

Not much is known regarding resistance of corn hybrids to head smut. In sorghum, where the disease is more important, resistant varieties are known and their use provides a means of control. Seed treatment and rotation are partly effective in reducing the prevalence of head smut in corn.

CORN IS SUSCEPTIBLE to three rust diseases—common corn rust, southern corn rust, and tropical corn rust. In the United States only common corn rust and southern corn rust are known. Both diseases are generally of minor importance, but occasionally they may become severe and cause considerable leaf killing. Infection that becomes

severe by silking time probably causes some actual loss in grain yield, but no accurate data are available on this point. In Mexico and Central America, corn rusts are frequently more severe and may prematurely kill plants. Tropical corn rust has been found only in the American Tropics. The three corn rusts differ somewhat in symptoms and in the morphology of the causal organisms.

COMMON CORN RUST is recognized by the appearance of circular to elongate, cinnamon-brown, powdery pustules scattered over both surfaces of the leaf. Their powdery nature is due to the masses of uredospores that form beneath and break through the epidermis of the leaf. As corn matures in the fall, black pustules are formed on both surfaces of the leaf because of formation of black teliospores in place of brown uredospores. Pustules will form on any above-ground part of the plant, but they are most abundant on the leaves.

Puccinia sorghi is the fungus that causes the common corn rust. Uredospores, or summer spores, are cinnamon brown, globoid to ellipsoid, and finely to moderately spined. The spores are spread about by wind. Under favorable conditions of moisture and temperature they germinate and penetrate the corn leaves. During the growing season, uredospores continue to produce new infections. Toward maturity of the host, teliospores are formed in the pustules. These spores are brownish black, oblong to ellipsoid, and rounded at both ends.

The teliospores are two-celled, and each is attached to a colorless pedicel once or twice the length of the spore. Teliospores overwinter and germinate in the spring to form small, colorless, thin-walled secondary spores, called basidiospores.

The basidiospores cannot attack corn, but are able to parasitize a number of species of *Oxalis*, or woodsorrel— the alternate host of the fungus. Following invasion of the woodsorrel leaves by the basidiospores, small, inconspicuous, pimplelike eruptions (spermagonia) are formed on both surfaces of the leaves. These spermagonia contain minute, colorless spores, called spermatia. The spermatia from one spermagonium must fuse with the hyphae that protrude from a spermagonium of opposite mating type before the fungus can continue growth and complete its life cycle. When such fusion takes place, the nuclei of opposite type associate in pairs in the mycelium, which then continues to grow and finally forms the cluster cup (aecial) stage of the fungus on the lower surface of the woodsorrel leaves. The cluster cups, called aecia, contain numerous aeciospores. These spores are globoid, finely spined, pale yellow, and each contains two nuclei. Aeciospores are carried by wind to young corn plants, where they germinate and penetrate the host tissues. Following infection by aeciospores, red uredospores are formed in pustules on the plant. Uredospores may overwinter in southern and central United States and initiate infections the following spring, thus bypassing the alternate host, woodsorrel, as a link in the life cycle of the fungus.

Uredospores are carried progressively northward by wind currents as the growing season advances and probably furnish the bulk of the initial inoculum of the corn rust in the Corn Belt.

MODERATE TEMPERATURES and frequent heavy dews favor development of common corn rust. Luxuriant and succulent growth of the host, as frequently occurs on soils high in nitrogen, is conducive to rust development.

Little attention has been given to the control of common corn rust because of its minor importance. Inbred lines differ in resistance to common corn rust, but because of the variation in distribution of physiologic races of the rust, the reaction of inbred lines may not be constant when such lines are grown in different localities. Seed treatment and crop rotation have no effect on the disease. Teosinte is the only other host for this rust.

Southern corn rust is found from Massachusetts westward to southern Indiana and southward to the Gulf of Mexico. It has been found in Mexico, Central America, South America, the West Indies, and Africa.

The symptoms resemble those of common corn rust, particularly in the uredial, or summer, stage. The cinnamon-brown pustules tend to be smaller and more circular in outline than those of common rust. Pustules of the telial, or winter, stage are chocolate brown to black and circular to elongate and are distinguished from common corn rust by retention of the epidermis of the leaf over the pustule for a long time.

Puccinia polysora is the fungus that causes southern corn rust. Uredospores are yellowish to golden, globoid to ellipsoid, and finely and sparingly spined. Teliospores, which differ from those of *P. sorghi*, are angular, irregularly ellipsoid or ovoid, and chestnut brown. Each spore is two-celled and borne on a pedicel one-fourth or less the length of the spore.

No alternate host is known for southern corn rust. Consequently, the spermagonial and aecial stages have not been described. Much of the initial inoculum in the southern part of the Corn Belt may be carried in by wind currents from warmer areas. Certain species of *Tripsacum* and silver plumegrass are the only other known hosts of southern corn rust.

Frequent heavy dews favor infection and spread of the disease. Southern corn rust requires somewhat higher temperatures for optimum development than common corn rust. Because of the minor importance of this rust, little attention has been paid to methods of control.

ARNOLD J. ULLSTRUP *is a plant pathologist in the Bureau of Plant Industry, Soils, and Agricultural Engineering cooperating with the Purdue University Agricultural Experiment Station.*

Several Ear Rots of Corn

Arnold J. Ullstrup

Diplodia ear rot, or dry rot, is a prevalent and destructive disease of corn ears. Bleaching of the husks is one of its earliest symptoms. Early infection results in complete rotting of the ear, which becomes grayish brown and shrunken by harvest. The growth of the fungus makes the husks adhere tightly to the ear. Such ears remain upright for a long time. Ears that become infected later show a grayish-white mold on and between the kernels at harvest. When infection occurs late in the season, the ears may show no external evidence of the disease; only when such ears are broken, or kernels removed, is infection apparent. Mold will be seen only on the cob and at the discolored tips of the kernels. Diplodia ear rot begins usually at the butt of the ear and involves all the kernels as it progresses toward the tip.

Diplodia zeae is the fungus that causes diplodia ear rot. Its spores are olive brown, long oval, straight to slightly curved, and two-celled. A second type of spore, often found, is tiny, colorless, and threadlike. Both types are borne in black, globose, flask-shaped structures, called pycnidia, which are formed partly embedded in the stalks, husks, shanks, and cobs. Mature spores are released from the pycnidia in wet weather. The spores are carried by wind and lodge between the husks where, in the presence of moisture, they germinate and penetrate the host tissue.

Corn is the only known host of the fungus. Besides ear rot, the fungus causes a stalk rot of corn. A similar species, *Diplodia macrospora*, causes an ear rot of corn in warm, humid areas. Its spores are about twice as long as those of *D. zeae*. No sexual stage of either species is known.

The disease is most prevalent in years when June and July are dry and August and September are wet. Hybrids with loose husks that permit exposure of the ear tip or that hold their ears upright for a relatively long time show a high incidence of ear rot. Upright ears tend to retain water between the husks and make conditions ideal for germination of the spores that lodge there. Early-drying hybrids usually show less disease than do those that dry slowly. Ears are most susceptible to infection within 2 to 3 weeks after silking. The inbred lines 540, Ill. R4, and Ill. 90 transmit resistance; the lines Ind. Tr, Ill. Hy, and M14 tend to transmit susceptibility.

GIBBERELLA EAR ROT, or red ear rot, is somewhat more prevalent in the northern and western parts of the Corn Belt. It is seldom of major importance over more than small areas. Infected corn is especially poisonous to hogs.

It is distinguished by a pink to brick-red fungus growth, which discolors the ears, husks, and kernels. Infection usually begins at the tip of the ear and progresses toward the base.

The causal fungus, *Gibberella zeae*, produces two types of spores. The colorless asexual spores tend to be crescent-shaped, with sharp, pointed ends, and have three to five cross-walls. The sexual spores, the ascospores, are colorless and long oval in shape and have one to three cross-walls. Ascospores are borne in saclike structures, the asci, each of which usually contains eight ascospores. The asci are produced in black, globose, flask-shaped structures, the perithecia. Perithecia develop on cornstalks and then mature the following spring and early summer. Mature ascospores ooze from the apex of the perithecia in wet weather. Wind carries the spores to susceptible hosts where, in wet weather, they germinate and penetrate the tissues.

G. zeae causes also a stalk rot of corn, a seedling blight of corn, and scab or head blight of small grains. Barley and wheat sometimes are severely damaged by scab.

Wet weather at silking time favors infection of corn ears. Hybrids with loose, open husks that expose the ear tips frequently show more of the disease than do those offering greater husk protection.

Rotation and clean plowing tend to reduce the spore population of the fungus, but little benefit from such measures can be expected unless they are practiced over a wide area.

FUSARIUM KERNEL ROT, or pink kernel rot, is widely distributed. Damage to individual ears usually is less severe than with diplodia or gibberella ear rot. The disease is frequently prevalent in the drier parts of the Corn Belt and in some of the Western States.

Infected kernels, often distributed at random over the ear, are recognized by pale-pink to lavender discoloration on the kernel caps resulting from growth of the fungus. The fungus often gains entrance to the ear through channels made by earworms and corn borers.

Fusarium kernel rot is caused by *Gibberella fujikuroi*. The asexual spores are of two types. Microconidia, which are most abundant, are small, colorless, oval shaped, and borne in chains and false heads. Macroconidia are produced sparingly and resemble generally the asexual spores of *G. zeae*. The ascospores, asci, and the perithecia are like those of *G. zeae*, except for minor differences. A closely related fungus, *G. fujikuroi* var. *subglutinans*, is also frequently associated with pink kernel rot. Microconidia are borne in false heads and never in chains. Both fungi are widely distributed and are weak parasites that frequently follow infections initiated by more vigorous pathogens. The fungi live over in the soil and on plant refuse from one season to another.

Some inbred lines are more susceptible than others to this disease. Inbred lines that tend to show "silk-cut" or "popped kernel" are more susceptible in that such breaks in the seed coat provide easy means for the fungus to establish infection. Inbred lines that transmit this tendency toward weak seed coats to their hybrids should be avoided where fusarium kernel rot is a problem.

NIGROSPORA COB ROT is widely distributed over the Corn Belt. The incidence of the disease is variable, but some may be found nearly every year.

The most typical symptom is the shredding of the cob. Shredding may begin at the tip or butt of the ear, but the latter site is far more common. The disease ordinarily is not conspicuous until harvest. Severely infected ears show a gray discoloration of the internal cob tissues because of growth of the fungus. The pith may be completely disintegrated, so that only the water-conducting strands remain intact. Chaff on normally red-cobbed hybrids is brown instead of red as in healthy ears. Kernels on infected ears will show masses of black spores near their tips. Ears are light in weight and kernels are bleached and loose on the cob.

Nigrospora oryzae is the causal fungus. The black spores are oval to spherical in shape and are borne on short branches of the fungus strands. The fungus lives on dead plant refuse from one season to the next. No sexual stage of the fungus is known. The organism is not an aggressive parasite.

The disease develops when corn plants have been checked in their growth by frost, drought, stalk rot, or leaf blight. Corn appears to be more susceptible when grown on poor soil than corn that is well nourished.

The use of adapted, full-season hybrids tends to reduce the incidence of the disease. Kernels from infected ears, which often germinate and produce normal seedlings in warm soil, may give rise to weak seedlings when cold, wet weather follows planting.

GRAY EAR ROT has been found throughout most of the eastern part of the United States, but the disease has been serious only in local areas.

Early symptoms of gray ear rot resemble closely those of diplodia ear rot. Husks are bleached and adhere to each other because of the growth of the fungus. The ear often remains in an upright position until harvest. Infected ears have tiny black specks through the pith of the cob. Severely infected ears are slate gray in color and light in weight. Kernels from infected ears have small black specks or stripes beneath the seed coat.

Physalospora zeae is the fungus that causes gray ear rot. The organism produces no spores on the ears. All spore forms are found in large lesions on corn leaves. The black globe-shaped perithecia are embedded in the dead tissue of the leaf lesions. Asci are cylindrical and straight or slightly curved and contain eight ascospores. The colorless ascospores are narrow, elliptical, and one-celled. The asexual spores are colorless, one-celled, and oval. They are borne in black, flask-shaped pycnidia, which are embedded in the dead tissue in the leaf lesions.

The spores are carried by wind to corn leaves and ears where they germinate and start infection. The fruiting structures (pycnidia and perithecia), produced on leaves, overwinter and mature the following summer. Wet weather during and following silking favors development of the disease. Hybrids that hold ears in an upright position for a relatively long time and those having poor husk protection tend to be susceptible.

PHYSALOSPORA EAR ROT occurs in the Gulf States. The symptoms are somewhat similar to those of gray ear rot. The causal organism, *Physalospora zeicola*, is similar to *P. zeae*. Asexual spores are two-celled and olive brown. *P. zeicola* does not attack corn leaves. Perithecia and pycnidia are produced on cornstalks in the field. Warm, wet weather during and following silking favors development.

Rhizoctonia ear rot is known to occur only in Florida. In early stages of infection husks and kernels are covered with a pink mycelial growth of the fungus. Later the color becomes dull gray. *Rhizoctonia zeae* is the fungus causing the disease. No spores are known in the life cycle of the organisms. The fungus is carried over from one season to another as dormant mycelium and sclerotia in the seed and on plant debris. The distribution of the disease suggests that it is favored by warm, humid weather.

A NUMBER OF other fungi attack and cause rotting of corn ears. These fungi, which are widely distributed, are not specialized in their parasitism and become prevalent only under conditions exceptionally favorable to their development. They often gain entrance to ears following insect injury.

Species of *Penicillium* cause a blue-green rot of kernels. A number of species of *Aspergillus* cause a powdery black rot of kernels. A kernel rot caused by species of *Hormodendrum* is recognized by the deep greenish-black rot on the caps of the kernels. Warm, wet weather after the corn is mature favors development of the fungi on and between the kernels on ears in the field. All these fungi may cause storage rots if the corn is stored when its moisture content is too high.

ARNOLD J. ULLSTRUP, *a graduate of the University of Wisconsin, is a plant pathologist in the Bureau of Plant Industry, Soils, and Agricultural Engineering cooperating with the Purdue University Agricultural Experiment Station. He has been engaged in the study of the nature and control of the diseases of corn since 1938.*

vegetable

crops

Field Diseases of Beans and Lima Beans

W. J. Zaumeyer, H. Rex Thomas

More than 50 diseases attack beans and lima beans in this country. In a season when weather favors their development, they may cause losses to American farmers of 15 million dollars.

No region of the United States is free of all bean diseases. Root rots cause serious trouble wherever crop rotations are not practiced. Frequent rains during the growing season are likely to lead to heavy losses from bacterial blights, especially if seed that carries the blight organisms is planted. Bean rust often causes serious losses in parts of the South and West. Virus diseases occur in all bean-growing districts. Downy mildew of lima beans often gives considerable trouble in the North Atlantic States.

About 30 years ago, when anthracnose and bacterial blights were causing heavy losses of snap beans, research revealed that the organisms causing those diseases, which are seed-borne, do not thrive in areas where low rainfall and high temperatures prevail during the growing season. Consequently the business of growing seed of snap beans moved from the East and Middle West to the drier intermountain region. Seed growers in parts of that region and in the Pacific States need have little fear of large losses from the two diseases, and crops grown from their seed all over the United States are less apt to be diseased than those grown from seed produced east of the Rockies.

393

Another line of research that has enabled farmers to grow healthier bean crops is the development of fungicides for control of certain diseases. Still another is the development of better systems of crop rotation and better methods of field sanitation. Possibly the most progressive step of all has been the development of disease-resistant varieties. A number of new varieties, each resistant to several diseases, have been introduced.

THE BACTERIAL BLIGHTS are among the most important diseases of beans wherever the crop is subject to frequent rains during the growing season. If occasional showers occur during the early part of the growing season the diseases are usually noted even though the total rainfall is not excessive. Only in certain sections of the Intermountain and Pacific Coast States, such as southern Idaho, eastern Washington, and California, are beans grown relatively free of these diseases. Practically all beans grown for seed purposes therefore are produced in a rather small area in the West. The severity of the diseases in any place varies with the weather and the presence of infected seeds.

The bacterial blights include common blight, fuscous blight, halo blight, and bacterial wilt. Each is caused by a different bacterial organism, but all, except the wilt organism, produce similar symptoms on bean plants. Under certain conditions the bacterial wilt organism produces a wilting of the plant unlike that caused by any of the other organisms. Under other conditions some of the wilt symptoms are like those of other bacterial diseases.

Water-soaked spots on the leaves usually are the first visible evidence of blight. The spots enlarge, turn brown, and finally kill the leaf.

Halo blight makes a halolike zone of greenish-yellow tissue around each water-soaked spot in cool weather. Leaves of newly infected plants are yellow.

Leaves of plants infected with the common or the fuscous blight organism turn brown rapidly and look burned. Positive identification of the two diseases cannot be made without laboratory tests.

The necrotic leaf lesions made by the bacterial wilt organism are hard to tell from those caused by the common and fuscous blight organisms. From a combination of all the symptoms of bacterial wilt, this disease can usually be told from the other three diseases.

Water-soaked spots similar to those on the leaves are produced on the pods by all of the organisms, except the wilt organism. The spots grow larger, and the tissue around each is reddish brown or brick red. The spots finally dry and are often covered by a dried bacterial ooze. Commonly the bacteria invade the upper suture of the pod, cause water soaking of the tissue on both sides of it, and later infect the seed. On light-colored bean seed a yellowish discoloration may be visible at the hilum, the point of attachment to the pod, but on colored seed the infection is hard to detect. Badly infected seeds usually are shriveled and yellow. Slightly infected seeds may appear healthy.

The only evidence of infection of pods by the bacterial wilt organism is a slight discoloration of the upper suture, but the seeds inside them often are yellow and shrunken. When the infected seeds are planted, the plant becomes infected internally, and the bacteria spread through it. General stunting and death may result. Some of the seedlings may grow to fairly good size, but usually a lesion, known as stem girdle or joint rot, occurs at the node where the cotyledons were attached. The affected stem, further strained by the increasing weight of the top, breaks at the node.

The bacteria that cause common blight (*Xanthomonas phaseoli*), fuscous blight (*X. phaseoli* var. *fuscans*), and halo blight (*Pseudomonas phaseolicola*) enter the plants through the stomata of the leaves, stems, and pods. The wilt organism (*Corynebacterium flaccum-*

faciens) enters through wounds. Rain, hail, driving winds, damp weather, and even sprinkler irrigation favor the spread of the organisms.

Plants grown from infected seed frequently develop lesions on the cotyledons and stems. From those spots bacteria are splashed by rain or hail to leaves of other plants. A few diseased plants scattered through a field as a result of infected seed may be the source of a general outbreak if weather conditions are favorable for the spread of the organisms. Warm weather favors common and fuscous blights and bacterial wilt. Cool weather favors halo blight.

The bacterial blight organisms can also live over winter on diseased bean refuse in the soil, possibly for 2 years.

The most effective control measure against bacterial blights is the use of disease-free seed. One should use only seed grown in areas where rainfall is scant and blight epidemics do not occur.

Because the blight organisms can overwinter in the soil, beans should not be planted for at least 2 years in fields that have been infected. Nor should bean straw from a crop that showed blight be applied to land that is to be planted to beans. Infected bean straw used for bedding farm animals may continue to harbor bacteria, and the use of such straw on fields to be planted to beans is unwise.

Crops like lima beans, soybeans, or cowpeas, which also are susceptible to one or more of the blight organisms, should not be included in the rotation.

Bacteria adhere to clothing and farm machinery. Picking, cultivating, and similar operations can spread the bacteria from a few infected plants to the rest of the plants in a field.

No variety of snap beans or dry beans is resistant to common or fuscous blight. Many of the varieties of dry beans, such as Pinto, Great Northern, Red Mexican, and Michelite, are highly resistant to halo blight, but all snap beans are susceptible to it. Not much is known about resistance of any of the varieties to bacterial wilt.

Seed treatment is of doubtful value in the control of the blights. Spraying or dusting the plants with fungicides or bactericides has not proved to be a practical control measure.

RUST is one of the most serious diseases of dry beans in irrigated sections of Colorado, Nebraska, Wyoming, and Montana some years. It also causes losses in pole snap beans along the coast of southern California, Oregon, Washington, and Florida, and in other States. In 1950 and in 1951 it caused considerable damage in western Nebraska. It was widespread in 1951 in northeastern Colorado. Bean rust infects only beans. None of the rusts of the other crops infects beans.

The bean rust organism commonly attacks the leaves. It attacks the stems and pods less commonly. The first symptoms are small white spots or flecks on the under sides of the leaves. In a few days the spots break open into rusty-colored lesions, which occur on both leaf surfaces. The leaf begins to yellow about a week after the lesions appear. Later it turns brown and dries up. In a seriously infested bean field the plants look as if they had been scorched.

A fungus, *Uromyces phaseoli typica*, causes bean rust. It reproduces by spores, of which there are several types. The organism cannot be grown on any known artificial media as many other fungi can be grown. It grows only on bean plants.

Usually the grower notices only one of the spore stages, the summer stage. It shows up as reddish-brown pustules, which contain thousands of spores. The spores, called uredospores, readily become detached and may be blown by the wind from plant to plant and field to field. Toward fall the rust produces another type of spore, which is black and known as a teliospore. These spores live over winter, mainly on old bean straw. A small percentage of the summer spores also survive the winter.

The teliospores germinate in spring. Each produces four smaller spores of still another kind, called sporidia. They are blown about by the wind. If conditions are favorable when they alight on a bean plant, they germinate and grow into the leaf. Later they produce a fourth kind of spore, known as aeciospores. These, in turn, infect bean leaves and produce the red summer spores.

The aeciospore stage is found only in some bean-growing areas, particularly in the far West—we do not know why. It has never been reported in the intermountain region. But there the small percentage of uredospores that overwinter may also be blown by the wind and later germinate and penetrate into the leaf of a young bean plant. Some days later occasional white flecks may appear on the under side of the leaves. The flecks soon break through the leaf surfaces and produce the rusty pustules of the type the grower observed the previous summer.

Since each pustule produces thousands of spores, the disease may develop readily if weather conditions are right. Each spore in turn may produce another pustule on a leaf in about 10 days. The cycle may be repeated for 5 to 6 weeks. Unless steps are taken to control the disease an epidemic may occur and the crop may be lost.

Bean rust develops most rapidly when the humidity is high, as the result of rain, dew, or irrigation. Heavy vine growth, which shades the ground and prevents air circulation, produces ideal conditions for rust.

Bean rust is not seed-borne. The spores live over winter on old bean straw and the disease may get started in the field if beans are planted on land that produced a crop of rust-infected beans the preceding year or on new land on which infected straw was spread. The spores on the straw may germinate and infect the new crop. The disease might also get started if beans are grown close to stacks of old, infected bean straw. Spores may be blown to nearby bean fields and infect the plants.

More than 30 races or strains of bean rust have been identified. Each reacts differently on different varieties of beans. Some varieties are susceptible to certain races but are resistant to others. No variety that resists all the known strains of rust has been developed. The few noncommercial varieties that resist a great many of them are used as parents in the breeding of new varieties resistant to as many strains as possible.

The most satisfactory artificial control is a dust of finely ground sulfur. It can be applied to the plants with a power duster on the ground or from an airplane. The dusting should be done fairly early in the season before the rust spots become numerous. A prompt application destroys the few pustules present at that time, stops the spread of spores from the spots, and prevents the production of others. If dusting is done after the rust is widespread, more applications are required and the control is not nearly so satisfactory. If the disease is widespread in a district, two or three dustings at intervals of 7 or 10 days are necessary. The best time to dust is when the wind is not blowing and the plants are dry. About 25 to 30 pounds of sulfur to an acre should be used for each dusting.

Bean rust can be almost eliminated in a district in a few years if growers cooperate and dust their beans with sulfur. This must be started fairly early in the season and before the plants overlap in the rows—usually about 6 weeks after planting.

All commercial varieties of dry beans are susceptible to most of the races of rust. Men in the Department of Agriculture developed two Pinto varieties, No. 5 and No. 14, which resist many of the races but are slightly too viny for commercial use. Other resistant types of Pinto, of more of a bush habit, and several Great Northern types should be ready for distribution to growers in a few years.

Most of the bush snap beans are highly tolerant of rust. Some of the pole snap beans, however, such as Blue Lake, McCaslan, and Kentucky Wonder are very susceptible. Among the tolerant pole beans are White Kentucky Wonder, the U. S. No. 4 Kentucky Wonder, Potomac, and the Rialto.

ROOT ROTS occur wherever beans are grown, but they cause more damage in the Southern States than elsewhere. They have become a problem in parts of the West. The organisms causing root rots live in the soil and attack beans when soil and weather conditions are unfavorable for best plant growth.

The organisms as a group form lesions or cankers on the stem below the soil level, on the taproot, and on the fibrous roots. The cankers, which are of various sizes and shapes, may be gray, black, brown, or brick red. Decay of the fibrous roots is common. Infected plants generally are stunted and somewhat yellowed.

The dry root rot organism usually causes a reddening of the taproot, which may extend to the soil line. The rootlets that develop from the taproot are killed. The main root and the lower part of the stem beneath the soil are often pithy and dry.

The rhizoctonia root rot organism causes reddish-brown, sunken cankers on the roots and the stem below the soil line. The cankers often girdle the stem.

The pythium wilt and southern wilt organisms cause sudden wilting and death of the plant. Pythium wilt usually occurs on the stem at the soil line. The affected tissues become soft and slimy. The infection often extends upward into the branches, but it does not extend much below the soil surface.

Southern wilt rots roots and stems, which later become dry and papery. A white fungus growth develops on the stem at the soil surface and grows into the soil around the plant. When an infected plant is pulled from the soil, a collar of fungus mycelium and soil often clings to it.

The causal organisms of dry root rot (*Fusarium solani* f. *phaseoli*), rhizoctonia root rot (*Rhizoctonia solani*), pythium wilt (*Pythium butleri*), and southern wilt (*Sclerotium rolfsii*) can live for fairly long periods in the soil where no cultivated crop is being grown. All the organisms, except the dry root rot organism, cause root rots of other crops. The southern wilt organism is found primarily in the South, but the other organisms normally are present in nearly all soils. They like cool weather and high soil moisture. None is seed-borne.

We know of no effective artificial control measures for the root rots. No varieties are resistant to any of them. Cultural practices that improve the general growing conditions of the crop will reduce the severity of the diseases. The most effective control is a 4- to 5-year rotation that includes cereals, clover, and alfalfa—plants on which the root-rotting organisms rarely cause damage. Anything that makes conditions favorable for bean plants tends to make conditions unfavorable for the fungi.

SCLEROTINIA WILT, or white mold, is a serious disease of beans in several parts of the United States—in parts of southern Florida, Wyoming, Montana, Idaho, and Oregon.

It affects the stems, leaves, and pods. Small, soft, watery spots appear first. The organism grows rapidly. If several days of cool, wet weather follow the infection, a cottony fungus growth spreads over the branches and leaves. Heavy vine growth in irrigated fields causes the plants to stay moist for a rather long time, and so the fungus becomes active. The affected tissues dry out and become light, punky, and often severely shredded. Irregular, hard, black bodies, one-fourth to one-half inch in diameter and called sclerotia, frequently occur about that time on infected tissue. Those are the resting bodies of the fungus. Severely affected plants usually die within a few days.

The fungus *Sclerotinia sclerotiorum* causes sclerotinia wilt. The black sclerotia fall to the ground; when moisture and temperature are right, strands of white mold grow out of the bodies and infect bean plants directly. If conditions are not favorable when the sclerotia fall to the ground, they may remain in a resting stage for as long as 10 years.

Infection takes place also by spores. From the sclerotia grow tiny bodies, like mushrooms, each of which may produce thousands of spores. Spores that are blown to nearby bean plants germinate and infect them. Soon new masses of mold appear. In them more sclerotia are formed. As each sclerotium can produce many spore-bearing bodies and each of the bodies may produce thousands of spores, even a few sclerotia in one field can sometimes cause widespread infection if conditions are suitable.

No bean varieties are known to be resistant. No spray or dust materials have been found to control the disease satisfactorily.

A high percentage of the sclerotia can be destroyed by flooding infected fields for 3 weeks or more. In parts of Florida where that practice is feasible, the best season for flooding is summer because high temperatures hasten decay.

Fields in irrigated areas where the disease occurs should not be irrigated oftener than necessary. Wider spacing of rows and reduced rates of seeding, which prevent the vines from meeting early in the season and allow better air circulation, reduce the moisture around the plants and thus check the development of the fungus.

Infested bean straw and cull beans contaminated with sclerotia should not be fed to animals if the manure is to be used on land where beans may soon be planted.

When possible, infested bean fields should be planted for 2 years or more to crops—including small grains, corn, and hay—that are not susceptible to sclerotinia wilt. That practice is not likely to eliminate the trouble entirely, but it will reduce losses.

COMMON BEAN MOSAIC has been known for more than 50 years and is world-wide. Since 1930 several other mosaics of bean have been reported.

Because the different mosaics generally produce similar field symptoms, they are discussed here more or less as one disease. Many growers underestimate the importance of bean mosaics because infected plants are rarely killed. The mosaics reduce yield and quality of the product. The annual losses from these diseases total several million dollars in the United States.

The important mosaic diseases of bean are common bean mosaic, a variant of that disease called New York 15 mosaic, and yellow bean mosaic. Two other bean mosaics, southern bean mosaic and pod mottle, have been found, and may become of economic importance if they become widespread. Several strains of yellow bean mosaic have been identified. In some years they have caused considerable damage.

Common bean mosaic is the most widespread of the bean mosaics. The New York 15 mosaic virus, which produces much the same symptoms, is less serious. Yellow bean mosaic, which is primarily a disease of sweetclover and is found also on crimson clover, red clover, and gladiolus, has entirely different symptoms. Plant lice spread it from those crops to beans.

The bean mosaics cause mottling and malformation of leaves and stunting of the plants. The symptoms are more intense at high temperatures. Symptoms are not noticed on stems or seeds. The patterns made by the mottled yellow and green areas may vary. Dark-green areas frequently develop near the veins and veinlets of infected leaves. Leaves of very susceptible varieties may be considerably puckered and may develop areas that look like blisters and warts. On less susceptible varieties, the leaves are ruffled, crinkled, or cupped downward.

With yellow bean mosaic, the contrast between the yellow and green areas of the leaves usually is more intense than it is with common mosaic. On some resistant varieties the common mosaic virus may produce occasionally a necrosis of the leaves, pods, stems, and roots. This symptom has been observed only rarely in the field.

Pods from infected plants are sometimes mottled, deformed, and rough. Some may be very shiny. Yellow mosaic (especially the pod-distorting strain), southern bean mosaic, and pod mottle viruses produce the worst symptoms on pods.

Each of the bean mosaics is caused by a different virus. Plant lice usually spread the viruses from diseased to healthy plants.

The viruses of the important mosaic diseases are not spread from infected to healthy plants by cultivation or picking, but the viruses of southern bean mosaic and pod mottle can be spread thus.

The virus of common bean mosaic and its variant are seed-borne. The infected seeds look normal, but they carry the virus and produce diseased plants. None of the viruses causing the other mosaic diseases is carried in the seed.

The only satisfactory way to prevent mosaic is to use resistant varieties. None resists all viruses. Some of the bush snap beans that resist common bean mosaic and its variant are Conender, Florida Belle, Logan, Improved New Stringless, Idagreen, Puregold, Rival, Idaho Refugee, Sensation Refugee 1066, Sensation Refugee 1071, U. S. 5 Refugee, Tenderong 15, Ranger, Topcrop, and Wade. The resistant pole varieties include Blue Lake, Kentucky Wonder, and U. S. No. 4 Kentucky Wonder.

Dry beans resistant to common bean mosaic are Michelite, Robust, Great Northern U. I. Nos. 16, 31, 81, and 123, Montana Nos. 1 and 5, Red Mexican U. I. Nos. 3 and 34, Pinto U. I. Nos. 72, 78, and 111. Only the Great Northern strains are resistant to the New York 15 variant strain.

No variety has yet been developed that resists yellow bean mosaic.

In sections where yellow bean mosaic is widespread it is a good practice to avoid planting beans too close to fields of sweetclover, red clover crimson clover, and gladiolus. Fence rows and ditch banks should be kept free of sweetclover, which commonly grows "wild" in many Western States.

CURLY TOP is a virus disease of beans and several other crops. It commonly is found in Utah, Idaho, Washington, Oregon, and California, and sometimes in other Western States. In some localities it is not serious every year, although when there are many beet leafhoppers, which transmit the virus, the bean crop may be ruined. In some parts of Idaho, Washington, and Oregon, the disease has been so serious every year that only resistant varieties survive.

Young plants infected with curly top are decidedly dwarfed. The symptoms are most pronounced on the trifoliate leaves which pucker, curl downward, and show a clearing of the veins. The young leaves cease to develop, turn yellow, and curl downward. They are thick and brittle and readily break off from the stem. Frequently they are cupped; sometimes they resemble small green balls. Plants infected when very young usually die; plants that are infected later do not die, and typical symptoms do not always develop. The pods produced on infected plants are usually stunted. The disease is not seed-borne.

Curly top is spread from plant to plant only by the beet leafhopper, usually called whitefly in the West. Before being able to infect beans, it must feed on some plant that is infected with curly top. It overwinters in desert areas where many weeds carry the curly top virus. In the spring the leafhoppers migrate to cultivated fields of beans, beets, tomatoes, and other crops and spread the disease. The symptoms appear about 10 to 14 days after infection. Within a few weeks after that an infected plant may die.

Because curly top is transmitted only by leafhoppers, the disease is prevalent only where that insect thrives. The severity of the disease reflects the population of the leafhoppers and the percentage carrying the virus.

Curly top can be best controlled by growing resistant varieties. Unfortunately, no commercially suitable resistant variety of snap bean has been developed, but progress is being made in obtaining such beans, notably in developing several resistant Blue Lake types.

Resistant varieties of dry beans are Great Northern U. I. Nos. 16 and 31, Red Mexican U. I. Nos. 3 and 34, and Pinto U. I. Nos. 72, 78, and 111, Pink, and Pioneer. Pioneer can also be used as a snap bean in home gardens in regions where curly top is prevalent, although as such it is only fair.

DOWNY MILDEW was first reported in the United States about 60 years ago. In later years it has caused considerable damage to lima beans in some of the Middle Atlantic and North Atlantic States. It is of minor importance elsewhere. The fungus that causes it develops best during periods of wet weather with cool nights, heavy dews, and fairly warm days.

The disease is recognized by the white, cottony growth that forms in large, irregular patches on the pods. Each patch may have a purplish border. When young pods are attacked and when older ones are covered with fungus growth they shrivel, wilt, and die. Downy mildew less frequently attacks young leaves, shoots, and flower parts. Infected leaves may show irregular spots, particularly near the veins, without much visible fungus growth.

Downy mildew is caused by a fungus, *Phytophthora phaseoli*, which attacks only lima beans. The organism may penetrate the seeds and live in them over winter. It can also survive in debris, which may be a source of infection of the new crop. During the growing season, the fungus may be spread to healthy plants by insects that visit infected flowers. Rapid natural spread depends on ideal weather conditions favoring the fungus.

Seed from an infected crop should not be used for planting. Seed produced in the far West where downy mildew is not found should be used. A 2- or 3-year crop rotation is wise. When the disease is first noted the crop should be dusted with a copper dust containing 5 to 7 percent actual copper, such as tribasic copper, at the rate of about 40 pounds of dust to the acre for each application. Dustings should be made at weekly intervals as long as the weather favors the development of the disease.

No commercial variety of lima beans is resistant. Several resistant noncommercial types have been found. A breeding program has been started to incorporate that resistance into suitable varieties.

W. J. ZAUMEYER, *a graduate of the University of Wisconsin, is principal pathologist in charge of bean and pea disease investigations in the division of vegetable crops and diseases of the Bureau of Plant Industry, Soils, and Agricultural Engineering. Since he joined the Department in 1928, his work has dealt particularly with the diseases of beans and peas. At present much of his time is spent in developing bean varieties that are disease-resistant and in determining other ways of controlling bean diseases.*

H. REX THOMAS, *a graduate of the University of California, is a plant pathologist in the division of vegetable crops and diseases of the Bureau of Plant Industry, Soils, and Agricultural Engineering. He joined the Department in 1937 and specializes in the diseases of beans and peas.*

Root Rots, Wilts, and Blights of Peas

W. T. Schroeder

The pea (*Pisum sativum*) is subject to various types of diseases—blights, root rots, and wilts. The formulation of control measures for them requires knowledge of their symptoms, causes, relations of host and parasite, and possible inherent resistance.

Blight refers to the discoloration, gradual drying, and eventual death of the affected plant parts. Bacteria and fungi cause blights, which usually are seed-borne and develop best during wet weather.

Only one major bacterial blight (*Pseudomonas pisi*) affects peas. A number of fungal blights, however, do occur in peas, among which are septoria blotch (*Septoria pisi*), downy mildew (*Peronospora pisi*), powdery mildew (*Erysiphe polygoni*), anthracnose (*Colletotrichum pisi*), ascochyta blight, and several minor ones.

Ascochyta blight is among the oldest and worst. Its nature and control are much like those of other fungal blights (except powdery mildew). Details about it therefore apply generally to the others.

ASCOCHYTA BLIGHT is a composite of three diseases resulting from infection, singly or collectively, by *Ascochyta pisi*, *A. pinodella*, or *Mycosphaerella pinodes*.

The nature of the disease was first determined in Europe in 1830. It was a constant threat in the United States until about 1915, when it declined with the shifting of the seed industry to areas in the West where the low rainfall before and during the harvest reduced the amount of infected seed. But in some years unseasonal rainfall during harvesttime in western seed-growing districts means contaminated seed, so that the disease remains something of a problem.

The symptoms the three parasites cause are almost alike. Most evident are the lesions that begin as small purplish specks on leaves and pods. When infection is caused by *M. pinodes* or *A. pinodella*, the specks may enlarge on the leaves into round, targetlike spots. If numerous, they join to make irregular brownish-purple blotches on both leaves and pods. *A. pisi* produces relatively few, rather definite, sunken, tan or brown spots, which have dark-brown margins and are circular on leaves and pods. The pod lesions usually become sunken.

Stem lesions are elongated and purplish black. They originate as separate infections or as a continuation of petiole infection around the nodal area. They also may coalesce and girdle the entire stem, weakening it so that it is easily broken.

Affected leaves eventually shrivel and dry into a blighted condition, which resembles freshly cured clover hay. *M. pinodes* may also blight the blossoms and young pods and cause withering, distortion, and eventual dropping.

All three organisms can attack that part of the stem and root at the soil line and produce a bluish-black foot rot. It is severest when it is caused by *A. pinodella*. *A. pisi* seldom causes severe foot rot.

The three organisms responsible for the ascochyta blight complex are closely related, but each has marks that classify it as a distinct species. In pure culture on artificial media, the light-colored mycelium and the abundant carrot-red spores of *A. pisi* readily distinguish it from the darker-colored mycelium and relatively scarce light-buff spore exudate of *M. pinodes* and *A. pinodella*. All produce water-borne spores, the pycniospores, but those of *A. pinodella* are only half as large as the spores of the other two species. The incubation period of the disease caused by *M. pinodes* and *A. pinodella* is 2 to 4 days, compared with 6 to 8 days for *A. pisi. M. pinodes* is the only species that produces ascospores. Such spores can be carried for considerable distances by air currents and largely account for the more aggressive nature of that pathogen.

The three disease organisms can infect the seed. Such infection serves to overwinter the pathogens and is a means of transporting the disease from one region to another. The pathogens also overwinter in infected pea straw. In regions of extremely mild winters, they may remain active on infected volunteer plants. The ascochyta blight organisms do not live indefinitely in the soil as in the case of the root rot and wilt fungi, but remain there only as long as the infected pea straw is not completely decomposed.

When infected seed is planted, the disease first appears as a foot rot on the young seedlings at the point of seed attachment and often kills or weakens the young plants. Spores are produced during wet weather on such plants and spread the disease to nearby plants.

Infected pea straw in the soil from the crop of the previous season may give rise to both pycniospores and ascospores. As pycniospores need spattering rain for their dissemination, they spread the disease only a few feet from the source. Ascospores, however, are shot out from the spore-bearing structures in the old plant tissue and are carried quite far by air currents. They usually are more abundant than pycniospores and spread the disease uniformly over the field rather than in small patches. If conditions are favorable, both types of spores may be formed continually on the dead parts of the infected plant. Because the ascospores are more widely and uniformly distributed, however, infection by *M. pinodes* (the only species producing ascospores) is more damaging.

Because moisture is required for spore discharge and infection, rainfall, dews, and high humidity are the most important environmental factors in the development of ascochyta blight. The number of periods of wet weather during the pea season largely determines how bad the disease will be.

Because there is no practical resistance in the pea to the ascochyta blight complex and because nothing can be done at present to change the weather, the disease is best controlled by avoiding, eliminating, or reducing the causal organisms—by the use of disease-free seed, crop rotation, and sanitation.

It is unwise to plant seed grown in humid sections of the East and Middle West. That seed is likely to be infected with the disease organisms. Furthermore, the straw from a seed crop is apt to be more heavily infected with the organisms than a crop cut in the green stage for processing. That increases the inoculum potential on the overwintered straw and affords a better chance for the disease to establish itself earlier and more severely. Seed grown in drier regions of the West is the best insurance against seedling infection. Treatment of seed with fungicides reduces the surface contamination but will not eliminate internal infection.

Rotation to control pea blights implies more than merely avoiding planting pea crops on the same land more than once every 4 or 5 years. Such a rotation undoubtedly would eliminate the organism from the soil. But, in addition, every effort should be made to locate new plantings as far as possible from those of the previous season. Even though most of the vines from the old fields are removed to the viner station, there may be enough infection on the stubble and debris to provide for the dispersal of ascospores the following spring.

Of equal importance is sanitation. Any infected plant parts—whether stubble in the field or vines on the viner stacks—offer a constant source of inoculum for the next crop. After the ensilage has been removed from the stacks, the outside part of the stack, which usually is raked off, should be destroyed before seeding the next spring. If mobile viners are used in pea fields, the vines and pods, instead of just the stubble, are left in the fields. That will create a situation comparable to one in which seed peas and processing peas are grown in the same area, for the fresh vines will dry, and the organisms will continue to develop, thereby increasing the inoculum potential for the next season.

A good practice would be to plow down all pea stubble and vines immediately and plant the field to a crop, such as grain, in which the soil will not be cultivated during the next season. In some places it is customary to plant early varieties alongside late ones or to stagger planting dates. In either event, ascospores may develop on the stubble of the earlier planting and provide for abundant dispersal of spores to the younger plantings nearby. Such practices should be discouraged.

Root rot is caused by a number of fungi, which singly or together attack the cortex, the tissue outside the water- and food-conducting cylinder of the roots and lower stem. Invasion of the cortex may be quite general, or it may be somewhat localized. The rot may be soft and watery, or it may be more like a dry, corrosive decay, depending on the causal organism. The various types of root rot are designated by the names of the fungi that cause them, such as aphanomyces root rot, fusarium root rot, and ascochyta root rot.

The damage done by root rot varies with the season and the causal organism. One year the crop may fail; the next year on the same piece of land the crop may be all right. The disease may act as a seedling blight and kill scattered plants at an early stage, or it may not attack the plant until quite late in its development. Two different pathogens attacking the same plant frequently cause more harm than either alone. Complete crop failures can occur. More often, however, yields are reduced in varying degrees as a result of an impaired or restricted root system. Under those conditions, the affected plants look as though they were suffering from malnutrition.

The disease pattern or symptoms and the conditions favorable for root rot development depend upon the specific pathogen. Practically all the types may occur wherever peas are grown, but certain ones are more prevalent in some areas than in others.

Aphanomyces root rot, caused by *Aphanomyces euteiches*, occurs to some extent wherever peas are grown and is often referred to as common root rot. It is especially prevalent in the older pea-growing regions of New York, New Jersey, Wisconsin, and Minnesota. Some 10,000 acres of canning peas were lost in 1942 in Wisconsin as a result of the disease.

The disease is first detected by a soft and watery condition of the stem an inch or two above the soil line. By then the roots have become similarly affected. The diseased tissue becomes discolored because other fungi invade the softened tissue. Ordinarily most of those fungi cannot infect the healthy tissue.

In time the affected tissue on the stem above the soil line collapses and shrivels. The outer tissues of the roots then are so rotted that when the plant is pulled all that remains of the root system is the stringy central core of the taproot. That condition usually distinguishes the aphanomyces from other root rots in the field.

Severe infection of young plants usually kills them before they blossom. Plants infected later seldom die but, because of a restricted root system, they are stunted; their leaves turn yellow and die from the ground up.

The fungus that causes aphanomyces root rot belongs to a group of fungi commonly called water molds. It has two kinds of spores. One, the oospore, or resting spore, is the thick-walled spore generally found in diseased tissue. It may also occur in culture on artificial media. The other, the zoospore, or free-swimming spore, has two long hairs, which enable it to move about in water.

In artificial culture media of relatively concentrated food materials, the oospore germinates directly into hyphae or fungal strands. If the nutrients are diluted or removed by washing, it germinates indirectly and produces the motile zoospores, which germinate into more hyphae. If the food supply is not too concentrated, the hyphae give rise to a multitude of zoospores capable of infecting the host tissue.

Very likely the nutrient concentration in the soil water affects hyphal growth and spore germination similar to that observed on artificial culture media. Aphanomyces root rot can occur on relatively dry soils, but it never becomes severe unless the soil is wet either as a result of a high water-holding capacity, as in clay soils, or frequent heavy rains. Severity of infection is associated generally with a large number of infection points on the root system. In relatively dry soil the nutrients are concentrated in the soil water; then few zoospores are apt to be produced and the infection points may be scarce. In wet soil, however, the soluble nutrients are leached or diluted and abundant spores may form, so that severe disease develops. That supposition is strengthened by the fact that commercial fertilizers, especially those high in nitrogen, sometimes aid in controlling root rot. The nitrogen fraction contributes heavily to the soluble salt content of the soil.

FUSARIUM ROOT ROT is serious in Colorado and the Pacific Northwest.

In some places, New York among them, it and aphanomyces often occur together, and then the damage is worse than that caused by either organism alone.

The disease usually starts on the seedling at the junction of the root and stem where the germinated seed remains attached. From there it extends upward as a wedge-shaped, reddish-brown lesion. The decay also may extend downward and involve primary and secondary roots. There is no pronounced water soaking of the invaded tissue, and the discoloration is immediately apparent.

Further progress of the disease causes the tissue to shrink. In time the stem is girdled, and often the plant breaks near the place of seed attachment. A reddish discoloration of the central water-conducting vessels may occur, but usually only in the zone of seed attachment and seldom more than an inch beyond. If the main root is severed from the plant in the seedling stage, the plant attempts to maintain itself by sending out new roots through the underground part of the stem, but eventually it dies or is severely stunted.

Many species of *Fusarium* have been described as causing a root rot of pea but the generally accepted causal organism is *F. solani* f. *pisi*.

Fusarium root rot occurs in fairly dry soils as well as wet soils. It flourishes when the soil temperature is around 80° F. It develops most severely when the spring planting time is warm or when the peas are planted late.

RHIZOCTONIA ROOT ROT of pea is primarily a disease of the seedling stage. It usually is of minor importance. The causal fungus is the sterile or *Rhizoctonia* stage of *Pellicularia filamentosa*. It causes injury to a wide variety of farm crops, particularly young seedlings and potato sprouts. The same fungus causes black scurf of potato tubers.

On peas, in the early stages, the

disease appears first as a slightly eroded, yellowish-brown zone on the underground stem and root in the region of the seed attachment. The tissue later turns a darker brown, and the lesions become sunken and heavily eroded. They may girdle the stem. More frequently, however, it attacks the growing tip of the emerging seedling, killing it before complete emergence. When that happens a new shoot is sent up, which also may be killed, so that the affected seedling may have a number of growing shoots with dead terminals. That is quite characteristic of this root rot.

Temperature is the primary factor in the development of this disease on pea. A soil temperature of 60° to 65° F. is most favorable.

VARIOUS SPECIES of *Pythium*, notably *P. ultimum*, can parasitize the tissues of the underground part of the pea plant. In the field, however, most of the damage from the organism results from seedling injury or seed decay.

Affected plants show a water-soaked, somewhat translucent and softened tissue extending above and below the region of seed attachment. As the disease progresses, the tissue becomes more and more discolored. It develops best in wet soil.

It is unlike *Aphanomyces* in being most aggressive during the seedling stage—it rots the germinating seed or kills the emerged seedling. If the plant survives and conditions are not unusual, *Pythium* by itself has little effect on root rot. High temperature, accompanied by high humidity or wet soil for a long time, may incite the organisms to further decay of the root system.

CONTROL OF THE ROOT ROT complex of pea is difficult because of the nature of the different causal fungi, most of which live indefinitely in the soil.

No resistant varieties are available. In infested areas growers have to depend on seed treatment, rotation, and good management of soil and crops.

Seed treatment offers protection against some phases of some of the root rots. It largely controls the seed decay and damping-off stages that result from infection by *Fusarium*, *Pythium*, and *Rhizoctonia*, but it does not preclude infection beyond those stages. Aphanomyces root rot, however, is not affected by seed treatment. The main purpose of seed treatment is to provide for healthier, more vigorous plants which are better able to ward off the effects of later infection.

Crop rotation, properly carried out, keeps the pathogens from accumulating in the soil. Because some of the pathogens—including *Pythium*, *Rhizoctonia*, *Aphanomyces*—attack different crop plants, rotation may seem of little value against them. Actually, though, a nonsusceptible crop immediately preceding the peas is of some value. Surveys of pea fields affected by *Aphanomyces* and *Fusarium* have demonstrated that the severity of root rot declines as the interval between pea crops increases. The main purpose of rotation, however, should be to prevent the build-up of the fungi in relatively healthy soil by 4- to 5-year intervals between crops rather than to attempt to reduce the pathogens after the soil has become heavily infested with them.

Good management of soil and crops deters the establishment of the fungi and enables the crop to produce if disease is present. High soil moisture favors aphanomyces root rot and others to some extent. Soils with good external and internal drainage should be selected therefore for peas. One should not return diseased pea straw to the soil immediately. Because peas affected by root rot have a restricted root system and behave as plants suffering from malnutrition, one should maintain high fertility in the soil. Applications of fertilizers sometimes make a crop possible despite aphanomyces root rot. In New York applications of commercial fertilizers at the rate of 50 to 100 pounds of nitrogen to the acre have given good results. At times, especially in bad disease years, the increase in yields does not justify the added cost of fertilizers. Gypsum at rates of one-half ton to 1 ton an acre have reduced aphanomyces root rot but not fusarium.

PEA WILT is one of a group of diseases that are incited by certain vascular Fusaria. It used to be confused with the root rot complex generally attributed to "pea-sick" soils. It differs from the root rots in that the cortical tissue is seldom affected under field conditions. Rather, the fungus establishes itself in the central core of water-conducting vessels and produces a toxin that causes a progressive yellowing and wilting of the foliage. Death of the plant may ensue.

The two distinct fusarial wilts of pea are wilt and near-wilt.

Fusarium wilt of pea was first discovered in Wisconsin in 1924. Since then it has been found in the major pea areas of the United States.

Its first noticeable symptom is a downward curving of the stipules and leaflets and a slight yellowing of the leaves. A superficial grayness like waxy bloom may also occur. The lower internodes thicken and the entire stem becomes somewhat rigid. Thereupon the plants may wilt abruptly at the top, followed by a shriveling of the stem. If soil temperature is low, such wilting may not occur. Instead the affected plant becomes yellow and withers slowly, leaf by leaf, from the ground upward. The central water core turns yellow or orange. Symptoms often occur in advance of the fungus in the vessels. At times wilt symptoms appear with very little vascular discoloration. The cortex, the outer part of the root and stem, is usually quite sound, unless root rot fungi enter it. In a newly infested field only a few scattered plants may show infection the first year. With repeated plantings to susceptible varieties the infestations appear as enlarged round areas, which eventually merge until the entire field becomes infested. The disease can spread rapidly.

Fusarium wilt of pea, caused by *Fusarium oxysporum* f. *pisi* race 1, exhibits features not altogether common among diseases caused by other forms of the species. But like the others the pathogen inhabits the soil and, once established, remains there indefinitely. The best temperature for growth of the fungus on artificial media is about the same as for other vascular Fusaria— about 80° to 85° F. The best temperature for disease development in soil differs from that of the other Fusaria. With most of them, disease development follows closely the optimum temperature for growth of the fungus, but in pea wilt it is distinctly lower, about 70°. If, however, peas are grown in nutrient sand culture and the sand is artificially infested with the pathogen, the optimum temperature for disease development is not different from that for the growth of the fungus. This suggests that a biological antagonism occurs at the higher soil temperature, which interferes with the infectivity of the pea wilt pathogen. That possibility is supported by earlier demonstrations that fusarium wilt would not establish itself in certain types of Wisconsin soils.

Fortunately for the pea industry in districts where the disease appeared, a heritable resistance was found among some varieties in the field. The resistance, a clear-cut character governed by a single dominant gene, was soon incorporated into desirable canning and market varieties. Today virtually every canning pea variety possesses wilt resistance and the disease is completely controlled.

After wilt-resistant varieties had been established, another vascular wilt appeared. It was discovered in Wisconsin in 1931 and was called near wilt, because it resembled the old wilt in certain respects. Soon the same or similar diseases were reported in other regions.

The symptoms of near-wilt in the early stages resemble those of wilt— the stipules and leaflets curve downward and the foliage yellows. Th wilting of the plant, however, resembles that in wilt when the soil temperatures are low; namely, a progressive withering of the leaflets upward from the base. The yellowing and wilting often occur up one side of the stem. There is less stunting of infected plants and the total progress of the disease is slower than in wilt. Usually the symptoms do not appear in a destructive manner until after bloom or pod set. As in wilt, there is a vascular discoloration, but in near-wilt the color is more of a brick red and occurs farther up the stem than in wilt. Sometimes the near-wilt fungus may cause some cortical decay, particularly of seedlings. In the field near-wilt appears on scattered plants, which may become quite numerous with repeated planting, but the spread generally is not so rapid as with wilt. Near-wilt does not occur in circular patches.

The near-wilt pathogen, *F. oxysporum* f. *pisi* race 2, has much in common with the wilt pathogen. It remains indefinitely in the soil. Its best growing temperature is the same as for the wilt fungus. It is unlike the wilt pathogen in that the best temperature for disease development in the soil is higher and follows that for the growth of the fungus.

Near-wilt is worse in warmer seasons, on late varieties, and on late plantings. The fungus that causes near-wilt establishes itself on all soil types. It enters the water-conducting vessels of the pea through either the root tips or at the cotyledonary node. The wilt fungus does not progress far enough up the stem to infect the seed, but the near-wilt fungus frequently travels the entire length of the stem. As a result, seeds (especially those of the dwarf, late varieties) are likely to become infected. The fungus can be disseminated to other fields by infected seed and surface-contaminated seed and by spreading diseased vines on the soil.

Workers at the Wisconsin Agricultural Experiment Station discovered one line of breeding material that appeared to have complete field resistance to near-wilt. The resistance is inherited as a single dominant gene. Delwich Commando was introduced as the first variety completely field-resistant to wilt and near-wilt.

BACTERIAL BLIGHT, although caused by a bacterium, behaves like some of the fungal blights. The disease occurs on all above-ground parts of the plant, but is most pronounced on the leaves, stems, and pods. The symptoms first appear as small, irregular water-soaked spots, which may enlarge to one-eighth inch across on the foliage and to about one-fourth inch on the pods. Streaks usually appear on the stems. The translucent leaf lesions usually turn to a golden-brown color. In time the lesions coalesce. The leaves wither and become papery. The stem lesions elongate and remain water-soaked or turn brown with age. On the pods the spots become slightly sunken but retain the water-soaked character. They may occur on the cheeks of the pods or along either suture.

The causal organism, *Pseudomonas pisi*, is carried over winter chiefly through the seed, either as a contaminant on the seed surface or internally as an infection. The organism can infect cowpea, sweet pea, hyacinth bean, and the perennial or everlasting pea. Possibly the bacterium overwinters in the vines of those hosts, although the seed-borne character is most important.

Spread and damage depend on weather. Spattering rains carry the bacterium from one plant to the next. Seedling infection may kill the plant. Usually, however, such infection provides the inoculum for spread to adjacent healthy plants. The extent of spread depends upon the frequency of rainy periods. If they occur often enough, within the span of a week, the primary infection from a tiny amount of infected seed can spread over a large field. In continued rainy periods the crop might be destroyed. Dry weather may check the disease.

The bacterium enters the plant through the stomata and through wounds. Any practice, therefore, that injures the plants, especially when they are wet, serves to increase infection. Hail injury frequently paves the way for rapid and severe infection.

The most effective control of bacterial blight is the use of disease-free seed. A 4- or 5-year rotation, recommended for the control of other pea diseases, would certainly eliminate diseased vines as a primary source of infection.

W. T. SCHROEDER *is a graduate of the University of Idaho and the University of Wisconsin. While doing graduate work at the University of Wisconsin, he conducted surveys of diseases of peas for several large canning companies in Wisconsin and Minnesota. From 1941 to 1943 he was with the Green Giant Co. of Minnesota as plant pathologist. Since 1944 he has conducted research on the diseases of canning vegetables at the New York Agricultural Experiment Station of Cornell University, at Geneva, N. Y., where he is professor in the division of plant pathology.*

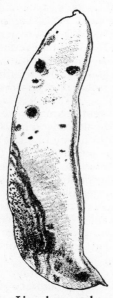

Lima bean scab.

Blights and Other Ills of Celery

A. G. Newhall

Celery is grown extensively as a truck crop on the muck lands and irrigated mineral soils of many States from Florida to Massachusetts, the Great Lakes States, and some of the Mountain and West Coast States. It is grown also as a market garden crop near many large population centers. It has an annual value of more than 50 million dollars.

In some districts celery has been grown intensively for nearly a century. The importation of much of our seed from Europe before 1920 and the free exchange of seeds and plants within the States at all times have meant that there are few if any celery diseases that we have not acquired. Appropriate control measures have been developed for many of them by Federal and State agencies and seed growers.

THE MOST WIDELY DISTRIBUTED and costly diseases of celery are the early and late blights, caused by the fungi *Cercospora apii* and *Septoria apii* var. *graveolentis*, and the rather minor bacterial leaf spot, caused by *Pseudomonas apii*.

Cercospora may be seed-borne, hence early blight occurs almost everywhere that celery can be grown. Because it requires hot weather for its most rapid development, the fungus is most troublesome on the early summer crops in the Northeastern and Great Lakes States. In Florida it may occur in the seedbeds in October and do some damage all winter, but the greatest losses occur on the late winter crop, which matures during the warm weather of March to May. It is checked by periods of cool weather below 40° F. Losses are due to stunting of growth, the necessity for heavy stripping of diseased stalks at harvest, and poorer keeping and market quality.

The fungus overwinters readily on debris from a previous crop. Early blight first appears on seedlings in the plant bed or on transplants in the field as small, pale-green or yellow spots a week after inoculation with the spores of Cercospora. The spots enlarge and often envelop much of the leaf. They turn brown to slate gray as the fungus fructifies on the lower surfaces of the leaves by pushing spore-bearing conidiophores through the stomatal openings. Spores are produced on the upper leaf surface also or on plant debris left on the ground. The spores, when abundant, give a delicate gray or pale-lavender sheen to the affected areas. Sunken, tan-colored, elongated spots may occur on the stalks just before harvest that require heavy trimming and loss of edible product.

L. J. Klotz, at the Michigan Agricultural Experiment Station, found the best temperature for growth and germination of spores of Cercospora apii to be about 70° F. Spores survived desiccation on dried leaves more than 170 days. They are well adapted to dissemination by air and can infect floral parts and grow into the seed coat. When the seed germinates, the fungus can attack the young cotyledons and from them pass to other leaflets. The life cycle takes 10 or 15 days. J. D. Wilson and I, working at the Ohio Agricultural Experiment Station, showed that the longer plants are left in the crowded seedbeds, the worse blight is apt to be later in the field.

An important leaf spot of carrot also is caused by a Cercospora, but it is nonpathogenic to celery as is the celery pathogen to carrot.

LATE BLIGHT, caused by the fungus Septoria apii var. graveolentis, can cause even more destruction than early blight in cool, wet seasons and on the later crop in the Northern States. It can attack any part of the plant above ground. As outer leaves and stalks turn dark and wither, the entire field may look scorched.

The fungus is seed-borne. It also overwinters on debris from a previous crop. It may get started in the seedbed where it forms small, circular, water-soaked spots on the leaves about one-sixteenth inch in diameter. In 10 or 20 days, the spots turn nearly black and become filled with many minute black dots, the fruiting bodies (pycnidia) of the fungus. Spores are formed in these closed, black, pear-shaped cups partly embedded in the plant. They are exuded during wet weather as gelatinous, snakelike tendrils, and require spattering raindrops rather than air currents for quick spread.

When celery is wet with dew, the clothes of workers can spread the fungus down the row. K. H. Lin, at the New York State College of Agriculture, found that the number of spores in a single pycnidium—a structure no larger than the dot over this i—varied between 1,448 and 5,493, with a mean for nine pycnidia of 3,675. Dr. Wilson and I found more than 2,000 spots on untreated plants, with an average of 56 pycnidia per spot; potentially, therefore, half a billion spores can be produced on one plant.

Germinating Septoria spores can penetrate directly through the epidermis as well as through stomata and as readily on the upper surface of leaves as on the lower surface, although there are only about one-third as many stomata on the upper surface.

THE BACTERIAL LEAF SPOT is caused by a soil-inhabiting bacterium, Pseudomonas apii. In the Lake States and

New Jersey it sometimes gives trouble on outer leaves in hot, humid weather. It makes small, circular, rusty-reddish-brown spots up to one-eighth inch in diameter; sometimes they have pale-yellow borders. The spots remain smaller than early blight spots and are a darker brown. They differ from septoria late blight in lacking the black pycnidia within.

The disease is not seed-borne but it often gets its start in the seedbed. It is most troublesome on the crop maturing in August and September. It was the first bacterial plant disease to be controlled by dusting with a fungicide, in 1922.

CONTROL MEASURES for all three celery leaf spots are practically the same. In the absence of resistant varieties, growers have relied heavily upon the use of copper fungicides in the field ever since the work of B. D. Halsted in New Jersey in 1891. No fungicide has exceeded bordeaux mixture in effectiveness, but the residues it leaves and the inconvenience of preparing it (compared with the low-soluble coppers, such as basic copper sulfate, copper oxide, and copper oxichloride, and the organic fungicides) have led more and more growers to abandon bordeaux.

The use of disease-free seed and a 2- or 3-year rotation, to eliminate the two important sources of primary inoculum, have helped many growers. Because the *Septoria* fungus embedded in the seed coat usually dies within 2 years and the seed retains its vitality 3 to 6 years, many growers buy their seed in advance or ask for 2-year-old seed when it is available.

In Bermuda the blight problem was greatly reduced by microscopic examination of samples of all imported seed and rejection at port of entry of all seed lots showing pycnidia. A free examination service offered at Cornell University to New York farmers similarly aided growers.

Fresh seed can be treated in various ways to kill the pathogens that cause early and late blights: A dip in hot water for 30 minutes at 118° to 120° F.; a dip in formaldehyde solution (1 to 300) for 3 hours at room temperature, followed by a rinse; a preliminary soak in tepid water for 30 minutes, followed by a dip in mercury bichloride solution (1 to 1,000) for 5 minutes and by a 15-minute rinse. The hot-water treatment is the best.

Dusting or spraying seedbeds with a copper fungicide two to four times (first practiced by growers in New York and Ohio) is an economical and effective way of reducing and delaying the onset of all three blights. It has been widely used.

If treatment of seed and seedbeds does not eliminate the blights, lack of rotation might be to blame. Growers who cannot rotate crops can hold the diseases in check by spraying or dusting in the field.

Local practices respecting materials and methods of field spraying and dusting vary a great deal. They depend upon variations in climate, on chances of losses at different times of the year, on growers' preferences, and on the extent of local experimental testing of the newer fungicides.

Bacterial blight can be controlled with a dust of 20 parts copper and 80 parts lime. That was a standard treatment among muck growers in New York between 1924 and 1935. But its high lime content and the need to apply it when plants are wet has led to its gradual abandonment in favor of the low-soluble coppers. The modern trend is toward materials that do not clog nozzles very much and leave no unsightly residues. This change was made possible by general adoption of the seed and seedbed practices I mentioned, which give better control of blights in the seedbed and hence a reduced amount of blight in the field. The low-soluble coppers have given fair satisfaction where disease potential was not too high, although the rate at which they wash and weather off has made it wise to shorten the interval between applications to 5 or 6 days on many farms, even to 3 or 4 days in southern Florida.

Heavy fertilization, the use of mulches between rows, side dressing with nitrogen, and adequate irrigation to keep celery growing rapidly are enough in some cool seasons up north to give growers a satisfactory crop despite early blight. But those practices are not so reliable in a hot, dry summer, on the early crop maturing in August, or on the late crop in Florida, which matures in April when temperatures are rising.

Nabam has been widely used in the Everglades in Florida. Ferbam, ziram, and the coppers have proved more suitable to the upland soils of the Sanford area.

In California the most satisfactory and inexpensive program against late blight includes spraying with 3–3–50 bordeaux mixture (3 pounds copper sulfate, 3 pounds lime, 50 gallons of water); in some localities zineb and the fixed coppers are preferred even though they adhere less well to the plant.

New York growers are giving up copper lime dust for the low-soluble coppers. A few use Dithane in liquid form. In most years control is satisfactory, but in some seasons many have been urged to go back to bordeaux mixture or to an alternate schedule of bordeaux and ziram, zineb, or captan.

In Massachusetts growers prefer a low-soluble copper to bordeaux, but the organics, zineb and ziram, if applied more often, are finding favor from the standpoint of safety and effectiveness. Zineb is generally considered more effective than ziram against *Septoria*.

Growers in Colorado have started using zineb sprays. Ziram and tribasic copper sprays have been favored in Oregon.

Extensive tests of fungicides in Michigan culminated in the development of a yellow cuprocide-sulfur-talc dust, 7–30–63, which is easier to use than liquid bordeaux, possesses less lime

than 20–80 copper-lime dust, is more lasting than other low-soluble copper dusts, and has better flowing and keeping qualities.

Still better control of early blight was obtained in 1951 with a Dithane Z–78-sulfur-talc dust (7–30–63). Sulfur by itself is of little value in the control of celery blights, but its presence is said to enhance the performance of both copper and nabam. J. D. Wilson in Ohio found Methasan and Manzate to be among the better replacements for bordeaux mixture.

BREEDING FOR RESISTANCE to celery blight has been made possible by the use of blight-resistant foreign plants brought in by the Eastern States Farmers' Exchange and the Department of Agriculture. The first was a hollow-stalked Danish celery, which was crossed in 1937 with Golden Self Blanching and given to plant breeders at Cornell University, who crossed it to their new yellows-resistant variety, Cornell 19, in 1940. Progenies were later crossed with Cornell 6 to improve quality. Further testing and selecting in New York and Florida resulted in the release in 1951 of Emerson Pascal, the first celery variety fairly resistant to early and late blights and highly resistant to fusarium yellows.

In 1940 and 1941, G. R. Townsend, then a pathologist at the Florida Everglades Experiment Station, discovered *Cercospora* resistance in a number of plants grown from seed that was brought from Turkey by the Department of Agriculture. The plants resembled celeriac. Because he was unable to induce them to set seed, he shipped seven plants to Cornell, where R. A. Emerson, after two more years, finally induced two of them to flower. Emerson made reciprocal crosses between Cornell 19 and P. E. I. (for Plant Exploration and Introduction, Department of Agriculture) 115557. Workers began a program whereby progenies highly resistant to both blights were being selected from that cross in Florida during the winters and in New York during the summers. As celery is a biennial, progress has been slow, but facts of value to vegetable breeders have emerged: Blight resistance is due to more than one gene. Hollow stalk and green color are each dominant in the F_1 generation and are governed by a single factor, and hence are easily eliminated. Susceptibility to black heart and to magnesium deficiency in the soil are both hereditary factors that can be eliminated by breeding.

THE YELLOWS DISEASE was next in importance to the leaf spots in most of the Northern States until resistant varieties were discovered and developed in Michigan, New York, and California. Ray Nelson, G. H. Coons, and L. C. Cochran, at Michigan Agricultural Experiment Station, found there are three distinct diseases in the sense that three separate strains of *Fusarium* may be involved. Stunting of the plant, vascular discoloration, and crown and root rotting are common to all three, but leaf symptoms clearly distinguish two of them. Hot, dry weather is necessary to bring on a full expression of yellows. When the weather turns cool and wet, even infected plants may recover partly.

The first symptom, a lagging in the growth rate, is sometimes seen even in the seedbed. In the field, plants lose their glossy appearance and there is a yellowing of the outer leaves between the veins. *Fusarium apii* form 1 is responsible for those symptoms. When temperatures are high, the entire plant, if not more than half-grown, may turn yellow in a few days. Often leaves of an infected plant when about to turn yellow become brittle. When they are crushed in the hands, they crackle like dead twigs. That is particularly true of green varieties, which usually never turn yellow; that and stunting may be the only visible indication above ground of the disease in such varieties. Petioles of affected plants often develop a bitter taste.

In the second type of yellows the earliest symptoms are a downward curling of the young heart leaves. Then the veins lose color. In this type *Fusarium apii* var. *pallidum* or form 2 is at work, and the areas between the veins are the last to turn yellow. Stunting, root rotting, and browning of the vascular elements in the roots accompany above-ground symptoms in both instances.

The California variation of the yellows complex lacks symptoms of leaf yellowing, curling, and brittleness even in warm weather. It is primarily a stunting, with secondary root rotting and primary vascular discoloration. The identity of the *Fusarium* that is responsible seems not to have been established. But it differs from the other two, which are more common causes of yellows in the Northeast.

In warm soil (77° to 85° F.), the symptoms below ground include brown discoloration and death of small secondary roots, vascular discoloration and dry rotting of the taproot and crown, and even splitting of the latter. Many plants die.

The fungi responsible for fusarium yellows have been isolated from vascular tissue of all parts of affected plants from lower roots to upper leaf stalks. *Fusarium apii* form 1 develops a pink to purple color on steamed rice, while *F. apii* var. *pallidum* or form 2 remains colorless. Some writers put both together under the name *F. oxysporum* form *apii*, but not this one. The fungi live in the soil for many years even in the absence of celery.

Green varieties generally are much less susceptible. Many of them can be grown on infested land without fear of much loss. There is also a difference in susceptibility of different strains of the same variety as well as a difference in apparent behavior of one variety in different seasons. The most extensive testing of varieties has been done in Michigan by Ray Nelson and L. C. Cochran and in Ohio by J. D. Wilson.

The following lists of varieties resistant and susceptible to yellows are based partly on their findings:

Yellow Varieties

More or less resistant: Michigan Golden, Michigan Green Gold, Cornell 19, Cornell 6, Morse's Masterpiece, Florida Golden, Tall Golden Plume, Golden 99, Golden Pascal, Emerson Pascal, and some strains of Wonderful.

Moderately susceptible: Wonderful, Golden Plume (some strains), Kilgore's Pride, Golden Prize, Kilgore's Pearl Special, Sneck's Florida Golden, Early Fortune, Superplume, and Paris Golden.

Very susceptible: Golden Self Blanching, Wonderful (some strains), Early Fortune (some strains), Meisch's Special, Hoover's Special, Gunson's Special, Golden Phenomenal, Golden 14, Golden Detroit, and Golden Plume (some strains).

Green Varieties

Highly resistant: Curly Leaf Easy Blanching, Pride of the Market, Fullheart Easy Blanching, Winter King, Autumn King, Woodruff's Beauty, Sweetheart, Crispheart, Krispgreen, Holmes' Crisp, Earligreen, and Newark Market.

Moderately susceptible: Winter King, Utah, Fordhook, Columbia, Epicure, Pascal, Emperor, Newark Market, Crystal Jumbo, and Winter Queen.

Very susceptible: White Plume, Houser, and Paragon.

Some varieties are classified as resistant at one time or by one worker and susceptible at another time or by another worker. T. C. Ryker, who grew plants in infested soils held at different temperatures at the University of Wisconsin, pointed out a possible reason for this discrepancy. He found some varieties or strains of a variety are resistant in soils up to a temperature of 79° F., above which they are susceptible. Early planting in the Northern States therefore enables a fairly susceptible variety to make good growth before soil temperatures become high enough to induce fungus infection. In wet, cool

seasons infection may be delayed until the crop is made.

CONTROL OF CELERY YELLOWS has been accomplished in Michigan by the selection of individual plants that grew well in fields, where nearly everything else died of the disease, and propagating directly from them. That was done between 1919 and 1926 with selections from a field of Dwarf Golden Self Blanching. The variety released was named Michigan Golden. A similar process of field selection and multiplication from a field of Tall Golden Self Blanching resulted in the Michigan Golden Tall strain between 1930 and 1933. Both were yellow varieties, but in 1951 a green variety, Michigan State Green Gold, was released. It was the result of hybridizing the Downing Strain of Fordhook with the tall strain of Michigan Golden. It has a light-green stalk and is widely grown in Michigan and elsewhere.

At Cornell University in 1933 Swarn Singh crossed Utah, a moderately resistant green variety, and Golden Self Blanching, a popular susceptible yellow one. His work culminated in the development of two new varieties, Cornell 19 and Cornell 6, both self-blanching and highly resistant to the eastern strains of yellows. By crossing the blight-resistant strain described under early blight with each of these in succession, New York workers developed Emerson Pascal, a variety resistant to both diseases. It was put on the market in 1951.

PHOMA ROOT ROT has occurred at times in the Northeast. The fungus that causes it, *Phoma apiicola*, can attack other members of the Umbelliferae, such as carrot, parsnip, parsley, and caraway, but not hemlock or dill. It can live over in the soil on plant debris and occasionally on the seed.

Its first appearance often is in the seedbed, where it causes stunting, yellowing of outer leaves, brown rotting of roots, and sometimes death of young plants. The fungus fruits on the roots and crown; spores from a diseased seedling thus can be spread at transplanting time to many other plants if they are pulled and soaked in water before they are set in the field. The fungus usually is confined to the crown, but sometimes it grows up into the outer leaf stalks far enough to turn them a dark bluish-green color and cause them to break over. Crown lesions take on a dark, brown, rough, scurfy appearance and frequently crack open in later stages. Plants may be killed in the field, although usually they linger on.

The fungus prefers a comparatively low temperature, 61° to 65° F., and requires oxygen and moisture for its most rapid development. Therefore it causes trouble principally on the spring crop and sometimes the late fall crop when temperatures and moisture are most favorable.

The pycnidia of the fungus, filled with very small one-celled spores, may be found partly embedded in the root lesions at any time. The fungus can occasionally become embedded in the seed coat, and it has been introduced by this means into new territories where it caused bad local seedling infections. Free spores once extruded from their pycnidia, however, cannot survive more than 30 days on the surface of seeds at room temperature.

No varieties are known to be resistant, although White Plume, Giant Pascal, and Easy Bleaching seem less susceptible. The fungus is not adapted to the climate of California, where most of our seed is grown. It has not been found in Florida, where much of our winter celery is grown. Losses can be kept down by treating infected seed with hot water, sterilizing infested seedbed soil, rotating crops, and destroying plants that show symptoms.

BROWN SPOT is a new fungus disease of leaf stalks, petioles, and leaflets. It is caused by *Cephalosporium apii*.

It occurred in Colorado in 1943 and later in New York, Ohio, and Ontario.

It has been confused with one or another of the blights of celery and with brown check and cracked stem but differs from them in several important respects. M. A. Smith and G. B. Ramsey, of the Department of Agriculture, have described the chief symptoms of brown spot as irregular, light-tan or reddish-brown, shallow lesions, which occur on any of the above-ground parts of the plant. The lesions may unite to form a scurfy brown streak all the way up the inside surface of the stalk. Transverse cracks may develop across the large lesions and the fungus fruits in the cracks as well as on the surface of stalk and leaf spots.

A certain amount of distortion of growth may occur. The fungus produces many small, elliptical or elongate, one- and two-celled spores on the surface of infested areas. Although the fungus was first found and is much worse on the Utah Pascal types of celery, it occurs also on the Golden Self Blanching types and has affected as high as 85 percent of the plants in a field.

Growers are concerned about this disease for several reasons. Because its fungus is a rapid, heavy sporulator, it probably requires more frequent applications of fungicides—if satisfactory fungicides can be found. Because it often attacks inner stalks and heart leaves, the plant cannot always be trimmed down to a sightly, marketable product. Furthermore, plants from diseased fields, which look fairly free at harvest, when packaged at the wash house directly from the field for retail markets may develop unsightly reddish-brown freckles in transit or in storage.

The spores of *Cephalosporium apii* germinate best between 68° and 75° F. and not at all above 90° or below 45°. The fungus grows best at 75°.

Bordeaux mixture is more effective than wettable sulfur in inhibiting spore germination in the laboratory, but control measures have not been worked out in the field. Growers in New York up to 1952 failed to get very good control with either a low-soluble copper or a liquid Dithane spray applied as for blight control. First attempts to isolate *Cephalosporium* from seed have failed. Fortunately a number of varieties are apparently resistant. These include Summer Pascal, Utah 52–70, Utah 15, a Department of Agriculture plant introduction 176789, and Tall Fordhook. Very susceptible varieties include Cornell 19, Golden Plume, Top Ten, Ten Grand, and Non Bolting Green Nos. 12 and 13 (from Hart and Vick), according to 1952 tests made at Cornell University by Ralph Segall.

STEM CHECK, brown check, or adaxial crack stem is another new disease of celery which has caused heavy losses from coast to coast since the introduction, in 1943, of the splendid variety Utah 10B. It begins as light-tan, shallow, sunken, greasy-looking spots on the inner surface of leaf stalks after plants are half grown. The spots or streaks turn dark brown and open up with a series of unsightly horizontal cracks. Sometimes typical symptoms of crack stem (known to be boron deficiency symptoms) occur on the outer ridges of the stalk but not always. Affected plants are not stunted; in fact, the disease seems to be worse where ample fertility increases growth rate. The disorder has been traced by P. A. Minges, J. T. Middleton, and other California workers to a deficiency of boron in the presence of excessive supplies of potash within the plant. Susceptible varieties seem unable to take up as much boron as needed to protect them. This inability is probably an inherited character as certain strains of Utah, notably 10B and Utah Special, are very susceptible. Utah 16–5 and Top Ten are also moderately susceptible, while Utah 52–70, Utah 16–8, Utah 16 PC, and Summer Pascal, in field tests by the California scientists, were practically free from the disease.

Control is only a matter of avoiding the use of susceptible strains, or if they are grown, then withholding of potash and excess nitrogen, or spraying with boron solution, or both, may be desirable.

AT LEAST NINE VIRUS DISEASES attack celery. Three or four of them are widespread and cause heavy losses. None is seed-borne. None remains in the soil after infected roots decay. Most of them have several common wild or cultivated plant hosts, which act as perennial reservoirs of infective virus. Aphids are the usual vectors, but thrips carry spotted wilt and leafhoppers carry virus yellows.

Cucumber mosaic virus, of which there are a number of strains, is common from coast to coast. The first symptoms are vein clearing and mottling of inner leaves. The most prominent symptoms develop about a month later and include stunting, fern-leaf growth of some leaflets, and raised, dark-green, blisterlike areas on others. A closely related virus, causing southern celery mosaic, is established in Florida, Cuba, and Puerto Rico. It also occurs in the Northern States, where it caused heavy losses in 1950.

Often buff-colored and translucent, sunken spots develop on outer petioles. F. L. Wellman correlated the spread of the disease in Florida with east winds and the spread of winged forms of the melon and cotton aphids. The corn leaf aphid and others also can transmit the virus. The disease has often been observed to start nearest to weeds or diseased economic plants. Eradication of *Commelina nudiflora*—dayflower or dewflower—in the Sanford area of Florida gave a large measure of control. The more than 140 host plants of the cucumber mosaic virus belong to more than 30 families, among them pokeweed, groundcherry, milkweed, and catnip.

Western celery mosaic occurs in California and Colorado. Its symptoms resemble those of southern celery mosaic, except that the leaf mottling is usually followed by necrotic spotting. On the petioles white spots or streaks develop instead of brown sunken ones. The disease became destructive in Los Angeles County, Calif., in fields where celery was grown continuously. It can be controlled if growers in an area observe a 3-month celery-free period beginning in September each year. The virus is restricted to umbelliferous hosts—celery, carrots, celeriac, dill, caraway, coriander—and wild weed hosts are unimportant. At least 11 different aphids carry the virus.

The viruses that cause southern and western celery mosaics apparently belong to the nonpersistent group of viruses. They are easily transmitted mechanically. A vector does not retain for long the ability to transmit it. This ability may be lost during the first feeding or in less than 15 minutes.

Spotted wilt occurs on celery chiefly in the cooler, coastal fog belt of California, where the virus attacks a wide range of truck crops and ornamentals.

Symptoms of spotted wilt on celery are most pronounced on the outer rather than inner stalks and begin on older leaf blades as numerous small yellow spots, which later become necrotic. Internal pockets of dead brown tissue develop inside the petioles and become more or less visual from without as sunken brown patches, which may rot and result in death of the entire leaf. Plants are stunted and worthless.

The vectors of spotted wilt virus are the tiny thrips, *Thrips tabaci* and *Frankliniella insularis*, which must pick up the virus while still a nymph and in which a period of 5 to 9 days must elapse before the insect can transmit it. Once infective, the insect remains so throughout pupation, emergence as an adult, and often until death. The virus is not transmitted through eggs of the infective female.

Control is through elimination of the host plants, including ornamentals, that harbor the virus in the off-season when celery is not being grown.

Spraying with one of the newer organic insecticides may be helpful in some cases. Tomatoes have been bred for resistance, but attempts to do that for celery have not been undertaken.

Celery virus yellows is caused by the aster yellows virus so common on lettuce and carrots. It is not to be confused with fusarium yellows, which is caused by a fungus in the soil. The symptoms on celery include shortening, twisting, yellowing, and delicate mottling of inner petioles and leaves; later many new shoots develop, and there is some stunting and a general yellowing. In California, 23 to 100 days may elapse before symptoms begin showing after inoculation of celery.

The vector is the six-spotted leafhopper. That insect overwinters in the egg stage on winter barley and to some extent on native grasses. After developing into adults, the leafhoppers begin in June to migrate to more succulent host plants; they do some feeding on infected plants, among them wild carrot, plantain, dandelion, chicory, perennial sowthistle, and some species of wild aster. After the insect has picked up the virus, an incubation period of 10 days must elapse, during which time the virus multiplies within the vector. The incubation period can be lengthened by heating the leafhoppers for periods up to 11 days at 91° F. After 12 days at this temperature they are no longer infective unless they feed again on a diseased plant. That accounts for the slower rate of spread of virus yellows during a hot summer.

Other celery virus diseases of less economic importance have been described in California under the names of western cucumber mosaic, celery calico, celery yellow spot, crinkle leaf mosaic, and tobacco ring spot.

CONTROL OF VIRUS DISEASES depends upon doing away with the wild host plants harboring the virus, destruction of insect vectors, or use of resistant varieties. The first has been used in the control of the southern celery mosaic with considerable success in Florida. Destruction of weed hosts around celery seedbeds and plant houses in the north is being employed to reduce losses in the field. It is well known that when hay is cut, when pastures dry up, or when weeds mature, great migrations of aphids and leafhoppers take place when the weather is warm and the air calm.

R. C. Dickson in the Imperial Valley of California calculated some 40 million winged aphids on a mile front may pass in an hour and flights may keep up for many days or weeks. He found that an individual aphid may feed for less than a minute, before flying on to another host, so each plant may play host to many aphids a day.

Weekly spray or dust programs against the insects after the diseases appear have been disappointing in California, probably because the migrating females that bring in the viruses are not killed quickly enough to prevent their first feeding.

CELERY is also subject to attack by several parasitic nematodes such as the root knot nematode (*Meloidogyne* species), the sting nematode (*Belonolaimus gracilis*), the stubby root nematode (*Trichodorus* species), and the awl nematode (*Dolichodorus heterocephalus*), as well as to damping-off disease (*Pythium* species), pink rot (*Sclerotinia sclerotiorum*), black crown rot (*Centrospora acerina*), rhizoctonia crater spot, a fusarium seedling root rot, a bacterial soft rot (*Erwinia carotovora*), bud failure, and two or more physiogenic diseases, such as black heart, crack stem (boron deficiency), and a pale-yellow mottle leaf (magnesium deficiency).

A. G. NEWHALL *is a graduate of the University of Minnesota and Cornell University. He has made research contributions in the fields of vegetable seed treatments; fungicide testing; and soil sterilization by heat, chemicals, and volatile fumigants. He is research professor of plant pathology at Cornell University.*

The Important Diseases of Lettuce

Guy Weston Bohn

American gardeners grow several types of lettuce—the loose leaf varieties, cos or romaine, butterhead, and iceberg. All are in the botanical species *Lactuca sativa*.

Most of the commercial acreage of lettuce is in the Southwestern States, where lettuce, most of it the iceberg type, is grown the year around and shipped in refrigerated cars to all parts of the country.

The lettuce plant has a compact mass of edible, tender leaves on a short stem. Its structure makes it very perishable. Harvesting and handling must be prompt. Lettuce is subject to a variety of diseases during its growth and its distribution to consumers.

SEED DECAY and seedling blight, diseases that reduce plant stands, are caused by several soil-inhabiting fungi, such as *Rhizoctonia solani* and *Pythium ultimum*.

The fungi attack the tender plants before and shortly after they emerge from the soil and cause the stems and roots to rot. Young plants may be attacked only at the soil surface. If that happens, a short section of the stem rots and the seedling falls over. The injury is called damping-off. Older plants are seldom attacked.

Conditions that reduce the rates of germination and emergence increase losses from seed and seedling rots in heavy, wet, poorly aerated soils, which tend to puddle. Losses in such soils are increased if seed is planted too deeply or if rain or irrigation water packs the soil about the seeds.

Lettuce seed germinates best at moderately cool temperatures in coarse, well-aerated soils. Losses from rots can be reduced, especially in heavy soils, by planting the seeds shallowly, and by irrigating before planting, or subirrigating. In districts where rain is likely to fall while the seedlings emerge, planting should be after, rather than before, a rain.

Seed decay can be reduced by dusting the seed with a fungicide, such as chloranil (Spergon), at the rate of 4 ounces to 100 pounds of seed; ferric dimethyl dithiocarbamate (Fermate), at 1 pound to 100 pounds of seed; or thiram (Arasan) at the rate of 1 pound to 100 pounds of seed. Yellow cuprous oxide (Cuprocide) is likely to injure the seed.

SCLEROTINIA DROP often causes severe losses in localities where rains come during the growing season, as in the Eastern and Central States. It is especially severe if lettuce and other susceptible hosts are grown repeatedly in the same soil. The disease causes occasional losses in Arizona and California, but it is seldom severe there because most of the commercial crop is grown on raised beds and harvested during rain-free periods.

Sclerotinia drop is caused by the soil-inhabiting fungi *Sclerotinia sclerotiorum* and *S. minor*. The fungi attack the leaves of older plants where they touch moist soil. They attack the stem at the moist axils of large leaves near the base of the plant. They cause a soft, watery rot, which spreads rapidly over the stem and leaf bases. The entire plant suddenly collapses. It becomes a soft, watery mass and then turns brown and dry.

A cottony fungus growth can be observed on the stem and leaf bases of plants that show early symptoms. Small black sclerotia of various shapes can be found in the decayed tissues as they become brown and dry. The sclerotia are resting bodies that enable the fungi to pass through periods of unfavorable weather. When moist, cool conditions favor their development, the sclerotia produce mushroom-like apothecia. The apothecia produce innumerable spores which distribute the fungus to new host plants by wind, rain, irrigation water, and cultivating tools.

The fungi can persist for long periods in the soil. They can also attack other crop plants, such as bean, cabbage, celery, eggplant, potato, and tomato. In places where the disease occurs on those crops, large populations of the fungi are built up in the soil and increasingly severe losses occur when susceptible crops follow susceptible crops in soils that harbor the pathogens.

Sclerotinia drop can be controlled in seedbed soils with steam pasteurization or with chemicals: One part of commercial formalin in 50 parts of water applied at the dosage of 1 gallon to a square foot, or calcium cyanamide at the rate of 1,000 pounds an acre, 15 days before planting.

Losses in seedbeds and greenhouses can be reduced by providing good ventilation and by using cultural methods that maintain a dry atmosphere and dry plant and soil surfaces.

In commercial lettuce fields it is best to grow the plants during rain-free periods and maintain a dry mulch around the bases of the plants.

In the West the plants are grown on raised beds and irrigation water is applied in semipermanent ditches. Irrigation water should be applied with care to prevent waterlogging and to prevent wetting the soil surface in contact with the plants.

The building up of large populations of the fungi in the soil can be prevented by rotating lettuce and other susceptible crops with grains and other crops that are not attacked by *Sclerotinia*.

No variety of iceberg lettuce is known to be resistant to *Sclerotinia*.

The cos varieties are also susceptible but often are less severely injured than the iceberg varieties. The cos varieties have an upright habit of growth and present fewer moist infection courts to invading fungi.

BOTRYTIS ROT and gray mold of lettuce are caused by the soil-inhabiting fungus, *Botrytis cinerea*.

The plants usually develop brown, necrotic lesions on the stem near the soil line, on the bases of leaves near the soil line, or on leaves in contact with moist soil. Infection usually proceeds upward along the stem and inward through successive layers of leaves. Hence, the rot often occurs in one side of the plant. In moist weather a gray mold appears on the dead tissues and on spots elsewhere on the leaves.

Botrytis cinerea grows upon decaying vegetable matter in the soil and attacks numerous ornamental and vegetable crop plants during moist weather. It is often troublesome in greenhouses and occasionally causes losses in fields during wet, muggy weather.

Control measures for sclerotinia drop also apply to botrytis rot.

SLIME OR BACTERIAL ROT of lettuce occurs in the field during warm, muggy weather; in transit, in lettuce shipped without refrigeration; and in markets. It often is troublesome in Eastern and Central States. In the West it is seldom seen during cool weather but often occurs in spring.

Slime causes a wet, slimy decay of the large internal head leaves. The outer leaves and the small leaves at the center of the head are usually not affected at first, and the plants often appear normal in the field. They can be detected by twisting the top of the head. The outer and inner firm tissues separate readily at the rotted leaves.

Similarly, the first symptoms of infection in nonheading varieties are observed in the rapidly growing large leaves between the older mature leaves and the younger central leaves. The decaying tissues at first appear water-soaked and soon turn brown. The decay proceeds until the entire plant is reduced to a loose, wet mass. Brown spots and marginal necrosis may occur on all exposed leaves.

Slime is caused by *Erwinia carotovora*, *Pseudomonas viridilivida*, *P. marginalis*, and other species of bacteria. The growth of those micro-organisms seems to start in dead tissues, such as those caused by tipburn. Once started, the rot spreads rapidly to healthy tissues, progressing most rapidly within affected leaves.

The disease occurs under conditions favorable for the development of tipburn. Losses from slime can be reduced by using the control measures recommended for tipburn. Losses in transit and in markets can be kept low by providing adequate refrigeration and ventilation.

DOWNY MILDEW of lettuce occurs throughout the year in the coastal lettuce districts in California, where it is most severe in winter. It is less severe in winter in the drier valleys of California and Arizona. The disease also occurs on lettuce grown under glass elsewhere in the United States and is especially severe during cool, wet weather in winter and spring.

The first symptoms of downy mildew in lettuce appear as scattered light-green to yellow areas on the upper surfaces of exposed leaves. Within a few days downy, white hyphae and conidia can be observed beneath the discolored spots. Old spots become brown. The fungus continues to grow under refrigeration and predisposes lettuce heads to decay by bacteria and other organisms in transit and storage. Symptoms of downy mildew are not spectacular. Secondary organisms may be identified as the sole causal agents of infections initiated by the downy mildew organism.

Downy mildew is caused by an obligate parasite, *Bremia lactucae*. If moisture is abundant, the fungus penetrates the exposed leaves and grows between the cells. Some hyphae penetrate host cells without killing them and form absorbing organs (haustoria). The fungus produces conidia on profusely branched hyphae that project into the air through stomata. The conidia are carried to new locations by wind and rain and initiate new infections. They enable the fungus to spread rapidly during moist weather.

The fungus that causes downy mildew produces thick-walled resting spores (oospores) within the host tissues. They are released when the host tissue disintegrates. They enable the fungus to survive freezing temperatures and other unfavorable conditions.

The fungus grows only on lettuce and some of its wild relatives. It may overwinter on weeds or in lettuce debris and volunteers in cultivated fields.

Serious losses can be avoided by growing lettuce in a dry atmosphere during rain-free periods, by avoiding excessive irrigation, and by practicing clean cultivation to eliminate lettuce crop residue, volunteers, and weeds. C. E. Yarwood, working at the University of California at Berkeley, reported that downy mildew on lettuce can be controlled in California fields with 0.2 percent zineb (Parzate or Dithane Z–78) spray with a spreader. However, F. A. Haasis and D. E. Ellis, at the North Carolina Agricultural Experiment Station, found that more potent 2.0 percent zineb drenches at seeding and at weekly intervals thereafter were required to control downy mildew on lettuce in propagation frames in North Carolina.

When conditions are very favorable for downy mildew, control is difficult and expensive. Besides, it is best to avoid the use of fungicides on plants such as lettuce, the edible part of which consists of a mass of leaves.

The varieties Imperial 44, Imperial 152, Imperial 410, Imperial 456, Imperial 615, Imperial 847, Imperial 850, and Great Lakes are resistant to some of the races of downy mildew. These varieties are protected from injury in localities where only those races of downy mildew occur.

Numerous races of *B. lactucae* exist. Some can attack all the varieties mentioned. Downy mildew has been observed on all of them at some places. Resistance to the different races is very specific; that is, resistance to one race of *Bremia* does not protect a variety from attack by other races. The value of a variety in controlling downy mildew at any specific location can best be determined by trying it out in that location.

MOSAIC OF LETTUCE causes losses in all parts of the United States. Its importance may not be recognized because the plants continue to grow and produce heads. Losses are often attributed to unknown causes.

A filterable virus, harbored in the seed and transferred from one plant to another by aphid vectors, causes the disease. It attacks plants of all ages.

Plants with seed-borne infection and those attacked while young are dwarfed and exhibit leaves that are mottled with irregular, pale-green or yellow areas. Occasional plants are uniformly pale, yellowish green. The leaves often have excessively ruffled margins and may be distorted. They are usually more prostrate than those of healthy plants. The plants may fail to form heads or they may produce small, loose heads of poor quality.

Plants attacked when the heads are developing show mild symptoms, often on one side of the plant. The heads may be irregular in shape because of the unequal growth of diseased and healthy tissues.

Mosaic plants produce seed stalks with mottled and distorted leaves. The plants lack vigor and produce little seed.

The lettuce mosaic virus overwinters in the seeds of lettuce and, perhaps, in the weed hosts, sowthistle and groundsel. Usually less than 1 percent of the seedlings are infected so that the disease causes little damage unless the virus is transmitted from the infected seedlings or from infected weeds to neighboring plants by aphids. The disease therefore causes little damage in winter lettuce. It often causes severe losses in summer lettuce in places where aphids are abundant while the plants are small.

Seed-borne infection can be reduced by producing seed in fields free from wild *Lactuca*, *Sonchus*, *Senecio*, and other weeds and isolated from other lettuce. The fields should be rogued while the plants are small to destroy plants that were infected from the seed.

R. G. Grogan and his associates, working at Davis and Salinas, Calif., demonstrated that mosaic can be controlled in market-production fields by the use of mosaic-free seed. Other control measures include isolation from other lettuce and from weeds that harbor mosaic or the insect vector, the reduction of insect populations with insecticides, and the prompt destruction of crop residue in harvested fields.

No variety of the iceberg type of head lettuce is known to be resistant to mosaic. The mosaic-resistant Parris Island variety of cos was made available to growers by the South Carolina Agricultural Experiment Station in 1951.

ASTER YELLOWS in lettuce is caused by a filterable virus, which leafhoppers transfer from one plant to another. The disease is widely distributed in the United States and causes severe losses in summer lettuce, especially in the East. Aster yellows has limited the expansion of lettuce production centers in the East and elsewhere. Most of the important production centers are in parts of California and Arizona where the disease seldom occurs.

Young lettuce plants affected by aster yellows have some curled and yellow or white leaves. Small brown spots of dried latex may occur along the margins of the leaves. The leaf veins may be more translucent than those of normal plants. The whole plant may be affected or the infection may be limited to one part. Plants attacked after heading have twisted and dwarfed heart leaves and do not become firm. The axillary shoots often grow before the head is mature. The flowering branches are chlorotic and slender and often bend down under their own weight. The flower heads on such branches are commonly dwarfed and may be distorted. The few seeds they produce are dwarfed and fail to grow.

Aster yellows in lettuce is caused by the aster yellows virus, *Chlorogenus callistephi*. It attacks many cultivated plants and weeds. The California strain of the virus differs from strains found elsewhere in the United States in its ability to attack certain host plants, such as celery and zinnia, which are immune to other strains.

The virus is transmitted from one host plant to another by *Macrosteles divisus* and certain other leafhoppers. It can be transmitted by grafting but not by mechanical means. It is not transmitted by aphids.

The virus commonly passes the winter in such perennial weed hosts as the common plantain. M. B. Linn, working at the Cornell University Agricultural Experiment Station, presented evidence that the vector does not pass the winter in the insect host or in cultivated fields and bordering weed areas in New York. His observations suggest that the insect overwinters in a milder climate some distance from the cultivated areas. The virus is apparently picked up from perennial hosts as the insects migrate into the fields.

A disease of this sort, with a wide host range and transmitted by migrating insects, is difficult to control. For the country as a whole, the disease is controlled by growing most of the commercial crop in districts free from the disease during the lettuce-production season.

The best potential method of control in areas where aster yellows is troublesome is the development of varieties of lettuce resistant to the disease. That is not easy. Ross C. Thompson, working at the Plant Industry Station at Beltsville, failed to find immunity or potent resistance in cultivated lettuce (*Lactuca sativa*) or in related species that can be crossed readily with it. Certain collections of *L. serriola* and *L. saligna* exhibited marked ability to escape infection. Those species may have value in breeding for resistance to aster yellows. *L. tatarica*, *L. bourgaei*, and *L. marschallii* appeared to be immune from aster yellows. Those species are cross-sterile with *L. sativa*. Some means must be found to cross them with cultivated lettuce before their immunity can be exploited.

Until resistant varieties of lettuce have been developed, it will be necessary to use other methods to control this disease in areas where it is troublesome. Dr. Linn recommended protection of seedlings from leafhoppers by cloth or metal screens; isolation of lettuce field plantings from weed areas and other yellows-susceptible crops by 200 feet or more; and weekly applications, from transplanting until 10 days before harvest, of either pyrethrum-sulfur dust (0.15 percent pyrethrum) or rotenone-sulfur dust (1.0 percent rotenone).

D. Ashdown and T. C. Watkins, working at the Cornell University Agricultural Experiment Station, reported success in the control of aster yellows in lettuce in New York with applications at 5-day intervals, from emergence until 2 to 3 weeks before harvest, of 5 percent DDT at 35 pounds an acre. They found no dangerous residue on harvested, marketable heads. It seems likely that care would need to be exercised to trim the outer leaves from heads moving to markets. Such trimmings would not be suitable feed for animals.

P. H. Bowser, working at the Michigan Agricultural Experiment Station, recommended the use of a DDT-treated trap area for migrating hoppers around lettuce fields in Michigan. If successful, this method would escape the residue hazard problem.

BIG VEIN OF LETTUCE is caused by a soil-borne virus. It occurs wherever lettuce is grown. It is more prevalent in the summer districts than in the winter districts. Big vein causes severe losses in some fields, especially where lettuce is grown repeatedly for several successive seasons. The importance of big vein may often be unrecognized because the plants do not die but continue to grow and produce heads. Losses result from reduced yields of salable heads and poor quality.

The first symptom of big vein, observed in plants with five or more leaves, is a slight yellow discoloration along the veins. The yellowing of veins becomes more pronounced and the entire leaf becomes thickened and crinkled. All leaves of the plant are affected. No killing of tissues occurs. The plant continues to grow and forms a head. The symptoms fade as the head matures, but the head is smaller and less firm than normal heads and the leaves have poor flavor and texture.

Although the above-ground parts of the plants exhibit marked symptoms, they do not contain the virus. The virus is limited to the roots, in which it multiplies. The amount of virus in infested soil is greatly increased when lettuce is grown. The big vein virus persists for long periods in the soil, but not in dried lettuce roots. The reason for this paradox is not clear.

The big vein virus can penetrate lettuce roots without the aid of nematodes or other known vectors. It is possible, however, that root aphids, nematodes, or other organisms act as vectors in natural infections.

No variety of lettuce is known to be resistant to big vein.

Big vein can be controlled in greenhouse and seedbed soils by treatment with heat, with D–D or chloropicrin at the dosage of 0.46 milliliters to a gallon of soil, or with formaldehyde (1.6 percent aqueous) at the dosage of 1 quart to a square foot.

Big vein can be controlled in the field by growing lettuce in virus-free soil. Losses can be held in check in infested soils by rotation of lettuce with other crops that do not harbor the virus. Sporadic infected plants in otherwise clean fields should be removed carefully and destroyed by burning. The infested soil can be treated locally with D–D, chloropicrin, or formalin. Saul Rich, working in Connecticut, recommended a mixture of 1 part commercial chloropicrin with 3 parts of xylene applied at the rate of 500 pounds an acre for the treatment of entire fields.

BROWN BLIGHT of lettuce is a soil-borne disease of undetermined cause. It is of little importance at present, but it has considerable historical importance. It was a serious disease in California and Arizona from 1917 or earlier until its conquest through the use of resistant varieties developed by the Department of Agriculture and the University of California. Nearly all of the commercial varieties now grown in California and Arizona are resistant to brown blight.

The conquest of brown blight of lettuce by Ivan C. Jagger and Thomas W. Whitaker and their associates had beneficial effects on the lettuce industry and on the quality of lettuce on American dinner tables. The varieties they developed were not only resistant to brown blight; they were also superior to older varieties in uniformity, firmness of head, adaptation to culture during different seasons, and high quality. They are widely grown in the United States and elsewhere, and they have served as high-quality parents in breeding programs.

Brown blight attacks lettuce plants after they have developed five to ten leaves. Seedlings do not show symptoms. Plants attacked while they are small develop small, light-yellow spots in the young, expanding leaves at the center of the plant. The spots enlarge slightly and the leaf areas between them become yellowish green. Those leaves and all subsequent leaves are reduced in size and tend to lie flat on the ground. The diseased plants are discolored, small, and rosettelike. Finally, the leaves turn brown and dry from the bases upward. Many plants die before harvest.

Plants attacked after heads form first show brown, irregular, disconnected, sunken blotches and streaks in the frame leaves or the larger head leaves. The streaks are usually associated with the midrib and larger veins, but they may occur between veins or along smaller veins. They are usually confined to the leaves, but they may extend into the stem. Many leaves or only an occasional leaf may show symptoms. The heart leaves are usually free from symptoms, but they may become brown and moist in nearly mature plants.

In early stages, the roots appear normal. In plants with advanced symptoms the roots may be discolored and have dead root tips.

The cause of brown blight is unknown. It may be a soil-borne virus. Observations by R. G. Grogan, of the University of California at Davis, and me in Imperial Valley suggest that the disease may be caused by the accumulation of toxic concentrations of substances in the soil about the lettuce roots.

Brown blight can be controlled by growing the resistant varieties Imperial 17, Imperial 44, Imperial 152, Imperial 410, Imperial 456, Imperial 615, Imperial 847, Imperial 850, and Great Lakes. Imperial 101 and most other varieties derived from those varieties are also resistant.

Brown blight can be controlled in susceptible varieties by growing them in disease-free soil.

TIPBURN OF LETTUCE is a physiological disease that occurs wherever lettuce matures during warm weather. It occurs as the plants approach maturity and is seldom observed in young plants. Tipburn causes severe losses during the spring and summer. It is less severe during the fall. It seldom occurs during the winter.

Tipburn is characterized by the death and dark-brown discoloration of marginal bands of the larger head leaves. In nonheading varieties, the symptoms appear in the rapidly expanding large leaves as they approach maturity. The mature leaves and the very young leaves are less often injured.

The first symptom of tipburn is usually the breakdown and brown discoloration of small spots of tissue near the edge of the leaf. The spots usually occur first between the larger veins. The spots increase in numbers and coalesce as the disease progresses until the entire marginal band of tissue is killed. The symptoms may appear on only one or two leaves or on most of the leaves in the head. Under very favorable conditions most of the leaves may be involved. The dead tissues remain dry and are confined to the marginal portions of the leaves unless they are invaded by micro-organisms. Various bacteria and other fungi may grow in the dead tissues, producing slime. Rotting then proceeds until the entire head is involved.

Tipburn in lettuce appears to be caused by the accumulation of excessive respiratory products in the sensitive tissues during warm nights. Injury seldom occurs at temperatures below 65° F. or during daylight.

Environmental conditions that favor rapid, succulent growth predispose the plants to tipburn injury—excessive soil fertility, excessive soil moisture, and warm temperatures.

Environmental conditions that favor rapid respiration and the accumulation of respiratory products in the large head leaves favor the development of tipburn—warm night temperatures and high relative humidity.

Tipburn can be controlled by growing lettuce during seasons when night temperatures do not exceed 65° F. as the heads mature; growing lettuce in soils that do not favor excessively rapid succulent growth; limiting the amount of fertilizers, especially nitrogenous fertilizers; using irrigation water sparingly when the heads approach maturity; and using resistant varieties.

The Department of Agriculture, in cooperation with several State agricultural experiment stations, has released several varieties of lettuce that are tolerant of conditions that cause tipburn. The most resistant varieties, Imperial 456, Progress, Great Lakes and some of its derivatives, and Alaska, are adapted to culture during the summer. The moderately resistant varieties, Imperial 410, Imperial 615, Imperial 847, Imperial 850, and Jade, are adapted to culture during the spring. Resistance to tipburn is not complete, and all varieties suffer tipburn when conditions are very favorable. The resistant varieties often show little or no tipburn, however, under conditions that render susceptible varieties worthless.

REDHEART OF LETTUCE, a physiological disease, is characterized by the chestnut brown discoloration and breakdown of the small, inner head leaves. The outer leaves may appear normal or they may develop numerous, elongate, brown pits on the midribs and veins and sometimes on the tissue between the veins. It often occurs in transcontinental shipments of lettuce, especially in spring.

The cause appears to be lack of sufficient oxygen, which results from poor aeration or prolonged exposure to low temperatures during shipment and storage. It also results from bacterial rot of the outer leaves, which occurs in shipments without adequate refrigeration.

Redheart can be controlled by providing adequate aeration and prompt and continuous cooling of lettuce to 39° to 41° F. in shipping containers, refrigerator cars, and terminal storage, and by prompt movement of the produce from the grower to the consumer.

PREMATURE YELLOWING, rib blight, and several other obscure diseases occur in head lettuce in the field and during shipping and marketing. The diseases occur most commonly during the spring and appear to be caused by various physiological disturbances.

Premature yellowing is associated with poor development of the root system and the production of small, infirm heads. Losses result from reduction in yield and from poor quality. Yellowing in early spring lettuce in Arizona was found to be associated with poor aeration, excessive soil moisture, and salt accumulation in the root zone. This complex of adverse conditions results from soil compaction by farm machinery and untimely applications of irrigation water. Losses can be reduced by avoiding the use of heavy machinery, especially on wet soils, and by avoiding excessive applications of irrigation water.

Rib blight is characterized by the occurrence of a dark-brown, necrotic strip of tissue along the midvein near the center of the leaf. This symptom occurs in only one or two or in several of the large head leaves. The plants often appear otherwise normal and the disease can be detected only by removing the outer leaves.

Rib blight appears to be associated with rapid, succulent growth; the plants are often vigorous and dark green in color. The disease predisposes heads to attack by bacteria and losses are often attributed to slime. The cause of rib blight is unknown. Excessive applications of fertilizers and irrigation water should be avoided—they favor rapid, succulent growth and predispose lettuce to injury by rib blight, tipburn, and other physiological disorders.

GUY WESTON BOHN *is a pathologist in the Bureau of Plant Industry, Soils, and Agricultural Engineering at the United States Horticultural Field Station, La Jolla, Calif. Before joining the Department, he was an instructor in genetics in Texas Agricultural and Mechanical College.*

Cauliflower, Cabbage, and Others

J. C. Walker

The cabbage tribe includes cabbage, cauliflower, broccoli, brussels sprouts, kohlrabi, kale, and collard. All have been derived from the leafy wild cabbage of Europe. They intercross readily with each other and with cabbage.

Somewhat removed from them botanically is radish, which does not ordinarily cross with members of the cabbage tribe. When it does, a rank-growing, sterile hybrid usually results.

Turnip and rutabaga are the other two important vegetables in this group. They are known to hybridize with each other. Their hybrids, too, generally are sterile.

All these vegetables belong to the family of plants known as crucifers, which includes also Chinese cabbage, water cress, rape, the wild and cultivated mustards, and many weeds, such as shepherds-purse and pennycress.

Some 60 diseases may affect one or more of the cruciferous vegetables. The most destructive are yellows, black rot, blackleg and dry rot, clubroot, and mosaic.

YELLOWS, a warm-weather malady, is most destructive throughout the Corn Belt and as far north as central Wisconsin and northwestern New York. It is not important on the midwinter crop in the South but may be destructive on autumn-sown cabbage and on the part of the crop that grows into late spring.

Yellows appears on young plants, in the seedbed or after transplanting, as a lifeless, yellowish-green color of the foliage. Often the yellowing is more intense on one side of the leaf, and on it a warping develops. Lower leaves are affected first. As the disease progresses up the plant, the leaves become brown and brittle and drop prematurely. The water vessels of leaf and stem turn brown. Severely diseased plants die early. Entire fields may be destroyed if susceptible varieties are used on infested soil. Yellows is especially severe on cabbage, a crop often grown in climates favorable for the disease. It is less common on other susceptible crops, which usually are grown in cooler regions.

The causal fungus, *Fusarium oxysporum* f. *conglutinans*, produces white or cream-colored threads, which form a cottony mass on culture media. On the threads are borne numerous microscopic spores, which propagate the fungus. The fungus can exist indefinitely in the soil. It is not seed-borne but is transported in transplants and in soil moved about by wind, water, implements, and animals. The fungus in the soil enters the plant through the young roots at or near their growing tips. Without noticeably injuring the outer parts of the root, it becomes established in the water vessels and progresses upward through them to the taproot and into the stem and leaves. The fungus remains confined in the water vessels until the plant is dead. Then it grows to the surface and produces spores.

How it acts on the plant is not known. It probably plugs the vessels and produces toxic materials, which cause discoloration of the bundles, yellowing of leaves, leaf drop, and death.

Yellows was so destructive by 1910 that it became the subject of a research project initiated by L. R. Jones of the Wisconsin Agricultural Experiment Station. The program was continued as a cooperative project with the Department of Agriculture.

It was one of the first studies of the relationship between soil temperature and plant disease. It brought out that when the soil was kept at 65° F. or lower little or no disease developed in plants grown in infested soil. As the temperature rose, the intensity of the disease increased up to about 81°. Then it declined. This temperature curve followed closely that of growth of the fungus in pure culture. The results explained why the disease increased in intensity as summer temperatures rose and also why it was severe in places where cabbage grew in warm months and was little noticed where the crop was grown in winter.

All attempts at practical control by chemical treatment of soils were unsuccessful. Dr. Jones noticed, however, that in any field that was almost completely destroyed occasional healthy plants survived. By growing seed from such plants and returning their progenies to infested soil, he got higher percentages of resistant plants in succeeding generations. After three generations of selection within the variety known as Hollander or Danish Ballhead, he obtained a strain sufficiently resistant to be of commercial value. It was released in 1916 under the name Wisconsin Hollander. It was still widely used on yellows-infested soil in 1953.

Two genetic types of resistance to yellows exist. One, known as type B, is found in Wisconsin Hollander. Wisconsin Hollander may show a considerable percentage of diseased plants in hot summers, but most of the plants are only mildly affected.

In the parent variety, Hollander, and in some other susceptible varieties, another type of resistance was found later. A single dominant gene controls it. This resistance, known as type A, has two advantages over type B resistance. As it is controlled by one gene, it is readily fixed and transferred from one variety to another. It also is stable at constant soil temperatures as high as 78° F.

Because breeding lines may carry

both types of resistance and the two are hard to tell apart in the field, a way was developed to separate them in breeding programs. Type A is expressed—more strikingly than type B—in young seedlings and in old plants.

By making use of the soil temperature effects studied earlier, technicians discovered that if young seedlings are grown in heavily infested soils at 75°, those that carry only type B resistance succumb to yellows while those which carry the gene for type A resistance are not affected. By growing seedlings in metal pans in thermostatically controlled water baths, known as Wisconsin soil temperature tanks, plants that carry type A resistance can be sorted out. The test is accurate and can be applied quickly and in small space to thousands of plants.

By selection and hybridization, type A resistance has been incorporated in many types of cabbage. Yellows-resistant varieties to suit most seasons and market requirements are available, but the work of breeding new varieties to meet changing requirements continues.

The chief yellows-resistant varieties now in use are Jersey Queen, pointed head, early; Wisconsin Golden Acre, round head, early; Resistant Detroit, round head, second early; Racine Market, round head, second early; Wisconsin Copenhagen, round head, midseason; Marion Market, round head, midseason; Globe, round head, midseason; All Head Select, flat head, midseason; Improved Wisconsin All Seasons, flat head, late; Improved Wisconsin Ballhead, round head, late; Wisconsin Hollander, a semiround head, very late; Bugner, semiround head, very late; Resistant Red Hollander, round head, late.

BLACK ROT, much like yellows in appearance, has been known since 1890 or so. It occurs on the same crops as yellows. It also affects turnip, rutabaga, radish, Chinese cabbage, rape, and other leafy crucifers. It occurs wherever those crops are grown in the United States except in places in the Pacific coast region where the crops are produced in dry seasons. The disease starts, often inconspicuously, at the water pores of the leaves. The organism progresses throughout the plant by way of the water vessels. The organism is known also to enter through the root system and through wounds made by chewing insects.

Marginal leaf infection is followed by browning and dying of the tissue. The lesion often forms a V, pointed toward the midrib. In the lesion the veinlets become black. As the organisms advance, the invaded vessels continue to turn black through leaf, stem, and heads of cabbage and through roots of fleshy crucifers. Nonmarginal yellowish places next appear on leaves; as they turn brown and drop prematurely the disease closely resembles yellows and is often confused with it on cabbage and other hosts susceptible to yellows. The chief points of distinction are: The veins in yellows tend to be brown and those in black rot are black; V-shaped lesions at the leaf margins are not so distinct in yellows as in black rot; soft rot of cabbage heads commonly follows black rot but seldom does in yellows.

The causal organism, *Xanthomonas campestris*, is a motile bacterium, which produces yellowish growth on culture medium. It was studied intensively in the 1890's by Erwin F. Smith, of the Department of Agriculture, and H. L. Russell, of the Wisconsin Agricultural Experiment Station. They worked out some of the essential features of the disease cycle. They learned that the bacteria entered the plant chiefly through the hydathodes at the edges of leaves on which guttation drops commonly accumulate during periods of high humidity, especially during cool nights which follow warm days. The bacteria soon gain access to the extremities of water vessels in that way. Only rarely do the bacteria enter stomata, the "breathing" pores that open and close—probably because in cabbage the substomatal chambers in leaves and stems seldom become filled with water in nature. When that condition is provided artificially, however, abundant stomatal invasion can be secured. In the first leaves of cabbage seedlings, a few stomata cease to open and close and serve more or less as hydathodes. Charles Drechsler at the Wisconsin Agricultural Experiment Station showed that that was the chief point of initial entry of the plant by bacteria carried with the seed. The seed coat is carried above ground as the seed germinates. It remains attached to the cotyledon, where it provides the infectious bacteria that penetrate the stomata.

Infected seed has been regarded as a major source of inoculum, but the disease cycle was not fully understood until the work of Allyn Cook, R. H. Larson, and me, of the Department of Agriculture and the Wisconsin Agricultural Experiment Station. It had been observed repeatedly that black rot epidemics appeared suddenly in cabbage fields approaching maturity, although there was no obvious source of the bacteria other than the seed used the previous spring. Plants that become infected in the seedbed commonly lose the infected leaves early. External signs of the disease disappear, although some bacteria have advanced into the stem before the infected leaf or cotyledon dropped. The plant may grow for weeks or months without any perceptible reduction in growth, but the bacteria become distributed more or less generally throughout the plant. At some later time, for reasons still not well understood, the bacteria multiply rapidly and cause many lesions along the leaf margins and in many plants in a field. The abundance of inoculum so produced may be spread rapidly in warm, moist weather, and the destructive disease epidemic is at hand.

Although men at the New York Agricultural Experiment Station pointed out that seed became infected in diseased seed plants, the exact relation of the bacteria to the seed was not known until our work was published in 1952. We noticed that just as young vegetative plants become diseased early and then grow without external signs for weeks or months, so cabbage plants in the head stage may go into the usual period of winter dormancy in the field or storehouse without showing infection. Seed plants usually grow to flower in cool temperatures, which tend to hold the disease back. The first signs on the seed plant therefore may not appear until the early pod stage. Inconspicuous lesions on the smaller stem leaves are followed by general blackening of the veins of branches and pods. The bacteria follow the veins to the seed coat. If they enter the latter, the seed usually aborts. Only an occasional seed is internally infected and viable. A few more have the point of attachment of seed to pod (funiculus) internally infected. Although the organism can be isolated from only a rare viable seed coming from a diseased seed plant, it takes only an occasional infected seedling in the seedbed to furnish enough inoculum to cause an epidemic later in the season.

To control black rot, it is necessary first to practice a 3-year rotation with noncruciferous crops to avoid infection by organisms in plant debris. The next remedy is to prevent introduction of inoculum with the seed. Liquid or dust chemical treatments are not effective in this case. Immersion of the seed for 30 minutes in water at 122° F. is effective against black rot germs in the seed. That is a standard seed treatment. It is unnecessary to treat seeds of cabbage, cauliflower, turnip, and rutabaga grown in the Pacific Coast States, where the dry spell in midsummer keeps the disease from spreading in seedbeds.

BLACKLEG—dry rot—affects cabbage, cauliflower, broccoli, brussels sprouts, kohlrabi, kale, collard, Chinese cabbage, turnip, and rutabaga. It is incited by a fungus, *Phoma lingam*, which, like the organism of black rot, subsists on infected plant debris for 1 or 2 years in the soil and in infected seed. All parts of the plants above or below ground may be affected. Spots appear on leaves as inconspicuous, indefinite, pallid areas. They gradually become well defined with ashen-gray centers, in which innumerable black dots, much smaller than a pinhead, are scattered irregularly; they are the fruiting bodies of the fungus, within which innumerable spores are formed and exude to the surface only in moist weather.

On the cabbage stems similar spots occur. Often they have a purplish border. When they are near the soil line, they gradually extend below ground, where the fungus eventually destroys the fibrous root system. That causes the plant to wilt or to topple over as the head increases in weight. When plants are carried through the winter to produce tall, branching seed plants, stems, branches, and seed pods are similarly affected. Here the fungus gains access to the young seeds. It burrows into the seed coat, where it remains dormant without necessarily stopping germination.

When turnip and rutabaga crops are infected, similar leaf lesions appear, and dry rot cankers on the fleshy roots develop before harvest or appear later in storage where heavy losses may follow.

The fungus of blackleg depends entirely upon dew and rain to promote discharge of spores and to spread them to uninfected plants. The disease starts from infection of young seedlings by the fungus from infected seed or from trash in the soil. Humid, rainy weather is essential for an epidemic and conversely in areas with dry growing seasons the disease is relatively rare. In Pacific coast areas the disease is so rare that seed produced there is considered safe without treatment. The only effective treatment, when it becomes necessary, is keeping the seed for 30 minutes in water at 122° F.

No resistant varieties are known, but the disease is controlled by 3-year

rotation with noncruciferous crops and the use of seed grown on the Pacific coast or treated with hot water. One should not plant crucifers in fields next to fields where crucifers were grown the year before, because surface water may spread infected debris.

CLUBROOT, a troublesome disease for centuries throughout Europe, is acute in many intensive crucifer-growing areas in our Northern States.

Most crucifers, wild and cultivated, are susceptible and thus the mustards, shepherds-purse, and pennycress can serve as perpetuating hosts of the causal fungus, *Plasmodiophora brassicae*.

As clubroot affects only the below-ground parts of the plant, it may run part of its course after infection without causing any noticeable symptoms above ground. Such signs, when they appear, are likely to be in the form of slowly reduced growth, sometimes temporary wilting, and occasionally premature death. When affected plants are pulled, various types and stages of root enlargement and malformation are found. The club may consist of a fleshy enlarged root in the shape of a spindle or it may consist of a spheroid gall. When many infections occur close together, most of the root system is transformed into variously shaped malformations. The clubbed tissue after a time is invaded by soft-rotting organisms. If the plant is not protected by production of additional secondary roots it may now wilt and die or, depending on the extent of root damage, slow down to stunted, unproductive growth.

The club tissue is permeated by the fungus, which first stimulates the growth of the host and then goes over into production of innumerable spores, which are released to the soil as secondary organisms decay the roots. The next spring the spores germinate and produce motile bodies, which enter the young roots of crucifers. Since the fungus does not gain access to the seed, it is not seed-borne. It is transported in diseased roots and transplants and in soil in various ways. There is no evidence that it lives as a saprophyte, but infested soil is known to remain infested for 10 years or more. Infection is favored by relatively high soil moisture.

Clubroot is hard to control. Alkaline soil is unfavorable to it. In places where the soil is naturally alkaline or can be made so by liming, the disease can be held in abeyance. Heavy liming, however, is not desirable for such crops as potatoes, which scab most readily on such soil. It is important to select noninfested soil for the seedbed. The disease may be reduced somewhat by dissolving 1 ounce of mercuric chloride (corrosive sublimate) in 16 gallons of the transplanting water. That is not a complete remedy, however, and can be applied only in small cultures.

Varieties of turnip that are somewhat resistant are used in Europe. The strains of the clubroot organism prevalent in the United States appear to be relatively mild on turnip and rutabaga, however, and the disease is thus of little import on those crops here.

A NUMBER OF VIRUSES infect crucifers. Disease is commonly caused on cabbage by the combined effect of two. One is a strain of turnip virus 1 and the other a strain of cauliflower virus 1. The first causes mottling of the foliage. The second causes a clearing or chlorosis along the veins of the leaves. Together they produce lifeless spots on leaves, stems, and pods, pronounced stunting, and premature defoliation. The viruses carry over from season to season in cruciferous weeds and in plants kept for seed production. They are both transmitted to healthy plants by the cabbage aphid. The mottle phase is most noticeable in warm weather and the vein-clearing phase is favored by cool weather.

Mosaic caused great damage in the early 1940's in cabbage seed crops growing near Puget Sound. By 1942 the reduction in seed production was so great that special measures were taken to study and control the disease. The research men found that the intensity of the disease was brought about by the fact that in seed production the viruses infect the cabbage during the first season, winter over in such plants, and bring about stunting and sparse seed production the second year. Moreover, aphids leave the maturing seed plants in midsummer and migrate to seedbeds nearby and infect the new crop. After several seasons of this close cycle, the first-year crop was almost completely infected before going into the winter.

Control was accomplished by breaking the cycle. Seedbeds were removed to isolated areas, and the first-year crop was thus protected from infection. The seed plants in the second year were found to be relatively free from disease, and the yields of seed were normal. In other areas relatively successful control may be assured by moving the seedbed to locations where cabbage or other cruciferous crops have not been grown recently and where weeds have not become heavily infected with the viruses.

Varieties of cabbage differ in their resistance to mosaic. The resistant plants become infected as do susceptible plants, but they produce nearly normal growth despite the virus. A program of improvement was started in the Department of Agriculture in cooperation with the Wisconsin Agricultural Experiment Station. By continuous selection of tolerant plants with yellows-resistant varieties, strains resistant to both diseases can be obtained. One such variety, Improved Wisconsin All Seasons, has been made available to growers.

J. C. WALKER *is professor of plant pathology in the University of Wisconsin. He has been a member of the faculty there since 1914. He also is a pathologist and agent for the Bureau of Plant Industry, Soils, and Agricultural Engineering. Dr. Walker holds three degrees from the University of Wisconsin.*

Hazards to Onions in Many Areas

J. C. Walker

Onions are grown in every State.

In the South, onions are an early spring crop, mostly for immediate shipment, and Yellow Bermuda, Excell, and Crystal Wax are the chief varieties.

In the North, the earliest crop is grown from sets produced the previous season, and the major part of the acreage, much of it on muck soils, is sown in early spring and harvested in September and October. Strains of Yellow Globe, Yellow Danvers, and Sweet Spanish predominate. White Globe and Red Globe also are planted.

Onion sets are grown mainly in northeastern Illinois and southeastern Wisconsin and near Greeley, Colo. The chief set varieties are Ebenezer, Yellow Strassburg, White Portugal, and Red Wethersfield. All northern-grown varieties are suited to winter storage. Onion seed is grown chiefly in California, Idaho, and Oregon.

Garlic, chive, and shallot are grown from sets. Welsh onion and leek are grown from seed. Welsh onion, like shallot, produces many small bulblets and both are used chiefly as "green" onions.

While many diseases affect onion and its close relatives—garlic, chive, shallot, Welsh onion, and leek—a few stand out as potential hazards, particularly to onions, in many areas.

Downy mildew is most destructive in New York, Michigan, Louisiana, California, and Oregon in an average year. In unusually cool, rainy seasons it is a major disease in other Midwestern States and once in a while in Texas and Colorado. It affects onion, Welsh onion, leek, shallot, chive, and garlic.

It usually appears in midseason as yellowish spots on the upper half of leaves of the onions. The fungus fruits on the surface of the spot as a bluish-gray, fuzzy mildew when humidity is high. The spots increase rapidly if moist weather continues. Spores produced on the surface are carried widely by air currents to cause new infections. The tops die back. The advance of the disease increases with high humidity and declines in dry spells. Plants are seldom killed, but growth of bulbs is reduced and the bulb tissue is inclined to be spongy and of poor keeping quality.

When expanding stems in the seed crop are infected, uneven, stunted growth follows. Spots on one side cause the stem to bend in the direction of that side. As the seed top grows heavier, weakened stems break over and seed is light in weight and poor in germination.

The causal fungus, *Peronospora destructor*, is spread by wind-borne, short-lived spores. In old leaves are formed winter spores, which remain viable in the soil until the next season. The fungus threads—mycelium—may also live in the bulbs and sets. From them infected plants may arise when they are used for the seed crop or for an early bulb crop.

Perennial onions may also become a source of summer spores in early spring. Summer spores are produced most abundantly during the night at about 55° F. They are spread during the day. As dew accumulates the following night, they germinate most rapidly at about the same temperature and penetrate the onion leaf or stem. Dew is required for germination and penetration. Windy weather favors spread of spores, but there is less dew then. That is why low muck areas with poor air drainage are the ones where onion mildew often appears first and causes greatest damage.

Downy mildew diseases usually can be controlled by protective sprays or dusts. Onion downy mildew has been an exception; many experiments have been conducted on it, but to little avail. At the Michigan Agricultural Experiment Station, Ray Nelson in 1951 reported encouraging results with a mixture of Dithane Z-78 and sulfur applied as a dust. We expect improvements in that line of control as other fungicides are developed.

Localities with dry summers have little to fear from mildew. The production of onion seed therefore has increased in Idaho and declined in California and Oregon.

A resistant variety, Calred, was developed by workers of the California Agricultural Experiment Station and the Department of Agriculture from a cross between a resistant strain of Italian Red and an Australian variety, Lord Howe Island. Its seed stalks are highly resistant and the leaves are moderately so. It is adapted to growing districts in California. We need to breed the resistant character into the more widely used varieties.

NECK ROT is one of the most serious of the storage rots of onion. It appears shortly after harvest as a softening of the scale tissue. It begins usually at the neck and occasionally at a wound elsewhere on the bulb. The affected tissue takes on a sunken, cooked appearance as it advances steadily down one or more of the bulb scales. There appear later on the decayed tissue grayish masses of fungus threads, which gradually form a compact mat on the surface. If conditions are even moderately moist, a gray, powdery mass builds up on the surface. Meanwhile the cooked-appearing zone advances while the fungus mass follows it down the scale. The scale gradually shrivels. If many scales are affected, the entire bulb dries down to a crisp mummy.

The causal fungi are three closely related species, of which *Botrytis allii* is the most widespread. The gray, powdery mass on the surface of the decaying scales consists of myriads of spores of the fungus, which are picked up readily by the lightest of air currents. They will live for some days or weeks, but not through the winter.

In the fungus mats there sometimes appear hard black bodies (sclerotia) about the size of a barley kernel. They are made up of finely woven fungus threads, which can survive freezing winter weather.

When cull onions are dumped from warehouses in the spring, the sclerotia give rise to spore masses in moist weather. The spores are carried to onion fields by air currents. They do not infect the growing plant, but when they germinate they grow saprophytically, principally on the oldest leaves which are sloughed off as the plant develops. As the plant matures it becomes susceptible at the neck. If the tops are cut while still green, the wounded neck is ideal for penetration and infection by the fungus.

The saprophytic stage of the fungus builds up most effectively in cool, moist seasons. If such weather persists into the harvest period, spores are most abundant and infection is greatest. If the crop matures in dry, warm weather, the build-up of spores is reduced to a minimum and the disease which follows is negligible. That is why neck rot is not a major disease in areas where the crop matures in dry climate, such as the Rio Grande Valley, central California, Utah, and Idaho. In the more humid upper Midwest and Northeast, neck rot varies from season to season, depending on the climate just before and during harvest.

With those facts in mind, growers there can do much to reduce neck rot. They should allow the bulbs to mature well before being topped. Bruising in harvest should be avoided. If there is adequate ventilation in storage, the disease does not spread very much.

Artificial drying at harvest and during early storage reduces somewhat the advance of neck rot, and many growers use it as a standard procedure.

All varieties of onion are susceptible once penetration has taken place, but a great difference still exists between varieties. White varieties are most easily infected. They therefore need the most attention at harvest. Yellow and red varieties are more resistant, but one must be careful with them also, especially when weather favorable to neck rot prevails. The mild varieties of all colors are more susceptible than pungent varieties of corresponding colors. It is therefore important that such types as Sweet Spanish be allowed to mature well and be given the best possible airing. They should be protected from rain and dew during the curing process. The best storage conditions for onions include a temperature of 32° F. or slightly above and a relative humidity of about 65 percent.

PINK ROOT first came into prominence in the Rio Grande Valley after 1921. It soon became important in central California. Since then the causal organism has been reported on onion in other areas. It is, in fact, a rather common soil inhabitant, which attacks the roots of many of our crop plants.

On onion the disease becomes manifest in young seedlings and at any subsequent time in the growth period of the host. Abnormal yellowing of roots is commonly associated with pink root but is not necessarily a stage of the disease. Affected roots turn pink, shrivel, and die. As the plant sends out new roots, they in turn become diseased and functionless. That happens throughout the growing season. The affected plants are not usually killed, but the reduced food supply results in the formation of mere scallions or small bulbs.

The causal organism, *Pyrenochaeta terrestris*, is made up of many races, which vary in growth characters and in virulence upon onion. Black fruiting bodies smaller than a pinhead sometimes appear on the diseased onion roots. Within them myriads of microscopic spores are formed. They are not important in the spread and perpetuation of the fungus, because the fungus seems to depend upon fungus threads, which grow and persist more or less indefinitely in infected soil.

I know of no practical way to eradicate the fungus from infested soil. The development of resistant varieties is therefore important. Such a program is under way in the Department of Agriculture and several State experiment stations. At the Wisconsin Agricultural Experiment Station, R. H. Larson has worked out a method of subjecting breeding progenies to pure cultures of the fungus as they grow in white quartz sand at controlled, constant temperatures. After 2 weeks of growth in a liquid medium, the fungus threads are chopped into fine particles, which are mixed in the clean, sterile sand. The sand is placed in shallow metal trays supported in tanks of water regulated at a constant temperature of 80° F. Seeds are sown in the sand, and after 28 days the diseased seedlings are discarded and the resistant ones are transplanted to soil and grown on to bulbs. Thousands of seedlings can be tested in a month in this way. Resistant individuals are then used for further breeding.

Yellow Bermuda is one of the most tolerant of the common varieties. Plant breeders have discovered that they can increase that level of resistance by rigid selection. Resistance is an hereditary character that can be transferred to other types by breeding.

Chives, the Nebuka type of Welsh onion, and Giant Musselberg variety of leek also have considerable natural resistance. The Evergreen shallot, developed at the Louisiana Agricultural Experiment Station, and the Beltsville Bunching, a nonbulbing onion derived from a cross between onion and Nebuka Welsh onion and introduced by H. A. Jones of the Department of Agriculture, are resistant types developed by selection and breeding.

ONION SMUT was first reported in 1869 in the Connecticut River Valley. By 1888 it was of great economic importance there on old onion soils. It has become an important disease in most of the onion-growing areas throughout the Northern States as far west as Oregon and central California. In the United States the disease has remained strictly a northern one, although very likely the fungus has been transported frequently to southern regions. The disease also occurs on leek and Welsh onion.

Smut appears on the first leaf (cotyledon) soon after it emerges above ground as a dark, slightly thickened area. If most of the first leaf or later leaves is involved, they are swollen and tend to bend downward. On plants starting to bulb, raised black blisters appear near the bases of the scales. Lesions may break open and expose black, powdery masses of spores.

Most infected seedlings die within 3 or 4 weeks after they emerge from the ground. Some plants survive weakly until midseason or later, and occasional plants produce bulbs with lesions on the outer fleshy scale and in one or more underlying scales. The fungus does not produce a rot in storage, but affected bulbs may be more subject than healthy ones to invasion by storage-rotting fungi and bacteria.

The causal organism, *Urocystis cepulae*, as seen in the black smut pustules in the leaves, consists of microscopic spores, which can live for many years in the soil. When soil is infested it remains so for many years, although there is no evidence that the organism grows and multiplies in the soil. The spores are not ordinarily seed-borne but are transferred widely on diseased sets and plants and locally by wind and water-borne soil.

The onion seedling is susceptible to infection by fungus threads growing from the spores only during the early seedling stage. If the plant escapes infection until the first leaf has reached its full growth it will continue entirely free from disease. Healthy sets or transplants that are planted in infested soil grow with complete immunity from infection. The fungus is sensitive to high temperatures, and if the young seedlings are growing in soil with temperatures of 80° F. or above they escape infection, because the fungus is very inactive and the plant grows through its susceptible period more rapidly. This phase of the disease cycle was worked out by the writer, L. R. Jones, and F. L. Wellman, of the Department of Agriculture and the Wisconsin Agricultural Experiment Station. We interpreted the results as explaining why the disease is of no importance in southern areas where seed is sown in late summer in very warm soil.

A great deal of research has been carried out on resistance of onion and its relatives to smut. R. I. Evans, of the University of Wisconsin, found that as the first leaf grew it became gradually more and more resistant and even though the fungus continued to enter, it had less and less success in establishing itself.

Welsh onion, especially the Nebuka type, is more resistant than onion, because the tissue of its first leaf becomes incompatible to the fungus earlier and much more rapidly. Three of us at the Wisconsin Agricultural Experiment Station and the Department of Agriculture studied resistance in crosses between onion and Welsh onion. Resistance was highly dominant and the hybrid scallion onion, Beltsville Bunching, has nearly as high resistance as Welsh onion. In 1952 we had not been able to introduce the resistance of Welsh onion to the bulb-onion type, by backcrossing the hybrid to onion.

Control of onion smut centers around protection of the young seedlings from infection. About 50 years ago at the Ohio Agricultural Experiment Station a method was developed in which a stream of dilute formaldehyde was introduced in the furrow with the seed. The method, known as the formaldehyde drip, has been a successful control measure ever since. The standard treatment is 1 pint of 37 to 40 percent formaldehyde solution in 16 gallons of water applied at the rate of 1 gallon to 150 feet of row, or 1 pint in 8 gallons of water applied at the rate of 1 gallon to 300 feet of row. The treatment, however, is cumbersome, formaldehyde injury may occur in very dry soil, and heavy rains immediately after application may reduce its effectiveness.

A. G. Newhall, of the New York (Cornell) Agricultural Experiment Station, devised a method in which Arasan is pelleted on onion seed with the aid of Methocel sticker; when seed is sown at the rate of about 5 pounds an acre for bulb-crop onions, the pelleting of 1 pound of Arasan to 1 pound of seed is necessary. Dr. Newhall later found that a much simpler and equally effective procedure is to apply 5 to 6 pounds of Arasan an acre in the furrow with the seed by a special attachment on the seeder. When seed is sown to produce set onions, about 65 pounds of seed to the acre is used. Then 1 pound of Arasan applied to 10 of seed without a sticker controls the disease, and no special attachment for the fungicide is required.

J. C. WALKER *is professor of plant pathology in the University of Wisconsin.*

For further reading:
W. C. Hatfield, J. C. Walker, and J. H. Owen: Antibiotic Substances in Onion in Relation to Disease Resistance, *Journal of Agricultural Research, volume 77, pages 115–135, 1948.*
Ray Nelson: Control of Onion Mildew with Dust Fungicides, *Phytopathology, volume 41, page 28, 1951.*
A. G. Newhall: New Methods of Controlling Onion Smut, *Phytopathology, volume 41, page 28, 1951.*
J. J. Taubenhaus and F. W. Mally: Pink Root Disease of Onions and Its Control in Texas, *Texas Agricultural Experiment Station Bulletin 273, 1921.*

Control of Diseases of Potatoes

Eugene S. Schultz

The Irish potato is susceptible to many diseases. The fungi that might attack it range from the slime molds to the smuts and rusts. It is subject to several viruses of the yellows and mosaic groups. Such nonparasitic diseases as black heart, sunscald, freezing injury, and a malnutrition caused by deficiency in magnesium, potash, and boron may cause damage. Several nematode diseases have been found on it.

Unless effective methods of control are practiced, serious diseases, such as late blight, ring rot, and leaf roll, can cause the total loss of a crop.

LATE BLIGHT of potato is a downy mildew caused by a fungus, *Phytophthora infestans*. The mildew, or flourlike spots, usually on the lower surface of the leaf, distinguishes the disease from other leaf spots on the potato plant. Humid conditions favor it. Despite its name, the first infection often occurs soon after the plants emerge when favorable moisture and temperature prevail. At 70° to 75° F. the fungus grows so fast inside the leaves that within a week after infection it causes dead spots one-half to 1 inch in diameter. The entire plant may be killed within 2 weeks. The brown discoloration of the foliage brings to mind the terms "blight" and "rust."

Late blight destroyed potato crops so often during the nineteenth century that it outranked other potato diseases and was called "the potato disease." In 1845 it was responsible for the potato famine in Ireland.

The late blight fungus produces a mycelium, or moldlike growth, which invades and kills the plant tissue. From the mycelium grow treelike sporangiophores, which bear sporangia, the agents involved in spreading infection. At about 70° and 90 percent relative humidity, sporangia develop in 5 to 7 days after infection. In water at 72° to 77°, sporangia form germ tubes. At lower temperatures, 58° to 63°, they develop swarmspores, or zoospores. The two methods of germination enable the fungus to adapt itself to a rather wide range of temperature. The higher temperature favors mycelial development, rapid invasion, and killing of the plant. The lower temperature favors formation of zoospores and rapid increase in inoculum to spread infection.

The fungus infects the potato tuber as well as the tops. Spores from infected tops are carried by rain to the tubers in the soil. Tubers also are readily infected if they are harvested before the blighted tops are killed. Infected tubers quickly show a brown discoloration, which changes to a purplish color. The fungus usually invades the tuber to about one-fourth to one-half inch below the skin. At about 36° to 40°, the affected tubers persist in a dry rot condition. Higher temperatures favor secondary infection with bacteria, and the blighted tubers develop soft rot.

The organism is carried into the following season in infected tubers. When such tubers are planted, the fungus invades the shoots on which form the spores that infect the foliage. Another source of infection is the blighted tubers in the potato refuse or dump pile. Late blight appears on potato tops on waste piles a few weeks before the plants in the fields emerge, so that the potato tops in the fields become infected as soon as the plants emerge and before spraying begins.

The spread of late blight is favored by humid conditions such as may prevail in the New England States, other regions along the Atlantic coast, and the North Central States. With favorable moisture, it also appears in the Middle Western, Southern, and Pacific Coast States. It occurs in long periods of rain, fog, and dew, which favor fruiting, infection, and dissemination of the fungus.

Control measures are sanitation, protection, and the use of resistant varieties.

Sanitation involves careful inspection and removal of blighted tubers from seed potatoes and elimination of piles of waste potatoes. Waste potatoes that have to be dumped should be given a dormancy or sprout-inhibiting treatment—0.25 percent isopropyl ester of trichlorophenoxy acetic acid—before dumping to prevent sprouting.

For many years a combination of copper sulfate and lime—bordeaux mixture—has been used to control late blight. Weekly spraying with it during the growing season effectively, although not absolutely, controls late blight even during epidemics. Copper-lime dusts control late blight if applied at rates of 25 to 30 pounds the acre at weekly intervals.

Some of the more recently developed products like Dithane and Parzate are less toxic to foliage and therefore favor higher yields than when bordeaux mixture is used. Because these products are not generally so effective for control of late blight as bordeaux mixture, some growers change to bordeaux mixture during the latter part of the season when conditions favor an epidemic of late blight.

Because lime in bordeaux mixture increases transpiration to a harmful degree and because one-half the amount of lime used formerly in bordeaux mixture is satisfactory, many growers use a recommended formula such as 10–5–100—10 pounds of copper sulfate and 5 pounds of lime in 100 gallons of water.

Search for resistant varieties began about the middle of the nineteenth century. Varying degrees of resistance appeared in different varieties, but no cultivated varieties manifested immunity from late blight. Sebago, Menominee, and Calrose, though not immune, are somewhat blight-resistant. The tubers in some varieties, such as Sebago, are more blight-resistant than the foliage.

Among certain wild species, such as *Solanum demissum*, some lines or strains are immune. Some lines of that species also are blight-susceptible. Empire, Ashworth, Chenango, Essex, Placid, Virgil, and Kennebec are varieties in which *S. demissum* was one of the parents and are immune to some races of late blight.

The development of blight-resistant varieties is a complicated procedure—actually, the plant breeder has to develop resistance to several biological races that vary in ability to cause disease. A blight-immune variety may be immune to one race but susceptible to other races. Within the past decade, however, efforts to develop blight-immune varieties show that varieties can harbor immunity to more than one race of the fungus of late blight.

COMMON SCAB, caused by *Streptomyces scabies*, is recognized by slightly raised spots or lesions of rough, corky tissue on the tuber. The lesions may be so numerous as to involve the entire surface. They may involve distinct russeting or deep scab. Scab lesions spoil the looks of the tuber and cause waste in peeling and reduction in grade.

The fungus lives in the soil and on infected tubers. It occurs in nearly every potato-growing region. Soil acidity, moisture, temperature, and aeration influence the development of scab. A soil reaction below pH 5.2 is unfavorable for most of the common scab races, although some strains are said to cause infection below pH 5. In general, the fungus is favored at pH 5.2

to 7. Common scab develops at a wide range of temperatures, 50° to 85°, but it thrives best at about 70°. Relatively high soil moisture tends to check the disease in some localities, but in other districts high moisture may favor scab. Lack of aeration inhibits development of the organism.

The several races of the fungus vary in type and color of mycelium, color in the medium, and pathogenicity. Apparently the races result by mutation and some races mutate more than others.

Treatment of seed tubers with disinfectants kills the scab fungus on the tuber, but it fails to control the disease if the treated tubers are planted in scab-infested soil. The use of 300 to 500 pounds of sulfur an acre reduces the severity of scab in some soils. The use of ammonium sulfate in fertilizer that increases soil acidity may inhibit the disease somewhat. None of the treatments has been entirely adequate for scab control, however.

The most promising method involves the development of scab-resistant varieties. Studies in Europe have disclosed that Jubel, Hindenburg, Ostragis, and Arnica are scab-resistant. In this country, scab resistance was noted in Russet Rural and Russet Burbank. Although the scab-resistant European varieties are not adapted to growing conditions in America, they do serve as resistant parents. From them the resistant Cayuga, Menominee, Ontario, and Seneca were derived. Investigations on scab resistance by the Department of Agriculture and State experiment stations are designed to develop varieties that are superior to them in scab resistance, quality, adaptability, and yield.

VERTICILLIUM WILT, caused by *Verticillium albo-atrum*, induces wilting of the tops and vascular discoloration of the stems, tubers, and roots—symptoms similar to those associated with other wilt-inciting fungi. Since *V. albo-atrum* is favored by lower temperatures than are wilt-inciting Fusaria, it often occurs in the cool seed-potato areas.

Verticillium wilt is recognized by flaccid, drooping leaves. Often only one stalk in the hill or a part of a stalk may be wilted. Later all the plants in the hill are involved and finally are killed.

Cross sections near the stem or stolon end of the tubers expose dark-colored vascular elements, the sap-conducting elements. The verticillium wilt fungus does not cause a disintegration or rot of the invaded tissues. Sometimes other organisms may enter the wilt-invaded parts, however.

Verticillium wilt on potato was reported in Europe and America early in the twentieth century. It occurs in the seed-potato areas in the New England, North Central, and Northwestern States.

The wilt fungus is harbored in the tubers and persists in the soil. If conditions are favorable, wilt-free soil can be infested by wilt-infected seed potatoes. Attempts at getting wilt-free seed tubers by cutting off the discolored stem end of infected tubers have met with failure because fungus hyphae may penetrate beyond the discolored section of the tuber.

Roguing wilted tops has reduced the amount of wilt of seed potatoes if the tops in the three hills on each side of the wilted hill also were removed. In some regions the wilt fungus persisted in the soil after a 2-year rotation, but infestation was practically eliminated after a 3- to 4-year rotation.

Some varieties—Menominee, Saranac, and Sequoia—are more resistant than others.

BLACKLEG, caused by *Erwinia atroseptica*, is recognized by an inky-black lesion on the base of the stem, which is a primary distinguishing character from similar soft rot caused by bacteria.

The blackleg bacteria invade tops and tubers. Infection may enter the stalks from the infected seed piece. Diseased tops manifest slight to severe dwarfing and somewhat rigid and rolled leaves that in the later stages yellow, wilt, and die.

In very wet weather, the inky-black lesions at the base of the stalk may spread to most of the plant. The bacteria enter the new tubers through the stolons of a blackleg stalk and invade the vascular elements, as well as other tissues of the tuber. Affected tubers show soft rot, involving the entire tuber. Under less favorable conditions the decay is arrested so that only the tissues in the center of the tubers are disintegrated.

The blackleg organism is spread from infected to healthy tubers with the seed-cutting knife and the picker planter as well as by contact of freshly cut, healthy seed pieces with diseased seed pieces. The seed-corn maggot and other insects carry the blackleg bacteria and infect the injured plant tissue of the potato.

In very moist weather, bacteria in the soil invade freshly cut or poorly healed seed pieces—a possible explanation for the more general appearance of blackleg in wet than in dry seasons in some places.

Because cuts, bruises, and other injuries permit the entrance of rot-inciting organisms, tubers should be handled carefully to avoid bruising. Storage should be provided with favorable temperatures and humidity for healing over (or suberizing) injured tissues. Removing from the seed potatoes all tubers showing rot and storing cut seed potatoes immediately after cutting at about 70° F. and 80 percent humidity to favor adequate healing of the cut surfaces have been effective control measures in some places.

We know of no varieties that are immune to blackleg, but some contract blackleg less easily than others. In 1947 Carl Stapp, a bacteriologist in Germany, reported that Carnea, Flava, Johanna, Priska, Robusta, Sickingen, and Starkeragis were more resistant to blackleg than the 56 other German varieties he included in his test.

Ring rot, caused by *Corynebacterium epedonicum*, is a bacterial disease. It is recognized by wilt of the foliage and rot of the vascular ring of the tubers. Chlorosis, or yellowing, and marginal browning and wilting of the leaves are symptoms. In the tubers the disease is detected by a light-yellow discoloration of the vascular elements, which break down and exude a cheesy bacterial and cellular ooze when a tuber is squeezed. When other micro-organisms enter, the lesions enlarge, and soft rot of the tuber results. Cankers or fissures often appear on the surface of infected tubers in the later stages.

Bacterial ring rot was found in Maine in 1932, a year after it was reported in eastern Canada. By 1940 it was detected in most of the potato States. In some areas it caused severe losses.

Ring rot apparently is not harbored in the soil, but infected tubers overwintering in the soil may develop infected volunteer plants, which may serve as sources of infection. The disease is spread from infected to healthy tubers by the seed-cutting knife, planting machines, grading equipment, and contaminated hands, gloves, bags, baskets, barrels, and bins that have come in contact with diseased potatoes.

Control involves prevention, sanitation, and the use of resistant varieties.

Control of ring rot is primarily the responsibility of seed-potato growers, who should propagate and maintain their own seed potatoes. Potatoes that are free from ring rot can be kept so if no infected seed potatoes are introduced from other sources. If a grower must bring in seed potatoes from other farms and localities, however, he will be safe if he plants them in separate fields for a few years or until he is absolutely certain that they are free from ring rot.

Seed-potato certifying agencies in most States set up a rigid zero tolerance for ring rot in certified seed potatoes in 1940. Largely as a result of those standards, the spread and extent of ring rot has been reduced greatly, and

growers of seed potatoes have access to an adequate supply of healthy potatoes even if they cannot grow their own seed stock.

Sanitation involves selling for table stock the crop that harbors ring rot and disinfecting all equipment, machinery, containers, and bins that in any way were in contact with the diseased potatoes. Bins, crates, barrels, and bags can be treated with copper sulfate (25 pounds to 100 gallons of water). Machinery can be treated with formaldehyde (1 part in 10). Ring-rot-free seed potatoes, such are produced by foundation seed-potato growers or on State foundation seed-potato farms, should be planted. By following this clean-up program many potato growers have eradicated ring rot from their farms.

Although no variety is immune to ring rot, some varieties contract the disease less easily than others. Teton, introduced in 1946, is an example.

Virus diseases of potatoes have been reported in every country. Leaf roll and latent mosaic apparently occur most widely.

The nature and cause of virus diseases have been under investigation for more than 100 years. Many investigators now regard them as filterable proteins that multiply in living cells.

The virus diseases of potatoes can be classified as mosaics and yellows. Distinguishing characters of the mosaic group are mottling and the ability to be transmitted in the sap. A mark of the yellows group is chlorosis; it cannot be transmitted in sap. The mosaic group includes several viruses, some of which have several strains or races that differ in pathogenicity. The yellows group includes the viruses that cause leaf roll, witches'-broom, and aster yellows.

As with most of the fungus diseases, the potato virus diseases are designated by common names that indicate the response or reaction of the plant to the virus. The reactions or symptoms are affected by temperature, host, and the strain or race of the virus. Mottling usually is absent at higher temperatures. Roll of the leaves is favored by relatively high temperatures. Some varieties manifest the effects of a virus; another variety might act as a symptomless carrier of the same virus. One race of a virus can cause a reaction in the same variety that differs from the reaction induced by another race. Most of the potato viruses are transmitted by sucking insects (aphids and leafhoppers) but some are spread also by chewing insects. Some viruses are spread by mere contact of diseased plants with healthy plants and by mechanical agents, such as the seed-potato cutting knife and planting machines.

ALTHOUGH SEVERAL MOSAIC diseases incited by as many different viruses affect the potato, I shall describe only three—latent mosaic, virus A, and vein banding mosaic, which occur in many potato regions.

Latent mosaic, caused by virus X, is so called because many varieties of potatoes are symptomless carriers. Synonyms of the latent mosaic virus are potato virus X, potato-acronecrosis virus, simple mosaic virus, potato virus 16, *Solanum* virus 1, and *Annulus dubius*.

Latent mosaic virus is harbored by potato varieties more generally than any of the other potato mosaic viruses. Almost every plant in most of the older varieties harbors the virus. Many varieties manifest the milder strains of this mosaic by slightly light-green and rugose leaves when the weather is cool.

Latent mosaic virus has several races or strains that induce a range of reactions, varying from weak or no apparent symptoms to severe necrosis. A plant harboring one race may be protected against infection from other races of this virus. More than one race may be harbored by a plant, suggesting mutation or simultaneous infection by more than one race.

Other plants in the nightshade family that are susceptible to latent mosaic are tomato, tobacco, pepper, jimsonweed, petunia, physalis, henbane, woody nightshade, and black nightshade. Jimsonweed is a good one for detecting different races of latent mosaic virus. It reacts to the races by manifesting no symptoms for the weaker races to severe necrosis for the more virulent races. Globe amaranth, or bachelor's button, which manifests red local lesions, also is a good host for detecting latent mosaic virus.

Latent mosaic is easily transmitted mechanically. Contact of diseased with healthy plants and the cutting knife spread the disease. Some sucking insects, such as aphids, fail to transmit latent mosaic, but grasshoppers are reported to transmit it.

Reductions in yield of 10 to 30 percent are reported for the common races of latent mosaic. Virulent races can cut yields more than 50 percent. Because most of the old varieties harbor latent mosaic, it is possible that yields from them are 10 or 15 percent lower than the yields of healthy stock.

VIRUS A often induces slightly light-green and rugose leaves, symptoms that are similar to those induced by virus X, the cause of latent mosaic. The symptoms are favored by cool temperatures and are masked at high temperatures. Some varieties merely show light-green foliage. Others develop dead spots in the foliage.

Although tobacco and some other species in the nightshade family are susceptible to virus A, the symptoms often are so like those induced by virus X that diagnosis is difficult.

Virus A is transmitted by aphids. It can also be transmitted in the sap. It is transmitted mechanically less easily than virus X. Virus A apparently involves several races, which vary in degree of reaction they induce on their host plants.

Virus A reduces yields by 15 to 25 percent in some varieties, apparently by causing plants to mature too early. It does not affect the set of tubers.

Since most of the old varieties generally harbor virus X, they carry a composite infection after contracting the aphid-transmitted virus A. On many varieties the two viruses induce more pronounced symptoms than those of one of them, such as distinct mottling and crinkling. This composite infection is recognized as mild mosaic, a term first used to designate mildly affected plants, as distinguished from severely dwarfed, curled, rolled, and necrotic plants.

VEIN BANDING MOSAIC, caused by virus Y, is distinguished by rugosity, or wrinkled surface of the leaf, and vein clearing in early stages and by necrotic spots and streaks and leaf drop in the later stages. The symptoms vary in different varieties, ranging from slight rugosity to severe dwarfing, curling, and necrosis. Synonyms for vein banding mosaic virus are potato virus Y, *Solanum* virus 2, and *Marmor upsilon*.

Vein banding mosaic occurs in leading potato areas of every country. In some places a high percentage of the crop is infected.

Susceptible hosts, besides potato, are tomato, black nightshade, henbane, woody nightshade, petunia, *Solanum nodiflorum*, *Datura innoxia*, and tobacco.

The several races of vein banding mosaic vary in virulence. Vein banding mosaic virus is readily transmitted by sap inoculation, grafting, and aphids. It is responsible for a greater reduction in yield than that caused by either virus X or virus A. Infected plants die prematurely; the result is undersized tubers. Usually less than half a crop is obtained from diseased plants.

Because the older potato varieties generally harbor virus X, they harbor two viruses after contracting vein banding mosaic virus (virus Y). This composite infection is known as rugose mosaic, which often causes more severe host reactions than either one of the viruses. On some varieties, however, the vein banding mosaic virus induces as severe reactions as the composite infection.

LEAF ROLL is recognized by upward cupping or rolling of the leaflets, first on the lower leaves and finally on the entire plant. An infected plant has a leathery texture. Chlorosis, or a generally light-green color, especially in the upper leaves, frequently appears, even before roll of the leaves begins. In colored varieties, reddish discoloration also may appear. The plants are barely half as tall as healthy plants. The tubers are smaller in size and number. In some varieties internal tuber discoloration, known as net necrosis, develops only as a result of current-season infection with the leaf roll virus.

Leaf roll occurs in potato regions in every country. In some areas all potatoes are infected so that growers in such areas do not know their stock is infected. They suppose that leaf roll symptoms are characteristic of a healthy crop.

Synonyms for the leaf roll virus are potato phloem necrosis virus, potato leaf roll virus, potato virus 1, *Solanum* virus 14, and *Corium solani*. Apparently the leaf roll virus involves more than one race. Other hosts are tomato, jimsonweed, woody nightshade, black nightshade, and groundcherry.

Leaf roll has not been transmitted by sap inoculation, but is transmitted by tuber and stalk grafts. Aphids, especially the green peach aphid, *Myzus persicae*, are vectors. Heavy infestations of aphids, mild temperatures, and absence of diseases and parasites of aphids contribute to the extensive spread of leaf roll.

Leaf roll is responsible for reduction in size of plants and tubers, as well as in set of tubers. Reductions in yield might be as high as 50 percent. In hot and dry weather, leaf roll infected plants produce chiefly culls.

CONTROL OF POTATO VIRUS diseases involves the use of isolated tuber-unit seed plots or fields and the resistant varieties.

Because insects transmit virus diseases, it is useless to attempt to grow healthy plants near potato fields that harbor the diseases. Healthy potatoes can be grown in fields that are surrounded by woods and located at a distance from other potato fields. The healthiest seed stock should be used for planting the isolated field, and it should be planted as soon as the soil is tillable. Planting the tubers in tuber units—planting seed pieces of the same tubers in consecutive order—facilitates detection and removal of diseased plants. Weekly inspections, beginning when the plants are about 6 inches tall, to detect and remove diseased plants will help control the diseases.

THE NUMBER of plants that contract diseases increases as the season advances. Some growers therefore practice early harvesting. That means harvesting seed potatoes about 10 weeks after planting. The most effective (but laborious) method is to pull the tops so that the tubers can be harvested later when storage conditions may be more favorable. Killing the tops with a weed killer frequently fails to kill the entire stalk that produces leaves, so that aphid infestation and virus transmission are encouraged unless the tubers are harvested a few days after the tops die.

In tests in northern Maine in 1932 to 1947, two highly susceptible varieties remained free from virus diseases when harvested August 1, even though they had been grown within 500 feet of diseased potatoes. Samples of the varieties, left on the same plots until harvest on September 15, had contracted 90 to 95 percent of mosaic and leaf roll in seasons when aphids were numerous. The tests show that susceptible potatoes can be maintained free from virus diseases in some seed-potato-producing areas, even with meager isolation, if the seed potatoes are harvested early in the season

before the dispersal of virus-carrying insects.

Seed-potato certification agencies in different States inspect and certify potatoes that meet their standards. To have potatoes inspected, the grower notifies the agency, which charges a small fee for the service. Certified seed potatoes, though not necessarily disease-free, usually are superior to noncertified potatoes for seed. Certification, more than any other factor, encourages growers to produce healthy seed potatoes.

POTATOES VARY in their resistance to virus X. Some varieties contract virus X in more than 50 percent of the plants. Under like conditions other varieties become infected in less than 10 percent of the plants. Still other varieties are immune. A variety that is immune to virus X is immune to all the races of virus X that have been tested so far. The varieties immune to virus X harbor this immunity not only against contact and sap inoculation but also against infection in stalk and tuber grafts. Grafting a scion that is susceptible to virus X onto a stock that is immune to virus X results in formation of aerial tubers on the scion and provides a method for identifying varieties immune to virus X in segregating progenies.

Protective inoculation against races of virus X involves inoculating a susceptible variety with a weak race of the virus for protection against infection from stronger or more virulent races of the virus. As the stronger races of virus X cause greater reductions in yield than the weak races, the potato stocks inoculated with weak races are protected against this reduction.

Some varieties susceptible to virus A contract it less easily than others. Some varieties are immune. Some are symptomless carriers, manifest top and tuber necrosis, and are light green and rugose, or show mottling. Immune varieties are of two types—virus-A, immune to aphid but not to graft infection, and virus-A, immune to both aphid and graft infection. Varieties included in the second type of virus A immunity manifest this immunity by top and tuber necrosis, a hypersensitive reaction. Examples of varieties of the second type of virus A immunity are Irish Cobbler, Earlaine, and segregating progenies of those varieties. Examples of the first type of virus A immunity are Katahdin and Chippewa, as well as segregating progenies of them.

Observations on the reaction of different varieties to virus Y disclose that many of them develop dead spots on the leaves and streaking of veins, petioles, and stems, which is associated with brittleness and leaf drop. Rugosity and vein clearing appears on some varieties. Other varieties manifest light-green and rugose leaves to so slight a degree that they may be mistaken for healthy plants.

Although no varieties immune to virus Y have been found, some varieties are highly resistant in the field. Katahdin and Chippewa are field resistant to virus Y under average conditions to aphid infestation. Under heavy aphid infestation, however, they contract considerable virus Y infection, an indication that the resistance is affected by the number of aphids.

In reaction to leaf roll, caused by the phloem necrosis virus, some varieties develop distinct foliage chlorosis, roll, and dwarfing. Others manifest those symptoms to a slight degree. Varieties vary in resistance to leaf roll. Under average field conditions Katahdin contracts leaf roll in less than 10 percent of the plants where less resistant varieties contract this disease in more than 50 percent of the plants. Some of the new seedling potatoes are more highly resistant to leaf roll than Katahdin.

Investigations on potato diseases by the United States Department of Agriculture and State experiment stations have contributed much helpful information on identification, means of spread, disease resistance, and control of late blight, scab, ring rot, leaf roll, and viruses A, X, and Y. There is need for additional knowledge on the causal agents as to the origin and development of races; pathological anatomy; disease development in relation to moisture, temperature, soil reaction and nutrition; and the nature of disease resistance.

Problems in control involve devising and evaluating new fungicides and studies on antibiotics designed to find a product that is systemic and persists during the growing season.

A primary objective in disease resistance involves breeding varieties that are immune from as many of the major potato diseases as possible and that possess other desirable characters such as quality, yield, and adaptability.

EUGENE S. SCHULTZ *is principal pathologist in charge of investigations of potato diseases, Bureau of Plant Industry, Soils, and Agricultural Engineering. He has been associated with the Department of Agriculture since 1917. Dr. Schultz holds degrees from the University of Wisconsin and Columbia University. Since 1930 he also has been associated with the National Potato Breeding Program in connection with testing, isolating, and developing varieties for resistance to late blight and viruses A, X, and Y.*

For further reading:
Reiner Bonde, E. S. Schultz, and W. P. Raleigh: Rate of Spread and Effect on Yield of Potato Virus Diseases, *Maine Agricultural Experiment Station Bulletin 421, 1943.*
T. P. Dykstra: Production of Disease-free Seed Potatoes, *U. S. D. A. Circular 764, 1948.*
E. S. Schultz, Reiner Bonde, and W. P. Raleigh: Isolated Tuber-Unit Seed Plots for Control of Potato Virus Diseases and Black Leg in Northern Maine, *Maine Agricultural Experiment Station Bulletin 370, 1934;* Early Harvesting of Healthy Seed Potatoes for Control of Potato Diseases in Maine, *Maine Station Bulletin 427, 1944.*
E. S. Schultz and D. Folsom: Transmission, Variation and Control of Certain Degeneration Diseases of Irish Potatoes, *Journal of Agricultural Research, volume 25, pages 43–118, 1923.*
K. M. Smith, A Text Book of Plant Virus Diseases, *P. Blakiston's Son and Co. Inc., Philadelphia, 1937.*

The Fungi That Cause Rot in Sweetpotatoes

Harold T. Cook

Diseases destroy 20 to 40 percent of the sweetpotato crop in the field, in storage, and in transit to market. The average annual production from 1939 to 1948 of nearly 62 million bushels had a farm value of about 119 million dollars. The losses thus might be set at 24 million to 48 million dollars each year.

More than 40 fungus diseases attack sweetpotatoes. Most of the damage is caused by seven of them. Diseases that affect the growing crop reduce the yield and the proportion of choice size potatoes and cause disfigurations and skin blemishes that reduce their salability. Those that affect the potatoes in storage, in transit, and at the market cause decay, shriveling, and unattractive appearance.

The greatest monetary losses arise from damage in storage, in transit, and at the market. Sweetpotatoes are extremely perishable after they are dug and many decay before they reach the consumer. The later the decay occurs, the greater the monetary losses because of the added costs of harvesting, storing, grading, cleaning, packing, shipping, and marketing.

STEM ROT is one of the worst field diseases. It is found in all our growing areas. It destroys more than 50 percent of the plants in some fields. It lowers total yield and the number of medium size, uniformly shaped sweetpotatoes preferred for marketing.

Stem rot is most conspicuous about 2 weeks after the sprouts are set in the field. By that time many of the diseased sprouts are dead or are yellow and dying. The inside of the stem and vines of infected plants are brown or black instead of the normal white color. The stem is often split near the ground level and decayed. Some of the diseased plants develop new roots above the decayed part of the stem and survive the entire growing season.

The potatoes produced by the infected plants are usually small and decayed at the stem end. Their vascular tissues are brown. Sometimes a tuft of new sprouts grows from the stem end at harvest. Diseased sprouts growing from diseased seed potatoes in the plant bed sometimes can be recognized by a faint purplish tint, which shows through the white part of the stem and is caused by the dark tissues.

Stem rot is caused by *Fusarium oxysporum* f. *batatas* or *F. hyperoxysporum*. The fungi can live indefinitely in the soil. They also overwinter in stored sweetpotatoes that are diseased. They are usually spread from one locality to another by the exchange or sale of diseased seed potatoes or plants. They also may be carried in soil that adheres to farm implements.

Varieties of the Jersey group, including Big Stem Jersey, Little Stem Jersey, Maryland Golden, and Nancy Hall, are very susceptible to stem rot. Porto Rico is intermediate in resistance. Southern Queen, Triumph, and Yellow Strassburg are quite resistant—but most of the more resistant varieties have poor table quality. A breeding program has been started to develop resistant kinds of good eating quality.

BLACK ROT is serious in the seedbed and field. It is especially destructive in storage and transit. It causes some reduction in yield, and some of the potatoes have visible black rot spots on them at harvest. Frequently, however, potatoes that appear free from black rot at harvest are so badly diseased at the end of storage or on arrival at market that they are nearly a total loss.

The most conspicuous symptom is the circular, dark-brown or black spots on the potatoes. The spots vary in size from mere specks to 1 or 2 inches in diameter. The blackening usually extends into the potato only as far as the vascular ring, but in some varieties it extends much farther. Sometimes small, black bristles, the fruiting bodies of the fungus, develop at the center of the spots.

Black rot may cause small, round black spots on the white underground stem of the sprouts or it may cause blackening and decay of most of the base of the stem, a condition that is sometimes referred to as black shank.

Black rot is caused by the fungus *Ceratostomella fimbriata*, which may remain alive in the soil for several years. It also lives from one season to the next on infected sweetpotatoes in storage. It is usually spread from one farm area to another by the exchange or purchase of plants and seed potatoes. Harvested potatoes become infected by spread of the fungus spores during grading, brushing, and washing. When lots containing a few infected potatoes are washed, the wash water becomes contaminated by the fungus spores and nearly all of the potatoes become infected. Such potatoes may appear sound when they are packed for shipping after washing, but they may be heavily infected when they arrive at the market.

The fungus grows best at temperatures of 73° to 81° F., but also makes good growth at 55°, the lowest temperature at which sweetpotatoes should be stored. Little or no growth occurs at temperatures above 95°. When infected sweetpotatoes are held at 110° for a day, the fungus is killed. Most infection takes place through wounds.

No commercial variety of sweetpotatoes is entirely immune to black rot, but several unnamed seedling varieties have been discovered to be highly resistant.

Soft rot is the most serious disease in storage and transit. It may start soon after the potatoes are stored and destroy nearly all of the potatoes before the end of the storage period or it may not affect the potatoes until they have been removed from storage and cleaned, packed, and shipped to market.

It is easily recognized by the soft, mushy decay and the accompanying fuzzy gray and black mold. The affected tissues are moist, brown, and stringy. The decaying potatoes have a rather pleasant aromatic odor, which is quite noticeable in storage houses when potatoes are affected with the disease. The affected potatoes lose moisture rapidly and finally become dry and brittle.

Soft rot is usually caused by the common bread mold fungus, *Rhizopus nigricans*, but several other species of *Rhizopus* also may cause it. *Rhizopus* spores are almost universally present, because the bread mold fungus grows on a wide variety of vegetable material.

Species of *Rhizopus* responsible for soft rot grow well at the usual storage temperatures and even better at higher temperatures. Infection rarely takes place except at wounds, such as those where the potato is broken from the stem and at cuts and bruises caused in digging, cleaning, and packing. Less infection occurs in bruised potatoes that are held at a high relative humidity and about 85° F. temperature for a few days immediately after wounding, because the injuries heal so rapidly at this temperature and high humidity that the fungus cannot get established.

All varieties are susceptible to soft rot, but some decay more rapidly than others. Southern Queen and Nancy Hall are quite resistant. Porto Rico, Big Stem Jersey, and Triumph are intermediate. Yellow Jersey is very susceptible.

Scurf, or soil stain, has little effect on yield, but it causes a brown stain on the potato skin and increased shriveling in storage. It does not spread to other potatoes in storage or cause decay.

The brown stain is only skin deep. It is usually worse at the stem end of the potato. It occurs as scattered blotches on lightly infected potatoes, but large areas may be brown or nearly black on badly infected ones.

Scurf is caused by *Monilochaetes infuscans*, a fungus that overwinters on potatoes in storage. It persists in the soil for several years. If potatoes are bedded, the fungus grows from the mother potato up to the base of the sprouts. After the sprouts are planted it spreads down to the new potatoes. Most of the infection apparently comes from the seed potatoes and is carried to the field on the sprouts.

Scurf is worse on heavy soils and those containing a large quantity of organic matter than on sandy soils.

Pox, or soil rot, is a widely distributed field disease, but generally it is less important than stem rot or black rot. It reduces the yield and the proportion of salable potatoes.

Its most conspicuous symptom is the pits it causes on the potatoes. The pits are one-fourth inch to more than an inch in diameter and have a jagged margin. In the early stages the infected spots are dark-colored and water-soaked. Later the skin of the potato covering the pit breaks and the contents fall out, leaving an empty cavity. The disease also kills the young feeding roots and causes dark lesions on the part of the stem below the soil line. Affected plants are usually stunted and have yellow leaves. Many of them die early.

Streptomyces ipomoea, the causal fungus, lives indefinitely in the soil and is spread in soil adhering to farm machinery or plants, by wind-blown soil, and by floodwaters. It likes soils that are less acid than pH 5.2. The addition of sulfur to the soil to make it more acid has reduced damage from pox in some places.

INTERNAL CORK, a new virus disease, was discovered in South Carolina in 1944. Since then it has been found in sweetpotatoes in many other areas, but it is most serious in South Carolina, Georgia, and North Carolina.

Sweetpotatoes affected with internal cork appear normal externally, but have dark brown to blackish corky spots scattered irregularly through the flesh. The corky tissues remain firm during cooking and have a slightly bitter taste. They vary in size up to about one-tenth inch in diameter and one-fifth inch in length. Closely grouped corky spots may affect large areas in the flesh. Leaves of plants affected with internal cork are sometimes marked with purplish ring spots.

Only a little internal cork is found when the sweetpotatoes are dug but corky spots increase in number and size during storage. The rate of increase is more rapid at 70° F. than at the recommended storage temperatures of 55° and 60°.

JAVA BLACK ROT ranks next to soft rot and black rot in importance as a storage disease. It occurs in all parts of the United States where sweetpotatoes grow and in many other countries. It was named Java black rot because it was first discovered on sweetpotatoes sent from Java. It is caused by a fungus, *Diplodia tubericola*.

It causes a dry rot of the roots. The decayed tissues, brown at first, turn black and hard. The fungus forms black protuberances on the surface of the potato. The decay usually starts at the ends, but sometimes at breaks on other parts of the potato. It progresses slowly and there is little evidence of the disease until about a week after infection. The potato rots in 4 to 8 weeks.

SURFACE ROT, a common storage disease, causes shallow, circular, depressed spots on the surface and a gradual drying out. It progresses so slowly that a great deal of damage may be done before the extent of the disease is recognized. The spots usually are not more than three-fourths inch in diameter and seldom penetrate below the vascular ring. They usually are grayish brown, but sometimes they may be so dark-colored that they resemble black rot.

The disease is caused by the fungus *Fusarium oxysporum*. Infection apparently takes place through the small rootlets that are damaged when the potatoes are harvested. The disease does not become conspicuous until the potatoes have been in storage for 2 months.

Surface rot is worse on potatoes harvested when the ground is wet and when the potatoes are in the storage house several days before the curing process is started.

All varieties are affected, but Big Stem Jersey and Little Stem Jersey are more susceptible than some of the darker skinned varieties.

THE MOST EFFECTIVE and practical control of the field diseases is to plant only healthy seed potatoes and plants in healthy seedbeds and fields.

Except for the fungi that cause stem rot and pox, none of the fungi that cause major diseases of sweetpotatoes remains alive in the soil for more than 2 or 3 years. A crop rotation of about 4 years generally rids a field of the fungi that cause black rot and scurf.

Plant beds should be thoroughly cleaned and filled with new soil or and or new plant beds prepared.

Plants free of black rot or scurf can be had even from affected sweetpotatoes by planting vine cuttings or sprout cuttings instead of pulled sprouts. The cuttings will be free of those diseases because black rot and scurf do not affect the above-ground parts. It is more practical to use sprout cuttings than vine cuttings because they can be obtained and planted as early as pulled sprouts; vine cuttings cannot be made until much later. The sprout cuttings should be made by cutting the sprouts about 1.5 inches above the soil line of the plant bed without disturbing the below-ground parts. Once black rot and scurf have been eliminated from the sweetpotato seed stock, it is all right to use pulled sprouts in succeeding years.

Because the fungi that cause stem rot and pox live indefinitely in the soil, neither the use of clean planting stock nor crop rotation will eliminate those diseases from a farm. The most practical control is by the use of resistant varieties when suitable ones have been developed. The addition of sulfur to the soil to lower the reaction to slightly less than pH 5.2 reduces the amount of pox.

Much of the losses caused by black rot and scurf in storage and transit may be avoided by storing and shipping only potatoes that are free of those diseases. Black rot and scurf may be eliminated from the potato stocks by use of clean plants and crop rotation.

Losses in storage and transit caused by soft rot, Java black rot, and surface rot can be greatly reduced by proper curing so that wounds caused in harvesting, handling, washing, and packing will heal rapidly and wall out the decay fungi. Temperature and humidity are important in curing sweetpotatoes. The temperature should be about 85° F. and the humidity should be high. Only enough ventilation should be used to keep the potatoes from becoming wet. Frequently outside temperatures are high enough to favor healing when the sweetpotatoes are harvested and additional heat in the storage house is not necessary. Sweetpotatoes may be cured to reduce decay after they are taken from storage and washed and packed for shipment as well as when they are placed in storage in the fall. Storing sweetpotatoes at temperatures even slightly below 55° F. causes chilling injuries that make the sweetpotatoes more likely to decay.

HAROLD T. COOK *is a pathologist in the Bureau of Plant Industry, Soils, and Agricultural Engineering.*

Preventing the Diseases of Peanuts

Coyt Wilson

Prevention, rather than cure, is the rule with the diseases of peanuts.

Some beneficial preventive measures are the application of fungicides to seed to prevent seed rot, the use of fungicidal dusts or sprays on growing plants to prevent leaf spot, and the treatment of soil with chemicals before planting to control nematodes and soil insects.

Prevention involves more than the use of chemicals, however. Management practices that promote vigorous growth enable the plants to escape infection or to survive after infection. Outstanding are rotations that include one or two crops of corn, oats, or similar crops before each peanut crop; adequate mineral fertilization; planting on light-textured, well-drained soils; and reduction of mechanical damage by cultivating implements.

SEED ROT is the most serious of the diseases that affect stands of peanuts. It is caused by mildly pathogenic or saprophytic organisms that live in the soil—mainly species of *Fusarium*, *Rhizopus*, *Mucor*, *Diplodia*, *Penicillium*, and *Aspergillus*. Their entrance is facilitated by broken seed coats and by other mechanical injuries produced by the sheller. Seed rot is most destructive under conditions that retard germination—cool, damp weather, abnormally deep planting, and water-logged soils. Most seed rot occurs within the first week after planting.

Beginning about 1940, when farm labor became scarce, a trend was started toward the use of machine-shelled seed. Poor stands often resulted. Work started by Luther Shaw in North Carolina in 1939—and later confirmed by research in Virginia, South Carolina, Georgia, Florida, and Alabama—showed that machine-shelled seeds treated with a seed protectant before planting produced stands comparable to those obtained by using hand-shelled and treated seed.

Although seed usually are treated at the time they are shelled because of convenience, the treatment may be applied with equal effectiveness just before planting.

Several good seed protectants are available commercially. Eight materials were tested in Alabama in 6 years. Best results were had with Ceresan M (7.7 percent ethyl mercury *p*-toluene sulfonanilide). Phygon (90 percent 2, 3-dichloro-1,4-naphthoquinone), Arasan (50 percent tetramethyl thiuramdisulfide), and Spergon (98 percent tetrachloro-*p*-benzoquinone) were somewhat less effective. Reasonably good results were obtained with Yellow Cuprocide (yellow cuprous oxide containing 47 percent metallic copper) and Dow 9–B (50 percent zinc trichlorophenate). Seedox (50 percent 2,4,5-trichlorophenyl acetate) and Merc-O-Dust (a compound of indefinite composition containing mercury and formaldehyde) were ineffective. Similar results have been obtained in other States.

Although the mercurial treatments such as Ceresan M are most effective, they are more dangerous to use. Overdosage results in poor germination. The radicle of the germinating seed does not elongate but becomes thickened and stubby. If a seedling is produced, it is stunted and never makes normal growth. Therefore—and because of the danger to warm-blooded animals that might eat treated seed—most States recommend one of the organic materials such as Arasan or Spergon in preference to the mercurial treatments.

The organic seed treatments have a tendency to be somewhat erratic in performance. In tests lasting 6 years at Auburn, Ala., Ceresan M was the most consistent of four treatments. Spergon was the best of the four in 1949 but the poorest in 1947. Dow 9–B was practically as good as Arasan or Ceresan M in 1946 but was considerably poorer than either in 1948. Arasan gave less protection than Ceresan M in 1944, 1946, 1948, and 1949.

Seed protectants are applied as dust treatments at the rate of 2 or 3 ounces to 100 pounds of seed. Slurry treatments—liquid suspensions of the fungicide—have not been popular on peanuts, probably because of the tendency of the seed coats to peel after the slurry treatments are applied. The tendency appears to be more common with Spanish-type seed than with seed of runner peanuts.

SEEDLING BLIGHTS may be destructive in some localities, but generally they do little damage in established stands. Damping-off is not a serious disease of peanuts.

One of the most common types of seedling blight in peanuts is caused by *Sclerotium bataticola*. This organism causes a disease known as charcoal rot in a number of other species of plants during periods of high temperatures. Infections result in the formation of lesions on the succulent stems. The initial infections usually are near the soil line, but the lesions may extend downward some distance into the soil. If plant growth is retarded by dry weather and if the temperature is high—above 75° F.—the lesion is likely to girdle the stem and kill the plant. The stem assumes a dull brown color and becomes quite dry. Sometimes the progress of the disease is stopped and the seedling is stunted rather than killed. Then the plant is made more susceptible to other diseases later in the season. Charcoal rot in peanuts can be recognized by the many small, irregular, black sclerotia that develop in the affected

tissues and give them a dark gray or black color on the inside.

Another form of seedling blight is dry rot, caused by *Rhizoctonia solani*. It is like charcoal rot in the early stages. Lesions develop on the stem near the soil line. The plant may be girdled and killed; if the infection does not spread, the plant may partly recover. The lesions are not likely to extend as far below the surface as those caused by *Sclerotium bataticola*.

There are no specific control measures for seedling blights. Losses may be reduced by planting treated seed of good quality on a well-prepared seedbed.

OF THE DISEASES of growing plants, leaf spot generally is the most destructive disease during the growing season. It is recognized by the brown or black and somewhat circular spots on the leaves. As the disease progresses, the spots enlarge until the entire leaf is affected. Defoliation follows. The detrimental effects of leaf spot are threefold: The yield of nuts is reduced; the quality of the peanut hay is lowered; and the fallen leaves provide organic matter on which inoculum of other fungi, such as *Sclerotium rolfsii*, is produced.

Two species of fungi cause leaf spot. Each produces characteristic symptoms.

Early leaf spot, caused by *Cercospora arachidicola*, produces spots that are light tan at first. With age the spots become reddish brown to black on the lower surface and light brown on the upper surface of the leaf. A yellow halo surrounds each spot. Late leaf spot, caused by *C. personata*, produces dark-brown or black spots on both surfaces of the leaf. The spots usually are somewhat smaller than those of early leaf spot and there is no distinct halo. The fungi can be distinguished by microscopic examination of the conidia.

The conidia of *Cercospora arachidicola* are colorless to pale olive green and often curved. According to measurements made by W. A. Jenkins in 1938, they are 37–108 by 2.7–5.4 microns and contain 3 to 12 septations. The conidia of *C. personata* are much shorter and considerably thicker; they measure 18–60 by 5–11 microns, with 1 to 8 septations. They are generally cylindrical and seldom curved. Both leaf spots attack the leaves, petioles, pegs, and pods of Spanish, bunch, and runner peanuts. No host plants other than *Arachis hypogaea* are known for them.

Primary infections of leaf spot are caused by ascospores formed in the spring on overwintered peanut leaves. Secondary infections result from conidia. Although the fungus has been reported to be seed-borne, this method of overwintering is of minor importance. The principal means of dissemination is by wind-borne inoculum. The ascospores or conidia germinate within a few hours and penetrate the leaf directly through the epidermal cells or through stomata. In both species, the mycelium is intercellular at first. Branched haustoria are soon formed by the mycelium of *Cercospora personata* and the host cells are not killed outright. *C. arachidicola* does not form haustoria; the host cells are killed in advance and the invading germ tubes enter dead cells. Infections on leaves are visible within 8 to 23 days after inoculation.

Leaf spot is controlled by fungicides applied as dusts or sprays to the foliage. Most commonly used are dusting sulfur or dusting sulfur containing approximately 3.5 percent metallic copper. Specific recommendations vary slightly in different States; three to five applications beginning about 90 days after planting often are recommended. Usually applications are repeated every 10 to 14 days; 15 to 25 pounds of dust per acre are applied each time.

Bordeaux spray—6 pounds of copper sulfate and 2 pounds of hydrated lime in 100 gallons of water—is effective, but offers no particular advantages over fungicidal dusts. The dithio-carbamate fungicides have not come into general use on peanuts, probably because of their higher cost. Increases in yield resulting from dusting depend upon the fertility of the soil on which the crop is grown, the prevalence and severity of leaf spot, and the type of peanuts being grown. Highest returns have been obtained on runner peanuts growing on fertile sandy loam soils in the Southeast. Increases of 1,000 pounds an acre have been reported by the Alabama Agricultural Experiment Station. The increases generally amount to 500 pounds an acre or less.

SOUTHERN BLIGHT, caused by *Sclerotium rolfsii*, is more destructive on Spanish and bunch types of peanuts than on runners. It may appear on the plants at any time during the growing season but is more likely to cause damage in late summer and early fall as the plants approach maturity. The fungus, soil-borne, attacks the plants near the soil line. It causes wilting and eventual death of the part of the plant above the infection. It may attack the central stem and affect the entire plant, or the infection may be limited to one or more branches. Diseased plants wilt; the leaves gradually turn brown or black and eventually fall off. The fungus destroys the succulent tissues in the stem; the vascular bundles that are left give a shredded appearance to the diseased area. When the humidity is high, light-tan to reddish-brown sclerotia are formed in abundance on the infected tissues and the surrounding ground. The sclerotia are usually spherical and about the size of mustard seed but may be larger and irregular in shape. In dry weather the sclerotia are not so conspicuous.

Sclerotium rolfsii attacks hundreds of species of plants. In the absence of suitable hosts it lives quite well as a saprophyte in the soil. Crop rotation is therefore of limited value for control. Most grasses are highly resistant, but among them usually are enough volunteer plants that are susceptible to enable the fungus to survive in the soil. Southern blight appears to be more destructive on peanuts following peanuts or cotton, however, than on peanuts following corn.

Occasional reports of strains of peanuts resistant to *S. rolfsii* have been made, but it has not been possible to incorporate the resistance into the commercial varieties that are available.

Collar rot of runner peanuts is a disease complex that sometimes resembles southern blight. The disease has been reported only from Georgia, Florida, and Alabama. The cause has not been definitely established. The fungi that can be isolated from diseased plants are either saprophytic or weakly pathogenic, and efforts to produce the disease by inoculating healthy peanut plants with these fungi usually are unsuccessful. *Diplodia theobromae* apparently is always associated with the disease. Other fungi that usually are present include various species of *Fusarium, Penicillium, Trichoderma,* and *Rhizopus nigricans. Sclerotium rolfsii* and *S. bataticola* sometimes are isolated.

COLLAR ROT may result when plants that have been wounded are invaded by any of those fungi. L. W. Boyle in Georgia has demonstrated that young seedlings of peanuts are subject to sunscald. The injured areas on the stem or branches become lesions or cankers through which the fungi gain entrance. If the lesion is small, the plant may continue to grow for several weeks before the disease becomes severe enough to cause death.

Other types of injury also may predispose the plants to attack—injury by cultivating implements, windblown sand, and chewing insects. It is possible that infections also develop in lesions produced by the charcoal rot and rhizoctonia dry rot organisms.

Collar rot may appear at any time during the growing season. It usually is most noticeable during July, August, and early September. It may involve the entire plant or only a single branch. The affected part wilts suddenly; the leaves become pale green and turn dark brown or black rather quickly. Death is usually complete within 2 or 3 days after wilting becomes evident. If the entire plant is diseased, the wind usually blows the leaves and stems away, leaving the ground completely bare. The taproot is usually shredded at or near the soil line.

There is no control for collar rot.

NEMATODES have become increasingly important on peanuts. Several species attack peanuts, among them the root knot nematodes (*Meloidogyne arenaria* and *M. hapla*), meadow nematode (*Pratylenchus leiocephalus*), and the sting nematode (*Belonolaimus gracilis*).

The root knot nematode attacks both roots and fruits and causes the formation of galls. The feeding roots are deformed. The knots on the roots usually are similar in size and shape to the nodules formed by nitrogen-fixing bacteria. On the fruits and peduncles the galls are corky and variable in shape. Symptoms on the above-ground part of the plant are not characteristic. Plants are stunted; leaves are likely to show chronic symptoms of wilting; and the color is light green. In advanced stages leaves are necrotic along the margins, and considerable leaf shedding results. Heavy infestations may reduce yields to 500 pounds or less to the acre.

The symptoms of meadow nematode injury consist of lesions on peanut shells and lateral feeding roots. The damage it does to plant tissues provides avenues of entrance for soil fungi that cause peg rot.

The most characteristic symptom of the sting nematode is an unusually long taproot with relatively few lateral roots. Those that are present are short, stubby, and deformed. This nematode causes damage by puncturing the roots with a needlelike "sting" and withdrawing the juices. The nematode does not enter the roots but feeds externally. The area punctured by the sting is attacked by soil fungi. Small dead spots develop; the result is root pruning, which accounts for the elongated taproot and the deformed lateral roots.

If the nematode infestation is light, control can usually be accomplished by rotation. Such crops as corn, oats, and grain sorghum are resistant to the root knot nematode but not to the sting nematode. Control by rotation is not successful if infestations are heavy.

If infestations are heavy, nematodes can be controlled by fumigating the soil before planting. A fumigant, such as Dowfume W–40, should be applied to the drill at the rate of 7 gallons to the acre about 3 weeks before planting. After fumigation the soil should be left undisturbed until planting time. Care should be taken to plant the seed directly above the area in which the fumigant was applied. The plows used for opening the furrows should be as small as possible to prevent mixing of fumigated and unfumigated soil.

The root knot nematode, *Meloidogyne arenaria*, attacks several plants other than peanuts, including sweetpotato, Ramie, coffeeweed, tomato, okra, onion, peach, and several weeds.

PEG ROT, strictly speaking, is not a disease of the growing peanut plant. The term includes all losses that result from rotting, sprouting, and other types of damage to the developing nuts or to loss of nuts in the soil at harvest by breaking of the gynophores.

The peanut flower is formed in the axil of the leaf on the stem. After pollination, the petals wither, and the peg (or gynophore) elongates and grows into the soil, where the fertilized ovary at the tip of the peg enlarges to form the pod or peanut fruit. The peanut fruit thus develops in an environment populated with soil micro-organisms and is subject to attack by them during all of its development.

Soil insects such as wireworms and the larvae of the southern corn rootworm do considerable damage to the developing pods and facilitate infection by fungi. Many soil fungi attack the slender gynophore near the soil line as the fruit approaches maturity and many gain entrance to the tissues. Their action weakens the gynophore so that when the plant is pulled or lifted from the soil the gynophore breaks, leaving the pod in the soil. Early defoliation of plants by leaf spot, leaf-eating worms, or other causes also causes the gynophores to be more brittle and to break more easily.

Injuries to the "shell" of the developing fruit by soil insects permit soil-borne fungi to gain entrance. Discoloration or decay of the seed follows. If harvest is delayed beyond maturity of Spanish or bunch peanuts, the seeds begin to germinate.

Miscellaneous fungi, including *Sclerotium rolfsii* and *S. bataticola* and species of *Rhizoctonia, Diplodia, Rhizopus, Aspergillus*, and *Penicillium*, may be isolated from developing pegs and mature fruits. Apparently any one of them may cause one form of peg rot under proper conditions.

The control of peg rot is a problem of crop management. The plants should be kept growing as vigorously as possible until harvesttime. Defoliation should be prevented by controlling leaf spot and leaf-eating worms. The crop should be harvested as soon as mature. With runner peanuts, that is quite a problem because the fruits are formed and mature in cycles. Thus it is necessary to decide when peak production has been reached, to sacrifice some of the earliest formed fruits, and to harvest before the later fruits are fully mature. The crop should be harvested with machinery adapted for the purpose so as to minimize unnecessary breaking of the pegs.

SEVERAL OTHER diseases of growing peanuts occur occasionally in the United States.

Peanut rust, *Puccinia arachidis*, has been found occasionally in Florida, Alabama, and Texas. A leaf spot caused by an unidentified species of *Phyllosticta* appears on young peanut leaves early in the spring, but infections do not spread to older leaves. Botrytis late blight of peanuts has been observed on overmature peanuts during cool, damp days of early fall in Georgia. It is sometimes destructive on peanuts grown in greenhouses in winter. Fusarium wilt of peanuts has been reported from Southeastern States many times, but apparently it has not caused heavy damage. Virus diseases and bacterial wilt—destructive in the East Indies and in Africa—are not serious in the United States.

As THE PEANUT DEVELOPS in the soil, a variety of fungi become established in the shell, the peg, and occasionally the seed. When peanuts are harvested, they usually are placed in stacks or small piles or windrows and allowed to cure. During the curing process the fungi continue their activity and frequently become established in the tissues of the seed or on the interfaces of the cotyledons. Activity of the fungi during curing, together with the activity of the enzymes within the peanut seed, results in various types of seed deterioration. In commercial circles all these troubles are grouped together under one heading—damage.

Concealed damage is first evident as a slight yellow discoloration on the interfaces of the cotyledons. A mat of fungal mycelium develops between the cotyledons as the disease progresses. The tissues become rancid and discolored. There is no evidence of the disease on the outside until its late stages. If conditions remain favorable, the entire seed becomes shriveled and blackened, assumes an oily appearance, and is unfit for human consumption. The percentage of free fatty acids in the oil increases markedly. The disease is more common in runner peanuts than in Spanish or bunch peanuts, and has been more prevalent in the southeastern peanut belt than in the Virginia-North Carolina area and the Texas-Oklahoma area.

Seeds with concealed damage may contain a variety of fungi, primarily *Diplodia theobromae*. Others are species of *Fusarium, Aspergillus, Penicillium, Rhizopus,* and *Rhizoctonia*. Occasionally, *Sclerotium rolfsii* and *S. bataticola* are found. The disease has been produced by inoculation only with *Diplodia theobromae* and *Sclerotium bataticola*. Although initial infections usually occur before digging, concealed damage makes its most rapid development during the curing process. The moisture content of the seed is the principal conditioning factor, as temperatures during the curing period are usually near the optimum for fungal development. Concealed damage develops most rapidly in partly cured peanuts that contain 15 to 35 percent moisture. The disease does not develop appreciably in seeds containing less than 10 percent moisture. Neither soil type nor fertilizer practice has any measurable effect on development of the disease.

Concealed damage can be controlled by rapid curing of peanuts as soon as they are harvested and the use of resistant varieties.

Freshly dug runner peanuts usually contain 40 to 55 percent moisture. If peanuts are allowed to wilt before being placed in symmetrical, well-capped stacks with provisions for air circulation at the base, curing usually is rapid enough to prevent development of concealed damage. If peanuts are stacked before wilting or if they are allowed to become brittle before stacking, curing is retarded and the disease is more pronounced. Peanuts that are cured in windrows instead of stacks usually contain very little concealed damage, but this method of curing is more hazardous because of shattering in unfavorable weather.

The Dixie Runner variety has a great deal of resistance to concealed damage, and that resistance has been incorporated into a number of other strains of peanuts. By using resistant varieties and by exercising reasonable care at harvest, most growers can keep losses from concealed damage to a minimum.

Blue damage is a discoloration that often occurs on the seed coat of Spanish peanuts cured during periods of warm, damp weather. The small spots usually have a "bull's-eye" appearance, with colors ranging from blue through black. Larger spots may be irregular in outline with no evident center. The discoloration does not produce detectable changes in chemical constituents, taste, or germination of seed. Quite often the discoloration does not extend into the cotyledons, but sometimes the cotyledons may be conspicuously discolored.

Experiments at the Georgia Agricultural Experiment Station showed that the discoloration results from an interaction between pigments in the seed coat and oxalic acid produced by *Sclerotium rolfsii.* Under favorable conditions *S. rolfsii* grows saprophytically on the peanut shells during the curing process. The fungus secretes oxalic acid, which diffuses into the tissues in advance of the hyphae. When curing conditions are unfavorable for growth of *S. rolfsii*, no discoloration occurs.

OTHER STORAGE disorders, including seed rot, rancidity, and reduced germination, may be the result of improper curing or of improper storage. Peanuts should contain less than 10 percent moisture at the time they are stored. Some deterioration occurs at moisture contents between 6 and 10 percent, but the rate is fairly slow. The relative humidity of the storage environment should be 65 percent or less. Under those conditions, well-cured peanuts will keep well in storage for several months.

COYT WILSON *is assistant dean of the School of Agriculture of Alabama Polytechnic Institute and assistant director of the Alabama Agricultural Experiment Station. He was graduated in agriculture by Alabama Polytechnic Institute. He has a doctor's degree in plant pathology from the University of Minnesota.*

Ways To Combat Disorders of Tomatoes

S. P. Doolittle

Every tomato grower is faced with the hazard of loss from disease. Infections by fungi, bacteria, or viruses are responsible for much of the loss, but extremes of temperature and moisture or excess or deficiency of mineral elements in the soil at times may damage the crop.

The symptoms thus caused can be classified as wilts, leaf spots, fruit spots or rots, and abnormalities of growth of the foliage or fruits.

Fusarium wilt, caused by the fungus *Fusarium oxysporum* f. *lycopersici,* is serious on tomatoes. Its first symptom is a yellowing of the oldest leaves, usually on a single stem. Beginning at the base, the yellowed leaves wilt and die until all the leaves are killed. Often a single shoot dies before others are severely injured, but eventually the entire plant is affected. There is no soft decay of the stem, but if one cuts it lengthwise near the ground, he can see in the woody portion next to the outer "bark," or cortex, a brown discoloration of the water-conducting tissues—fibrovascular bundles—which is characteristic of the disease.

The fungus that causes fusarium wilt can persist in the soil for many years. Infection occurs through the roots. From them the fungus passes into the water-conducting vessels of the stem. Apparently it produces a toxic substance that causes the wilting of the foliage and eventual death of the plant. The fungus is most active at temperatures between 80° and 90° F. Losses from the wilt are most common and severe in the warmer sections of the country. Clean fields can be infested by planting diseased seedlings, or by drainage water, farm implements, or any agency that carries infested soil—even in small amounts—to the clean field.

Other wilt diseases of tomato are caused by soil-borne bacteria and fungi. Unlike fusarium wilt, they are characterized by a decay of the stem near the ground and a wilting of the entire plant with little or no yellowing of the leaves.

Bacterial wilt, caused by *Pseudomonas solanacearum*, is an example. That organism causes a watery decay of the pith, which soon causes the wilting and death of the plant. These wilt diseases are most common in the southern United States but are of much less economic importance than fusarium wilt.

LEAF SPOT DISEASES of tomato cannot be described solely on a basis of leaf symptoms, since certain of their causal agencies also are responsible for serious spotting of the stems and spotting or rot of the fruits.

The most common and destructive leaf spots are caused by bacteria and fungi that produce spots in which the cells of the leaf have been killed. In some of the diseases an area of yellowed tissue surrounds the dead spots. With the exception of one fungus that destroys areas of tissue almost too large to be called spots, the organisms invade only a limited area around the point of infection and produce spots of characteristic size and appearance. They may be irregular or circular and vary from one thirty-second inch to one-half inch in diameter. Both the petioles and leaflets may be spotted, and those injuries commonly cause the death of many leaves. Some viruses also cause dead spots or patches on the leaves but the spots are of a type that usually is not confused with those caused by bacteria or fungi.

The leaf spot caused by the fungus *Septoria lycopersici* is an example of a disease that severely injures the leaves but does no appreciable harm to the fruit.

On the other hand the fungus (*Alternaria solani*) that causes alternaria leaf spot and the fungus (*Phytophthora infestans*) that causes late blight produce severe injury to the foliage and are also important because of their effect on the fruits.

Septoria leaf spot is characterized by numerous water-soaked spots that soon become roughly circular and have gray centers with dark margins. Later the centers of the spots show tiny dark specks (pycnidia), the bodies in which the fungus spores are produced. The spots are from one-sixteenth to one-eighth of an inch in diameter and may occur in such numbers as to cover the leaf. The fruits rarely are affected, but stems and blossoms may have spots.

The fungus also attacks wild solanaceous plants, such as horsenettle, jimsonweed, and nightshade. It overwinters in the soil on the remains of tomato plants, its weed hosts, and other decaying vegetation. Spores produced on such material cause the infection of tomato leaves near the soil. Spores then are produced in the spots on those infected leaves and, in wet weather, are exuded on the surface of the spot. From there they are splashed to other leaves by rain and may be carried on the hands or clothing of farm workers or on farm equipment.

The disease may occur on plants of any age, but in the field it seems to develop more rapidly after some fruit is set. If temperatures are moderately high and rains frequent, there is a progressive loss of foliage until only a few leaves may remain at the tips of the stems. When that occurs, yields are reduced and many of the fruits are injured by exposure to the sun. In hot, dry seasons the disease is much less damaging.

Septoria leaf spot causes serious loss in some sections of the Central and

Atlantic States as far south as Arkansas, Tennessee, and South Carolina, but is of minor importance in the Mountain and Pacific States.

The first symptoms of alternaria leaf spot (early blight) consist of small, dark-brown spots on the older leaves. The spots may enlarge until they are one-half inch in diameter and have an irregular or circular outline. The large spots often are marked with rings in a target pattern. The tissues surrounding the spots often turn yellow and this discoloration may cover the leaflet. The disease is common on seedlings, where the spots usually are small and dark. In the field, the spotting and yellowing of the leaflets, together with spotting of the petioles, often kills much of the foliage.

Plants in the field also show many spots on the stems. They are light brown, with darker margins, and from one-eighth to one-half inch in size. On seedlings the fungus causes large, dark cankers (collar rot) that may girdle the stems. The varieties Southland and Manahill have high resistance to collar rot and some resistance to alternaria leaf spot.

Alternaria solani also causes a disease of potatoes known as early blight. Occasionally it affects peppers. It can live on decaying plant tissue in the soil. Most of the primary infection in tomatoes comes from that source, although contaminated seed may possibly cause occasional infection.

On tomatoes, the spores of the fungus produced on the leaf spots are spread by wind and rain. In periods of frequent, warm, rainy weather its spread is rapid and infection soon becomes general. Usually the leaf spotting is largely confined to the older leaves until the fruit is well set. When that stage is reached, however, the plants seem to become more susceptible and a general spotting of the leaves kills much of the foliage before the end of the season. This defoliation reduces both the yield and quality of the fruit.

Alternaria spot is the most common leaf spot disease of tomatoes in the Central and Atlantic States and occurs in all tomato-growing regions, although it is of less importance in the Mountain and Pacific States.

Late blight is characterized by irregular, greenish-black patches, which first appear on the older leaves. They rapidly enlarge until they may cover one-fourth to one-half of the leaflet. The spots soon turn brown and many of the infected leaves wither, yet frequently remain attached to the stem. When weather conditions favor a rapid development of the disease, so much of the foliage may be affected that the plants look as though injured by frost. The fungus also produces water-soaked, brown streaks on the stem. In moist weather there often is a white, downy growth of the fungus on the under surfaces of the spots on the leaves and stems.

The fungus that causes late blight also causes a disease of the same name on potatoes. It is not carried in tomato seed and does not live over in the soil. It infects potato tubers, which can produce diseased plants in the spring. From them spores can be carried by the wind and infect plants in other fields.

Late blight of tomatoes is caused by a strain of the fungus somewhat different from that which ordinarily occurs on potatoes. The tomato strain can infect potatoes, however, and has been recovered from blight-infected potato tubers as a typical tomato strain. What appears to be the typical potato strain of the fungus may produce only mild symptoms when first transferred to tomatoes but can develop the virulence of a typical tomato strain after a number of passages through tomato plants.

Late blight commonly occurs on potatoes and tomatoes grown in the Gulf States during the winter and early spring. The disease works northward with those crops as the season progresses. Most of the canning tomatoes of the Central and Atlantic States are produced from seedlings grown in the South, and late blight occasionally appears in some plant fields. If the infected transplants are shipped north they become a possible source of infection to other fields. Besides that possible hazard and that of infection from diseased potato plants, there also is an occasional carry-over of the fungus on greenhouse tomatoes in winter. Seedlings grown in those houses in the spring often become infected and carry the disease into the field. Cool nights and only moderately warm days, with abundant moisture, favor the rapid development and spread of late blight.

Late blight of tomatoes was of little or no importance in many tomato-growing sections until 1945, although the disease had caused some loss in the Northeastern, Middle Atlantic, South Central, and South Atlantic States. Occasional damage also had occurred in Texas and on the Pacific coast. In most of the sections where the processing tomatoes are grown east of the Mississippi, however, the disease was almost unknown.

In 1945 there were some losses in the North Central States. Early in the season of 1946 several unusually long periods of cool, moist weather were followed by an epidemic of the disease along the Atlantic seaboard, which destroyed nearly half the crop. The damage was all the worse because the growers had no previous experience with the disease and were not equipped to apply the fungicides that would have prevented much of the loss. Since then, late blight has occurred to some extent each year in many tomato areas of the Central and Atlantic States, but the loss has been greatly reduced by increased use of fungicides.

A NUMBER OF FRUIT ROTS are caused by bacteria and fungi that produce no other significant injuries to the tomato plant. The most serious are due to soil-borne fungi that can infect uninjured fruits. There also are organisms that can only enter the fruit when the epidermis is broken by growth cracks, mechanical injuries, or the lesions caused by the common fruit-spotting organisms. Such decays are unimportant in the field but may cause losses of fruits in transit, in ripening rooms, and in the markets.

Anthracnose of tomato, caused by the fungus *Colletotrichum phomoides*, is the most serious of the fruit rots caused by organisms that produce little or no injury to the leaves. Uninjured fruits can be infected at any stage, but in green fruits the fungus remains latent and no spotting occurs until the fruits ripen. Ripe fruits show dark, depressed spots whose centers have concentric markings. The centers are tan with dark specks (acervuli). In moist weather the masses of spores, which give the spots a salmon-pink color, are produced in the dark specks. The spots are circular and about three-eighths inch in diameter. They penetrate a short distance into the fruit and must be removed when the fruit is processed.

Anthracnose is a serious pest of processing tomato crops in the Central and Atlantic States, but is of little importance where tomatoes are picked green for shipment to distant markets. The fungus occurs in the soil and the first infections come from that source. The spores produced on the surfaces of the fruit spots later are splashed by rain or otherwise spread to healthy fruits. In warm, moist weather many fruits are thus infected.

Fruit spots also are produced by some organisms that spot the leaves. Some of them penetrate the epidermis of the fruit and produce spots that do not extend very deeply into the flesh. The spots vary from one-sixteenth to one-half inch in diameter and have a roughened, broken surface that is brown or gray in color.

Alternaria leaf spot and late blight, however, are characterized by rots that cover a considerable area of the fruit and extend deeply into the tissues. Spotting and ring markings of the fruits also are associated with some viruses that cause spotting of the leaves. Losses from them are not of major significance.

The fungus that causes alternaria leaf spot attacks the green fruits at the point of attachment to the stem. Here the fungus produces dark, leathery, sunken spots, which have concentric markings and may be an inch or more in diameter. A dark, dry, decay extends well in the fruit and makes it unfit for use. This fruit rot phase of the disease, however, causes less damage than the defoliation caused by the leaf spotting.

The fruit rot associated with late blight often is a cause of major loss. Fruit infection occurs at any stage of growth and is most frequent on the upper half of the surface. The grayish green, water-soaked spots enlarge until they may cover half the fruit and eventually become brown, with a firm, slightly wrinkled surface. In moist weather, a downy, white growth of the fungus often appears on the surfaces of the spots.

TOMATOES ARE SUBJECT to a number of diseases caused by viruses that produce a mottling or yellowing of the leaves and are accompanied by varying amounts of curling, twisting, and malformation of the leaflets. Some of them also cause a streaking of the stem and a spotting of the leaves and fruits. Most of the viruses may occur wherever tomatoes are grown in the field or greenhouse, but the destructive virus known as curly top is confined largely to the Mountain and Pacific States as it is transmitted only by a leafhopper whose breeding grounds are limited to semiarid sections in the West.

Tomato mosaic, as the name is commonly used, is the most common virus disease of tomatoes. The name refers to the disease caused by the tobacco mosaic virus (*Marmor tabaci*), which also affects peppers. The common green strain of the virus causes a light- and dark-green mottling of the leaves, a slight curling, and occasional malformations of the leaflets. Infected seedlings are stunted, but plants that become infected after they reach the fruiting stage show no severe check in growth although yields are reduced. There also are "yellow" strains of

the virus which cause a pronounced yellow mottling of the leaves and some mottling and blotching of the stems and fruits.

The tobacco mosaic virus is rarely, if ever, transmitted in commercial tomato seed. It does not persist long in field soils, although in greenhouses, where one crop may follow another in a few weeks, some infection may occur from plant remains in the soil.

Perennial weeds, such as horsenettle, groundcherry, and plantain, sometimes are infected with the virus and may be a source of infection. The virus remains active for years in dried tobacco leaves and is known to occur in pipe, cigar, and cigarette tobaccos. Smokers, therefore, may carry the virus on their hands, and some of the initial infection of tomato seedlings may come in that way. The virus is transmitted so readily by successive contact with mosaic-infested and healthy plants that it is almost certain to become widespread after it appears in the greenhouse or field.

Aside from its own effect on the plant, the tobacco mosaic virus is a menace to the crop because infected plants also may become infected with the virus X of potatoes (*Marmor dubium*). The virus is present in the tops and tubers of all the older varieties of potatoes but usually causes little visible evidence of disease. Tomatoes that are infected with both the tobacco and potato viruses develop a disease known as double-virus streak. Such plants show small, dead, brown spots on the leaves, which are mottled, dwarfed, and curled. Stems and leaf petioles develop the narrow brown streaks that give the disease its name. The plants set few fruits and those produced are often misshapen and have irregular brown spots on their surfaces. Streak can be very destructive in the greenhouse where the necessity of handling the plants in pruning and tying leads to its rapid spread.

Tomatoes also are sometimes infected with the cucumber mosaic virus (*Marmor cucumeris*). Such infection is much less common than that with the tobacco mosaic virus. The leaves show only a mild mottling but often are dwarfed or malformed. Frequently the leaflets are reduced to little more than a central rib, and this "shoestring" symptom is one characteristic of the disease. The plants that are infected with the cucumber mosaic virus are dwarfed and often have an abnormally compact, bushy appearance. The few fruits they set are small and often malformed.

Unlike the virus of tobacco mosaic, the cucumber mosaic virus does not withstand drying. It can be transmitted by mechanical means, but on tomatoes that occurs less readily. It is commonly disseminated by aphids, particularly the species that feed on cucumbers and melons. As they prefer to feed on plants other than tomatoes, the aphids cause less infection on tomatoes than on certain other crops. The virus is not transmitted in the seed and does not persist in the soil. It does infect a wide range of cultivated and wild plants and is common on cucumbers, muskmelons, celery, peppers, and some ornamental plants. It lives over winter in some ornamentals, such as perennial phlox, and in some perennial weeds, such as milkweed, groundcherry, and catnip. Aphids feeding on such infected plants in the spring later carry the virus to cultivated crops.

THE MOST COMMON nonparasitic disorders involve dropping of the blossoms, surface injuries, malformations, and hollowness of the fruits.

Some evidence of such diseases can be found in many fields every season. Usually the losses are minor, although the drop of blossoms, caused by hot, drying winds, sometimes is a serious factor.

Blossom-end rot, a common nonparasitic disease, usually appears on tomato fruits when they are about half-grown. It consists of a brown discoloration that enlarges until it covers one-third or more of the fruit. The dark tissues shrink and form a flattened or slightly concave area with a dry, leathery surface. There is no rot of the fruit unless the dead tissue is later invaded by fungi or bacteria.

Blossom-end rot usually appears when plants that have made a rapid growth are subject to high temperatures and drought. Then the cells at the blossom end of the fruits apparently fail to receive enough moisture to maintain their growth, and the tissues break down. Plants that have had heavy applications of nitrogenous fertilizer are especially susceptible to blossom-end rot. Marked fluctuations in soil moisture increase the likelihood of injury. Plants that are pruned and staked consistently show more blossom-end rot than those growing naturally in otherwise similar conditions. That may be due largely to the restriction of the root system that results from drastic pruning of the tops.

DISEASE CONTROL is essential in the profitable production of tomatoes. The first step consists of measures that help to prevent the occurrence of seedling diseases.

Wherever possible, seedlings should be started in soil that has not grown diseased plants. If that is not feasible, the soil can be disinfected by treatment with formaldehyde or chloropicrin or by steam.

Seed treatments are used to disinfect the surface of the seed and to coat the seed with a fungicide that will protect the seed and germinating seedling from fungi in the soil that cause seed decay and damping-off of seedlings. Tomato seed can be dusted with such materials as New Improved Ceresan, Semesan, Phygon, Arasan, or Thiram 50. They generally are used at a rate of 0.3 to 0.5 percent of weight of seed.

Losses from wilt diseases and fruit rots caused by soil-borne organisms can be reduced somewhat by crop rotation and the avoidance of fields where such diseases have damaged previous tomato crops. Seedbeds should always be located on clean soil.

If plants are purchased, they should be obtained from plantings free from disease.

In the greenhouse, wilt diseases and injury from the root knot nematode can be controlled by disinfection of the soil by chemicals or steam. In the field, the use of steam is impracticable and chemical treatments, other than those effective only against nematodes, have as yet been too expensive for large-scale use.

Resistant varieties offer the most effective means of preventing losses from wilt diseases, but we do not yet have varieties resistant to all diseases of this type.

Breeding of varieties resistant to fusarium wilt by the Department of Agriculture and State experiment stations has made it possible to maintain a profitable tomato industry in regions where the disease is prevalent. Some of the resistant varieties that have had most general use are Rutgers, Marglobe, Indiana Baltimore, Pearson, and Pritchard. They are not immune to wilt and occasionally are damaged by it. Since 1940, however, varieties have become available that have extremely high resistance. Among them are Pan America, Southland, Homestead, Cal 255, Manahill, Manasota, Fortune, Boone, Tipton, Kokomo, Tucker, Sunray, and Golden Sphere. Another such variety, Jefferson, has been introduced by a private seed company. Resistant varieties suited to greenhouse use include Ohio W-R Globe (which possesses high wilt resistance), Blair Forcing, and Michigan State Forcing. A race of the fusarium wilt fungus, which can attack plants of the highly resistant varieties, has been reported in Ohio and Missouri, but we have had no report of widespread infection of those varieties in commercial plantings.

Varieties resistant to verticillium wilt, caused by the fungus *Verticillium albo-atrum*, have been developed for use in sections in the West where the the disease has caused serious losses. The varieties Riverside, Essar, and Simi have tolerance of verticillium wilt but are injured when conditions are very favorable to the development of the disease. They also have moderate resistance to fusarium wilt. Two newly introduced varieties, Loran Blood and VR Moscow, are highly resistant to verticillium wilt but not to fusarium wilt. Varieties highly resistant to both diseases are now being developed.

Losses from the leaf spot diseases and certain fruit rots caused by parasitic organisms can be reduced by the timely application of fungicides. They are particularly necessary in the Central, Atlantic, and Northeastern States, where a humid climate favors the occurrence of such diseases. The use of fungicides there has become much more general because of the continued appearance of late blight in sections where it was not a problem before 1945 and 1946. The routine use of fungicides also has been accelerated by the development of the very effective dithiocarbamate compounds. which have increased the possibility of reducing losses. Proper spraying and dusting and improved cultural methods have increased tomato yields markedly since 1940.

The fungicides most commonly used on tomatoes are copper compounds and organic compounds of the dithiocarbamate group.

The neutral copper compounds (which include basic copper sulfates, copper oxychloride, copper oxychloride sulfate, and copper oxide) largely have supplanted bordeaux mixture because they are less injurious to tomato plants.

As sprays, they are generally used in formulations that give the equivalent of 2 pounds of copper to 100 gallons of water. For seedbed spraying, however, this often is reduced to 1.5 pounds to 100 gallons. Bordeaux mixture cannot be safely used on tomato seedlings, but often is employed after the fruit is set. An 8–4–100 mixture (in which the first figure represents pounds of copper sulfate, the second hydrated lime, and the third water) is probably that most generally favored, but 8–8–100, 6–6–100, and 6–3–100 preparations are used on tomatoes.

Dusts containing the neutral coppers are formulated so as to give 5 to 7 percent of actual copper in a suitable inert carrier.

The dithiocarbamate compounds commonly used on tomatoes are zineb (zinc ethylene bisdithiocarbamate), nabam (sodium ethylene bisdithiocarbamate), which is used with zinc sulfate, and ziram (zinc dimethyl dithiocarbamate). A newly introduced compound, manganese ethylene bisdithiocarbamate (Manzate), also appears to be effective against a number of tomato diseases. Zineb, ziram, and the manganese salt commonly are used at the rate of 2 pounds of the commercial preparation to 100 gallons of water. With nabam, 2 quarts of the commercial preparation are added to 100 gallons of water and then 1 pound of zinc sulfate is added. Zineb and ziram also are used in dust preparations containing from 6 to 8 percent of the fungicides.

Other compounds such as Phygon (2, 3-dichloro-1, 4-naphthoquinone), captan (n-trichloromethylthio tetrahydrophalimide), Cop-O-Zink (tribasic copper sulfate and zinc sulfate), and Crag 658 (copper-zinc-chromate) also are being used. In many instances they have given satisfactory results but more experience with some of these materials is needed. New organic compounds constantly are being tested for tomato disease control.

Both the copper fungicides and compounds of the dithiocarbamate group are quite effective for the control of alternaria leaf spot. Late blight can be controlled with copper compounds and with those of the dithiocarbamate group other than ziram. Losses from gray leaf spot, caused by the fungus *Stemphylium solani*, and septoria leaf spot can be reduced by applying either copper or dithiocarbamate fungicides. Manganese ethylene bisdithiocarbamate appears to be very effective against gray leaf spot. Ziram is particularly effective for control of anthracnose fruit rot but other dithiocarbamate compounds also will reduce losses from this disease. It is not satisfactorily controlled by copper fungicides.

In the Central and Atlantic States, the control of anthracnose is a problem wherever tomatoes are grown for processing. Ziram is commonly used to reduce losses from anthracnose but, since it does not control late blight, other fungicides must be used to prevent losses from the disease. Where copper fungicides are used to control late blight, one or two applications of ziram often are made at the start of the season and copper fungicides are used thereafter. An alternating schedule of applications of ziram and a copper fungicide also is sometimes used. When that is done, the schedule begins with an application of ziram and ends with one or two applications of a copper compound.

The relative extent of the use of copper and dithiocarbamate fungicides varies with the section in which tomatoes are grown. In southern Florida, zineb and nabam have proved to be superior to the copper fungicides for late blight control and have been generally used. There has seemed to be some preference for the dithiocarbamate materials throughout the South Atlantic States, although copper fungicides also are recommended for use in tomato disease control.

In the North Central, North Atlantic, and Northeastern States, copper fungicides are commonly used for control of late blight although the dithiocarbamate materials also have been extensively used.

Seedbeds need protection from leaf spot diseases. Often they are sprayed or dusted three or four times before the plants are taken to the field. In the field, the first applications of fungicides usually can be made about 30 days after the first flower cluster blooms. Later applications can be made at 10-day intervals unless there are frequent rains, when the interval may have to be reduced to 7 days, or even less, to secure good control.

Spraying has proved to be superior to dusting in the control of tomato diseases but, when wet soil makes it impossible to use heavy spraying equipment, dusting is a very valuable adjunct.

The coverage obtained with ground dusting machines has been superior to that secured from applications of dust by airplane.

We have no commercial varieties of tomatoes resistant to mosaic diseases and must depend on measures of sanitation to prevent infection. After the diseases appear in the field or greenhouse, it is hard to check their further spread. Therefore the best means of control consists of preventing infection in the seedling plants and thus delaying the appearance of the disease until a crop is well started. If that can be done, the loss is likely to be less severe.

One should never handle seedlings without first washing his hands with soap and water to remove any virus from the hands. Because manufactured tobacco may carry the virus of tobacco mosaic, no one should smoke or chew tobacco while handling the plants. Workers can stop at intervals for a smoke and then wash their hands before again touching the plants.

All perennial weeds around the seedbeds and in or near the fields should be destroyed because they may carry viruses of tobacco or cucumber mosaic.

Every effort should be made to prevent aphid infestation of the seedbed by using insecticides regularly.

When seedlings are grown in a greenhouse used for commercial tomato production, the seedlings should not be handled after working with older plants unless the hands have first been washed. Anyone who has worked in a potato field or peeled or cut potatoes should wash the hands before working with tomatoes.

The removal of mosaic plants in the field usually is of little value in checking the spread of mosaic diseases and often leads to further infection through brushing the infected plants against healthy ones in the course of removal.

Because many nonparasitic diseases are induced wholly or partly by extremes of temperature or moisture, the grower is somewhat at the mercy of the elements where those disorders are concerned. In some diseases, however, both nutrition and weather have a part, and some losses may be avoided by care in the use of fertilizers, particularly nitrogen.

S. P. DOOLITTLE *is a pathologist in charge of investigations of diseases of tomatoes, peppers, cucurbits, and other vegetable crops in the division of vegetable crops and diseases of the Bureau of Plant Industry, Soils, and Agricultural Engineering. He is author of Farmers' Bulletin 1934,* Tomato Diseases.

Gray ear not on corn.

Transplants Grown in the South

Huey I. Borders

More than 90 percent of the seedlings used to produce tomatoes for canning in the Central and Atlantic States are grown in the South. Field-grown tomato transplants are produced in Florida, Mississippi, Texas, North Carolina, Arkansas, Tennessee, and Virginia, but most are grown in southern Georgia, where the industry was established in 1908.

Field-grown seedlings are sturdier than plants produced in greenhouses or cold frames and can be produced as early in the spring as the northern grower needs them. Their low cost gives them a competitive advantage over plants grown under glass in the North. Consequently the industry has grown to comprise more than 5,000 acres in Georgia alone. Each year hundreds of millions of plants are shipped to northern growers by truck, train, and airplane.

The production of disease-free transplants is vital to the grower and to the producers of tomato crops for canning in the North. A few leaf spots on a large tomato plant in the field may not greatly affect the yield of fruit, and the grower can obtain a good crop despite the presence of some disease. But a few leaf spots on a tomato seedling, up to transplanting size, may profoundly affect the ultimate vigor and yield of the plant. Infected seedlings are likely to become unthrifty plants that may die shortly after they are transplanted.

Furthermore, the presence of one or two diseased seedlings in a bundle of plants may lead to the infection of others under the moist conditions that occur in a closely packed package of plants during shipment and before they are transplanted after arrival. Therefore it is vitally important to keep even a small amount of disease out of a field of tomato seedlings; growers of tomato transplants try to have perfect—not merely good—control of disease in their fields.

To that end, the Georgia Department of Entomology maintains a system of plant certification. Fields registered for certification must meet requirements as to crop rotation, seed treatment, and spraying for control of insects and diseases. The fields are inspected regularly during the season. Those that meet the requirements are certified as free from disease.

The diseases most common on field-grown tomato seedlings are caused by fungi, bacteria, and nematodes. Most important are late blight, caused by the fungus *Phytophthora infestans*, and alternaria or early blight, caused by *Alternaria solani*.

They cause stem and leaf infections that severely damage seedling plants and also are the cause of serious losses in field-grown tomatoes.

Another group of diseases is caused by organisms that attack the plants through the roots and underground parts of the stem or at the ground line. In plant fields the most common diseases of this type are southern blight, caused by the fungus *Sclerotium rolfsii;* bacterial wilt, caused by *Pseudomonas solanacearum;* and injury from the root knot nematode, *Meloidogyne* species, formerly known as *Heterodera marioni*. The organisms live in the soil and attack the seedlings during the warmer parts of the season.

Fortunately for the southern grower, the control of virus diseases is not a difficult problem, as the mosaic diseases that are so common in commercial tomato fields and greenhouses are rarely found on field-grown seedlings—probably because the aphids that transmit the viruses are not particularly active during the early spring, or because there is little handling or other contact with the plants until they are pulled for shipment, or because the viruses are not often seedborne.

The control of diseases starts with the soil.

Root knot nematodes are microscopic eelworms that attack and invade the roots of the seedlings and cause swellings or galls. The seedlings may become sickly and develop into unproductive plants.

Of the diseases caused by the soilborne fungi and bacteria, the most serious are southern blight and bacterial wilt. The organisms that cause them grow best at higher temperatures and consequently are generally confined to the South.

So far, from the standpoint of the grower of tomato seedlings, the best means of control is to plant only in soil free of soil-borne pathogens. A field can be used for the production of certified tomato seedlings only three or four seasons. By that time either southern blight or bacterial wilt or both will usually appear and make the field unfit for the production of certified seedlings.

The Georgia State authorities require that only land that has not been planted during the previous 3 years to crops susceptible to root knot nematodes be used for certified tomato seedlings. An exception: A grower may replant a field to tomato seedlings following a tomato seedling crop that was approved for certification or that was not disapproved because of infections by bacterial wilt or southern blight or infestations of the root knot nematode.

Clean seed is important. The seed is usually treated with 5 percent ethyl mercury phosphate (New Improved Ceresan), a fungicide that destroys surface-borne fungi and bacteria and protects the germinating seedlings from the attacks of damping-off fungi.

Dry seed can be treated by applying the material as a dust at the rate of 0.05 percent by weight of seed. Seed also can be treated by a liquid soak method—soaking the seed for 5 minutes in a 1–1,200 solution of the commercial compound. The treatment can be used on either dry or freshly extracted seed.

Georgia regulations require that the plants shall be grown from certified seed obtained from a source approved by the Georgia Department of Entomology. To determine the efficiency of the seed-disinfectant treatment, a composite sample from each day's treatment is tested by certification authorities to determine the efficiency of the surface disinfection. Only seed that meets these requirements is acceptable for the production of certified plants.

The seeds are sown in open fields in Georgia in the early spring. Planting usually begins around the last week in February and continues up to the middle of April or so. Such plantings give a succession of seedlings of the right size and obviate the need to hold plants after they have reached commercial pulling size. Plants held in the field after reaching commercial pulling size become hard and fibrous and deplete the available nitrogen in the soil as they grow older. Such old, nitrogen-deficient plants are more susceptible to alternaria infection than young, vigorously growing seedlings. Successive plantings therefore help in reducing the amount of disease. Another factor that encourages disease is wilting or mechanical injury to seedlings during harvesting and packing.

The control of alternaria blight and late blight, which affect the leaves and stems of the plants, depends on the use of the proper fungicides but also on the selection of disease-free soil and the maintenance of a sufficiently high level of nutrition in the seedlings to assist them in resisting disease.

Tomato seedlings that are allowed to develop hunger signs were found to be susceptible to alternaria stem canker and leaf spot. In regulating fertilizer applications, however, the grower must remember that periods of warm, wet weather will cause increased growth and nitrogen intake by the plants with the result that they may become too soft or succulent. Such plants will suffer injury during shipment and when exposed to hot, dry weather after transplanting.

In spraying tomato seedlings for disease control many factors must be considered: Row width; number, angle, and height of the spray nozzle; size of spray disk orifice; pressure of the spray pump; and speed of spray rig, as well as the choice of spray materials.

The rows must not be too close together or it will be impossible to achieve proper coverage of the plants with the spray. Although tomato seed is sown in rows of various widths, rows spaced 16 inches part—18 inches is better—will permit a much better spray dispersal and coverage than can be had in the narrower rows.

Fungi of late blight and alternaria blight produce their spores or conidia in greatest abundance on the under side of the leaves. Therefore spray nozzles should be placed low enough so that the cone of spray will be directed upward to cover that area. If the side nozzles are too high the leaves may be forced downward around the stem of the plant. Then spray material would not only be prevented from reaching the under side of the leaves but also would be kept from portions of the stem where canker spots or lesions can develop.

To protect the seedlings from late blight, alternaria leaf spots, and stem cankers, the grower should start spray applications as soon as the seedlings have produced their first pair of true leaves and continue them at intervals of 5 to 7 days until the plants have reached commercial pulling size (more than $\frac{5}{32}$ inch in diameter of stem). A final fungicidal spray immediately before pulling may protect plants against disease during shipment and until the first sprays can be applied after transplanting in the North.

A spray should be applied with sufficient force to break it up into a fog of fine droplets that will cover both surfaces of the leaves and the stem but without sufficient excess spray to cause coalescence of the drops and runoff. A power sprayer is needed. Pump pressures of 200 to 400 pounds the square inch will give adequate coverage without injury to the plants. The best results are obtained by using No. 3 disks in the spray nozzles and by maintaining a tractor speed of not more than 4 miles an hour. Approximately 150 gallons of spray material an acre is applied.

Our experiments have shown that some sprays give almost perfect control of alternaria blight but that the same materials used in the form of dusts give practically no control. Dusts can be properly applied only in early morning or late evening when the dew has formed and the wind has died; sprays can be applied at any time during the day after the dew has dried on the plants unless the wind velocity is excessive.

Of many fungicidal materials tested at the Vegetable Seedbed Investigations Laboratory of the Department of Agriculture in Tifton, Ga., dithiocarbamates as sprays gave the most effective control. The four best spray materials were nabam (Dithane D–14) plus zinc sulfate and lime; ziram (Zerlate); zineb (Dithane Z–78); and tribasic copper sulfate. Besides good control of alternaria blight under severe disease conditions encountered in these tests, zineb and nabam plus zinc sulfate and lime also gave a high degree of control of late blight and stemphylium or gray leaf spot of tomatoes (*Stemphylium solani*).

HUEY I. BORDERS *is a plant pathologist who conducts research on diseases of vegetable seedlings grown in the South. He joined the Department of Agriculture in 1947. Previously he was extension plant pathologist in Georgia and was engaged in research at the Subtropical Experiment Station, Homestead, Fla.*

Diseases of Peppers

S. P. Doolittle

Peppers are subject to diseases that cause wilts, leaf spots, fruit rots, and mottling, yellowing, and malformation of the leaves. Some of the most serious ones are caused by the agencies that produce diseases in tomatoes.

Wilt diseases due to the bacteria or fungi are common on peppers and often cause serious losses. They are of a type characterized by a decay of the stem at the ground line and a rather rapid wilting of the plant. These diseases are most common in the southern and southwestern United States.

Southern blight is serious on peppers in the Southeastern and Gulf States. It is caused by a fungus, *Sclerotium rolfsii*, which attacks many vegetables and other crops.

The fungus attacks the stem of the pepper plant at the soil line and causes a soft decay of the outer tissues. This girdling of the stem causes a wilting and yellowing of the leaves and an eventual drying of the stem and branches. The stems of diseased plants become covered with a white growth of the fungus in which are light-brown bodies (sclerotia) about the size of a mustard seed. When dead plants are pulled, a clump of fungus-infested soil often stays attached to the roots.

The fungus lives for a long time in the soil and requires warm, moist weather for its active development. It seems to be most active in poorly drained, light, sandy soils. The sclerotia can live in the soil for some time and are spread by cultivation or washing rains. Under favorable conditions the bodies can put out fungus threads and infest new areas in the field.

Bacterial wilt, caused by *Pseudomonas solanacearum*, affects peppers, tomatoes, potatoes, eggplants, and a number of other cultivated and wild plants. Like southern blight, it is most common in the warmer sections of the United States.

The first symptoms consist of a drooping of the leaves that is soon followed by wilting and death of the plant. When the stem of a wilted plant is cut across near the soil, the inner tissues have a dark water-soaked appearance. If the stem is pressed, there is a gray, slimy exudate from the vascular elements.

The bacterium causing this disease lives in the soil and infects the plant through the roots or stem. The organism usually is most destructive in low, moist, sandy soil and is most active at temperatures above 75° F.

Phytophthora blight of peppers occasionally occurs in the Southern States in moist, warm weather. The disease is caused by a fungus, *Phytophthora capsici*, which attacks stems, leaves, and fruits. The fungus infests the soil and may be carried on the seed.

The stem usually is infected near the soil and shows a dark, water-soaked band that may girdle the stem. Plants so affected soon wilt and die. Similar infection may occur higher up on the stem and single branches may be girdled and wither. Infected leaves show dark spots of irregular shape and size. They become dry and look as though scalded and bleached by the sun. On the fruits are dull, water-soaked patches, which soon cover the entire surface. The fruits shrivel and may remain attached to the plant.

Chili peppers in the Southwest are damaged by a wilt caused by the fungus *Fusarium annuum*. This fungus attacks the roots and the stem just below or at the soil line. Infected plants wilt and die rather rapidly from the injury to the stem.

The fungus lives in the soil but does seem to be carried on the seed. It is spread by irrigation water and on wind-blown particles of soil. The disease is most severe on heavy, poorly drained soils.

PEPPERS SUFFER from leaf diseases characterized by spots or large areas in which the leaf tissues are killed. To blame are fungi or bacteria, some of which also cause spotting or rot of the fruits. The most common are bacterial spot, caused by a bacterium, *Xanthomonas vesicatoria* (which also affects tomatoes) and cercospora leaf spot, caused by the fungus *Cercospora capsici*. Bacterial spot affects leaves and fruit. Cercospora spot attacks leaves and stems.

Bacterial spot causes severe injury to sweet peppers but is not serious on hot peppers. When infection occurs on young leaves of pepper, the spots are small, yellow green, and slightly raised on the under side. On older leaves the spots are not noticeably raised. If there are only a few, they may be one-fourth inch across and have a pale-tan center with a dark margin. If there are many, they remain small and dark in color. Severely spotted leaves turn yellow and drop. Infected seedlings may lose nearly all their leaves. Plants in the field often lose much of their older foliage. Some spotting of the stem occasionally occurs. The bacterium is carried on the seed and apparently lives over winter on the remains of diseased plants in the soil. Contaminated seed appears to be the chief source of initial infection. Infected seedlings are a source of further infection in the field. Severe outbreaks often follow long periods of warm, rainy weather, particularly when driving rain and wind cause slight injuries to the plants.

Cercospora leaf spot is sometimes known as frogeye spot, because the spots on the leaves and stems have pale-gray centers with a wide and darker margin. They are oblong or circular and may be one-half inch in diameter. Severely spotted leaves generally wither and drop. A spotting of the leaf petioles also is a factor in the defoliation of the plants. The loss of leaves often is so great as to cause serious reduction in both size and quality of the crop. Hot and sweet peppers seem to be affected with equal severity.

The fungus causing cercospora leaf spot does not live very long in the soil but is carried on the seed. Field infection commonly can be traced to seedlings grown from contaminated seed. Spores of the fungus are produced in the tissues of the spots. Their spread is favored by the same conditions that favor the dissemination of the organism that causes bacterial spot.

PEPPERS ARE SUBJECT to a number of fruit rots. The most prevalent is the one that is known as anthracnose. It is caused by a fungus (*Gloeosporium piperatum*), which produces dark, sunken spots up to an inch across on sweet peppers. The spots occur on green or ripe fruits and eventually are covered with dark, raised specks—the bodies in which spores are produced. The surface of the spots may be covered in moist weather with a salmon-pink mass of spores. A similar spotting of the fruit is caused by another fungus (*Colletotrichum nigrum*), which can attack the fruit only through wounds or injuries such as those caused by blossom-end rot. The symptoms it causes can easily be confused with those caused by *G. piperatum*.

The fungus causing anthracnose can grow through the flesh of the fruit and infect the seed internally. The surface of the seed also may be contaminated by spores from the surface of the fruit during the seed harvest. If the fungus is carried by the seed, it can infect the leaves and stems of young seedlings and remain on the plant through the season, although it causes little evident injury other than that on the fruits. After the fruit is infected, the spores produced on the surfaces of the spots are washed or spattered by rain to other fruits and spread by handling the plants. In rainy, warm seasons the loss from anthracnose often is severe.

Ripe rot, caused by the fungus *Vermicularia capsici*, is more damaging than anthracnose on pimiento peppers in the South. Fruits may be infected when green but show no spotting until they turn red. At this stage, fruits in the field may show only small, inconspicuous yellow spots. When they are picked and held in the containers in warm, moist air, however, the spots enlarge so fast that many fruits become unfit for use within 24 hours. The fungus, like the one that causes anthracnose, can grow into the seed cavity and infect the seed. Seedlings grown from such seed show spotting of the seed leaves, but there is little injury to the foliage.

The organism causing bacterial spot of the leaves also causes a damaging spotting of the fruits. The spots, roughly circular, are raised in small blisterlike swellings that may be one-fourth inch across. They turn brown and become cracked, roughened, and warty. In damp weather various decay-producing organisms can enter through the spots.

Mosaic diseases of peppers cause serious losses in yield and quality of the fruit. The most common are those of tobacco mosaic, cucumber mosaic, and the tobacco etch virus (*Marmor erodens*). They sometimes are found in combined infections of the same plant.

Younger leaves of plants affected with the tobacco mosaic virus are mottled with yellow-green spots and may be slightly curled and crinkled. Infected plants often show a streaking of some of the branches. Later the leaves drop; often the branches die. Some green strains of the virus cause little if any mottling of the fruits, but with others the fruits may turn yellow and have a wrinkled surface. Yellow strains sometimes cause a mottling of the fruit.

The cucumber mosaic virus causes a leaf mottling like that of tobacco mosaic, but the young leaves are more often curled upward at the edges and the darker areas are raised and slightly blistered in appearance. Such leaves often are narrow and pointed. The plants often are abnormally short and bushy. Fruits sometimes are misshapen and have dark raised spots on their surface. One strain of the virus causes large yellow rings on the leaves and fruits.

The tobacco etch virus often affects peppers and causes a mottling of the leaves that may be much like that of cucumber mosaic. At times it is very mild. With the etch virus alone, there is no evident mottling of the fruit. When sweet peppers are infected with both the etch and tobacco mosaic viruses, however, the fruits are yellowed and wrinkled and show rough, slightly raised, circular spots.

NONPARASITIC DISEASES like those that attack tomatoes sometimes affect peppers. Sunscald and blossom-end rot are a common cause of considerable loss of sweet peppers. Blossom-end rot is caused by the same factors that lead to its development in tomatoes. Sunscald injury is particularly severe where peppers have been defoliated by leaf spot diseases.

The symptoms of both disorders consist of large areas with a dry, light-colored, papery appearance. Blossom-end rot, however, occurs on or near the blossom end of the fruit. Sunscald injuries may occur at any point. With spots of both types, the injured areas are commonly overgrown by fungi that later give them a dark appearance.

As FOR CONTROL: The prevention of disease in the seedbed is of prime importance, because several of the most serious pepper diseases are caused by organisms that may be present on the seed or infest the soil.

It is best not to grow seedlings in soil that recently has been planted with peppers; if that must be done, the soil should be disinfected by one of the means mentioned for tomato seedbeds (see page 460).

The seed should be disinfected before planting. One method consists of soaking seed for 5 minutes in a 1–2,000 solution of bichloride of mercury (corrosive sublimate). After treatment, it is washed for 15 minutes in running water and dried at once. The treatment will destroy organisms present on the surface of the seed. It is particularly effective in the control of bacterial spot.

Some organisms, such as those that cause anthracnose and ripe rot, also may cause internal infection of the seed. That can best be prevented by harvesting seed only from sound fruits, as surface treatments will not destroy the fungus within the seed. Treatment with bichloride of mercury does not protect seedlings against damping-off, and it is advisable to treat the seed afterward with Arasan, Thiram 50, or Phygon.

Losses from wilt diseases can be reduced by crop rotation and the avoidance of fields where wilt diseases have previously been destructive. Poorly drained, moist soils should be avoided. The variety College No. 9 chili is resistant to the fusarium wilt, which damages hot peppers in the Southwest.

The use of fungicides for the control of leaf spot and fruit rot diseases of peppers has not become the general practice that it is with tomatoes. Peppers sometimes are sprayed with a 6–6–100 bordeaux mixture or a neutral copper fungicide used in a formula that gives the equivalent of 1½ pounds of actual copper to 100 gallons of water. Neutral copper dusts with a 5-percent copper equivalent also have been used. The dithiocarbamate fungicides zineb, nabam (used with zinc sulfate), and ziram also can be used at the strengths commonly employed with tomatoes (page 461).

The copper compounds seemed to give the best control of bacterial spot, but that is not necessarily true with such diseases as cercospora spot and anthracnose fruit rot.

If leaf spot diseases appear in the seedbed, the plants should be sprayed at once. When such diseases appear on the leaves of occasional plants throughout the field, it is wise to apply a fungicide and continue applications at intervals of 7 to 10 days, depending on the weather. If leaf spot diseases do not appear until late in the season, however, the use of fungicides may not be profitable. There is evidence that the copper fungicides may cause some injury to peppers, particularly when several applications are made during the season.

In general, the methods for reducing losses from mosaic viruses are the same as those for the prevention of losses in tomatoes. Care in handling seedlings is as important with peppers as with tomatoes.

Aphids commonly infest peppers. It is essential to control them, especially in the seedbed. Because peppers are commonly infected with the cucumber mosaic virus, perennial hosts of that virus should be destroyed near seedbeds and in and along the margins of the field. It is best to try to avoid having pepper fields next to cucumber, muskmelon, and celery fields because they all are highly susceptible to cucumber mosaic.

The varieties Rutgers World Beater No. 13, Burlington, and Yolo Wonder are resistant to the tobacco mosaic virus but are not resistant to the viruses causing cucumber mosaic and tobacco etch.

S. P. DOOLITTLE *is a principal pathologist in charge of investigations of tomatoes, peppers, cucurbits, and certain other vegetable crops in the division of vegetable crops and diseases of the Bureau of Plant Industry, Soils, and Agricultural Engineering. He was graduated from Michigan State College and, after graduate study in plant pathology at the University of Wisconsin, joined the Department of Agriculture in 1918. He was one of the earlier workers on virus diseases of vegetable crops.*

Diseases of Beets

Glenn S. Pound

Garden beet, or red beet, is grown the country over as a common garden vegetable. It is grown as a canning crop on large acreages of the Great Lakes area, especially in Wisconsin and New York. Large acreages for fresh-market shipments are grown as winter crops in the South and Southwest, especially Texas and California. The production of beet seed represents an entirely different culture and is centered primarily in western Washington, Oregon, and California.

INTERNAL BLACK SPOT—boron deficiency or heart rot—is a common ailment of garden beet in many parts of the world. Applications of boron to the soil generally give good control, but it is still probably the worst disease of garden beet in the Northern States, where most of our canning beets are grown.

Young leaves are the first to show symptoms. They become redder and narrower than normal and stunted. Sometimes the leaf blades roll downward and die early. Growth of adventitious buds follows a similar pattern, and a cluster of dead leaves is left at the crown. The most conspicuous symptom on garden beet is the spotting of the root. The spots are black, corky areas, masses of dead cells that might be very small or involve much of the roots. The spots inside cannot be detected at harvest without cutting, and canners often have to reject fields where the disease is prevalent.

The first effect of boron deficiency in beet is one of increased cell division and growth, followed by death of the tissues and a reduction in the conductive tissue of the plant. Stunting or even death of the entire plant may result.

Many soils, especially alkaline soils or soils high in calcium, are naturally deficient in boron. Overliming thus tends to increase the disease. In other soils the boron may be fixed and unavailable to the plant. The application of 40 to 75 pounds of borax to the acre before seeding will control the disease. The borax can be applied with the fertilizer. Boron in excess is extremely toxic. If it is applied in fertilizer beside the row, one must be careful to keep the fertilizer 2 or 3 inches away from the seed.

Sometimes black spot develops even when borax has been added to the soil, notably on heavy soils and when growth resumes after a drought. Apparently the boron becomes unavailable in dry weather. In such conditions the application of 10 pounds of borax to the foliage as a spray once or twice in midseason gives good control.

Some variation in susceptibility exists among varieties. Long Dark Blood is one of the least susceptible.

BLACK ROOT (damping-off), a seedling disease of beet, may be caused by any of a number of fungi. Beet and its relatives are very susceptible to fungus attack as seedlings because of the rapid growth of hypocotyl cells at or slightly below the soil line.

Several fungi may produce black root. The major ones are *Rhizoctonia solani*, *Phoma betae*, *Aphanomyces cochlioides*, and species of *Pythium*.

The organisms differ in importance according to localities concerned. In some areas *Pythium debaryanum* has been described as the primary incitant of black root; in other areas *Aphanomyces* is the chief incitant. The fungi differ in the time they attack seedlings. *Pythium* is the chief cause of preemergence damping-off. Usually *Pythium* effects are during the first 2 weeks after seeding. *Phoma* is carried on beet seed and may also cause preemergence damping-off. *Phoma* is not common on domestic seed, however, and it is thus of much less importance than the other fungi, all of which commonly inhabit the soil.

Symptoms of black root vary slightly according to the fungus involved. *Pythium* attacks any part of the germinating and emerging seedling, especially the taproot and hypocotyl, and turns them soft and black. Seedling leaves wilt and the plants topple over. It usually occurs in the very young seedling stage and rarely occurs after the first true leaf is formed.

Rhizoctonia attacks slightly older seedlings. It darkens the affected area, but the lesions are less extensive than those caused by *Pythium*, brown instead of black, and dry instead of soft. They also have definite margins. The fungus also incites a crown rot of mature sugar beets.

Aphanomyces attacks seedlings as *Pythium* does, but much later. It seldom causes preemergence damping-off. It also causes tip rot, a rot of mature sugar beet.

Aphanomyces, *Pythium*, and *Rhizoctonia* all persist for a number of years in the soil. Close cropping of soil to beets increases the incidence of disease. A high level of soil fertility helps control black root, probably by producing rapid and sturdy growth of the seedlings. The disease is most severe in rainy seasons. *Pythium* attacks are most severe at temperatures of about 55° to 70° F.; those of *Rhizoctonia* at about 60° to 85°; and those of *Aphanomyces* at about 65° to 90°.

Pythium can be controlled by such seed protectants as New Improved Ceresan, Arasan, Phygon, and copper oxide. They have less effect on *Rhizoctonia* and little or no effect on *Aphanomyces* because it attacks so late. *Phoma* can be eradicated from seed by

treatment with hot water, but that may not be practical. L. D. Leach, of the University of California, has shown that spraying seed with a suspension of New Improved Ceresan greatly reduces the amount of seed transmission.

CERCOSPORA LEAF SPOT is the most common and most destructive leaf disease of beet and sugar beet. In the United States it is prevalent only in areas that are relatively humid or get regular rains during the growing season. In the Midwest it may be serious in rainy seasons and almost absent in dry seasons. It is generally much less serious on garden beet than on sugar beet. The fungus can attack *Amaranthus*, lambsquarters, lettuce, celery, sweetpotato, dock, soybean, spinach, potato, and other plants.

Symptoms are small, circular spots, about one-eighth inch in diameter, which have a well-defined border usually darker than the rest of the lesion. Lesions on petioles are long. The lesion center is tan to brown. Sometimes the grayish masses of spores on the lesion surface can be seen easily. Lesions may be numerous enough to coalesce and produce extensive dead areas. Often they are numerous enough to kill the entire leaf. Older leaves are more susceptible than young leaves. Progressive defoliation therefore occurs throughout the season.

The causal fungus, *Cercospora beticola*, produces sclerotial masses in infected tissue, which probably are the source of overwintering inoculum. The spores, which are borne on the lesion surface, are wind-blown and provide the secondary inoculum. Spores may also be carried on the seed, but that source of primary inoculum is much less important than the debris of infected plants. When humidity is high, the spores germinate and send infection threads into the stomata to initiate the leaf lesions. Spores are not produced at low temperatures. Spread of the disease therefore is not great until midsummer. The fungus develops rapidly in the leaf for a short time until the plant develops a layer of cells, which wall the lesion off and limit its size. Hence the smallness and regularity of size of the spots.

The disease can be controlled by fungicidal sprays and dusts such as bordeaux mixture, fixed coppers, and the organic carbamates, but proper rotation is the most practical way. Resistant varieties of sugar beets have been developed. Among them are U. S. 215 x 216 and its derivatives.

DOWNY MILDEW is restricted almost entirely to Pacific coast areas. It attacks sugar beet, chard, and several species of wild beet, but not such related plants as spinach and lambsquarters. It is more important on beet seed crops than on root crops.

The fungus, *Peronospora schachtii*, attacks plants in all stages. The leaves of seedlings are extensively yellowed and curl downward. Attacks on older leaves result in more restricted spots, which sometimes are ringed with darker pigmentation. If dry weather prevails after lesions begin, the spots may become dead and produce few spores. In wet weather the under side of the lesions becomes covered with spore-bearing growth of the fungus. The mycelium develops systemically in the cortex and invades the crown of the plant. Subsequent leaves are infected as they expand, and the entire crown becomes a rosette of small, distorted, mildewed leaves.

When crown-infected roots are planted the following spring for seed production, the floral stalk is systemically invaded and shows marked symptoms. Growth is severely retarded and distorted. Leaves are curled and thickened. Occasionally adventitious buds develop to give an effect of witches'-broom. Infected floral parts are swollen and distorted. Various affected parts may be covered with the downy fungus growth.

Downy mildew is serious only in cool weather when there are frequent showers or heavy dew or fog. Conidia germinate best at about 40° to 45° F., although germination will occur in a range of 35° to 85°.

Sexual resting spores (oospores) are produced abundantly in infected tissue. Probably they carry the fungus over long periods of unfavorable conditions. The organism also is carried in seed which may initiate the disease in the spring. The chief source of primary inoculum, however, especially in seed-growing areas, is the overwintering roots that were infected in the steckling beds. Adequate control measures have not been worked out but in the culture of steckling beds prevention of the disease by foliage fungicides is important.

MOSAIC and curly top are the worst virus diseases of beet in the United States.

Mosaic occurs in many other parts of the world, notably Europe, England, Australia, and New Zealand. It is conspicuously associated with seed production of beet and sugar beet, because of the cultural methods used in seed production. Beet roots for seed mostly are grown in steckling beds and transplanted to the seed row after overwintering either in the steckling bed or in pit or warehouse storage. Since steckling beds are planted some 2 or 3 months before seed harvest, there is an overlapping period between crops during which the virus is transmitted from seed plants to seedlings.

Because of a marked restriction in host range, overwintering in wild hosts is of little importance and the disease is of little importance in areas growing market beets only. The virus infects most species of the Chenopodiaceae—the goosefoot family. Hosts in other families are pigweed, chickweed, zinnia, shepherds-purse, yellow sweetclover, and crimson clover. It can be found commonly on lambsquarters, pigweed, and spinach in beet-seed-growing areas.

Symptoms on beet consist of a transparency of the veins followed by many small rings that have red centers or are solid yellow spots with reddish borders. Concentric rings—alternating pigmented and light areas—are characteristic. Young leaves often show a conspicuous, irregularly etched pattern along the veins. Infected plants usually develop an excessive amount of anthocyanin pigment and are thus easily detected in the field. With age, seed plants may develop considerable necrosis of leaves; defoliation then is severe. Leaves of infected plants often are leathery and markedly stunted and distorted.

Sap from infected beet plants loses its infectious properties when it is diluted 2,000 times, or allowed to age at room temperature for 2 or 3 days, or heated for 10 minutes in a water bath at 140° F.

The virus is transmitted from diseased to healthy plants by a number of aphids, notably the bean aphid (*Aphis fabae*) and the green peach aphid (*Myzus persicae*). The virus is not infectious enough to be spread on equipment. It is not seed-borne or soil-borne.

In seed-growing areas a marked measure of control can be had by growing the steckling beds in areas isolated from infected seed fields.

GLENN S. POUND *is associate professor of plant pathology in the University of Wisconsin and collaborator with the Bureau of Plant Industry, Soils, and Agricultural Engineering of the Department of Agriculture. He is a native of Arkansas and has a bachelor's degree from the University of Arkansas. After receiving his doctorate from the University of Wisconsin in 1943 he spent 3 years at Mt. Vernon, Wash., studying diseases of vegetable seed crops in the Pacific Northwest. Since 1946 he has been engaged in research on vegetable crop diseases.*

For further reading:
Glenn S. Pound: Beet Mosaic in the Pacific Northwest. *Journal of Agricultural Research*, volume 75, pages 31–41, 1947.
J. R. Warren: A Study of the Sugar Beet Seedling Disease in Ohio, *Phytopathology*, volume 38, pages 883–892, 1948.

Diseases of Carrots

Glenn S. Pound

Carrots are grown the world over as a garden vegetable. They also are processed in great volume. In the United States several areas produce large acreages of carrots for fresh-market consumption, the bulk of this acreage being grown in Texas, Arizona, and California as winter crops. Acreages for canning are greatest in the Great Lakes States, notably New York and Wisconsin. Production of carrot seed is primarily in the Pacific Coast and Rocky Mountain States.

BACTERIAL BLIGHT of carrot has become an important disease of market carrots in the Southwest and carrot seed crops in the Pacific coast and Rocky Mountain areas.

First symptoms are yellow spots on the tips of leaf segments. They rapidly turn brown and get a water-soaked appearance. A yellowish halo often subtends the black center of the lesion. Entire leaf segments or leaflets may be killed and lower leaves die and dry up as the disease advances. In severe infections, long, dark-brown, water-soaked lesions develop on the petioles and main stem. A gummy bacterial substance frequently collects on them.

On seed plants the symptoms on the floral organs are most conspicuous. If infection occurs before the umbel emerges from the sheath or before it opens up, the entire umbel is usually killed outright. If the umbel opens before infection occurs, several of the umbellets may escape. A gummy exudate is usually present and frequently may cover the entire umbel.

The affected roots of market carrots may show small, water-soaked, greasy flecks or scablike lesions at any point on the surface. They first appear as brown or maroon spots, which may become raised pustules or sunken craters. A grayish ooze may cover the surface of the lesions. The larger craters usually crack open and are filled with soil particles embedded in the bacterial ooze. Often internal pockets are formed when surface lesions heal over to enclose the scab lesion. Another symptom is a marked constriction of the root, which may let it break in two at harvest.

The bacteria (*Xanthomonas carotae*) persist in the soil and are commonly carried with seed. Seed may be disinfected by soaking in hot water at 126° F. for 10 minutes. Control also requires adequate crop rotation.

BACTERIAL SOFT ROT is one of the most destructive diseases of carrot and other vegetables in storage or transit. It also may cause considerable rot before harvest, especially if organs are injured by insects or other diseases. It is caused by the bacteria *Erwinia carotovora* and *E. atroseptica*. It was one of the earliest bacterial diseases of plants to be studied. The bacteria attack storage organs of almost all vegetable crops, especially onion, cabbage, potato, carrot, parsnip, and celery. The latter bacterial species causes the important blackleg disease of potato. Leafy vegetables, such as spinach, are often attacked in the field and in storage.

The disease is characterized by a watery, smelly, soft decay of storage tissue.

The bacteria are common in most soils, particularly soils closely cropped with plants susceptible to attack. They normally invade plants through wounds. Injuries from harvesting, freezing, and insects make plants susceptible to attack. The bacteria must have relatively high moisture and high temperature for rapid development. Cool, dry storage or transit conditions therefore are helpful in control. A storage temperature just above the freezing point and a relative humidity below 90 percent check the development of the disease. Care in harvesting to avoid bruises is important. If vegetables are washed before storage or shipment, drying in warm forced air immediately after washing reduces the chances of soft rot.

Several species of maggot flies (especially *Hylemya cilicrura* and *H. brassicae*) carry the bacteria. Adult flies, which have the bacteria in their intestinal tract, lay eggs about the plant. As the larvae emerge they become contaminated with the bacteria, which cover the egg and are necessary for the normal development of the larvae. As the contaminated larvae bore into potato seed pieces or storage organs of other vegetables such as carrot roots and cabbage heads, they introduce the bacteria into the host tissue.

The pathogenicity of the soft rot bacteria depends on the production of an enzyme, protopectinase, which moves through the tissues ahead of the bacteria, loosening and destroying cells as it does so. Byproducts of bacterial growth cause the cell contents to flow into the intercellular spaces, where they are a nutrient medium for the bacteria. Thus the rot is watery.

THE ALTERNARIA AND CERCOSPORA BLIGHTS, leaf spot diseases caused by *Alternaria dauci* and *Cercospora carotae*, are world-wide in distribution and commonly occur together. In many areas, however, cercospora blight appears earlier in the season than alternaria. Cercospora is more severe on young leaves than on old leaves and thus builds up when the plants are relatively young. Alternaria blight is much more pathogenic on old leaves than on young leaves and does not become prevalent until the plants approach maturity. Temperature requirements are about the same for both fungi.

Symptoms of the two diseases are quite similar. Alternaria blight appears first as irregular brown spots with yellowish centers near the margins of the leaves and yellowish areas surrounding the spots. The leaflet tip or entire leaflet may be invaded and turn brown. Under severe infections entire fields may be bronzed as if scorched by heat.

Cercospora lesions are also usually marginal although any part of the leaf or petiole may be attacked. Spots are quite circular and usually have a whitish or tan center. Under very moist conditions, lesions of cercospora may be quite extensive and dark-colored, closely resembling alternaria. Both organisms attack petioles on which lesions are usually elongate. Neither organism attacks the fleshy root.

Spores of the two fungi are borne on the surface of the lesions. Those of alternaria are dark-colored, club-shaped, and have cross walls in both directions. Those of cercospora are colorless, long, and have cross walls only in a transverse direction. They are wind-borne and germinate over a wide range of temperature. Both fungi persist in the soil, in refuse of infected plants, and are commonly seed-borne. Seed can be freed of the organisms by soaking for 5 minutes in a 1–1,000 solution of mercuric chloride or dusting with New Improved Ceresan. Crop rotation and sanitation will reduce carry-over in the soil. Both diseases are amenable to control with fungicides. Bordeaux, fixed coppers, and the carbamates are all effective.

YELLOWS, a virus disease, is probably the worst disease of carrots. It is caused by the aster yellows virus.

Its first symptom is a yellowing of young leaves as they emerge from the crown. Almost at the same time come yellow side shoots, which may later give an appearance of witches'-broom to the plant. As the disease develops, the entire cluster of shoots may become a sickly yellow color and the older outside leaves may become bronzed or reddened and twisted. By late season the crown often becomes dead and blackened. Such roots are usually attacked by soft rot bacteria. The roots are smaller in size and a profusion of fine roots on the surface of the main root is not uncommon. Such unsightly roots are unsuited for bunching and the shortened, rosetted tops are often missed by mechanical harvesters. Affected roots are off-flavor and give a bitter, stringent flavor to canned products.

The virus attacks a wide range of cultivated and wild hosts. Two strains have been described, western and eastern, as being pathogenic and non-pathogenic to celery, respectively.

H. H. P. Severin, of the University of California, was first to show that the aster yellows virus was the cause of yellows in carrot. L. O. Kunkel, of the Rockefeller Institute, had earlier shown that the six-spotted leafhopper (*Macrosteles divisus*) was the vector of the disease on aster. Severin learned that the insect was also the chief vector of the western strain of the virus but that it also could be transmitted by at least 16 species of leafhoppers. No vector other than the six-spotted leafhopper has been reported in the East and Midwest.

The relationship of the virus to the vector has received much attention. Kunkel observed that insects were unable to transmit the virus until a lapse of a few days after feeding upon diseased plants. L. M. Black, of the University of Illinois, has shown that the virus multiplies manyfold within the insect vector and an incubation period in the vector is apparently a necessary prelude to transmission. Infected hoppers may carry the active virus for 100 days or longer. Kunkel showed that if infected hoppers were subjected to exposure to an air temperature of about 90° F. for 12 days, the virus was permanently inactivated in the hoppers. With less exposure at 90° it was so reduced in some hoppers that several days were necessary before they could effect transmission. In still others, the virus was apparently changed so that when transmitted to the plant host a much milder disease occurred.

The virus may be carried from season to season in adult leafhoppers, but in most areas, especially the Northern States, overwintering occurs in perennial hosts. The six-spotted leafhopper overwinters in Northern States primarily as eggs laid in winter grains and grasses. The first-generation insects in the spring obtain the virus by feeding on diseased perennial plants. In 1952 Darrell Drake and R. K. Chapman, of the Wisconsin Agricultural Experiment Station, showed that in Wisconsin primary inoculum introduced in the spring by migrant leafhoppers is of more importance than the overwintering inoculum.

No variety of carrot has been shown to have any appreciable amount of resistance. The disease in carrots can be controlled by reducing the leafhopper vector with DDT sprays or dusts. Applications are made at intervals of 7 to 10 days beginning when hopper populations are prevalent and continuing until about 1 month before harvest.

GLENN S. POUND *is associate professor of plant pathology in the University of Wisconsin and collaborator with the Bureau of Plant Industry, Soils, and Agricultural Engineering of the Department of Agriculture.*

For further reading on carrot diseases:

W. L. Doran and E. F. Guba: Blight and Leaf-spot of Carrot in Massachusetts, *Massachusetts Agricultural Experiment Station Bulletin 245, 8 pages, 1928.*
James B. Kendrick: Bacterial Blight of Carrot, *Journal of Agricultural Research, volume 49, pages 493–510, 1934.*
Glenn S. Pound and R. K. Chapman: Control of Aster Yellows in Carrot by Control of *Macrosteles divisus* with DDT, *Phytopathology, volume 37, page 18, 1947.*

Diseases of Spinach

Glenn S. Pound

Most of the large spinach-growing areas are in coastal States. The largest acreage for fresh-market spinach is in southern Texas. For fresh-market spinach, savoy (wrinkled leaf) types are generally grown; for processing, the smooth-leaved types are generally used. However, the important canning acreage in the Arkansas River Valley of Arkansas and Oklahoma is predominantly of savoy type. The production of spinach seed in the United States is centered in the Puget Sound area of Washington.

DOWNY MILDEW—blue mold—is one of the most serious diseases of spinach. It develops when the weather is cool and moist and generally is most severe in coastal areas. It is especially severe at times in southern localities that grow fresh-market spinach. Although downy mildews occur on closely related plants, the fungus (*Peronospora effusa*) does not affect any other host.

The disease appears on plants of any age. It is first noticed as large yellow blotches on the leaf, the under side of which becomes covered with a fuzzy growth that is white at first and bluish purple later. The growth contains a mass of spores (conidia), which are easily detached and are carried by air currents from plant to plant.

At night or in cloudy, rainy weather when temperatures are low and plants are covered with a film of water, the spores germinate and penetrate the plant. In about a week the newly infected leaves produce a crop of spores, which can start another cycle of the disease. Many such cycles occur within a growing season.

The conidia are vegetative spores and will not remain viable more than a few hours in a dry atmosphere. However, the fungus produces in the host tissue sexual spores (oospores), which are very resistant to unfavorable conditions and which serve to carry the fungus from one season to another. Their germination has not been observed, but it is generally believed that they are the important source of overwintering or oversummering inoculum, as the case may be.

The oospores may be carried as a surface contaminant of spinach seed. Seed may even be internally infected by the fungus. It has never been proved that contaminated or infected seed will give rise to infected seedlings, however. First infections probably occur from oospores germinating in the soil, or in areas of extremely mild climate the conidial stage may extend from one crop to another on volunteer host plants. The fungus is an obligate parasite, and cannot persist except on spinach.

Copper-containing fungicides are said to give successful control but have not been generally practical. A foreign introduction of spinach (P. I. 140467) carries a single dominant gene for immunity. The development of resistant varieties is the best hope of control.

WHITE RUST of spinach is caused by the fungus *Albugo occidentalis*, an obligate parasite. It was first reported on spinach in Virginia in 1910 but did not assume importance until it became established in the Winter Garden region of Texas about 1935. As a field disease it has been practically restricted to southern Texas, although it has occurred in the Arkansas River Valley of eastern Oklahoma and western Arkansas. Periodically it has been severe in the Winter Garden, Coastal Bend, and lower Rio Grande Valley areas of Texas.

The fungus has been reported on two or three wild plants closely related to spinach, but it does not attack any cultivated plant other than spinach.

Early symptoms consist of yellow spots, similar to those of blue mold, on the leaves. The under surfaces are distinct—white, blisterlike, circular or elongate pustules develop, which may have a concentrically zonate pattern. The pustules (sori) break open to release a mass of conidia to the air. Severely affected leaves often die and turn brown and give a frosted or blighted appearance to a field.

The conidia are short-lived and do not germinate well until they lose some of their moisture—usually during the day in the dry atmosphere of the Southwest. At night, if temperatures drop enough to cause dew, the conidia germinate to produce six to eight swimming spores, which in turn germinate and send infection threads into the host. Mature pustules are produced on these newly infected leaves in about a week.

The fact that conidia require a certain amount of dryness before germination probably explains why the disease has become severe only in the Southwest. In the Arkansas River Valley, spinach is growing during the rainy part of the year and only sporadic periods are favorable for its spread. The failure of the disease to spread during foggy or rainy periods probably explains its absence in other spinach-producing areas.

The fungus produces sexual spores in great abundance in the infected tissue, especially in seed plants and under warm temperatures. They are even produced abundantly on seeds, but such seeds have never given rise to infected seedlings. The spores in the soil are probably the means by which the fungus is carried from one season to the next although their germination has never been observed. No adequate control measures have been devised.

BLIGHT, caused by the cucumber mosaic virus, is the most widespread and serious virus disease of spinach. The virus is transmitted from a number of wild and cultivated hosts to spinach by aphids, and the disease is most severe on fall and winter crops because of a greater build-up of inoculum in other hosts.

Symptoms of the disease appear as a general yellowing. Plants ultimately become completely yellowed, twisted, and stunted. If warm temperatures prevail, death of the plants quickly follows, but if air temperatures are cool, death does not occur for several days.

Virginia Savoy, a resistant variety, was developed in 1920. It is a hybrid of Bloomsdale Savoy and an Asiatic variety. Old Dominion, a second resistant variety, was developed by selection following a cross of Virginia Savoy and King of Denmark. This was one of the first successful attempts to control plant virus diseases by breeding resistant varieties. Virginia Savoy and Old Dominion are both savoy varieties and have been widely used for fresh-market spinach.

The resistance of Viginia Savoy is due to a single dominant gene that is dependent on certain air temperatures for expression of resistance. At temperatures below 80° F. resistant plants show no symptoms when inoculated, but at temperatures above 80° F. inoculated plants rapidly succumb with a systemic necrosis. Thus, in breeding programs the control of air temperature is of prime importance.

J. P. Fulton of Arkansas has isolated a strain of the virus from spinach to which Virginia Savoy and Old Dominion are readily susceptible.

GLENN S. POUND *has specialized in the diseases of vegetable crops since 1943.*

J. P. Fulton: Studies on Strains of Cucumber Virus 1 From Spinach, *Phytopathology,* volume 40, pages 729–736, 1950.

M. C. Richards: Downy Mildew of Spinach and Its Control, *New York (Cornell) Agricultural Experiment Station Bulletin 718, 1939.*

Diseases of the Common Mushroom

Edmund B. Lambert, Theodore T. Ayers

The mushroom industry in the United States has developed around one type of mushroom—the common commercial mushrooms that are sold in the markets of all our large cities and are grown in caves or special sheds in which temperature and humidity can easily be controlled. Near almost every large northern city are several mushroom houses.

The industry is only about 50 years old in the United States, but it has developed rapidly to a production of about 60 million pounds of mushrooms a year.

Progress in the development of the techniques of growing mushrooms and the expansion of the industry have been due in large degree to progress in the recognition and control of diseases and insect pests. Before 1920 growers were never sure when an individual crop would be a total failure. Average yields were less than three-fourths of a pound to the square foot. The average yield now is about twice that. Cooperative work of the technical staffs of the spawn makers and the plant pathologists of the Pennsylvania Agricultural Experiment Station and the Department of Agriculture has made that possible. Further progress is in sight: Rather consistent yields of about 5 pounds the square foot have been obtained in small-scale experimental culture at Beltsville, Md.

Strangely enough, both the mushroom itself and many of the organisms of the diseases that attack it are fungi.

The fleshy part of the mushroom that spreads out above the stem is known as the cap. Its function in nature is to produce and disperse the spores, the reproductive bodies. Each mushroom is nourished from the soil and compost beneath it by a system of threadlike moldy growth, which can be compared to the roots of the higher plants. But unlike the higher plants, the "root system" develops extensively before the mushroom appears above ground. The mushroom plant has no chlorophyll with which to manufacture its own carbohydrates from water and the carbon dioxide of the air. Therefore the mushroom "roots" must seek and assimilate organic nutrients in partly decomposed organic matter derived from plants and products of other organisms.

THE FIRST STEP in cultivating mushrooms is the collection and germination of spores. That is done under controlled laboratory conditions. The finished propagative material—the spawn—is a pure culture of threadlike growth in a solid medium. It is produced and sold in large amounts by specialists; the average mushroom grower need not be trained in the techniques of making spawn.

The grower's first step is to prepare a compost. For years horse manure has been used, but artificial composts of straw or old hay, fortified with corncobs, organic nitrogen, phosphates, and potash, have been gaining favor. Large heaps of the materials are moistened and mixed at weekly intervals to maintain a warm, moist, aerated, well-mixed pile. The object is to use up the food materials that might serve as food to the common airborne molds and leave a material in which the mushroom "root system" can better compete with the molds for nutrients.

After the heap has attained a proper degree of decomposition, the compost is adjusted to a favorable moisture content and placed in mushroom houses on shelf beds about 6 inches deep. There are usually several tiers 5 to 6 beds high in a mushroom house, which can hold 50 tons of compost when filled. The compost continues to develop a warm fermentation in the beds. The grower closes the doors and all openings of the house so that, with the aid of supplementary heat, he can raise the inside temperature to 130° or 140° F. That temperature is maintained for about a week. The process is known as a "sweating out" or pasteurizing period.

The temperature then is lowered to about 65° or 70°, and spawn is placed in the bed. The spawn is allowed to grow undisturbed for about 3 weeks. By then it has spread as a threadlike growth through two-thirds of the compost in the beds, and the grower places a 1-inch layer of soil, a process called casing, over the surface of the bed. The spawn continues to grow in the beds and into the casing soil to form a coarser rootlike growth, which produces the mushrooms on the surface of the soil and serves to translocate the food to them from the compost.

The first mushrooms appear about 4 weeks after the beds have been covered with the soil. As growth proceeds, new mushrooms appear above the soil in a succession of waves of rapid growth and large numbers called flushes. Under good conditions the flushes occur every 4 or 5 days for 2 to 4 months, depending on the temperature in the growing houses. During the cropping period the grower waters the soil and maintains a temperature of 50° to 65°. At its end the nutrients in the compost are depleted and the beds are emptied.

The major causes of mushroom disorders, besides fungi, are nutrient deficiencies, toxic chemicals, bacteria, and nematodes.

We know of no disease of mushrooms that is caused by a virus, although the symptoms of one, the mummy disease, suggest that it may be caused by a virus.

Under certain conditions, some undesirable fungi competing for food in the beds will crowd out the growth of the planted spawn. Such undesirable fungi are called weed molds and are considered disease-producing agents. Traces of gaseous impurities in the air also produce abnormalities in mushrooms.

Years ago beds were "spawned" or inoculated by merely transferring pieces of grayish mushroom mold from an old bed to a new one. Later the mold growth was pressed into bricks, which were broken up and used for planting beds. Both methods failed to exclude diseases and insects from the spawn and from the new beds. To reduce contamination of the spawn, growers attempted to select wild spawn from the fields for use in the beds, but that was only trading trouble, for now they were unable to control the varieties grown or maintain favorable strains.

A half century ago, methods of germinating spores of known parentage under control, discovered in France and in the United States, made possible the production of disease-free spawn on a large scale—no longer could growers blame their troubles on poor spawn; they had to look to their methods of culture.

A powdery mold—the white plaster mold—appeared in the mushroom beds of many growers in the early days. It frequently crowded out the mushroom spawn. Growers noticed that this weed mold was usually associated with a wet, greasy condition and with traces of ammonia odor in the compost. This weed mold is seldom encountered now in mushroom houses. French growers were the first to add gypsum during the composting to control white plaster mold. An English scientist gave the explanation of the way in which gypsum acted. He showed that the white plaster mold was usually associated with a dispersion of the colloidal material in the compost resulting from an excess of ionized potassium and that the addition of gypsum (calcium sulfate) to the compost served to flocculate these colloids.

Growers in the United States about 1920 began to allow their beds to sweat out immediately after filling them. The process drove insects to the surface of the beds, where they could be killed by fumigation. But frequently the process caused the beds to fill with an olive mold, which reduced yields and often caused complete crop failures. Control of this weed mold was accomplished by a refinement in the pasteurizing process.

It was shown about 1930 that the olive mold rarely appeared unless the temperature in the beds had gone above 150° F. during the last days of pasteurizing. Most growers therefore maintain their bed temperatures below 145° during pasteurizing. Recently it has been shown that if the temperature goes above 150°, the compost can be reconditioned by subsequently holding it for a few days below 140°. The explanation is that certain nutrients, presumably proteins, that cannot be assimilated by the olive mold are partly broken down by temperatures above 150° and thus made available to it. Under those conditions the mushroom spawn cannot successfully compete with the olive mold for food and is crowded out.

The reconditioning of the compost by holding it at 140° or below for a few days is accomplished by the conversion, by the microbial flora of the compost, of the available nitrogen into microbial protein, which is again unavailable to the olive mold but readily assimilated by mushroom spawn. All commercial growers in the United States now pasteurize their compost and rarely suffer losses from the olive mold.

Another puzzling problem that growers used to encounter was that some soils gave satisfactory yields when they were used to case the beds but other soils gave very poor yields. The reason was found to lie in the intolerance of mushroom spawn to acid soil. Most of these unsuitable soils can be made into good casing soils by bringing their reaction to between pH 7.0 and pH 7.7. Care is needed, though: Some limestone is toxic to spawn because it contains too much magnesium.

Casing soil often harbors the causal organisms of bubbles, brown spot, and mat diseases and parasitic nematodes, which can cause crop failure. Soils in many localities are free from harmful organisms, but if only contaminated soil is available it can be freed of disease organisms by treatment with chemicals or by steaming. In areas where mushrooms have been cultivated for many years nearly all growers fumigate or steam the soil.

Truffle disease, another weed mold, appeared in mushroom beds of a few growers about 1927. Soon many houses in this country and England, Australia, and South Africa had it. It cut the crops in half. It was suspected at first that the appearance of the mold was associated with high temperatures during the growing period but that idea was dropped when experiments showed that a pure culture of the truffle fungus grew well at 50° to 70° F., temperatures that are suitable for the growth of the mushroom spawn, and that the truffle fungus could withstand a temperature of 180°. In 1944 the mystery was solved: The fungus can grow vegetatively and produces fruiting bodies at temperatures below 60°, but its spores do not germinate below 60°. It became apparent that the widespread appearance of the disease was associated with a new practice, beginning about 1926, of growing the spawn in the beds at temperatures between 70° and 80°. Spawn now is grown below 70°, or below 60° if the disease has been prevalent in a grower's house. As the mushroom crop itself is always grown below 65°, the spores of the truffle fungus do not germinate. They are held in a dormant condition by the low temperature and can do no harm even though they are present in the beds.

During the cropping period, growers dust their beds with zineb, which con-trols the verticillium spot disease and reduces late outbreaks of the bubbles disease. The lack of injury or reduction in yields when this fungicide is dusted on mushrooms in different stages of growth for the control of fungus diseases is remarkable since the host plant itself is a fungus—especially in view of the fact that the growth of spawn is sharply arrested when zineb is added to the compost or mixed with the casing soil.

Mushroom growers ventilate their houses as much as possible without excessively drying out the layer of soil on the surface of the compost. This practice is based on an obvious depression of growth or "sulking" of the mushrooms and reduced yields when mushroom houses are closed up for several hours. Experiments indicate that two gases given off by the growing mushrooms themselves, carbon dioxide and an unsaturated hydrocarbon gas, can cause toxic effects in tight houses.

Even when the crop is finished and the houses are empty, growers must take precautions against diseases. They heat the houses to 135° and introduce formaldehyde fumes to combat several diseases that otherwise could be carried over from one crop to another.

NEMATODES are a serious problem wherever mushrooms are grown commercially. They are hard to control and cause heavy losses. They may be actually parasitic on the hyphae or "rootlet system" of the mushroom. With other organisms, they may produce toxic substances. Probably they act as disease carriers.

Although nematodes were present in enormous numbers in mushroom compost, they were not known to be parasitic on mushrooms until 1949. For many years, the reduction in yields in some beds after two or three "breaks" and the total lack of production of mushrooms in others could not be satisfactorily explained. The cause of the trouble was believed to be due to a fungus always present on the affected beds until it was pointed out that the

fungus is not parasitic on the mushroom hyphae but acts as a predator on
nematodes, which are the prime
causes of the disease. Subsequent study
showed that an undescribed nematode
is parasitic on the mushroom hyphae
and is responsible for the decreases in
yields or the disappearance of the
mushroom fungus from the compost.

The nematode has a stylet, or spear,
with which it makes punctures in the
hyphae. The punctures are avenues of
entrance for bacteria, which otherwise
would be unable to enter the hyphae.
E. J. Cairns and C. A. Thomas in 1950
reported that the failure of many beds
in the Kennett Square area of Pennsylvania was due to the activity of
nematodes and bacteria in the compost. They believe that the tremendous
numbers of both organisms produce
metabolic products that inhibit the
production of mushrooms but do not
visibly injure the hyphae.

Most of the nematodes involved in
the complex are free-living, nonstylet
forms. The only known way to control
the nematodes is to raise the temperature of the compost to at least 140° F.
for several hours during pasteurization.
The casing soil also should be heat-
treated for several hours to eliminate
the nematodes in it and prevent their
introduction into the mushroom beds.

Nematodes were reported earlier to
aid in the dissemination of bacteria
responsible for injury to mushroom
caps. A free-living and nonparasitic
species is believed to be a carrier and
distributor of the bacterium *Pseudomonas tolaasii*, the causal organism of
the "blotch" disease of mushroom
caps. The nematode also is suspected
of disseminating other bacterial diseases of mushrooms. There are no
means of controlling it after it has
become established in the beds. More
ventilation is recommended to lower
the moisture on the mushroom caps so
that the nematode will not be able to
move about so freely and disseminate
the bacteria causing the "blotch" and
other diseases. It can be eliminated if
the temperature of the compost is held

at 140° or more for several hours during the pasteurization process. The
casing soil must also be treated similarly to prevent contamination of the
compost with the nematode.

EDMUND B. LAMBERT, *senior mycologist
in the Bureau of Plant Industry, Soils, and
Agricultural Engineering, received his doctor's degree in plant pathology at the University of Minnesota in 1926. He has been
in charge of the Bureau's research on the
diseases and cultivation of mushrooms since
1928. He represented the Department at an
international conference on the scientific aspects of mushroom culture in England in
1949.*

THEODORE T. AYERS, *a graduate of the
Pennsylvania State College and Harvard
University, is associate plant pathologist in
the division of vegetable crops and diseases
of the Bureau of Plant Industry, Soils, and
Agricultural Engineering.*

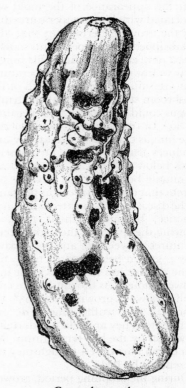

Cucumber scab.

Cucumbers, Melons, Squash

John T. Middleton, Guy Weston Bohn

Most cucurbits are perishable and are consumed shortly after harvest—cucumber (*Cucumis sativus*), muskmelons (*C. melo*), summer squash (*Cucurbita pepo*), and watermelon (*Citrullus vulgaris*) are some of them.

A few, such as winter squash (*Cucurbita maxima* and *C. moschata*) and pumpkin (*C. pepo*, *C. moschata*, and *C. mixta*) can be stored for later use.

Others are processed, such as some varieties of cucumber and gherkin (*Cucumis anguria*). Some are used as ornamental gourds (mostly *Cucurbita pepo* and *Lagenaria siceraria*) and for commercial fibers, such as the luffas (*Luffa aegyptiaca*).

A variety of diseases affect the fruits and other parts of the plant, rotting the produce or affecting the plant in such a way that the yield is reduced.

Seed decay and seedling blight are diseases that reduce plant stands. Good stands of cucumber, muskmelon, squash, and watermelon are usually had by seeding in moist, warm soils in warm weather. Poor stands usually result when seeds are sown in cool, wet soils in cool weather. Poor stands are due to decay of the seed or to the death of seedlings, caused by action of such soil-inhabiting fungi as *Pythium irregulare*, *P. ultimum*, and *Rhizoctonia solani*. The severity of seed decay and seedling blight is related to the relative growth rates of the attacking fungi and the cucurbit plant.

Cucurbit seeds germinate best and seedlings grow most rapidly when the soil temperatures are between 85° and 95° F. and soil moisture is moderate and not excessive. Seeds planted in cold, overly wet soils, or planted too deep, germinate and emerge slowly; they may decay before they break through the seed coat. After they break through, the slow-growing, tender seedlings are susceptible to attack by *Pythium* and *Rhizoctonia* for several days.

If the soil temperature and moisture are right, the cucurbit grows fast, the period of exposure to the causal fungi is shortened, and the more robust seedling escapes infection or is able to overcome the effects of attack.

Seed decay may be controlled by dusting the seed with a protectant fungicide such as chloranil (Spergon) at the rate of 6 ounces to 100 pounds of seed, or thiram (Arasan) at the rate of 4 ounces to 100 pounds. Seed protectants do not control blight of seedlings after they break through the seed coat.

The best stands and minimum losses from seedling blight will be assured by coating the seeds with a protectant fungicide, sowing the seeds as shallow as possible consistent with adequate soil moisture supply, and planting during the warm season when soil temperatures are above 80° F.

Root rot occurs on cucurbits at all stages of growth. The first symptoms are usually stunting, production of small and somewhat yellowish leaves, wilting, failure of fruit to set and mature, and sometimes collapse and death of the plants.

The roots of affected plants may appear water-soaked and flaccid, with some sunken, darkened lesions on the larger, fleshy roots. Occasionally the crown of the plant may become girdled and the top break off.

The two most common root rots are incited by fungi. One, pythium root rot, is caused by the soil inhabitors *Pythium aphanidermatum*, *P. irregulare*, and *P. ultimum*. The other, fusarium root rot, is caused by *Fusarium (Hypomyces) solani* f. *cucurbitae*.

Pythium root rot may affect all cultivated cucurbits, but the disease becomes important only in certain seasons on particular crops.

Cucumber, squash, and watermelon are affected by root rot incited by *P. irregulare* and *P. ultimum* only in the spring and fall when the soil temperatures are comparatively low and hence favorable for the growth of the fungi and unfavorable for the growth of the plants. Pythium root rot is most damaging in soils that are poorly drained and have been cropped to cucurbits or other plants, such as peas and spinach, which provide an increase in abundance of *Pythium* in the soil. Land previously cropped to alfalfa, carrots, cereals, crucifers, lettuce, and some other plants that do not support a large population of these species of *Pythium* in the soil will usually yield satisfactory harvests of cucumber, squash, and watermelon.

Root rot of muskmelon, incited by *Pythium aphanidermatum*, occurs during the warm season and not when the soil temperatures are low, for the causal fungus grows best at high temperatures and sufficiently better than the muskmelon so that root decay results. Root rot of muskmelon is usually most severe in land previously cropped to alfalfa and sugar beets, for the fungus is able to increase in numbers on those crops, providing a large fungus population for infection of the muskmelon crop. Damage from pythium root rot may be minimized by planting on land which was not sown to muskmelon at least the preceding year and which is adequately drained and by planning an appropriate rotation system that avoids alfalfa and sugar beets the preceding year.

Fusarium root rot primarily affects pumpkin and squash. It occasionally occurs on muskmelon, watermelon, and cucumber. The fungus may affect the fibrous and fleshy roots, but it is most commonly found on the main root and crown of the plant, usually girdling it at the ground level and causing the collapse of the plant. The fungus can persist in the soil for years, but is able to attack only cucurbits. Fruits on the ground are frequently rotted by the fungus. Seeds harvested from such infected fruits carry the fungus on their surface, providing a ready means for introducing it into clean, uninfested soils. Seed may be disinfested by soaking it for 5 minutes in 1–1,000 mercuric chloride and rinsing well in water. Land known to be contaminated by the fungus should not be planted to susceptible cucurbits.

FUSARIUM WILT in muskmelon and watermelon is caused by fungi that enter the root system from the soil and grow in the water-conducting vessels of the plants.

If very young plants are attacked the seedlings may rot before or after emergence or the plants may become stunted. When mature plants are attacked, the tips of the runners wilt, and gradually the entire plant wilts and dies. The woody part of the stem is discolored brown. The roots may exhibit cankers.

The disease is most severe when soil temperatures are comparatively high, about 80° F., favoring growth of the causal fungi, and sufficiently below the optimum for plant growth, about 90° F., to retard plant growth enough to render them more susceptible to damage.

The fusarium wilts of muskmelon and watermelon are caused by two different biological races of the causal fungus. The race that causes watermelon wilt is *Fusarium oxysporum* f. *niveum*, which is able to infect watermelon and citron but not muskmelon. The race that causes muskmelon wilt is *F. oxysporum* f. *melonis;* it can infect only muskmelon. Both fungi can survive in soils for many years. Their populations are increased when the respective hosts are grown.

Crop rotation omitting muskmelon

nd watermelon will reduce the populations of the causal fungi, but the diseases are best controlled by growing muskmelons and watermelons in soils that are free from these parasites or by planting wilt-resistant varieties.

VERTICILLIUM WILT resembles fusarium wilt in many respects, but differs in that it is caused by the fungus *Verticillium albo-atrum* and affects not only muskmelon, citron, and watermelon, but also cucumber, pumpkin, and squash.

Verticillium wilt is most commonly observed in California, but it may occur in many Eastern and Southwestern States. It usually becomes severe when the plants are fairly large and the fruits are ripening and when the soil temperatures are about 70° to 75° F. Like *Fusarium*, the fungus is able to persist indefinitely in soils. Unlike *Fusarium*, the fungus attacks a wide variety of plants such as tree crops, small fruits, ornamentals, and many vegetables, making it difficult to find uninfested land suitable for cropping to cucurbits. Muskmelon, pumpkin, and squash are most susceptible to attack. Cucumber and watermelon are fairly resistant. Verticillium wilt may be definitely distinguished from fusarium wilt only by isolation and identification of the fungus from the infected plant tissue.

Verticillium wilt in cucurbits can best be controlled by growing the crops in soils free from the fungus. In districts where verticillium wilt occurs, losses can be minimized by growing cucurbits so that they mature their crop during hot weather when temperatures of the soil are high. No verticillium wilt resistant varieties of cucurbits are available. Fusarium wilt resistant varieties are susceptible to verticillium wilt.

BACTERIAL WILT is a serious disease of cucumber and muskmelon, principally in the Middle West, North Central, and Northeast. It is rare in the Southern or Western States. Pumpkin and squash are susceptible to infection but are rarely severely damaged. Plants infected with the causal organism, *Erwinia tracheiphila*, show first a wilting of a single leaf which remains green. Eventually all the leaves wilt and the plant dies. Freshly cut wilted vines display a viscid white ooze of the bacteria, which is stringy and may be pulled out into strands of an inch or more.

Plants become infected after bacteria-infested spotted and striped cucumber beetles feed on them. The bacteria overwinter in the body of the insect. As the adult beetle feeds on the cucurbit plant it introduces the bacteria, which soon multiply and become distributed throughout the vascular system.

Since the only way in which plants may become infected is through the feeding of the cucumber beetles, it is advisable to use insecticides to destroy the insects.

Although cucumber varieties differ in their susceptibility to bacterial wilt, there are as yet no highly resistant varieties available for commercial use. No resistant muskmelons or other cucurbits have yet been developed.

ANTHRACNOSE seriously affects muskmelon and watermelon and to a lesser extent cucumber and gourd, but not pumpkin or squash. The disease occurs principally in the Middle West, Northeast, and Southeast in areas of summer rains and rarely if at all in the Southwestern and Western States.

The causal organism is a fungus, *Colletotrichum lagenarium*, which overwinters on diseased vines and may also be carried on seeds taken from infected fruits. The organism is disseminated by means of rain and surface water and may infect not only leaves and stems but also fruits.

Spots formed on leaves of cucumber and muskmelon are at first light brown and more or less circular. Later the lesions turn dark brown to red. They may coalesce, consuming the entire leaf and giving it a scorched appearance. Similar leaf spotting occurs on watermelon, the spots becoming dark brown or black. Elongated, narrow, slightly sunken, water-soaked lesions often appear on the stems and petioles. These later may turn yellow or brown. Infected fruits bear circular to oval sunken lesions, in which the pink fruiting spore masses of the fungus may be seen.

In districts where the disease is troublesome, western-produced, disease-free seed should be used. If such are unavailable, the seed should be soaked for 5 minutes in 1–1,000 mercuric chloride, rinsed in water, and planted in land that has not been recently planted with cucurbits. Clean cultivation and crop rotation should be practiced to prevent the building up of large populations of the parasite in the soil.

Losses from anthracnose can be reduced by spraying or dusting with copper fungicides, ziram, or zineb, or spraying with nabam used with zinc sulfate.

ANGULAR LEAF SPOT is serious only on cucumber. It causes water-soaked spots on leaves and fruits. The spots on the leaves become angular (because their margins are confined by veins), turn gray to tan in color, and form an exudate on the lower surface of the leaf. Finally a good many of the infected spots loosen and fall out. Infected fruits show a brown, firm rot extending into the flesh.

The inciting organism is a bacterium, *Pseudomonas lachrymans*, which like the causal agent of anthracnose, overwinters on infected vine refuse, is seed-borne, and is spread by rain and surface water. Although the chances of seedling infection may be greatly reduced by soaking the seed for 5 minutes in 1–1,000 mercuric chloride, rinsing in water, and quickly drying or planting, the treatment may not prevent an occurrence of the disease if conditions favor its development.

SCAB is primarily a disease of cucumber. It may cause some damage to muskmelon. The small, circular, water-soaked lesions that occur on leaves of cucumber and muskmelon are usually first bound by a faint yellow halo. The halo later disappears, and the infected tissue turns brown and becomes necrotic.

Sometimes the causal fungus, *Cladosporium cucumerinum*, infects the petioles and stems, producing spots similar to those on the leaves, but smaller. The fungus can also cause sunken, dark-brown spots on cucumber and muskmelon fruits. Usually young muskmelon fruits do not develop conspicuous fruit-spotting symptoms, the infection remaining minute and of no consequence until the fruit ripens. When the fruit is shipped to market, the fungus becomes active and causes a serious blemish and decay on the fruit.

The disease is most severe during cool, moist weather. Losses can be held to a minimum by growing cucumbers and muskmelons at locations and during seasons in which high temperatures and low humidities prevail and rains seldom occur. Where scab occurs, the resistant varieties of cucumber, Maine No. 2, SR 6, or Highmoor, can be used. Resistant varieties of muskmelons are not available.

DOWNY MILDEW is a destructive disease of cucumber, muskmelon, and watermelon. Occasionally it causes damage to gourd, pumpkin, and squash. It is favored by warm, moist weather. It is most prevalent in regions where rain falls during the growing season. Downy mildew is particularly destructive in the Eastern and Southern States, is usually less damaging in the North Central States, and rarely occurs in the Southwest.

The disease is incited by the fungus *Pseudoperonospora cubensis*. The causal organism is able to infect leaves only. It first appears as a gray-tinged spore mass on older leaves. It causes small angular, yellowish spots, which later increase in number and size. Severely infected leaves become chlorotic, turn brown, and shrivel. The disease begins to appear on the young foliage as the older leaves die. The loss of foliage precludes normal flower set and fruit development. Maturing fruits fail to color properly, are tasteless, and usually are sunburned.

The fungus attacks several species in related genera of wild cucurbits. Its spores can be carried from naturally infected native cucurbits to cultivated ones by wind, splashing rain, and such insects as cucumber beetles.

The observations of several investigators in eastern and southern agricultural research centers suggest that the fungus does not overwinter in northern areas but that it grows on cucurbits at all times of the year in frost-free areas in the South and migrates northward each season to the Atlantic seaboard. The time of appearance and the severity of the disease depend on the severity of the disease in localities further south and on local weather conditions.

Losses from downy mildew may be reduced in areas adjacent to native sources of the causal fungus by eradicating the wild cucurbits. Where that is not practicable, susceptible cultivated cucurbits should be planted some distance away. Production fields should be isolated from one another and especially from small home-garden plantings, where plant disease control measures are not practiced. Sanitation practices will also help reduce losses from downy mildew. Harvested and abandoned fields should be disked promptly. Late plantings should be isolated from earlier ones. Insect pests should be controlled. Men and equipment should stay out of fields when the plants are wet from dew or rain.

The disease may be controlled by the application of fungicidal dusts and sprays. Among the most promising materials are nabam, 2 quarts to 100 gallons of water plus 1.5 pounds of lime or zinc sulfate; zineb, 1.5 pounds

to 100 gallons of water; tribasic copper sulfate, 3 pounds to 100 gallons. A variety of other copper-containing compounds may also be used successfully. A wetting and sticking agent should be added to all the sprays.

Dusts may be used with some satisfaction when the disease is not severe or following a spray program that has reduced the incidence of the disease. Dusts are usually applied at the rate of 40 to 50 pounds per acre and sprays at the rate of 200 to 400 gallons per acre. Fungicides should be applied before the disease appears and continued through the season in districts where downy mildew is known to be troublesome.

Satisfactory control can only be had by applying enough material to cover the upper and lower surfaces of the leaves and applying often enough to cover new foliage and replace old residues that have been removed by rain. Such a schedule usually requires treating plantations once a week during rain-free periods and perhaps twice a week during rainy periods.

Resistance to downy mildew has been found in cucumber and muskmelon from Cuba, China, and India by a number of investigators at several research stations. The resistant importations are poor in quality and are not suitable for commercial culture.

Hybridization with American varieties and several years of breeding and selection in Texas yielded a resistant cantaloup that is also resistant to aphids. It is Texas Resistant Number 1. Resistance to downy mildew has been combined with resistance to powdery mildew and aphids in a cantaloup variety released by the Georgia Agricultural Experiment Station as Georgia 47.

Several years of hybridization and selection in South Carolina resulted in the development of the downy mildew resistant varieties, Palmetto and Santee. They are somewhat susceptible to a race of the fungus that appeared after their development, but it has been reported that the disease may be more readily controlled with fungicides on these varieties than on more susceptible varieties.

The progress made in the combined efforts of investigators at several State and Federal experiment stations indicates that downy mildew may be controlled by an integrated program that embraces sanitation practices, the use of resistant varieties, and the application of fungicides coordinated with the forecasts of the Plant Disease Warning Service.

POWDERY MILDEW affects the leaves and stems of cucumber, muskmelon, squash, and occasionally gourd, pumpkin, and watermelon. The disease causes the greatest damage in the warm, dry, rain-free growing season of the Southwest.

Powdery mildew first appears as round, white spots on the under side of the older leaves. The spots enlarge, increase in number, coalesce, appear on the upper surface of the leaf, and eventually cover both surfaces with a white, powdery growth. Severely affected leaves lose their normal dark-green color and become pale yellow green, then brown and shriveled. When the fungus attacks the stems and young leaves of plants, they become chlorotic, grow poorly, and may be killed. Fruits on infected vines ripen prematurely and lack the desired texture, flavor, and sugar content. Late-set fruits are often small, irregular, and sunburned.

The causal fungus of powdery mildew is *Erysiphe cichoracearum*. It is obliged to grow on living plant tissue and is not confined to cultivated or native cucurbit species. It is found on many kinds of plants, such as aster, lettuce, and sunflower. Although the fungi that occur on these several hosts look alike, and are included in the single morphologic species, *E. cichoracearum*, they are not identical biologically and are differentiated into numerous biological forms that differ from one another in their ability to attack particular kinds of plants.

T. W. Whitaker and his associates have demonstrated the occurrence of two distinct races of the fungus on muskmelon and have shown that one of the races successfully infected 18 species in 9 genera but failed to infect 3 species in 2 genera of the Cucurbitaceae.

The powdery white growth on the leaves and stems of susceptible cucurbits is made up of a tangled web of fungus threads. Some of the threads remain upright and form chains of countless oval or barrel-shaped spores. The masses of spores give the spot its powdery appearance and the disease its name. The chains of spores break up; the individual units are carried by the wind to other leaves and other plants and are capable of producing new infections. The spores may germinate in the absence of water and in relative humidities of 20 percent or less. In that regard they differ markedly from the spores of *Pseudoperonospora cubensis*, which germinate best in water and only rarely when the relative humidity is 80 percent or lower. The spores of powdery mildew are viable for only a few hours when air temperatures are 80° F. or above. They last much longer with air temperatures below 40° but are killed by temperatures below 30°.

Erysiphe cichoracearum produces on some plants perithecia and ascospores, which permit the fungus to overwinter in cold climates, but those fruiting structures are rarely produced on cucurbits and have never been observed on cucurbits in the Southwest. The fungus overwinters in the warm climate of the Southwest in the mycelial and conidial stage in sheltered locations on a variety of volunteer and cultivated cucurbits as well as on a number of susceptible evergreen herbaceous perennials.

Powdery mildew can be controlled by dusting with sulfur on sulfur-resistant cucurbits such as the gourd, pumpkin, squash, and watermelon. Sulfur is the most effective fungicide currently available for the control of powdery mildew on cucurbits and may effectively control the disease with as little as 10 pounds of material an acre. Sulfur can be safely used on some varieties of muskmelon and cucumber and not on others, for different species and varieties of cucurbits vary in their sensitivity to sulfur.

Resistance to sulfur injury in muskmelon was discovered by J. B. S. Norton in commercial fields in California many years ago. This type of resistance has been introduced into desirable commercial strains of cantaloup and made available as sulfur-resistant cantaloup varieties V–1 and S. R. 91. Those varieties are susceptible to attack by powdery mildew and must be dusted with sulfur or some other fungicide in order to yield satisfactory crops.

Powdery mildew on susceptible sulfur-sensitive varieties of cantaloup may be controlled by spraying them with liquid lime-sulfur, 38 ounces per 100 gallons of water, plus a suitable wetting agent, and applied at the rate of 200 to 400 gallons per acre when air temperatures will not go above 95° F. for at least 3 days following application. This should be followed about 2 weeks later with a spray application of cuprous oxide, 1.5 pounds per 100 gallons, plus wetting agent, at the same dosage.

Other copper-containing fungicides tested to date are less effective for the control of the disease. None of the copper fungicides is especially effective when applied as a dust. Iscothan, Ovotran, and possibly some other miticide dusts may be safely and effectively used against powdery mildew.

Powdery mildew of cucumber can be controlled by 15 percent sulfur dust applied at the rate of 40 to 50 pounds per acre when air temperatures do not exceed 90° F. This dust is comparatively ineffective when air temperatures are below 70° F. A dust mixture containing 15 percent sulfur and 7 percent copper (expressed as metallic) such as basic copper sulfate or cuprous oxide satisfactorily controls the disease when temperatures are above or below 70° F. Iscothan and Ovotran are also highly effective for the control of the disease on cucumber, but zineb gives only fair control.

Resistant varieties of sulfur-sensitive muskmelon offer the best bet for commercial production of melons when powdery mildew is present. I. C. Jagger and his associates at La Jolla, Calif., utilized resistance found in wild muskmelon from India to develop the varieties Powdery Mildew Resistant Cantaloup No. 45 and No. 50. Those varieties were found susceptible to a new race of the powdery mildew fungus.

Additional breeding work was undertaken by T. W. Whitaker and his associates at the same research station. It yielded Powdery Mildew Resistant Cantaloup No. 5, No. 6, and No. 7. They are not immune to races 1 and 2 of the fungus prevalent in the Southwest, but are resistant and productive. Other muskmelon material with still greater resistance is used in breeding work for new and improved lines and as a bulwark against the eventuality that additional races of the powdery mildew fungus may appear. Georgia 47 has resistance not only to powdery mildew but to downy mildew as well and moderate resistance to aphids.

VIRUS DISEASES are numerous and widespread throughout the United States. They are responsible for substantial crop losses, especially in cucumber and muskmelon and occasionally in squash and watermelon.

Cucumber plants infected with mosaic display a mottled leaf pattern of yellow and green areas, which are most conspicuous in the young terminal leaves of the vine. The mosaic usually becomes less marked as the plants grow older and become dwarfed. Fruits on the infected vines are mottled in a green and yellow pattern and become distorted and malformed. Cucumber mosaic is sometimes referred to as white pickle disease because fruits on severely infected vines lose practically all their normal green color and turn almost completely white, with wartlike malformations.

Cucumber mosaic is caused by a group of strains of a virus that can infect not only a number of cucurbits but also a wide variety of agricultural and ornamental plants and a large number of annual and perennial weeds. The cucumber mosaic virus is also the causal agent of a mosaic of bean, pea, spinach, and sugar beet, southern celery mosaic, and "shoe-string" of tomato, to name only a few.

The cucumber mosaic virus is rarely seed-transmitted in cucumber, but some strains are carried by muskmelon seed. The virus is known to overwinter in a number of perennial hosts in fields and gardens. It is readily transmitted from its plant source to cucumber by means of aphids, primarily the melon and green peach aphids.

Control of the disease through eradication of weed host plants is impracticable because of the large variety of plants that harbor the virus. Control of the insect vectors by currently available insecticides fails to control the disease because, even though the insect population is reduced to a level wherein the insect is no longer considered a pest, enough carriers remain to permit spread of the virus. The time required for the kill of a vector is usually long enough to permit the insect to feed, introduce the virus, and infect the plant before it is killed.

Development of resistant cucumbers offers the best means of control. The Ohio Agricultural Experiment Station has developed a pickling variety, MR 17, and the New York (Cornell) Agricultural Experiment Station has introduced York state Pickling and Niagara. Early Surecrop Hybrid and Burpee Hybrid have been developed by commercial seed companies.

Squash is sometimes affected with mosaic, which causes a yellow-green mottle, crumpling, and considerable leaf distortion. The leaves of severely infected plants often are reduced to no more than the veins and narrow strips of attendant leaf tissue. Infected fruits are irregular in shape and distorted by numerous raised, circular areas, which color prematurely. Seed taken from infected fruits is usually light, poorly filled, and deformed in comparison with seed from healthy fruits.

The squash mosaic virus produces typical disease symptoms in gourd, muskmelon, and pumpkin, but infects very few other plants except a few perennial cucurbitaceous weeds such as *Cucurbita foetidissima* and *C. palmata*. The virus can infect cucumber but rarely produces any marked pattern other than a faint yellowing about the veins of the leaves. The virus is seed-transmitted in gourd, muskmelon, pumpkin, squash, and in the two *Cucurbita* species mentioned before, but not in cucumber. The transmission in muskmelon and squash ranges from none to 3.4, and is usually 0.24 percent. The poorly filled, deformed seed carry a notably higher percentage of the virus than normal seed. Although originally the virus was believed to be transmitted by both aphids and cucumber beetles, it is now thought to be transmitted only by beetles.

Some relief from squash mosaic may be obtained by planting virus-free seed. Although that does not assure freedom from the disease, mosaic does not usually become serious enough to reduce yields until late in the growing season after the bulk of the crop is harvested and when the virus is introduced from other sources by migrating cucumber beetles.

Seedsmen can remove a fairly large proportion of virus-infected seed by not harvesting infected fruits and by careful cleaning to remove light, deformed seeds, which are known to be the principal seed source.

Eradication of the few weeds known to overwinter the virus will effectively reduce outside sources of squash mosaic. New plantings of squash should not be sown adjacent to old plantings, which may be reservoirs of the virus.

Muskmelon mosaic is another disease caused by a virus. Leaves of infected plants show a conspicuous dark-green banding about the larger veins. Later leaves usually do not show vein banding but display a severe to mild yellow and green mottle. The margins of many leaves are serrated. Some leaves may become distorted and curled. Flowers on infected plants are often deformed and generally fail to set. The pollen grains are irregular in shape and fail to germinate normally. Only rarely are there mild mosaic patterns on immature fruits. The symptom normally disappears with the development of the normal fruit net, but sometimes the virus appears to inhibit normal netting. The total soluble solids of infected fruits are lower than normal.

The muskmelon mosaic virus infects only cucurbits. It causes typical mosaic symptoms on gherkin, pumpkin, and squash and only a faint mottle on cucumber. The virus is commonly seed-transmitted, ranging from more than 95 percent in fresh seed to less than 5 percent in seed 3 years old. It has been recovered from seed stored 5 years. It is readily transmitted by aphids.

Although the planting of virus-free muskmelon seed will assure freedom from the disease in young plantings, it fails to assure continued freedom from infection as the plants mature when grown in the vicinity of other sources of the virus.

Muskmelons grown in the Southwest frequently are affected by mosaic caused by all three of the viruses we described and by a complexity of strains. Usually one virus is predominant over the others. Symptoms may vary somewhat from year to year depending on the particular virus, but the similarity of the symptoms produced by the several viruses is such that they cannot be readily distinguished in muskmelon. Crop losses due to the reduction of foliage and exposure of fruits (so that many are sunburned) usually are great. A fairly large number of the fruits fail to develop a satisfactory net and are discarded; others appear normal but are of inferior quality.

Mosaic in muskmelon has been observed in the Imperial Valley of California for many years, but not until 1946 did the disease appear in epiphytotic form. Since then it has been of considerable economic importance.

Attempts to control mosaic of muskmelon through control of insect vectors by airplane application of DDT, parathion, benzene hexachloride, and nicotine were unsuccessful.

R. C. Dickson and his associates determined that the causal viruses were spread principally by transient populations of aphids, chiefly the green peach aphid, which did not originate from melons but came mostly from sugar beets and weeds and moved across the melon fields in great swarms. The aphids usually fed for less than a minute on the melon plant and moved on in short flights to feed on a large number of plants. Such a feeding pattern is efficient in distributing the viruses and allows a large increase in the low initial incidence of the disease on weeds, escaped and cultivated melons, and squash.

In the absence of methods for reducing aphid populations at their source, intensive efforts are being made to develop muskmelons resistant to the several causal viruses.

FRUIT ROTS of cucurbits occur in the field, in transit, in storage, and in market. Many of the decays observed on harvested produce originate from infections initiated while the fruits were maturing upon the plant. For a discussion of some of these disorders, the reader is referred to our earlier discussion of angular leaf spot (also known as bacterial spot of cucumber); anthracnose, the most serious fruit decay of muskmelon, squash, and watermelon; fusarium root rot, also a rot of gourd, pumpkin, and squash fruit; and scab (sometimes referred to as cladosporium rot), a fruit rot of cucumber and muskmelon.

Fusarium rot of muskmelon and pumpkin is an important market disease. Many small, scattered lesions are found on the surface of infected fruits which are tan to light brown and often difficult to separate from healthy tissue. Later the spots become sunken, more extensive, and covered by a white or pink growth of the fungus. Infections are usually confined to the rind but may sometimes extend into the flesh and seed cavity. The seeds then appear clumped and embedded in the fungus mycelial mat. The disease is caused by *Fusarium moniliforme*, *F. roseum*, and *F. solani*. Those fungi can enter the fruit only through ruptures in the skin. The common occurrence of the rot on ripe muskmelons is associated with appearance of minute rifts and abrasions on the surface, many of which result from handling practices.

Fusarium rot can be fairly well controlled by reducing the frequency of handling muskmelons, shipping under refrigeration at about 45° F., and marketing promptly.

Rhizopus soft rot may affect all cucurbits but is of most importance on muskmelon, pumpkin, and squash. The disease appears first as soft, water-soaked spots on the rind. As the affected area increases in size, it becomes soft, sunken, and easily broken. The fungus *Rhizopus* appears after the skin has been broken and develops a profuse mold growth when the temperature ranges from 80° to 90°. Decay may be controlled by avoiding skin ruptures, shipping under refrigeration at 40° to 45°, and by prompt disposal of ripe fruit.

Soft rot may also be caused by bacteria, such as *Erwinia aroideae* and *E. carotovora*, which usually gain entrance through breaks in the skin of fruits and cause a putrid collapse of tissue. Bacterial soft rots are not common and are usually unimportant. Soft rot due to fungus infections are more common and of economic importance. Perhaps the most important of the fungal decays are those caused by *Phytophthora* and *Pythium*.

Phytophthora rot occurs naturally on muskmelon and watermelon. It affects cucumber and squash by artificial inoculation. The diseased tissue is first water-soaked, then turns brown, and becomes soft; the result is a sunken and wrinkled lesion. Infections generally occur in the field and are caused by *Phytophthora capsici*, *P. drechsleri*, and *P. parasitica*. Decay of fruit can be arrested by shipping under refrigeration at 45°.

Pythium rot is similar to phytophthora rot. It naturally affects muskmelon, watermelon, cucumber, pumpkin, and squash. Diseased cucumber and squash fruits are conspicuously water-soaked; the tissue is soft and flaccid and ruptures readily under pressure. In cucumber and squash the disease is sometimes referred to as leak. It is incited by *Pythium aphanidermatum* during hot weather and by *P. irregulare* and *P. ultimum* in cooler weather. The fungi infect fruits in the field and serve as a source of further infections during transit and storage. Quite often a luxuriant white fungus growth covers the affected tissue. Losses may be reduced by careful sorting of field-picked fruit, shipping under refrigeration at 45° to 50°, and rapid distribution to retail market.

Muskmelon, pumpkin, and watermelon fruits affected by pythium rot are water-soaked and soft, but are also discolored a light tan to brown. As the infections increase, the lesions become sunken and wrinkled, breaking open easily and discharging quantities of watery fluid. Primary infections are initiated in the field, but secondary infections result from contact of healthy fruits with diseased ones. The rot in muskmelon is usually incited by *Pythium aphanidermatum* and *P. ultimum;* in pumpkin by *P. ultimum;* and in watermelon by *P. acanthicum*, *P. myriotylum*, and *P. periplocum*. Careful sorting of fruit to exclude infected merchandise in the packed container and shipping under refrigeration at 45° to 50° will reduce transit losses.

Stem-end rot of watermelon, induced by the fungus *Diplodia natalensis*, is an important disease and is responsible for a high percentage of the watermelons lost in transit. The fungus infects the stem end of the fruit following its cutting from the vine. The fungus does not infect fruits other than through cuts or other wounds. Infected tissues turn brown and shrivel, and the fungus may produce pycnidia and a grayish-white mycelium on the fruit surface. The disease develops most rapidly between 85° and 90°. Prompt coating of the freshly made stem cut with bordeaux paste containing no less than 6 percent copper sulfate prevents its development. Field cutters should be careful to avoid contaminating the cutting knife by faulty harvest of an infected fruit. All harvesting and packing equipment should be washed down thoroughly each day and disinfected with phenol or formaldehyde. Shipment of watermelon at 50° will deter development of the disease in transit and assure satisfactory arrival condition. The disease sometimes affects muskmelon; it is not restricted to stem end but occurs over the entire fruit surface, making surface sterilization impracticable. Temperature control and careful field selection offer some relief from losses.

JOHN T. MIDDLETON *is associate plant pathologist, University of California, Riverside. He holds degrees from the University of California and the University of Missouri. He has investigated vegetable crop diseases, especially root rots and their control and the biology of root-rotting fungi.*

GUY WESTON BOHN *is a pathologist in the Bureau of Plant Industry, Soils, and Agricultural Engineering at the United States Horticultural Field Station, La Jolla, Calif. He has conducted research on the causes and control of diseases of crop plants and on the breeding of vegetable crop plants for disease resistance and other economic characters.*

201500°—53——33

Developing Healthier Vegetables

H. Rex Thomas, W. J. Zaumeyer

Work progresses steadily toward the important goal of breeding vegetables that can withstand the ravages of disease. How close are we to it?

The latest edition of the vegetable seed catalog of one company lists more than one-half of the varieties of pea, approximately one-third of the varieties of watermelon, and one-fourth of the varieties of tomato and cabbage as resistant to one or more diseases. The proportion would be higher if all of the new varieties released within the past few years were included. That is an excellent record for an endeavor that had barely started in this country before 1900.

What are some of the problems facing us today and how are we prepared to meet them? Emphasis currently is directed toward incorporating higher degrees of resistance into a wider range of varieties and resistance to several diseases—multiple resistance—within one variety. Superior quality, resistance to insects, wide adaptation, high nutritive value, and good qualities of processing, shipping, and storage also are essential.

The need for multiple resistance is becoming more and more important. It is no longer enough to have varieties resistant to only the diseases present in the areas where the crop is grown for market or processing. They must also be resistant to the diseases in the seed-producing areas. For example, most of the seed of snap beans is produced in the drier sections of Idaho and California, where the bacterial blights and anthracnose rarely occur. In parts of Idaho, however, the curly top virus is destructive, and resistance to it is necessary for the safe production of the seed crop, even though the virus does not occur in the southern and eastern production areas of the United States where snap beans are grown most extensively for market and processing.

Progress in multiple resistance has already been demonstrated. The Southland tomato, introduced by the Department's Southeastern Vegetable Breeding Laboratory at Charleston, S. C., possesses high resistance to collar rot and fusarium wilt and moderate resistance to early blight and one race of late blight. The Hawaii Agricultural Experiment Station has developed and introduced several varieties of tomato that resist the spotted wilt, fusarium wilt, and gray leaf spot. The rapidity with which the varieties were developed was the result of using new, streamlined methods of eliminating susceptible plants in the seedling stage. The Hawaiian workers made crosses between varieties that would produce progeny with resistance to the three diseases mentioned above and would also add good horticultural characters.

When the crossing program has progressed far enough for disease testing, the seeds are planted in gallon cans filled with sterile soil. After 12 to 15 days, the seedlings are sprayed with a suspension of gray leaf spot spores and placed in a humidity chamber for 2 days to allow the spores to germinate and infect the leaf. Within 2 to 3 days after the plants are removed from the humidity chamber, the plants with infected cotyledons—seed leaves—are discarded. A high correlation between cotyledon infection and mature plant resistance had previously been determined. The seedlings are allowed to harden off for 4 to 8 days. They are removed from the gallon can and the roots are dipped into fusarium inoculum previously produced in the laboratory. A few seedlings are then transplanted again to gallon cans, which are placed in the spotted wilt nursery, where virus-infected host plants are grown and a large population of thrips is maintained as a carrier for the virus. After 3 to 4 weeks, the plants susceptible to spotted wilt and fusarium wilt are removed. Notes on horticultural characters—earliness, growth habit, vigor, type of flowering—are evaluated. The most promising plants are finally transplanted to the field to mature. During this period further eliminations for poor horticultural type are made. With this procedure many thousands of plants can be tested and the few resistant and promising types selected with the minimum of effort, space, and expense.

Plant breeders are utilizing the greenhouse as a substitute for field plots for testing the disease resistance of the young hybrid seedlings because the soil, temperature, nutrition, and moisture can be controlled in a manner most favorable for the development of disease. As many as four or five generations a year can often be tested where only one could be tested in the field.

Improved pathological techniques that insure consistent, severe disease tests provide the means for separating the hybrids with high resistance from those with only low or moderate resistance. Marglobe tomato is moderately resistant to fusarium wilt and will often stand up in infested field plots. In badly infested greenhouse soil, however, it is killed in the seedling stage, but a highly resistant variety like Pan America survives. The high resistance in Pan America, which was derived from a tomato species introduced from South America, has been included in most of the new tomato varieties developed since 1947.

Two types of resistance to fusarium yellows, a serious disease of cabbage in the warmer climates, occur in cabbage. The higher type of resistance is effective at both high and low temperatures. The other type is active only at low temperatures. To obtain hybrid cabbage seedlings with the high degree of resistance, they are grown in infested soil at 75° F. for 2 to 3 weeks. All seedlings with no resistance or only a low degree of resistance are eliminated.

For many diseases no resistance has yet been found. The search continues. New, valuable sources of resistance are continuously being made available because of an extensive screening of large collections of vegetable seeds made in foreign countries by the Department of Agriculture and other organizations.

Often the plant breeder must settle for a moderate degree of resistance to a disease. If a foliage disease is involved, the addition of a spray or dust schedule may permit the successful culture of the crop that otherwise might be impossible if a susceptible variety were grown.

It is important that the degree of resistance and the number of diseases to which the variety is resistant be fully explained when it is released. If additional chemical control is necessary this should be mentioned. Any particular susceptibility to other diseases should be noted. A plant breeder's enthusiasm should not overbalance his judgment as to the limitations of his new creation.

How difficult is it to develop an acceptable disease-resistant variety once a source of resistance has been found? Sometimes it is easy. Resistance may be found within individual plants of a commercial variety. In that way were wilt resistance in peas and yellows resistance in cabbage found.

Sometimes an off-type resistant plant may be found in a commercial variety. Resistance to common bean mosaic virus was found in an off-type Stringless Green Refugee plant. The selection, named Corbett Refugee, was of poor commercial type. Crosses to Stringless Green Refugee were necessary to improve the quality. But even that was relatively easy, as both plants had stringless pods and similar habit of growth.

Compare this with the development of the anthracnose-resistant Congo watermelon. No commercial varieties resistant to anthracnose could be found. A poor-quality melon, supplied by a missionary in South Africa, had to be used. Crosses were made between it and the commercial variety Iowa Belle. After several generations, a promising selection was crossed to another commercial variety, Garrison. After several generations of selections of that, the Congo variety was produced.

When the plant breeder cannot find disease resistance within a species he must turn to a related species. Crosses between species—interspecific—have been used successfully in potatoes to obtain resistance to late blight and in tomatoes for resistance to fusarium wilt and leaf mold.

Sometimes the crosses are easily made. More often they are difficult, as when a cross was attempted between tomato and the related species *Lycopersicon peruvianum*, which is resistant to tobacco mosaic virus and nematodes. Some of the newer techniques, however, made the cross possible and enough hybrid plants were obtained to give hope of controlling these two serious diseases of tomatoes.

Some breeders have used colchicine, a narcotic alkaloid chemically related to morphine and codeine, to double the number of the chromosomes, the small bodies in the cell that contain the genes that control the development of inherited characters. That can be done by soaking the tomato seed for a short time before planting or by applying a dilute solution on the growing tip of the plant. If the latter method is followed, only the new growth on the treated stem will have the double number of chromosomes. When the flowers on the treated plants are used to cross with *L. peruvianum*, fertile seed develop.

Another approach to the problem has been embryo culture. When the cross between plants in which the chromosomes have not been doubled is made, normal fruit (but not seed) development occurs. About 30 to 40 days after pollination the tissue around the young developing embryo collapses. Shortly after, the embryo dies. Occasionally a few immature seeds have an embryo sufficiently developed to grow when aseptically removed from the seed and transferred to a nutrient medium and cultured at a warm temperature. The young seedlings are planted in soil later and handled in the routine manner.

Other techniques have aided vegetable hybridization. Some plants will flower only in a short day. Others will flower only in a long day. We now retard or induce flowering at will by controlling the length of day, either by using dark curtains to shorten the day or a few minutes of light in the middle of the night to lengthen the day. Growth regulators have been applied to the pedicels of flowers to aid in securing set of fruit and seed. Flies have been used to make controlled pollination in onions and carrots, thus saving the plant breeder many hours of work. The control of temperature, moisture, and nutrition have aided in flowering and fruit set.

Because of the expense involved, most of the disease-resistant varieties of vegetables are developed by public-supported State and Federal agencies or large seed companies. The search for a source of resistance may take years of testing and involve many thousands of plants.

For more than 20 years breeders have been striving to develop a tomato resistant to the curly top virus. Few private companies could have financed such a program. Yet the acute need for solving this as well as other difficult problems remains. Well-equipped laboratories, greenhouses, and field plots must be available. Often a particular disease can be studied only in a particular locality, and facilities must be provided in that area if they do not already exist. Besides the plant breeders, other trained specialists are needed for the work, among them pathologists to help

eliminate susceptible plants, cytologists to study the chromosome behavior, and chemists to make analyses of the content of vitamins, sugar, and fiber.

The plant breeder may or may not have a great deal of formal training. He may have specialized in horticulture and agronomy, pathology, plant breeding, or genetics. To be successful he must like his work and know the crop or crops with which he is working. The new disease-resistant variety he develops must be equal to or better in all respects than the commercial variety which it is to replace. Disease resistance itself has seldom been enough to induce the grower to plant a variety of poor quality.

The large number of agencies and individuals involved in plant breeding has necessitated some measure of coordination. Establishment of the national potato-breeding program, the national onion-breeding program, and the Southeastern Vegetable Breeding Laboratory, along with the efforts of the professional societies and other groups of workers in cataloging and exchanging available sources of resistance, have been of major importance. The rapid increase and introduction of new varieties developed by private, State, and Federal workers is due to the close cooperation of the seed companies. They have been very generous in increasing, evaluating, and maintaining new varieties at little or no cost to the State or Federal agencies.

How well new resistant varieties are accepted by growers is illustrated by the new potato varieties released since 1932. They account for approximately 50 percent of all the certified seed grown in 1951. The mosaic-resistant Topcrop bean was released to the seed trade for increase in 1947 and to the public in 1950; in 1952 it ranked third in the volume of bush snap bean seed produced. Congo watermelon, released in 1950, was grown on 6,000 acres that year and on more than 40,000 acres in 1951. How long some resistant varieties persist is illustrated by the rust-resistant Mary Washington asparagus. It was introduced about 40 years ago, but it is still by far the most popular variety grown. The moderately wilt-resistant Rutgers tomato was introduced in 1934, but in 1951 approximately 50 percent of all the tomato seed raised in this country was Rutgers.

Some of the accomplishments in developing resistant vegetable varieties, together with some hint of things to come, are presented here.

ASPARAGUS

RUST (caused by *Puccinia asparagi*) was first noticed in the United States in 1896. By 1902 it had become serious throughout our commercial asparagus-growing sections. In 1906 an intensive breeding program was initiated, and by 1919 the two resistant varieties, Mary Washington and Martha Washington, had practically replaced the other varieties. Their resistance was obtained from a male plant of unknown parentage and two female plants selected from the Reading Giant variety from England. Mary Washington is still the most widely grown variety of asparagus, although current strains have been reported somewhat less resistant to rust in the East than the original strain.

BEAN AND LIMA BEAN

ANTHRACNOSE (caused by *Colletotrichum lindemuthianum*) before 1920 was possibly the most important disease of beans. The wide use now of western-grown seed has reduced it to a minor position. About 1901 an anthracnose-resistant selection was made in a badly diseased field of red kidney bean in New York. Later tests revealed that the progeny of the selection resisted the two races of the organism known at that time. In 1915 the selection, described as Wells Red Kidney, was used as a parent in developing a resistant strain of White Marrow. Because of the relative unimportance of the disease at present,

little emphasis is directed toward developing anthracnose-resistant varieties in the United States.

POWDERY MILDEW (caused by *Erysiphe polygoni*) often attacks the fall crops of beans in the Southern States and also is serious in bean crops along the Pacific coast. Differences in varietal resistance have been observed. Frequently varieties resistant to the race of the fungus that occurs in one location may be susceptible in other places to different races of the organism. Some of the recent varieties listed as being resistant to certain races of powdery mildew are Contender, Florida Belle, Logan, Wade, Fullgreen, Ranger, Tenderlong 15, and Flight.

RUST (caused by *Uromyces phaseoli typica*) attacks pole beans particularly. Most of the efforts to obtain resistance have been with them. The existence of more than 30 races of rust makes it difficult if not impracticable to breed varieties resistant to all of them. One of the parents in a cross may be resistant to all the races known at the time the cross was made, and yet a variety developed from it may be susceptible to races present 10 years later when the new variety is ready for release. Numerous resistant varieties have been introduced. Some are of use in only a limited area. The development of new resistant pole varieties is being carried on in several Southern and Western States. Rust is not often a serious problem in growing bush snap beans and therefore little effort has been made to develop rust-resistant bush varieties.

Some of the pole snap beans resistant to certain races of rust are Coaster, Kentucky Wonder Rust Resistant Brown Seeded, Kentucky Wonder Wax, Morse Pole No. 191, Potomac, Rialto, Stringless Blue Lakes Nos. 228 and 231, and U. S. No. 4 Kentucky Wonder.

HALO BLIGHT (caused by *Pseudomonas phaseolicola*) is often serious on beans when the environment is favorable for its development. Many of our important field bean varieties have acceptable field resistance to halo blight. One, Great Northern, has been used as a source of resistance by several workers in developing resistant snap beans. It was one of the parents of Fullgreen, a bush snap bean with good field resistance to halo blight. Tenderlong 15 has also been reported to have some tolerance to halo blight.

VIRUS DISEASES. The most important virus disease of beans is common mosaic, but with the rapid development of resistant varieties it may soon be of minor importance. Resistance to this mosaic in most of the new bush varieties was derived from Corbett Refuge, a resistant selection made in 1931 from the susceptible Stringless Green Refugee variety, but a poor commercial type. The first-developed resistant varieties were U. S. No. 5, Wisconsin, and Idaho Refuges. All of the new Refugee varieties are resistant. Some of the new resistant bush snap beans are Topcrop, Wade, Tenderlong 15, Improved New Stringless, Ranger, Contender, Idagreen, Improved Brittle Wax, and Pure Gold Wax. Many of the pole varieties such as Kentucky Wonder, most of the Blue Lake strains, and Ideal Market are resistant to common bean mosaic.

Curly top frequently occurs on beans grown in Utah, Idaho, Washington, Oregon, and California. From a cross made in 1936 between the Burtner variety, a white pea bean type, and Blue Lake, the resistant snap bean Pioneer was released in 1943. Pioneer is not grown commercially but is used in home gardens in areas where curly top is severe. Two resistant strains of Blue Lake beans have been developed. The resistant Red Mexican variety has also been used and crosses of it with commercial snap bean varieties have given some promising resistant green and wax-podded snap bean types which have not been released.

Southern bean mosaic and pod mottle viruses have been reported as causing serious damage on fall-grown crops of snap beans in southern Illinois. Susceptible varieties affected with pod mottle sometimes have severely mottled pods at Charleston, S. C. Most of the new varieties resistant to common mosaic virus are resistant also to this virus. Most pole bean varieties are resistant to southern bean mosaic virus. Low's Champion, Ranger, Corbett Refuge, strains of Idaho Refuge, and Tennessee Green Pod are the only bush snap bean varieties known to be resistant to this virus. Several groups of breeders are developing promising new resistant bush snap beans.

DOWNY MILDEW (caused by *Phytophthora phaseoli*) has seriously damaged lima beans in the North Atlantic States since 1945. Resistance was found in some selections from India, Guatemala, southeastern United States, and California. None was acceptable commercially, but crosses were made between them and several small- and large-seeded market and processing types. It will be several years before resistant commercial types are available.

ROOT KNOT, to which beans are very susceptible, is caused by certain nematodes (*Meloidogyne* species). The disease is prevalent in the Southern States on light, sandy soils. Two resistant selections of pole beans have been released as Alabama Pole No. 1 and Alabama Pole No. 2. Spartan and State are resistant half-runner types.

Some lima beans collected from the Hopi Indians and possessing high resistance to nematodes have been crossed with commercial varieties. Some promising highly resistant green-cotyledon baby lima types may be available for distribution within a few years. Bixby, released in 1951, is a bush baby lima somewhat tolerant to nematodes.

CELERY

EARLY BLIGHT is caused by *Cercospora apii* and LATE BLIGHT by *Septoria apii-graveolentis*. In Massachusetts in 1936 a row of celery plants grown from a seed sample from Denmark was more resistant to early blight than the others. The plants were not of an acceptable quality, and a cross was made with Golden Self Blanching, a leading commercial variety. Additional crosses were made later with Cornell 19 and Cornell 6. A selection from this final cross resistant to early blight, late blight, and fusarium yellows was introduced as Emerson Pascal.

FUSARIUM YELLOWS (caused by *Fusarium oxysporum* f. *apii*) became serious in Michigan between 1912 and 1919. A resistant selection from a dwarf strain of Golden Self Blanching was made in 1919, and seed was made available to the growers in 1926. In 1933 the variety Michigan Golden, derived from a resistant survivor in a susceptible variety of the Golden Plume group, was released. Some of the other resistant varieties are Florida Golden, Cornell 6, Cornell 19, and Michigan State Green Golden. The green varieties generally are resistant. The resistance in Cornell 6 and Cornell 19 was obtained by crossing a green with a yellow type.

CRUCIFEROUS CROPS

YELLOWS (caused by *Fusarium oxysporum* f. *conglutinans*) is especially serious on cabbage in the warm climates, but it is not serious in the extreme northern sections of the United States or along the northern Pacific coast. Varieties of cauliflower, broccoli, and brussels sprouts are resistant to yellows. Kohlrabi, kale, and most of the older varieties of cabbage generally are very susceptible to the disease. In 1910 resistant plants were selected in several diseased cabbage fields in Wisconsin. From those selections the variety Wisconsin Hollander was released in 1916 and Wisconsin All Seasons in 1920. In later genetic studies on the inheritance of yellows resistance in cabbage, it was shown that there are two types of resistance, now referred to as "A" and "B." Type A resistance is effective at high and low temperatures, while plants with only type B resistance become susceptible at high temperature. Wis-

consin Hollander was found to have type B resistance; about 20 percent of Wisconsin All Seasons plants had type A resistance and 80 percent had type B. Most of the present fusarium-resistant varieties now carry type A resistance. Resistant varieties of all the important market types of cabbage have been developed.

CLUBROOT is caused by *Plasmodiophora brassicae*. No varieties of cabbage, cauliflower, broccoli, kohlrabi, brussels sprouts, or collards now available commercially are resistant to clubroot. Most of the rutabaga varieties grown in the United States and many turnips are highly resistant. The garden varieties of kale are susceptible, but some of the forage varieties are resistant. Kale-cabbage hybrid rogues were found in 1941 in a Wisconsin cabbage field. From them resistant plants were obtained, which, when crossed to a commercial cabbage variety, yielded some promising resistant types of cabbage. Yellows resistance has been added to many of the types. A line of cabbage of the Wisconsin Ballhead type resistant to both clubroot and yellows was ready for increase, before introduction, in 1952.

MOSAIC has been serious on the cabbage seed crop in the Pacific Northwest. In the Middle West and Pacific Northwest cabbage mosaic is caused by two viruses. Several selections within Wisconsin All Seasons variety were found highly resistant to mosaic caused by a strain of turnip virus A and a strain of cauliflower virus 1. One was released in 1947 as Improved Wisconsin All Seasons cabbage. It was the first variety to be bred with a high degree of resistance to mosaic. Highly resistant lines have also been developed by selection within Wisconsin Ballhead and Wisconsin Hollander, lines that are also resistant to fusarium yellows.

CUCUMBER

ANTHRACNOSE is caused by *Colletotrichum lagenarium*. Resistance to it has been found in several importations from India. They are very late types and produce fruits with black spines. Crosses have been made to incorporate resistance to both anthracnose and downy mildew into a slicing variety.

DOWNY MILDEW (caused by *Pseudoperonospora cubenis*) has been serious along the Atlantic seaboard. All the commercial American varieties were found susceptible to it. A Chinese variety introduced into Puerto Rico from China and another received in Louisiana from Bangalore, India, were found to be highly resistant. From the Chinese variety, Puerto Rico 39 and Puerto Rico 40 were developed. They are resistant to the races of downy mildew found in Puerto Rico. Resistant varieties (including hybrids) recently developed in the United States are Palmetto, Santee, and Surecrop. When their vines become old and weakened, infection occurs on the older leaves, but nevertheless they can produce a crop while other commercial varieties are killed. Downy mildew infection was observed on Palmetto in 1950 and 1951. Perhaps a new race of downy mildew has developed. The combination of the now partially resistant Palmetto in conjunction with a fungicide has given satisfactory control which has not been possible in certain areas when the susceptible commercial varieties were planted.

SCAB is caused by *Cladosporium cucumerinum*. Resistance to scab was found in the late-maturing, long-fruiting, slicing varieties Longfellow and Windermoor Wonder. The resistant variety Maine No. 2 was released in 1939 for use in home gardens. It was selected after crossing Boston Pickling with a scab-resistant inbred line obtained from a cross of Longfellow x Davis Perfect. It has been used as a resistant parent in developing improved resistant pickling and slicing types. In 1947 the scab-resistant slicing variety Highmoor was released. Scab-resistant National Pickling types Wisconsin SR 6 and Wisconsin SR 7 have been released.

MOSAIC was a problem until 1927, when the variety Chinese Long was observed to be highly resistant to common cucumber mosaic virus. Later Tokyo Long Green also was found to be resistant. These varieties have been extensively used as a resistant parent in hybridization. A number of mosaic-resistant varieties, such as Ohio MR 17, Shamrock, Niagara, Surecrop, Yorkstate Pickling, Puerto Rico 10, and Puerto Rico 27, are now available.

EGGPLANT

PHOMOPSIS BLIGHT AND FRUIT ROT (caused by *Phomopsis vexans*) attacks the plants just above the ground level, causing stem cankers and fruit rot. In 1942 a resistant variety from India was crossed with Fort Myers Market. Two resistant varieties originating from this cross, Florida Beauty and Florida Market, have been introduced.

BACTERIAL WILT is caused by *Pseudomonas solanacearum*. In Puerto Rico a highly wilt-resistant noncommercial variety was found in gardens and crossed with several commercial varieties. Seed of two resistant varieties, Puerto Rico Beauty and E. 12, were made available in 1939.

LETTUCE

DOWNY MILDEW (caused by *Bremia lactucae*) is serious in the coastal lettuce-growing areas of California. A resistant European variety was crossed with several strains of the New York variety from which desirable progeny, resistant to the four known races of downy mildew, were selected and released. Later a new physiologic race of mildew appeared; all of the previously resistant varieties were susceptible to it. Factors for immunity from this race were found in *Lactuca serriola* and were incorporated in Imperial 410, which was released in 1945. New strains of mildew to which none of the varieties mentioned are resistant have appeared since then.

Bronze Beauty variety is highly tolerant to mosaic in that it stands up under field and greenhouse tests better than any of the varieties tested. A strain of lettuce tolerant to mosaic was obtained from progeny of a cross between Paris White and another European cos type. This was released to the trade in 1951 as Parris Island.

TIPBURN, a physiological disease, occurs during warm weather and causes necrosis in the marginal and submarginal parts of head leaves of lettuce. Great Lakes, "456," and Progress, of the present commercial varieties, are somewhat resistant. A much higher degree of resistance has been developed in an interspecific hybrid between *Lactuca virosa* and common lettuce, but no varieties have yet been released.

MUSKMELON

ALTERNARIA LEAF BLIGHT is caused by *Alternaria cucumerina*. Resistance to this fungus, which defoliates the plants and sometimes causes sunken spots on the fruit, was found in a selection of New Seed Breeders, a variety of the Hale Best type. It was released in 1944 as Purdue 44. Workers in the East, South, and Middle West have begun the task of developing resistant types, using Cuban Castilian and an importation from India as sources of resistance.

DOWNY MILDEW (caused by *Pseudoperonospora cubensis*), a destructive disease of muskmelons in the Atlantic and Gulf Coast States, defoliates the plants. Resistance to it was found in several foreign varieties and in a wild type growing in Texas. Texas Resistant No. 1, a shipping type released in 1945, was the first resistant variety developed. It was a selection out of a cross between the resistant West Indian melon Rocky Dew Green Flesh and New Seed Breeders variety, a variety of Hale Best type. It also is highly resistant to aphids. Riosweet is another downy mildew resistant variety, which is moderately resistant to aphids. Its resistance was obtained from a naturalized wild, small, inedible melon growing in Texas, which is orange yellow, smooth-skinned, and cucumberlike in flesh. The new Georgia 47 is resistant to powdery mildew, downy mildew, and aphids. Its resistance was obtained from a plant in a mixed lot of melon seed obtained from Canada. The seed had been increased by open pollination of plants grown from seed brought into Canada by settlers from Russia. The resistant selection was crossed and backcrossed with Hearts of Gold variety; after five generations of selection a resistant line was crossed with Smith's Perfect. Granite State is a resistant cantaloup developed primarily for the short growing season in the North. Another resistant variety is Smith's Perfect, which was originated in the West Indies.

FUSARIUM WILT (caused by *Fusarium oxysporum* f. *melonis*, a soil-borne fungus) is important in some sections of the Central and Eastern States. The Persian, Honey Dew, Honeyball, and Casaba varieties are relatively resistant but are not adapted to culture in those States. The resistant variety Golden Gopher was developed from crossing the resistant Honey Dew with the susceptible Golden Osage. Other resistant varieties are Iroquois and Delicious 51. Burrell Gem, Paul Rose, and Pollock 10–25 have fair tolerance. Promising resistant lines are being developed for shipping, local marketing, and home gardens.

POWDERY MILDEW (caused by *Erysiphe cichoracearum*) may occur wherever the crop is grown. It is serious in the Southwest. In 1925 it became destructive on muskmelons in the Imperial Valley of California. A year later work was under way to develop a resistant variety. In 1928 a resistant inedible type from India was found. A cross between it and Hale Best produced several promising lines, three of which were introduced from 1931 to 1933 and grown to a limited extent. In 1936 Powdery Mildew Resistant Cantaloup No. 45 was released. It was grown extensively because of its excellent qualities. A new race of mildew appeared in 1938 on all varieties, including No. 45. Another Indian type was found resistant to the new race; in 1942 Powdery Mildew Resistant Cantaloup No. 5 was released; in 1944 Powdery Mildew Resistant No. 6 and Powdery Mildew Resistant No. 7 were released. Resistant types of Honey Dew and Persian melons then were developed, but further improvement of them is needed.

MOSAIC virus causes dwarfed plants and small mottled fruits. In the Central and Eastern States the most common form of mosaic is caused by the ordinary cucumber mosaic virus. Resistance to it has been found in the Freeman Cucumber, White Melon, and Gin-Makuwa (Kin-Makuwa) varieties of the oriental pickling melon (*Cucumis melo* var. *conomon*). Crosses with this melon and certain types resistant to fusarium wilt have been made to develop lines resistant to both mosaic and fusarium wilt.

Although the ordinary cucumber mosaic virus is found in the Southwest, the greatest damage there is caused by certain other cucurbit virus strains. No immunity or high resistance to them is known, but some tolerance has been found among many Asiatic types and is being incorporated into a shipping variety for the Southwest.

ONION AND SHALLOT

DOWNY MILDEW (caused by *Peronospora destructor*) has been reported in most States, but in the North the damage is chiefly to the bulb crop. Losses in the seed crop in winter and spring in California are often heavy. Italian Red 13–53 was observed in 1934 to be resistant to downy mildew. It was crossed with Lord Howe Island, and a resistant selection named Calred was released in 1947. The seed stalks of Calred show a higher degree of resistance to downy mildew than do the leaves. As the seed stalks are highly resistant to the race of onion downy mildew present in central California, it is now possible to grow a seed crop in that region where downy

mildew is prevalent in epidemic form every year. The resistance in Calred is being incorporated in a Creole type.

PINK ROOT (caused by *Pyrenochaeta terrestris*) is an important soil-inhabiting disease in the onion-growing districts of California, Texas, New York, Ohio, Indiana, Michigan, and shallot-growing districts of Louisiana. Yellow Bermuda is one of the most resistant of the commercial varieties. The green bunching onion Nebuka (*Allium fistulosum*), leek (*A. porrum*), and chives (*A. schoenoprasum*) are highly resistant. The green onion variety Beltsville Bunching, released in 1945, is resistant. It is a cross between White Portugal, a common bulbing variety, and Nebuka, with the chromosomes doubled. Work has been started to incorporate the resistance to pink root of Nebuka into the shallot types. Yellow Bermuda and Crystal Wax have been used as sources of resistance to develop resistant commercial and hybrid onions.

SMUT (caused by *Urocystis cepulae*) attacks the bulbing onions, in none of which has resistance been found. The green bunching varieties Nebuka and Beltsville Bunching are resistant.

YELLOW DWARF is a virus disease. Selections immune to certain strains of it have been made in some of the commercial varieties of the Spanish type, such as White Sweet Spanish and Yellow Sweet Spanish, and also in Yellow Bermuda, Lord Howe Island, and Crystal Grano. Resistance to the yellow dwarf virus and to three other viruses known to attack onions is found in Nebuka and Beltsville Bunching. Shallots resistant to yellow dwarf have been selected among hybrids with double the normal chromosome number from a cross of shallot with Nebuka.

PEA

WILT is caused by *Fusarium oxysporum* f. *pisi* race 1. In 1924 it was observed that the variety Green Admiral remained healthy, while other varieties were infected with the wilt fungus.

Later tests showed that some other varieties were resistant. Because of intensive and successful breeding of peas by State and commercial agencies, most of the varieties listed in seed catalogs are wilt-resistant.

NEAR-WILT (caused by *F. oxysporum* f. *pisi* race 2) is another race of *Fusarium* that attacks most of the varieties resistant to race 1 of the fungus. Delwiche Commando is resistant to both races. The resistance in this variety was found in a single plant line from a cross between the varieties Admiral and Pride, neither of which is tolerant to near-wilt. Recently introduced is the canning variety New Era, which is resistant to both races of *Fusarium* and also to the mosaic disease of peas caused by yellow bean mosaic virus. Its parents were Wisconsin Perfection and a line similar to Delwiche Commando.

One strain of Perfection is tolerant to septoria leaf spot (caused by *Septoria pisi*). Other strains of the variety are resistant to several viruses, including yellow bean mosaic and common pea mosaic.

PEPPER

MOSAIC is due to several viruses, which cause mottling of the leaves and distortion of the fruit of garden pepper. Resistance to one of these, tobacco mosaic virus, has been found in several pungent varieties including Tabasco. In these varieties, infection is expressed by local necrosis on the inoculated leaves 2 or 3 days after inoculation, followed by dropping of the infected leaves, which prevents spread of the virus to other parts of the plant. This type of resistance is being incorporated into mosaic-susceptible sweet peppers. Rutgers World Beater No. 13, a new mosaic-resistant variety, was selected out of World Beater. In this variety the virus spreads slowly in the plant and a successful crop can be grown, while World Beater may be severely infected. Burlington is another resistant variety, released in 1945, which was developed from a cross of the Elephant Trunk and susceptible California Wonder. It resembles World Beater in plant habit and fruit type. Yolo Wonder, also resistant, originated from the same cross but resembles California Wonder in fruit type. The reaction of Yolo Wonder, Burlington, and Elephant Trunk to tobacco mosaic is identical but different from that of Tabasco. Several lines of a California Wonder type resistant to a pepper mosaic occurring in Puerto Rico have been selected out of a cross between the susceptible California Wonder and the Mexican hot pepper known as Cuaresmeno.

Several pepper varieties—Santanka, Anaheim, Chile, and Italian Pickling—have high degrees of natural resistance to nematode galling. Santanka has also been reported as resistant to bacterial spot. Tabasco was observed by workers in the South to be more resistant to southern blight (caused by *Sclerotium rolfsii*) than other varieties when infection occurred about the time of first blossom formation. This resistance is being introduced into pimento types.

POTATO

LATE BLIGHT, caused by *Phytophthora infestans*, is severe in cool, humid regions. Factors for resistance are recessive. They have been found in several varieties and kinds of potatoes. From crosses between susceptible lines the mildly resistant varieties Sebago and Sequoia have been selected. The latter has resistance to vine infection but not to tuber infection. A resistant German variety, Ackersegen, was used in developing the moderately resistant Calrose. Immunity from field infection occurs in *Solanum demissum*, which is related to our cultivated potato but lacks most of the characters of commercial importance. The resistant progenies of the crosses between it and cultivated varieties have thus far been of poor quality. It has been necessary to cross the best selections back to cultivated varieties many times to obtain promising seedling varieties with a high degree of late blight resistance. Workers at Cornell University have used *Solanum demissum* as a source of resistance in developing Empire, Placid, Virgil, Chenango, Ashworth, and Essex. The so-called "W" lines from Germany are believed to have derived their resistance to late blight from *S. demissum*. They have been used in this country as a source of resistance in developing the resistant varieties Kennebec, Pungo, and Cherokee.

VERTICILLIUM WILT (caused by *Verticillium albo-atrum*) is increasing in importance throughout the potato-growing areas of the United States. It has been present in Maine, in the South, in sections of California, and in rather large areas in Idaho and Washington. Field tests have shown that several varieties are resistant. Among them are Menominee, Saranac, and Sequoia.

RING ROT is caused by *Corynebacterium sepedonicum*. The varieties Friso and President from the Netherlands and a number of seedling varieties developed in the United States resist this bacterial disease. One of these seedlings, released as Teton, has shown a high degree of resistance in Maine and Wyoming. Saranac is also highly resistant. Promising seedling varieties with even a higher degree of resistance are being tested.

SCAB (caused by *Streptomyces scabies*) is the result of a soil-borne organism that infects the tubers and causes losses wherever potatoes are grown. Three resistant but poor-quality European varieties, Hindenburg, Jubel, and Ostragis, have been used in this country for hybridization. Crosses between these and American varieties have yielded some commercial lines possessing high resistance to scab. Some of the resistant varieties that have been released in this country are Menominee, Ontario, Cayuga, Seneca, Yampa, and Cherokee.

Extensive breeding work by several cooperating agencies is under way to develop resistance to the common virus diseases such as mild mosaic, latent mosaic, rugose mosaic, leaf roll and net necrosis. Virtual immunity from virus A, one of the component viruses causing mild mosaic, has been found in several breeding lines. Some lines can be infected by grafting, but the virus does not reach the tubers and the resulting crop is healthy. Immunity from virus X, one of the component viruses causing mild and rugose mosaic, is available as well as apparent immunity from the virus causing net necrosis of the tubers. A hypersensitive type of resistance to virus Y, one of the component viruses causing rugose mosaic, has been found. Chippewa, Earlaine, and Katahdin are immune to virus A. Katahdin is also resistant to virus X, virus Y, and the virus causing leaf roll. Warba, Sebago, Red Warba, Mohawk, Kennebec, Menominee, and Houma are resistant to virus A. Houma is also resistant to the leaf roll virus. Unnamed seedlings for test or breeding purposes are available with resistance to one or more of the following virus diseases: Mild mosaic, latent mosaic, rugose mosaic, leaf roll, net necrosis, and yellow dwarf.

SPINACH

DOWNY MILDEW is caused by *Peronospora effusa*. In a collection of spinach varieties made in Iran in 1940 two lines contained a mixture of plants resistant and susceptible to downy mildew. The resistant plants had small, thin leaves, which had a high content of oxalic acid, and the plants were early bolters. By crossing the resistant plants with the different popular commercial varieties, good progress is being made in developing resistant shipping, canning, and freezing types.

MOSAIC, OR BLIGHT, on spinach is due to several viruses, but the chief cause of spinach blight in this country is the cucumber virus. A wild spinach from Manchuria was found to be highly resistant. It was crossed with several commercial varieties, and a

Savoy type was selected and introduced about 1921 as Virginia Savoy. From a selection of a cross between Virginia Savoy and King of Denmark, mosaic-resistant Old Dominion was developed. It was released in 1930. These two varieties are widely grown today. Since then Domino and a strain of Virginia Savoy, resistant to fusarium wilt, have been released.

SQUASH AND PUMPKIN

CURLY TOP is a serious virus disease of many vegetables in some sections of the Pacific Northwest and the Mountain States. Marblehead, Long White Bush, and some strains of Vegetable Marrow squash have been found resistant.

Resistant varieties of pumpkin are Big Tom, Cushaw, Large Cheese, and Tennessee Sweet Potato.

SWEETPOTATO

FUSARIUM WILT (caused by *Fusarium oxysporum* f. *batatas*) attacks almost all of the present market varieties of sweetpotato. Goldrush, a new, resistant, orange-fleshed, moist type, was released in 1951. Its resistance was obtained from a seedling of a Cuban variety, Americano. A higher type of resistance is present in breeding lines from crosses of a selection from Tinian Island with commercial types. In a few years several resistant varieties of commercial value should be available.

TOMATO

EARLY BLIGHT (caused by *Alternaria solani*), a fungus disease, is often serious on tomato stems, foliage, and fruit. When infection occurs at the soil line, the lesion is known as collar rot. This phase of the disease is serious on tomato seedlings grown in the Southern States for transplanting in the North. Resistance to it was found in several wild types collected in South America, in some European forcing varieties, and in a few domestic varie-

ties. By using an English forcing variety as the source of resistance to collar rot and Pan America as the fusarium wilt resistant parent, crosses were made with several popular commercial varieties, and the variety Southland was developed. It possesses high resistance to collar rot and some resistance to early blight. The new Manahill variety is reported to be somewhat resistant to foliage infection.

FUSARIUM WILT (caused by *Fusarium oxysporum* f. *lycopersici*) is a soil-borne disease that is particularly serious in the Southern States. It is not surprising that the early work for disease resistance in tomato was directed toward finding a variety resistant to it. In 1910 selections were made by workers at the Tennessee Agricultural Experiment Station, and in 1912 Tennessee Red was released. In the same year Louisiana Wilt Resistant was distributed by the Louisiana Agricultural Experiment Station. Then followed many moderately resistant varieties. Two of them, Marglobe (1925) and Rutgers (1934), are still widely grown. If infection is severe, all these so-called resistant sorts may become diseased. The finding of near immunity in a wild small-fruited species known as the Red Currant tomato from Peru was a real advance in the development of truly wilt-resistant tomatoes. Since 1935 it has been crossed with a number of commercial types. Pan America, introduced in 1940, was the first variety to possess the new type of resistance. Since then other varieties with this resistance have been developed; among them are Cal 255, Sunray, Southland, Jefferson, Golden Sphere, Fortune, Ohio W. R. Globe, Boone, Tipton, Kokomo, Homestead, Tucker, Manahill, and Manasota. A race of *Fusarium* that attacks plants with resistance of the Red Currant type was reported in Ohio in 1945 and in Missouri in 1951. In both cases the infection was found on experimental plantings and no widespread infection in commercial plantings was reported.

LEAF MOLD (caused by *Cladosporium fulvum*), a leaf-spotting disease, is serious on tomatoes grown in greenhouses. Resistance to it was observed in Ohio in an off-type plant of the Globe variety. This plant was probably the result of a natural cross with Red Currant tomato, which was the only known resistant type. By using that species as a source of resistance, several varieties (Globelle, Bay State, and Vetomold) have been developed. Those varieties are not resistant to all four races of the fungus that have been identified, but work is progressing in developing resistance to them.

VERTICILLIUM WILT is caused by *Verticillium albo-atrum*. The Riverside variety, released in 1937, had tolerance to both verticillium wilt and fusarium wilt. It was a cross between Cal 2, moderately resistant to fusarium and verticillium wilts, and Marvana, resistant to only fusarium wilt. This variety and Essar, released in 1939, are adapted to areas in California where the wilts are a factor in production. In 1952 Simi was described as being adapted for trial in the Southern California coastal plain and valleys near the coast. Its resistance to verticillium and fusarium wilts was obtained from the Riverside variety. These varieties are susceptible when conditions are extremely favorable for the development of verticillium wilt. A high degree of resistance was found in a small-fruited strain of tomato called Peru Wild. Crosses between this and commercial types have yielded promising lines, two of which, Loran Blood and VR Moscow, are now available.

CURLY TOP is a virus disease, to which none of the domestic tomatoes are resistant. It is serious in some sections of the West. Three wild species, *Lycopersicon glandulosum*, *L. peruvianum* var. *dentatum*, and *L. peruvianum* var. *humifusum*, have an appreciable degree of resistance. Progress in the development of resistant commercial varieties has been slow because hybrids obtained by crossing these species with commercial types have shown much sterility

and some other undesirable features. Recently, promising selections which possess approximately the resistance of the wild species have been made among the progeny from the cross between *L. peruvianum* var. *dentatum* and commercial varieties.

MOSAIC: A line of *Lycopersicon hirsutum* with high resistance to ordinary tobacco mosaic virus, which causes a mosaic disease of tomato, has been crossed with several of the commercial tomato varieties. Some of the progeny have shown tolerance to the virus when artificially inoculated. Mostly, however, the resistance is expressed as a delay in symptom development.

SPOTTED WILT, a virus disease spread by thrips, is serious in parts of California and Oregon. Strains of the Red Currant tomato, of *Lycopersicon hirsutum*, of *L. peruvianum*, and of the variety German Sugar are resistant. Pearl Harbor, a resistant variety, was released in 1945. It was a selection from a cross of Bounty with an advanced breeding line received from California that had Red Currant as a resistant parent. It was followed by seven other varieties resistant to spotted wilt in Hawaii as well as to several other diseases. In California, Pearl Harbor and German Sugar are only moderately resistant, possibly because of the presence of a different strain of the virus. As yet, the high resistance in the Red Currant tomato has not been fully recovered in any of the progeny of crosses made with commercial varieties.

Immunity to the gray leaf spot fungus (*Stemphylium solani*) was found in the currant tomato. The Hawaii Agricultural Experiment Station has released seven varieties immune to the disease. They are named after the islands: Hawaii, Kauai, Lanai, Oahu, Maui, Molokai, and Niihau. Another resistant variety, developed in Florida, is Manahill.

Some resistance to septoria leaf spot (caused by *Septoria lycopersici*) occurs in *Lycopersicon hirsutum*, *L. peruvianum*, and the Australian variety Targinnie Red.

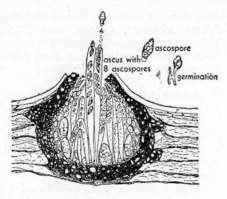

Diagrammatic section of a perithecium.

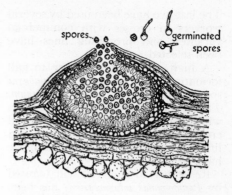

Diagrammatic section of a pycnidium.

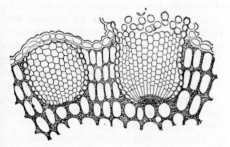

Cross-section of an aecium.

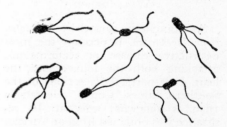

Bacillus carotovorus.

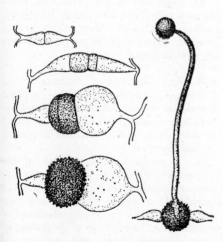

Zygospore formation.

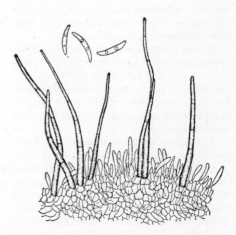

Section through an acervulus.

The last two have been used by several workers in crosses with commercial varieties, and promising lines have been selected.

A high degree of resistance to gall formation by nematodes (*Meloidogyne* species) was found in *L. peruvianum*. This species is a difficult one to cross with commercial varieties. Several crosses have been made, however, and lines having a high degree of resistance have been selected.

Resistance to bacterial wilt (caused by *Pseudomonas solanacearum*) has been reported.

One line of currant tomato is reported to have mature plant resistance to southern blight (caused by *Sclerotium rolfsii*).

WATERMELON

ANTHRACNOSE, caused by *Colletotrichum lagenarium*, is perhaps the most destructive disease of watermelons, attacking both the foliage and the fruit. It is particularly serious in the Southern States. Congo, released in 1949, is somewhat resistant. Its resistance was obtained from an African melon. Fairfax, introduced in 1952, is the first shipping variety available to southern growers which offers combined resistance to anthracnose and to fusarium wilt. The resistance to anthracnose came from the same source as Congo and the resistance to fusarium wilt from Leesburg and Hawkesbury.

DOWNY MILDEW is caused by *Pseudoperonospora cubensis*. A source of resistance to it was found in native watermelons of poor quality from the Dominican Republic. They were crossed to varieties resistant to fusarium wilt and anthracnose.

FUSARIUM WILT is caused by *Fusarium oxysporum* f. *niveum*. Since the release of Conqueror in 1911 there have been developed many resistant varieties that are adapted to the principal watermelon-growing areas. Among them are Improved Kleckley No. 6 and Stone Mountain No. 5 for the Midwest; Leesburg, Hawkesbury,

Blacklee, Georgia Wilt-Resistant, Miles, Missouri, Queen, and Ironsides for the South; and Klondike R-7, Baby Klondike, and Blue Ribbon for the West.

MANY SERIOUS DISEASES remain for which resistance is needed: Common blight of bean, bean and pea root rots, ascochyta blight of pea, aster yellows and mosaic of lettuce, and curly top and late blight of tomato, to mention only a few.

Often resistance has been found in a related species, but it has not been satisfactorily transferred into a good horticultural type. A higher degree of disease resistance is needed in many of our so-called resistant varieties. Recently the moderate type of resistance to fusarium wilt in tomato has been increased to near immunity; many of the newer potato varieties are more resistant to late blight than the earlier resistant introductions; most of the yellows-resistant cabbage varieties now have the type of resistance which is effective at both high and low soil temperatures.

New diseases and strains of old diseases will appear as cropping becomes more intensive and as vegetables are grown in new areas. New sources of resistance will be needed.

To meet the future problems, continuous research by plant breeders, pathologists, and other biologists is needed. There will be no time to rest on past laurels.

H. REX THOMAS, *a graduate of the University of California, has been a plant pathologist in the division of vegetable crops and diseases of the Bureau of Plant Industry, Soils, and Agricultural Engineering since 1937.*

W. J. ZAUMEYER, *a graduate of the University of Wisconsin, joined the Department of Agriculture in 1928. He is a pathologist in charge of bean and pea disease investigations in the division of vegetable crops and diseases of the Bureau of Plant Industry, Soils, and Agricultural Engineering.*

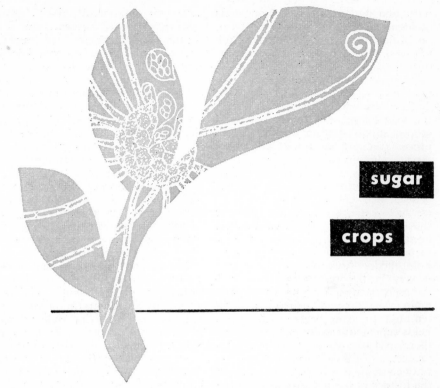

sugar

crops

Some Problems in Growing Sugar Beets

George H. Coons

Sugar beets are grown for sugar in 22 States—Michigan, Ohio, Indiana, Illinois, Wisconsin, Minnesota, Iowa, Kansas, Nebraska, South Dakota, North Dakota, Colorado, Montana, Texas, New Mexico, Utah, Idaho, Oregon, Washington, Arizona, Wyoming, and California. They are grown in New Mexico, Arizona, Utah, Nevada, California, and Oregon for seed.

Almost 20 percent of the national sugar requirement is obtained from the domestic production of sugar beets.

Beet sugar produced in the United States is in demand for food and for the chemical, pharmaceutical, fermentation, and heavy industries.

The byproducts of the sugar beet—tops, molasses, and pulp—are used chiefly as a feed for livestock. Beet molasses is also highly important in the fermentation industry, particularly for the production of citric acid. Beet pulp, the slices of beet from which the sugar has been extracted, is fed in wet or dry form to cattle.

Nearly 670,000 acres of sugar beets were harvested in 1952. On that acreage 10,217,000 tons of sugar beets were grown and were processed in 68 factories. The approximately 1,532,000 tons of sugar (raw value) produced from the sugar beet roots contributed nearly 20 percent of the estimated national sugar consumption of 7,900,000 tons. Production in 1951 was much like that of 1952, 700,000 acres being

201500°—53——34

509

harvested and about 10,500,000 tons of sugar beets being grown. In 1950, on 924,000 acres, 24.5 percent of the national sugar requirement was produced.

Disease-resistant varieties have been used almost exclusively to grow the American sugar beet crop. To obtain the seed for growing the commercial crop of sugar beets for the factories to process, the industry maintains several seed-producing enterprises.

Beet sugar can only be produced in factories equipped to carry on the complicated chemical processes necessary to extract and purify the sugar that is stored in the roots. Usually the beets are grown within a radius of 40 to 60 miles of the factory. A highly intensified culture on the best lands nearby is the result; on the farms themselves, sugar beets are usually the main cash crop, and farmers have been tempted to grow beets on the same fields repeatedly rather than to make them part of a rotation system. Twin problems of diseases and lowered fertility consequently have arisen; indeed, the history of the industry as it moved from the Eastern States westward, and then sought in place after place for suitable production areas, reflects the damage done by curly top, leaf spot, and root diseases.

Curly top by 1926 had caused repeated failures of the sugar beet crop in States west of the Rocky Mountains. In years of outbreak, the average acre yields from some districts dropped from an expected 15 tons to 5 tons or less. The history of sugar beet culture in the Truckee project of Nevada, Salt River project of Arizona, Delta and other areas in Utah, the San Joaquin Valley of California, the Yakima Valley of Washington, and many others is all much the same—a brief period of fine prospects and then crop failure because of curly top, with ultimate abandonment of sugar beets by farmers.

Congress in 1929 appropriated funds for investigations of curly top and the beet leafhopper. All aspects of the problem were attacked quickly. Thanks also to some earlier research, progress in the development of varieties resistant to curly top was immediate. By 1933, seed was being increased of the resistant variety that was introduced in 1934 as U. S. 1. Since then, U. S. 1 and the other resistant sorts that followed in quick succession—U. S. 34, U. S. 33, U. S. 12, and U. S. 22—have removed from western agriculture the threat of crop failure from curly top.

It cannot be said that curly top is vanquished. Severe exposure in the worst years still takes its toll. But farmers may now plant the new varieties with confidence that the crop will be carried through to a reasonably high yield despite disease.

Meanwhile the producers farther east were being plagued by sporadic epidemics of leaf spot. Leaf spot, caused by the fungus *Cercospora beticola*, blights the tops so that root growth is dwarfed and the percentage of sucrose is cut. Its effects are less dramatic than those of curly top, but it occurs more widely and is more damaging to the industry.

Leaf spot is a wasting disease. It can reduce tonnage and sucrose enough to make the beet crop unprofitable to farmer and factory. The blight years are those in which rainy periods are frequent in the early half of the season and total rainfall is abundant—the very conditions that should give a bumper crop bring only disappointment as wave after wave of leaf blighting occurs. In epidemic years, leaf spot may kill back the entire foliage bouquet several times in a season. New growth is pushed out only to be blighted in 2 or 3 weeks. Replacement of blighted leaves is at the expense of root growth and stored sugar, hence the crop is lacking in weight and quality. Between 1915 and 1930, blight years were frequent. Factories in the Midwest and in the more eastern districts were in financial distress.

The first leaf spot resistant variety, U. S. 217, was introduced in 1938 by the Department of Agriculture. Its average production of sugar was 5 percent more an acre than that of the susceptible European varieties. It was soon replaced by U. S. 200 x 215, a hybrid variety that served the industry from 1940 to 1944. It gave higher root yields than U. S. 217 and was at least 8 to 10 percent superior to European varieties if leaf spot was prevalent. U. S. 215 x 216 was introduced in 1945. It became the leader in the humid area. Without leaf spot, it is as productive as the nonresistant European types; if leaf spot is serious, it is at least 15 percent superior in production of sugar.

Still another disease contributed earlier to the general instability of our beet sugar industry—the seedling and root disease complex that farmers call black root. It occurs all over the United States but is worse in the humid area. The primary cause of black root of seedling beets is the water mold, *Aphanomyces cochlioides*. Other damping-off organisms are associated in the seedling disease complex but are less important or more readily controlled. Black root may kill so many of the seedlings that the stands after thinning are below or on the border line of profitable production. If rainfall in spring is slightly above normal or if the soil is infested with damping-off organisms, the initial stands of seedlings are so reduced by fungi that only gappy stands can be left after thinning.

Heavy planting rates were used formerly in an attempt to have extra large numbers of seedlings from which a fair stand of thinned beets could be saved. In recent years, to save manpower in singling sugar beets, seeding rates have been reduced. Destruction of the meager initial stands by black root thus causes even greater damage than before. According to factory records, parts of Michigan and Ohio often have had average stands in their fields considerably below 70 percent— much too low for profitable growing of the crop.

In seasons of severe black root, re-

planting of 25 percent of the acreage around a factory has been necessary.

The sugar beet cannot attain stable production and full mechanization is not possible until disease-safe varieties are available. U. S. 216—a leaf spot resistant inbred—was also found to be outstanding in its resistance to black root. The superimposing of resistance to black root upon resistance to leaf spot seems entirely feasible in varieties built around U. S. 216 and its close relatives. A number of selections resistant to black root have been made from varieties resistant to leaf spot. Varieties that were ready for introduction in 1953 combine resistance to leaf spot with moderate resistance to black root. They are equal to nonresistant strains when disease is absent and superior when leaf spot and some black root occur. Plant breeders hope they will solve the problem of black root.

WEATHER CONDITIONS sometimes produce effects on sugar beets that resemble symptoms of disease. Hot, dry winds may cause scorching of the edges of leaves. Such leaf scorch should not be confused with blighting by fungus. Sugar beets are relatively hardy, but early frosts may injure the emerging plants. Such an injury may be distinguished readily from damping-off of seedlings.

Heavy fall frosts kill the upper leaves, which become black and water-soaked and then dry out and turn white. Growers recognize this condition, even though they might not understand the effects of severe freezes and the reduction in sucrose of the roots that may follow. Low temperatures in late October or November may kill all leaves. If warmer weather follows, the killed foliage is replaced by a new growth at the expense of the food reserves in the root, thus lowering the sucrose percentage. Often a farmer is puzzled by sugar tests after a freeze that show a much lower sugar content than the earlier tests. Wherever feasible, after tops are severely frozen the harvest should be delayed to permit the foliage to be replaced and the plant again to store sugar in the roots.

A bolt of lightning may kill all plants in an area 10 to 50 feet in diameter in a field. The plants die suddenly, as if affected by disease. Each day for nearly a week the circle of dead plants widens. The lightning, hitting the field just after the surface soil was wet by rain, distributes itself and grounds through the beet roots, electrocuting them. The least affected plants in the outer parts of the circle die more slowly.

Hail may cut and bruise petioles and crowns of plants but (except when the plants are very young) does not kill the beets. The plants put out new leaf growth. The loss caused by hail is therefore according to the amount of injury to foliage, except that wounds may offer points for the entrance of disease organisms. Because sugar beets can recover from hail injury, farmers in districts subject to frequent hailstorms include this crop in their farming program as a safeguard.

SHORTAGES OF NUTRIENTS in the soil produce definite reactions on the sugar beet plants. A deficiency of phosphate produces telltale effects that are especially marked on the older leaves, which then curl upward and inward. The edges of the leaves and the tissue between the veins die and turn black. An affected plant stands out markedly from its neighbors. A single plant may show this evidence of phosphate deficiency—the surrounding plants being apparently normal—or a number of plants in a group may be affected. Less severely affected plants show reduction in growth, greater susceptibility to black root, and secondary invasion by weak parasites of the *Cercospora beticola* spots on the leaves. The enlargement of the lesions by the secondary organisms that follow leaf spot is so striking in fields deficient in phosphate that the cercospora spots, instead of appearing grayish brown, take on the form that growers call black blight.

When the soil is low in boron, the heart or bud leaves turn black, and half-grown leaves around the bud may be darker green than normal and distorted. A black or brown scabbiness develops on the inner face of the petioles. The scabby streaks are crossed by breaks that produce ladder markings. Cankers may occur in the flesh of the roots about one-fourth inch under the skin. Affected tissues turn pale brown or gray. The dead tissue may be sterile at first, but later secondary organisms such as *Phoma betae* may invade it.

Shortage of potash is characterized by a bronzing of the foliage. Manganese deficiency causes whitish spots on the younger leaves. A lack of magnesium shows up by producing pale blotches and whitened leaf margins of the maturing leaves. Sulfur deficiency, known to be characteristic of some Oregon soils, gives a pale-yellow cast to the foliage. Nitrogen deficiency shows itself by producing a yellowing of the foliage, particularly the older leaves. A severe shortage of nitrogen depresses growth and makes the plants pale yellow and unthrifty.

The application of adequate amounts of the fertilizer element that is lacking controls the deficiency diseases. Heavy dosages of phosphate may be necessary. Minute amounts are needed of some, such as boron. Where 400 to 500 pounds an acre of superphosphate (15 percent P_2O_5) would be applied to meet a serious phosphorous deficiency, boron is added in the form of borax at not more than about 10 to 12 pounds an acre, unless the soils are known to have the capacity for fixing boron. With such soils, much heavier treatments are given.

LEAF SPOT, a seed-borne, fungus disease, has been found everywhere that the sugar beet is grown. It attacks leaf blades, petioles, seed stalks, and floral parts, on which it forms small, necrotic spots. The spots on the leaves are circular with grayish centers. With a hand lens, one can see pin-point black dots in the center of the spots. The spots occur so densely in heavy infections that the whole leaf may be speckled. Often the spots run together. As the disease progresses, the leaves turn yellow and brown and finally die. On the petioles and seed stalks the spots are large and elongate and have conspicuous grayish centers. The floral envelopes that dry and form part of the seed ball show the lesions of the fungus on the bracts and old ovary tissue. The fungus (*Cercospora beticola*) does not attack the root.

The fungus has a rather simple cycle of infection—spot formation, spore formation, reinfection. It is known only in its asexual stage. Commonly the leaf spot organism is brought to the field in the lesions on the seed ball. When sugar beets follow sugar beets, however, diseased material from the previous crop leads to early and severe infection.

The fungus on a seed ball or on the infected leaves and petioles left as the trash from a previous crop (or from a weed host) remains alive and starts to grow in the spring. Spores are produced that are blown by the wind or dashed by rain to the young beet plants. As the seedlings push out from the seed balls, occasionally a ball is carried above ground by the developing plantlet. Then the fungus develops on the infected floral parts, and spores are produced. The spores infect the cotyledons. Typical cercospora spots can be found by search on the cotyledons of the young plants in any field. Obviously the old leaves and petioles from an infected previous crop would supply a very heavy inoculation if beets were to follow beets. The fungus grows rather slowly in cool spring weather. About 3 weeks are required for the cycle from spore to spore. The growth rate is much faster in warm weather.

Cotyledon infection in early April leads to spore production in early May. If rainy periods are numerous in May or June, two or three cycles of the fungus may occur. Each spot that arises from spore infection produces in its turn countless spores, which, when spread in the field by wind or dashing rain, produce new infections, thereby widening and greatly extending the circle of affected plants. If weather conditions favor growth and sporulation and if frequent rains supply the moisture necessary for infection, then leaf spot—starting on one infected plant in about 100 or 500 in a field—becomes by mid-July (as the circles of infection overlap) an entrenched disease affecting all the older leaves on most of the plants in the field. With such a start, unless August is very dry, ordinary light rains are enough to bring about severe blighting and death of the foliage.

When leaf spot had to be controlled by spraying or dusting with fungicides, treatment had to be started before the middle of July to keep the fungus from becoming prevalent in the field. The fungicides used for direct control were bordeaux mixture (applied as a spray) or monohydrated copper sulfate and lime (applied as a dust). Fixed copper dusts later were used. If the disease was severe enough to do heavy damage, the fungicides, properly and plentifully applied, produced average gains of about 2 tons of roots an acre and a two-unit increase of sucrose in comparison with untreated parts of the fields.

Resistant varieties have given such good control of leaf spot that it is no longer necessary to spray or dust sugar beet plants. They yield well, so no penalty is involved in their use in blight-free years. In the more eastern districts, the "U. S." varieties have given exceptionally high percentages of sucrose and high tonnage.

The resistant varieties are not immune to leaf spot but the degree of resistance is such that no crop failure occurs, and, even in epidemics, the sugar beets hold their foliage—green and functional—until the leaves are fully mature. Blighting and killing down of tops from leaf spot no longer occur. Such a loss of tops would make it inefficient to use the Scott-Urschel type of beet harvester, which carries the lifted sugar beet plants up to the topping disks by grasping the tops between rubber-faced belts. The saving of the tops means also that there is definite gain in the feed value from the crop. The roots of resistant varieties keep better in storage since they have higher sucrose and are better nourished than roots from the blighted plants.

DOWNY MILDEW, caused by *Peronospora schachtii*, attacks the foliage of sugar beets in the coastal area of California. The fungus is not known elsewhere in the United States except on sugar beets grown for seed in Oregon and Washington, where humidity often equals that of the California fog belt. The hosts of the fungus are *Beta vulgaris* (sugar beets, red beets, mangel-wurzels) and *Beta maritima* (the sea beet). No other species of *Beta* or other genera are known to be attacked. The mildew attacks the young growing leaves, which thicken, curl, and eventually die. It is a disease of late winter and early spring. The dead parts turn brown or black. When the disease is active, the sooty-gray growth of sporophores and spores of the fungus identify downy mildew.

Young plants may show the disease on cotyledons, primary leaves, and growing points. Ordinarily the beet has reached the 4- to 10-leaf stage before conditions favor the attack by the fungus. The disease seldom kills the plant, but checks growth and 'destroys the primary bud. Subsequent growth has to be from accessory buds. Recovery from mildew commonly occurs when weather becomes warmer and drier in late spring.

The fungus produces resting spores and perennial mycelium. These remain alive in the trash and debris from an affected crop and presumably are sources of infection to a crop of sugar beets planted on the same field. The fungus also is carried on seed. In addition to these sources of infection, co-nidia from living beet plants may be carried by the wind to nearby sugar beet fields. If they land on a film of water on a beet leaf, they germinate and cause infection. Then the fungus occupies the beet tissue and produces fruiting threads on the beet tissue and an enormous number of spores. The spores again spread the fungus in the field. Under favorable conditions, susceptible varieties may become 80 to 100 percent infected. A resistant variety such as U. S. 15 under similar conditions may show infection of 1 to 10 percent, and recovers better than susceptible types do.

Downy mildew no doubt could be prevented by copper sprays or dusts, but resistant varieties are good enough to control downy mildew satisfactorily. Breeding work started in 1945 seeks to combine resistance to downy mildew and rust, the character for nonbolting, and adequate resistance to curly top to give a variety that is adapted for winter plantings and is disease-safe. U. S. 75, a product of this work, has been introduced to replace U. S. 15.

RHIZOCTONIA FOLIAGE BLIGHT, caused by *Pellicularia filamentosa*, may attack leaves of beets if weather is moist in June or July. The strains of the fungus causing foliage blight are nonpathogenic to half-grown or mature roots. The fungus attacks only leaf tissues and the tender fibrous roots of seedlings. On the leaves, black spots from one-quarter to one-half inch across are formed.

Affected tissue dies and dries, and the primary spot soon becomes surrounded by a circular zone of secondary spots. With the hand lens one can see the *Rhizoctonia* threads on the leaf surface. The dead areas break away from the sound tissue, and the leaves get a ragged look. About 3 weeks after infection, a filmy, gray-white growth appears on the leaf surfaces. It is the spore-bearing stage. The growth consists of threads and spore-bearing structures called basidia. Air currents and rain spread the spores, so that a single primary infection may become the center of an infected circle 15 to 30 feet in diameter. The original source plant usually can be recognized by its older infection. The air currents may carry the fungus far wider in the field and set up foci beyond the area of heaviest infection.

The disease has been found in Maryland, Virginia, Michigan, Ohio, Minnesota, Nebraska, and Colorado. In most fields, in a dry spring, it occurs only in trace amounts, but losses may be serious if the spring weather is wet.

It commonly has been overlooked or confused with cercospora leaf spot, and outbreaks on resistant varieties, said to have been caused by leaf spot, sometimes actually have been caused by this *Rhizoctonia*. Dry weather in midseason usually checks the foliage blight, so that as yet no direct control measures have been taken against it.

Because the fungus persists in the soil, a good rotation practice, in which beet crops are spaced at least 4 or 5 years apart, helps reduce primary infections.

A RUST FUNGUS, *Uromyces betae*, causes a serious leaf disease of sugar beets in the coastal areas of California. Affected plants take on a rusted appearance—leaves, petioles, or seed stalks are covered with minute pustules filled with a rusty brown powder, the spores of the fungus.

The rust apparently attacks only plants in the genus *Beta*. The fungus occurs in Europe and Asia Minor. It has been collected on *Beta lomatagona*, *B. trigyna*, and *B. intermedia* in Turkey. It occurs generally on *B. maritima* in Europe and on *B. patellaris* in the Canary Islands. In the United States it has been found in California and Oregon, where it may do considerable damage to sugar beets and red garden beets, and in Arizona and New Mexico, where it was of minor importance.

The rust apparently persists over off-seasons in volunteer plants or in trash and debris. Presumably it has been introduced into United States as pustules on seed. The occasional appearance of beet rust in Arizona and New Mexico may be attributed to seed-borne infection.

The damage done by beet rust on winter-planted beets has been recognized by the industry, but no direct control measures have yet been used against it. The only control achieved so far has come from use of resistant varieties. U. S. 15 has definite resistance to beet rust; its good performance in winter plantings in California, in comparison with other varieties, has been due largely to its resistance to rust and to downy mildew, as previously discussed.

SEVERAL MINOR DISEASES affect the foliage of sugar beet.

A bacterial disease, black spot (*Pseudomonas aptata*), seldom does damage in sugar beets grown for sugar but has been known to blight plants grown for seed in Oregon. No control measures have been developed for it.

A leaf spot caused by *Ramularia beticola* damages sugar beets grown for seed in Oregon, Washington, and northern California. The spot is of the same size and character as cercospora leaf spot, but its center is white, not gray, and the small tufts of fungus growing in the spot are white and not black, as with cercospora. The fungus, apparently limited by climate, grows only in cool places. *Cercospora beticola* grows best when day temperatures exceed 75° F. Sugar beets that are resistant to leaf spot are also resistant to ramularia leaf spot. If necessary, ramularia leaf spot in sugar beets could be controlled in seed fields by spraying with copper sprays.

A leaf spot of minor importance is caused by the fungus *Phoma betae*. Affected leaves show tan, round spots, up to one-half inch in diameter and characterized by a series of concentric markings. Affected leaves may be found here and there in the field by midseason. Usually the small fruiting bodies of the fungus can be found forming a series of concentric rings on the dead tissue. The fungus attacks the seed stalks and seed balls of the sugar beet and is definitely known to be seed-borne. *Phoma betae* causes a serious seedling disease of sugar beets, and is especially important as a cause of rotting of the roots in storage. No control measures have been worked out for the disease on the leaves.

Saltgrass rust, *Puccinia aristidae*, often attacks sugar beets in the Western States. It should not be confused with the beet rust caused by *Uromyces betae*. The salt-grass rust produces its telial and uredial stages on *Distichlis* species and its pycnial and aecial stages on a very wide range of host plants. Its fruiting bodies often can be found in spring on seedling sugar beet plants. The yellow cluster cups and the swollen overgrowth dotted with pycnia are conspicuous. No control measures are necessary because the fungus does not produce any lasting injury.

BLACK ROOT is the common cause of poor stands wherever sugar beets are grown. The diseases that reduce or destroy seedlings are called black root because of the appearance of dead or dying plants. Of the many fungi able to attack seedlings, *Pythium* species, *Phoma betae*, *Rhizoctonia solani*, and *Aphanomyces cochlioides* are the most serious. If the seedling is killed during germination or a week or two after it emerges from the soil, the attack is acute. All the organisms listed can produce such effects under certain conditions of soil and climate.

Plants that escape the acute form may be subject to the chronic form of black root. That form does not kill the plant but causes death and sloughing-off of lateral roots or terminal parts of the taproot. *A. cochlioides* chiefly produces the chronic type. The black root it causes may persist throughout the life of the plant. Affected plants show a great lag in growth in comparison with healthy plants because of the persistent and continued attack on the feeding roots. When a plant diseased with chronic black root is carefully

removed from the soil, most of the lateral roots will be found dead and blackened. The main root will show bunches of dead, black side roots, which indicate that as one root was killed the plant pushed out others, which succumbed in turn.

In the early stages of black root, the leaves may become yellow and mottled, possibly because of a poisoning effect of the fungus. Because affected plants never establish proper root relationships in the soil, they remain stunted and may never reach marketable size. When the terminal part of the taproot is killed, the root becomes sprangled as lateral roots replace the killed terminal.

The fungi causing seedling diseases are found everywhere in the United States. They do greatest damage in sections of greatest rainfall. In the West there is reasonable assurance that properly planted and watered seed will give a good stand of seedlings, regularly distributed in the row. In the humid area there is no such assurance. Emergence of seedlings may be irregular, or most of the plants that do appear may die from acute seedling disease or become infected with chronic black root.

Among the organisms causing black root, only *Phoma betae* is known to be seed-borne. The others probably are present in any field likely to be planted to sugar beets. The amount of injury they do is tied in with their prevalence in the soil. This is greatly influenced by the crops that are grown ahead of the sugar beets. Legumes such as alfalfa, sweetclover, and the clovers also are subject to the same damping-off organisms that attack sugar beets; hence, they harbor and increase them. Furthermore, the roots and residues from the legumes are favored foodstuffs for these black root fungi and they bring about their strong build-up in the soil. Weeds such as red root pigweed (*Amaranthus retroflexus*) and related species also increase the degree of soil infestation. Corn, soybeans, and small grains, however, repress the sugar beet pathogens, probably because their residues are cellulosic and support an entirely different fungus flora, and one that is antagonistic to the flora supported by residues from legumes and sugar beets. Organisms in the soil have their cycles of development which are influenced by the nature of the food supplied by crop residues, with soil moisture and soil temperature acting as controlling factors on when and how fast the organisms grow.

When it was discovered that residues from legume crops build up black root infestation in the soil and that the contrary effect is produced by corn stover and corn roots, and when it was found that after 2 or 3 months the residues from legumes disintegrate and no longer favor the black root fungi, the proper ways to clean up soils and to utilize sod-forming legume crops to precede sugar beets were shown.

For badly infested soils, the growing of a corn crop immediately to precede the beet crop is an effective clean-up measure against black root. With such crop sequence, good stands of sugar beets can be obtained in fields that have had a long history of black root damage. The practice is now followed in many districts. Since plowing under cellulosic materials tends to lock up nitrogen, applications of fertilizers rich in nitrogen are made at planting time and often as side-dressings.

If sugar beets are to follow alfalfa, sweetclover, red or crimson clover, then a proper timing of the operations in fitting the soil for the beet crop must be observed. If the legumes are plowed in late fall or early spring, then the residues offer the black root fungi abundant food which the organisms use just as soon as the soil warms up in the spring. Thus, planting time and the germination of the sugar beet seed will come just when the black root fungi are at their peak of development.

An entirely different set-up is presented if the legume sods are plowed in late summer or early fall. The alfalfa or clover roots die, and the black root organisms flourish during September and October, using up the nitrogen and quickly soluble carbohydrates. When these are gone the cellulose framework of the residues supports a different set of fungi, and the forms that produce black root are crowded out.

Thus, by timing properly his plowing of legume sods, the farmer can gain the advantages that come from growing legumes and avoid the very definite bad effects that the legume sods exercise if they are plowed too late in the fall or in the spring immediately before beet planting.

Black root of sugar beets is so serious in its effects on stands in the more eastern sugar beet growing districts that the relationship of the various crops to the prevalence of the disease-producing organisms is stressed. The experimental work on which the conclusions are based is described in some detail as a means of relating the laboratory and greenhouse experience with what the grower himself can observe on his own farm. The method used in following the increases and decreases of black root fungi in soil has not been the well-nigh impossible job of finding these microscopic forms and counting them, but instead the amount of killing of sugar beet seedlings that takes place in a soil flat treated in a given way is taken as the direct indicator of what is happening.

It has been found that if red clover, sweetclover, alfalfa, or other legume is grown in a flat in the greenhouse for about a month and this growth turned under, and then after a week or 10 days sugar beet seed is planted, the stand of sugar beets obtained is very poor—usually not over 10 percent. The soil without legumes gives a stand of from 50 to 75 percent. If corn is grown for a month, and then the young plants turned under, and after a week or 10 days sugar beet seed is planted in the flat, the stand is nearly 100 percent.

The flats that failed because a legume was grown, if planted to corn, can be made to give nearly 100 percent stands of sugar beets. The flats giving fine stands can be made to fail simply by planting legumes for a month, turning them under, as a preliminary treatment before planting sugar beet seed.

That these results are brought about by changes in the black root organisms in the soil has been shown by treating the soil initially with formaldehyde to ·kill the black root organisms. With such soil, after the formaldehyde vaporizes and disappears, it makes no difference whether a legume or a corn crop precedes the beets or if the beets are grown on fallowed soil; all give 100 percent stands.

These effects are related to the nutrition of the soil organisms. This is shown by incorporating nitrogen-bearing materials such as ground legume hay, dried blood, cottonseed meal, or urea into the soil. Those substances increase the amount of damping-off of sugar beets over that which occurs when the soil is untreated. On the other hand, if ground cornstalks, corn meal, ground filter paper, or sugar is put into the soil the stands of beets are improved over those in nontreated soil.

If alfalfa hay is incorporated into the soil and the sugar beets started directly thereafter, bad effects on stands are noted. After 2 or 3 weeks in the warm greenhouse, however, the stands following the addition of alfalfa residues are greatly improved. In other words, when the nitrogenous substances and soluble carbohydrates are used up, the effects from the cellulose portions appear.

The conclusions from these experiments have been tested by field experiments and observations in Michigan, Minnesota, Colorado, South Dakota, and other States. Replicated tests have shown that the effects in the field of the legumes and corn as preceding crops for beets are comparable to those of the greenhouse cultures. But if the alfalfa and sweetclover sods are turned under in August, Septem-

ber, or possibly even October, and if the conditions of moisture and temperature permit disintegration of the residues, stands are good in the sugar beets planted the following spring. This is in sharp contrast with the prevailingly poor showing of the sugar beets in the spring-plowed part of the experimental plots.

If the farmer understands what takes place in the soil when he incorporates the crop residues, he may use legume sods to advantage with sugar beets. A blanket recommendation to plant sugar beets on legume sods without specification of the time of turning-under the sods is ill-advised and may invite an outbreak of black root.

A rather definite relationship exists between soil fertility and the incidence of black root. Tests in many localities have shown the effectiveness of adequate phosphate applications. In a test at Holgate, Ohio, superphosphate (15 percent) at a rate of 200 to 400 pounds an acre increased stands and nearly doubled the sugar production. A complete fertilizer, 2–16–8, at 500 pounds an acre doubled yields and gave the highest sugar.

The increase of the aphanomyces type of black root, as well as the acute forms, seems related to the progressive lowering of the supply of available phosphate that has taken place on many soils of Michigan, Ohio, Minnesota, and other States. Evidence is available that a low status of plant nutrition, especially with phosphate, reduces resistance to *Phoma betae* of stored sugar beet roots. Deficiency of phosphate appears to lower the resistance of young sugar beet plants to *A. cochlioides*. Abundant evidence is at hand that raising the fertility level of the soil, particularly with respect to phosphate, can bring about decisive reduction of losses caused by *A. cochlioides*. Fertilizer practice with sugar beets has shown marked improvement in recent years, but many farmers still apply fertilizers so sparingly that little or no benefit is obtained.

Treating seed with copper, mercury, and other fungicides helps prevent acute phases of black root. Even better are organic mercury compounds, such as Ceresan and New Improved Ceresan. They used to be the standard treatments, but Arasan, Phygon, and other nonmetallic fungicides have mostly replaced the mercurials for seed treatments. Treatment of seed gives fairly satisfactory stands of seedlings if the exposure is not extremely severe. When soil infestation is high and soil moisture conditions are favorable, seed treatment is not enough to assure a stand. Seed treatment does not prevent the chronic form of black root caused by *A. cochlioides.*

Effective control of black root is not simple. Many factors of the environment affect it: The field chosen for the beet crop must be plowed at the proper time and its fertility must be high. Liberal application of commercial fertilizer is needed. Seed treatment to protect against acute forms of the disease is necessary. When the beets emerge, prompt cultivation assists in soil aeration and may prevent an excessive loss of stand.

Those general measures will prevent the acute forms of damping-off. The chronic type, caused by *Aphanomyces,* is to be met by use of resistant varieties. They give excellent results. By 1953 and 1954, they will be available for the worst-affected sugar beet districts.

RHIZOCTONIA CROWN ROT (*Pellicularia filamentosa*) occurs on half-grown or nearly mature sugar beet roots. *Rhizoctonia solani,* the pathogenic stage of the fungus, also causes decay of the fleshy parts of the root. Plants here and there in the field die. The leaves turn brown or black, wither and dry, and persist on the dead crown. The entire crown or only a part of it may be rotted. The disease spreads along the row, rather than across rows, so that one or two affected plants commonly are found on either side of the disintegrating plant first to show crown rot.

The fungus causing crown rot is in all agricultural soils and is capable of persisting indefinitely. The spore stage of the fungus probably does not constitute a significant factor in its spread.

Sugar beet seedlings attacked by *Rhizoctonia* may be killed outright or only cankered. The cankered plants continue to grow, and some recover. Such plants, however, may develop crown rot. Sugar beets will be found in July and August with their crowns cleft horizontally, much as if injured with a hoe. The cause is a canker contracted in the seedling stage. Rapid growth cracks the flesh away from the dead spot. The fungus then advances into tissue as a crown rot.

Rhizoctonia solani comprises countless strains or biotypes. Some cause diseases. Some are nonvirulent forms. The highly virulent strains can penetrate sound tissue; they can invade without wounds. The fungus persists in the soil. Continuous cropping with beets or other susceptible types of crops increases the infestation. *Rhizoctonia* causes a serious disease of potatoes, but apparently the strains attacking potatoes are different from those that cause root rot of sugar beets. The Rhizoctonias that attack cereals also seem different from those that attack sugar beets, legume sod crops, and vegetables. The disease is worse when the level of nutrients is allowed to drop.

Selections of sugar beets made under conditions of severe *Rhizoctonia* attack have shown outstanding resistance to a few strains of the fungus, but this resistance has failed with exposure to other strains. The outlook for the control of crown rot by breeding *Rhizoctonia*-resistant varieties is not promising because of the enormous number of biological strains of *Rhizoctonia.*

Sanitation measures should be used, especially proper crop rotations, to reduce the prevalence in the soil of the *Rhizoctonia* strains that attack beets. Sugar beets may be grown following corn, small grains, potatoes, soybeans, and probably field beans without serious loss from *Rhizoctonia*, as these crops do not build up strains that are highly virulent against sugar beet. The control of *Rhizoctonia* by rotations also has direct relation with the reduction of seedling disease. Sugar beets should not be grown on legume sods unless these sods are plowed in late summer or early fall, so that the residues disintegrate fully in winter.

FUSARIUM YELLOWS (*Fusarium conglutinans betae*) affects sugar beets in Colorado, Nebraska, South Dakota, Montana, Wyoming, and possibly other States. It causes wilting of the plants. The characteristic symptom is a yellowing and dwarfing of the foliage of the half-grown plants. Affected leaves become pale yellow and mottled. The pathogen belongs to the group of fungi that invade the water-conducting tissues of the plant. With fusarium yellows of sugar beet, the central core of the root turns yellow, or brown, and eventually black. Surrounding tissues may also be injured. The fungus gives off toxic substances that cause wilting and collapse of the leaf tissues when carried upward in the transpiration stream. In a diseased root that is cut lengthwise, the diseased vascular system shows up as a yellow or brown discolored area. That and the effects on the leaves make it easy to recognize the disease.

The fungus can persist in soils for many years. With ordinary rotation practices, the organism has not shown the capacities for soil infestation that characterize related organisms that cause cabbage yellows, celery yellows, aster wilt, tomato yellows, flax wilt, and cotton wilt. With continuous culture of sugar beets for 5 years, incidence of disease increased until about 40 percent of the crop was affected.

No effective control measures are known for fusarium yellows. No resistant varieties have been introduced. The disease is worse when crop rotation is neglected. Heavy dosage with P_2O_5 fertilizer is beneficial. Fields that one time showed infection of more than 10 percent have been greatly improved and incidence of disease lessened by growing alfalfa 3 years, and some crop such as corn, lima beans, or cantaloups 1 year, before growing sugar beets again. The sugar beet crop was given adequate fertilization with superphosphate.

BACTERIAL CANKER (*Phytomonas beticola*) can cause overgrowths on petioles or on the root, but are chiefly to be found on the crown. The central parts of the overgrowths are water-soaked and yellow. These are cells of the sugar beet root that are almost completely invaded by the organism.

Bacterial canker occurs in Virginia, Maryland, Michigan, Wisconsin, Colorado, Wyoming, New Mexico, and Utah. No other natural hosts are known.

The disease normally affects a plant here and there in the field but sometimes the galls have been found on almost every plant. Such an outbreak follows a hailstorm that has wounded the crowns and afforded entrance for the bacteria. The bacteria have been found in agricultural soil and have been isolated from irrigation water. The organism can persist a long time in the soil. It does only minor damage to the sugar beet. No specific control measures are used other than crop rotation, in which beets do not occur more often than once in 4 or 5 years, and good fertilization.

SCLEROTIUM ROOT ROT (*Sclerotium rolfsii*) in 1933 and 1934 killed entire fields of sugar beets in California. The fungus growth, a coarse, rapidly growing mycelium, can invade sound or wounded root tissue and quickly rot it. The fungus attacks many vegetable crops in the South. It was serious on carrots and peas in southern and central California. Sugar beet roots rotted by *Sclerotium rolfsii* are covered with a filmy, whitish growth, on which the fungus forms its resting bodies—small, brownish, seedlike bodies about the size and appearance of a radish seed. Thousands of these sclerotia are formed on rotted roots and identify the organism. The fungus requires warm soil conditions. Attempts to grow sugar beets in Louisiana and southern Texas have largely been fruitless because of *Sclerotium rolfsii*.

The disease in California was found only in a few fields. The California Agricultural Experiment Station cooperated with the industry in making a survey of *Sclerotium*. Soils were sampled and laboratory tests were made to determine the degree of infestation. Seriously infested fields were taken out of beet production and planted to alfalfa and other nonsusceptible crops. The practice of returning dump-dirt of the beet receiving stations to the fields was prohibited in order to prevent introduction of the fungus into clean fields.

If the disease appeared in the field in serious amount, heavy applications of nitrogen—usually accomplished by adding nitrogen as ammonia gas to the irrigation water—checked it. The steps taken in California controlled the disease and removed it as a threat to sugar beet production.

THE SUGAR BEET NEMATODE, a parasitic worm, is one of the worst pests of the sugar beet. Failure to practice proper crop rotation leads to serious infestation.

Practical control depends on starving out the nematodes by rotation of beet crops with crops not attacked by the nematodes. Usually such crops are grown for 5 years between sugar beet crops. Alfalfa, grains, tomatoes, potatoes, beans, peas, and sweetclover may be used as rotation crops. Cabbages, cauliflower, table beets, mangel-wurzel, turnips, rutabagas, and radishes must be avoided as they are attacked by the sugar beet nematode and not only permit the nematodes to increase instead of decrease, but are often injured severely. Special attention should be given to weed control during the rotation period as the sugar beet nematodes can also live on many common weeds. Thus, in California, mustards in alfalfa fields must be killed. The long period between beet crops is necessary because the female sugar beet nematode develops into a tough cyst which remains in the soil for many years. Enclosed in the cyst are eggs with larvae which can remain alive and capable of attacking plants for many years. In the absence of a host crop, only a small proportion hatch each year and die of starvation and other natural causes, so that it takes several years to reduce their numbers sufficiently so that a good sugar beet crop can be grown.

Success of the 5-year period, or more, between beet crops in restoring the land to its former productivity for sugar beets is remarkable. It should not, however, encourage the grower to follow up with a second crop of sugar beets, since the starvation period does not kill all nematodes and sugar beets will have brought back a high nematode population.

ROOT KNOT NEMATODES cause distinct knots or galls on the roots of sugar beets. These are generally more numerous on the lighter type soils than on the heavier ones, but may be a serious problem wherever sugar beets are grown. They also are controlled by soil fumigation or by crop rotation, but since no cyst is formed shorter rotation periods can be used. Since several species of root knot nematodes attack sugar beets and these differ in their host relationships, no definite rotation system can be specified. Rotation details must be worked out on a local basis.

AMONG THE MINOR ROOT DISEASES is verticillium wilt, caused by *Verticillium albo-atrum*. It occurs to a limited extent in Colorado and Nebraska. It is serious in the Yakima Valley of Washington. The foliage becomes yellow and dries. Roots show only slight evidence of small, blackened fibrils here and there in the flesh. The lateral root through which the fungus entered the plant usually can be detected because it becomes black and water-soaked. Probably crop rotations with several years between sugar beet crops would reduce the incidence of the disease.

Crown gall, caused by *Agrobacterium tumefaciens*, is an overgrowth that usually takes the form of a smooth, gall or knot on the shoulder or central part of the beet root. It is caused by the same bacterial organism that attacks fruit trees and other plants. Occasional affected plants have been found in nearly all sugar beet districts. The overgrowth excites attention because frequently the gall is as large as the beet root itself. No control measures are necessary as the disease is limited on sugar beets.

Texas root rot, caused by *Phymatotrichum omnivorum*, attacks sugar beets in New Mexico and Arizona, on soil in which Texas root rot, well known as a cotton disease, occurs. The tissue of an affected plant is rotted completely. The fungus produces a thin, feltlike coating of hyaline or yellowing mycelium on the surface of the root. It advances on the root surface as a whitish or yellow fan-shaped growth. Sugar beets are not grown for sugar production to any extent in areas where Texas root rot is common. No loss in the seed-producing areas of Arizona or New Mexico has been reported.

STORAGE ROTS are caused by *Phoma betae, Botrytis cinerea, Rhizopus nigricans, Rhizoctonia solani*, several species of *Fusarium*, and other fungi.

To prevent cold weather from interfering with harvesting, factories in nearly all the beet-growing districts must accept deliveries of sugar beet roots in excess of their capacity for prompt processing—so huge tonnages of roots are piled at the factories and their receiving stations.

The roots stored in the huge piles are alive; like all living things, they respire. Respiration involves the oxidation of the sucrose in the root. Temperature influences the rate of respiration;

therefore, if the storage piles are kept cold, the loss of sugar from respiration is at a minimum. Because respiration produces heat, if a storage pile contains layers of dirt and masses of leaves and trash, the dissipation of heat by air currents may not take place and a chain of conditions is set up that leads to the generation of heat in pockets of the pile. First, respiration is accelerated; finally, roots become subject to fungus rots, and the rotting organisms feeding on the rich sugar stores of the roots produce excessive heating in the piles. These manifest themselves as "hot spots." In some years the losses from storage rots are staggering.

Experiments by Myron Stout and Charles A. Fort a few years ago started active prevention of sugar losses from stored sugar beets by cooling the roots by forced ventilation of the piles with chill night air. Engineers at beet sugar factories promptly capitalized on this finding, and today piles of sugar beets at the factories very commonly have ventilating ducts laid through them. Thermostats are located at critical points to control the operation of blowers. Cold air is forced through the piles by blowers as the temperatures within the piles may require.

Sugar losses still occur with roots in storage piles, and after a period in storage such losses may sharply rise. Studies to reduce losses further are continuing. Beets grown with abundant nutrients, particularly phosphorus and nitrogen, and with adequate soil moisture, are resistant to storage rots, particularly to *Phoma betae*. Drying in the field before piling has bad effects on keeping qualities. High temperatures have been shown to break down the resistance of roots to the attack of organisms that ordinarily are saprophytes unable to attack a live root. Thus, a period of 60° F. is enough to change the character of the sugar beet root so that the bread mold, *Rhizopus nigricans*, can rot the tissue.

Roots have been exposed to invasion by *Phoma betae* and *Botrytis cinerea*, chief rotters of roots in storage, and the most resistant roots selected. Progenies from such selections keep better than parents. Sugar beets with good keeping quality may be bred, since apparently this is governed by the genetic make-up of the sugar beet.

BEET MOSAIC occurs in Colorado, Nebraska, Utah, Idaho, Oregon, California, and other Western States. This virus disease produces mottling of the young leaves of sugar beet. Sometimes veinlet clearing develops on the youngest leaves of an affected plant. The green peach aphid (*Myzus persicae*) and other aphids transmit the virus from plant to plant.

The disease is apparently limited to the sugar beet, red garden beet, chard, and mangel-wurzels. Spinach and other plants have been artificially inoculated.

Other than in California, mosaic is chiefly to be found close to infected commercial seed fields or near breeding stations where mosaic-affected roots are carried over winter for transplanting in spring. Ordinarily it is not prevalent beyond the flight zones of aphids—usually a matter of a few miles. In California, mosaic is very common. Since sugar beet crops overlap from year to year and seed crops of both sugar beet and red garden beet are grown, there is no break in the cycle of development. Furthermore, the aphid vectors are abundant and have year-round activity. The absence of mosaic in the more eastern beet-growing sections, such as Michigan, Ohio, and Minnesota, is not understood. It is probable that wherever the virus has been introduced, a cycle of development has been broken because affected plants have not been overwintered.

Any damage that sugar beet mosaic may do to sugar beets grown for sugar has not been appraised. It is known that plants affected with mosaic are significantly poorer than healthy plants as seed producers. As yet no control measures are employed against sugar beet mosaic, or its insect vectors.

SAVOY, which is a virus disease that is transmitted by the lacewing bug, *Piesma cinerea*, curls and distorts the leaves and dwarfs the root of sugar beet. The disease also affects red garden beet, chard, and mangel-wurzel, but is not known on other hosts. Usually the disease appears as a plant here and there in the field, but 10 to 15 percent Savoy has been found in fields bordering wood lots or weedy areas where the insect could overwinter. The disease occurs from Maryland and Virginia westward through Wyoming and Montana, but it has not been found in sugar beets west of the Rocky Mountains—although the insect vector occurs throughout the United States.

The most definite symptom of Savoy is the swelling and thickening of the veins. Their growth is reduced and they show up as prominent network on the under side of the leaves. The leaves curl and roll downward. The tissue between the veins bulges out; the whole leaf becomes whiplike and distorted. The roots show darkened vascular rings, the flesh between becoming glassy white. Affected plants make very limited growth, and the roots show much reduced sugar storage.

Ordinarily the disease is minor in its effects, the lessened growth being compensated by greater growth of the neighboring plants. No direct control measures are employed against the disease.

VIRUS YELLOWS, long known as the most serious disease attacking sugar beets in Europe, was found in 1951 in Michigan, Colorado, Utah, Oregon, and California. It is probably widespread in the United States and may have been here for some time but overlooked. This virus is spread by aphid vectors, of which the green peach aphid, *Myzus persicae*, is most important. Only the older leaves show the disease symptoms. They turn a greenish yellow, particularly at their tips. The veins stay greener than the interveinal tissue. The leaf blades become thick and brittle. Apparently the disease does its damage to the sugar beet plants by interfering with the movement to the root of the food elaborated in the leaves. If a plant is attacked early, its root growth is checked and storage of sugar is strongly reduced. With early attack, sugar production may be cut from 40 to 50 percent. If the attack occurs in August, damage may be much less.

Totally infected fields were found in California in 1951 and 1952. Instead of a normal green color, the fields were canary yellow. The condition has been known for several years in California as "Salinas yellows," but now is identified as virus yellows. Because infection was total, there was no measuring stick of healthy fields for determining effects of the disease. In 1952 the disease was prevalent in Colorado, where it appeared in late August. Early records indicate the disease probably occurred in Colorado as far back as 1940.

Studies in California have shown that the disease may strikingly reduce root weight, and cause strong declines in sucrose percentage. In light of present knowledge, virus yellows may rank with curly top as a serious menace.

Control measures now in use in Europe are not likely to be of particular applicability in the United States. There is some evidence that breeding for resistance to virus yellows may be fruitful, but no resistant varieties have as yet been developed.

GEORGE H. COONS *was loaned in 1924 and 1925 to the Bureau of Plant Industry, Soils, and Agricultural Engineering by the Michigan State College, where he was professor of botany, to initiate the research program of breeding sugar beet varieties resistant to curly top and to leaf spot. After his return to the College, he continued as plant pathologist on a half-time basis with the Bureau until 1929, when he left Michigan State College to become principal pathologist in charge of sugar beet research projects in the division of sugar plant investigations.*

Rots, Blights, and Leaf Diseases of Sorgo

E. V. Abbott, P. E. Bouchereau

Sorgo is the term applied to the juicy, sweet-stemmed members of the genus *Sorghum* that are grown for sirup production. Sorgo is grown for sirup on approximately 90,000 acres in the Great Plains and the South. More than 80 percent of the acreage is in 11 Southern States.

Sorgo might some day be a commercial source of sugar, but it is not that now because we do not have varieties with the necessary productiveness, disease resistance, and adaptability to the areas where they would be grown as a sugar crop.

The sweet sorgos are subject to the same diseases as the forage and grain sorghums, but the relative importance of some of the diseases varies.

The head smuts, for example, which are important in the grain sorghums, do less damage to the sorgos. Some leaf and stalk rot diseases are much worse in the sorgos, particularly those grown in the more humid regions. The longer growing period required for sorgo grown for sugar production leads to greater difficulty with stalk rots.

Three groups of diseases affect sorgo: Seed rots and seedling blights, leaf diseases, and stalk rots.

The seed and seedling diseases may be caused by several different fungi. Their severity depends on weather and soil conditions. They are more severe when cool, wet weather follows planting. They often reduce stands, but satisfactory stands can usually be obtained, even though the diseases are not completely controlled, by treating the seed with fungicides before planting. The hazard of loss is reduced by delaying planting in the spring until favorable temperatures for germination are in prospect. These diseases are not considered a major obstacle in the development of sorgo varieties for sugar production.

Of greater importance are the major leaf diseases, anthracnose (caused by *Colletotrichum graminicola*), zonate leaf spot (*Gloeocercospora sorghi*), and rust (*Puccinia purpurea*). They are worst in the humid sections near the Gulf.

Anthracnose causes small, roundish, discolored spots on the leaves. The young lesions are reddish orange or dark purple and later become grayish or dark straw-colored. In moist weather their surfaces are covered with the pink masses of fruiting bodies of the fungus. Long, rather oval lesions also occur commonly on the leaf midribs. Destruction of leaf area may seriously injure the plant, particularly by delaying maturity.

Zonate leaf spot, so called because of the large spots with wide bands of reddish purple alternating with straw-colored tissue, may defoliate some plants before they mature. Some of the more vigorous and otherwise desirable varieties now available are susceptible to it. They may mature sufficiently for satisfactory sirup production, but the destruction of leaf area prevents the degree of maturity necessary for sugar production in humid sections. The disease limits the production of sugar sorgos in the sugar-producing areas of southern Louisiana.

Rust on sorgo resembles the leaf rusts of small grains. Its raised pustules are covered with a thin membrane, which eventually breaks and permits the escape of the powdery, reddish-brown spores of the fungus. Sometimes only a few scattered rust pustules are present on a leaf, but in warm, humid weather they may become so numerous on the leaves of the susceptible varieties as to cause pre-

mature death and drying of the leaves.

The three leaf diseases occur also on Johnsongrass. Where the weed is prevalent, as it is in the sugar-producing area of southern Louisiana, it provides a ready source of initiating epidemics of disease in commercial plantings of sorgo. The disease organisms presumably live over the winter on Johnsongrass. Zonate leaf spot and rust generally decline somewhat in severity northward from the Gulf of Mexico.

Other leaf diseases that may be important on some sorgo varieties in some years are leaf blight (caused by *Helminthosporium turcicum*), gray leaf spot (*Cercospora sorghi*), rough spot (*Ascochyta sorghi*), and bacterial stripe (*Pseudomonas andropogoni*).

The major disease problem to be met in developing varieties of sorgo suitable for sugar production is red rot of the stalk. The causal organism, the same fungus that causes leaf anthracnose, is closely related to *Colletotrichum falcatum*, which causes a similar disease of sugarcane. Strains of the sorgo red rot fungus occur on several other grasses, including Johnsongrass.

Red rot of the stalk is characterized by reddish, purplish, or orange discoloration of the pith (depending on the variety). Lighter bars extend crosswise through the darker background. The general pattern of the disease is like that produced by red rot of sugarcane. The fungus may break through the rind, producing elongate, sunken lesions, which are frequently covered with the fungus fruiting bodies. Besides lowering the quality of juice for sirup or sugar, the disease, by causing the stems to break, greatly reduces tonnage. Its critical importance in considering varieties for sugar production arises from the fact that the disease gets worse as plants mature.

Ordinarily the stalk-rotting phase of red rot is not of major importance in sorgo grown for sirup. But sorgo grown for sugar needs a greater degree of maturity and hence a longer growing period; red rot might therefore rot completely the stalks of some varieties.

Breeding varieties that resist red rot and have other essential qualities is the main problem to be met in the development of sorgo for sugar production.

Neither the leaf diseases nor red rot is yet amenable to economic control through the use of fungicidal dusts or sprays. Practical control depends on varietal resistance. In the genetic material now available to the sorgo breeder, resistance to all of the important diseases fortunately is present in one or more varieties.

The task of combining through breeding this resistance with the other qualities that would be required of a commercially adaptable sugar-producing sorgo is being carried forward by sorgo breeders in the Department.

While encouraging progress has been made, hybrid varieties satisfactorily meeting all of the requirements have not yet been produced.

E. V. ABBOTT *is a pathologist in the Bureau of Plant Industry, Soils, and Agricultural Engineering.*

P. E. BOUCHEREAU *is a pathologist of the division of sugar plant investigations of the Bureau, and has headquarters at Beltsville, Md.*

Sugar beet curly top.

Sugarcane and Its Diseases

E. V. Abbott

Sugarcane is native to or is grown in some 50 countries or political units within approximately 40° north latitude to 32° south. It is an important crop for thousands of small farmers with only a few acres. It also is the basis of large plantation enterprises. It is native to the Eastern Hemisphere, but since the Second World War the Western Hemisphere has produced about 55 percent of the world's cane sugar.

Sugarcane is commonly thought of as a thick-stemmed, tall grass, cultivated in tropical regions for the production of sugar from its juices. That conception is correct only in a limited sense. It does not take into consideration the numerous wild forms of the sugarcane genus *Saccharum* that are not thick-stemmed, high in sucrose content, or grown in tropical regions.

Even the present commercial sugarcanes often disappoint the person who sees them for the first time, particularly in the southern United States, where, instead of the large-stemmed, broad-leaved sugarcane of the textbook, the visitor finds a plant with narrow leaves and stalks of more slender girth—a plant that, while possibly lacking some of the physical attractiveness of its noble-type ancestors, has gained the vigor, disease resistance, and adaptability to other elements of its environment that are essential in this section. It is, in fact, a new plant, created to meet specific requirements through the blending by cross-breeding of the so-called noble and wild forms of the genus *Saccharum*.

The known forms of sugarcane are classified into five species: *Saccharum officinarum*, the traditional sugarcanes, which have thick, soft stems, broad leaves, and attractive appearance and therefore are commonly termed "noble" canes; *S. barberi*, the slender-stemmed canes of northern India; *S. sinense*, also slender-stemmed types, native to China; *S. spontaneum*, native to continental and insular Asia and to parts of Africa, a diverse group of grassy forms, which do not have direct commercial use for sugar production, but which are important sources of vigor and disease resistance in breeding; and *S. robustum*, wild forms of great vigor, indigenous to New Guinea and some adjacent islands.

Disease epidemics are known to have occurred in Mauritius and Reunion in the 1840's and in Brazil in the 1860's. Complaints of "degeneration" were heard elsewhere. Since the true nature of the difficulties was not understood at the time, however, the outbreak of sereh disease in Java in the early 1880's, which seriously threatened the industry there, stands out as of greater historical importance because of its influence on the future of sugarcane breeding and disease investigations. Sereh disease, presumed to be caused by a virus, forced a complete change in field practices, including the adoption of an expensive system of growing seed cane in elevated areas and the abandonment of ratoons. Satisfactory control was not attained until the Black Cheribon variety was eventually replaced with more resistant ones.

Sereh did not become widely distributed over the sugarcane-growing areas of the world. But another virus disease, mosaic, which was first observed in Java in the early 1890's, was carried to practically every cane-growing country before its true nature and seriousness were suspected. In most of them it assumed epiphytotic proportions that forced changes in varieties and caused enormous economic loss. In Louisiana, where it was superimposed on varieties already declining from the combined effects of root rot and red rot, it brought the industry to the brink of ruin in the 1920's. No other sugarcane disease has attained the universal importance of mosaic; yet, while it can still be considered a potential danger wherever it occurs, it has become one of the first major sugarcane diseases to be brought under a satisfactory degree of control in most countries through the development of resistant or tolerant varieties.

A third trouble, which caused widespread concern to the sugarcane world beginning in the late 1890's and continuing into the present century, was attributed to what was variously termed root rot, root disease, or root disease complex. In Java, the West Indies, Hawaii, Louisiana, and elsewhere, the declining yields and crop failures of the period were attributed in varying degree to root disease, but with less than universal agreement as to the specific cause. In the West Indies in particular, some of the losses at first attributed to root disease were later found to be due to red rot.

Species of the fungus genus *Marasmius*, to which the noble cane varieties are susceptible, were at first believed to be the main cause of root disease, but *Rhizoctonia* and other fungi were also blamed by some workers. Those fungi, however, are much less aggressive parasites than a member of the genus *Pythium* (*P. arrhenomanes*), which later was found to be the chief cause of root rot. Nevertheless, while all of the factors concerned in the growth difficulties of the period were not correctly diagnosed at the time, it was concern over root disease that stimulated the search for resistant varieties and the investigations that led to a better understanding of this and other diseases and their control.

BESIDES SEREH AND MOSAIC, five other diseases of sugarcane assumed to be of virus nature have been identified—Fiji disease, streak, chlorotic streak, dwarf, and ratoon stunting.

There have been unverified reports of the occurrence of sereh in the Philippines, Formosa, and India, but it has not assumed commercial importance outside Java. The disease has no certain diagnostic symptoms. Its effects vary widely on different varieties. A composite picture would include the extreme stunting of affected plants, with the arrested growth of successive shoots in the stool and a bunch-grass appearance; sprouting of the lateral buds on affected canes into leafy shoots; and excessive production of aerial roots at the nodes. No insect vector has been determined.

Fiji disease, named for the islands in which it was first observed, was identified in 1910, although it is believed to have been present there for at least 20 years before it was recognized as a disease. It caused serious loss to the industry of the islands before being brought under control by the use of resistant varieties. It has been definitely identified only in New Guinea, Queensland, and the Philippines, outside of Fiji. The disease causes extreme stunting of affected plants. It has one distinctive diagnostic symptom—the elongate galls it produces on the veins of the under surface of the leaves. Its insect vectors are members of the genus *Perkinsiella*.

Streak is also of limited geographic distribution. Its known occurrence is confined to South Africa, Egypt, India, and the island of Mauritius. It is characterized by the production of many narrow, elongate, sharply defined white streaks on the leaves. Its principal effect on the plant is reduced growth, with consequent loss in tonnage. While causing important loss to the Uba cane predominant in South Africa at the time of its discovery, losses have been greatly reduced by the substitution of more resistant clones. Its insect vector is *Cicadulina mbila*.

A comparative newcomer in the list of sugarcane diseases is chlorotic streak, first observed and described in Java in the late 1920's. It has since been found in Hawaii, Australia, Mauritius, Puerto Rico, Louisiana, and British Guiana. It is most prevalent and severe in cane growing on heavy, poorly drained soils, where it may markedly reduce germination, growth, and ratooning. Its only known insect vector is the leafhopper *Draculacephala portola*.

Two other diseases, presumed to be caused by viruses, dwarf and ratoon stunting, have been described in Queensland. Dwarf is not known to occur elsewhere, but what is apparently the same as the ratoon stunting disease was identified in the United States in 1952. This disease is of particular interest because it has no well-defined symptoms other than the retarded growth of affected plants. Because of this insidious nature, its presence was not suspected until experiments showed that the growth stunting could be transmitted. It is transmitted in infected cuttings, by knife cuts, and by inoculation of seed cuttings with juice of infected plants.

IN ANY PLANT that is propagated vegetatively, as sugarcane is, with the seed pieces consisting of succulent stems rich in carbohydrates, it is not surprising that rots of the seed cuttings are serious causes of poor stands. At each node of the stem is an axillary bud, which, when planted under required conditions of moisture and temperature, germinates to produce a new plant. Also at the node is a narrow band of rudimentary root buds from which the rootlets develop as the shoot bud germinates. The young plant depends on these roots, called seed roots, until it has produced sufficient stem tissue of its own for the permanent root system, or shoot roots, to develop. The seed roots are only temporary, but they serve the plant during a critical period between germination of the bud and establishment of the system of shoot roots.

Commercial practice with respect to the use of planting material varies in different countries. In the Tropics, where the high temperatures and adequate moisture usually favor a quick germination of the buds, the immature upper parts of the stem are used for planting. The more mature lower part of the stalk is left to be milled. In the subtropical sugarcane areas, such as Louisiana, where low temperatures following planting often mean a delay of several weeks before the new plants are established, the whole stalk is used as seed. It may be planted without segmenting, but more often is cut into shorter sections before planting, or, as in Louisiana, after being laid down in the furrow. In the Tropics, where there is little delay in germination of the buds after planting, seed-rotting diseases are much less important than in the subtropical fringes of the sugarcane-growing area, such as Louisiana, India, South Africa, and Queensland.

Of the seed-rotting diseases, red rot is one of the most serious. It rivals mosaic in its nearly universal distribution in the sugarcane world. First described in Java in 1893, it has since been identified in all countries where sugarcane is important.

A second widely distributed seed-rotting disease is caused by *Ceratostomella paradoxa*. Commonly it is termed pineapple disease because of the characteristic odor of the rotting cuttings, which is like that of decaying pineapples. The interior of affected seed pieces becomes sooty black. Eventually only the vascular bundles are left as fibrous strands in the hollow, blackened core. In contrast to red rot (which is favored by excessive soil moisture), pineapple disease is most destructive when cane is planted in soil that is too dry. Another major difference is that the red rot fungus is not soil-borne and infection occurs before planting, whereas the pineapple disease fungus lives in the soil. That fact makes the pineapple disease more susceptible to control through the use of protective fungicides. It may also

cause a rot of the stalk of growing cane, but that is not common.

Seed rots have also been ascribed to several other fungi, including *Ceratostomella adiposum* (black rot), *Fusarium* species (probably the same organism described as *Cephalosporium sacchari* as the cause of wilt in India), *Cytospora sacchari*, and *Phytophthora* species (in Louisiana).

ALTHOUGH ASSOCIATION of a species of *Pythium* with sugarcane roots was noted in Java in the 1880's, a member of this genus was not implicated as a primary cause of root rot until some 30 years later. During the intervening years, when root disease occupied such a prominent place in the minds of those concerned with the varietal troubles of the period, its true cause was not recognized.

In fields of young cane where the plants have a general unthrifty appearance, pythium root rot (*Pythium arrhenomanes*) is to be suspected. On the highly susceptible noble varieties, destruction of roots by the disease causes severe wilting and yellowing of the leaves, stunting, and sometimes death of the plant. Deficient tillering is also characteristic. On the more resistant hybrid varieties now commonly grown, the above-ground symptoms are less marked, though the effects of the disease may be recognized in the stunted growth, shortened internodes of young plants, deficient tillering, and (during hot, dry weather) varying degrees of yellowing of the leaves and wilting. When such plants are dug up, pythium injury is evident in the flabby, water-soaked appearance of the young roots, rotted root tips, and a deficiency of secondary roots. In stubble or ratoon fields, root rot often prevents or greatly delays sprouting of the stubbles, with resultant gappy stands and frequent failure.

Differences in the physical, chemical, and biological conditions of the soil exert an important influence on the severity of root rot. So marked is this influence that early workers sometimes cited one or another soil condition as the sole cause of root rot. In Louisiana, as elsewhere, the disease is more severe on soils with a high percentage of clay, mainly because of the greater moisture-holding capacity of those soils and their poorer drainage, which results both from their texture and commonly lower-lying position in the field. Aside from the fact that the higher moisture content generally associated with soils of heavy texture is favorable to the *Pythium*, the presence of toxic organic compounds in such soils may predispose the cane plant to infection by the fungus.

The main injury occurs during winter and early spring, when low temperatures and commonly excessive moisture resulting from heavy rainfall and poor drainage provide good conditions for the root rot fungus. Destruction of the seed roots by root rot or other causes may thus interfere directly with satisfactory establishment of the new plants and indirectly by favoring the spread of rots in the seed piece as a result of the delayed germination. Injury caused by root rot during the winter may not be fully evident until some months later, when during hot, dry weather the plants with deficient roots may suddenly wilt and die.

As with other diseases of cane, the losses caused by root diseases have been greatly reduced by the breeding of resistant varieties. Nevertheless pythium root rot is still a factor in areas such as Louisiana, where on inadequately drained soils the disease may cause injury in winter. It may, in fact, be more important than is generally believed, because of the absence of well-defined symptoms and the difficulty of fully appraising the role of a growth-retarding disease that is active only on the roots and that has effects so closely related to those of seed-rotting diseases.

BASAL STEM ROT, attributed to *Marasmius sacchari*, was found in Java in 1895, but it was soon discovered that the organism only rarely was associated with true root rot. However, during the next 20 to 30 years it was quite generally assumed in several other countries that the conspicuous *Marasmius* (including also *M. stenophyllus*) was the cause of root rot. On the susceptible noble varieties then grown, *Marasmius* doubtless was a contributing factor in the root-disease complex, but later investigations disclosed that *Pythium* is the primary cause of root rot troubles. The disease caused by *Marasmius* has therefore assumed an historical role out of proportion to its true importance.

Basal stem rot affects the lower part of the stem both above and below ground level. The sheaths commonly are tightly cemented to the stem by the mass of grayish-white mycelium, from which the toadstool fruiting bodies arise. Young shoots may also be invaded and are sometimes killed. Healthy and actively growing plants are seldom attacked, but the disease may further injure those already weakened by root rot, which probably accounts for its greater development during periods of drought when the effects of true root rot are most pronounced. Of minor economic importance, the disease now is less prevalent than formerly because the more resistant hybrids have replaced the susceptible noble types.

SMUT (*Ustilago scitaminea*) is characterized by the production from the growing point of a long, whiplike shoot, often several feet in length. The smut spores are scattered when the membrane covering this shoot bursts. Infection takes place through the seed piece and through the axillary buds of the growing plant. Germination of buds from infected cuttings may be seriously reduced, the plant is stunted, and ratooning ability is weakened.

Until 1941 we thought the disease occurred only in the Eastern Hemisphere. It was discovered in 1941 in Argentina and later in southern Brazil. It has caused serious losses in

Argentina. In Brazil it appears to be localized in occurrence.

The noble canes are resistant. Where they have been the predominant varieties, the disease has been of less importance than where varieties carrying ancestry of *S. spontaneum* and *S. barberi* were grown. The latter fact makes it potentially important for the southern United States, where breeding lines and commercial varieties carry a strong infusion from those two species.

Two fungus top-rotting diseases are of minor importance, pokkah boeng, caused by *Fusarium moniliforme (Gibberella fujikuroi)*, and dry top rot, caused by *Plasmodiophora vascularum*. First described in Java, pokkah boeng, a Javanese term meaning damaged top, has since been noted in most of the important sugarcane countries. Injury varies from slight chlorosis and splitting of the base of young unfolding leaves to top rotting, which may kill the growing point. While common in certain susceptible varieties during warm, rainy weather, it is seldom of commercial importance.

Dry top rot causes drying, wilting, and sometimes death of the plant because of clogging of the vascular tissues of the lower part of the stalks. First described in Puerto Rico, it has not been found outside the Caribbean area.

OF THE SEVERAL FUNGUS leaf diseases of sugarcane, only two, eyespot (*Helminthosporium sacchari*) and downy mildew (*Sclerospora sacchari*), are of major importance.

Eyespot is widespread and was serious in Hawaii and Florida until susceptible varieties gave way to resistant ones. The principal loss is from the reduced growth and lowered sucrose content of the juice that result from the destruction of leaf area. The disease produces elongate, oval spots, which at first are water-soaked, then yellowish, and later reddish brown, and are surrounded by a yellowish halo. Size of the lesions varies according to the resistance of the variety. On susceptible varieties long runners develop from the ends of the lesions. Sometimes they extend most of the length of the leaf. Coalescence of the reddish-brown lesions and runners may give a fired appearance to the leaf. The disease is favored by cool, moist weather.

Downy mildew occurs only in the Eastern Hemisphere. Once a major disease in Queensland, it has been controlled by the use of resistant varieties. It makes yellowish-green streaks on the leaves between the veins, a whitish down on the under surface composed of the mycelium and spores of the fungus, and pronounced abnormal elongation of some of the canes, causing them to stand out like flags 2 to 3 feet above the surrounding plants. The elongated part of the stem is extremely thin. The leaves are sparse and stunted. In the late stages, affected leaves become shredded by the death of tissue between the bundles. The disease seriously reduces growth. Transmission is by wind-borne spores that infect the immature lateral buds, through which the disease is transmitted to the new plants.

Corn and teosinte are also susceptible. Species of the genus *Sorghum* become infected, but they are resistant and there is little likelihood that they are factors in spreading the disease.

Other leaf diseases that are generally of minor importance, but sometimes of local importance, are brown spot (*Cercospora longipes*), yellow spot (*Cercospora kopkei*), brown stripe (*Helminthosporium stenospilum*), and ring spot (*Leptosphaeria sacchari*). All but yellow spot occur in the Southern States.

FOUR DISEASES caused by bacteria have been described: Gummosis (*Xanthomonas vasculorum*), leaf scald (*X. albilineans*), red stripe (*X. rubrilineans*), and mottled stripe (*X. rubrisubalbicans*). Gummosis and leaf scald are regarded as major diseases. Local outbreaks of red stripe have been serious. Mottled stripe is of minor importance.

Gummosis is the oldest disease of sugarcane to be recognized as such. It was described in Brazil in 1869. Its cause and true nature were not determined until some years later. It is believed to be native to Brazil, from which it was apparently carried in seed cuttings to Mauritius, Australia, and Fiji. It also occurs in several islands of the Caribbean area. In all countries where it occurs it has caused epidemics that were brought under control only by changing to resistant varieties. Consequently it has subsided to a position of potential rather than actual major importance.

It is primarily a disease of the vascular system. It receives its name from the slimy gum that oozes from cut ends of affected stalks. Yellowish streaks, usually dotted with red or brownish spots, are produced on the leaves, usually near the tips. Narrow at first, they may broaden to about one-half inch in width and elongate to nearly the length of the leaf. Frequently they widen to a V-shape toward the apex of the leaf, the tips and margins of which become dried and withered. Top rotting may result when the terminal bud is invaded. That often is followed by shooting of the lateral buds. The disease is transmitted in infected cuttings used for seed and by knife cuts and other means of physical contact.

Leaf scald used to be confused with gummosis, but the two were eventually recognized as distinct diseases. Like gummosis, scald is primarily a vascular disease, but differs from the former in the type of streaks produced on the leaves and in the absence of oozing of gum from cut ends of diseased stems.

The leaf streaks begin as sharply defined, narrow, white pencil stripes which may extend the entire length of the blade and onto the sheath. As the leaves grow older the streaks tend to broaden and become more diffuse. There may be only one or several streaks on a leaf. Sometimes, instead of the definite stripes, the entire shoot is chlorotic to nearly white. Diseased plants have a characteristic stunted appearance and the terminal whorl of leaves curves inward at the tips, which are often dried or withered. Sprouting of the lateral buds beginning at the base of the stalk is characteristic and may occur when there is no apparent injury to the top. In the acute stage, some shoots or the entire stool may suddenly wilt and die. The disease causes marked reductions in growth, tillering, and ratooning ability of susceptible varieties.

The known distribution of leaf scald was limited to the Eastern Hemisphere and Hawaii, but in 1944 it was found in Brazil and in 1950 in British Guiana. The disease is highly infectious. It is spread through infected cuttings, knife cuts, and probably by other means of physical contact. Insect vectors of the disease are not known but the disease may be spread by rats.

Red stripe produces narrow, sharply defined blood-red stripes, which may be short or extend nearly the length of the leaf. They are usually more prevalent on the younger, fully unfolded leaves; when conditions particularly favor the disease, however, infection spreads to the younger leaves and the growing point, often resulting in top rotting. The rot may extend into the mature portions of the stem to ground level, and is accompanied by a characteristic disagreeable odor. At one time the disease had some importance in several countries, but outbreaks now are infrequent and localized.

WEATHER markedly affects the severity of several diseases of sugarcane and sometimes may be a determining factor in their distribution. Red rot, for example, is important as a rot of seed cuttings only in the subtropical fringes of cane-growing regions in the Temperate Zone, while in the warmer Tropics, where uniformly high temperatures favor quick germination of the cuttings after planting, it is of minor importance.

Prolonged periods of wet, cool weather, such as commonly occur in Louisiana in winter, are unfavorable for the germination and growth of sugarcane, but they favor the development of fungi that cause seed rots and root rot. Growth of cane is slow between 60° and 70° F., temperatures which may occur for considerable periods during the winter months, but the fungi causing red rot and root rot are able to grow at those temperatures. Consequently, if the red rot fungus has gained entrance into the seed piece, it will continue to develop during cool periods when the cane is unable to grow. Likewise, the young rootlets produced by the cane during relatively warm periods may be attacked and largely destroyed by root-rotting fungi when their growth is checked by cool weather. For the same reason, freezing temperatures that kill leaves and shoots of young cane in winter or spring may cause more damage than merely killing the foliage itself. The cane plant loses what progress it has been able to make during favorable periods and because of exhaustion of food reserves may not be able to recover. But the disease organisms do not lose the progress they have made. Instead, they may continue to develop, destroying roots and further depleting food reserves in the seed cuttings. Therefore young cane that apparently has established a good stand may fail to recover following a freeze, and stands may die out during cool, wet spells in the spring even though a freeze does not occur.

During the growing season, particularly in summer, hard, dashing rains and winds aid in the spread of fungus and bacterial diseases that affect the leaves and stalks of cane. Dissemination of the stage of the red rot fungus occurring on the leaf midribs is favored in this way. The leaf disease, brown spot, spreads most rapidly during the rainy summer months. The top-rotting diseases, pokkah boeng and red stripe are most severe during hot, humid weather. Eyespot, on the other hand, is favored by cool, humid weather. The leaf diseases, brown stripe and mottled stripe, and the basal stem rot caused by *Marasmius* are more prevalent during dry weather.

CERTAIN DISEASES are more severe on some soils than others. It is common experience that root rot, red rot, and other seed-rotting diseases are more severe on the heavy clay soils than on the lighter-textured sandy soils. That largely is due to the higher moisture content of such soils resulting both from their physical structure and consequent greater moisture-holding capacity, but often also from their lower-lying position in the field, which makes drainage more difficult. Those conditions are unfavorable for germination of sugarcane seed cuttings and for root development, but they do favor root- and seed-rotting organisms.

ASIDE from those more obvious relationships, other biological factors are involved. Toxins may develop under the partial anaerobic conditions that often prevail in waterlogged soils. Antibiotic organisms affect sugarcane pathogens. Soil biological problems as related to sugarcane diseases have not been studied adequately. From practical experience, however, it is known that improvement of drainage results in increased yields, partly because there is less injury from diseases.

Chlorotic streak is more prevalent and severe on heavy, poorly drained soils than on lighter, well-drained ones. That fact has been observed in all countries where the disease has been studied, but the reason for it is not known. As we have no proof that the causal agent is soil-borne or that the activity of the one known vector (*Draculacephala portola*) is related to soil differences, it may be that the less favorable growing conditions for cane on heavy soils influences the metabolism of the sugarcane plant in such a way as to make it more susceptible to the disease.

THE SUGARCANE GROWER controls diseases mainly by replacing susceptible varieties with resistant varieties.

As a result of the ceaseless race between the growers and diseases, with the resultant never-ending varietal changes, probably no group of farmers is as conscious of varieties as are the growers of sugarcane. So spectacular have been some of the past achievements resulting from replacement of disease-susceptible with resistant varieties that to many growers a new variety still holds the possibility of a miracle and often, unfortunately, a fascination that cannot be resisted when the opportunity arises to obtain a new variety from other than approved sources.

Many diseases owe their spread from their native habitats to other countries to this search for new varieties. An unrecognized disease often is introduced in a variety that was brought into a country in an effort to overcome one already there. Before it was recognized as an infectious disease, mosaic was thus distributed over most of the sugarcane areas, and gummosis moved from the Western to the Eastern Hemisphere. Belated recognition of what was occurring resulted in the institution of quarantines in most countries, prohibiting the importation of sugarcane except through authorized government-controlled agencies. While those measures have greatly deterred the further distribution of diseases, as evidenced by the numerous interceptions that have been made in quarantine, they have not been entirely successful. Smut and leaf scald have become established in South America and chlorotic streak in Louisiana since the institution of quarantines.

Doubtless some of the earliest spread of diseases from one country to another resulted from the desire of migrating peoples to carry their favorite eating canes with them in moving from one region to another. It may be assumed that some of the early unrecorded dissemination of disease occurred in this way, while in more recent times importation of contract laborers who carried chewing canes with them is believed to have been the means of spreading the diseases.

THE CHANCE DISCOVERY of Kassoer, the supposedly natural hybrid between the wild cane of Java and the Noble Black Cheribon, which proved to be resistant to sereh, presented dramatically to the Dutch scientists the possibilities of obtaining disease-resistant varieties through the crossing of different parent stocks. The result has been the development in many cane-growing countries of breeding programs, a primary aim of which is the production of resistant varieties.

Observations of differences in reaction to disease among varieties of different species of sugarcane led to a search for resistant germ plasm by breeders and pathologists.

FORMS of *S. officinarum*, noble canes, were almost universally the world's commercial sugarcanes before the outbreaks of epiphytotics of disease. Because of disease susceptibility, few now remain in large-scale commercial cultivation. They are, however, important in breeding work as sources of many of the qualities required in a commercial cane other than disease resistance, such as large diameter of stalk, low fiber, and good quality of juice. With few exceptions, the noble varieties are susceptible to the major diseases, including mosaic, sereh, streak, red rot, root rot, and gummosis. As a group, their greatest resistance is to smut, although some varieties are also resistant to leaf scald.

Varieties of *S. barberi* are generally susceptible to red rot. They are susceptible to, though tolerant of, mosaic. They are intermediate in resistance to pythium root rot, moderately susceptible to smut, and resistant to sereh, streak, and gummosis.

The wild, grassy members of *S. spontaneum* are important sources of resistance to several diseases. They are resistant to sereh, pythium root rot, and gummosis; some of them are resistant to red rot and (with the exception of the forms from Turkestan) are resistant or immune to mosaic. On the other hand, they are susceptible to smut, Fiji disease, red stripe, downy mildew, and some of the leaf-spotting diseases.

Forms of *S. sinense* are resistant to sereh, pythium root rot, gummosis, and generally to mosaic. They are very susceptible to smut. Most forms for which there are records are susceptible to red rot and streak. This species has been used relatively little in breeding.

Relatively few forms of *S. robustum* have been tested for disease resistance. In the United States they have proved to be susceptible to mosaic, pythium root rot, and intermediate in resistance to red rot. Both resistance and susceptibility to gummosis have been recorded. Fiji disease and downy mildew have been observed on them in their native habitat in New Guinea.

COMPARED with the use of resistant varieties, other means of controlling sugarcane diseases are less important. Disease injury sometimes may be minimized by planting at such time as to escape severe infection or by avoiding the planting of varieties susceptible to certain diseases in soils where the effects of such diseases are most severe.

Progress has been made in the control of the seed-cane rot, pineapple disease, by the use of protective fungicides in South Africa, Hawaii, and Queensland. For several reasons, economical methods for the use of fungicidal seed treatments have not been developed in the southern United States. Certain leaf-spotting diseases could be controlled by the application of fungicides but the losses caused by them are not sufficient to justify the expense.

Considerable work has been done on the control of the diseases by treating the seed cuttings with hot water. The pioneer experiments in this field were done by the Dutch in Java in an effort to control sereh, and it has since been tried there and elsewhere as a curative for other diseases that are transmitted in the seed cuttings. Various temperatures and time intervals have been used, as a result of which exposure at 125.6° F. for 20 minutes is generally considered the standard treatment. Mature buds of most sugarcane varieties can be subjected to the treatment without injury; in fact, it usually results in stimulation of germination. Lower temperatures or shorter periods of exposure may not be effective in killing the disease organisms, while higher temperatures or longer intervals of exposure frequently injure the cane buds.

The standard hot-water treatment eliminates infection by the virus diseases sereh and chlorotic streak and the bacterial disease gummosis. It is partly effective against leaf scald and is not effective against mosaic or streak. Spores of some leaf-spotting fungi that may be present on the cuttings are killed by the treatment. Although certain diseases can be controlled by the hot-water treatment and some increase in germination and yields of cane often results aside from any control of the diseases, the treatment has not been widely adopted in plantation planting. That is because the benefits derived generally have not been sufficient to justify the expense. A deterrent also is the fact that the very exact temperature control required is often difficult to maintain in large-scale handling of the bulky seed material. If the temperature falls below the required level, the purposes of the treatment will not be accomplished; if it goes much above, the cane buds may be injured. Hot-water treatment is widely used by quarantine authorities in the movement of planting material from one country to another.

E. V. ABBOTT *is a pathologist in the division of sugar plant investigations of the Bureau of Plant Industry, Soils, and Agricultural Engineering. He is stationed at Houma, La.*

Red Rot of Sugarcane

E. V. Abbott

Red rot is a serious disease of sugarcane in the southern United States. It causes a rot of seed cuttings that commonly results in faulty stands of plant cane or sometimes complete failures, reductions in stands of stubble or ratoon crops because of the rotting of the underground parts of the stem from which the crops arise, and annual losses of sucrose in mill cane from infection of the stalks that usually follows injury by the sugarcane moth borer, *Diatraea saccharalis*.

Besides the loss in tonnage from reduced stands of cane, red rot lowers the amount of recoverable sugar at the factory because of the inversion of sucrose in the stalk, which is accompanied by lowered purity of the juice and other untoward chemical changes.

Because it is most destructive as a rot of seed cuttings, red rot causes little injury to seed cane if conditions favor the early germination of the buds after planting, as in the Tropics. In the subtropics, however, such as India, South Africa, and Queensland, where considerable time may elapse between the time of planting and the establishment of new plants, it frequently reduces stands badly. As a rot of mill cane, on the other hand, it may be more important in the tropical areas, where the longer growing season gives the fungus more time in which to spread through the stalks between the time of infection and milling of the cane.

Red rot was first described in Java in 1893. Shortly thereafter it was identified in the West Indies, where it was considered at first to be a cause of the then prevalent root disease. Within the next 20 years its occurrence was recorded in Queensland, India, Hawaii, and Louisiana. It now is one of the most widely distributed of the diseases of sugarcane.

Red rot has been a major cause of the decline of several varieties of sugarcane in the Southern States. First identified in Louisiana in 1909, it doubtless was a factor in the general downward trend in the average yield that began early in this century in Louisiana. It was one of the causes of the failure of the Louisiana Purple and D–74 varieties in Louisiana in the 1920's and of those and other noble-type varieties in the other Gulf States. It forced the discontinuance as a commercial cane of the variety P. O. J. 2714 in southern Florida.

The noble varieties were replaced in Louisiana with hybrids from Java, one of which, P. O. J. 213, became the leading commercial variety in the State by 1931. Classed as resistant to red rot when it was released, it suddenly failed from red rot in the early 1930's. In the sirup-producing districts of the Gulf States, Cayana 10 and P. O. J. 213 became the most popular replacements of the older canes, but both eventually succumbed to red rot. Some of the other varieties that have succeeded them as important commercial canes have also declined from red rot, but they were tested more rigidly before they were released to growers, and their potential weakness in this respect was recognized at the time of their release.

THE FUNGUS that causes red rot may infect any part of the sugarcane plant. Its principal importance is as a rot of the stalk of standing cane, of seed cuttings, or of the stubble pieces remaining in the ground after the cane is harvested. It produces long lesions on the leaf midribs. The lesions usually cause no serious injury to the plant but are important in the life history of the disease because they are sources of the spores that cause infection of the stalk.

Red rot often cannot be told on external examination of the stalk unless it has rotted the interior so completely as to cause the rind to lose its natural bright color and to look dull. Plants so affected may be detected by the yellowing, shriveling, and dying of the upper leaves. More certain identification may be made by splitting the stalk or seed cutting. Then one recognizes the disease by the reddening of the normally white or creamy-white internal tissues and cross-barring of the reddened area with occasional white or light patches. Unless the cross bars are present, identification of red rot may be uncertain without microscopic examination or culturing of the fungus. Almost any sort of wounding causes a reddening of the stalk tissues next to the wound, but when red rot is present the characteristic discoloration usually extends considerably beyond the point of origin. In advanced stages of rotting, the interior of the stalk darkens and the tissues shrink, leaving a cavity, which may be filled with the mycelium of the fungus.

The lesions on the leaf midribs are dark or blood red, and may occur as short, discontinuous blotches or as long ones that extend nearly the length of the leaf. The centers become straw-colored with age and are later covered with the black, powdery masses of the spores of the fungus.

The fungus causing red rot is commonly known by its imperfect stage, *Colletotrichum falcatum*, although *Physalospora tucumanensis* is the perfect stage of the fungus. If a fairly large number of isolates of the fungus obtained from different cane varieties or geographic areas are studied on artificial culture media, considerable variation in the type of growth and color of the fungus colony usually is seen. Some isolates or races are light gray and form a loose cottony colony. Others are dark gray and form a restricted velvety colony. Others are intermediate in those respects. If they are inoculated into stalks of sugarcane, the fact that they differ also in pathogenicity—their ability to infect and rot the stalks—will be seen.

It is this variability of the fungus that makes it appear that some sugarcane varieties are unstable in their resistance to the disease. Often a new variety, when it is released to growers, may be resistant to the races of the fungus then prevalent. If a race that is virulent toward that variety is present or appears later, however, it may build up on it and eventually cause serious injury. We have evidence that that occurred with the variety P. O. J. 213 in Louisiana in the early 1930's. Some growers believe this change in predominance of races of disease organisms indicates an inherent change in the sugarcane variety with respect to its disease resistance. The real explanation, though, is to be sought in changes in the prevailing populations of the disease organism.

THE INFECTIONS of the leaf midrib provide the means of dissemination of the disease during the growing season and the source of inoculum for stalk infections. The infections appear in Louisiana in the late spring and continue to develop on new leaves as they are produced during the summer.

On the midrib lesions the fungus produces an abundance of spores, which are carried by wind or splashed by rain to other leaves and plants. Heavy dews and rains wash the spores down the leaf blade to the attachment of sheath to the stalk, where the spore-laden moisture may be held for some time in contact with the nodal region of the stem. The spores may also be washed down the stalk, where they cause infections through the tunnels made by the moth borer.

During the growing season, infection of various parts of the plant may occur at the nodal region, including the buds, leaf scars, and root buds. In very susceptible varieties the fungus may penetrate into the internal stalk tissues of standing cane. As a rule, however, that does not occur until the stalks are cut and planted as seed cane. Then if temperature and moisture conditions do not favor early germination of the buds and establishment of new plants, the fungus may invade the stalk and impair germination. The extent to which the stalks are invaded through the nodal region varies greatly with different varieties.

In countries where freezing weather does not occur and the cane grows throughout the year, the fungus is always active. Where freezes occur, however, there may be periods of weeks or months when no living portion of the plant is above ground. Then the fungus survives in trash or crop refuse in the planted seed pieces or on stubble from the previous crop. In the spring when growth starts, infection of the new leaves occurs from such overwintering sources. Apparently the fungus does not survive in the soil.

After the fungus invades the tissues of the stalk, the mycelium may spread sidewise and up and down from cell to cell. More rapid longitudinal spread may occur by migration of the spores through the vascular bundles.

Varieties differ in the extent and rapidity of the spread of the spores in this way, because some have many bundles that are continuous through the nodes from one internode to the other. In other varieties few bundles are continuous. In varieties with a large number of continuous bundles, the spores may spread through the entire stalk; if the bundles are discontinuous, the fungus may be checked for a time at the nodes. Thus it happens that some varieties whose tissues have little resistance may not be seriously damaged by the disease because of the checking of longitudinal spread through the nodes. This type of resistance offers less protection, however, if the variety is highly susceptible to infection at the nodes, or if the stalk is seriously damaged by the stalk borer; since the tunnels of this insect in successive internodes offer a ready means of separate infection.

Injury to seed cuttings by red rot is not limited to conditions of excessive soil moisture that often prevail in heavy soils, but they do favor greatly the development of the disease. Often the severity of red rot then is also associated with injury by pythium root rot. If the rootlets arising from the seed cutting are destroyed by root rot during germination, the development of the new shoot may be retarded. If red rot has invaded the seed piece, the spread of the disease during the period of delayed establishment of the new plant may kill the young shoots. Thus the degree of injury from red rot may be greatly influenced by the susceptibility of the variety to root rot. A variety that is susceptible to red rot but resistant to root rot may be less injured than one that is only moderately resistant to red rot but very susceptible to root rot.

A common source of infection of the stalk by red rot is through the tunnels of the moth borer. Frequently the degree of injury to mill cane by the disease depends on the extent of infestation by this insect—particularly in areas like Louisiana, where during the relatively short growing season infections of the stalk (other than those that occur from insect injury) do not have time to develop sufficiently to cause important damage to the cane before it is milled. Red rot damage to seed cuttings also is often increased by borer damage and in some varieties may relate directly to the extent of infestation by the moth borer.

Infection of the underground parts of the stem after harvest, from which the stubble or ratoon crops arise, may occur through the tunnels of the sugarcane weevil (*Anacentrinus subnudus*). At times germination of the buds on the stubbles may be impaired by the combined effects of insect and disease injury.

As a seed-rotting disease, red rot is hard to control. Because infection of the stalk to be used for seed has occurred to a great extent before the time of planting, the fungus is largely beyond the reach of fungicides that control many seed-borne diseases of other crops.

Heat treatments that might reduce or eliminate the infection in the stalk are not economically feasible for large-scale use. Furthermore, the fungus is extremely variable; it comprises many parasitic races that apparently are being continually increased by mutation or hybridization. Thus there can be no certainty of the permanence of resistance because of the possibility of the development of virulent, specialized races on initially resistant varieties.

Also, red rot as a seed-rotting disease is favored by the very conditions that retard germination and growth of the cane plant. The balance may be thrown so far in favor of the parasite that ordinarily resistant varieties may at times be seriously damaged by the disease.

Finally, breeding for resistance to red rot is handicapped by the lack in parent material of the high degree of resistance or immunity that is available for some other diseases, such as mosaic or root rot.

Effective control, however, depends on the planting of resistant varieties. Progress has been made in developing resistant varieties under the breeding program of the Department in cooperation with State agricultural experiment stations. The varieties C. P. 36/105, C. P. 44/101, and C. P. 44/155, important commercial varieties in Louisiana, are resistant to red rot, as is C. P. 36/111, recommended for sirup production in Mississippi and other areas of the Gulf States.

Where it is feasible to do so, red rot injury can be avoided to a great extent by planting cane at a time that favors early germination and establishment of the new plants. In Louisiana, for example, part of the acreage commonly is planted in August, when high temperatures usually result in quick germination and establishment of stands. That practice avoids the danger of the injury that accompanies planting in fall, when there may be little growth for several weeks.

Improvement of drainage and the use of resistant varieties in heavy or inadequately drained soils lessen the hazards of injury. The use of seed cane that is as free as possible of borer infestation is desirable to avoid loss from both insects and red rot.

E. V. Abbott *is a pathologist in the division of sugar plant investigations, Bureau of Plant Industry, Soils, and Agricultural Engineering, and superintendent of the United States Sugar Plant Field Station, Houma, La.*

For further reading the author suggests his U. S. D. A. Technical Bulletin *641*, Red Rot of Sugarcane, *published in 1938, and the following:*

R. E. Atkinson: On the Nature of Resistance of Sugarcane to Red Rot, *Sixth Congress of the International Society of Sugar Cane Technologists, Proceedings, pages 684–692, 1938.*

E. J. Butler: Fungus Diseases of Sugarcane in Bengal, *India Department of Agriculture Memoirs, Botanical Series, volume 1, number 3, pages 2–24, 1906;* Red Rot of Sugarcane, *with Abdul Hafiz Khan, India Department of Agriculture Memoirs, Botanical Series, volume 6, number 5, pages 151–178, 1913.*

Fernando Carvajal and C. W. Edgerton: The Perfect Stage of Colletotrichum falcatum, *Phytopathology, volume 34, pages 206–213, 1944.*

C. W. Edgerton: Colletotrichum falcatum in the United States, *Science (new series), volume 31, pages 717–718, 1910;* The Red Rot of Sugarcane. A Report of Progress, *Louisiana Agricultural Experiment Station Bulletin 133, 22 pages, 1911;* Host-Parasite Relations in Red Rot of Sugarcane, *with F. Carvajal, Phytopathology, volume 34, pages 827–837, 1944.*

F. J. LeBeau: Pathogenicity Studies with Colletotrichum Isolates From Different Hosts on Sorghum and Sugar Cane, *Phytopathology, volume 40, pages 430–438, 1950.*

A. McMartin: Pineapple Disease of Sugarcane Cuttings and Its Control, *South African Sugar Journal, volume 28, pages 241–245, 1944;* Sugarcane Smut, *South African Sugar Journal, volume 32, pages 737–749, 1948.*

R. D. Rands and Ernest Dopp: Pythium Root Rot of Sugarcane, *U. S. D. A. Technical Bulletin 666, 96 pages, 1938.*

E. M. Summers, E. W. Brandes, and R. D. Rands: Mosaic of Sugarcane in the United States, With Special Reference to Strains of the Virus, *U. S. D. A. Technical Bulletin 955, 124 pages, 1948.*

F. A. F. C. Went: Het Rood Snot, *Archief Java Suikerindustrie, volume 1, pages 265–282, 1893.*

the tobacco

plant

Developments in Growing Tobacco

E. E. Clayton

During the early years of tobacco culture in the United States, the established practice was to grow tobacco only on new land. Trees were cut down, forests cleared, and the fields so made were planted to tobacco for a few years. The round was repeated as new lands and settlements opened farther west.

Under the system there was no tendency for disease problems to accumulate. But the supply of new land began to run out just before the turn of the century, and the next 30 years saw a rapid increase in disease problems. Granville wilt, black shank, and blue mold appeared then; under the new system of continuous cultivation in the same areas, growers found out that tobacco as a cultivated crop is subject to a whole series of diseases.

The uncertainty of the crop and the unhealthy conditions of many fields that were cropped repeatedly to tobacco led to the belief that tobacco was "hard on the land." Growers of burley in Kentucky learned that their crops did not grow well unless the land was "rested" a number of years between crops. We now know that the rest period was needed to reduce the amount of black root rot in the soil and to improve the physical condition of the soil—not because of exceptional demands on fertility.

The first line of defense against the diseases has been crop rotation. It is only moderately effective. It does most good against nematodes (root knot) and least against black shank and Granville wilt.

Hopes next were pinned to resistant varieties. Now we combat the diseases by using both rotations and disease-resistant sorts—a combination that is better than either one alone against such diseases as wilt and black shank. Soil treatments are available for plant beds as supplements to control weeds and diseases. Fungicides can be used to control blue mold. But chemical control measures are not popular with the tobacco farmer, who is typically a small operator, although fungicidal treatments for blue mold are well established in major areas.

BLUE MOLD is commonly a disease in plant beds. It first became established in the commercial tobacco-producing areas of the Southeast in 1931. Before then it occurred on wild *Nicotiana* (related to our cultivated tobacco) in Texas, California, and other Western States. Before 1931 the disease appeared in northern Florida, but failed to establish itself there.

The fungus that causes the disease produces a durable resting spore that lives over winter in the soil. For that reason old plant beds are primary sources of mold infection each spring. The first occurrence is generally in early February in the southern part of Georgia.

The early symptoms of blue mold vary somewhat with the age of plants at the time they become infected and the severity of attack. Because the effective use of control measures often depends on early detection of the disease, it is important to know the first symptoms.

When infection develops while the plants are very small—plants with leaves up to the size of a quarter—the first evidences of blue mold are small patches of seedlings with erect leaves. When plants are a little older—leaves up to the size of a dollar—the first evidence of blue mold is round, yellow areas. In either case, distinctly cupped

leaves grow in the center of each affected area. Some of the cupped leaves have a whitish or violet mold growth over the lower surface. About 2 weeks later one can expect to find the disease throughout the beds. When the infection is limited to the small patches, there is still time to begin a control program with fair chance of success. After the disease has spread through the bed, spray or dust treatments have little value.

The damage caused by blue mold depends on the age of the plants when attacked and on weather conditions at the time that the infection becomes widespread.

Sometimes the disease merely kills irregular areas of leaf tissues, giving the appearance of a burn caused by scalding water. Sometimes all leaf tissue, except the growing tip, is invaded and killed. Actual killing of the plants is most apt to happen if blue mold attacks young plants. The growth of affected plants may be delayed up to 4 or 5 weeks, although delays of 2 weeks or less generally are not serious. Plants that are not killed do recover and produce new foliage.

The new leaves are healthy and are temporarily immune to attack by the fungus. The immunity lasts 3 or 4 weeks, but it gives time for transplanting and the recovered plants grow normally.

It is best not to transplant from a bed infected with blue mold until the recovery is definitely under way. Recovery can be hastened by watering, if the beds are dry, or by fertilizing, if the plants need food. Indiscriminate applications of concentrated fertilizers, such as nitrate of soda, are likely to do more damage than good.

The spores of the fungus spread the disease and are produced in tremendous numbers. Winds can carry them for miles. Each year nearly every plant bed from Florida to Pennsylvania may become infected—even beds surrounded by woods. Wisconsin is the only tobacco area in which the disease does not occur—otherwise the area in which blue mold occurs each year is the area occupied by the crop.

The question that faces the growers, then, is not whether the disease will occur. It is: Will the attack be severe? In Georgia a destructive epidemic may be expected about 1 year in 3. In South Carolina destructive outbreaks are slightly less frequent. In North Carolina and Virginia the disease has been serious about 1 year in 5, but never so destructive as in Georgia. In Tennessee and Maryland really destructive outbreaks are unknown, but localized damage is not uncommon.

Blue mold illustrates how wasteful can be some attempts to control disease by fungicides. One has to spray or dust before disease occurs. Therefore in many areas and years, when the disease does little damage, the labor and materials used are largely lost. Growers often start to use control measures too late, stop too soon, or decide to take a chance. As a result, thousands of beds are poorly protected or unprotected.

An effective system for predicting the occurrence of blue mold would be helpful. On the basis of experience, if one merely predicted each year that blue mold attack would be moderate to light, however, his average accuracy would be 67 percent in Georgia and South Carolina, 80 percent in North Carolina and Virginia, and 95 percent in Maryland and Tennessee.

Conditions most favorable for the disease prevail in Georgia. What are those conditions? The first is low temperature. Blue mold develops best during maximum daytime temperatures of 60° to 75° F. and minimum night temperatures between 40° and 60°. Disease activity is slowed by minimum temperatures in the 30's and 40's, but ultimate damage then may be most severe because the recovery of affected plants is retarded even more than the disease is. Thus there is no true lower limit to the activity of blue mold. Blue mold ceases to become active when minimum night temperatures rise above 65°. Maximum day-

time temperatures above 85° also check the disease.

Low light also is important. When plants are shaded, the disease can flourish at considerably higher temperatures. Shading also greatly increases the percentage of plants killed. That is why blue mold is occasionally destructive in the Connecticut Valley shade-tobacco fields, while Havana and Broadleaf tobacco growing nearby in full sunlight is not seriously attacked.

Heavy rains do not favor the disease, but light rains and the foggy, humid periods lasting 2 or 3 days are most favorable. The cycle of blue mold from infection to the production of another crop of spores is only 7 days. Consequently a succession of three or four moist periods, about a week apart, plus cool weather, provides ideal conditions for blue mold.

The age and vigor of plant growth are other factors. In plant beds, blue mold can kill plants from the time they appear above ground until they are about half transplanting size. The smaller they are the more quickly are they killed. After plants are half transplanting size or larger, they may be completely defoliated by blue mold, but the growing tip and the stem usually remain alive. Such plants usually produce new leaves and recover, although transplanting may be delayed. Under field conditions, damage is limited to the killing of localized leaf areas, and rarely are entire leaves destroyed. Vigorous, rapidly growing plants are most susceptible to attack; plants that are retarded for any reason may escape serious damage.

Let us now see how those factors may operate to cause serious damage in an area like Georgia and less harm in an area like Maryland.

In Georgia:

Seed sowed.....................	Dec. 27.
Plants up.....................	Jan. 15.
Blue mold appears..............	Feb. 7.
Plants half-grown.............	Mar. 15.
Blue mold peak................	Mar. 15.
End of blue mold..............	Apr. 5.
Period of blue mold activity: 57 days.	

The dates in Maryland are:

Seed sowed................. Mar. 7.
Plants up.................. Apr. 1.
Blue mold appears.......... May 1.
Plants half-grown.......... May 15.
Blue mold peak............ May 25.
End of blue mold.......... June 5.
Period of blue mold activity: 36 days.

The figures may be considered average for the two areas. One important difference is the length of time the disease is likely to be active—57 days in Georgia and 36 in Maryland. Equally important is the fact that in Georgia the disease is active 5 weeks before the time the plants are half-grown, February 7 to March 15. In Maryland this critical period is only 2 weeks long, May 1 to May 15. Again, with a warm January in Georgia, plants come up early, and the blue mold may be observed as early as January 22. February weather in Georgia typically has many cool, foggy days, which favor the spread of blue mold. In Maryland the weather after blue mold appears is typically bright and clear. The differences explain why a disease with a destructive record in Georgia is only moderately troublesome in Maryland, although practically all beds in each State are infected each year.

Conditions in South Carolina approach those in Georgia. Tennessee, Kentucky, and Pennsylvania have conditions much like those in Maryland.

When blue mold became established in the flue-cured area in 1931, the disease had behind it a long history in Australia. Control was first attempted in the United States by spraying with bordeaux mixture. It failed. An extensive investigation of fungicides was made. An effective gas treatment was announced in 1935. Benzol was the material used. Benzol vapors held in by a heavy muslin cover were effective in Australia in preventing the disease and checking its development after infection had occurred.

A modification of the benzol gas treatment, worked out in this country, substituted paradichlorobenzene, a crystalline material. It was found that the crystals, scattered over the ordinary cotton used over tobacco beds and then covered with a heavy muslin, slowly vaporized. The vapors given off controlled the disease. Between 1.5 and 3 pounds of paradichlorobenzene are needed for 100 square yards, depending on whether the weather is cool or warm and on whether the cover is well above or down close to the plants.

A good practice is to wait until the disease is at hand and treat three successive nights the first week, and then twice a week. Five or seven treatments are usually enough for the season. Gas treatment is effective but laborious and expensive. It has been largely superseded by fungicidal sprays and dusts.

A combination of cuprous oxide and cottonseed oil makes a good spray. Its effectiveness is due to the protection it gives the leaf surface and its penetration into the leaf tissues. When the infection occurs, the size of the lesions is limited and the plant suffers only a slight attack.

The new carbamate materials, of which the first was Fermate-ferbam (ferric dimethyl dithiocarbamate), are effective against blue mold. Somewhat more effective is a similar material, Dithane Z-78; or Parzate; or zineb (zinc ethylene bisdithiocarbamate). They can be used as dusts or sprays equally effectively.

In areas where mold is very destructive, it is well to begin treatments when the plants are the size of a dime. Elsewhere treatments may be delayed until mold is first reported in the locality. The recommended rates for spraying are Fermate, 4 pounds to 100 gallons of water; Dithane Z–78 and Parzate, 3 pounds to 100 gallons. In mixing, the powder should be thoroughly worked into a little water before the bulk of the water is added. One should start applications in time, apply enough material so that the leaf surfaces are visibly coated, and make applications twice a week until the plants are in the field or mold has disappeared because of warm weather.

The usual schedule is two applications a week. Depending on the season and area, 7 to 12 applications will be needed. Spraying is usually done without removing the cotton covering from the bed. For 100 square yards when the plants are very small, about 3 gallons are needed; 5 or 6 gallons are needed when plants are half-grown. If mold appears in a bed that is being sprayed, the affected spots should be sprayed with a double-strength mixture for one or two applications, or the amount of spray mixture should be increased until the spread of the disease has been checked.

Failure to control blue mold with these methods very likely is due to too late a start (after the disease is spread throughout the bed) or an inadequate application that does not coat the leaves with the fungicide. During a wet period, instead of missing an application, as often happens, one should make an extra application.

The materials recommended for spraying are equally effective as dusts. Satisfactory dust formulations are Fermate, 15 percent; and Dithane Z–78 or Parzate, 10 percent. Talc or Pyrax (pyrophyllite) are satisfactory diluents. Fuller's earth, clays, lime, and land plaster are undesirable.

Dusting should be done when there is no wind. Early morning usually is the best time. If beds are 4 yards wide or less and the cotton cover is at least 6 inches above the ground, the dust can be applied without removing the cotton. If the bed is wide and the cotton close to the plants, one should remove the cotton.

The amounts of dust needed for 100 square yards of bed are about 2 pounds an application when plants are small and about 3 pounds when they are half-grown or larger. As with spraying, if blue mold does appear in a bed that is being dusted, the affected area should be treated heavily until the disease is checked. The regular dust schedule is two times weekly, but the leaf surface must be kept visibly coated and the protective coating must be renewed after every rain. Occasionally, because of rains, three or four applications are required in a week. Usually the total number for the entire season is 7 to 15.

Dusting takes less time than spraying, and does away with the need for carrying water. Since it requires about twice as much material, and because dusts are bought ready-mixed, their cost is greater but growers generally regard the greater convenience of dusting as more than counterbalancing the increased cost.

BLACK SHANK can spread rapidly into new areas and is a serious threat wherever it occurs.

It almost always appears first in a low place in a field. Usually about midsummer a few plants begin to wilt. If you pull one of these plants in the early stages of the disease and examine the roots, you will find that one or more of the large lateral roots is blackened and dead. At this early stage the stalk will be free from decay or discoloration. As the disease progresses, the entire root system and the base of the stalk decay, and the plant dies. Black shank in its first year of occurrence is easily confused with other troubles like bacterial wilt.

Black shank appeared near Quincy, Fla., about 1915, but it was not identified until some years later. In 1924 the situation in the Florida shade-tobacco area became desperate, and remained so until resistant varieties could be developed. Only a type resistant to black shank is grown there.

Black shank appeared in North Carolina near Winston-Salem about 1921 and spread slowly. It was identified there in 1930, and the damage built up with increasing rapidity. Growers there tried without great success to reduce losses by using long rotations. Resistant flue-cured varieties, which became available after 1941, relieved the situation, even though they were less desirable agronomically than the best susceptible varieties.

Black shank appeared in eastern North Carolina in 1937. By 1945 it was a major problem. Within 10 years it built up to epidemic proportions. Growers whose farms became generally infested had to discontinue growing susceptible varieties.

Black shank was found in central Tennessee and Kentucky in 1934. It became serious in 1951, and growers looked to the development of resistant varieties for solution to the problem.

One cannot forecast with certainty how black shank will behave in a new area. In the Florida shade-tobacco area and in North Carolina and Virginia, once a farm or field became infected it remained infected, although a rotation of 5 or 6 years might reduce the infection to a trace. There is one locality in which the disease has never persisted—the flue-cured area of east Georgia where black shank has been identified twice, in 1933 and 1947. Both times the infection disappeared without any effort on the part of growers. For reasons we do not know, the disease, which spreads so rapidly in North Carolina and Virginia, has not been able to establish itself in eastern Georgia and Florida.

Black shank has occurred also since 1948 in South Carolina, eastern Tennessee, Maryland, and Pennsylvania.

A word of caution to growers in areas where black shank is a new problem: The experience in the older areas has been that during the build-up period (which has been anywhere from 7 to 15 years) growers often have had a false feeling of security. A moderate amount of rotation has worked quite well, and losses have been limited for a few years. After the epidemic stage was reached, however, rotation was less successful. It has been the same with regard to resistance in plants. In the early years even a little resistance stood up very well. After disease infection had accumulated, the need was for much higher resistance.

Thousands of tobacco growers have yet to experience black shank, and suitable resistant varieties are not available to many. The question of what to do to avoid the infection as long as possible is important.

Black shank is spread by moving water, soil, and plants. The fungus is related to the water molds, and the disease spores can contaminate ponds or streams into which infested fields drain. In areas where black shank is present, it is unsafe to use stream or pond water in the plant bed or when setting out plants. Well water and city water offer less hazard.

The infection is readily carried in soil, and so it has often been spread by road workers, as indicated by infection coming in from the roadside. The disease can be carried from field to field in the soil on cultivators, tractors, and trucks. Plants also carry black shank. The best protection is for the grower without black shank to grow his own plants. Never should he get his plants from an area where black shank occurs. It is impossible to tell whether a bed is free of infection, because during the cool weather of the plant-bed season the disease is quite inactive.

For the grower who finds black shank in a field the first time, the best procedure is: Stop cultivating the field as soon as possible, because cultivation spreads the disease by moving the infection, injuring roots, and facilitating entry of the fungus. Keep out of the diseased field as much as possible to reduce spread to a minimum. Sow the affected field to grass or another noncultivated crop as soon as possible, and do not bring it back into tobacco for 5 years or more. Locate future fields so as to avoid drainage from the diseased field.

The problem of varieties is acute in the flue-cured area wherever black shank occurs—Virginia, North Carolina, and South Carolina. Epidemics of black shank are due largely to favorable weather and a build-up of infection. Variety may be an important factor. At the time of the original outbreak in Florida, it was noted that the disease had spread gradually until 1924, when the highly susceptible variety Round Tip was planted extensively for the first time. In 1924 the disease spread alarmingly. In North Carolina epidemic development has followed extensive planting of the 400 series of varieties—400, 402, Yellow Special, and Golden Harvest. Those varieties are tolerant to many diseases but are highly susceptible to black shank. Hicks and Gold Dollar are less susceptible. Growers who live in areas where black shank now occurs but do not have the disease on their farms might well plant one of the less susceptible of the common varieties.

Some of the resistant flue-cured varieties, developed in 20 years of effort, are Oxford 1, Vesta 47, and Dixie Bright 101. Plant breeders have learned that flue-cured varieties highly resistant to black shank have been so low with respect to returns per acre that it has rarely been practical for the grower to plant them. The results with the moderately resistant varieties I listed have been better; Dixie Bright 101 has yielded on a level with such a successful susceptible variety as 402. Dixie Bright 101 is not equally well adapted to all areas, however.

In any event, growers of flue-cured tobacco must depend largely on varieties that are only moderately resistant to black shank; plant breeders may be able to develop varieties that probably will be better in yield and quality but not in resistance. There is no indication that it will be possible to produce flue-cured varieties resistant to black shank that can be planted continuously on the same land. A combination of resistance and rotation is the best answer at present to the problem for the grower of flue-cured tobacco; that probably will apply in other areas as resistant varieties become available there. The soil fumigants that are used against nematodes may have some value.

BACTERIAL (GRANVILLE) WILT in the field looks very much like black shank. Plants wilt and die and the roots decay. In stalks of diseased plants that are sliced lengthwise 12 to 18 inches above the soil line, dark-brown, threadlike streaks show up in the woody tissue. They are a certain symptom of bacterial wilt.

The disease appeared first in North Carolina about 1900. Gradually it spread until thousands of farms were involved. Growers came to expect a loss of 20 to 25 percent of their crops each year.

Rotation became the standard recommendation for control, but failures were numerous.

The organism attacks many plants besides tobacco—some common weeds, peanuts, potatoes, tomatoes, eggplant, and peppers.

An intensive search was made to find tobacco resistant to bacterial wilt. Finally it was discovered in a collection made in Colombia. It was crossed with the flue-cured type, and the first commercial wilt-resistant variety—Oxford 26—was produced. It has since been used to produce Dixie Bright 27, 101, 102, and Golden Wilt.

The wilt-resistant varieties are not immune to the disease, although they stand up well under ordinary conditions. The parasite invades the roots and base of the stalk. However, if tobacco is grown continuously on the same land, infection may build up to the point that the tobacco is damaged. The remedy is to grow the resistant variety in a short rotation with other crops. Long rotations cannot be depended on to control the disease if the variety grown is wilt-susceptible.

BLACK ROOT ROT causes dark lesions that may be scattered over the roots. Above-ground symptoms are growth retardation plus wilting on bright days. Root rot is common in Tennessee, western North Carolina, and Virginia. It was the major disease of tobacco in 1910–20, when highly susceptible varieties—especially of burley and Havana—were grown. As long as new land was constantly cleared for growing tobacco, root rot did not accumulate, but as culture was discontinued on new land, the black root rot infection built up rapidly in the old fields. A contributing factor was the widespread use of lime, which encourages root rot. Liming tobacco land is advisable only if the land is very acid, below pH 5.0 to 5.5. After 1925, varieties resistant to root rot became available, among them 142, 211, 307, K1, and K2 (Havana) and Kentucky 16, 41A, and Burley 1 and 2 (burley).

ROOT KNOT used to be thought the only nematode root disease of tobacco. It is characterized by swollen roots, which have numerous galls that later decay. It is caused by a group of nematode species, all of which attack tobacco. One of the species also attacks peanuts; so, in places where peanuts suffer from root knot, peanuts are not a good crop to rotate with tobacco.

Rotation and fumigation are effective ways to control root knot.

Nematode root rot (*Pratylenchus*), the second important root nematode disease to be identified, is especially common in South Carolina and other Coastal Plain areas. The nematodes burrow through the smaller roots and cause a red-brown decay. They freely attack crabgrass, corn, cotton, and other crops, and are not so effectively controlled by rotation.

Two more recently identified nematode parasites that attack tobacco are the *Tylenchorynchus* and *Helicotylenchus*. They do not enter the roots, but they thrust in their sucking tubes and feed on the roots. Both nematodes sharply reduce the growth of tobacco plants, but the only general symptom is failure of the plants to make normal growth.

WILDFIRE AND BLACKFIRE leaf spots (bacterial leaf spot) are quite common in plant beds. Wildfire is especially harmful. The lesions it makes on the leaves are yellow and usually have a small white area of dead tissue in the center. The blackfire lesions in the field are large, often angular, and dark. In the field, wildfire lesions show much less of the yellow border, so conspicuous in the beds. The lesions generally are more rounded and lighter colored than the blackfire lesions. Aside from the difference in appearance, the two diseases may be considered as a single bacterial leaf spot disease.

The leaf spots have long been known under such names as red rust and black rust. Between 1917 and 1927, this leaf spot trouble was epidemic in every major tobacco area. Damage was heavy. In some areas—notably central Tennessee and Pennsylvania—wildfire remained severe until 1938. Beginning in 1947 and continuing each year since wildfire has been steadily building up throughout the burley area of Kentucky and Tennessee. The disease was widespread and destructive in 1952 and spread into western North Carolina and Virginia.

As to control in plant beds by chemicals: Applications of copper, as a drench or spray, will protect plants in the beds. The recommended mixture is bordeaux 3–4–50 (3 pounds of copper sulfate and 4 pounds of hydrated lime to 50 gallons of water) or 4–6–50. The first is applied as a drench with a sprinkling can at the rate of 25 gallons to 100 square yards of bed. The second, stronger bordeaux mixture is applied with a sprayer. Either way is effective if properly done. A commercial fixed copper (Copper A or Tennessee Tribasic) may be substituted for the bordeaux—1.5 to 2 pounds of a 50-percent material to 50 gallons of water.

Effective treatment depends on an early beginning. The initial application must be made as soon as plants are above ground. Then it is important that the framing boards or logs, the cotton (unless it is new), the soil surfaces, and, of course, the plants be wet thoroughly. A second treatment should follow in 7 to 10 days, and a third as much later.

The three-treatment program has been adequate in Tennessee, Kentucky, and Maryland. In Pennsylvania and

Wisconsin it has been found necessary to continue weekly treatments until setting time. Keeping plants free from wildfire-blackfire in the beds helps field control and should be a regular practice in places where the diseases occur.

The breeding of varieties immune to wildfire and blackfire is well advanced.

MOSAIC causes leaf chlorosis and mottling. Symptoms are most pronounced in the young leaves. Mosaic is found wherever tobacco is grown. It has been rare in Georgia but prevalent in Maryland. It also is common in Kentucky, Tennessee, and Virginia.

Its virus can be spread from plant to plant merely by rubbing first diseased and then healthy leaves. The infection spreads throughout the plant. Cured leaves of diseased plants may carry infectious virus for 25 years. Cured tobacco is an important source of infection because growers often handle the leaf of the previous crop in the spring when stripping and grading it; at that time plants for the new crop are in the bed. Plants often become contaminated when workmen chew natural leaf, get juice on their hands, and then handle plants. It is important to avoid infecting plants in the beds or at transplanting time.

Adequate resistance to mosaic is now available. Mosaic-resistant types of all sorts are being developed. A few varieties have been introduced.

IN SUMMARY: Some progress has been made in efforts to control tobacco diseases, but the situation is far from stabilized. It seems certain that farmers in many areas are going to suffer heavy disease losses for years to come —from wildfire leaf spot, nematodes, and black shank. New diseases have appeared in recent years; others may appear.

E. E. CLAYTON *is a pathologist in the Bureau of Plant Industry, Soils, and Agricultural Engineering.*

The Genes That Mean Better Tobacco

E. E. Clayton

From all over the world American plant breeders have collected hundreds of specimens of tobacco to test for factors that might be useful in developing disease-resistant tobacco plants.

Many came from Mexico, Central America, and South America, where tobacco is a native plant. Among the specimens were 59 other species of *Nicotiana* that, with *N. tabacum*, make up the genus. From Australia a group of *Nicotiana* species was obtained that represents a "lost" branch of the family, separated from the main American stock countless ages ago. They were wild, stunted, ill-smelling plants of no commercial value but of great scientific value. Some American species obtained from our own far West grew only a few inches tall. Other South American relatives were the so-called tree tobaccos. Types of cultivated tobacco were obtained in endless variety.

The studies have been going on since 1912, when James Johnson, at the Wisconsin Agricultural Experiment Station, began what might be termed scientific tobacco breeding, with definite procedures and objectives.

Some success has been attained. We have Havana and burley varieties that are resistant to black root rot, flue-cured varieties that resist wilt, and flue-cured and cigar-wrapper types that resist black shank. A beginning has been made in combining, in one variety, resistance to more than one disease.

The goal is to breed varieties that resist all major diseases.

To do that one has to know how much—and which—resistance is available, and that is why plant explorers went to the uninhabited interior of Australia, native Indian villages in remote sections of South America, and to many other places to get their thousand-odd collections of tobacco plants. We hope the study of all those specimens will yield two kinds of information.

The first is information about where the genes—the carriers of heredity for resistance to each disease—are located and whether they can be used. Much resistance is not usable because the species cannot be crossed, there are undesirable linkages, or inheritance is too complex to permit backcrossing.

The second type of basic knowledge concerns the parasitic potentialities of the disease-producing organisms: Is the organism in question a single race or is it a group of races that have varying parasitic ability.

Although breeding and selection work were carried on long before the underlying scientific principles had been worked out, James Johnson added greatly to our knowledge by his attempts to control black root rot by breeding better varieties. He found that in varieties and seed collections occasional plants appeared to be resistant. From that selection and testing, Havana 142 was developed, the first root rot resistant variety to be introduced. It is still grown extensively.

Resistance to black root rot depends on many genes. Furthermore, the root rot fungus is an assemblage of races that differ in their pathogenicity. Some are weakly parasitic. Others are strongly parasitic. If a series of varieties possessing resistance is tested with different races of the fungus, one finds that a variety may be highly resistant to one race and quite susceptible to another.

Resistance is a matter of degree. A variety may be slightly resistant—it is only a little less severely damaged by the disease than the variety recognized as susceptible. In similar fashion, varieties may be moderately or highly resistant. The ultimate is immunity, which means complete freedom from disease. Immunity is not a matter of degree.

The varieties resistant to black root rot so far released are at least moderately susceptible to some races of the fungus. Some people report that certain varieties are "losing their resistance." Actually they have lost nothing; it is merely that the constant growing of one variety makes easier the multiplication of fungus races to which it is susceptible. With polygenic resistance—which depends on the accumulation effect of a number of genes—it would be possible to find genes with which to meet this situation temporarily.

We have evidence, however, that linkage problems make the accumulation of high-level root rot resistance extremely difficult or impossible. For example, in 1935, certain tobacco collections having high-level resistance to root rot were crossed with susceptible burley, and a program of backcrossing and selection was started. The highly resistant selections from those crosses consistently proved to be low in yield or otherwise undesirable, and the variety finally released (Burley 1) was not nearly so resistant as the original highly resistant parent line.

Among the species of *Nicotiana* that are related to cultivated tobacco are some that are immune to black root rot and some that are moderately or highly susceptible. So, in addition to the work with polygenic resistance that made possible such varieties as Havana 142, Kentucky 16, Burley 1, and Connecticut 15, plant breeders began the work of transferring a black root rot immune reaction from wild species to the cultivated tobacco. The species selected was *N. debneyi*, a native of Australia. The immune reaction provides resistance far beyond the parasitic ability of any race of the fungus; so, in a practical sense, it eliminates the fungus race problem. The transfer of black root rot immunity from *N. debneyi* to *N. tabacum* was in its final—and successful—stages in 1953. When immunity to root rot is available and is incorporated in our commercial tobacco varieties, one more problem will have been solved.

The study of the tobacco collections made in Central America disclosed that some had marked resistance to root knot nematode disease. Subsequent backcrossing to commercial varieties and careful selection made it possible to increase the original resistance to root knot, but all the highly resistant lines proved to be low in yield because their leaves were small. So now we have a good level of root knot resistance, the inheritance of which depends on many genes. Because of unfavorable linkages involving small leaf size, the resistance so far has not been usable. The difficulty is being overcome, however.

Plants resistant and susceptible to root knot are invaded freely by the nematodes. Once they are in the roots of resistant plants, however, the nematodes cease development after a time, and few eggs are produced. Gall formation also is reduced.

The resistant plant, in a sense, is a nematode trap. At McCullers, N. C., in 1950, winter peas were sown in the field following resistant and susceptible tobacco. The peas grew luxuriantly when they followed resistant tobacco, but after the susceptible tobacco they were severely attacked by root knot and made little growth. It seems that planting tobacco resistant to root knot reduces the number of nematodes in the soil, and hence can protect other crops that follow on the same land.

Even higher resistance to root knot (and perhaps complete immunity) is found in some of the *Nicotiana* relatives of cultivated tobacco. Most resistant are *N. repanda* and *N. megalosiphon*. A successful cross with the latter has been

obtained, but it is a long way from anything of practical value. Growers consequently may have to depend for some time on rotation and chemicals to control root knot. The nematodes also enter the roots of a species such as *N. megalosiphon*, but form no eggs.

Nematode root rot, the common meadow nematode disease, has been studied in connection with resistance to root knot. Many of the selections resistant to root rot also show good resistance to meadow nematodes. The resistance is being preserved so that if varieties with resistance to root knot are perfected, they will also have a good level of resistance to root rot.

The story of developing plants resistant to black shank begins with the work of W. B. Tisdale. At the Florida Agricultural Experiment Station he intercrossed and selected many varieties in order to develop a resistant commercial shade tobacco out of the Florida-grown types, which were largely of Cuban origin. The variety Florida 301 was used as the source of resistance when breeding work was started with flue-cured tobacco in 1931 in western North Carolina. The resistance of 301 to black shank is of the usual polygenic type.

More than 20 years of work have gone into the flue-cured breeding program with black shank resistance. Several problems have arisen. It has become necessary to breed burley, dark-fired, and Maryland and Pennsylvania broadleaf varieties that resist black shank. Flue-cured varieties have been produced that have the major part of the black shank resistance of the Florida 301, but they are not grown widely because they tend to be low in yield and quality. The high-yielding and better quality varieties have turned out to have only moderate resistance to black shank. The kind of resistance used in 1953 is least effective in seedlings. Resistance increases as the plants grow older. The roots of these moderately resistant varieties are freely invaded by the black shank fungus, and young plants are readily killed. Root invasion in older plants results usually in death of only a part of the root system, and there is slight or pronounced stunting. One answer to this situation is higher level resistance or immunity, but apparently neither can be obtained in flue-cured tobacco with the Florida 301 type of resistance, so we have had to look elsewhere.

We have long known that *Nicotiana rustica* is highly resistant or immune to black shank. More recently that was found to be true with regard to *N. longiflora* and *N. plumbaginifolia*. Work on the transfer of high resistance to black shank from one or more of these species has been started. Successful interspecific crosses have been made with the three species.

The moderate level of black shank resistance coming from Florida 301 has made possible such commercial varieties as Oxford 1, Vesta 47, and Dixie Bright 101. Efforts to increase the level of that resistance have been fruitless because the more highly resistant types have proved to be lower in yield and quality. The related wild species of *Nicotiana* provide a new prospect for obtaining gene material with which to build new varieties with higher resistance. Resistant varieties constitute the only effective method for combatting black shank. Consequently better resistance is highly important.

The need for resistance to Granville wilt became so critical that in 1934 and 1935 the Department of Agriculture sent men to Mexico, Central America, and South America to collect tobacco seed. The aim was to get material that could be searched for wilt resistance. Out of a thousand seed collections so obtained, one showed good resistance. A selection from it, T. I. 448A, was the source of wilt resistance that has now been incorporated into Oxford 26, Dixie Bright 101, and Golden Wilt. The resistance is polygenic. There is evident linkage between one or more of the resistance genes and some plant-growth characters; namely, short, broad leaves and height of plant. The

linkages already have been broken to some degree, however. There is also a favorable linkage between resistance to wilt and resistance to black shank.

The behavior of the T. I. 448A type of wilt resistance is interesting. The resistance is lowest in young plants, which, under field conditions, may be freely invaded. Early in the summer it is not unusual to find a field of wilt-resistant tobacco with many plants showing symptoms of wilt that would kill plants of a susceptible variety. Rarely do more than 5 percent of the resistant plants die, however. Most recover and show no ill effects except one or two malformed lower leaves. Some roots of the resistant plants are killed, but usually not enough to affect normal growth. Wilt resistance is scarce. All the *Nicotiana* species tested are as susceptible as cultivated tobacco. Resistance constitutes the only effective method for combatting the wilt.

Fusarium wilt is serious only in limited areas. Resistance is available within the cultivated tobacco species. It may be found in various types. The Robinson strain of Maryland Broadleaf is resistant to fusarium wilt in Maryland. In the flue-cured area the varieties resistant to Granville wilt, Golden Wilt, Oxford 26, and Dixie Bright 101, have fusarium resistance, which derives from T. I. 448A. Fusarium resistance is incorporated in Kentucky into Kentucky 35. All fusarium resistance is inherited on a polygenic basis.

Collections from all parts of the world have been surveyed with the aim of finding resistance to blue mold. Some varieties from Argentina have a slight amount of resistance but not enough to be of practical use. In related species of *Nicotiana* native to western North America there is no resistance to blue mold. High resistance is found in some of the Australian group and in some South American species. As a start toward the transfer of the resistance to cultivated tobacco, *N. debneyi*, an Australian species, was crossed with tobacco. By a series of backcrosses, plus selection, it has been possible to transfer resistance from this source into the tobacco genome. Additional resistance is available in the South American species, *N. plumbaginifolia* and *N. longiflora*, in case it is needed. Ultimately the tobacco grower may be relieved of the trouble and expense of using fungicides against blue mold.

Wildfire and blackfire, from the viewpoint of resistance, may be regarded as a single bacterial leaf spot disease. The organisms that cause them are similar. Selections resistant to wildfire also are resistant to blackfire. Collections of cultivated tobaccos from different places have been tested. Many levels of resistance were found. Investigations showed that this resistance, due to complex inheritance, was of doubtful value in a breeding program. Search through the species, on the other hand, revealed complete immunity in some. One of the best is *N. longiflora*, which was successfully crossed with tobacco. The immune reaction has been transferred into the tobacco genome. This immunity is a simple monogenic dominant and the immune reaction holds from the very earliest seedling stage in the plant bed until the end of the field season. Therefore, it provides complete protection.

A study of tobacco with *N. longiflora* genes to ascertain its immunity to wildfire has shown two effects, besides the disease reaction: A degree of extra seedling vigor and a tendency toward low nicotine content in the wildfire-resistant lines. The latter can be eliminated easily, but it is being conserved as a valuable asset because much tobacco today has a higher nicotine content than is desirable.

Brown spot is a minor disease because the common varieties have a considerable degree of resistance to it.

Resistance to mosaic was first reported in a cultivated tobacco, Ambalema, from Colombia. The virus invaded it but did not multiply very much, and the plants showed no symptoms of mosaic. Some 30 seed collections from different parts of Colombia and Venezuela had the Ambalema type of resistance. Some, including T. I. 448, had modifying genes that made them more resistant than Ambalema. The resistance of Ambalema has not been satisfactory in combination with varieties grown in the United States. The resistant lines tended to be semi-drooping and susceptible to leaf scald.

A second type of mosaic resistance was developed by F. A. Holmes, of the Rockefeller Institute. It was obtained by crossing *N. tabacum* and *N. glutinosa*. It may be classed as immunity, for the virus cannot multiply in the plants with the *glutinosa* genes. It is a strange type of immunity. The tissues of the immune plants are so sensitive to the virus that leaf invasion results in a dead area—the so-called local lesion reaction. The death of the invaded tissues stops the infection. In ordinary tobacco the virus, once it enters, multiplies and spreads into every part of the plant. The *glutinosa* type of mosaic immunity is controlled by a single pair of genes. This immunity is readily incorporated into commercial varieties by backcrossing. (Backcrossing means an original cross, and then the hybrid plants are repeatedly crossed back to a specific variety of desired type.)

The tobacco grower, whether he be a grower of flue-cured tobacco in South Carolina or a grower of burley in Tennessee, needs better disease-resistant varieties.

They need to be more resistant in the case of a disease such as black shank, and resistant not to just one disease but to a whole group of diseases. Slowly but surely research is building a solid foundation of high-level resistance or immunity to all major tobacco diseases. Future varieties will be more and more resistant as these different types of resistance are perfected and combined. Out of this will evolve a new, improved type of tobacco that will reduce or eliminate many disease hazards that trouble the tobacco grower today.

Future varieties will be fundamentally different. When black root rot resistance was established and the first root rot resistant variety Havana 142 was distributed, nothing new had been added that did not already exist in the cultivated tobacco species. On the contrary, the transfer of mosaic immunity to cultivated tobacco from the wild species *Nicotiana glutinosa* and the transfer of wildfire-blackfire immunity from *N. longiflora* introduced into cultivated tobacco genes that had not existed previously in the species. Such transfers of desirable genes from distantly related wild plants means that the cultivated crops we grow are being steadily improved.

In the past, tobacco variety improvement was limited to the genes and characters found within the one cultivated species. In the future, desirable characters may be transferred from any of the 60 plant species that make up the genus *Nicotiana*.

Resistance depends on genes. In tobacco the genes for resistance may come from two sources: The many different types of cultivated tobacco and the wild plants that are related to tobacco. A vital difference exists in the quality of the resistance that comes from the two sources. The resistance obtained within the cultivated tobaccos was always a degree of resistance and never immunity. Also it was controlled by many genes. On the other hand, in the related *Nicotiana* species we found immunity; and in several instances the immune reaction has been demonstrated to be simply inherited. In a word, resistance within the cultivated species is easy to obtain, but hard to use, and it may not be adequate. Resistance in the related wild species is difficult to obtain but, once obtained, it is easy to use, and it may prove to be immunity and therefore completely adequate.

E. E. CLAYTON, *principal pathologist, has been in charge of tobacco breeding and pathology research for more than 20 years in the Department of Agriculture.*

Crop Rotations and Tobacco

J. G. Gaines, F. A. Todd

Crop rotation is of unusual importance in the production of flue-cured tobacco.

Rotation crops, such as sweetpotatoes and tomatoes, encourage the early establishment of destructive soil-borne diseases. The use of small grains often prevents disease losses. Other plants, such as crotalaria, may be effective in preventing disease, but have undesirable crop effects that result in poor quality of leaf.

Cultivated plants are not alone in exerting those influences. Weeds growing between seasons may be beneficial or harmful. Nor do the responses to crops and diseases remain constant. They have less influence in some seasons and more in others. So, too, with some soil-borne diseases, which may remain localized and be more destructive in some seasons and areas than in others.

Consequently, we have to consider a complex of crops, weeds, diseases, season, and location when we evaluate rotations in tobacco culture.

It used to be the custom in the Southeast to locate tobacco fields in areas newly cleared from pine forests and to grow tobacco continuously there until the soil failed to produce good crops. Then more new ground was cleared, and the process was repeated as long as any virgin land remained. Finally, growers were forced to use rotations, primarily because of root knot.

The fact that many growers in Georgia have reduced the amount of injury from root knot enough for successful tobacco culture for 30 years points to the value of crop rotation as a practical disease-control measure.

GRANVILLE WILT, or bacterial wilt, in North Carolina has been reduced by growing corn for 2 to 4 years. Redtop (*Agrostis alba*), hairy crabgrass (*Digitaria sanguinalis*), lespedeza, soybeans, and crotalaria also could be included in the rotation. Horseweed (*Erigeron canadensis*), ragweed (*Ambrosia artemisifolia*), jimsonweed (*Datura stramonium*), and horsenettle (*Solanum carolinense*) were susceptible to infection, but the occasional growth of those weeds in a corn rotation did not nullify the beneficial effects of corn. Four years of bare fallow failed to eliminate wilt. Crop rotation was not uniformly successful when the soils were heavily infested. Limited short rotations and the use of a tobacco variety slightly resistant to wilt have proved adequate. The growing of tomato, pepper, peanuts, and potatoes and the continuous culture of tobacco encouraged wilt.

Fusarium wilt has been controlled in Georgia by 3-year crop rotations plus the use of the slightly resistant standard tobacco varieties. Rotations that failed to control root knot also failed to prevent wilt. Two successive years of oats plus weeds effectively controlled this root knot-wilt complex. Sweetpotatoes encouraged the establishment of fusarium wilt in tobacco soils. The same fungus disease attacks both crops. Wilt was limited in small areas before 1950. The rate of spread and establishment may be governed to a large extent by whether or not sweetpotatoes are grown in tobacco soils and by the degree of susceptibility of new tobacco varieties. There is also the possibility that more virulent strains of the causal fungus may appear in some areas.

Stem rot is influenced more by season than by rotation. Over a 20-year period, in a 3-year rotation test, however, less stem rot followed cotton and tobacco than cowpeas, corn, weeds, and peanuts. The greatest amount of disease, averaging 4 percent, followed velvetbeans. As much stem rot followed bare fallow rotations as corn and weeds. More stem rot occurred after leguminous cover crops if the residues remained than if the tops were removed. Increased stem rot was associated with severe root knot in those rotations.

Black shank also responds to crop rotation, but rotations alone are not always successful. Longer intervals are required between tobacco crops. Two years of clover, lespedeza, small grain, or grass crop followed by 2 years of corn (or cotton or harvested Spanish peanuts) have been reasonably successful. Limited rotations plus a moderately resistant tobacco variety have been adequate. Root knot sometimes influences the amount of black shank damage. At Attapulgus, Ga., the resistant Rg cigar-wrapper variety develops severe black shank if root knot is present. This variety remained highly resistant in the absence of root knot. Highly susceptible varieties of tobacco, however, succumbed to black shank in nematode-free soil. Thus control of root knot alone is not enough to control black shank, unless it is combined with a variety that is moderately resistant to black shank. Growth of tobacco, pepper, tomato, and related plants encourages the development of black shank, even if resistant varieties of tobacco are used.

Nematode root rot is a little-known disease complex that also has been associated with crop rotation. Three-year rotations with small grain plus weed fallow or bare fallow were helpful in South Carolina. Corn, cotton, and crabgrass, as well as continuous tobacco culture, permitted the disease to become destructive. The oats-plus-weeds rotation helped materially in controlling the nematode root rot-root knot combination.

No accepted variety of tobacco has pronounced resistance to root knot, and since the control of root knot is an important tool by which it is possible to keep other soil-borne diseases in check, rotation becomes more urgent than ever, especially in districts where black shank and fusarium wilt develop along with nematode diseases. Root knot nematodes occur over the entire flue-cured region from Virginia to Florida. Thousands of tobacco growers, particularly in the Carolinas, are faced with the grave problem of attempting to produce profitable crops on lands infested with two or more diseases. Good varieties of tobacco, which have adequate multiple resistance to these infestation complexes, are not available; existing varieties have to be supplemented by rotation. On the other hand, limited rotations are inadequate without the use of moderately resistant tobacco varieties.

To complicate matters, there are several recognized species of root knot and root rot nematodes. Some of them vary in ability to infest different crops. Closer attention than ever must be paid to them by grower and research worker alike. If previously effective crops fail to protect tobacco, one has to know that quickly so that other crops can be substituted in time. Also nematodes in time may become adapted to crops that are considered resistant.

Because root knot is more widespread than other recognized nematode diseases, extensive experiments designed for nematode control have been made at McCullers, N. C., and Tifton, Ga. A number of field crops were grown in continuous rotations with tobacco between 1925 and 1951 at Tifton and between 1937 and 1951 at McCullers. Experiments of shorter duration were conducted at both locations and at Florence, S. C. Annual records were kept of root knot in tobacco at the close of harvest. Yields, leaf grades, and occurrence of other important diseases were recorded. In general, wherever peanuts, soybeans, cowpeas, velvetbeans, and similar cultivated legumes were grown,

the tops were removed in an effort to avoid the danger of adding objectionable amounts of nitrogen to the soil. Uniform fertilizer and cultural practices accepted in the respective States were followed throughout.

Leaf quality and yield usually are not affected by the equivalent of less than 50 percent severe root knot at the close of harvest. Unlike black shank, fusarium wilt, stem rot, and Granville wilt, which may cause death of the plant from a single infection, severe nematode infestation after midseason may not cause measurable reduction in leaf grade or yield. Sometimes a root disease of 80 percent severity causes no measurable crop loss. If a well-developed root system is attacked by root knot nematodes and the roots do not break down readily, little damage may be done. Only when the weakened roots break down from secondary decay, caused by common soil organisms, do serious losses generally occur. If seedling roots are infested, marked stunting of plants may be evident from the outset. The earlier the attack the likelier is the secondary breakdown before plant maturity is reached. Usually the breakdown is slow acting, but when weakened roots are attacked by black shank and fusarium wilt, early death is more certain.

Root knot and other root nematode diseases commonly cause reductions in yield of 200 to 400 pounds an acre. Occasionally maximum losses resulting from root knot exceed 1,000 pounds an acre. Leaf grades, as well as yields, are materially reduced when a big part of the root system becomes affected by secondary decay.

Leaves harvested from these wilted and stunted plants are immature and may cure with a green or dull cast. If they are left on the stalk until ripe in appearance, they will be trashy, dark, lifeless, and of very low value when cured. Such immature leaves from severely wilted plants may contain excessive nicotine and too little sugar.

Crop rotation controls nematodes by partial starvation through growth of resistant crops. Root knot nematodes require susceptible growing roots in which to develop and reproduce. The resistant crop plants are readily invaded by the nematode parasites, but the nematodes fail to mature and reproduce in them.

Two-year rotations, with tobacco grown alternately with a single resistant crop, are adequate in North Carolina and Virginia. Farther south, where the seasons are longer and conditions more favorable for year-round nematode and plant development, 3-year rotations are needed to give the same reduction. If an intermediate or susceptible crop is included in the rotation, longer intervals than 2 years are required between tobacco crops. Two years of bare fallow, used as an experimental check to compare with crops, were adequate to insure against root knot damage, but at least 3 or 4 years were needed to eliminate all infestations.

Crop rotations in which a resistant crop is grown may reduce root knot but will never eliminate it.

ROTATION CROPS are rated according to their ability to prevent root knot in tobacco that follows them. Crops most effective in reducing subsequent nematode occurrence are regarded as most resistant.

Peanuts and oats, or other small grains, were the most effective field crops tested. Weeds were permitted to grow in the summer and fall after the small grain. Spanish (bunch) and runner peanuts were of equal value against disease. Over a 20-year period of systematic 3-year rotations in Georgia, harvested Spanish peanuts and oats-weeds permitted infestations to reach or exceed the danger level, 70-percent infestation, only once. The average for peanuts was 30 percent and for weeds 56. While those differences were highly significant in favor of peanuts, there were no differences in yields.

The bare fallow rotation (2 years of fallow and 1 year of tobacco) showed only 23 percent of slight to moderate root infestation, the lowest average of any rotation.

Crotalaria (C. spectabilis and C. intermedia) was of equal value to peanuts in other rotations. Highly effective grasses and sods were Dallisgrass (Paspalum dilatatum), the Pensacola variety of Bahiagrass (P. notatum), and centipedegrass (Eremochloa ophiuroides).

Of intermediate value in Georgia (but effective in 2-year rotations in North Carolina) were cotton, velvetbeans, and weed fallow where crabgrass grew among the weeds. In one 20-year test, excess root knot occurred in tobacco six times after two successive years of weeds, seven times after velvetbeans, and eight times after cotton. Other crops of only intermediate effectiveness at Tifton were Korean lespedeza (Lespedeza stipulacea), common lespedeza (Lespedeza striata), root knot resistant soybean, pearlmillet (Pennisetum glaucum), and grain sorghum (Sorghum vulgare).

Corn was still less effective against root knot. It was followed by severe infestations in 16 tobacco crops out of 20. The test was on Tifton sandy loam soil. On Norfolk lowland sandy loam, where root knot was less destructive, corn rotations were more reliable. At no time did a maximum of 100 percent severe disease develop after corn, velvetbeans, and weeds. Cowpeas resistant to root knot were not much better than corn; the succeeding tobacco showed severe root knot 12 out of 20 years. Sudangrass (Sorghum sudanense) behaved about the same as corn.

Least effective of the rotation crops were cowpeas that were susceptible to root knot and sweetpotatoes. The only difference between the two varieties of cowpeas was that the more susceptible variety permitted maximum disease to develop within 3 years instead of 6. After that, the same amount of root knot appeared after both varieties. Severe disease was the rule after perennial lespedeza (Les-

pedeza cuneata), carpetgrass (*Axonopus compressus*), Bermuda-grass (*Cynodon dactylon*), chufa flatsedge (*Cyperus esculentus*), susceptible soybeans, tomatoes, pepper, squash, cucumber, okra, snap beans, and similar truck crops.

At McCullers, corn was slightly less effective than weeds, oats-weeds, peanuts, and cotton, but all were adequate to insure against severe losses throughout the 15-year test period. Redtop also was of value there. Thus it was easier to control root knot by rotation in North Carolina than in Georgia.

Small grains are the only reliable winter cover crops in tobacco rotations. Oats or rye, turned under in time for planting tobacco, have given slight but consistent reduction in nematode disease—not enough, however, to prevent excessive damage if tobacco was grown every year in the same field. The practice is of slight value only as a supplement to a good rotation. Winter legumes, such as vetch, Austrian winter peas, and lupine, are highly susceptible to root knot and tend to increase damage from disease.

IN ORDER TO DETERMINE weed influences on root knot, a number of common weeds were cultivated in 3-year rotations with tobacco. It appeared that related species of weeds brought about different root knot responses. For example, sickle senna, or coffeeweed (*Cassia tora*), reduced root knot to a minimum, while another species, coffee senna (*Cassia occidentalis*), permitted severe disease in succeeding tobacco. The common Canada fleabane, or horseweed (*Erigeron canadensis*), was more effective than a similar fleabane (*E. pusillus*).

The weeds most effective in preventing root knot were no better than peanuts and crotalaria when used in 3-year rotations. Among the most resistant were coffeeweed, horseweed, ragweed, beggarweed (*Desmodium tortuosum*), and goldenrod (*Solidago microcephala*). Mexican clover (*Richardia scabra*) permitted slightly more root

knot than peanuts or crotalaria but was more effective than dogfennel (*Eupatorium capillifolium*). Weeds that had intermediate value but permitted occasional excess disease were crabgrass, camphor plant (*Heterotheca subaxillaris*), bitterweed (*Helenium tenuifolium*), and fleabane (*Erigeron pusillus*). Of still less rotation value were dogfennel and bull paspalum (*Paspalum boscianum*). Weeds that permitted severe disease consistently in a 7-year experiment were spiny amaranth (*Amaranthus spinosus*), slim amaranth (*A. hybridus*), cocklebur (*Xanthium chinense*), lambsquarters (*Chenopodium album*), drug wormseed (*C. ambrosioides* var. *anthelminticum*), and coffee senna (*Cassia occidentalis*).

The best natural weed fallow in North Carolina consisted of ragweed and horseweed, but crabgrass frequently predominated between annual row crops. Cultivation after a row crop or after small grain encouraged crabgrass. In Georgia, Mexican clover, crabgrass, bull paspalum, and camphor plant predominated after oats the first year, with occasional beggarweed, horseweed, and ragweed. The second year of weeds showed less grass and Mexican clover, with more horseweed, camphor plant, beggarweed, dogfennel, and goldenweed, *Aplopappus divaricatus*. The clean-cultivated cotton and peanuts discouraged all weed growth. Corn encouraged beggarweed, crotalaria, cocklebur, coffeeweed, crabgrass, and bull paspalum. Normally root knot susceptible weeds soon disappeared in a long weed rotation, but in short ones that did not occur. If soils are very fertile, a long period may be necessary to eliminate the susceptible weeds. Root knot has been observed in old abandoned barnyards 15 years later on lambsquarters and Jerusalem-oak (*Chenopodium botrys*). Such places, however, are not suitable for flue-cured tobacco.

CONCLUSIONS regarding rotation effects cannot be drawn from short-time experiments—those continuing only 4 or 5 years.

At McCullers, root knot remained severe during the first rotation cycle. Then there was a steady decline in disease until a minimum occurred in 1946, 10 years later. During the following 5 years, there was a slight but unimportant increase. Those trends occurred in all 2-year rotations with oats, weeds, peanuts, cotton, and corn, but root knot remained severe throughout the 1937–51 period in continuous tobacco plots.

Striking differences occurred at Tifton between some rotation crops during the 1925–51 period. All the tested crops in 3-year rotations there permitted an increase in root knot up to or beyond the danger level. In contrast, bare fallow consistently prevented an increase in disease, and at no time was there any indication that this starvation method would fail.

The time required for nematode populations to build up to a crop-destructive level varied with the different rotations. In these 3-year rotations, maximum root knot occurred after 2 or 3 years of sweetpotatoes, susceptible cowpeas, or tobacco; after 4 years of corn-corn-tobacco; 6 years of nematode-resistant cowpeas; and 9 years of velvetbeans or native weeds; but not until 27 years after peanuts-peanuts-tobacco.

The results with the cotton rotation were quite unexpected. Like sweetpotatoes, cotton permitted a rapid increase in disease the first 2 years. Maximum root knot occurred the third and fourth years, after which there was a steady decline in nematode activity until this rotation reached the bare fallow level of minimum root knot activity 14 years later. An average of 100 percent of the tobacco plants after cotton were severely affected by root knot in 1930–31. This was in contrast to only 2 percent during the 1942–46 period.

The long-time rotation experiments have shown many successive periods of ascending and descending disease developments, plus some trends that extend over long periods. At both McCullers and Tifton there was a low disease activity in 1946, followed by a higher peak of activity in 1951. Many factors exist in the crop-soil complex. Some of them we do not understand fully. Rotation effects need to be evaluated on a basis of averages and not on the basis of results of 3 or 4 years. Any rotation is considered dangerous, however, if it permits several successive years of severe root knot.

A good rotation crop may lose its value temporarily if grown too often. In the 1925–51 peanuts-peanuts-tobacco rotation, root knot damage was negligible for the first 15 years, but remained excessive after 1946. In additional rotations, begun in 1944 where peanuts had not been grown before, infestations were reduced by peanuts between 1946 and 1950 but were increased to the destructive level in 1951. When one rotation crop permitted excess disease damage, the substitution of another one reduced disease.

EXTENDED ROTATION experiments have shown that certain crops, notably oats and peanuts, have outstanding value and wherever possible the rotation should be varied. Behavior of the tobacco will indicate when the rotation crop should be changed. A number of crops, which are not highly effective in nematode control when used alone, can be used in combinations to good advantage.

For example, in the effective peanuts-oats-tobacco rotation for controlling root knot, corn can be substituted in place of peanuts. The substitution would make a better rotation in an area where Granville wilt is present, because peanuts are susceptible to it and corn is not. The crop sequence that places the most resistant crop immediately in advance of tobacco generally is to be preferred. Thus cotton-peanuts-tobacco is more effective than peanuts-cotton-tobacco.

Where it is practical to utilize a number of crops on the farm, it is desirable to change their sequence in succeeding 3-year cycles. For example, corn-oats-tobacco might be followed by cotton-peanuts-tobacco, and that in turn by peanuts-oats-tobacco. Millet, corn, and grain sorghum may be substituted occasionally with safety. Another plan might be to grow corn-oats-tobacco in succeeding cycles until that rotation begins to show excess root knot, and then change to another three-crop system. It is important to remember that any systematic two-crop or three-crop system, continued for long periods without change, may become less effective. For example, after 15 years in one location, peanuts-oats-tobacco rotations permitted severe root knot development. The expert grower will watch his tobacco crop closely each year and adjust his rotation to check disease build-up before it becomes destructive. He will also consider rotation in its relation to soil fertility.

WHEN TOBACCO FIELDS are abandoned and permitted to revert to weeds and finally to broomsedge and pines, the soil again becomes suitable for flue-cured tobacco. No better plants are known to condition the soil for tobacco than the original native vegetation. Early growers felt that cropping practices that kept the soil close to its virgin state were best for producing good leaf quality. That was sound reasoning. Of the crops compared in rotation tests, the best leaf quality followed small grain, cotton, corn, and some nonleguminous weeds. Quality was almost as good after harvested Spanish peanuts.

While crotalaria is an excellent rotation crop for nematode control, its use in a tobacco rotation is limited to poor and sandy or low and wet lands that have insufficient organic matter. With soils of average fertility, one crop of crotalaria may cause poor quality in the following tobacco crop.

In a time when emphasis is placed on increasing soil fertility to insure bountiful yields of food and fiber, it may seem a paradox that the best flue-cured tobacco can be grown only on relatively infertile soils. One important reason is that flue-cured leaf of the desired composition, texture, and aroma can come only from relatively healthy plants that receive limited amounts of nitrogen. To promote best yields, sufficient readily available nitrogen is essential during the period of most active growth. After that the supply must diminish.

Legumes, used as main crops or cover crops, are apt to cause too much nitrogen to be available late in the season, particularly if they are grown immediately preceding the tobacco. In the heavier soils, excess nitrogen may occur 2 years following legumes. This organic nitrogen causes the cured tobacco to be dark and thick; chemically the leaf is high in nicotine and low in sugar. It is not suited for cigarettes.

Consistently high yields followed oats or other small grain plus weeds, harvested Spanish peanuts, and nonleguminous weed fallow. Highest dollar returns followed those crops. Optimum yields as well as good leaf quality also followed ragweed and horseweed. Still higher yields occurred after leguminous crops such as crotalaria, beggarweed, and runner peanuts, but the tobacco was of poorer quality and dollar returns usually were reduced. Any increase in yield at the expense of quality is always undesirable.

The 1927-46 average yield of tobacco after weeds and harvested peanuts at Tifton exceeded 1,450 pounds an acre. Similar high yields, as well as top quality, followed oats during a 15-year period. As long as they effectively controlled root knot, the crops remained in this favorable position, whether they were grown in a two-crop system or included in sequence with still other crops.

All yields were approximately 200 pounds an acre less at McCullers than at Tifton. But at both locations total production was approximately 500 pounds less an acre after continuous tobacco than after good rotation crops. Yields after root knot susceptible cowpeas averaged 100 pounds an acre more than continuous tobacco. Thus almost any rotation proved better than none.

While low yields were associated consistently with very severe root knot, highest production did not necessarily accompany the most effective rotation. Although control of root knot was commercially perfect after bare fallow, yields here were fully 200 pounds an acre less than in good crop rotations. These lower yields were associated with lack of organic matter and poor physical condition of the soil. In the absence of sufficient organic matter, cover crops of rye or oats have increased yields 100 or more pounds an acre without affecting leaf grades. On the other hand, lower yields comparable to those after bare fallow followed heavy sods of Bahia and Dallis grass where the sod had not completely decomposed.

IN SUMMARY, nematode root diseases are serious problems throughout the flue-cured area, Virginia to Florida. They increase in seriousness with the more southern latitudes, being most destructive in Florida and least in Virginia. The basic system of crop rotation is adjusted to control nematode diseases, to maintain the soil in proper condition for production of quality flue-cured tobacco, and to aid in the control of other diseases, such as black shank, Granville wilt, and fusarium wilt.

For nematode control the small grains, especially oats, are helpful. Native weeds are good. Harvested Spanish peanuts are effective in most areas, but not if peanut-infesting nematodes are abundant.

Over long periods, a mixed rotation is better than any set system followed year after year, and almost any rotation involving nonlegumes is superior to continuous tobacco. There

is also the possibility that as new varieties of rotation crops are released, their resistance to nematode diseases may differ from the old, and their value in the rotation will vary accordingly.

Maintaining the soil in proper condition to produce good tobacco involves careful watch over organic nitrogen residues in the soil. Crotalaria and runner peanuts, excellent nematode-controlling crops, must be used sparingly and only on the very poor soil types. Harvested Spanish peanuts gave the best results of any legume, but when used excessively they sometimes caused depressed stalk and leaf size and lowered quality of the top leaves. From the viewpoint of quality, small grains and native weeds have been best. It is noted, however, that such a native legume as beggarweed may become troublesome in a weed rotation because of excessive residues of organic nitrogen.

Rotation serves a double duty in relation to the control of black shank, Granville wilt, and fusarium wilt. It reduces the build-up in the soil of the organisms causing these fungus and bacterial diseases, and it reduces the nematode population, thus preventing root-infesting nematodes from opening the way to invasion by parasitic fungi and bacteria.

This over-all protective effect from rotation is not realized if the varieties of tobacco grown are highly susceptible to the other diseases. If nematode diseases are the major problem, rotation alone is adequate, but in the presence of black shank and wilt, it is necessary that rotation be combined with the use of resistant varieties. Rotation alone gave uncertain control of black shank in the 1930's, when only black shank susceptible varieties were grown. Even 5- to 6-year rotations were not completely successful. By contrast, in 1951 tobacco following 1 or 2 years of a rotation crop withstood black shank almost perfectly when the moderately resistant varieties Oxford 1 and Dixie Bright 101 were planted. The same situation now exists with respect to Granville wilt and the resistant varieties now available. Short rotations plus wilt resistance are highly effective in controlling the disease.

The fusarium wilt situation appears to be about the same, with rotation and resistance supplementing each other. An added factor here is that sweetpotatoes are subject to the same wilt and are unsafe to include on land to be used later for tobacco.

Lastly, it is a good policy not to grow rotation crops closely related to tobacco, and those include tomatoes, pepper, eggplant, and Irish potatoes.

J. G. GAINES, *a graduate of Clemson College and Rutgers University, has been a pathologist in the Department of Agriculture since 1929 to investigate root knot and other diseases of tobacco.*

F. A. TODD, *a graduate of the University of North Carolina, is a pathologist in the Department of Agriculture. He has studied the control of tobacco diseases in Southeastern States for a long time.*

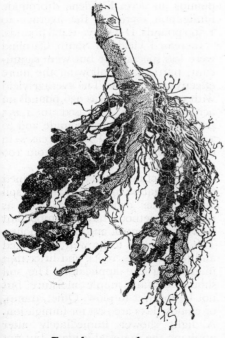

Root knot on tobacco.

Soil Fumigation To Control Root Ills

J. G. Gaines, T. W. Graham

The Coastal Plain from Virginia to Florida is a center of tobacco production. Its light, sandy soils and mild, humid climate are ideal for growing cigarette tobacco of high quality. But the soils and climate likewise are favorable for the development of soil-borne diseases, especially the ones caused by nematodes.

Many farmers do not have enough good tobacco soil to permit the long rotations required for control of root diseases. They need a safe and efficient soil treatment that will enable them to use shorter rotations.

Early experiments with chloropicrin, urea, and formaldehyde demonstrated that some diseases can be controlled by adding chemicals to the soil. But they were either too expensive and cumbersome to apply, or they adversely affected growth and quality of leaf. Cheaper and more practical chemicals later became available. They are not safe enough to be recommended without qualification, but some of them are being used increasingly on tobacco farms in the Southeast.

Gaseous chemicals, whose vapors penetrate to all parts of the soil, have been more satisfactory than those that require mechanical mixing. Such gasforming chemicals are called soil fumigants. The present materials are liquids that volatilize when they are exposed to the atmosphere. One in common use is ethylene dibromide. Dowfume W–40 is one of several commercial mixtures of it. It is 40 percent by weight and 20 percent by volume of ethylene dibromide. Another one is dichloropropene-dichloropropane, which is supplied as D–D mixture.

To fumigate tobacco land, one of them is poured or injected into the soil under suitable conditions and with special equipment. The job must be done carefully, otherwise it will do no good. If it is done at the wrong time or if excessive amounts are used, the tobacco may be seriously damaged.

Nematode diseases are the principal ones controlled by soil fumigants. Treatment does not eradicate nematodes but reduces them sufficiently to make it possible to grow a crop without measurable loss from disease. The major nematode diseases are root knot and root rot.

Besides controlling nematode diseases, the fumigants have given some control of black shank, fusarium wilt, and stem rot. It seems that roots injured by nematodes are more readily invaded by other disease organisms. Consequently fumigation treatments most effective against nematodes may greatly reduce the amount of other soil-borne diseases.

Extensive experiments with soil fumigants have been conducted at Florence, S. C., and Tifton, Ga. Careful data have been taken on the control of root diseases, yields, quality (as indicated by grade and price of the cured leaf), and rates of application.

Experiments in Georgia showed that fumigation with 40 percent ethylene dibromide reduced root knot from a disease index of 91 in untreated soil to 29 in treated plots. (In the index numbers, 100 means all roots are severely diseased and 0 means all roots are healthy.) Under the same conditions D–D mixture reduced infestation to index 35. A great variation occurred because of soil condition and method and rate of application. Thus in treated plots the amount of disease varied from 0 to 70. The most effective control of root knot and root rot was obtained in Norfolk sandy loam soil,

where tobacco had been grown for 22 consecutive seasons. At Florence, where root-knot infestations were less severe, similar results were obtained. Ethylene dibromide reduced root knot from disease index of 56 in untreated soil to 20 in treated plots. Following D–D mixture it was 27. Thus, both in Georgia and South Carolina, the 40-percent ethylene dibromide mixture used was slightly the more effective. The difference was fairly consistent, but usually it was not enough to influence yields very much.

If there were no nematodes, fumigation did not increase yields. On the contrary, excess amounts of either fumigant have sometimes lowered yields because of injuries to roots. In diseased soil, however, marked increases in yield have been obtained consistently. In fact, fumigation gave just as effective nematode control and as large yield increases as were obtained with the very best crop-rotation practices. On nematode-infested Georgia land, the 6-year average yield from untreated soil was 920 pounds an acre. Ethylene dibromide fumigation increased the average to 1,590 pounds. D–D gave 1,468 pounds.

Increased yields in South Carolina were less spectacular but were significant, particularly following the more effective treatments. The average yield with untreated soil was 936 pounds an acre. That was increased to 1,255 pounds by ethylene dibromide and to 1,276 pounds by D–D. Increases in different experiments varied from 100 to 500 pounds an acre.

Wide fluctuations in results obtained from fumigation indicate that both soil and weather conditions, as well as rates and methods, have an important bearing on control and crop response. The land needs to be well pulverized and free of clods, roots, and litter that might clog the applicator. The soil should contain ample moisture but not be too wet to plow. Quiet, damp, or cloudy days are best for fumigation. A light shower immediately after applying the material is ideal, but not essential if the soil is in proper condition. It is important that the weather be mild and not windy and that the temperatures should remain above a minimum of 40° F. and below a maximum of 75° for the first 2 days after the application.

Row treatment involves applying a stream of the liquid directly under each tobacco row. Equipment may consist of one-row and two-row rigs for attaching to tractors.

For small tobacco fields, a simple one-horse rig attached to a single-foot plow stock has been cheaper and more practical. It consists of a small horizontal (preferably flat) tank, which rests between the plow handles or on the beam. An outlet in the bottom, provided with a ¼-inch nipple and valve, permits the liquid to flow out at controlled rates. A ⅜-inch flexible or plastic delivery tube extends from the valve to the heel bolt or to the rear of the plow shank. The end of the tube should be a few inches higher than the plow point and almost against the rear of the shank. The shank is equipped with a small plow not over 2½ inches wide. The tank is fastened to the beam or handles in such a way that the outlet is directly over the shank, so that the delivery tube will extend straight downward. This is necessary for best results with gravity flow rigs where there is no pressure to regulate the flow. A breather tube may be installed in the tank if desired, provided the filler cap can be fitted in an airtight position. This will keep the flow more constant if properly used. If no breather tube is used, a small opening will be necessary in the cap to permit air to replace the liquid which flows out. The flow from gravity tanks is not perfectly uniform, but the slight variation has caused no difficulty.

The first thing to decide is how much to apply. Rates may vary from 5 to 7½ gallons of 40 percent ethylene dibromide and 7½ to 10 gallons of D-D mixture to the acre. If tobacco is planted in 4-foot rows, a 5-gallon application to the acre requires 1 pint of liquid to each 272 feet of row; 7½ gallons require 1 pint to 181 feet; and 10 gallons call for a pint to 136 feet. The important thing to remember is that the minimum and safest rate for 40 percent ethylene dibromide is 1 pint to 272 feet of row; whereas the corresponding rate for D-D mixture is 1 pint to 181 feet, irrespective of row width. If rows are less than 4 feet apart, those concentrations will slightly increase the amounts per acre. For rows wider than 4 feet, the amounts per acre will be slightly less than 5 and 7½ gallons, respectively, for the two fumigants.

If 7½ gallons are to be applied, the applicator valve must be adjusted to deliver 1 pint in the time it takes the rig to move 181 feet. If the adjustment is not marked on the valve, four steps will be necessary to determine the correct opening: Mark off 181 feet. Count the number of seconds required for the rig to move 181 feet at operating speed. With the tank half full, hold a pint measure under the delivery tube, and by making several trial openings with the valve, determine the exact position required to deliver 1 pint in the measured amount of time. Mark that position on the valve handle so that the correct opening can be adjusted at will.

If convenient, a second valve may be installed just above to act as a cutoff. The machine should always be kept free of trash and grit. The liquids should be strained into the tank.

Making the necessary adjustments, preparing the soil, and selecting the appropriate time for treatments are the most important preparations. The rest is only a matter of carrying out a few simple procedures.

The first step in row fumigation is to mark off the 4-foot rows with a shovel plow, making a shallow furrow to remove all trash that might clog the applicator foot.

The second step: With the first row as a trial run, and moving at regular speed, hold the plow foot in the center of the row mark so that the liquid is buried 10 inches beneath the normal soil surface. Practice will determine when to cut the valve off and on when turning. It is a good plan to open the valve wide occasionally and close it immediately to clean out grit that might change the rate of flow. Keep the tank filled as near as practical to the same level. See that several inches of soil fall back into the applicator furrow immediately covering the liquid. Check the flow from time to time.

The third step is to follow a few minutes later with one turnplow furrow on each side of the row to make a large bed. This bed should be considerably larger than usual to insure treating a wide strip. A disk lister may be used if it is set to make a large bed.

If the soil is subject to washing, it may be advisable to run out the middles with a sweep, so that drainage water will be confined to the middles and not wash over the beds. If the soil is cloddy and does not settle well after treatment, the beds may be rolled immediately afterward with a log or similar equipment. If the soil is in proper condition, rolling is neither necessary nor beneficial. Beds that are rolled must be opened again and reworked before planting. Under no condition should the beds be opened until 1 week after fumigation, however.

Our directions imply that the fumigant is to be applied in a single stream. There has been some question as to whether more effective row fumigation could be obtained by applying the fumigant in two streams 8 to 12 inches apart. The single- and double-stream methods have been compared. While the double stream was slightly more effective, the differences were too slight to influence yield.

BOTH FERTILIZER and fumigant may be applied at the same time and in one operation with one- and two-row tractor rigs if the tobacco is to be set within 3 weeks. With the one-horse rig, fertilizer may be put in immediately after marking off the rows or in advance of the fumigator.

When fertilizer is applied 2 and 3 weeks before planting, however, it usually is advisable to put in only 60 to 75 percent in the row, and then to side-dress with the remainder 20 days after planting. If row fumigation is done 4 to 6 weeks before planting, it is best not to apply the fertilizer along with the fumigant. In that event, any time after 1 week following treatment, the beds may be carefully opened with a small shovel plow and the fertilizer applied and mixed in the usual way. Rows are then rebedded; the second bed is made smaller than the first to lessen the danger of bringing in untreated soil from the middles. Opening the bedded rows in that way has not reduced effectiveness of treatment. In all operations between fumigation and planting, however, it is important to keep the row exactly in its original location.

Broadcast fumigation involves treating the entire field by applying parallel streams of fumigant about 12 inches apart. It usually is done best with a tractor rig equipped with a pump to force the fumigant into the soil at controlled rates. The rig may be equipped with 6 to 10 shanks, each with a delivery tube attached to the rear. It is necessary to have the field leveled or smoothed in order to prevent too shallow applications in low spots. If parallel streams are applied 12 inches apart, each shank must deliver 1 pint to each 272 feet of furrow for 20 gallons an acre, and three-fourths of a pint for 15 gallons. With broadcast treatments it is necessary to follow the applicator with a drag to level the soil and reduce evaporation loss.

Repeated tests in Georgia have shown that 7½ gallons of 40 percent ethylene dibromide or 10 gallons of D–D mixture in the row per acre gave more efficient disease control than twice those amounts broadcast. Broadcast treatments reduced disease from a 90 level of infestation in untreated soil to 42; row applications reduced the disease index to 27. The difference often was not enough to influence yields significantly, however.

In South Carolina the situation was reversed. Broadcast treatments repeatedly proved better than row applications. Disease was better controlled and yields were higher. The fact that extensive experimentation in Georgia showed that row treatments were more economical and effective, while similar work in South Carolina gave results that consistently favored broadcast treatments, indicates that generalization is not possible for all areas with respect to method of application.

The most effective broadcast rate of 40 percent ethylene dibromide was 15 gallons an acre, although 20 gallons sometimes slightly increased yields. The minimum effective broadcast rate of D–D mixture was 20 gallons an acre. More than 20 gallons of either material did not increase disease control sufficiently to justify the additional cost. The higher rates sometimes damaged tobacco, particularly if they were applied a short time before planting.

Repeated tests with 7½ gallons an acre of 40 percent ethylene dibromide and 10 gallons of D–D mixture gave better disease control than 5 and 7½ gallons, respectively, but the more efficient control was not reflected consistently in higher yields. Sometimes the 7½- and 10-gallon rates stunted the tobacco, particularly if the soil remained wet after treating or the beds were rolled. Ten and fifteen gallons in the row caused still more damage and lowered quality as well as yields. The minimum amounts of 5 and 7½ gallons an acre gave the maximum benefit per unit of fumigant and were least likely to cause damage.

An interval of 3 weeks or longer between fumigation and time of planting is desirable for both row and broadcast applications. Under ideal conditions and with minimum applications of ethylene dibromide, the period may be reduced to 2 weeks. A longer interval is required with D–D mixture to be on the safe side; also,

the higher the rates, the longer the waiting period. With row treatments the waiting period may be increased to 6 weeks without any great loss in efficiency. With broadcast treatments it is practical to apply the materials in the fall or, in areas of mild climate, in winter. Fall and winter applications usually have been safer than those made in the spring and as effective. But treatments in early fall or September in Georgia have failed to control root knot the following season. Late fall applications are better there.

Soil type has been a definite factor in determining the length of time between treating and planting. Light, sandy soils, particularly lowlands, require at least a week longer than the heavier soils. Wet, cold soils need as much as 6 weeks, particularly if D–D mixture is used.

Growers are cautioned not to be misled by good disease control that may be obtained from heavy row applications made shortly before planting. Repeated tests have shown that even when plants are not visibly injured, such a practice often has resulted in depressed yield and lower quality.

A fumigation depth of 10 inches has been more effective in the soils tested than 6 inches or less. Root knot nematodes occur abundantly in upland Georgia soils between the 4- and 16-inch depths. Maximum concentrations are at 12 inches or so—the zone where fumigation must be most effective. Soils that remain waterlogged several months of the year need more shallow treatment because nematodes may be nearer the surface.

The risk in shallow treatments of 4- to 6-inch depths is that much of the fumigant may be lost too soon by evaporation. The danger in deep applications of 10 to 12 inches in wet soils is that the fumigants may be retained in the soil too long and cause damage to crops. Comparatively deep applications are essential for row treatments because they permit a wider strip of soil to be sterilized.

One good treatment will remain effective long enough to protect one crop. More than that cannot be predicted. Some treatments put in during January in Georgia controlled root knot during early summer but offered no protection after the first of August. Sometimes second-year benefits are apparent but may not be important. Minimum annual treatments therefore are preferred in heavily infested areas. Residual protection cannot be guaranteed even by heavy treatments. Thus, 30 gallons an acre in South Carolina tests did not always give measurable protection the second season. Ethylene dibromide showed more second-year benefits than D–D mixture.

To understand the immediate problem of quality arising from fumigation, one has to consider the materials used and their composition. One gallon of 40 percent ethylene dibromide mixture contains about 3 pounds of bromine. Thus, with 7½ gallons an acre of the mixture in the row, the bromine application is 22.5 pounds. One gallon of crude D–D mixture contains approximately 6 pounds of chlorine; 10 gallons an acre in the row means an application of 60 pounds of chlorine. With broadcast applications, and twice the amount of fumigant applied, the respective bromine and chlorine figures would be 45 and 120 pounds an acre. All the amounts may be dangerous from the point of view of quality.

Normally tobacco does not contain more than 0.01 percent of bromine. Both row and broadcast ethylene dibromide treatments have increased the bromine content from 0.04 to 0.31 percent. The average was less than 0.20 percent.

The tolerance limit for bromine in tobacco has not been established. Minimum applications therefore are advised. When as much as 0.30-percent bromine increase occurs from 7½ gallons of mixture containing 22.5 pounds of bromine, it is evident that considerable amounts of bromine may remain in the soil to be taken up by the tobacco plant. Calculated on a basis of

samples analyzed and normal yields, up to 20 percent of the total bromine application has been taken up by the tobacco leaf in extreme cases. Usually the amount is less than 10 percent and sometimes it is negligible.

Fumigation with D–D mixture has increased the chlorine content of the leaf and at times greatly lowered fire-holding capacity. In extreme instances, 10 gallons an acre of the material in the row 3 weeks before planting have raised the chlorine content of the leaf a full 0.60 percent higher than unfumigated tobacco. Calculated from leaf samples analyzed and assuming normal yields, that amounts to approximately 14 percent of the original 60 pounds of chlorine applied as fumigant. At other times the chlorine increase is scarcely perceptible and is not enough to affect fire-holding capacity.

The tolerance limit for chlorine in tobacco varies with the type. Some flue-cured tobaccos may tolerate up to 1 percent of chlorine as a maximum, if other qualities are suitable, but half that amount is excessive for cigar types. Low chlorine is always preferred.

With both fumigants, the greatest increase in bromine or chlorine and the lowest fire-holding capacity followed row treatments of 10 or more gallons an acre 3 weeks before planting. Packing the beds when it was not necessary to do so had similar adverse influences on leaf composition.

It might be assumed that such unfavorable effects on quality caused by excess chlorine and bromine would be reflected in lower grades and hence in lower prices for the tobacco grown on fumigated soil. That—perhaps unfortunately—has not been the case. Actually tobacco with an excess of chlorine or bromine, and, for that matter, tobacco low in sugar and high in nicotine, may grade and sell very well. Over a 6-year period at Tifton, tobacco from fumigated plots averaged 20 percent or less of undesirable grades (common leaf and nondescript), while leaf from untreated plots averaged 30 percent of those undesirable grades. Also tobacco from the fumigated plots has repeatedly sold for a higher price than leaf from diseased, untreated plots. In fact, in an extensive series of comparisons the over-all average has been 3 to 8 cents a pound in favor of leaf from fumigated plots. That price differential was caused primarily by visibly poor tobacco from the untreated diseased soil. Where both fumigated and untreated plots were free from disease damage, usually there was no difference observed between grades and prices.

It has been possible with fumigation to produce tobacco that graded poorly. That has happened when tobacco was grown on fumigated land that contained more than the usual amount of organic matter. Under those conditions, fumigation delayed nitrification and the result was excess nitrogen late in the season. As a result, the top leaves remained green; that in turn lowered leaf grade and adversely affected leaf composition. Again, when heavy applications of fumigants were made 2 weeks before planting and root injury occurred, the resulting cured leaf has tended to be soggy and to turn dark upon aging.

The best protection against undesirable quality effects is to use the minimum effective dosage of fumigant, treat well in advance of planting, and treat only land that does not remain waterlogged long after fumigation.

Quality effects with D–D mixture are further complicated by the fact that some tobacco fertilizers contain up to 2 and 3 percent chlorine. Some Georgia soils produce tobacco containing up to 1 percent chlorine or more when the fertilizers are used. D–D fumigation of such soils tends to make a bad situation worse, unless chlorine is eliminated from the fertilizer. With a nonchlorine fertilizer and with a 6-week interval between treating and planting, the chemical composition of flue-cured tobacco after D–D usually has been satisfactory. In wet soils an interval of 4 weeks between treating

and transplanting has resulted in chlorine injury even when chlorine was eliminated from the fertilizer. The unpredictable breakdown of both fumigants, particularly in wet soils, is added reason for using the smallest applications. Low quality resulting from delayed nitrification, particularly in the presence of excess organic nitrogen, is reason for using minimum rather than maximum rates of nitrogen fertilizer.

A combination of 100 to 150 pounds of granular calcium cyanamide plus 2 quarts of soil fumigant (40 percent ethylene dibromide or D–D mixture) to 100 square yards is one of the most effective and practical plant-bed soil treatments for control of weeds and nematodes in southern areas. Less damping-off usually occurs after cyanamide than in soils where that weed killer is not used. Three-fourths of the cyanamide is uniformly broadcast and worked in thoroughly not more than 3 inches deep. The soil fumigant is applied at a rate of 20 gallons an acre or slightly more. One-row applicators for field use are satisfactory. The furrows may be spaced 10 inches apart, instead of 12, to increase the rate slightly. The bed is again leveled and the remaining cyanamide is broadcast. This is raked in several times only 1 inch deep.

It is important that both fumigant and cyanamide be applied in the fall, or at least 60 days before seeding. If fumigant is not put in until a month or less before seeding, roots may be injured and plants stunted. In addition the plants may be induced to bloom prematurely in the field as a result of this plant-bed injury. The injuries can be avoided by early treatment plus location of beds in well-drained soil.

J. G. GAINES, *a pathologist, has investigated tobacco diseases in Georgia since 1929.*

T. W. GRAHAM, *a pathologist in the Department of Agriculture, has received degrees from the Universities of Louisiana and Minnesota. He has studied extensively the nematode diseases of tobacco.*

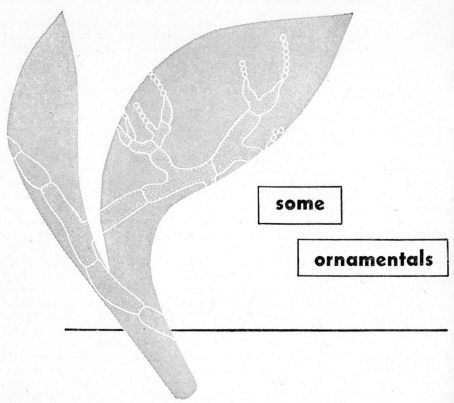

Rust and Other Disorders of Snapdragon

W. D. McClellan

Of the numerous diseases of snapdragons, rust probably causes the most concern.

Rust itself seldom kills the plant, although in dry weather the affected leaves may dry up, and in humid regions the rust-infected spots are entrances for the secondary fungi that may kill leaves and stems.

Rust can be told by its reddish-brown pustules on the under sides of the leaves. The powdery chocolate-brown masses in the mature pustules are the spores of the rust fungus (*Puccinia antirrhini*).

Rust affects snapdragons at all stages of growth. The leaves are most heavily infected, but often stems, petioles, and calyx structures may be attacked severely. The first indications of the disease are small yellow flecks, less than one-sixteenth inch in diameter, just under the epidermis on the under side of the leaves. If conditions are favorable, the brown, powdery spore masses may appear 48 hours later. Leaves that are severely attacked droop as though they needed water.

Snapdragon rust has an interesting history. It is one of the few plant diseases whose spread can be traced from its origin. Rust was first collected on snapdragons at Santa Cruz, Calif., in 1879 by C. L. Anderson. Next it was found at Berkeley, Calif., in 1895 by W. C. Blasdale, a chemist at the University of California, who reported his studies on rust in 1903. The fungus soon spread throughout California and was found in Portland, Oreg., in 1909. Rust appeared in Lake Forest, Ill., in 1912, in the New England States in 1915, and in Canada in 1916. It reached Bermuda in 1922 and was first found in Europe at Grignon, France, in 1931. By 1933 rust had spread throughout northwestern France and to England. Three years later it had been reported throughout Europe and in Egypt. It was observed in Russia in 1937 and in southern Rhodesia in 1941.

Wind-borne spores account for the local spread of snapdragon rust. Probably the long-distance spread of the disease began (50 years ago or so) when snapdragons were propagated by cuttings that were shipped widely to florists, nurserymen, and private gardeners. It is also possible that rust may have spread in infected seed or in rust-infected plant materials associated with the seed.

Snapdragon rust is confined to members of the genus *Antirrhinum* and a few other genera of the Scrophulariaeae, such as *Linaria* and *Cordylanthus*. C. O. Blodgett and G. A. L. Mehlquist, working at the California Agricultural Experiment Station, tested a number of species and varieties of *Antirrhinum* and found that seven species, *A. asarina*, *A. chrysothales*, *A. glandulosum*, *A. maurandioides*, *A. orontium*, *A. ibanjezii*, and *A. siculum*, were resistant to two races of rust. Those species, however, are so far removed from *Antirrhinum majus*, the common snapdragon, that I doubt whether they would be of much value in a breeding program.

Harold E. White, of Massachusetts State College, tested 56 wild species and strains of *Antirrhinum* and found *A. charidemi*, *A. calycinum*, *A. ibanjezii*, *A. siculum*, and four strains of *A. glutinosum* to be resistant. Other strains of *A. glutinosum*, as well as *A. molle*, vary in susceptibility to rust. Other species of *Antirrhinum* said to be susceptible include *A. nuttallianum*, *A. virga*, *A. vagans*, *A. assurgens*, *A. tor-*

tuosum, *A. coulterianum*, *A. glandulosum*, and *A. vexillo-calyculatum*.

Many rusts have life cycles that involve alternate hosts. No such alternate host is known for snapdragon rust. Only the uredial and telial stages are known.

E. B. Mains, working at Purdue University, obtained no infection with germinating teliospores on young snapdragons. He deduced that this rust is heteroecious and has pycnia and aecia on an alternate host. The rust probably lives over on parts of infected plants that survive the winter in greenhouse or out-of-doors. Such infections provide inoculum for infection the following spring.

The best temperature for uredospore germination and infection is 50° to 55° F. The optimum temperature for the completion of the life cycle of the fungus is 70° to 75°. Still higher temperatures may result in the abortion of some of the infections previously established at lower temperatures, however, for only a low percentage of incipient infections will survive temperatures of 90° F. Uredospores are killed by prolonged exposure to temperatures above 94°.

In cooperative tests at Beltsville, Md., Urbana, Ill., Wooster, Ohio, Los Angeles, and Ithaca, N. Y., A. W. Dimock and Kenneth F. Baker discovered a close correlation between the observed intensity of rust and that expected on the basis of temperature and moisture records. At the first three locations, rust development was prevented or greatly restricted by high temperature or insufficient moisture or both. At Los Angeles and Ithaca, temperature and moisture conditions were more favorable and severe rust developed.

In the drier weather that prevails in Los Angeles, host injury resulted almost exclusively from drying of the rust-infected tissues. Under conditions of high average relative humidity and frequent rainfall, as at Ithaca in summer, injury was due primarily to the action of secondary fungi (principally

Fusarium species), which invaded through the rust pustules, destroyed the rust, and advanced into the previously healthy host tissues, killing the leaves and stems. Where secondary fungi were controlled at Ithaca by the use of selective fungicides or by the prevalence of unfavorable low temperatures, however, there was relatively little host injury even though rust infection was severe.

On the basis of their results, the severity of snapdragon rust can be predicted from the climatic characteristics of a given area. For instance, if temperatures remain at 45° to 65° F. when plants are wet with rain or dew for 6 to 8 hours, infection by air- or water-borne uredospores is certain. If, in addition, the day temperatures reach 70° to 75° but do not often exceed 80° or 90°, the development and sporulation of the fungus are rapid, and the complete cycle from infection through pustule formation and sporulation to infection may be completed every 12 days.

An area or season in which those conditions commonly occur is favorable for severe rust development. The Pacific coast is such an area. In other districts that have such high temperature as to prevent either infection or sporulation or both, rust would be expected to be unimportant except when snapdragons are grown in greenhouses in winter—probably much of the Mississippi Valley, the Atlantic Coastal Plain, and the South.

Control measures include selection of resistant varieties and healthy cuttings, the use of fungicides, and the avoidance of syringing and excessive humidity.

S. L. Emsweller and H. A. Jones, after extensive research in California, reported that resistance is controlled by a single dominant gene. That makes for easy development of resistant varieties, providing good flower types can be obtained. They also found that there are modifying genes that permit the selection of immune plants from highly resistant parents. Later, in 1937,

C. E. Yarwood, of the California Agricultural Experiment Station, found a race of snapdragon rust that would affect the so-called resistant strains in the California seed fields. Apparently that new race had not been prevalent before that time in the district where the earlier work had been done.

C. O. Blodgett and G. A. L. Mehlquist, also working at the California Agricultural Experiment Station, then searched for resistant or immune types that could serve as parents in breeding desirable resistant types. They inoculated about 140 samples of different species and strains of *Antirrhinum* with mixtures of the two rust races. No commercial strain was found to be immune to both races of rust, but several strains were found to exhibit considerable resistance.

Research workers have gotten widely different results in tests of fungicides. In British Columbia and England bordeaux mixture gave good control, and poor control was had with sulfur fungicides. In the United States, Egypt, Belgium, and Poland, opposite results have been obtained. The explanation might be that bordeaux mixture is ineffective when average maximum temperatures and other factors favor good rust development; when the average maximum temperature is above the favorable range or if other conditions are unfavorable for the rust, bordeaux is effective.

Research by Dimock in New York and Baker in California helps explain these discrepancies. They found that under semiarid conditions, bordeaux mixture fails to control either rust or the damage from desiccation caused by the rust; in humid and rainy conditions, however, serious plant damage is prevented because invasion of secondary fungi is controlled by bordeaux although rust is not controlled.

An example of apparent rust control was the effectiveness of both Bioquin 1 and bordeaux mixture at Ithaca, N. Y. Rust control with the two materials was poor there, but the secondary fungi, which invade through the rust pustules, were effectively controlled, and the plants remained relatively normal in appearance and bloomed profusely.

At Los Angeles the bordeaux-sprayed plants were severely damaged by desiccation of the rust-invaded tissues. Zineb gave excellent control at all places; rosin-lime-sulfur, good control; and wettable sulfur, poor control.

PHYLLOSTICTA BLIGHT, caused by the fungus *Phyllosticta antirrhini*, affects outdoor snapdragons. Occasionally it attacks those grown in greenhouses. Plants of all ages and varieties are susceptible.

The disease is characterized by large, circular, dark-brown or black zonate spots, which are small and cream-colored at first and darken as they age. Usually they become zonate because of an abundance of black dots—pycnidia—that develop in rings. Leaves attacked when young become distorted and curled; the whole leaf may die but clings to the stem. Dark-green, water-soaked spots form on the stem several inches from the tip. The spots spread rapidly and girdle the stem. In a few days the affected tissue shows a firm, dark-brown rot. These stem lesions soon become covered with numerous pycnidia, arranged over the surface in close circles. The stem lesions on a young seedling may girdle the plant near the base and cause rapid wilting and death.

Blight apparently occurs wherever snapdragons grow. In England it is more common as a stem disease than as a foliage disease. The fungus may overwinter in plant debris or on plants that live through the winter. The disease, like most leaf diseases, is favored by a moist atmosphere. Temperatures below 60° are unfavorable for the development of phyllosticta blight. Consequently it is most serious in summer.

Control consists of cleaning up all debris of snapdragon plants in the fall and spraying the plants during the growing season with bordeaux 4-4-50 (4 pounds of copper sulfate, 4 pounds of lime, and water to make 50 gallons). In the greenhouse, surface watering and temperatures below 60° are recommended.

BOTRYTIS BLIGHT, caused by *Botrytis cinerea*, frequently causes serious losses in greenhouse snapdragons and in coastal seed fields. It occurs most commonly in poorly managed greenhouses where the humidity is often excessive.

It causes the flower spikes to wilt. When one examines such spikes, he finds tan areas on the stem near the lowest flowers or the base of the shoot. Those areas enlarge rapidly, girdling the stem and causing the death of the spike. Infection takes place through old blossoms; through the glandular trichomes, which occur on the flowering part of the stem; through wounds; or through tissues previously attacked by other diseases, such as rust or powdery mildew. The gray-brown spore masses soon appear if humidity is high.

Control involves cutting the spikes as soon as they are marketable, removing infected parts, cleaning up all plant debris, and avoiding excessive humidities by proper control of greenhouse temperature and ventilation.

ANTHRACNOSE, caused by the fungus *Colletotrichum antirrhini*, is more destructive in the greenhouse in fall and spring than in winter. It is most conspicuous outside in August and September.

Many elliptical sunken spots are produced on the stem. Round dead spots appear on the leaves. At first the spots on the stems are dirty white, with a narrow, brown or reddish-brown border. Minute black acervuli appear later at the centers of the spots. The fungus may attack stems of all ages. Several large spots may girdle the plant at the base. A single large spot may cause death

of a succulent terminal part. Anthracnose can be controlled out-of-doors by
spraying with bordeaux mixture or
other good fungicides, such as zineb,
ferbam, lime-sulfur, or wettable sulfur. In the greenhouse, one can control it simply by keeping the foliage
dry.

AMONG THE OTHER DISEASES of snapdragons are:

POWDERY MILDEW (*Oidium* species)
has been confined to greenhouse-
grown snapdragons in the United
States. It is characterized by white
powdery growth on both leaf surfaces and occasionally on young
stems. It can be controlled by sulfur
dust or a wettable sulfur spray plus
a suitable spreader to insure complete
coverage.

DOWNY MILDEW (*Peronospora antirrhini*) is most common on seedlings,
on which it causes a characteristic
paling and downward marginal curvature of affected leaves. The ter-
minal-shoot growth is checked and the
disease can cause the death of all
aerial parts. The fungus sporulates
on the lower surface of leaves as a
white, sparse downy growth.

ROOT KNOT (*Meloidogyne* species) is
evidenced as gall-like swellings on the
roots. This nematode disease is controlled by soil sterilization.

STEM ROT AND WILT (*Phytophthora
cactorum*) is characterized by a girdling
of the stem at the root level, followed
by wilting and death. The disease can
be controlled by soil sterilization.

W. D. McCLELLAN, *a native of California, studied plant pathology at the
University of California and Cornell University. He was on the staff of the University of Maryland and the Bureau of
Plant Industry, Soils, and Agricultural
Engineering before he became director of
research for the Mid-State Chemical Supply
Co. at Lindsay, Calif., in 1951.*

Fusarium Wilt of China Aster

Kenneth F. Baker

The fusarium wilt disease—stem rot,
black stem, aster wilt—caused by
Fusarium oxysporum f. *callistephi*, is generally the most serious disease of China
aster (*Callistephus chinensis*) in commercial and home-yard plantings over
most of the world.

The China aster was introduced from
China into France about 1731 and into
the United States before 1800. Commercial aster culture had developed in
this country by 1890. The first definite
report of fusarium wilt was made by
B. T. Galloway from several places in
northeastern United States in 1896,
but it probably was present and unnoticed before then. The fungus was
widely distributed during the next 25
years, probably with the seed.

In many places it is the factor that
determines whether asters can be
successfully grown. Soil once infested
with the fungus is essentially ruined for
growing asters. Growers in California,
therefore, avoid land that is known
ever to have been used for the crop.
Some home gardeners have found
asters so unreliable because of disease
that they are replacing them with
zinnias.

Losses result from three phases of the
disease: Damping-off of the seedlings
at any time from emergence to time of
transplanting; the typical wilt of mature plants; and the decay of flowers in
storage. Wilt of mature plants usually
causes the greatest loss, but damping-
off is important because seedlings fre-

quently are infected in the seedbed and fail to show the disease until much later, when they have already infested the land with the fungus.

THE SYMPTOMS of fusarium wilt may appear at any stage of plant growth. Following emergence, seedlings may fall over from damping-off caused by the fungus. The warmer the soil (up to about 80° F.) and the greater the soil infestation, the sooner that will occur. The stems of tiny seedlings may rot near the soil surface and the cotyledons wither. Symptoms may be delayed at lower soil temperatures or lesser soil infestation, or with somewhat resistant plants.

Diseased seedlings about 2 inches high may show nothing more specific than the death and browning of basal leaves, stunted plant growth, drooping of leaves during the heat of the day, and perhaps poor green color. The typical diseased plant 4 inches or more high has a black streak up one side of the stem, and all leaves originating from the streak are dead. A single branch may be killed.

Plants grown in heavily infested soil or at high soil temperatures, however, usually have dead leaves on a blackened stem base, and do not have unilateral development. In a dry climate, as in southern California, such stems may be harder and woodier than those of healthy plants. In a humid area that symptom may be lacking, but just above soil level there is often a pink crust consisting of masses of mycelium and spores of the fungus. The roots usually have few or no rotted areas unless they are growing in very wet soil. When infected stems are cut longitudinally, one can see brown or black streaks that extend upward through the woody tissues. The black color of the basal stem may extend into the pith.

All those symptoms do not necessarily appear in any one plant, but most of them may be observed in a large planting. The one-sided development, the black streak in the stem,

and the pink spore mass at soil level are the most dependable symptoms.

Other diseases may be confused with fusarium wilt.

Verticillium wilt causes much the same symptoms but lacks the pink basal spore layer.

Phytophthora root rot may cause death of tops, but the roots are then discolored and decayed, whereas fusarium wilt plants have nearly clean roots.

Phomopsis stem canker in humid areas causes a basal stem canker, in which tiny black fungus fruiting bodies are seen; the pink spore crust, the one-sided development, and dark streaks in the wood are lacking.

A stem rot caused by *Fusarium roseum* produces pink spore crusts on the cankers, but it does not extend up one side of the stem nor become vascular. Symptoms progress from outside inward, in contrast to wilt that develops outwardly from the inner tissues.

The spotted wilt virus causes dead tan areas in leaves and brown surface blotches on stems. Although symptoms may be unilateral, no black streak or pink spore crust is produced.

Root aphids sometimes cause wilting of the plants, but can be recognized by the insects on the roots.

Stem miners can produce wilting of aster plants in California. The tiny tunnels formed in the pith differentiate this trouble from fusarium wilt.

Flowers produced on plants infected by *Fusarium* under cool conditions may not show obvious external symptoms. The fungus has been found by W. C. Snyder to grow out from infected stems of such flowers and cause them to decay in warm storage.

The host range of the pathogen of fusarium wilt is not known to include plants other than China aster, nor does it even include all varieties of the single species, *Callistephus chinensis*. Varietal differences in susceptibility have been noted by many workers.

Resistant varieties have been developed several times, only to be lost when introduced into commerce. After

1925, efforts to develop resistant varieties by selection on heavily infested land were conducted by L. O. Kunkel at Yonkers, N. Y., L. R. Jones and R. S. Riker at Madison, Wis., E. R. Honeywell in Indiana, and D. J. MacLeod at Fredrickton, New Brunswick.

Mr. Kunkel's selections were turned over to Jones and Riker, who supplied material to seed companies in California and Illinois in a cooperative arrangement from 1929 to 1932.

The resistant varieties first offered to the trade in 1931 were American Branching Mary Semple, A. B. Azure Blue, Ostrich Feather Deep Rose, Crego Deep Rose, Royal Azure Blue, and Heart of France. More recently, P. E. Tilford at Wooster, Ohio (1940–42) and K. F. Baker at Los Angeles (1940–44) selected resistant plants under more favorable conditions for elimination of susceptible plants.

In the latter instance, only 0.75 percent of 78,000 plants of nearly 100 varieties survived in 1942, while 38.3 percent of 13,500 plants grown from 1942 selections survived in 1943. We have considerable evidence that satisfactory resistance can be obtained in three to five selection generations in heavily infested warm soil. Mr. Tilford's selections were marketed by the Ohio Florists' Association until 1950, when they were discontinued. Mr. Baker's selections were released to several seed companies.

Despite those and other efforts, one seedsman wrote in 1948: "Asters today are at their lowest ebb . . . for petalage and susceptibility to stem rot. Little is usually done except order 'rot resistant' strains, and regardless of where they come from, all too frequently they are disappointing."

Resistance was lost through one or more of the following factors:

(1) Making single-plant selections for flower type under conditions of very low wilt losses and correspondingly great risk of selecting susceptible plants. Selections thus made in commercial seed fields where soil was either poorly infested or too cool for severe wilt have lost resistance in a single generation.

(2) Planting in cool or poorly infested soil in all or in most years. Resistance to this disease is not stable or homozygous, and continuous selection is necessary to maintain it. The variable low percentage of natural crossing among even highly double varieties in seed fields contributes to this instability.

(3) Expense of maintaining resistance, which involves special procedures and single-plant lines. To develop or maintain resistant lines one must be able to sacrifice plants and seed yield. That in turn means more costly seed. Resistance consequently is basically an economic problem.

(4) Use of alternative plants, such as zinnia, in home yards and the disinfestation of soil and seed in commercial plantings have reduced the demand for resistant varieties.

The China aster is peculiar among hosts of wilt Fusaria in that it is the sole representative of the host genus and probably was developed from plants cultivated from antiquity by the Chinese. Indeed, it is not certain that the true wild progenitor is even represented in herbaria. It is possible that the full complement of potential resistance factors of the genus is not represented in the present commercial aster, and that if such factors were incorporated into commercial varieties a stable high-level resistance could be maintained.

Present commercial resistance seems to be best explained as the result of more than one genetic factor, perhaps several, which may be cumulative in effect. There is no correlation between resistance and flower color, but single varieties such as Single Chinensis and Rainbow types often, but not always, are quite resistant.

THE CAUSAL FUNGUS is *Fusarium oxysporum* f. *callistephi*. Other Fusaria (*F. roseum*, *F. lateritium*, *F. solani*, and *F. episphaeria*) have also been suggested as causal, but it is now known that some of them (*F. roseum* in particular) produce stem decay under moist conditions, rather than a vascular wilt of China aster. In earlier literature the wilt *Fusarium* has gone under such names (now synonyms of *F. oxysporum* f. *callistephi*) as *F. conglutinans* var. *callistephi* and *F. conglutinans* var. *majus*. Likewise the existence of several strains of forma *callistephi* has been postulated in explanation of the "breakdown of resistance" in commercial varieties since 1930. The assumption here that the level of resistance of aster varieties has not changed since 1930 is unwarranted, however.

Riker and Jones in 1935 presented evidence for the existence in Indiana and Japan of fungus strains of greater virulence to aster than those from Germany, Canada, and other sections of this country. It is not known, however, whether they were dealing with a greater *degree* of virulence or with a different *type* of pathogenicity.

Different isolates of the aster wilt *Fusarium*, as well as those from other hosts, are known to vary from weakly to strongly parasitic. In practice this affects severity of injury but not the host range, because a plant truly resistant to a virulent isolate under the most favorable conditions will not be susceptible under any circumstances. This differs greatly from *type* of pathogenicity (selective pathogenicity), in which the parasite has the ability to attack a new host, or against which a new set of genetic factors is necessary for resistance. This latter situation is clearly known among vascular Fusaria in garden pea and tomato, but is thought to be uncommon.

Because of the great importance of environment in the occurrence of aster wilt, the fact that no completely resistant aster varieties have been developed, the fact that verticillium wilt has not always been differentiated from that due to *Fusarium*, and the uncertainty that the tests of Riker and Jones were conducted with maximum soil infestation and optimum temperature, it is considered that evidence is still lacking for differing types of pathogenicity in forma *callistephi*. The selections directly or indirectly derived from those developed in Wisconsin proved highly resistant in field tests in California, Illinois, Maine, New York, the District of Columbia, New Brunswick, England, Sweden, Tasmania, and Germany, and were partially resistant in South Africa and Indiana. The selections developed at the University of California (Los Angeles) were highly resistant in various places in California, New York, Connecticut, Indiana, and Illinois, the only places where they were tested.

THE LIFE HISTORY of the fungus is similar to that of other wilt Fusaria. The organism persists in the soil, even in the absence of aster plants, for many years and reduces the usefulness of the land for the crop. The disease potential may decline after 5 years, but it builds up rapidly with return of the crop. The fungus is carried from place to place on tools and workmen's shoes, in irrigation water, and perhaps with soil particles by the wind.

Conidia formed on the stems are sticky and probably not airborne, although readily spread by water. These spores can germinate at once or remain alive under dry conditions for several months. The fungus can persist in plant refuse as dormant, thick-walled chlamydospores and be spread through the medium of the compost pile. These spores are more resistant to drying, heat, and fungicides than are the conidia or mycelium. The fungus also is commonly distributed with transplants from the seedbeds, where it may or may not have had time to produce disease. An infested seedbed may therefore introduce the disease to several fields or home yards.

The more delicate type of spore (conidium) is carried on the surface of the seeds. Presumably it gets there during threshing operations, either from dust or from the pink masses on stem bases. Spores are also carried on debris mixed with the seed. Whether a crop grown from contaminated seed will show wilt depends in part on soil temperature; it may do so at 77° F. but appear tardily or not at all at 60°. In either case the soil becomes infested. The fungus establishes most readily in soil freed (*i. e.*, pasteurized) of other competitive organisms, and will produce heaviest losses in such soil. This seed-borne fungus is initially most destructive in steamed soil under warm conditions, and is thus most rapidly damaging in glass houses and seedbeds.

Plants are susceptible to infection at any time from germination to maturity. Infection generally occurs through uninjured roots, but inoculations may be made into stem wounds. Infection in most instances is between the cells of the root cap and between the epidermal cells in the region of elongation.

In susceptible plants the fungus develops copiously in the xylem of the root, from which it spreads upward through the xylem of the stems. From the xylem it may spread outward into phloem and cortex in roots or stems. Stem cankers thus arise in moist, warm weather. In resistant plants there is little development of mycelium in the root tip, and it remains localized, though still alive, in tiny lesions. Resistance is of the physiological type, as in cabbage and tomato fusarium wilts, rather than of the morphological type. It is reported that lower losses result from seeding in place than from transplanting, but the results in all instances may have been due to higher soil temperature in the seedbed than in the field, rather than to transplanting injuries.

The damage to the plant results from toxins formed in the water-conducting tissues and carried to the leaves and stems, where cells are injured or killed. Insufficient mycelium is formed to block the xylem vessels and interfere seriously with water movement.

ENVIRONMENTAL CONDITIONS are important in determining the severity of the disease. Soil temperature is of such significance as to determine largely whether the disease occurs or not. Thus A. B. Jackson found in 1927 that parallel series in naturally infested soil at 63°–68° F. and 68°–77° developed 12.5 and 100 percent wilt, respectively. The optimum for growth of the fungus in culture is about 80°–86°, and no growth is produced at 39° or 95°. No symptoms other than slight loss of weight develop on asters grown in infested soil at 54°. Slight wilt develops at 61°. The optimum for wilt is about 80°, and the maximum is 90°.

Thus, even in heavily infested soil at about 55°, plants will sustain little loss from fusarium wilt, and only in heavily infested soil will symptoms develop at about 60°. On the other hand, lightly infested soil (such as clean soil planted with infested seed) will produce wilt plants if temperatures are 77° to 80°. To a certain extent, then, temperature and amount of fungus in the soil are interchangeable factors—an increase of one will offset a decrease of the other.

A certain length of time is required for wilt symptoms to appear. The lower the soil temperature or soil infestation, the longer that interval will be. Other things being equal, the shorter the exposure to heavily infested warm soil, the less will be the disease. However, winter planting of asters in coastal California has led to excessive losses from botrytis gray mold and rhizoctonia stem rot. The losses in a given field grown continuously to asters will vary greatly from year to year, depending on soil temperatures. Asters grown in the cool soils along the coast of California consistently have less wilt than those grown in the warm soils of the interior valleys of that State and are undesirable for a wilt-selection program.

A new commercial area planted to asters normally may pass through several stages. In the first year scattered diseased plants will appear through the field, their number depending on whether spread is restricted by seed sown in place and whether infected transplants were used and on the prevailing soil temperatures. The next year the disease will appear more uniformly through the field; if the soil is warm, severe losses may occur. By the third season a profitable crop will be produced only if the soil remains very cool. Usually the venture is then abandoned as uneconomic.

THE CONTROL of fusarium wilt is made difficult by the unavailability of commercial asters of high resistance, although advertisements may claim the contrary. Should truly resistant varieties again become available they would provide the ideal solution for home-yard and commercial plantings. In the meantime some benefit may be gained by using seed saved from the few plants surviving in heavily infested warm soil.

The protection of uninfested soil from introduction of the wilt fungus is highly important. Treatment of seed is essential in this, but one should recognize that it is done to protect the soil from infestation from the seed, rather than the seedling from the soil-borne fungus.

The best treatment at present is a mercuric chloride (corrosive sublimate) soak. A glass jar is filled about one-third full of seed and filled up with corrosive sublimate (1 to 1,000, or one 7½-grain tablet per pint of water), unheated and without any spreading agent. The lid is replaced and the seed intermittently shaken for 30 minutes. Then the fungicide is poured out through a cheesecloth held over the top of the jar. Three separate changes of water are used in rinsing. The jar is shaken each time. The seed is then spread out to dry in a warm place. The treatment lowers germination somewhat, particularly of seed whose cracked coats permit the mercury to reach the embryo. Heating the solution above room temperature is highly injurious. W. O. Gloyer found that seed treatment permitted the growing of asters in the same field in New York for five consecutive years without wilt.

To avoid infestation of land it is further necessary to prevent carrying the fungus on tools, machinery, shoes, and such. Formaldehyde solution (1 part commercial formaldehyde in 15 parts of water), may be prepared for dipping infested tools, for applying to shoes, and for spraying machinery before it is used on clean land.

Once soil becomes infested, three courses are open if resistant lines are not available: It may be abandoned for asters; it may be used once every five or more years for this crop, being rotated with any other in the interim; the soil may be steamed or treated chemically to free it of the organism.

The third is imperative for seedbeds as a routine procedure. If steam is used, the soil should be heated to at least 180° F. and held at this level for 30 minutes. A formaldehyde drench (diluted 1 to 40) has been recommended; enough of it is applied to penetrate the soil to at least an 18-inch level. The soil is covered with canvas for 2 days, and then aerated for at least a week before planting.

Old infected plant parts, in which the fungus can survive for at least a year, should be burned. They should never be used in a compost pile unless it is to be steamed before use.

Because of the restrictive effect of cool soil on the occurrence of wilt, losses may be reduced by shading if shading keeps soil temperatures near 60° F.

KENNETH F. BAKER, *a plant pathologist in the California Agricultural Experiment Station, Los Angeles, has been engaged in studies on diseases of floricultural crops for more than 15 years. He has conducted pathological investigations in Washington, Wisconsin, Nebraska, Hawaii, New York, and California.*

Petal Blight of Azalea

D. L. Gill

Azalea petal blight, or flower spot, is a striking disease. One day all the flowers on a plant or in a garden may appear normal to the casual observer. The next day they may be blighted as though hot water had been poured over them.

The disease was first noticed near Charleston, S. C., in 1931. In 1932, men who conducted a survey for the Department of Agriculture found the disease in all the gardens they visited within 20 miles of Charleston on both sides of the Ashley and Cooper Rivers. The disease spread rapidly. In 1935 it was discovered in Wilmington, N. C., and in 1936 in Savannah, Ga., Mobile, Ala., and New Orleans.

Freeman Weiss, then of the Department of Agriculture, found the disease in 1937 along the Coastal Plain from Wilmington, N. C., to Lafayette, La., where his survey stopped. It was not present in some of the isolated azalea plantings into which no new plants had been brought shortly before. The disease was reported in 1940 in Texas, where apparently it had been present for several years. California reported its presence in 1941, Maryland in 1946, and Virginia in 1947.

Moved by the severity of the disease and the great value of the azalea flowers throughout the South, Dr. Weiss began investigations in 1933 at Charleston. He believed at first that the sudden appearance and rapid spread of the disease meant it was spread otherwise than by wind or rain. As insects were considered possible vectors, Floyd F. Smith, an entomologist in the Department, joined Weiss in the investigation in 1935. They continued to work together on the project through 1938.

Azalea petal blight appears first as small white spots on the colored flowers, or as brown spots on white-flowered varieties. The spots enlarge rapidly under favorable conditions until the whole petal or flower softens and collapses. Affected petals fall apart if rubbed gently between the fingers. Flowers injured by insects or weather or otherwise will not do so. The diseased flowers cling to the plant and present an unsightly appearance. Normally healthy flowers of Indian azaleas fall to the ground while still displaying their original color and shape and thus prolong their attractiveness.

Weiss and Smith found the fungus most commonly associated with the diseased flowers to be the cause of it. That point had been hard to prove because the fungus grows slowly and fails to produce spores in artificial culture. Because the fungus was previously unknown, Dr. Weiss named it *Ovulinia azaleae.*

Hard, black objects—the sclerotia—are produced on the old, diseased flowers while they still cling to the plant or after they fall to the ground. The sclerotia are one-eighth to one-fourth inch long. In that stage the fungus can live through the period when flowers are not present. Their presence confirms diagnosis of the disease.

Sclerotia spread *Ovulinia* into new areas when some of the surrounding soil is moved with the plants in transplanting. In spring, about the time azaleas bloom, the sclerotia on or just below the soil surface produce on the ends of short stalks small, brown, cup-shaped bodies, known as apothecia. The apothecia are one-sixteenth to one-eighth inch across. Apothecia continue to be produced for 4 or 5 weeks. They flatten as they mature, and spores (ascospores) of the *Ovulinia* are forcibly discharged from their flat upper surface. A spore may reach a flower by the force of its discharge, or it may be caught in wind currents and carried to a nearby plant. If such a spore reaches a flower when conditions are favorable it germinates, sends a germ tube into the flower, and initiates a new infection. A few days later, as the flower blight progresses, secondary spores (conidia) are produced.

Up to several hundred thousand conidia are produced on a single flower. They spread the disease quickly. Infection thus is produced on successively opening flowers. Spores can produce infection at 40° to 80° F.; infection normally occurs between 50° and 72° and is at a peak at 65°.

High humidity, rain, fog, and dew favor the development of the petal blight disease—conditions frequently present in the South during the azalea season.

Azalea petal blight attacks all varieties of azaleas (*Rhododendron* species).

Early-blooming varieties like Elegans may largely escape infection because there is not enough inoculum when they flower. The Macrantha azaleas usually bloom so late that conidial inoculum is again very low.

Weiss and Smith found the disease on several unidentified hybrid rhododendrons growing interplanted with azaleas. Two true rhododendrons (*R. catawbiense* and *R. carolinianum*) became infected following inoculation.

Ovulinia attacks mountain-laurel (*Kalmia latifolia*) when it grows near azaleas.

Flowers of highbush blueberry (*Vaccinium corymbosum* and its varieties *fuscatum* and *tenellum*) and of huckleberry (*Gaylussacia baccata*) were experimentally infected. The disease has been of little importance on them. All plants known to be susceptible belong to the family Ericaceae. Research workers could not infect plant parts other than flowers.

Because many insects visit azalea flowers, Weiss and Smith undertook an investigation to determine their relationship to the spread of petal blight. They soon learned that insect injuries were not necessary for the fungus to enter the flower. Early in the study, they thought it probable that spores carried by insects were responsible for the initial infection in the spring. It seemed unlikely that honey bees harbored the fungus in their colony or initiated early infection.

Because primary infection occurred near the ground, soil-inhabiting insects and animals and insects emerging from the soil were investigated, but these workers rarely found that they harbored *Ovulinia*. They could not indict them as carriers of primary inoculum.

Insects, they learned, can carry *Ovulinia* conidia from flower to flower but are not effective carriers until infection becomes general and large numbers of conidia are present. Some of the spore-bearing insects were observed to travel 5 miles in 8 days. Inoculation tests showed that they sometimes released spores gradually for several days. Insects therefore may be responsible for the introduction of the disease into nearby uninfected azalea gardens. Consequently any eradication program must be on an area basis if it is to succeed.

Some combined insecticidal-fungicidal dusts had no repelling effect on bees lighting on the flowers. The combination, or fungicidal dusts alone, did reduce the number of spores produced on the flowers and so reduced the number carried by the insects. Dusts made of stomach poisons had no effect on the insects carrying the fungus. Dusts that contained a contact insecticide, derris, pyrethrum, or nicotine sulfate killed adults of most species in 1 to 4 days. The insects were not attracted to poisoned sugar spray applied to the flowers.

The entomological investigations were closed with the conclusion that disease control, rather than insect control, appeared the logical method of attacking the problem. The studies showed that insects were involved in the secondary spread of the disease, but that their role was less important than it had been thought to be.

Weiss and Smith pointed out that since the *Ovulinia* persists in the sclerotial stage from one flowering season to another, the chief control efforts should be prevention of sclerotial formation, removal and destruction of sclerotia that may form and reach the ground, and prevention of apothecial development by sclerotia that escape.

In accord with those recommendations, large numbers of diseased flowers were picked from the plants and destroyed. The suggestion was made that in isolated plantings the entire bloom for 1 year be destroyed as a means of eliminating the disease—but that was of no value, because some sclerotia were found to live at least 2 years. Because picking off all infected flowers proved to be an almost impossible task, the mulch around the plants was removed and destroyed after the old flowers had fallen. Many sclerotia were destroyed. A heavier mulch replacing the old then tended to prevent apothecia from pushing through to a point from which they could eject spores onto the flowers.

Those practices effected little or no control—at least a few apothecia were always produced to initiate infection, and (except in isolated plantings) secondary infections could be initiated by conidia from outside the treated area. Besides, old sclerotia sometimes remained hanging on plants a year after they were produced, and some sclerotia produced apothecia in the second flowering season.

Drenches applied to the soil about the plants were also tested. The shallow root system of azaleas makes injury from such applications a hazard. Surface applications of sulfur and copper, commonly used as dormant sprays, were ineffective. Acetic acid (1–1,000 to 1–600) did not injure azaleas even with repeated applications and was toxic to the *Ovulinia*.

Fungicidal sprays were applied to the plants before the flowers opened. Because *Ovulinia azaleae* infects only flowers after they show color, the sprays were valueless.

Spraying the open flowers with fungicides was also tried. Effective control by this method was considered unlikely by Weiss and Smith because the waxy surface of the blossoms prevented wetting, there was difficulty in obtaining coverage in the dense masses of blooms, and frequent spraying was necessary because of continuous opening of the flowers over several weeks. Lime-sulfur and copper sprays gave no control but produced no injury in azaleas except flower discoloration. Acetic acid (80 percent diluted to 1 part to 600 parts water) offered some promise when sprayed on open flowers and on the ground, but—because of its solubility in water —rains, dews, and fogs removed it and left the flowers exposed to infection.

A copper-clay or copper-lime dust containing 6.5 percent copper was effective in laboratory tests. Dusting azaleas in the open failed to control the disease if secondary infection was severe. The dusts left an objectionable residue on the flowers. Weiss and Smith concluded that overwintering sources of *Ovulinia* must be largely eliminated if spraying or dusting was to be effective.

Philip Brierley, of the Department of Agriculture, followed Weiss and Smith at Charleston, working through the 1941 season. His approach was to attempt suppression of apothecial formation by application of chemicals to the soil just before the apothecia developed.

Other workers had found cyanamide (calcium cyanamide) effective against apothecia of the fungus causing brown rot of stone fruits and Elgetol (sodium dinitrocresylate) toxic to perithecia of the fungus causing apple scab. Cyanamide applied to plats containing large numbers of sclerotia at the rates of 200, 400, and 800 pounds an acre prevented apothecial formation. No apparent damage was produced in azalea plants when 400 pounds an acre of cyanamide were applied around them. Elgetol was applied as a 1-percent solution at 450, 900, and 1,800 gallons an acre. It also prevented formation of apothecia. Similar results were obtained later with cyanamide at Spring Hill, Ala., and Baton Rouge, La.

I treated an entire isolated planting at St. Francisville, La., with 400 pounds of cyanamide an acre in 1942. Petal blight appeared later and failed to become as severe as in previous years. I could not determine whether infection originated from apothecia that escaped the treatment or from conidia from another planting. I observed no injury in azaleas and no lasting injury in other plants.

Dr. Brierley pointed out that two factors weigh against the practical use of a material suppressing apothecial formation: The danger of injury to azaleas or other plants grown in association with them and the need for application on a community-wide basis to accomplish significant reduction of the disease.

During the azalea seasons of 1944 and 1945, Cynthia Westcott represented the Department of Agriculture at Spring Hill, Ala. She assembled a number of new and old fungicides. These she tested in the laboratory and garden as protectants against conidial infection. Two offered good control of petal blight with a minimum of discoloration or injury to the flowers. They were: (1) Dithane D-14 (nabam), 1⅓ quarts; zinc sulfate, 1 pound; lime, one-half pound; and Triton B-1956, 1 fluid ounce to 100 gallons of water; and (2) Phygon (2,3-dichloro-1,4-napthoquinone), 1 pound to 100 gallons of water. Applications were made three times a week. Satisfactory control resulted on sprayed flowers even when only half a plant was sprayed and infection was severe on the other half.

Those preparations were used in 1946 in a number of parks, estates, and gardens. All reported excellent control, but some found objectionable injury to the flowers. I followed Dr. Westcott at Spring Hill in 1946. I tested other fungicides, wetting agents, concentrations, and frequencies of application, and studied the nature of the flower injury.

Nabam (Dithane D-14 and Parzate Liquid) and zineb (Dithane Z-78 and Parzate) have been outstanding fungicides against petal blight in comparison with other materials. Dithane D-14 and Parzate Liquid sprays were prepared at the strength Dr. Westcott used. Dithane Z-78 and Parzate were used at the rate of 1.4 pounds to 100 gallons. A reduction in the concentration was considered desirable to reduce spray residue on the flowers and possibility of injury. Dithane D-14, 0.9 quart; zinc sulfate, 0.67 pound; lime, 0.34 pound; and Triton B-1956, 1 fluid ounce to 100 gallons, was found satisfactory. The quantity of zineb (Parzate and Dithane Z-78) was successfully reduced to 0.97 pound to 100 gallons.

Santomerse S (2 fluid ounces in 100 gallons) or Dreft (4 ounces in 100 gallons) were found to be satisfactory wetting agents to replace Triton B-1956 in making the Dithane D-14 spray. The wetting agents cause the spray to spread over the flowers in a film instead of forming drops that roll off. Lime is not essential in the spray.

Tests were conducted for 4 years with Dithane D-14 and for 2 years with Phygon, using one, two, and three applications a week. Spraying three times a week gave consistently better results than spraying twice, although many gardeners would have been satisfied with the control obtained with the latter. One application a week was unsatisfactory.

Dr. Westcott found some injury to azalea flowers by Phygon, but did not consider it objectionable in view of the control obtained. In later tests and in the hands of some gardeners, the injury proved objectionable, particularly after three or more applications of the material. Injury consisted of bleaching and burning of the flowers from the margin inward. It was present to a lesser extent when the concentration was reduced beyond that affording satisfactory control. Some other quinone compounds produced similar injury. We no longer recommended Phygon.

In preparing the Dithane D–14 spray, Dr. Westcott used zinc sulfate containing 25 percent metallic zinc. Some growers who reported injury following the Dithane D–14 spray recommendations were using the same amount of 36 percent zinc sulfate. Comparisons of sprays prepared with equal quantities of the 25- and 36-percent material showed that injury resulted from the latter spray under conditions which tended to dry out the flowers. A reduction in the amount of 36 percent zinc sulfate reduced the injury. If the flowers were deficient in water for a longer period, injury was produced by Dithane D–14 sprays containing any concentration of zinc sulfate. A slightly greater water deficiency resulted in injury to unsprayed flowers. Spray injury consisted of burning and drying of the petals from the margins inward. Because large amounts of water are lost through the flowers and injury is severe with low water content, azaleas in flower should be watered during dry periods. Varying the zinc sulfate contents of the sprays had no effect on the control of petal blight. If no zinc sulfate was added, injury also resulted although control was obtained with three applications a week.

Use of dusts was investigated because of the ease of application, particularly in small gardens. Six-percent dusts of zineb (Parzate and Dithane Z–78) gave satisfactory control but were not as effective as the sprays. Use of dusts is recommended for small gardens not equipped to spray.

Applications of a protectant fungicide should begin at the first evidence of the disease—usually about the time early varieties (such as Elegans) are in full bloom or when midseason varieties (such as Formosa or Pride of Mobile) are beginning to bloom. Applications may be less frequent when all the flowers have opened and are covered with a fungicide. Spraying should be in the form of a fine mist directly into the flowers, but should not be continued until there is runoff of the material. In a number of show gardens, parks, parkways, estates, and home gardens, one of these control methods is used as a regular procedure.

D. L. GILL *is associate pathologist in the Bureau of Plant Industry, Soils, and Agricultural Engineering. He studied at Louisiana State University and Cornell University. From 1935 to 1941 Dr. Gill taught ornamental horticulture at Louisiana State University. He has been with the Department of Agriculture since 1941, conducting research on diseases of azaleas, camellias, and other ornamental plants in Southeastern States. He is stationed at the Georgia Coastal Plain Experiment Station at Tifton, Ga.*

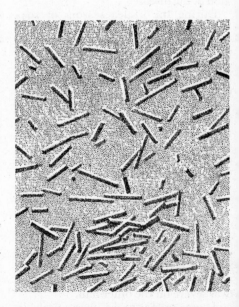

Tobacco mosaic virus.

Infectious Diseases of Carnation

Emil F. Guba, Ralph W. Ames

Growing carnations under glass is an extensive industry in the United States, one with a long history of progress despite ever-present disease problems.

Control of the diseases embraces a sequence of practices associated with each of the stages of culture, beginning with propagation.

Propagation by cuttings is an important consideration because it is the source of most of the disease problems. It offers the means for diseases to spread to places where the stock is sent. The problem is not easily avoided because of the varying conditions of growing and the widespread dissemination of stock.

The mother stock must be kept healthy by rigid controls. The danger of infection must be avoided by discriminate selection and segregation. Outbreaks of systemic diseases in certain classes of stock, even after rooting, are unquestionably linked with the source of the stock. There are ways of meeting this problem.

After the cuttings are rooted, they are transplanted in soil and pinched to make plants with a potentially productive frame. Conditions having to do with water, drainage, physical and chemical properties of the soil, and insect and fungus contamination affect the survival and growth of the young plants. Soil and the insects, weeds, and pathogens it contains may be cleansed by steam or chemicals. Efforts have been made to control diseases with chemicals applied to the soil to disinfest it, to prevent spread from centers of infection, or to be absorbed into the plant to ward off infection or even to cure the plant of infection after attack.

Field growing in the early part of summer is still practiced in some places. It favors stronger growth than inside culture, but it may also expose the plants to weather that favors disease. Plants that are brought indoors may bring infection with them.

Inside culture provides better control over growing conditions, easier control of pests by fumigation, greater security from disease, and economies in labor. Therefore the trend has been toward greenhouse culture entirely.

THE LEAF SPOT diseases mainly destroy foliage. They also attack the stems and calyxes of flowers. They progress from the lowest leaves upward and cause dead spots, which join or expand across the leaf and ultimately wither and kill either the part beyond or the entire leaf. Infection is favored by syringing, overhead watering, excessive moisture in the beds, and moist, stagnant air. Strong, dense growth and close planting favor the diseases. Those conditions can be made worse by long spells of wet weather. The inoculum of the pathogens is transmitted on the surface of the cuttings, especially if the cuttings come from infested growing areas. The susceptibility of different varieties to the diseases varies markedly.

Bacterial leaf spot, caused by the bacterium *Phytomonas woodsii*, produces spots that are elliptic, barren, brown, and surrounded by a purple zone within a light-green halo or margin. The spots dry out, but under moist conditions beads of bacterial ooze appear on their surfaces. When the spots are numerous, the leaves twist, wither, blight, and turn completely brown, but the outline of the spots remains clearly apparent. The disease spreads easily. Widespread epidemics have occurred in cycles, one of them between 1930 and 1940.

The disease is controlled by removing diseased leaves, careful bottom watering, and spraying the plants with phenyl mercury acetate (Tag Fungicide or Puratized Apple Spray), ½ pint to 100 gallons of water. A spray of zinc sulfate, 3 pounds, lime 4 pounds, and alum 1½ pounds to 50 gallons of water is said to give satisfactory control. The addition of a spreader (Dreft, Penetrol, or Dupont Spreader-Sticker) helps to get better wetting of the foliage.

Fairy ring spot is caused by the fungus *Heterosporium echinulatum*. Its spots are usually circular, about one-fourth inch in diameter, zoned, ash gray or brown, surrounded by a pale-green halo, and beset with an olive-brown mold, which is most prominently confined to the centers of the spots. The stems break off easily at points of infection. The olive-brown spore stalks arise in tufts from the stomata and bear three- or four-celled brown spores with spiny walls.

Bottom watering to avoid wetting the plants and ventilating and heating to avoid too low temperatures and excessive dampness are advisable for satisfactory control. Spraying with ferbam or copper fungicides is necessary if infection persists. Sanitation of diseased foliage is also important.

Septoria leaf spot, caused by the fungus *Septoria dianthi*, attacks leaves stems, and calyxes and causes light brown, elliptic spots that have violet or purple borders and unite to form irregular areas. The spots are dotted with black, pin-point spore sacs of the fungus. Control measures are the same as those for fairy ring spot.

Carnation rust is caused by the fungus *Uromyces caryophyllinus*. It is prevalent wherever carnations are grown. The round or elongate fungus pustules, filled with rusty-brown spore powder, break out on both sides of the leaves and occasionally on the stems. The area about the infected tissue at first is yellowish, then brown.

Infection causes constriction and curling of the foliage, stunting, and death. Varieties vary in susceptibility to infection. The same conditions contributing to the development of the leaf spot diseases apply to rust, and the same cultural practices apply to its control. Careful bottom watering and a frequent dusting with zineb, ferbam, or a mixture of ferbam and sulfur are advised. Dry lime-sulfur, 4 pounds to 50 gallons of water, applied once also gives good results. The spore inoculum is carried on the cuttings into the propagation. Protection from such infection may be obtained by dousing the cuttings in ferbam, 1 ounce to 4 gallons of water, with spreader (Dreft three-fourths to 1 level teaspoonful to each gallon) added before planting.

Gray mold rot, due to the fungus *Botrytis cinerea*, attacks many kinds of plants. With carnations the fungus attacks the sepals and petals, wilting and rotting them. On the decayed parts it produces a dense growth of mold and spores. The fungus is favored by cool, excessively damp conditions in the greenhouse and mild winter temperatures that are at the low range of temperature for carnation culture. Flowers that are packed for market during the incubating stage of infection show serious gray mold in transit and upon arrival. The fungus grows profusely on carnation debris in the greenhouse. Hot-water heat appears to control the disease better than steam heat. Fluctuations in temperature and rises in humidity encourage the disease. Control is obtained by a drier atmosphere by means of more pipe heat, more uniform distribution of heating pipes, more ventilation, and colder and drier outside weather. Sanitation and the removal of plant debris are helpful.

Bud rot, caused by the fungus *Fusarium poae*, keeps the buds from opening or causes them to open partly and imperfectly. The inside is decayed and moldy, brown or pink, and usually infested with the grayish-white grass mite, *Pediculopsis graminum*. Many spores of the fungus are also present on the rotted tissue. The fungus and the mites live together. The mites introduce the spores into the buds. The decay that follows infection provides favorable conditions for the mites. Both mites and fungus infest various grasses, notably Kentucky bluegrass, *Poa pratensis*, on which it causes the so-called silver spike disease. Excessive dampness and wide extremes of temperature under glass favor bud rot of carnations. Diseased buds should be removed and destroyed. Heating and ventilation should be managed to avoid abnormal temperature and moisture conditions. Fumigants, such as organic phosphate compounds as aerosols, will control the mites. Soil from outside grassland used in resoiling beds should be steam-sterilized as a precautionary measure. Improvements in cultural practices, more general soil steaming, and the less frequent use of new sod have reduced the number of grass mites and the incidence of bud rot.

Stem rot, caused by the fungus *Corticium* (*Rhizoctonia*) *solani*, is the most generally destructive disease of carnations in greenhouse and field when excessive water and high temperatures appear together. Losses from it can be serious in summer. When the fungus causes bad rotting of cuttings in the propagating bench, it is referred to as the cutting bench fungus; its spawn binds the sand into masses. The foliage loses its green color. The entire plant wilts, collapses, and turns straw-colored. The part of the stem in contact with the soil is attacked. Its bark becomes a soft shredded rot, but the underlying wood remains firm. If pulled, the plant breaks off easily at the rotted stem, and the firm root remains in the soil. Threads and brownish knots of fungus sometimes appear about the rotted stem and nearby soil. Even branches in contact with the soil may become infected and wilt independently of the rest of the plant.

The fungus occurs even in virgin soil and attacks all kinds of plants. The carnation is susceptible in all its stages of growth. Cleanliness and cautious watering and airing throughout the growing period are desirable control measures. The use of clean sand, soil steaming, shallow planting to assure that the stems are well above the soil line, shading, and cool temperatures are important. The use of plant bands helps. In the bands the plants grow compact blocks of roots and are planted three-fourths of their depth so that the stem is exposed well above the soil. Without plant bands, it is hard to plant at the proper depth in relation to the soil line.

Blight (leaf spot and canker) is caused by the fungus *Alternaria dianthi*. It is manifested by brown spots on leaves, flowers, and stems; blighting of foliage; and cankers in stems and branches, sometimes followed by wilting and death. The brown spots are overlaid with a black deposit of spores, which give the blighted parts and plants a blackish appearance. Infection in the blade causes constriction and twisting of the leaf. Often the tips of the leaves are killed. If weather conditions favor a progressive development of the disease, infections appear in the calyx and corolla lobes. Spores lodged in the leaf axils may infect nodes of branches and girdle them. Ordinarily the disease is restricted to the bark and to the outside of the cambium, but occasionally the fungus grows deeper into the tissue of the branch and causes a localized, dry, brown or black rot and the death of the branch above. Black crusts of spores appear on the surface of the cankers, especially if unusual moisture is present. Then, also, injuries from chemicals and pests can contribute to attacks of alternaria blight. Injuries of all kinds favor infection indirectly, although infection may also be direct.

Spores of the fungus are carried with the cuttings, especially those from contaminated places. The disease appears in the propagating bed as a leaf spot or blight and as a basal stem decay. The black deposit of spores, generally associated with the disease, is a diagnostic sign. Outside culture is not advised. Preventive and protective spraying with copper or ferbam or ziram fungicides, to which is added a spreader and sticker, is recommended. Bottom watering and the avoidance of excessive dampness are important. Varieties show marked differences in susceptibility. Highly susceptible varieties should be avoided.

Canker, dieback, stem, crown, and root rot are caused by the fungi *Fusarium culmorum and F. avenaceum.* They attack all parts of the carnation plant. The rotting of roots, root head, and stem causes a progressive wilting and collapse of the plant. The diseased tissue is brown, red, and crimson. The snags rot and branches die back because of localized infections in the nodes. A destructive rot of roots and stems of cuttings occurs in the propagating bed and among young plants. Cuttings carry infection from mother stock, and contamination of the sand may lead to the loss of the entire class of stock. Red or crimson tissue is usually associated with infection and is frequent in stock 2 and 3 years old. The organisms are commonly associated with the decay of roots and crowns of plants attacked by bacterial wilt.

Infection occurs only through injuries or weak and old tissue. Well established, uninjured plants, having good root action and growing under favorable conditions, are never affected. Wet soil, warmth, poor drainage, excessive mulches, root injuries from chemicals, symphilids, and similar conditions favor infection.

THE SYSTEMIC DISEASES include another smut. It is caused by the fungus *Ustilago violacea,* which attacks various plants in the pink family. Infected plants make slow growth. Many weak axillary shoots develop and give the plants a grassy or bushy habit. The internodes of the stems are shortened. The flower buds are short and squatty.

The calyxes tend to split. The flowers are sprinkled with a violet-black, sooty dust from the anthers, which may be observed even in the unopened buds. The female structure of the flower is completely suppressed by the fungus. The smutted anthers are produced in abnormal numbers. The smut spores replace the pollen grains in the anthers and infect other plants when they are dispersed. Infection, which occurs through injured surfaces and flowers, becomes systemic in the plant but persists mainly in the young growing tissues. It eventually invades the male structures of the flowers. Infection is readily carried along from diseased plants in cuttings. Except for flowers, infection by spores is only through broken surfaces. Young growth is much more apt to be infected than old growth. Infection does not arise from contaminated soil.

Anther smut can be eliminated by a progressive roguing of affected plants just before they come into flowering—an important step to prevent spore dispersal. Plants showing the characteristic grassy or bushy habit must be removed. They must be avoided when cuttings are gathered for propagation. A grower who follows that advice can eliminate the disease in 2 or 3 years.

VASCULAR WILT DISEASES include many distinct forms. In all of them the first symptoms are a dull color of the foliage and loss of turgidity. The branch or entire plant dies and becomes straw-colored. The true wilt diseases are caused by pathogens that invade the water-conducting tissues and discolor them throughout the roots, stem, and branches—that is, as a brown ring in cross section and brown streaks or bands in long section under the bark. Sometimes one can tell one wilt disease from another only by examination through a microscope. Other pathogens cause localized infections in stems and branches and lead to symptoms of wilt, such as those of alternaria blight, rhizoctonia stem rot, and *Fusarium culmorum.* Those are not true vascular diseases.

The vascular wilt diseases may appear in all stages of growth. Generally they develop fastest in the warm months. Young plants succumb quickly. Symptoms may be marked in older plants, although the plant and axillary shoots used for cuttings may be infected. Infection tends to become general or systemic in the plant, although temperature, moisture, and other conditions influence the rate at which symptoms develop.

In all these diseases, the causal organisms infest the soil and can be transmitted by soil and water, but serious outbreaks of wilt among young plants originate with infection in the stock. Plants showing the first symptoms of wilt should be destroyed, because infection will certainly spread. An entire flat of plants should be destroyed even if only one plant among them shows symptoms of disease.

Bacterial wilt, caused by the bacterium *Phytomonas caryophylli*, makes plants wilt and die rapidly. The symptoms are like those caused by the rhizoctonia stem rot fungus, but with bacterial wilt the roots are rotted and sticky and the tissue under the bark in stems and branches is yellow or brown and sticky. The bark about the stem is soft, disintegrated, and sticky. Usually nothing remains of the root.

Fusarium wilt, or branch rot, is caused by the fungus *Fusarium dianthi.* Young plants die slowly after infection, which occurs through injuries in the root, stem, or branches. Older plants show a slow and progressive dying of the branches. The conductive tissue is brown and dry—not moist, as in bacterial wilt. Bacterial ooze and stickiness are absent. In the stems the fungus eventually progresses beyond the conductive tissue, producing a dry rot, which may girdle the stem and kill the plant.

Symptoms of phialophora wilt, which is caused by the fungus *Phialophora cinerescens*, resemble those of fusarium wilt. The vascular tissue is discolored but there is no dry rotting and browning of other parts of the tissue, such as the pith or cortex.

The control of vascular wilt diseases starts with the propagation of healthy stock. Stock derived from cultured cuttings is the best. Steaming the soil at temperatures of 180° to 200° F. is advocated, because the pathogens are also soil-borne. Flats of plants in which disease occurs should be discarded. In planted beds or benches, areas showing loss should be treated with phenyl mercury fungicide, 1 pint to 100 gallons of water, 1 quart to a square foot, before planting replacements. Cuttings must not be doused in water. Subirrigation is inadvisable. Flowering stock in which there is loss from disease should not be carried beyond the first year. Injuries to plants should be avoided. Too much handling and transplanting is inadvisable.

Tests at Ohio State University in gravel culture gave best control of bacterial wilt at high calcium levels of 150–200 parts per million of nutrient solution at pH levels of 5.5–6.5. Application of these results to soil culture of carnations is wanting. Where calcium is needed, gypsum is recommended.

VIRUS DISEASES are extremely infectious. The contagion or substance that causes them is ultramicroscopic and characterized by peculiar properties. It cannot be cultured artificially. Virus diseases are recognized principally by changes induced in living cells and by characteristic symptoms.

The virus diseases of carnations—mosaic, streak, and yellows—assume greater importance in the carnation-growing industry as they become better known. Mosaic is caused by the carnation mosaic virus; streak, by the streak virus; and yellows, by a combination of the two viruses in the same plant.

Carnation mosaic is the most widespread. Symptoms are not evident at the time cuttings are normally taken and the effects of the diseases are so obscure that they may pass unnoticed until the stock is completely infected and unfit for propagation. A slight mottling of the leaves with light-green, irregular to elongate blotches is the most marked symptom. The mottling is usually more pronounced in the younger leaves than in the older ones. Foliage from virus-free plants is smooth and uniformly green. Flowers of colored varieties infected with carnation mosaic virus often show somewhat lighter streaks that parallel the veins of the petals. The most striking symptoms generally appear in late fall, winter, and early spring.

Carnation streak is characterized by broken lines or streaks in the leaves. The streaks may be white, yellow, brown, or purple. The streaks are plainly indicated in older leaves of established plants in the spring, especially during March to May. They may be so severe as to lead to the death of the plant. Symptoms are erratically indicated during the rest of the year. The disease therefore is not accurately recognized during the usual time of propagation but appears prominently in cuttings in spring.

Plants affected with carnation yellows show mottling and flecking of the leaves and stems, distortion and color breaking of the flowers, and a general reduction in vigor and production. Young leaves show mottling of light and dark green patches or streaks that run parallel to the midrib and cause the affected leaves to appear lighter green than healthy leaves. Older leaves have whitish, sunken, elongated flecks or streaks, which may become reddish, purplish, or brown. Severely affected leaves sometimes are blighted. Yellows has caused the death of nearly all flower stems of some varieties in March and April. Death of severely spotted foliage is more common from the combination of streak and yellows than from streak alone. Stems also may show white or light-colored streaks like those on the leaves. Color break-ing of the flowers, characteristic of mosaic, is intensified in yellows. Broken flowers show white or light-colored streaks that parallel the veins of the petals, fanning out from the base toward the tip. The streaking does not show in white varieties, but all varieties often have distorted flowers of poor quality.

Environment influences the symptoms of yellows. Unfavorable growing conditions that injure the root system or check plant growth increase the development of symptoms in diseased plants. Low fertility, excessive amount of salts in the soil, too heavy or too frequent application of water, and excessive application of fertilizer are apparent causes for severe symptoms.

Carnation mosaic can be transmitted readily by mechanical inoculation, grafting, or by the green peach aphid, *Myzus persicae*. There may be other vectors.

Carnation streak has been transmitted experimentally by grafting, although insect vectors, more common in the field than in the greenhouse, are suspected. Studies at the Colorado Agricultural Experiment Station indicate that streak can be caused by the aster yellows virus and transmitted by the aster leafhopper.

Carnation yellows has been transmitted only by grafting, although it may be transmitted by insect vectors. Vegetative propagation is an important method of spreading the diseases.

None of the virus diseases of carnation are transmitted through the seed. They are not carried over from one season to the next in the soil.

Roguing and selection of stock have not given complete control of the carnation virus diseases because the appearance of symptoms in diseased plants is not distinct enough at any given time to allow for complete eradication. From the time of removal from sand until benching, however, the selection of young plants with no symptoms should be of great value.

Recommended measures for the control of carnation virus diseases involve four steps.

First is the selection of healthy plants for propagation. It may be desirable to start a special propagating plot each year. Stock with a high percentage of disease should be discarded, and new virus-free stock obtained. New seedlings are virus-free and, where they are commercially acceptable, are to be desired over standard virus-infected varieties. The use of Sweet William as a test plant is beneficial in determining whether the stock is free from mosaic.

Second is rigid control of insects at all times, for aphids, thrips, and such may be carriers of the infective agents.

Third, the plants should be grown in the greenhouse the year around, because the diseases, especially streak, spread much faster in the field. Certainly the specially selected mother plants for the propagation plot should be kept inside and free from insects.

Fourth: New carnation plants or cuttings should be as free as possible from virus diseases. It might be advisable to secure stock from firms specializing in the propagation of carnations.

We know of no treatments with chemicals or heat that are available on a practical scale or effective in eliminating or controlling the virus diseases of carnations.

THE CONTROL OF VASCULAR WILT diseases, like the bacterial and fusarium wilts, requires infection-free plants in the beginning and culture in soil that has been freed of the pathogens by disinfestation or sterilization.

In view of the indiscriminate transplanting in soil for several months before the plants are established in the benches, the value of soil disinfestation with steam or chemicals can be negligible unless it is complete all the time the plants are growing.

Other approaches to the control of carnation wilt diseases have been proposed, notably chemotherapy and soil disinfestation by applications of chemicals to the topsoil during the growing period.

Chemotherapy is the treatment of internal disease by the introduction of chemicals. To be effective, the chemicals must be completely distributed through the plant tissues in concentrations sufficient to destroy or modify the growth of the pathogen without injuring the plant.

The chemical may act directly on the pathogen or may counteract toxins produced by the pathogen. Chemicals may be injected directly into the plant or they may be absorbed through the roots or other plant parts. In chemotherapy the action of the chemical is exerted upon the organisms or its toxins within the plant body rather than on the surface of the plant.

Chemotherapy may be a promising method of controlling vascular wilt diseases. Knowledge of its possibilities is still limited, and the practicality of its application is doubtful. Until quite recently the only positive cure credited to plant chemotherapy has been the cure of diseases due to deficiencies of nutrients. Reports of studies on infectious diseases indicate that internal treatment with certain chemicals may have some value in controlling certain plant diseases or in masking their symptoms.

It has been reported that 8-quinolinol sulfate (1:4,000), 2-norcamphane methanol (1:16,000), or 4-chloro-3,5-dimethyl phenoxy ethanol (1:64,000) applied in water solutions to the topsoil every other week is effective against fusarium wilt of carnations. Control of the disease has been reported by treating rooted cuttings at weekly intervals for 4 months. Soaking cuttings from healthy plants for 12 to 18 hours in a 1:20,000 water solution of 8-quinolinol sulfate and then spraying the rooted plants with the same solution are claimed to reduce considerably the losses from the wilt.

These experimental findings must be corroborated and their practicality established before definite recommendations can be made.

The pathogens causing wilt, stem rot, and root rot diseases inhabit the soil. Some form of soil disinfestation or sterilization is desirable as an aid to their control.

Because serious losses from wilt and stem rot frequently occur after planting, a chemical topsoil treatment that would arrest or control the disease on its appearance would be of great value at that time. This idea, in relation to carnations, was introduced in 1948 and has stimulated investigators to search for a satisfactory treatment.

Some control of rhizoctonia stem rot may be realized from periodic treatments of topsoil with ferbam, New Improved Ceresan, or Semesan at the rate of 2 pounds to 100 gallons, 1 pint per square foot, or 3 to 4 ounces mixed with sand per 100 square feet; or phenyl mercury acetate fungicide (Tag Fungicide or Puratized Apple Spray), 1 pint to 100 gallons at the rate of 1 pint to 1 quart per square foot.

The diseased plants are removed, and the area is drenched with the diluted chemical. Further treatments are at intervals of 3 or 4 weeks.

Such topsoil treatments are costly considering the little value received in the control of rhizoctonia stem rot. A high regard for proper planting and desirable details of culture and greenhouse management are much more effective and economical. In addition, steam sterilization of the soil before planting is recommended because of its wide application and effectiveness in the control of soil-borne pathogens.

Growers have developed ingenious methods of steaming soil in ground beds and benches. The common method is to inject steam under pressure into tile lines either buried in the soil or placed on the surface and covered and secured with fabricated paper to confine the heat. Soil temperatures of 180° to 200° F. are maintained for 1 hour.

Some control of fusarium wilt and root rot has been reported by topsoil treatments with Tri-lig 74 (an extract of the fungus *Trichoderma lignorum*), 2 ounces of 7-percent solution; Dithane Z–78, 4 ounces; and Crag 531, 2 ounces to 100 square feet. The materials are worked into the soil four times at 3-month intervals, but it is best to apply the first treatment just before planting.

The idea of applying chemicals to carnation beds to control disease appears to be purely novel and psychological. We are not aware of any materials that warrant endorsement, nor can we recommend the method on the basis of what is known about the subject. The novelty of the idea appears to have worn away, and we must repeat that it is best to pay attention to infection-free stock and to proper planting, cultural, and management practices.

A CULTURED CUTTING is one that has been tested by means of a laboratory technique to determine the absence or presence of systemic bacterial or fungus infection. Cuttings from which no organism is recovered in artificial culture are considered healthy or free from infection. Such healthy cuttings may then be used to establish mother blocks to supply healthy propagation material for production plantings. The cuttings are not disease-resistant— they are merely infection-free, and the plants in subsequent culture require strict sanitary measures and good cultural practices.

The culturing of carnation cuttings and the use of cultured cuttings have been practiced by some commercial concerns with a significant reduction in plant loss. The evidence we have points to the fact that visual symptoms are not a good enough basis on which to cull out all diseased plants. Ample equipment and laboratory room for a culturing program are not overly expensive, and anyone who has the time, patience, industry, and some training can develop the technique. The work might best be done, however, in a central laboratory supported by pooled resources of an organization of growers.

Through culturing one can establish stock that is free from fusarium wilt and bacterial wilt. Every precaution must be taken, however, to prevent reinoculation. Stock plants therefore should be isolated from other carnations. One person should be responsible for them. The method will be successful only if the plants are grown the year around in the greenhouse. If all steps are followed carefully, a clean mother block of plants can be built up in a short time. Once a mother block is established it should not be necessary to culture cuttings every year, if rigid sanitation and proper cultural practices are maintained.

D. Noordam, T. H. Thung, and J. P. H. Van Der Want in the Netherlands have developed an antiserum for carnation mosaic. The reaction of the serum with sap from diseased carnations indicates the presence of virus and may be used as a method of screening diseased plants before symptoms are evident.

CARNATION CUTTINGS may carry infection from the mother stock internally as localized spotted or rotted tissue, as systemic and hidden infection, or as inoculum of the fungus in the form of spores existing superficially on the cuttings. Consequently it generally is unwise to soak cuttings in water to freshen them because of the risk of contaminating the water and inoculating the entire lot.

Cuttings may be planted promptly and directly without trimming or wetting them, and they should root well. Good drainage in the cutting bed, shallow planting hardly in excess of 1 inch in the rooting medium, proper temperature and light conditions, and sanitation require attention.

Sometimes the medication of cuttings before planting to kill surface-borne inoculum of pathogenic fungi is useful. Dousing cuttings for an instant in ferbam or zineb, 1 ounce to 4 gallons of water, is recommended for controlling rust and alternaria spot. A light powdering of the base of the cutting with a 10-percent fungicide-hormone dust mixture helps to prevent infection at the base of the cutting. The phenyl mercury fungicides have a disinfesting action, and the immersion of untrimmed cuttings for 15 minutes in phenyl mercury acetate solution, one-fourth teaspoonful to 1 gallon of water, is effective. After immersion, the base of the treated cuttings is snapped off to the next node and then planted; otherwise, the cuttings will not root well. The addition of a wetting agent to the medicant is recommended (Dreft, three-fourths to 1 level teaspoonful to 1 gallon of water).

Cuttings are freely distributed in the trade without restriction, and all the diseases in the mother stock may be transmitted with cuttings. The word and reputation of the propagator is the only assurance of the quality and health of the stock. Among other crops propagated vegetatively, such as potatoes and nursery stock, standards of certification for freedom from disease and regulations governing certification are recognized.

The carnation industry has been interested in the possibilities of cultured cuttings for eliminating infection and developing healthy mother stock—actually an effective standard of certification. The conventional method of propagating can be supplemented with these further efforts to guarantee the distribution of clean stock. Some form of certification would appear to be desirable in the industry.

THE GROWING of commercially desirable carnations resistant to disease is a logical and practical method of controlling disease. Research workers, however, have not given it enough consideration. With the exception of stem rot, caused by the fungus *Corticium (Rhizoctonia) solani*, and canker, dieback, and crown and root rot, caused by the fungi *Fusarium culmorum* and *F. avenaceum*, resistance and susceptibility to every carnation disease have always existed among varieties in the long history of commercial carnation culture.

Disease-resistant varieties offer the breeder valuable parent stock for breeding purposes. These evident and distinct contrasts in the reaction of standard varieties to disease in commercial culture can be established scientifically and confirmed for each pathogen by artificial infection techniques—a necessary preliminary step, we think, to the actual breeding program. In this work, selfing and hybridizing should be confined to parent varieties consistently resistant to one pathogen or more than one pathogen. By that procedure, the high degree of resistance peculiar to both parents will appear in most of the seedlings of the first generation. These resistant progenies can be used for further breeding—selfing, backcrossing, and outcrossing.

The successes in breeding crop plants for disease resistance and horticultural desirability are numerous. Examples of the effort in behalf of the carnation industry are the varieties Mrs. E. F. Guba, Waltham Pink, Spicy Rose, and others resistant to fusarium wilt. A breeding program for disease resistance with broader application has been started in the Department of Agriculture.

EMIL F. GUBA, *a native of Massachusetts and a graduate of the University of Massachusetts and the University of Illinois, has been on the staff of the Waltham Field Station, University of Massachusetts, since 1925, specializing in carnation diseases, mycology, and general plant pathology.*

RALPH W. AMES, *a native of Wyoming, holds degrees from the University of Wyoming and the University of Illinois. He has been identified especially with the study of carnation virus diseases and florist crop diseases. He was formerly on the staff of the Waltham Field Station, University of Massachusetts. He now teaches plant pathology in Utah Agricultural College.*

Control of Three Ills of Chrysanthemum

A. W. Dimock

The chrysanthemum, one of the most popular and profitable of our common flowering plants, is subject to serious attack by a diverse array of disease organisms.

The common and serious diseases include, for example, a powdery mildew (*Erysiphe cichoracearum*), a rust (*Puccinia chrysanthemi*), two fungus leaf spots (*Septoria obesa* and *S. chrysanthemella*), a leaf nematode disease (*Aphelenchoides* species), a fungus wilt (*Verticillium albo-atrum*), two petal blights (*Mycosphaerella ligulicola* and *Botrytis cinerea*), and a virus stunt disease.

Despite the importance of chrysanthemums as garden plants and commercial cut flowers, little progress toward the solution of the important disease problems was made before 1940. It is my aim to discuss here the rapid progress made since 1940 in the control of three of the most important diseases—septoria leaf spot, leaf nematode disease, and verticillium wilt.

SEPTORIA LEAF SPOT could be found almost every season in field or clothhouse plantings of chrysanthemums throughout the eastern part of the United States before 1940. In dry seasons it caused only minor damage, but in wet seasons it frequently reduced the quality of the crop so seriously that a profit could not be realized. Pathologists could easily identify the cause of the trouble but could suggest only the then current panacea, bordeaux mixture. Sometimes it seemed to help, but often the results were inadequate.

To one better-than-average chrysanthemum grower the situation was not at all satisfactory. He wanted to know not only how to control the disease; he also wanted to know why he was not obtaining control with bordeaux mixture. A visit by pathologists confirmed that he was spraying with bordeaux mixture and that no control was resulting. More important, it was noted that although the upper surfaces of the leaves were thoroughly coated with the bluish spray deposit, the lower surfaces were not covered. Experiments were conducted at once. They showed that nearly all infection with septoria leaf spot occurs through the lower surfaces of chrysanthemum leaves. Once this was ascertained, a simple shift of spraying practices to cover the lower leaf surfaces and forget the upper surfaces enabled the grower to obtain excellent control of the disease with the same spray material—bordeaux mixture.

That still did not satisfy the grower, because bordeaux mixture leaves an unsightly deposit, which detracts from the sales appeal of the product and causes some reduction in growth. At that point, current progress in the development of new fungicides provided the answer. A newly recognized fungicide, ferric dimethyl dithiocarbamate, now known as ferbam, was being supplied for trial by a manufacturer of agricultural chemicals. Careful tests showed it to be highly effective for septoria leaf spot control, to lack objectionable residue when properly utilized, and to be noninjurious to the plants. It could safely be used as a preplanting dip for the rooted cuttings, a procedure that eliminated infection of the lower leaves, which could not be adequately protected by field sprays.

The results with the new material were good. After two seasons of use, septoria leaf spot could not be found in the 3 acres of chrysanthemums

grown by the producer. The program was soon adopted generally by chrysanthemum growers throughout the United States and has been so successful that the septoria diseases, which had once been considered constant and uncontrollable hazards of chrysanthemum culture, are now rarely seen in commercial plantings.

THE LEAF NEMATODE DISEASE has been a running mate of septoria leaf spot. It is present over much the same geographical range, causes similar symptoms, and is, or was, encountered about as frequently. During wet seasons, however, it often was even more destructive than septoria leaf spot; sometimes it caused death of 100 percent of the foliage on infected plants. Although the gross effects on the plants is similar to that produced by the septoria disease, which is caused by a fungus, the nematode disease is caused by microscopic worms, which invade the leaves and feed on the cell contents. Unfortunately, the ferbam spray, which proved so effective against septoria leaf spot, had no perceptible effect against the nematode.

Investigations, initiated about 1940, confirmed that the nematodes cannot spread from infected leaves to healthy ones except in splashed water or in a film of water on the plants. Thus it appeared that if the parent plants were grown in greenhouses and if all splashing were eliminated, terminal cuttings taken from the plants should be completely free of leaf nematode infection.

That, indeed, proved to be the case. A solution was at hand to the problem of producing nematode-free young plants. It was further found that the nematodes cannot survive the winter in dead, infected leaves, but can survive in infected suckers or leaves that are sufficiently hardy or well-protected to come through the winter without being killed. If the old plants were either pulled up or plowed under rather deeply in the fall so that there was no over-winter survival of infected plants, the healthy plants brought out from the greenhouse would not become infected in the field. Careful adherence to this program has resulted in complete elimination of the disease in many plantings.

But the need for a chemical means of control in the field remained, because the practices I just mentioned cannot always be employed in the culture of the garden chrysanthemums.

At about that time, W. E. Blauvelt, of Cornell University, was developing the use of sodium selenate soil treatments for the control of insect pests of ornamental plants. In this method of control, the poisonous selenate was taken up through the roots of the plants and permeated the tissues of the leaves. Sucking insects feeding on such tissues got lethal doses of the poison.

Because leaf nematodes also were known to feed on the cell contents, it was reasoned that they also might be controlled by sodium selenate applied to the soil. Just so: The leaves of chrysanthemums grown on selenate-treated soil were essentially immune to attacks of leaf nematodes. The method was recommended primarily for the treatment of parent plants from which cuttings were to be taken; it proved to be a good means of producing nematode-free young plants, particularly in situations where splashing of the parent plants could not easily be avoided. It has also been used for field and garden plantings.

THE SELENATE treatment, at dosages effective for nematode control, occasionally caused a degree of stunting and leaf burn under certain temperature and soil moisture conditions.

Consequently the search was continued for safer methods of field control that would be as effective as the selenate treatment. Once again industry and the entomologists provided the answer. Shortly after the end of the Second World War a material known as parathion, which had been developed by the Germans, was brought to this country to be tested. Research

workers found that it was highly effective as an insecticide and it could be absorbed to some extent by the sprayed foliage. Nearly perfect control of leaf nematodes was achieved with about four spray applications. Parathion also proved to be compatible with ferbam, so that a single combination spray could be employed to control leaf spot, rust (against which ferbam had proved to be effective), foliar nematodes, and most of the more important chrysanthemum insects.

UNLIKE septoria leaf spot and the leaf nematode disease, which are caused by organisms that make a direct attack on the leaves, verticillium wilt is caused by a soil-inhabiting fungus that invades the water-conducting tissues of the plant, grows upward in them, and eventually causes the leaves to wilt. It may attack through the roots of healthy plants set in infested soil, or it may be introduced to healthy soil in cuttings taken from diseased plants.

Before 1940 the disease was to be found in nearly all greenhouses in which chrysanthemums were grown, its severity varying with variety. With the more susceptible ones it was common to see entire crops rendered essentially worthless. Many such varieties, otherwise highly desirable, were discarded because of the seeming impossibility of freeing them of wilt.

The difficulty in obtaining adequate control lay in the fact that the disease is readily transmitted through cuttings or divisions taken from diseased plants, and, further, that the disease is rarely obvious in the parent plants at the time cuttings are taken.

Control procedures consisted of roguing out obviously diseased parent plants in the fall, when symptoms are most evident; taking terminal cuttings from rapidly growing, vigorous shoots and planting in new or sterilized soil. Those procedures provided a measure of control and still yielded results far better than mere chance selection, but at best the degree of control left much to be desired. A more satisfactory solution to the problem was developed by the adaptation of a common laboratory procedure of plant pathology to the needs of the industry.

As one phase of an investigation on the verticillium disease it was desired to determine how closely the growth of the fungus within the plant kept pace with the growth of the shoots during the normal season of propagation. Laboratory cultures were made on nutrient agar of segments of the shoots at various distances back of the growing point. If the fungus grew from the segments it was obviously present within the water-conducting tissues at that point. If the fungus did not grow out, it was felt to be a safe assumption that the fungus growth had not advanced to the particular point in question. The results confirmed the reliability of the method and further showed that a fair percentage of the shoots from diseased parent plants either were free of the fungus or were infected only at the base. A most significant fact was that culturing provided the only means of distinguishing between healthy and infected shoots—superficially they were indistinguishable.

What possibility was there that this procedure of culturing from the base of prospective cuttings might provide a means of reliably selecting verticillium-free cuttings to be used as parent plants for subsequent propagation of wilt-free flowering stock? Although it was felt that such a process might not be adaptable to commercial practice, a test was set up in which a large block of cultured plants of a very susceptible variety were compared with a similar block of plants propagated in the usual manner from the same parent plants. The results were outstanding—a high percentage of the noncultured plants were severely diseased, but nearly 100 percent of the cultured cuttings remained healthy.

A representative of a large chrysanthemum-plant-producing concern saw the test. He started at once to develop a program of culturing of the parent stocks of the 300-odd varieties offered by his firm. Many problems had to be solved, many cultural practices had to be changed, and a staff had to be trained in specialized techniques before the process could be put on a mass-production basis. But through the efforts of the firm's own scientists and cooperation with experiment station workers, a satisfactory program was developed. The cost was high, but the results were satisfactory.

The benefits of this undertaking by a single firm have been reaped by nearly all growers of chrysanthemums throughout the country because that firm supplies much of the planting stock of all the commercial chrysanthemums grown. Serious cases of verticillium disease have been rare in commercial greenhouses since the program was developed, and a number of the fine varieties that had been discarded because of their susceptibility to the disease have been reintroduced. In fairness it must be stated that the full value of cultured stock is realized only in greenhouse culture, where the soil can be sterilized to free it of the wilt fungus. In field plantings, where adequate sterilization is as yet impractical, susceptible varieties may still suffer seriously even though the planting stock is free of the fungus.

The stories of the conquest of these three diseases of chrysanthemums might well be joined by those of equally successful attacks on two other major diseases—virus stunt and mycosphaerella blossom blight. Mastery of these diseases, paralleled by similarly effective development of insect control procedures and improvement in cultural practices, has eliminated the major hazards in chrysanthemum cultivation and has put the industry on a sound, reasonably predictable, and profitable basis.

A. W. DIMOCK, *professor of plant pathology at Cornell University, has specialized in the study of the diseases of ornamental plants since 1937.*

Virus Diseases of the Chrysanthemum

Philip Brierley

For more than 50 years florists have grown chrysanthemums in the greenhouse as potted plants and as cut flowers for autumn bloom, and amateurs have grown them as garden perennials. The garden chrysanthemum gained popularity with the introduction about 1935 of early-flowering sorts in a wide range of color and form.

Before the development in the 1930's and 1940's of techniques for controlling the time of flowering by adjusting the photoperiod as well as the temperature, florists' chrysanthemums were seen only in the fall and the early winter months. Rooted cuttings were planted in the greenhouse in April or early May and grown on to natural flowering, which extended from September through January with a succession of early and late varieties. Precision timing of flowering enabled growers to produce cut flowers of chrysanthemums at all seasons. A great expansion in production resulted, and the chrysanthemum became one of the five leading florists' crops in terms of value to the grower. Acres of mums were produced in cloth houses out of doors. Production in greenhouses was expanded.

Together with those increases in volume and in efficiency of production, there appeared about 1945 a disease called chrysanthemum stunt, which threatened to ruin the business.

Chrysanthemum stunt was first described by A. W. Dimock, of Cornell University. He noticed the disease in florists' mums as early as 1945. He directed attention to the reduced size of plant, leaves, and flowers; the bleaching of bronze, pink, and red flowers to lighter shades; and a tendency to early flowering in plants affected with stunt. The disease became generally prevalent in the United States and Canada in 1946 and 1947. Infection reached 50 to 100 percent in many greenhouses, and affected plants were so short or so inferior that they were unsalable.

By that time the disease was familiar to most producers of florists' chrysanthemums, but its nature remained a mystery. The symptoms and the rapid extension of the stunt disease immediately suggested a virus as the causal agent, but growers who had not previously contended with any virus disease of major importance were slow to accept that explanation. Many ascribed the trouble to overpropagation, to the use of hormones in propagating, or to the lack of the normal winter rest period that mums were believed to require for normal growth.

Convincing evidence of the virus nature of stunt was presented by several workers in 1948 and 1949. M. F. Welsh, at the Summerland Laboratory in British Columbia, produced a stunt-mottle disease, now known to include stunt and a mosaic disease, by experimental grafting. Floyd F. Smith and I found the stunt virus transmissible by grafting and by manual inoculation with sap from a stunt plant.

J. R. Keller, of Cornell University, confirmed our findings, showed that the yellow spotting in Mistletoe chrysanthemums is a symptom of stunt, and also transmitted the stunt virus from plant to plant by dodder connection. C. J. Olson, pathologist at Yoder Brothers, Inc., of Barberton, Ohio, discovered that contamination of healthy plants by the knife and hands in taking cuttings can transmit the stunt virus. He and I learned that contamination by the hands in pinching may effect transmission of the virus. Shears used in cutting flowers can also transmit it.

Olson presented evidence that stunt is not carried through the seeds of chrysanthemums. Earlier claims of transmission by insects have not been confirmed. Present evidence indicates that contaminations during commercial handling operations, such as taking cuttings, pinching, and cutting flowers, are responsible for all transmission of stunt in florists' mums. Even in garden chrysanthemums those contaminations during handling are of chief, and perhaps sole, importance in spreading stunt, for commercial propagators bring garden mums into greenhouses for increase during late winter and spring.

Symptoms of stunt are first expressed several months after contamination takes place. Most varieties show the first recognizable symptoms of stunt 6 to 8 months or longer after infection. Such a long delay is not uncommon in virus diseases in woody plants, but is exceptional in herbaceous plants, such as chrysanthemums, that make extensive and rapid vegetative growth.

This slow expression of stunt is an advantage to the grower of chrysanthemums who does not propagate his own plants. It is feasible to buy stunt-free cuttings, now available from specialists in propagation, and to bring them to flowering without taking precautions against stunt contaminations, because stunt expression is too slow to affect the quality of the first crop. Any contamination that took place during the production of the first crop, however, will be expressed in a second crop propagated from the first one. The propagator who is attempting to reselect stunt-free plants from partly contaminated stocks, therefore, must contend with recently contaminated plants that seem perfectly normal but are stunt-affected.

Stunt was recovered from normal-appearing plants of the variety Mary MacArthur 1, 2, and 3 months after inoculation, although the plants did not show recognizable symptoms until after 6 to 7 months. Also some varieties of chrysanthemums express ill-defined

symptoms or none even after long-standing infection.

Clearly some reliable method of detecting stunt is essential to any program of eliminating the disease from stocks of chrysanthemums.

Many methods have been tried. Microscopic examination of affected tissues failed to reveal any characteristic abnormalities. Studies of stunt tissues under the electron microscope by W. C. Price and R. L. Steere at the University of Pittsburgh and by James Johnson at the University of Wisconsin failed to detect any foreign particles of the types that characterize some other plant viruses.

An intensive search for plants that would express well-defined symptoms following manual inoculation has not been successful. All species of chrysanthemums that have been tested and a large number of other plants of the family Compositae are susceptible, but most of them produce no recognizable symptoms, although the stunt virus can be recovered from them in chrysanthemum. Only the florists' cineraria and Matricaria Golden Ball proved to be of some value as test plants; each became dwarfed and rosetted in 2 or 3 months after manual inoculation.

Such test plants that could be grown from seed were eagerly sought in the early stages of the stunt problem because of the difficulty of finding strictly stunt-free chrysanthemums. The need for them has diminished with the discovery of chrysanthemum varieties that express stunt symptoms clearly and relatively early.

Elimination of stunt from such varieties is a simple task. Mistletoe chrysanthemums, a group of florists' "standards" or large-flowering sorts, come in several flower colors and all react to stunt with distinctive yellow leaf spotting. Mistletoe varieties react in 4 to 6 weeks when inoculated by grafting. On manual inoculation, some stunt is expressed in 5 weeks, but it is necessary to hold the plants for at least 6 months for full expression. Blazing Gold, another florists' standard variety, expresses yellow vein banding 6 to 8 weeks after graft inoculation, and becomes typically stunted in habit later. Both Blazing Gold and the Mistletoe varieties are now used to detect stunt. Each has advantages in detecting mosaic diseases as well as stunt, as I explain later. Graft indexing is the standard procedure because of the more prompt and consistent expression of symptoms. For some purposes, such as property studies, manual methods of inoculation must be used. Mistletoe chrysanthemums are preferred for that purpose because of their distinctive expression of symptoms, but the long time required for full expression is a handicap.

The only method of controlling stunt that is known to be feasible is the reselection of healthy stock with suitable precautions against further contamination. Two systems of reselection have been used by different commercial firms with marked success.

Mikkelsen and Sons, of Ashtabula, Ohio, devised a system of reserving tip cuttings from the most vigorous plants, which are usually the healthy ones, for a propagation block, which is renewed each year. The next best cuttings are used for the flowering crop. All weak or questionable ones are discarded. The only precaution against contamination is to break off the cuttings instead of cutting them with a knife. This procedure makes use of the superior vigor of healthy shoots, and thus tends to eliminate other diseases that depress vigor as well as the stunt disease. The program, which is relatively simple and involves a minimum of records, has worked well for the Mikkelsens in supplying disease-free planting material for several acres of year-around chrysanthemums.

Yoder Brothers designed a program to eliminate stunt from the millions of plants maintained by them for propagation. The best plants selected in vegetative condition were later flowered to detect further stunt expression at the flowering stage, and they were even pruned to bring all shoots to bloom, with the result that additional partial infections, known as "splits," were detected. The Yoders have used paper shields, flamed tools, and sterilized soil to eliminate all possible hazards of recontamination. The nucleus, or foundation, stock is maintained in a separate greenhouse and handled by a separate crew of trained workers as insurance against contaminations in handling. More recently, as suitable test varieties became known, graft indexing on Blazing Gold was adopted to speed recognition of stunt in new acquisitions. The foundation block, now free of stunt by all known tests, is a permanent one, which furnishes cuttings to the production line, where they are further increased. The success of such reselection has brought a sharp decline in the importance of stunt in the florists' chrysanthemums. Stunt-free cuttings of most florists' varieties are now available, but only a beginning has been made toward supplying similar reselected stock of the garden varieties.

Some attempts have been made to eliminate stunt from chrysanthemums by heat or by cold treatments.

Heat cure of virus disease is possible only when the virus is less tolerant of heat than the host plant, and that is true for a few viruses only. In tests by Yoder Brothers and also at the Plant Industry Station at Beltsville, the stunt persisted at all the temperatures that the chrysanthemums withstood. Some growers reported that stunt plants were cured if stock plants were wintered in outdoor frames and if cuttings were taken as early as suitable shoots were available in spring. In trials during three seasons at Beltsville, such wintering in outdoor frames retarded expression of stunt symptoms but failed to eliminate the stunt virus or to alter its final expression of symptoms.

The sap extracted from stunt plants remains infectious after heating for 10 minutes at 208° F. or even after boiling for a like interval. The stunt virus is not diminished in potency by extracting in 95 percent alcohol and standing in the alcohol for an hour. It withstands aging in crude sap extract at 65° for about 6 weeks, and remains infectious in drying leaves for more than 8 weeks. Some preparations prove infectious after diluting 1 to 10,000 with water, and many losing potency at lesser dilutions. These properties do not correspond to those of any other known plant virus, and indicate that stunt is a new disease rather than an old one in a new host.

The origin of stunt is still a mystery. One can hardly assume that it is a recent import from some other country. Stunt was reported from Australia in 1951 and from Holland in 1952, long after it had become generally distributed in North America. Possibly stunt is endemic in one of the many species of Compositae that are capable of carrying the disease without symptoms, and perhaps it spread to chrysanthemums in recent years, but no evidence can be cited in support of that assumption.

THE SEARCH for stunt and the methods devised for detecting it have brought to notice other virus diseases of chrysanthemum. Some of them doubtless were present before stunt but remained unnoticed or were dismissed as unimportant.

Aster yellows, a common virus disease of many plants, notably plants of the aster family, has been known to affect chrysanthemums since the work of L. O. Kunkel at the Boyce Thompson Institute in 1926. Symptoms in chrysanthemums are variable. When the flowers produced are green instead of the color normal for the variety, aster yellows is clearly present. Sometimes the upper branches of a flowering stem are thin, pale or yellowish, and more upright than usual. Again, a number of thin, weak shoots bearing tiny leaves may arise from the base of the plant.

Aster yellows appears in outdoor chrysanthemums and also in the greenhouse when plants are brought in for propagation or for flowering.

Affected plants are unsalable and commonly die in a few months after becoming diseased. In most sections of the United States aster yellows is infrequent in chrysanthemums, but in places where the virus is common in other host plants and the leafhopper vector, *Macrosteles fascifrons*, is abundant, a considerable number of garden chrysanthemums may be infected each year.

Chrysanthemum mosaic was known to commercial growers in the variety Good News before stunt appeared. J. R. Keller, of Cornell University, first showed that this mosaic is due to a virus by grafting apparently normal Blanche to Mistletoe. The causal agent, which he called Q virus, is symptomless in Blanche and several other florists' sorts and many garden chrysanthemums. In Blanche the mosaic virus and the stunt virus combine to form a complex known as crinkle or stunt-mottle, with crinkling of leaves and marked stunting. Mistletoe varieties show a yellowish-green vein banding followed by mottling, sometimes with marked reduction of leaf size, and even with necrotic effects such as bud and leaf blasting and dieback of young shoots. Strain variation in the mosaic virus seem to account for these gradations in severity of symptoms.

Cross inoculations showed that the Q virus induced News mosaic in Good News and that News mosaic virus reproduces Q symptoms in Mistletoe. Symptoms in Good News include a well-defined yellowish-green mottling with crinkling of leaf margins and reduction in vigor of the plant. Viruses of the mosaic type have been demonstrated also in chrysanthemums from England and Denmark. The mosaic virus is manually transmissible but less readily than is the stunt virus. Prevalence of mosaic in garden chrysanthemums and in florists' varieties that have been grown outdoors in summer suggests that natural spread of the mosaic virus occurs in the open, but no vector is known.

Chrysanthemum rosette occurs in

apparently normal plants of the Ivory Seagull variety but induces marked dwarfing with yellow vein banding and crinkling in Blazing Gold. The disease was detected in Ivory Seagull and in Mamaru by C. J. Olson, of Yoder Brothers, Inc., and by me in Matador at Beltsville. Variation in intensity of yellowing, crinkling, and dwarfing in the Blazing Gold variety suggested that strain variation occurs in this virus. Manual transmission of the rosette virus is difficult, with one of ten plants infected in each of two trials. No evidence of natural spread has been detected thus far and no vector is known. The Good News variety develops marked rosetting with dull-yellow mottling when infected, and serves to distinguish the rosette virus from the mosaic virus.

The occurrence of other virus diseases in addition to stunt complicates the problem of virus detection by graft indexing. Chrysanthemum mosaic and rosette are much less important than stunt, for they are damaging to few varieties, while stunt is injurious to practically all. Nevertheless anyone taking the trouble to index chrysanthemums for virus disease will not wish to let one of these diseases pass undetected. Blazing Gold provides prompt and distinctive symptoms for stunt and for rosette. Mosaic is expressed by slightly lower vigor, smaller leaves, and occasional distortion of the terminal lobe of the leaf. Mistletoe expresses distinctive symptoms of stunt and of mosaic, but is slow to respond to rosette. Good News offers clear reactions to mosaic and to rosette, and distinguishes those diseases from each other. It expresses stunt as transitory yellow veining. The ideal variety that will express promptly clear and distinctive symptoms for each of the three viruses is not yet known.

Tomato aspermy, a virus disease of tomatoes and chrysanthemums, has been known in England for several years, but was first distinguished from cucumber mosaic in 1949. Affected tomatoes often fail to set seed after infec-tion takes place, hence the name aspermy. Chrysanthemums are commonly affected in England and chrysanthemums are important reservoirs of the virus, which spreads to tomatoes in the mixed nurseries common in England. The tomato aspermy virus infects also tobacco and many other plants but not cucumber. It is carried in the nonpersistent manner, by the green peach aphid.

Additional viruses of chrysanthemums were described in 1952 by Dirk Noordam of the Instituut voor Plantenziektenkundig Onderzoek at Aalsmeer, the Netherlands. He found two viruses common, one of which he classed as a strain of cucumber mosaic virus, and a second which he called virus B. His B virus, infectious to petunia but not to tobacco, is also common in chrysanthemums in the United States. Noordam's chrysanthemum strain of cucumber mosaic virus is similar to the aspermy virus in many respects, but is serologically related to the cucumber mosaic virus. In chrysanthemums it is associated with distortion and changes of color in the flower, perhaps together with virus B. Aspermy and the chrysanthemum strain of cucumber mosaic may be merely two names for the same virus, although Noordam did not reach this conclusion. He did include many English chrysanthemums in his studies; and English workers frequently refer to cucumber mosaic in chrysanthemums. However, regardless of its technical name, this chrysanthemum virus differs in important respects from the cucumber mosaic virus strains common in the United States.

At Beltsville we detected the aspermy virus in 1951 by manual inoculation to tobacco from two varieties of chrysanthemum recently imported from England, from one plant from Denmark, and from the variety Nightingale from Ohio. The virus apparently has been introduced into the United States repeatedly with European chrysanthemums which have been in popular demand here since 1945. In our tests the aspermy virus has infected more than 35 plant species, including tobacco, tomato, pepper, lettuce, spinach, and several ornamental plants and weeds. Marglobe tomatoes were severely diseased and bore some seedless fruits. Floyd Smith found the aspermy virus transmitted in the nonpersistent manner by four species of aphids, the foxglove aphid, the green peach aphid, the black chrysanthemum aphid, and the green chrysanthemum aphid. Aphids transmitted the virus readily from chrysanthemum to tomato and tobacco, as well as chrysanthemum to chrysanthemum and tomato to tomato. The aspermy virus is thus well equipped to persist in perennial plants such as chrysanthemum and to spread to vegetable crops that grow near them in gardens.

At Beltsville we graft-inoculated 13 varieties of chrysanthemum with scions of the Nightingale variety, now known to carry both the aspermy virus and the B virus. The flower distortions described by European workers failed to develop. Most varieties expressed mottling or veining in young actively growing leaves but some never showed clear symptoms. Leaf symptoms were generally masked as the chrysanthemums approached flowering. The variety Good News expressed well-defined mottling without leaf distortion. The B virus, not the aspermy virus, produces these symptoms in Good News. The four species of aphids that transmitted the aspermy virus also transmitted the B virus from chrysanthemum to chrysanthemum. Present evidence indicates that the B virus is more injurious to American chrysanthemums than the aspermy virus; however, the aspermy virus is the one that damages vegetables.

PHILIP BRIERLEY, *a pathologist in the Bureau of Plant Industry, Soils, and Agricultural Engineering, has been with the Department of Agriculture since 1922, and has studied diseases of various ornamental plants. He has degrees from the University of Minnesota and Cornell University.*

Some Fungi That Attack Gladioli

Robert O. Magie

The modern gladiolus has been developed during the past 125 years by cross-breeding several gladiolus species native to Africa and by crossing many of the hybrids and varieties obtained thereby. It is adapted to a wide range of soils and climate and is now grown in many countries as a garden flower.

In the United States gladioli are grown extensively for cut flowers—on hundreds of acres in States bordering the Great Lakes, in New England, in some of the Atlantic and Gulf Coast States, and along the Pacific coast. About 7,000 acres are planted in Florida each year for winter and spring production of flower spikes, which are shipped to all but the most distant sections of the country.

The growing of glads is estimated to be a multimillion-dollar industry in the United States. Bulbs—properly called corms—are produced principally in areas where the flowers are grown for market because most bulb growers sell flowers as well as bulbs. The corms are sold to flower growers and to thousands of gardeners. Each year millions of corms are transported from State to State and country to country. Often the traffic is two-way and makes ideal conditions for dispersal of insect and disease pests.

Diseases are not only dispersed on corms. Some are also carried from year to year in the corms and cormels. The control of disease, especially the fusarium disease, therefore is much more difficult.

The worst disease is caused by *Fusarium oxysporum* f. *gladioli*. That fungus invades the vascular tissue of roots, corms, and leaf bases. It causes a rot of the underground parts of the gladiolus, a yellowing of leaves, and distortion or modification of leaf, stem, and flower growths. In Florida the disease is estimated to cause an average loss of 200 dollars an acre. Some of the best commercial varieties are most susceptible to the corm-rot phase of the disease, which is conspicuous both in storage and in the field.

Two distinct fusarium diseases have been reported, fusarium yellows and brown rot of corms. Apparently in the Southeast only one fusarium fungus is involved. Fusarium infection of corms or roots is accompanied by yellowing or other symptoms typical of a vascular fusarium disease. All corm stocks with corm rot have shown these symptoms. Some varieties resistant to corm rot show "yellows" symptoms as a result of root or vascular infection. Corm rotting is not always a part of the fusarium yellows disease, but the vascular disease symptoms have always been associated with fusarium brown rot.

Symptoms of fusarium infection include bending of the young leaf stalk, cupping of leaf stalk in older plants, and limber flower stem, often crooked just below florets and greener than normal. Curving of the leaf growth is always away from the side of corm showing rot. There is a modification of floret shape, size, and color as a result of slight or recent corm infection. Those symptoms may appear on only one side of the spike.

A dark-pink color in the Picardy variety is a response to partial rotting of the mother corm. Some growers mistakenly refer to that color transformation as a sport or as the result of soil conditions. The commonest symptom seen on most varieties in the field is a gradual yellowing and dying of the foliage, beginning with the oldest leaves. Leaf yellowing is not very pronounced in some of the more resistant varieties.

Symptoms of corm rot may vary greatly in different varieties and in different stocks. Rotting may begin anywhere on the corm surface, but most spots are found at the base next to the core. By scraping lightly at that place, one may find a slight amount of browning. Rotting may involve the core before spreading out along the vascular tissues, or one side of the corm may rot before the core is completely discolored. In some stocks only the core is rotted.

Rot spots may show up where the corm was cut or bruised in digging, handling, or grading. The spot, usually round or oval, becomes depressed as the rotted tissue dries. The surface often wrinkles and forms concentric rings. The rotted tissue becomes compressed and tough on drying. Rotted corms are mummified or are greatly shrunken in storage and sound like a stone when dropped. When rotting begins after corms are planted, the rotted tissue remains soft and is invaded by other organisms.

Picardy, an outstanding commercial variety, is so susceptible that it is no longer grown on some farms. Nearly 200 million Picardy corms have been shipped into Florida since 1944, mainly to replace rotted corms. Fusarium infection was found to be carried in the corms; losses were great even though corms were treated with fungicides and planted in uncontaminated land. Few commercial stocks of Picardy have been found to be free of fusarium infection of corms.

The infection often does not show up until after the corms have been planted. Commercial stocks of other varieties usually carry fusarium infection, although losses from rotting are generally less severe than in Picardy.

Fusarium infections tend to remain dormant in the corms. They pass from one crop to the next and break out as rot when temperature and nutrition favor the growth of the fungus or when the natural resistance of the host is weakened by adverse conditions.

Volunteer stands of Picardy plants, which seem healthy, are found in fields abandoned because of severe loss from fusarium disease. Some of the stands continue to grow in uncultivated fields for several years. Seeing this, growers have propagated the corms, hoping to find a resistant strain of Picardy. They learned, though, that the corms carry latent infections that are activated when the plants are fertilized for the production of flowers.

The fusarium disease is most destructive in areas with light sandy soils, heavy rainfall, and warm climate. To grow quality flowers on such soils, large amounts of fertilizers are used. But corm rot is increased with the use of nitrogen fertilizers and manures, especially in places where the phosphate supply is low in comparison to available nitrogen. Dried blood, tankage, fresh manure, and ammonia nitrogen are especially undesirable because of their tendency to bring about extensive rotting. These relationships between plant nutrition and disease were discovered by W. D. McClellan and Neil Stuart at the Plant Industry Station.

GROWERS USUALLY TREAT corms with chemicals to control the disease. Many fungicides have been tested in the search for good treatments.

The more effective chemicals, including mercury compounds and trichlorophenates, delay the rotting of infected corms but do not effectively reduce the percentage of corms carrying the fungus into the next crop season. Despite fungicidal treatment, annual losses of corms in the major cut-flower areas range from 5 to 40 percent in susceptible varieties.

Growers used to treat corms only before planting. Because many corms rotted during storage, I investigated the possibility of applying a treatment after harvest and, in 1948, pointed out the advantages of treating the corms immediately after they are "cleaned." Cleaning is the removal of the old corms and roots from the new corms after harvest. The best post-harvest treatment at present is a dusting of the corms immediately after the cleaning operation with a 48-percent formulation of tetrachloro-*p*-benzoquinone (Spergon).

Corms of susceptible varieties contaminated with the fungus are treated again, immediately before planting, by soaking them for 15 minutes in a solution of ethyl mercury phosphate, 8 ounces of a 5-percent formulation (New Improved Ceresan) in 50 gallons of water. Gardeners and small growers often soak their corms in a solution of Lysol (1 quart in 50 gallons) for 2 to 3 hours just before planting.

Some varieties are very resistant to the fusarium disease, but one or more stocks of some have developed serious cases of the disease because of unusually virulent strains of the fungus. By replacing infected stock with disease-free corms, growers have been able to continue with the same variety with little loss from disease.

Replacement of diseased stocks with healthy corms helps control the disease in susceptible varieties, too.

With fusarium-free stocks, growers have demonstrated—on land used for gladiolus every third year—that susceptible varieties such as Picardy and Spotlight may be grown for 2 to 3 years without severe losses of corms. Some stocks obtained from an area in western Washington were found to be free of the gladiolus *Fusarium*.

C. J. Gould, at the Western Washington Agricultural Experiment Station, suggested that low temperatures of the soil may explain the disappearance of fusarium disease from corms grown in that area during several successive years. Observations in other cool climates suggest that low soil temperatures suppress disease expression but may not eradicate the fungus. Antibiotics produced by soil microorganisms may be one factor in the eradication of fusarium from corms in certain soils.

Replacement of susceptible varieties with resistant varieties is not always sstisfactory in growing flowers for long-distance shipping. Those substituted for such susceptible varieties as Picardy, Leading Lady, Corona, and Spotlight are generally less suitable for cutting in tight bud. But growers catering to nearby markets have a wide choice of resistant varieties that produce satisfactory flowers if one or two florets are allowed to open in the field before the spike is cut.

Growers can exclude the fusarium disease from their plantings. We found on a few farms that disease-free corms planted in uncontaminated soil remained disease-free until the introduction of contaminated soil or diseased corms. The usual source of contamination is the latent infection of corms. In 1953 no corm stocks were certified as free of the fusarium fungus. Such stocks are greatly needed as foundation stocks for propagation of corms. Freedom from latent infection may be tested by growing corms for at least 2 years in warm, sandy soil and fertilizing for maximum flower production. Stocks of fusarium-free corms are found occasionally in gardens, and some bulb growers are trying to propagate large stocks of healthy corms of the more important varieties.

No chemical method of eradicating the fungus from corm stocks is known, nor has it been feasible to eradicate the fungus from the soil in commercial acreages. A search has been started for a systemic fungicide that is taken up by the roots so as to kill the fungus in the corms. Such a chemical which would eliminate latent infections would greatly help in disease control.

Infection from contaminated soil can be avoided by fumigating the soil with methyl bromide. That is recommended for growing seedlings, if the soil is contaminated. Some corms of each seedling stock should be tested for disease resistance by growing them in contaminated soil for at least 3 years. The propagating stock, however, should be grown only in clean soil so that latent infections may be avoided.

I give several recommendations for the control of fusarium disease.

Acquire healthy corm stock.

Grow corms on clean land.

Rotate plantings if corm stocks are infested with *Fusarium*, so that the soil is planted to gladiolus not oftener than once every 3 or 4 years.

Replace diseased stocks with healthy corms, never mixing healthy with diseased stock.

Cut off tops at harvest and avoid bruising corms.

Soak mechanically harvested corms 10 minutes immediately after digging in a solution of 3 pounds Dowicide B in 50 gallons water.

Cure corms at temperatures between 80° and 90° F. for a week immediately after corms are dug.

Avoid too rapid drying of corms.

Remove old corm and roots from new corm within 2 weeks after digging.

Dust corms with Spergon wettable powder as they are cleaned.

Pick out diseased corms and treat sound ones immediately before planting in a ½-percent solution of Lysol for 2 hours or a ⅛-percent solution of N. I. Ceresan for 15 minutes.

Rogue diseased plants as soon as they can be identified.

Grow disease-resistant varieties.

Use nitrogen fertilizers sparingly, if at all; never place them in the planting furrow and always add phosphate fertilizer with the nitrogen. For soils where potash is needed, ratios of 1–3–2 or 1–3–3 are often advised.

THE GLADIOLUS BOTRYTIS, *B. gladiolorum*, has been present in this country at least since 1940 and before that in Europe. The fungus causes a spotting and rotting of all parts of the plant. The disease, which is favored by cool moist weather, has been destructive in Eastern and Southern States, in States bordering the Great Lakes, and in places along the Pacific coast.

The relation of weather to the severity of the botrytis disease in gladiolus-growing areas of the United States was pointed out by W. D. McClellan, Kenneth F. Baker, and C. J. Gould. During the unusually wet, cool seasons of 1950 and 1951, destructive outbreaks of the disease occurred for the first time in the Midwest, indicating that the disease may appear in all our important gladiolus-growing areas during long rainy spells and at the lower temperatures that usually accompany such weather.

The disease is primarily a corm-rotting problem in northern bulb-growing areas. In southern flower-growing areas it causes most damage as a rot of flowers in transit to northern markets. In all areas, particularly along the Pacific coast, the disease may cause severe damage by the spotting and rotting of leaves.

The three types of leaf spots are large, round to oval, brown spots; smaller, pale-brown spots with reddish-brown margins; and very small, rusty-brown spots, which usually show only on the exposed side of the leaf. Smaller spots predominate, especially during drier, warmer weather and on the more resistant varieties.

Large and small spots also occur on the flower stem. At first they are pale brown, then dark brown. A soft rotting at the bases of florets may follow after a heavy rain. The petals of most varieties are very susceptible. When spores are placed on wet petals in the evening, one may see by the following morning, translucent, water-soaked spots, pin-point in size. As the spots increase in size, the watery, dead tissue turns light brown. In a moist, cool atmosphere, the whole flower becomes slimy with the rot. Flowers that show no spots when cut and packed may be ruined as a result of the spread of botrytis infection in transit or storage.

Stalk or neck rot caused by *Botrytis* may develop at any stage of growth but is most common after the flowers are cut. Infection may spread down the stalk and into the corm, giving rise to dark-brown spots, irregular in shape and size and most numerous on the upper surface. The leaf scar rings may be lined with small black spots. When corms are cured at about 85° F. for a week immediately after they are dug, the infections generally become inactive and remain shallow. Without the use of artificial heat, the surface infections frequently extend through the vascular tissue to invade the core and eventually the whole corm, causing a soft, spongy rot. In some varieties the diseased vascular tissue is tubelike and can be lifted out cleanly.

Core infections may originate at the top of the corm or at the base. Core rot usually spreads out along the vascular bundles to involve the whole corm. Infection at the top is usually the extension of rotting from the flower stem remnant. Basal infection is believed to result from the previous year's infection of the mother corm.

Corm infection has persisted from year to year without any sign of the disease on the growing plants. As the rotted corms dry out, they shrink only slightly. Botrytis-rotted corms are soft and spongy, with white mold among the rotted tissues and on the surface of the corm. Nests of rotted corms with white mold occur in stored corms. Infection often spreads from one corm to those in contact with it.

The fungus produces sclerotia, the resting bodies. They are oval, flat, black, and about one-eighth to one-fourth inch long. Sclerotia may live in the soil for many years before germinating to produce the spores that initiate infection in each growing season. Sclerotia are formed on rotting tissue in the field, in refuse piles, and on rotted corms in storage. They are commonly found at the time of corm harvest on plants killed by the disease and are located between leaves just above ground and in the hollow flower stems of plants from which spikes were cut.

Botrytis disease is easily identified by the clear, pin-point spots on petals, the spore signs on leaf spots and dead florets, the sclerotia on the stalks and corms, and the soft rotted corms with white mold.

Spores are produced in grapelike bunches on the ends of short "hairs" that have the fuzzy appearance of velvet, especially when wet with dew. Spores are usually found only on brown dead tissue. Dead petals on an old spike standing in the field may produce countless thousands of spores daily for weeks.

As THE DISEASE is carried in corms, it may not be practical to prevent its introduction to a farm or an area. It would be impractical to eradicate the disease from areas where it has been epidemic. It has been amply demonstrated, however, that the disease can be controlled effectively by protecting the plants with zineb or nabam fungicides. Arthur Holloman, Jr., and Roy A. Young in Oregon reported that ferbam is also effective, but may be less desirable on flower spikes because of the black spray residue. The fungicidal spray or dust is applied every 3 or 4 days in wet weather. To protect rapidly growing leaves and spikes, applications are made as often as every other day in plantings where the disease is already present. Dusting is most useful for renewing protection between showers and when speed of application is important.

The amount of spray mixture applied on each acre varies with the frequency of spraying. Although 80 or more gallons are used for weekly applications, only 20 or 30 gallons an acre are required at each spraying when repeated every day or every other day. A pump pressure of about 300 pounds per square inch is effective in producing a desirable spray mist. A spreading agent, such as Triton B–1956, is added to the spray mixture so that the droplets will tend to cling to the new leaves and spikes without running together.

A heavy drift of *Botrytis* spores from a nearby planting may endanger spikes that are to be shipped, even though the planting was sprayed every other day. Some control is obtained by dipping the cut spikes for 2 seconds in a solution of 1 pint Puratized Agricultural Spray in 100 gallons of water with enough wetting agent, such as Glim or Joy, to cause the solution to film over the hard-to-wet petals. Some growers prefer dipping the spikes in a spray mixture of nabam and zinc sulfate. The dip is not a substitute for spraying or dusting.

Sanitation may be helpful in controlling the disease, but has not made spraying unnecessary. Diseased material should be buried deeply or burned. Bloomed-out spikes should not be left standing in the field but should be removed from the field by hand if possible; otherwise they may be cut off and dragged out of the rows with cultivators. Covering them with soil promotes rotting.

CURVULARIA LEAF SPOT, a new disease, swept over the gladiolus fields of Alabama and Florida in 1947. We had no previous record of it on gladiolus, but a few growers believe they saw it in 1946 on gladiolus in Tennessee and Alabama. Its rapid spread through Florida and from Southern to Northern States indicated travel through the air and on the corms. The disease has been identified on corms or flowers received up to 1951 from New Hampshire, Vermont, Connecticut, New Jersey, New York, Indiana, and most of the Southeastern States. It has been reported to occur also in Illinois and Michigan.

Caused by a soil fungus, *Curvularia lunata*, the disease is favored by high temperatures and moisture and is a serious threat to gladiolus culture in areas having long periods of summer temperatures of 65° to 90° and frequent rainfall or heavy dews.

Leaves from cormels and seed are much more susceptible than leaves from large corms. Young leaves are more susceptible than old leaves. The rapidly growing flower spikes of some varieties are very susceptible. Infection of above-ground parts of the plant is serious in Southern States, although corm infection is slight or rare. In some Northern States, infection of corms has been severe, compared to flower infection. In all areas having warm, moist weather, the disease would be expected to be severe on seedlings and on plants grown from cormels.

Curvularia spots on large leaves are oval and tan, with a dark-brown margin. They may be as large as 2 inches long by one-half inch wide. There is a sprinkling of black spore specks near the center of the older spots. Typical spots seldom are seen on small leaves. Infection of cormel and seedling plants frequently appears as a damping-off and as a severe yellowing and browning of leaf tips. Large, oval, brown or black spots develop on stems and floret buds. Petal spots are large, brown, and nearly round. Infection of the flower bud often prevents its opening.

Corms and the leafy stalk below ground may be partly or completely rotted by the Curvularia fungus held over in ground where the disease occurred the previous year. Stalk infection may be very damaging to small plants but is generally outgrown and seldom noticed on larger plants. Diseased spots on corms are sunken, dark brown or black, and irregular in size and shape. They are hard, shallow, and usually separate easily and cleanly from the healthy tissue, although corms of some varieties have been rotted completely.

THE CURVULARIA FUNGUS lives in the soil for 3 years and probably longer. Gladiolus should not be replanted for 3 years in a soil where a severe attack of the disease occurred. Crop rotation will help to control infection of underground parts but will not prevent reappearance of the disease on leaves when the weather is favorable.

Infection of leaves and flowers is controlled by spraying or dusting the plants with nabam or zineb. Applications of the fungicide are made once, twice, or three times a week, depending on the weather, the presence of infection, and stage of growth. Young or newly exposed growth is most susceptible and requires frequent applications for protection during moist weather. The spray is more effective if a spreader is added and if applied as a fine mist.

Many varieties are resistant to the disease and need no fungicidal protection. The leaves of some varieties are susceptible only when grown from cormels. Some varieties need protection also at the time of flowering. A few varieties, such as Picardy, Picardy sports, Corona, Purple Supreme, and Vredenburg, may be attacked severely at almost any stage of growth, except on mature, weathered leaves. Some varieties with good resistance to aboveground infection have shown little resistance to below-ground infection.

Growers no longer fear this disease as they did in 1947 and 1948, when losses were severe in the South. They have learned that timely, preventive spraying of the plants will control the disease, even on the most susceptible varieties.

R. O. MAGIE, *pathologist in the Florida Agricultural Experiment Station, was born in Madison, N. J., and was educated at Rutgers University and the University of Wisconsin. Dr. Magie conducted research at the New York State Agricultural Experiment Station before taking up research on gladiolus in 1945 at the Gulf Coast Experiment Station, Bradenton, Fla.*

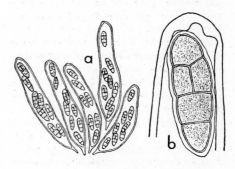

a, Group of asci; b, single spore at apex of ascus.

Virus Enemies of Gladiolus

Philip Brierley, Floyd F. Smith, Frank P. McWhorter

When a virus infects the gladiolus plant the probability is that it will soon become a permanent resident of the plant and of all its vegetative progeny.

Thus, the recent great increase in production of gladiolus, the growing of corms in very many places, and the interstate and international commerce in them offer unusual opportunities for transporting viruses and for increasing them in the crop. Such factors are partly responsible for the increase in number of virus diseases as the growing of gladiolus has expanded. Before 1928 no one had described a virus disease of this crop. By 1952 workers had demonstrated four diseases of this class and had described several other suspected virus diseases of gladiolus.

The first report of a suspected virus disease of gladiolus was by Louise Dosdall at the Minnesota Agricultural Experiment Station in 1928. She described a disease of Gretchen Zang and other gladiolus varieties. It was distinguishable by wartiness and mottling of the corms, mottling of leaves and flower bracts, breaking of the flower color, and bunching of the blossoms. The disease reappeared the following season when affected corms were replanted. Miss Dosdall therefore considered it a degeneration disease, although she presented no proof of transmissibility of a causal virus. Later students of gladiolus diseases have not recognized a virus disease with distinctive wartiness of corms. Colin D. McKeen, of the University of Toronto, in 1943, described ring patterns in gladiolus corms, but found no proof of virus as a causal agent. We have seen corm symptoms resembling McKeen's disease, but the causal agent is still unknown.

A. W. Dimock, of Cornell University, in 1940 described a damaging mosaic disease of gladiolus, characterized by short spikes, fewer florets than normal, and bleaching of the petals of colored varieties. We have termed this disease white break to distinguish it from the more common and milder mosaic caused by bean yellow mosaic virus. In white break the flowers are blotched with white or with yellow rather than streaked. The bleached areas are sometimes recognizable in the buds as they begin to show color. Affected flowers open irregularly and fade early. Bleaching is often so extensive that the flower is no longer recognizable as to variety. The flower bracts are streaked or bleached and may wither while the flowers are still opening. Affected plants are often notably shorter than normal plants. No leaf symptoms are consistently linked with white break.

White break caused some concern among producers of gladiolus when it was first recognized. Affected plants are unsalable, and such a disease could assume major importance if it would spread rapidly. It appears commonly along the eastern seaboard and is known in southern Oregon. Natural spread at Beltsville, Md., has reached 15 percent in one season. There has been little evidence of natural spread in other areas in which glads are produced commercially, so that white break is feared less than formerly. The disease is a nuisance because it is not recognizable in plants that do not bloom and is commonly overlooked in flowers that are cut for shipment when the first floret shows color. It thus persists in field plantings and frequently enters the wholesale markets in cut blooms. No insect vector has been found for the white break virus, although aphids, leafhoppers, and thrips have been experimentally tested as suspects.

The virus of common mild mosaic of gladiolus is transmitted by the green peach aphid and by the crescent-marked lily aphid. The mosaic is expressed as angular light- and dark-green mottling in young leaves and as stripe breaks in the flowers.

Similar mosaic mottling appears in plants of related genera of Iridaceae, such as *Babiana, Freesia, Ixia, Sparaxis, Streptanthera, Tritonia,* and *Watsonia,* grown from corms from commercial sources. Those plants, like gladiolus, however, are free from leaf mottling and from flower breaks if grown from seed. Extensive cross-inoculations, mostly by means of the green peach aphid, showed that the mosaic diseases occurring in those plants are the same as the mild mosaic of gladiolus or much like it. Flower breaks were observed in affected plants of *Babiana.* The effects of this mosaic on the other hosts are usually mild mottling comparable to the symptoms in gladiolus, but freesias die back when infected with some strains of the virus from gladiolus.

A VIRUS DISEASE caused severe loss in commercial pole beans in 1946 in Oregon, especially when the beans were grown next to gladiolus fields. The gladiolus were shown to be the source of the virus when the virus was experimentally transmitted from gladiolus to beans and reproduced the bean disease in question. Next, abnormalities characteristic of the previously known bean yellow mosaic, or bean virus 2, were found also within the cells of bean infected experimentally from gladiolus. Thus gladiolus were shown to be carriers of this bean virus—a wholly unexpected relationship, for gladiolus is remote from bean in the plant kingdom and the bean yellow mosaic had not been detected previously in plants other than members of the pea family. Finally we transmitted the mild mosaic of gladi-

olus to beans by means of the green peach aphid. Symptoms typical of bean yellow mosaic resulted, and the virus, on further transfer by this aphid from these beans to gladiolus seedlings, produced the mild mosaic symptoms again. This showed that mild mosaic in gladiolus is a form of bean yellow mosaic.

Proof that the mild mosaic of gladiolus is the same as bean yellow mosaic made it possible to apply earlier studies on the bean virus to the problem in gladiolus. The virus was found not to be seed-borne in gladiolus; it had been shown not to be seed-borne in legumes. Other species of aphids, notably the pea aphid, were known vectors. The virus is of the non-persistent type; it is acquired by the vector aphids in a few minutes feeding on a diseased plant, but is soon lost by the vectors if they later feed on nonsusceptible plants or if they do not feed for a time. Thus susceptible crops are usually safe from infection when grown at relatively short distances from sources of virus. Furthermore, many strains of bean yellow mosaic are known to occur; and strain variation in the causal virus may account for minor variations found in the mosaics from several iridaceous plants. Commercial gladiolus now take their place along with red clover, sweetclover, and alfalfa as reservoirs of bean yellow mosaic as sources of infection for crops like beans, peas, and the sweetpeas. Considered solely as a gladiolus disease, bean yellow mosaic is of minor importance, for few varieties are seriously disfigured by infection. On the other hand, gladiolus have consistently proved bad neighbors for beans in the West.

CUCUMBER MOSAIC virus was detected in gladiolus in Tasmania and in England before it was found in North America. It and the tobacco ring spot virus were isolated from gladiolus in Ontario and Wisconsin in 1951. Subsequently at Beltsville, Md., we isolated cucumber mosaic virus and tobacco ring spot virus from a number of variously diseased gladiolus submitted from several States for diagnosis. In our experiments the tobacco ring spot virus has been successfully introduced into gladiolus seedlings and isolated again from them, but no symptoms occurred in leaves or flowers. Gladiolus seedlings experimentally infected with cucumber mosaic showed white streaking in petals and white or yellowish streaks in the leaves. Cucumber mosaic evidently is responsible for some of the streaking not infrequently encountered in gladiolus. Gladiolus also must be recognized as a reservoir of these viruses as well as the bean yellow mosaic virus.

ASTER YELLOWS, a common virus disease well known in a wide range of plants, also affects gladiolus. Diseased gladiolus develop green flowers and uniformly straw-yellow leaves in Eastern States. The plants usually shrivel and die down rapidly after the symptoms appear. We proved in 1948 that aster yellows causes these effects. The disease is damaging but usually is infrequent in gladiolus, even in areas of high intensity of aster yellows. The reason for this low prevalence in gladiolus is unexplained, for the six-spotted leafhopper, the vector of the virus, feeds readily on gladiolus.

A DISEASE called grassy-top developed in up to 50 percent of the plants of some commercial fields of gladiolus in Florida and Alabama in 1952. The corms that gave rise to the disease were all grown the previous season in one locality in Oregon. Affected plants developed several weak yellow shoots instead of the single vigorous shoots of normal plants. Roots also were thin and weak. Corms had rough, hard bases, small warts at the nodes, and enlarged and irregular cores. From such grassy-top gladiolus the six-spotted leafhopper transmitted western aster yellows to China aster, celery, and zinnia. When the virus was returned to gladiolus in early stages of

growth, the plants were killed. Gladiolus infected in later stages of growth, after new corms were well developed, survived to the next season. Such gladiolus, infected after flowering, apparently give rise to grassy-top symptoms when planted again. This outbreak is the only one known in which aster yellows has assumed commercial importance in the gladiolus crop.

OTHER GLADIOLUS DISEASES possibly caused by virus are mentioned briefly in gladiolus publications. They have symptoms similar to known virus diseases. Visible pathogens are lacking and proof is lacking that virus is the cause.

R. O. Magie, of the Gulf Coast Experiment Station, Bradenton, Fla., mentioned green petal stunt in the varieties Spic and Span and Golden Arrow, in which stunted petals show green veins, florets often fail to open, and plants are stunted or killed.

The disease called white pitting, known in Florida and sent to workers at Beltsville, has been found to persist from year to year in the corms. White pitting, characterized by short, stiff brittle leaves, white pitting of petals, and white or brown streaking in leaves and stems, is known only in Florida thus far.

GLADIOLUS STUNT, distinguished by plants and spikes much shorter than normal, with no mottling, streaking, or distortion, may prove to be a virus disease. Stunt is difficult to recognize until the symptoms are fully expressed. It is said to be widely distributed and responsible for much of the decline in vigor of old varieties, and, therefore, is feared more by growers than the other known or suspected virus diseases.

The gladiolus thus is known to be subject to four well-known viruses of wide host range—bean yellow mosaic, cucumber mosaic, tobacco ring spot, and aster yellows viruses—and to several suspected virus diseases. But we do not have all the information we should have about the agents that transmit them, their host range, and varietal reactions. Until more detailed knowledge is available there is little basis for suggesting a sound program of control.

Dr. Magie, in the North American Gladiolus Council Bulletin No. 20, December 1949, suggested the value of certifying planting stock of gladiolus, comparable to the program of certifying white potatoes. The stocks, he wrote, might be "produced in parts of the country where disease spread is naturally light or absent." He was concerned mainly with fusarium rot control, but he also mentioned virus control. Such a program would be good if it could be put into practice. But no one knows now which areas are favored by light spread of gladiolus viruses; more research is necessary before the gladiolus industry can follow the path of the potato industry; and the number of gladiolus varieties in the trade, already enormous, is continually augmented by the new productions of hundreds of amateur breeders. Therefore we find less interest in protecting the present commercial varieties than in developing new sorts. Of course the situation would improve if breeders of gladiolus would take all possible care to avoid exposing their seedlings to sources of infection so that only disease-free new varieties might enter the trade.

PHILIP BRIERLEY, *a senior pathologist in the Bureau of Plant Industry, Soils, and Agricultural Engineering, has been employed by the Department of Agriculture since 1922.*

FLOYD F. SMITH *is a senior entomologist in the Bureau of Entomology and Plant Quarantine. For many years he has done research on insects that affect greenhouse and ornamental plants. He holds degrees from Ohio State University.*

FRANK P. McWHORTER *in 1930 entered cooperative employment by the Oregon Agricultural Experiment Station and the United States Department of Agriculture. Since then he has specialized in virus diseases of bulb and legume crops.*

Blights of Lilies and Tulips

C. J. Gould

Whether one grows tulips or lilies for fun or for profit—in Brooklyn, Keokuk, or Seattle; in the garden, field, or greenhouse—he probably has more grief from botrytis blights than from any other cause.

The blights, or "fire" as they are sometimes called, are world-wide in distribution and most prevalent in cool, moist areas. They are caused by similar, but distinct, fungi. Most common on tulips is *Botrytis tulipae.* Most common on lilies is *Botrytis elliptica.*

Tulip blight begins with a diseased bulb or with contaminated soil in which the fungus is living on old remains of the tulip plant. As the young tulip shoot pushes through the ground, it becomes infected if it comes in contact with the fungus and may be changed into a distorted, grayish-brown body covered with powdery masses of spores. Sometimes only part of a leaf is diseased. Often the entire shoot is affected. Soon the leaves of the nearby tulip plants become spotted with small, circular, yellow or brown dots. Many of the spots remain small and dry up, but others, (especially if the weather is cool and moist) enlarge rapidly. Their color becomes a grayish brown or brown, with a dark water-soaked margin. Powdery masses of spores often form in the center. These, when blown to other plants, initiate more spots, which may become visible within 24 hours.

Large spots near the leaf base often

cause the leaf to break. Several spots may fuse and decay a leaf completely. Spots on stems are similar and may also cause the stems to break. Flowers are very susceptible and often are made unsalable by white or brown spots covered with spores. Not even the bulb escapes. On its outer fleshy scale the fungus may produce sunken, yellow or brown craters. In them, on the outer bulb husk, and on spots on the upper plant parts, small, hard, black circular masses of the fungus may develop. Such black bodies, the sclerotia, have a function somewhat similar to seeds in that they enable the fungus to live over winter, either on the bulb or on dead tulip parts. Then, when infection from the sclerotia occurs in the spring, the cycle is continued by the spores.

The disease probably occurs wherever tulips are grown, but it is most serious when conditions are cool and moist. Consequently it is prevalent in the Netherlands, southwestern England, and the Pacific Northwest.

Local conditions, however, are important: In western Washington, for example, the disease is more serious in the valleys near Puyallup than it is 90 miles to the north near Mount Vernon, where the plants are exposed to a more or less constant wind from Puget Sound.

The method of planting tulips commercially in beds about 3 feet wide, as practiced in Holland and some parts of the United States, is more conducive to botrytis blight than is the row system used in the Pacific Northwest. Not only is the relative humidity higher in the beds, but there is also a greater opportunity for infection. Likewise the disease is often found in gardens in massed plantings or on plants in shaded places.

Most, if not all, tulip varieties are susceptible, but there is some variation. Among varieties that are very susceptible are the popular William Copland, William Pitt, and Bartigon. Baronne de la Tonnaye is supposed to be resistant. This species of Botrytis can also attack bulbous plants other than tulips

under certain conditions according to tests by Neil A. MacLean at Washington State College. Other species of Botrytis, including B. cinerea, can sometimes attack tulips.

Although B. tulipae can attack healthy leaves, its entrance is facilitated by injuries from frost, hail, and equipment. The Dutch have tried to reduce frost injury by treating the bulbs to delay growth in the spring until the danger is partly over. This artificial retarding is accomplished by storing the bulbs at approximately 70° F. and delaying planting until October or November.

Much can be done to control the disease in commercial fields and home gardens by proper cultural practices: Digging every year; not replanting tulips in the same location for at least 3 years; planting so as to provide good air circulation and low humidity by proper selection of site, proper spacing, and thorough weeding; removing promptly and destroying diseased shoots, old and infected flowers, and dead plant remains; and planting only healthy bulbs.

Since the original infections arise from diseased bulbs that escape detection, it would seem logical to treat them with a fungicide in order to destroy the fungus. Many treatments have been tested and a few have been recommended, such as Uspulun and Aretan, in Europe. Such treatments have not met with general success, however. Either they injured the bulbs or failed to control the disease adequately.

Early attempts to prevent plants from becoming diseased by using fungicidal sprays were likewise not very successful. Although copper-containing compounds such as bordeaux mixture were found capable of controlling the fungus, they often caused considerable injury to the leaves and flowers. However, in New York in 1940 L. W. Nielson and C. E. Williamson found that silver nitrate sprays compared favorably with the 1.5–4.5–50 bordeaux mixture in fungicidal action. One spray, containing silver nitrate, manganese sulfate, and hydrated lime was adopted by bulb growers on Long Island.

Meanwhile tests in 1938 in the Netherlands had shown promising results with thiram, one of the new organic-sulfur compounds. I tested it and related sulfur compounds in comparison with silver and copper fungicides at the Western Washington Agricultural Experiment Station beginning in 1942. Then and later the best results were had with ferbam, another organic sulfur compound. Large-scale tests by growers in 1943 corroborated the experimental trials. Afterwards it came into general use in the Pacific Northwest and the Netherlands.

Four applications of ferbam are usually enough in the Northwest, beginning when the shoots are 2 to 4 inches tall and continuing at 7- to 10-day intervals. The spraying must be accompanied by the prompt removal of infected plants as soon as detected. By combining the proper cultural practices and a spraying program, the disease can now be conquered.

BOTRYTIS BLIGHT OF LILIES, like tulip blight, is an old enemy. Apparently distributed all over the world, it is infectious to all species and varieties of lilies. Some species, such as *Lilium candidum*, the Madonna lily, may be killed to the ground if conditions favor development of the blight. The fungus most often responsible is *Botrytis elliptica*, but a few other species of *Botrytis*, including the common *B. cinerea*, can parasitize lilies under certain conditions.

Although *B. elliptica* may occasionally rot the growing point of small plants, the usual visible symptom is a leaf spotting. The spots at first are small, circular or elongated, and brown or reddish-brown, with a yellowish or water-soaked margin. Under cool, moist conditions they may enlarge, becoming paler in color, and sometimes completely rotting the leaf. The fungus may attack stems near the soil level and so injure them that the foliage above turns yellow.

Spots on the flowers usually are brown and in cool, moist weather rapidly convert the flowers into wet, slimy masses covered with powdery layers of spores. In warm, dry weather the spots on leaves and flowers stop enlarging and dry up. With ample moisture and an optimum temperature near 60° F., however, a new spot may develop within 24 hours and new spores within a few days thereafter. Given suitable moisture and temperature conditions, the cycle may repeat itself every few days throughout the growing season. Meanwhile, hardened masses of the fungus are forming in the diseased portions. These masses, the sclerotia, are first white and later black. They may be rounded, elliptical or irregular, and one-thirty-second to one-quarter inch in size. Under favorable conditions the sclerotia germinate the following spring to produce spores.

The fungus overwinters in at least three ways: It can survive in the form of sclerotia. It can live saprophytically in lily debris. It can survive in the basal rosettes of leaves of such lilies as the Madonna lily. It may also possibly survive in nonlily hosts, since Neil A. MacLean of the State College of Washington discovered that some other plants are susceptible to the fungus. He demonstrated also that the fungus sometimes could rot lily bulbs. That implies another method of overwintering of the fungus, although it apparently seldom happens in nature.

Moisture is necessary for the germination of spores of the fungus and also for their formation. A saturated atmosphere is required for formation at 80° F., although at lower temperatures a slightly lower humidity permits development. Under favorable conditions spores may form on infected spots and become mature within 9 hours. Germination can only occur in a film of water. Under favorable conditions the fungus can produce visible water-soaked areas within 10 hours after lodging on a leaf. Although the optimum temperature for infection is near 6o°, once the fungus has entered the plant it then grows best at 70°.

Since a high relative humidity is necessary for both spore formation and germination, it is evident that areas of high rainfall or heavy dews should be favorable for the fungus, provided the temperature is cool enough. Thus the heavy rainfall of the west coast and Gulf States accounts for the severity in those places; according to C. E. F. Guterman, the heavy dews explain the prevalence of the disease in Long Island and Bermuda. The disease is also common in greenhouses, especially during periods of cloudy, wet weather in the fall before heat is turned on.

Although all lilies are apparently susceptible to botrytis blight to a certain extent, they vary in susceptibility. The very susceptible species include *L. candidum, L. chalcedonicum, L. humboldtii,* and *L. testaceum. L. speciosum* is somewhat less susceptible. Among the resistant types are *L. giganteum* and *L. willmottiae.* The Easter lily, *Lilium longiflorum,* is classed as susceptible, but F. P. McWhorter has pointed out that the variety Ace is more resistant than the more commonly grown Croft.

CONTROL MEASURES are largely a matter of changing the factors that favor the survival of the fungus. Although not much can be done about rain and dew, it is possible to lower the humidity by planting lilies in locations with good air circulation, avoiding low or shaded spots, avoiding massed plantings, and preventing weed growth.

One should also avoid cultivating or otherwise disturbing the plants when they are wet with dew or rain. In greenhouses the judicious use of heat and ventilation together with proper watering should help keep the humidity down to a point unfavorable for the fungus.

Protection with fungicides is usually a necessary addition to good cultural practice, especially in commercial plantings and in home gardens on such very susceptible types as the Madonna lily. Bordeaux mixture, with a wetting and sticking agent, gives good results if it is applied before the disease has become extremely serious. A weekly application is necessary in wet weather, but otherwise a spray every other week is usually sufficient.

Many other types of copper sprays and dusts would likely serve as well as bordeaux mixture if proper coverage is obtained. Ferbam has given good control of the botrytis blight of tulips, but it failed to give more than fair control of the lily blight in tests I have conducted in Washington.

Also necessary is sanitation—the elimination of the sources of spores. The diseased leaves and old flowers should be removed in home gardens. Many growers also have found it desirable to remove the flowers from commercial plantings. If all debris is destroyed at the end of the growing season, a major source of infection is eliminated. It has also been suggested that the basal rosette leaves of *L. candidum* be cut off just below the ground line in midwinter. This variety should be separated from less susceptible ones and all types should be replanted in a different location whenever dug.

Control measures therefore for lily blight are nothing more than the application of general good growing procedures, supplemented with fungicidal sprays when necessary.

ONE OF THE MOST POPULAR lilies is *Lilium longiflorum,* the Easter lily. Of the several varieties, the one usually seen in florists' shops at Easter is the Croft, which was developed in the West Coast States, where the center of production still exists. At the time of its introduction and for many years thereafter Crofts were grown in greenhouses without much trouble from diseases. Then a puzzling leaf spotting or scorching began to be reported occasionally in different parts of the country. Finally, in the 1947–1948 forcing season it became prevalent on Croft lilies in many greenhouses in the East, and since has become increasingly serious in many sections.

The condition has been called leaf spot, leaf burn, tip burn, and leaf scorch. The last is the generally accepted term. The symptom usually seen begins near the end of the leaf as a semicircular spot, which may enlarge until the entire tip is affected. Such spots develop most often on the upper part of the plant and after the flower buds appear. Usually only a few leaves are affected, but in severe cases nearly all may be spotted. The condition is usually most severe on plants with light-colored leaves or on those forced rapidly. It appears more frequently following bright sunny days than cloudy ones. Such spots so disfigure the plants that the leaves may have to be trimmed with scissors before they can be marketed.

Although fumigation with nicotine for insect control had produced somewhat similar injury, leaf scorch sometimes appeared where nicotine had never been used. The disorder also resembled botrytis blight in many respects, but the usual blight control measures were ineffective. It differed from the blight in that the spots regularly occurred on the margins of the leaves, usually an inch or two from the tip, and never on the flowers; the botrytis spots were scattered on the leaves and numerous on the blossoms. The possibility that it was caused by a fungus was discarded when research workers demonstrated that the fungus could not be detected in typical scorched spots. So it appeared to be a physiological problem, and investigations since have proceeded on that basis.

Neil W. Stuart at the Plant Industry Station at Beltsville, Md., noticed in 1945 that lilies fertilized with nitrogen during forcing showed fewer scorched leaves than unfertilized plants. He followed the observation with experiments in the greenhouse, using various types of fertilizers. He found that under his conditions nitrogen fertilizer alone reduced the leaf burning, but the inclusion of phosphorus and potash in the mixture counteracted the beneficial effect of the nitrogen. He reported the experiments in 1949 with the statement that "more than one factor is concerned in the leaf-spotting problem."

The soundness of the statement has been emphasized by later work. The beneficial effect of nitrogen has been substantiated generally by experiments by John G. Seeley at Pennsylvania State College and A. N. Roberts and his associates at Oregon State College. Many treatments have responded quite differently in various parts of the country, however. Deficiencies of boron and magnesium, for instance, appeared to increase scorch in one sand-culture test and and not in another. Results with nitrogen have not always been consistent.

Some of these variable results can perhaps be explained now as a result of cooperative tests made by Stuart at Beltsville and William Skou and D. C. Kiplinger at Ohio State University. One of their treatments gave particularly interesting results. Ammonium sulfate at a rate of 1 ounce in 2 gallons of water was applied every 2 weeks to lilies in the greenhouse. At Columbus the treatment produced the least scorch. The total numbers of scorched leaves were much below those occurring on unfertilized plants. The treatment produced the most scorch at Beltsville, however, and nearly three times as much as occurred on the unfertilized plants.

The average number of scorched leaves per treatment was 32 at Ohio and 188 at Beltsville. What factors could be responsible for such different results? The investigators suggest that perhaps they were due to the differences in soil acidity and water. At Columbus the unfertilized soil had a pH value of 7.3; the water had a pH of 10.5; the soil after treatment with ammonium sulfate had a pH of 6.7. At Beltsville the original soil had a pH of 5.8; the water had an average pH of 7.3; and the soil after treatment with ammonium sulfate had a pH of 3.9. Thus, the soil acidity was markedly different at the two locations. They also reported that in another experiment at Beltsville the least scorch was present on plants grown in quartz sand with a complete nutrient solution plus 25 grams of calcium carbonate per pot. A similar benefit was obtained by adding dolomitic limestone to infertile acid soil.

The effectiveness of lime in preventing scorch of Croft lilies during forcing was investigated by A. N. Roberts, R. E. Stephenson, and S. E. Wadsworth at Oregon State College in 1950 and 1951. Although an application of nitrogen alone completely prevented scorch, the plants were poor and were apparently severely affected with a deficiency of phosphorus or potassium or both. Plants that received a complete fertilizer (nitrogen, phosphorus, potash, and sulfur) and lime at a rate of 8 tons an acre grew very well with only a small amount of scorch. The complete fertilizer without lime resulted in a high rate of scorch, especially in the presence of high amounts of manganese and aluminum. Lime at a rate of 5 tons an acre was less effective than at the 8-ton rate. Also, a high rate of lime overcame the scorching tendency of an unbalance of nitrogen and sulfur in one combination and phosphorus plus potassium in another combination. The lime naturally changed the pH of the soil somewhat; generally the scorch was more severe in the most acid soils. V. A. Clarkson at Oregon State College showed that typical scorch could be induced within about 10 days by the addition of dilute sulfuric acid to the soil.

Such data indicate that the pH might be the determining factor, but some of the additional data from Oregon show that there was no significant difference in scorch on two soils, one with a pH of 6.2 and the other with a

pH of 5.0. They raise the question whether the value of the lime is in its neutralizing effect or in its ability to supply calcium to the plant.

In those studies and others it was noticed that plants grown from bulbs produced on different farms varied in the amount of scorch. In the 1950–1951 season, F. P. McWhorter assembled bulbs from 21 growers in California, Oregon, and Washington. The bulbs were forced at Beltsville, Ohio State University, and Oregon State College. Not only was there a different response by different stocks—the relative performance often was different at the three locations. It was evident that the field "history" of the bulbs had a marked effect on the amount of scorch that developed when no fertilizer was used during forcing.

Mr. Roberts and others at Oregon State College in 1948 began studying the possible carry-over effect of fertilizer treatments in the field on forcing performance and scorch development in the greenhouse. Their experiments demonstrated also that the field "history" of the bulbs had a definite bearing on the amount of scorch that developed but that none of the field treatments tested prevented subsequent scorching in the greenhouse. One field treatment containing nitrogen, phosphorus, potassium, sulfur, and manganese actually increased the number of scorched leaves in the greenhouse. A field treatment with nitrogen, potash, potassium, sulfur, and lime was ineffective in reducing scorch, but in that test the lime was used at a rate of 3,480 pounds an acre, which may have been too low. In general, they found that the more complete the nutrition was in the field and the better the growth, the greater was the likelihood that scorch would appear in the greenhouse.

In addition it may be more of a field problem than has been realized heretofore, since F. P. McWhorter and C. J. Anderson in Oregon pointed out in 1951 that "it is probable that a considerable portion of the injury

'ormerly attributed to Botrytis blight
may have been due to the physiological
disease, scorch."

Our knowledge of the cause and
control of scorch is far from complete,
although the studies I have reviewed
have helped greatly. Apparently scorch
follows unbalanced nutrition. The disorder is generally most severe in very
acid soils and can be prevented to a
great extent in them by heavy applications of calcium and nitrogen. In
moderately acid soils it can apparently be alleviated by the use of nitrogen fertilizers alone. But the exact role
of nitrogen and calcium and the
possible influence of aluminum, manganese, and magnesium are not entirely clear.

Finally, in developing a suitable
treatment, commercial factors other
than leaf scorch must also be considered—height of the plant, color of
leaves, number of flowers. The control
program ultimately based on the cause
must be one that not only prevents
the development of scorch but also
one that promotes a good culture.

C. J. GOULD *is a plant pathologist at
the Western Washington Experiment Station
(State College of Washington). He has
been investigating diseases of ornamental
bulbs since 1941. Dr. Gould has degrees
from Marshall College and Iowa State
College. He has studied bulb diseases in
Holland under a Fulbright grant and has
received with Dr. Neil Stuart the Society
of American Florists' Award for outstanding research in 1950.*

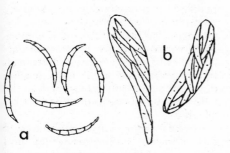

a, Fusarium spores; b, asci.

Narcissus Basal Rot

W. D. McClellan

Considerable concern was felt in
England in 1890 about a troublesome
rot of narcissus bulbs. The affected
plants were stunted, the tips of the
leaves turned brown, the flowers developed imperfectly, and the base of
the bulb was soft and rotten.

The cause of the rot was not determined. Some investigators blamed unfavorable conditions of soil or climate.
One person thought it was due to a
fungus. But little effort was made to
investigate the trouble until the hot
summer of 1911, when large numbers
of bulbs rotted during storage in England and the Netherlands.

J. Jacob, in an article in The Garden in 1911, stated that the rot was
due to the combined action of heat and
Fusarium bulbigenum. That fungus, described in 1887, had been found on
narcissus bulbs but had not been recognized as the pathogen. Later studies
indicated that the fungus was nearly
always present with nematodes, which
also can cause a rot of daffodils. Johanna Westerdijk in the Netherlands
in 1917 distinguished between the
nematode disease and the bulb rot due
to *Fusarium.*

Before 1924 about 77 million narcissus bulbs were imported annually
into the United States, primarily for
greenhouse forcing. The Secretary of
Agriculture promulgated a quarantine
against narcissus because of nematodes
and bulb flies, to become effective July
15, 1926. Increasing numbers of bulbs

were imported in 1924, 1925, and 1926 for use largely as planting stock to establish a domestic bulb supply. By 1926 the imports reached 142 million bulbs.

Along with the establishment of narcissus culture in the United States, basal rot became a serious commercial problem, for several reasons. At first many growers were unfamiliar with the culture of narcissus. The Hollanders who undertook production in this country were unfamiliar with the factors of climate and soil they encountered. The soil temperatures at harvest and planting seasons and the temperatures during summer storage and shipment along the eastern seaboard, where bulb production was started, were higher than the temperatures in England and the Netherlands. Most of the stock planted from the imports was made up of susceptible varieties, such as Golden Spur, Victoria, Spring Glory, Empress, and Emperor. The hot-water treatment of 110° F. for 2½ hours, which was required for treatment of narcissus bulbs if nematodes were present in the stock, proved to be a way of spreading basal rot. Finally, basal rot was a new problem. Little was known about its cause, development, or control.

Losses due to basal rot often were heavy. For instance, one grower near Babylon, N. Y., had a stock of 70,000 Golden Spur bulbs in 1927. They were treated with hot water to control nematodes, and they seemed healthy when they were planted. The bulbs emerged the following spring and made good growth until shortly before digging time, when a period of hot, moist weather began. The high temperature continued through the digging period and the disease spread rapidly until fall. Half of the stock was so badly rotted that it had to be destroyed. Enough of the remaining bulbs were available to plant 808 flats of approximately 40 bulbs each for greenhouse forcing. The rot continued to spread so that only about 250 of the flats had healthy bulbs of any kind and

none had more than three or four live bulbs. The entire planting was completely destroyed by basal rot in less than 18 months.

Because of the alarm felt by narcissus growers, the Department of Agriculture was directed in 1926 to study the disease—the first specific directive that the Department had had to study a disease of ornamental plants.

Dr. Freeman Weiss began the study of the disease, and soon found it to be caused by the fungus *Fusarium*. That *Fusarium* had been assigned the name *Fusarium bulbigenum*, but American pathologists follow Snyder and Hansen's classification and call it *F. oxysporum* f. *narcissi*.

The basal rot *Fusarium* is highly specific for narcissus, although closely allied forms attack other ornamental and vegetable crops. The large trumpet types of narcissus, especially the bicolor and white trumpets, are most seriously affected. Some of the Poeticus varieties also are susceptible, but most of the Incomparabilis, Barrii, and Leedsii varieties are resistant or at least do not ordinarily rot under conditions in which the trumpet types rot so badly. The Polyanthus types, or paper whites, are also resistant but less hardy and are therefore limited to the warmer parts of the United States. Trumpet varieties with hard bulbs, such as King Alfred, are a little less susceptible to *Fusarium* than the soft-bulb types. The susceptible bicolors have nearly disappeared from commercial culture because of basal rot.

Growers call the disease basal rot because the decay usually begins in the root plate or at the base of the scales, whence it spreads through the bulb. Basal rot is primarily a disease of narcissus bulbs during storage or transit, but in warm regions it may develop during the later stages of growth in the field and harm the bulbs before they are dug.

In early summer in warm areas, the tops of infected bulbs turn yellow and die down before the normal time of maturity. Bulbs only slightly affected at digging time often have many purplish roots, which die back from the tips towards the base of the bulb. Penetration of the bulbs by the fungus is primarily through the young roots.

After infection has begun at the base of a scale, extension of the rot becomes rapid if the weather is warm. In partly resistant varieties such as Sir Watkin, the disease tends to advance in streaks and layers. The rotted tissue has a characteristic chocolate-brown or purplish-brown color, and the mycelium of the fungus appears as a weft of delicate white or pinkish-white webs between the scales. The tissue is softened. Later one can easily tell the affected bulbs by touch, but the rotted tissue remains somewhat dry and spongy. In a humid environment a small amount of white mycelium may be evident at the juncture of the scales and root plate, but otherwise there is little external evidence of the disease. It is hard therefore to eliminate all infected bulbs by sorting.

Neil W. Stuart and I, investigating the disease at Beltsville, have shown that fertilizers, some growth regulators, and nitrogen bases (purine ring compounds) markedly affect the severity of basal rot. Field plots of narcissus fertilized with nitrogen or phosphate had greater amounts of basal rot than did similar plots not fertilized. The increased amount of rot in the plots fertilized with nitrogen or phosphate was correlated with increased growth of the *Fusarium* in culture when the levels of nitrogen or phosphate were increased.

Dr. Stuart has suggested that many fertilizer practices may be of greater benefit to the *Fusarium* than to the narcissus. Organic manures also were found to increase the amount of basal rot. Many organic manures contain purine ring compounds, such as uric acid, allantoin, guanidine, and adenine.

Some of the synthetic growth regulators have been recommended for use in fertilizers for bulbs to stimulate root growth. Stuart and I dipped narcissus bulbs in water solutions, or in talc,

containing indolebutyric acid, naphthalene acetic acid, naphthalene acetamide, allantoin, guanidine, uric acid, and nucleic acid (which on hydrolysis yields a pentose, three pyrimidines, and two purines, guanine, and adenine) before planting in the field. Those bulbs had a much higher percentage of basal rot when dug the following year than did similar bulbs dipped in water or untreated. Furthermore, greater growth of the *Fusarium* occurred in nutrient solutions to which the materials had been added.

Temperature markedly influences the amount of basal rot. In the Netherlands and England losses due to basal rot in the field are not nearly so extensive as those along our east coast. Also, losses from basal rot are much less in the Pacific Northwest than on the east coast.

We have grown King Alfred narcissus at Beltsville, in soil temperature tanks at temperatures of 45° to 70° F. and learned that uninoculated plants grow best with soil temperatures of 55° to 60°. When inoculated plants were grown in the tanks, *Fusarium* infection was most rapid at the higher temperatures. There seemed to be a sharp break in the rate of infection between 55° and 60°. That correlates well with experience in the Northwest and the East. King Alfred narcissus bulbs grown in Beltsville in 1947 and 1949 had 26.6 and 25.8 percent of rot, compared with 5.1 and 6.7 percent of rot in similar lots of bulbs shipped to Puyallup, Wash., and grown there. Late spring and summer temperatures at Puyallup average 8° to 12° lower than at Beltsville. The lower temperatures are believed to account for the lower incidence of basal rot at Puyallup. Attempts to reduce soil temperatures by mulching practices at Beltsville did not reduce the severity of basal rot.

CONTROL OF BASAL ROT involves attention to a number of details.

Rotation to avoid infested soil is one of the prime requisites. Bulbs should be harvested before soil temperatures get too high. In fact, a sacrifice in bulb size in order to dig early often is advocated. In handling the bulbs during digging, grading, and storage, injuries should be avoided, and bulbs should not be allowed to overheat. They should be stored in shallow layers in cool, well-ventilated storage houses. The rotted bulbs should be culled before and after storage. Quick drying of the bulbs immediately after they are dug helps reduce losses.

Soon after Weiss began the study of basal rot in 1926 he sought methods for controlling the disease. He demonstrated that the hot-water treatment for nematodes resulted in contamination of healthy bulbs and he added fungicides to the water to kill the spores. He found that formaldehyde or mercurials were effective, and the use of 5 percent formaldehyde in the water bath is now a regular practice.

Since nematodes are not always present, the hot-water treatment is not always used each year. Consequently some other treatment was needed to control the *Fusarium*. Chemical treatments are feasible at two different periods in the control of narcissus—in early summer, between harvest and storage, or in the fall, before the bulbs are planted.

In the first tests, various mercurials proved superior. Mercuric chloride, calomel, Semesan, 2 percent Ceresan, and New Improved Ceresan were effective in reducing rot, but all caused some injury. Two standard treatments were developed—a dip for 5 minutes in New Improved Ceresan (1 pound in 40 gallons of water) for the eastern sections, and a dip for 15 minutes in 2 percent Ceresan (1 pound in 8 gallons of water) for the Northwest. Such treatments have been credited with saving the narcissus industry in the East.

Treated bulbs far outyielded untreated bulbs. For instance, in a test at Beltsville, 200 King Alfred bulbs were treated with New Improved Ceresan in 1946. The bulbs were given the same treatments in 1947, 1948, and 1949. After harvest and storage in 1950, there were 821 healthy bulbs.

Although growers were reluctant to use treatments before storage because of the danger of severe injury to flowers produced the next season from treated bulbs, heavy losses from basal rot in storage turned the attention of workers to such treatments. They developed the double dip (before storage and before planting) with New Improved Ceresan. Treatments applied 3 days after the bulbs were dug gave best protection against storage rot but also induced maximum flower injury. Late treatment, 15 days after digging, caused no flower injury but gave little rot control.

A 5-MINUTE DIP in Mersolite 8 (phenyl mercury acetate) or in Puratized Agricultural Spray (phenyl mercury triethanol ammonium lactate) is as effective in controlling basal rot as the Ceresans but does not cause flower injury. Mersolite P, a phenyl mercury acetate dust, also has been effective. Arasan dust or Arasan SFX have been fairly effective when a low amount of *Fusarium* was present in the stock. The organic mercurials, Mersolite 8 and Puratized Agricultural Spray, have come into commercial use as prestorage and preplanting treatments in North Carolina and other bulb-growing areas. Bulbs have been treated with Mersolite 8 immediately after digging and have been kept wet for 10 days with no detrimental effect on flowering. Furthermore, bulbs dug immature were not injured by treatment with Mersolite 8, although there was a reduction in bulb yield the following year because of the immaturity.

W. D. McCLELLAN *was trained in plant pathology at the University of California and Cornell University. He was on the staff of the University of Maryland in 1940 and 1941, and was an employee of the the Bureau of Plant Industry, Soils, and Agricultural Engineering from 1941 to 1951, when he became director of research for Mid-State Chemical Supply Co., Lindsay, Calif.*

Nematodes in Bulbs

Wilbur D. Courtney

A number of parasitic nematodes—eelworms—may infect ornamental bulb crops.

Root knot nematodes (*Meloidogyne* species), lance nematode (*Hoplolaimus coronatus*), and meadow nematodes (*Pratylenchus* species) have occasionally caused severe damage to bulb crops, especially in the warmer sections of the United States.

In cooler sections where the hardier types of bulbous irises, Easter lilies, and narcissi are grown for sale to florists for greenhouse forcing rather than for immediate flower production the bulb and stem nematodes (*Ditylenchus* species) and the bud and leaf nematode (*Aphelenchoides olesistus*) are the most serious pests. This chapter concerns the latter two nematodes as pests in the bulb industry of the Pacific Northwest.

BULB AND STEM NEMATODES usually attack the bulbs, crowns, and aboveground parts of plants. More than 350 kinds of plants have been reported as infected at some time or place. The type species, *Ditylenchus dipsaci*, was first discovered in 1857 causing a disease in the flower heads of fullers teasel, *Dipsacus fullonum*. These nematodes are less than one-sixteenth inch long.

Infected narcissus plants show characteristic discoloration and swellings in parts of leaves or stems and discoloration in bulbs.

Infected bulbous iris seldom show malformations of leaves, but spots or blotches often are present at the place the stem joins the bulb. Nematodes enter iris bulbs near the base. They produce a dark depression around the basal plate and cause the dry scales to fall away. In more advanced stages, dark streaks and blotches of lifeless tissue may be found in the fleshy scales from the base toward the bulb tip.

The nematodes on infected plant tissue appear under the microscope as tiny worms among the plant cells. Nematodes exist as males and females and reproduction is by means of eggs, from which hatch tiny larvae, which are shaped like the adults and grow rapidly. They shed their cuticles ("skins") and become second-stage larvae. The procedure is repeated to form third- and fourth-stage larvae and finally adult nematodes. The life cycle requires 25 to 30 days and is repeated as long as the plant grows.

When the narcissus plant dies, because of infection or final ripening, many nematodes leave the plant tissue and, if the soil is moist, migrate into the surrounding earth. Those that do not migrate become dried in plant debris and enter an inactive stage known as quiescence. In that condition they are able to withstand unfavorable conditions, such as extremely high temperatures, and have been revived, upon moistening, after remaining more than 5 years in dry plant tissue. The same thing happens if the soil becomes dried after the nematodes migrate from the hosts, but they remain active as long as there is enough moisture. Bulb and stem nematodes infecting narcissi have remained active in moist soil free of plant growth for 18 months. It took that much time for them to starve to death, as they can exist only on food stored in their bodies.

Control measures for nematodes in bulbous crops must be efficient enough to eradicate them entirely—regulatory measures allow no tolerance of nematode-infected bulbs in salable stocks.

Control measures must include sanitation, proper soil management, and the treatment of bulbs with hot-water-formalin.

The sanitary measures insure the destruction of infected plant materials and prevention of contamination by infested soil. Infected plants with adhering soil should be carefully removed from the field, placed in a deep, isolated trench, covered with quicklime, and buried with a layer of soil. Dry materials from fields and sheds may be burned. To prevent the spread of nematodes by scattering soil and debris from an infested field, adhering soil should be removed from tractors, trucks, diggers, shovels, and other tools. The implements should be washed thoroughly with water and then freely sprayed with formalin (1 part commercial formaldehyde solution U. S. P. to 9 parts of water). That solution may also be used to dip bulb trays and other equipment and to drench soil along paths to free them of the pests.

Proper management of infested soil must destroy the nematodes by an adequate starvation program or by the use of soil fumigants. The success of the starvation method is based upon the removal of all volunteer host plants from the field in question. Infested fields must be kept free of bulbs for at least 2 years following the eradication of host plants in order to starve the plant parasitic nematodes remaining in the soil. Because rapidly decaying plant material tends to lower the number of bulb and stem nematodes in the soil, the frequent use of fast-growing green-manure crops may be recommended during the starvation period. Corn, or most grains, when used as fast-growing annuals, may be used during the starvation period as cash crops.

Soil fumigants may be used to free the soil of plant parasitic nematodes after all volunteer host plants have been removed from an infested field. Fumigation probably is most economical when it is used to treat infested spots or parts of fields for eradication. The materials for fumigation may cost

up to 100 dollars an acre. A grower who is thinking of fumigating soil will do well to consult local or regional horticultural officials about the source, cost, and choice of the various fumigants and applicators.

Proper hot-water-formalin treatment is the best method known at present for curing bulbs infected with nematodes. The use of heat for curing plants infected with nematodes was tried in Germany in 1909. Definite experiments with bulb crops were performed some 10 years later. As a result of those tests, Federal legislation in the 1920's, designed to protect our new bulb industry from pests and diseases carried by imports from other countries, required that nematode-infected stock be treated with hot water. The imported bulbs usually arrived in late autumn after root development was well started and were severely injured by the hot-water treatment. The injury was overcome by a year's growth, but treated bulbs could not be forced in greenhouses without being field-grown for a year. Many other methods of killing the nematodes in the bulbs were then tried, but none proved superior to hot water. It was found, however, that treatment with hot water at 110° to 111° F. for 3 to 4 hours, without the addition of formaldehyde solution U. S. P., did not kill all the nematodes.

When I was located at the Ornamentals Insect Research Laboratory at Sumner, Wash., in 1934, I added a presoak period of 2 hours in water at 75° F. in order to activate quiescent nematodes before the killing treatment. Commercial formaldehyde solution U. S. P. also was added to the treating water at the rate of 1 pint to each 25 gallons of water (0.5 percent) to kill the nematodes more rapidly and prevent the spread of rot organisms during treatment.

When the bulb industry was becoming established in the United States in the late 1920's and early 1930's, the small circular tanks used in England were found to be too small to be practical on American farms and a substitute had to be found. Therefore, equipment for treating bulbs in hot-water formalin has been largely developed by the growers themselves. Using materials at hand, they constructed tanks of wood, metal, or concrete large enough to handle many bulbs in less time. Steam from a nearby boiler, liberated near a motor-driven propeller at the bottom and end of the tank, usually heated the water. A false bottom formed a channel under the load of bulbs through which the heated water was forced to the opposite end and eventually back to the propeller. Baffle plates helped distribute the heat uniformly through the tank. A thermometer was kept immersed near the manually operated steam valve, which was opened occasionally to keep the water between 110° and 111°. Bulbs in containers were lowered to the false bottom by hand or with hoists.

After 20 years of experience, growers have made several improvements.

The false bottom is now a movable platform that may be raised to the top of the tank (which is at shed-floor level), quickly loaded by trucking stacks of trays filled with bulbs and covered with wire netting or empty trays secured in place, and again lowered into the treating bath. As several tons of bulbs may be treated at one time, the platform must be strong and sufficiently weighted to carry the bulbs into the bath. The hoist for raising and lowering the platform is geared to operate smoothly. Another improvement is a thermostat connected with an electromagnetic steam valve through a relay. When operated properly, it maintains the temperature more closely than manually operated valves. Some installations have alarm systems that give warning if the temperature drops below 110° or above 111° F.

One grower, unable to get a dependable steam boiler, substituted two propane-gas burners in two watertight flues, which looped along the bottom from the propeller end of the tank, down and back again and exhausted through a joint chamber. A fan in the chamber maintained a constant outward draft. Both burners are activated from a pilot light, but one is controlled by a thermostat and the other is manually operated as a booster heater.

Because high temperatures harm bulbs and low temperatures do not control nematodes, great care is needed in the operation of the equipment. The growers who do custom treating for other growers have installed recording thermometers so that a permanent record is made of each lot.

The present methods for a complete control of nematodes in bulbs consist of the presoak bath and the treating bath. The presoak bath is water maintained at 75° F., with Vatsol O. S. added at the rate of 8 ounces to 100 gallons of water. Infected bulbs are soaked in this bath for 2 hours immediately before treatment. Its purpose is to revive dried or inactive nematodes, which are more difficult to kill than active ones. Vatsol O. S. is a wetting agent that assures the thorough wetting of all bulbs immersed in the treating bath by removing air pockets from parts of individual bulbs or from between the bulbs. Newer wetting agents have not been tested in bulb treatments and should be avoided until it is definitely known that they will cause no injury. Vatsol O. S. has been used with good results and no apparent injury to the treated bulbs.

The treating bath consists of water with 1 pint of commercial formaldehyde solution U. S. P. to each 25 gallons of water. The bath is maintained at 110° F. for different periods in the treatment of narcissi, bulbous irises, and Croft Easter lilies.

An efficient treating bath must meet several requirements. Agitation or circulation must be adequate to insure a rapid and constant flow of the bath to all parts of the tank. That is accomplished by electrically driven propellers and by properly placed baffle plates in the tank, which assure an even temperature throughout the bath.

It is necessary to have the correct amount of treating bath to maintain the ratio of 4 to 5 parts of liquid by weight to 1 part of bulbs. In order to maintain the correct amount of formaldehyde solution, the tank is calibrated to determine the number of gallons required to fill it to its working level and the amount of water necessary to raise this level of the bath 1 inch. With that information at hand, the operator can add the correct amount of commercial formaldehyde when the bath is first prepared and can also determine the correct number of gallons of water and amount of formaldehyde solution to add between runs. If steam is discharged into the bath as a heat source, the bath is measured before the valves are opened because it is necessary to know how much water is added by condensation of steam.

The concentration of 1 pint of commercial formaldehyde solution U. S. P. to 25 gallons of water must be maintained so as to complete the nematode kill and prevent the dispersal of rot organisms from one bulb to another during treatment. Exact amounts must be added to compensate for any water added to the bath, either by steam or other methods. The commercial formaldehyde solution should be clear and free of any waxy sediment or thickening. If it has been stored in a cool place such a condition may exist and is likely to result in an unreliable concentration. The bath solution should be replaced when it has an excess amount of discoloration, sediment, or both from the soil brought in with the bulbs, which usually occurs after 6 to 8 uses.

The proper temperature is 110° F. for narcissi, bulbous irises, and Croft Easter lilies. The bath temperature must not fall below 110° nor rise above 111° for the entire treatment period, if results are to be satisfactory. In order to maintain this exact control, a reliable mercury-type thermometer, checked for variation with the one used by the State horticultural inspec-

tor, is a necessity. The cheap, spirit type of thermometer is not reliable enough to risk with a tank of bulbs which may be worth several hundred dollars. Growers doing custom treating should also use a recording thermometer and keep the records.

Duration of treatment is determined in hours after the bath has been stabilized at 110° F.

Bulbous irises are treated for 3 hours. Bulbs must be harvested early (about the same time as King Alfred narcissi) and treated within 3 to 4 weeks, or before any evidence of root development or basal swellings start.

Narcissi are treated for 4 hours. Bulbs should be harvested early, when about one-third of the foliage is yet greenish. Planting stock should be treated within 3 weeks after harvest.

Posttreatment care of irises and narcissi should consist of immediate cooling followed by planting or drying. Bulbs must be placed in shallow, sterilized containers and located where adequate air movement will dissipate the stored heat and excess moisture.

THE BUD AND LEAF NEMATODE, *Aphelenchoides olesistus,* was reported by me in 1945 as a serious pest of Croft Easter lilies in the Pacific Northwest. I later found that the infection can be controlled by a 1-hour treatment in the bath and temperature as used for irises and narcissi. Best results were obtained when bulbs were harvested 8 to 10 weeks following full bloom and their bulblets treated within 3 weeks. Only bulblets were treated, because we found that older stock may produce an excess of basal bulblets as a result of treatment, especially in late season. Treated bulblets are cooled immediately after treatment and planted in the field. If that is not feasible, they are kept moist and cool in well-ventilated storage.

WILBUR D. COURTNEY, *a nematologist in the Bureau of Plant Industry, Soils, and Agricultural Engineering, is stationed at Puyallup, Wash.*

Four Diseases of Garden Roses

L. M. Massey

Of the numerous diseases of roses, four are of chief importance in plantings in North America: Black spot, powdery mildew, rust, and the brown canker.

Because of its wide occurrence and destructiveness, black spot is the worst disease of roses in this country. It causes unsightly spots on the leaves. Yellowing and premature dropping generally follow.

Black spot is confined to the rose. Probably all classes of roses are affected but not equally so. The hybrid perpetuals, introduced in 1843; the hybrid teas, introduced in 1867; and the Pernetianas, which appeared in 1890, were more susceptible than their wild or almost wild forerunners. Most of the present-day popular varieties are sufficiently susceptible to black spot to require protection by fungicides.

But more attention is now being given to the development of resistant or immune varieties through the use of such parents as *Rosa wichuraiana*, *R. multiflora*, *R. cinnamomea*, and *R. pendulina*, which tests have shown to be resistant or immune. A start has been made, and progress is sure to be made. Some varieties—Radiance, for example—while possessing no true resistance regularly have but little black spot because the foliage is not easily wetted and therefore escapes infection.

No one knows when or where black spot started, but by the time the early botanists knew something of diseases and began to collect and identify fungi, they found the roses affected with the disease. Early reports of it came from Sweden in 1815, France in 1822, Germany in 1833, England in 1840, and Holland in 1844. The disease was noted in North America in 1831 and has now been reported in practically all States and Canada and South America. It probably occurs throughout the temperate and tropical regions of the world wherever roses are grown. The disease is most serious in areas of heavy rainfall during the growing season.

All aerial parts of the plant may be affected. The spots on the leaves are conspicuous and often are half an inch or more across. They are black and have margins marked by rays and tiny fibrils. A number of spots may merge to form larger ones and cover nearly the whole leaf. The spots may be on either surface—usually the upper.

The leaf tissue next to the black spots becomes yellowish. Sometimes the entire leaf becomes yellow before defoliation occurs. The leaflets may turn yellow in spots, or the yellow area may be limited to a band outside the black spot.

Premature loss of leaves is one of the most pronounced characteristics of the disease. Plants affected by black spot generally show naked stems except for a few young leaves at the tips. Defoliated plants are less vigorous than healthy ones and produce fewer and less desirable blossoms. Also, defoliated plants often send out a late, second crop of leaves; in doing so they fail to mature and develop normal resistance to low temperatures.

The sizes and shapes of the black spots and the rapidity and extent of yellowing and defoliation vary with the varieties as well as the conditions under which the plants are growing.

Spots on the canes look much like those on the leaves. Spots on the petioles and stipules are relatively inconspicuous, as are those on the flower receptacles, sepals, and petals. Discoloration and distortion of the flower may occur.

Black spot of the rose is caused by the fungus *Diplocarpon rosae*.

In sections where the rose loses its leaves in the autumn and becomes dormant, the fungus hibernates in the old leaves on the ground and in the lesions on the stems. If the rose is in leaf throughout the year, as in greenhouses and in the warmer areas, the fungus lives the year around in the infected leaves on the plants. In any event, spores will be produced in the spring to initiate infections on the season's new leaves. The spores will be either ascospores or conidia if they are produced in the old leaves on the ground. They will be conidia if they are produced in the spots on the stems. The ascospores are forcibly discharged from the asci (little sacs), which are produced in fruit bodies, called apothecia. The ascospores are disseminated by wind. The conidia are liberated only if water is present. They are disseminated by splashing and dripping water. Spores—conidia—produced in the spots on the overwintered stems probably are the most important in initiating the infection in the garden following dormancy.

The spores must have water for germination and infection. They will germinate in a humid atmosphere if they have been previously wet. It takes about 9 hours for germination to occur. Infection will be assured if favorable temperatures and humidities continue for at least 6 or 7 hours. Penetration takes place through the cuticle. The black spots become visible in 3 to 10 days, depending on temperature and moisture. Within a day or two after the appearance of the spots on the leaves, mature fruiting bodies (acervuli) are present within the spots. The conidia will be found in these fruiting bodies, which are barely visible to the unaided eye. The spores can be liberated only in the presence of water and are disseminated by splashing rain, by wind-borne rain, by dew, and by water from the hose.

The spores of *D. rosae* can germinate and produce infection immediately after dissemination. The increase in the amount of black spot in the garden depends on the frequency of rains, which favor dissemination and germination, and in the greenhouse on the frequency of syringing. The development of the disease is favored by temperatures around 70° F. and by wet foliage, or at least a saturated atmosphere.

Black spot is controlled through the use of sprays and dusts applied at the proper times to the foliage to protect it against infection.

Wettable-sulfur sprays have replaced lime-sulfur. The "fixed" coppers, such as tribasic copper sulfate, copper oxychloride, and copper oxychloride-sulfate have largely replaced bordeaux mixture. A number of the newer fungicides, including several salts of dithiocarbamic acid gave promising results in tests in 1953.

Fungicides in dust form are as effective as those applied as sprays, and the method has advantages in ease and speed of application. A sulfur dust of at least 325-mesh fineness is often used with success. A dust mixture of 90 percent 325-mesh sulfur and 10 percent fixed copper has been found to be especially effective in Texas.

As sulfur in any form will cause injury to the foliage when the temperatures get into the 90's and above, many gardeners find advantage in turning to the use of a fixed copper, as spray or dust, during periods of high temperature. Copper fungicides are more injurious during cool, wet weather.

Ferbam, an organic sulfur, is effective against black spot and less injurious than ordinary inorganic sulfur during hot weather. It is also effective against rust but not against powdery mildew. It can be used as a spray at the rate of 2 level tablespoonfuls in a gallon, or ½ cupful for 5 gallons of water. As a dust it is used at 10 percent concentration.

Because most gardeners need a fungicide effective against both black spot and mildew, mixtures of sulfur and ferbam are commonly used. Combinations tested and found satisfactory are: For spraying, 2 level teaspoonfuls of ferbam and 2 level tablespoonfuls of wettable sulfur per gallon; for dusting, 10 percent ferbam and 90 percent dusting sulfur. If the problem of high temperatures during the summer (with resulting burn) must be met, a straight ferbam spray, or a 10 percent ferbam and 90 percent pyrophyllite (talc) dust may be substituted for the ferbam-sulfur mixtures. Insecticides may be added to the mixtures as needed.

Roses must be protected against infection by the black spot fungus—not cured after infection takes place. Practically, then, the fungicide must be on the plant in advance of the rainy weather. The gardener should keep in mind that whenever the leaf is wet continuously for 6 hours or longer, conditions are favorable for infection and that the fungicide must be on the plant and operating throughout the period. That is the key to adequate protection.

Many gardeners proceed on a schedule of weekly applications, or at least a fixed schedule. This program may prove satisfactory under ordinary conditions, but frequently such schedules may be inadequate. During the spring when rains are frequent and growth is rapid, it may be necessary to spray or dust twice a week to protect the new growth. During the summer, when rains are less frequent and growth is less rapid, it may be feasible to go 2 or 3 weeks between applications.

With either spray or dust, coverage of both surfaces must be thorough. Sprays must include a wetting and spreading agent, as otherwise they will fail to wet and spread over the surface and adhere to the waxy covering of the leaf. Adequate pressures and nozzles with discs with small holes to break the spray into a fine mist are essential for effective coverage.

Dusting has the advantage of being easier and faster than spraying—the plants can be covered quickly, on short notice of approaching rain, between the showers, or, indeed, during the rain. Dusting is best done in the early morning or evening when the air is quiet and the plants are dry.

POWDERY MILDEW is a common disease of the rose. It is rarely absent from plantings in the garden and the greenhouse. It may make plants unsightly. It may cause severe injury.

The seasonal and regional prevalence of powdery mildew has focused attention on the relation of temperature and humidity to its occurrence.

Powdery mildew of roses does not attack plants outside the genus *Rosa*. Although we have many reports on the susceptibility of varieties to the disease, we have little information based on reliable experimentation. The climbers and ramblers frequently are mentioned as being highly susceptible; the evidence supporting that contention for such varieties as Crimson Rambler, Dorothy Perkins, and others, is impressive. Certain hybrid teas, for example Rome Glory, are known to be more regularly mildewed than others. Varieties having *R. wichuraiana* as a parent, many of which have thick, glossy leaves, are said to have some resistance. Many species of *Rosa* are reported as being susceptible. Few of the reportedly resistant roses escape in seasons favorable to the disease.

The powdery mildew of roses was probably known before its causal organism was described in 1819. It has been reported in most European countries and Asia, Australia, North America, and South America. In the United States it has been reported in almost all States and Alaska.

All above-ground parts of the rose may be affected by powdery mildew. The leaves and the young shoots are most seriously attacked.

The first symptoms are raised, blisterlike areas on the young leaves, which may become covered with a white, powdery, fungus growth. The powdery appearance of the lesions is due to spores of the fungus, which are produced in great abundance. Older leaves may be affected, usually with little distortion, but growing leaves become twisted and misshapen. Some discoloration of the leaves may occur with an early reddening and eventual yellowing. Dark spots somewhat resembling black spot may be produced as the cells are killed. Young growing tips are commonly completely covered by the mildew; the result is dwarfing and curling of leaves, stems, and buds. The tips of severely infected canes may be killed. Often infected buds do not open. Petals, sepals, and receptacles of the flower buds are subject to attack. The petals may become discolored and dwarfed and finally die.

Powdery mildew on roses is caused by the fungus *Sphaerotheca pannosa* var. *rosae*.

Some question exists as to whether the powdery mildew on peach (*S. pannosa* var. *persicae*) is the same as the one on the rose. The evidence we have indicates that they are different. Some workers have thought that the hop mildew, *S. humuli*, is to be found on roses in the United States, but more research is needed on that point. The conclusion is favored that there is but one powdery mildew fungus on roses, namely, *S. pannosa* var. *rosae*. It is probable that pathogenic races of the fungus on roses will be found.

The white patches on the leaves and stems are seen under the microscope to consist of a moldlike growth (mycelium), composed of slender, white threads, with numerous branches that form a network over the surface. Many upright branches bearing chains of egg-shaped summer spores (conidia) arise from this network of fungus threads. At many points these threads are attached to the surface of the host by means of minute specialized branches or feeding organs—the haustoria—formed in the outer cells. The fungus gets its food supply through the haustoria. The cells into which the haustoria are sent may be stimulated

at first but are killed sooner or later. The conidia are colorless and are about one-thousandth inch long. They are easily detached. Air currents carry them away. They are thin-walled and sensitive to environmental influences after they have been separated from the stalks on which they are borne. They serve to disseminate the fungus over short distances.

Like many fungi, powdery mildew has a spore stage that helps tide it over cold spells. Globose fruit bodies, at first brown, finally black, may appear near the end of the growing season. They can be seen with the unaided eye. They are more or less buried in the mycelial cushions on canes, thorns, and leaves. Although the winter fruit bodies, the perithecia, have been observed more frequently on stems, especially around thorns, than on the mildewed leaves, they do occur on leaves, particularly on the under sides close to the midrib, and on the petiole.

Within each perithecium may be found a small sac, or spore case, the ascus. Within each ascus may be found eight spores, the ascospores. These winter spores are about the size of the summer spores.

In greenhouses, sheltered locations, and areas with warm winters where there are living leaves on the plants the year around, the fungus may be able to hibernate in the summer stages (mycelium and conidia) on the canes and leaves. Mycelium and conidia exposed to freezing temperatures will be killed. Under such circumstances, the fungus may still overwinter in the leaf buds, where it is protected somewhat by the scales.

The hibernation of *Sphaerotheca pannosa* var. *rosae*, however, is left less to chance than it would be by the overwintering of persistent mycelium in the buds. As I mentioned, the fungus produces a winter spore stage that lives in the coldest climate. The spores (ascospores) are mature and ready for dissemination in the spring; thus they bridge the periods of low temperatures, which kill exposed mycelium and conidia. These perithecia are probably more generally prevalent than some reports would lead one to believe.

The perithecia absorb water and crack open in warm, moist weather. The single large ascus in each perithecium protrudes its tip and discharges the eight mature ascospores, which the wind carries away.

In the case of overwintering mycelium in the buds, the mildew is said to renew growth and rapidly cover the newly formed leaves when the rose resumes growth in the spring. Formation of stalks producing conidia follows, the spores being carried to other leaves by even slight air currents or splashing water. There is evidence that the conidia are actually shot away when mature. The conidia and the ascospores behave similarly with respect to germination and infection and lead to the formation of identical structures.

The spores germinate at once on reaching a new, favorable location on the leaf or stem. They germinate best in a relative humidity of 97 to 99 percent and at temperatures between 64° and 75° F. Free water is unnecessary for germination; submergence in water lessens germination. After being separated from the stalks on which they are borne, the conidia die quickly when exposed to adverse conditions, such as low relative humidities and high or low temperatures.

Under favorable conditions of temperature and humidity, the conidium puts out a germ tube quickly and thus penetrates the cuticle and epidermal cell of the rose leaf, resulting in the formation of a haustorium within the cell. The germ tube and its haustorium are formed within 24 hours. On completion of the haustorium, the apex of the germ tube resumes its growth. From the same conidium one to three secondary germ tubes may grow out directly into hyphae (mycelial threads), thus initiating the felty mass on the surface of the leaf or stem.

The haustorium serves as the food- and water-absorbing organ for the mycelium, which otherwise is entirely

on the surface. Many such haustoria are formed by the mycelium as it spreads over the leaf surface. Within 48 hours after germination of the conidium, young spore stalks are present. Soon a new crop of spores—conidia—is being produced on the stalks. The conidia fall off or are shot away.

With the coming of the cool weather of autumn, conidia production ceases, and perithecia may be formed. They carry the fungus through the winter, as does the mycelium formed within the buds, thus completing the life history.

Both temperature and relative humidity are important in influencing the initiation and development of powdery mildew, the humidity being more important than temperature. Maximum germination of spores takes place at about 70° F.; the most rapid germination occurs between 76° and 82°. One reason is that the higher temperature hastens the processes that lead to the death of the spores as well as those that cause germination. But with the proper relative humidity infection occurs rapidly around 80°, before the loss of viability becomes a serious factor. At 76°–82° spore production is speeded up and germination increased. The fungus has a short cycle, as short as 4 days. The disease may quickly become epiphytotic.

The spores of the fungus germinate best at high relative humidities, above 95 percent. But some germination will take place at a relative humidity as low as 25–30 percent. Mycelium development is much poorer at 20 percent relative humidity than at 97 percent. Far fewer spores are produced at low humidities, and the spores are shorter lived.

Statements are to be found that high nitrogen favors powdery mildew and high potassium discourages it. The use of wood ashes, a source of potassium, as a fertilizer is sometimes recommended. The evidence seems to warrant the conclusion that soft, succulent growth as produced by high nitrogen and low potassium is favorable to mildew. It is doubtful, however, whether any combination of fertilizing elements alone will enable the gardener to have plants free from mildew and at the same time have good roses.

Under conditions of temperature and moisture not especially favorable for powdery mildew, the disease is not particularly difficult to hold in check through the use of fungicides as dusts or sprays.

It can be eradicated from the plant through the use of fungicidal sprays that wet and kill the oily mycelial growth on leaves and stems. One can get advance protection by sprays and dusts applied before infection starts. But under conditions of favorable humidities and temperatures in the greenhouse or in the garden, and especially when the plants are making rapid, succulent growth, all fungicides and procedures seem to fail and the disease runs rampant.

Spraying and dusting with fungicides are the accepted ways to eradicate the fungus and to protect the plant against infection. It is important to start early to guard against the first infections and to make applications often enough to give season-long protection.

Because the mildew fungus occurs externally on the rose (except the haustoria which enter only the epidermal cells) it is possible to kill it by spraying with disinfectants. Fungicides used for it include lime-sulfur, potassium sulfide (liver of sulfur), wettable sulfur, oil emulsions, mineral and vegetable oils, sodium bicarbonate, bordeaux mixture, copper oxide, malachite green, and others. A newer fungicide, dinitro capryl phenyl crotonate, tested under the names of Arathane and Karathane and sold under the name of Iscothan, has given promising results at the rate of 1 level tablespoonful to 3 gallons of water, along with a suitable wetting agent. Often the wetting agent itself is reasonably toxic and somewhat effec-

tive. Dusts are less effective than sprays against the fungus.

The best garden practice is to protect the plants against infection. Fungicides that function both as eradicants and protectants have an advantage. The materials that are effective against black spot, rust, and other diseases and can be used in combination with insecticides save time and simplify the problem in plantings beset by other diseases and insect pests.

Sulfur is preferred to most of the other fungicides for powdery mildew and is generally used except when temperatures are high. Whenever the temperature gets into the 90's, and above, injury may be expected from any form of sulfur, spray or dust. The fixed coppers are probably less effective than bordeaux mixture. The salts of dithiocarbamic acid used as fungicides generally are not effective against powdery mildew. Malachite green causes discoloration of open blossoms. Sodium bicarbonate may be effective in mild infections, especially as an eradicant, but it probably would not be effective as a protectant against mildew and other fungi. The oils are not satisfactory as protectants and are not generally safe. The efficiency and safety of some of the newer fungicides such as Phygon and captan remain to be established.

Wettable sulfur should be used at the rate of about 1 pound in 25 gallons of water, or 2 level tablespoonfuls in a gallon. In using a proprietary material, the manufacturer's directions should be followed. To the suspended sulfur should be added, following dilution and just before spraying, enough wetter to assure that the spray wets the waxy surface of the leaf and also the oily patches of mildew, if the fungus is present. Detergents, such as Dreft, Orvus, Swerl, and Vel, or prepared wetters such as Vatsol, B-1956, Triton X-100, and Grasselli Spreader Sticker, may be used. A concentration of 1 part in 1,000 parts of water (for solids about one-third teaspoonful per gallon) is usually adequate. It is important to use ample pressure and a nozzle that breaks the spray into a fine mist.

In dusting with sulfur, a dust of at least 325-mesh fineness should be used. Ordinary sulfur is too coarse. Mixtures of sulfur and arsenate of lead, ferbam, and other materials are satisfactory as long as there is 50 percent or so of sulfur in the mixture. The dust applications must be started early in the season, before infection occurs, and continued at regular intervals.

NINE SPECIES OF THE RUST genus *Phragmidium* have been reported attacking members of the genus *Rosa*. Of these nine species, only one occurs on the cultivated roses, such as the hybrid teas and hybrid perpetuals, that have large, firm leaflets. This rust fungus is *Phragmidium mucronatum*, frequently called *P. disciflorum*. The disease it causes has been called common leaf rust to distinguish it from other rust diseases.

Only members of the genus *Rosa* are attacked. Some 20 or more species have been reported to be susceptible, although it is not clear that the persons making the reports were always dealing with rust due to *P. mucronatum*. One report lists the hybrid perpetuals as the most susceptible; the polyantha and tea roses as the most resistant; and the Bourbons, hybrid teas, and Noisette groups as intermediate in susceptibility. Most of the hybrid teas and climbing hybrid teas grown in California and elsewhere in the country probably are susceptible.

Common leaf rust of roses has been known at least since 1665, when it was identified in England. The fungus was described in 1790. The disease has been reported throughout Europe and in Western Asia, South Africa, North and South America, Hawaii, Ceylon, Australia, and New Zealand.

Common leaf rust is of economic importance only along the Pacific coast in the United States and in England and parts of Australia. It has been collected many times in the United States east of the Rocky Mountains, but so far it has not flourished except along the west coast, especially in California, where it may be severe in nurseries and gardens.

As the range of the disease in epidemic severity is limited and as the fungus is shipped into Eastern States on plants from nurseries on the west coast, attention has been given to factors that determine its occurrence and severity. Like black spot and mildew of roses, common leaf rust is a good example of the manner in which temperature and moisture determine the range and importance of a disease.

The common leaf rust of cultivated roses is most conspicuous in its summer stage. It is characterized by the formation of reddish-orange pustules on the under sides of the leaves. The pustules, or sori, consist of a powdery mass of spores—the uredospores, or summer spores, of the fungus. The pustules average about one-fiftieth inch in diameter. Viewed from above, the lesions appear as angular dead spots in the tissue, up to one-sixth inch in length, and surrounded by a narrow zone of pale-green or reddish color. The summer stage reproduces itself every 10 to 14 days during the summer if conditions are favorable. It is the stage that causes serious damage. Infected leaves may wilt as early as the fifth day after the appearance of the orange spots and soon fall from the plant.

But there are two other stages of common leaf rust—the aecial, or caeoma, stage, which appears in the spring and the black, or telial, stage, which appears in the autumn. In the spring stage, affected leaves bear one to many circular spots about one twenty-fifth inch in diameter. The spots are bright orange or yellow. The spots may be surrounded by a narrow zone of pale green. The bright-orange color is due to the formation of masses of spores. Affected leaves are malformed by the lesions protruding downward to form cuplike depressions.

The "black rust," or telial, stage appears in the autumn. Large-stalked, black spores are formed in the uredo sori with the reddish-orange summer spores, which they gradually replace, to the end that these pustules change to a black color. The black spores live over the winter and initiate a new cycle the next spring.

Common leaf rust on roses growing in areas with cold winters have those three stages. In a milder climate the reddish-orange stage is dominant and may occur throughout the year. Under such circumstances the spring and autumn stages are less important.

All four spore forms of the causal fungus, *Phragmidium mucronatum*, are borne on the rose. The fungus is confused in European reports with *P. subcorticium*. Before 1905 the two species were apparently considered as one. Probably physiological races exist within *P. mucronatum*.

In areas with winter temperatures low enough to defoliate roses and force them into dormancy, as in our Northeastern States, the fungus passes the winter as black teliospores in the sori in the leaves. When these thick-walled, black spores germinate in the spring they produce another type of spore (sporidia), which infects the newly developing leaves and stems to initiate the aecial stage of the rust.

The aeciospores in turn germinate and give rise to the summer spore (uredospores) stage—the reddish-orange sori so conspicuous on the under sides of the leaves. The uredospores germinate, infect leaves, and produce additional spots within 10 to 14 days. Finally the resistant black winter spore stage replaces the orange-colored summer spore stage and thus completes the cycle.

The relation of temperature and moisture to the occurrence and prevalence of the common leaf rust of the rose has been studied in some detail. The information thus obtained has supplied data to enable the plant pathologist to explain the prevalence and severity of the disease in California and its isolated occurrence east of the Rocky Mountains. Correlations between temperatures and humidities, determined under controlled conditions, and the weather records at Ithaca, N. Y., and San Diego, Calif., made the explanation possible.

Spore germination and infection in the summer stage (uredospore) are favored by temperatures of 64° to 70° F. At 75° both are noticeably lower. At 81° practically no infection occurs under otherwise favorable conditions. High temperatures are also unfavorable for the survival of the uredospores. At a medium humidity such spores remain living for about a year at 37°, about 7 weeks at 64°, and about 1 week at 81°.

Leaf infection will not occur unless the surface of the leaf is wet for at least 4 hours and a favorable temperature prevails. Even at very high relative humidity a leaf will not become infected unless it is actually wet. Dry weather, therefore, prevents the spread of the disease, while rain, dew, or fog aid in the further spread.

At Ithaca and in the Northeast generally, the common leaf rust has been comparatively unimportant because of unfavorable temperatures. The long, cold winter kills the summer spores, so that any new spring infections must come from the spores of the black rust stage. Assuming that a few infections were to get started in the spring, perhaps from introduced plants bearing rust, the generally high summer temperatures would prevent extensive spread of the rust. The weather would be favorable for a few weeks in the autumn, but that period is ended soon by the coming of winter and the defoliation of the rose plant.

The temperature in southern California is uniformly favorable for the rust. From October through April, rainfall also is adequate to allow for the spread of the disease; moisture from fog or dew supplements rainfall in the drier periods. Defoliation may be incomplete or not last long, so that the fungus may live through the year in the summer spore stage and cause infection when active growth starts again. One of the worst years in recent times for rust in southern California was the fall-to-spring season of 1940–1941, when twice the normal amount of rain fell and the winter was so mild that defoliation was not complete.

Roses in the Southeast do not suffer seriously from rust. Summer temperatures there are even higher than in western New York; the long hot period may be the reason that the rust is not prevalent.

Roses with common leaf rust are known to occur in a few gardens in Midwestern and Northeastern States. Some of those plants have had the disease for several years. While injury is serious, the rust is less damaging than it is in California. Apparently the rust was brought into those gardens on plants from California. There is always a chance of a new strain of rust arising through hybridizing, or as a sport, that will have different potentialities with respect to survival under conditions of temperature and humidity in the Midwest or Northeast. Consequently the occurrence and prevalence of common leaf rust east of the Rocky Mountains are watched with interest.

A combination of clean culture and a good fungicide will hold common leaf rust in check. Care should be exercised not to bring diseased plants into the garden even in districts where the disease is not known to be important because it may become established.

Diseased leaves should be removed and burned as they appear. The garden should be given a complete cleanup in midwinter or when the plants are dormant and are being pruned. If feasible, the old leaves clinging to the stems should be removed and burned.

Spraying or dusting for protection should begin with the development of new leaves following the winter cleanup or dormancy. One should begin spraying or dusting before the periods of wet foliage, because it is during those periods that infection occurs. Thus the timing of applications depends on the frequency of rains or periods when the foliage is wet. A special effort should be made to cover the under sides of the leaves—where infections occur—with the fungicide.

Sulfur-containing fungicides are preferred to those containing copper. A mixture of sulfur and ferbam either as spray or dust is good. The concentrations given for black spot are satisfactory for rust. Thoroughness and sharp timing are of utmost importance.

BROWN CANKER OF ROSES, of the several diseases of garden roses characterized primarily by injury to the canes, is probably the most destructive in the United States. In many home plantings and nurseries the disease persists despite efforts to eradicate it.

Brown canker is restricted to members of the genus *Rosa*. It seems doubtful that any class, variety, or species is immune, although rugosa, moss, and brier roses may have some resistance. Certainly the teas, hybrid teas, and hybrid perpetuals are susceptible.

Brown canker has been known in the United States for 50 years. Its present range includes most of the United States, from Maine to California, and England. It may cause serious losses.

All parts of the plant above ground may be attacked. Greatest damage is done by the cankers on the stems. A cane lesion or canker is typically a dead area in the wood surrounded by a reddish-purple border, which gives it a striking appearance. The color of the dead area is raw umber. Over the surface of the canker can be seen tiny black dots, the fruiting structures of the fungus. The stem often is girdled by the advance of the fungus, and the part above it is killed. That type of injury is frequently called dieback.

Leaf spots due to the fungus that causes brown canker are not always distinguished readily from those caused by other pathogenic organisms. The spots are usually purple at first and later have white or cinnamon-buff central regions. Black pycnidia may be found in the centers. Leaf spots are prevalent on certain species and varieties, such as *R. setigera*, *R. multiflora*, Blaze, and others. Lesions on petioles and stipules are similar to those on the leaf blades.

Lesions on the petals are discolored areas, often cinnamon buff in color, and usually bear the black, dotlike fruiting structures of the fungus. The fruiting bodies—pycnidia—are frequently in concentric circles. The infected blossoms may fail to open. The hips also may be affected and may bear the pycnidia.

Brown canker of rose is caused by the fungus *Cryptosporella umbrina*.

The fungus overwinters in the cankers on stems and perhaps in lesions on the leaves and other parts. As with the pathogens that cause black spot and mildew, there are two spore forms, sexual and asexual. The mycelium, having lived through the winter, renews growth with the warmer weather of spring, extends the area affected, and produces spores. The asexual, or imperfect, form, is produced in brown or black pycnidia and is called pycnidiospores. The sexual, or perfect, stage, is produced in little sacs (asci), which in turn are borne in fruit bodies called perithecia.

To what degree pycnidiospores live through the winter is not known; the point may not be important, because with favorable weather a new crop can be produced by the mycelium within a few days. The occurrence of perithecia bearing asci and ascospores is not uncommon and would be expected to carry the fungus over winter. Both fruiting forms, pycnidia and perithecia, have been found during each season.

The pycnidia and the perithecia usually soon rupture the epidermis, and the spores are exposed. Spore masses, or tendrils of spores, exuding from the mouths or pores of the fruit bodies, are often visible. Both pycnidiospores and ascospores are liberated in water and are largely spread by splashing, dripping, and wind-blown rain. The ascospores are probably shot from the asci; if so, they would be disseminated by wind.

Infection occurs from both pycnidiospores and ascospores. The resulting lesions are evident in 4 to 15 days. Spores, both pycnidiospores and ascospores, may be produced within a few days after the lesions are visible. They initiate additional infections, which may occur through wounds or directly through the uninjured epidermis.

Infections on the current season's canes result in many instances in shallow white lesions, in some of which the fungus passes the winter and renews growth in the spring to extend the boundaries of the cankers. Some of the tiny white cankers fail to enlarge the following spring; others may remain inactive for another year or two and then become active. Just what determines whether such a lesion is to become active, and when, is not yet known.

Temperature and moisture relations of the brown canker fungus have not received much critical attention. Observations on the fungus outside in early spring and in cultures in the laboratory would indicate that it is active at relatively low temperatures. The pycnidiospores survived for 4 months at 62° F. in a dried culture in the laboratory. Water is necessary for the production, dissemination, and germination of the spores.

The occurrence of brown canker in epidemic severity usually has been associated with injury to the canes. Injuries made by the careless use of the pruning shears or other tools may serve as infection points. When the disease was noted in test gardens of the Department of Agriculture in April 1927, the records indicated that the unusually severe hailstorm of the previous July had been an important factor. The cankers were predominantly located about the wounds produced by the hailstones. Brown canker flourished in gardens in California following the severe winter of 1932–33, when cold weather injured varieties such as the softwooded Golden Emblem, Ville de Paris, Los Angeles, Angèle Pernet, Souvenir de Claudius Pernet, and others. Reports from Georgia and other places where extremes of temperature and late spring frosts prevail indicate that injuries from freezing may increase the amount of brown canker.

The overwintering of the fungus in cankers on such roses as *R. setigera* and *R. multiflora* that may be growing in nearby hedges or plantings somewhat removed from the rose garden is often an item of importance. Such roses seem to thrive despite the disease and they usually get little attention. The mycelium in the cankers on such hedge plants may be a source of spores for the more formal planting in the garden and make eradication of the disease more difficult.

A control program for brown canker may also help combat the more prevalent but less injurious stem canker caused by *Coniothyrium fuckelli* and perhaps also brand canker caused by *C. wernsdorffiae*.

Such a program should include the following: Normally vigorous plants maintained so by attention to drainage, exposure, winter protection, and fertilization; prompt removal and destruction of all dead, dying, and weak parts of plants; systematic spraying and dusting for disease and insect control; care to avoid injury to stems, even small breaks in the epidermis; care in pruning and blossom cutting to avoid leaving stubs, crushing stems, or doing any more damage to the plant than is absolutely necessary; and careful scrutiny of any large, old plants (such as those of *R. setigera* and *R. multiflora*), which are back in the shrubbery and may be neglected.

Since wounds serve as infection courts for the canker fungi, it is desirable to handle the plants so as to prevent breaks in the epidermis. Wounds on the rose do not heal quickly. The maintenance of the plants in a vigorous condition may help in the formation of callus. Wounds heal more readily during the early growing sea-

son, so there is probably advantage in pruning just before, or just after, growth starts. Care, a pair of sharp shears, and clean cuts immediately above strong eyes will enable one to avoid leaving stubs that so frequently serve as infection courts.

Heavy pruning probably is to be preferred to light pruning insofar as brown canker is concerned. That practice will eliminate many of the initial cankers. Frequent inspection, with the prompt removal and destruction of all ailing plants and plant parts, is advisable if one has a canker problem. A single overlooked canker may supply the spores for general infection through the entire garden.

Regular spraying or dusting, as for black spot or rust control, will assist in canker control in that it will prevent many of the new infections that would otherwise occur. With proper conditions of temperature and moisture, infection can take place directly through uninjured tissue and it is such infection in particular that a fungicide will prevent. But spraying and dusting must be part of a program in which general vigilance and skillful handling are combined with practices making for a clean garden and vigorous growth.

Both copper- and sulfur-containing fungicides are effective in preventing infections by the fungus of brown canker. Maybe the new fungicides effective against black spot will also serve for brown canker. Either spraying or dusting will give protection. Application should begin in the early spring as soon as new growth starts and should be made often enough to provide protection throughout rainy periods and to keep the new growth covered. On the average, an application once a week will be needed from early spring until the plants are dormant.

Frequently the fungus is brought into the garden on infected plants from the nursery. That emphasizes the importance of patronizing reliable nurserymen and of giving new plants

a careful examination to be sure they
are free from blemishes and infection
before being accepted. Particular attention should be given to incipient
cankers at the cut made just above the
main bud in removing the top of the
stock that constitutes the root. Many
first-year failures result from infection
at this point.

L. M. MASSEY *is professor of plant
pathology, New York State College of
Agriculture, Cornell University. He went
to Cornell as a graduate student assistant
in plant pathology in 1912 and was granted
the doctor's degree in 1916. He served as
head of the department of plant pathology
at Cornell from 1922 to 1950. He has
worked with rose diseases since 1917. Dr.
Massey was president of the American Rose
Society in 1940 and 1941 and was awarded
the Society's Gold Medal in 1947 for in-
valuable research on rose diseases and distinguished service to the Society.*

*In preparing his discussion, Dr. Massey drew on
published articles of other authors, as well as those
of his own that have appeared largely in the publications of the American Rose Society, Harrisburg,
Pa. Among them are:*
Anna E. Jenkins: Brown Canker of Roses
Caused by Diaporthe umbrina, *Journal of
Agricultural Research, volume 15, pages 593–599,
1918;* Brown Canker of the Rose, *American
Rose Annual, 1927, pages 161–183;* Development
of Brown Canker of Roses, *Journal of Agricultural Research, volume 42, pages 293–299, 1931.*
Vincent W. Cochrane: The Common Leaf
Rust of Cultivated Roses, caused by Phrag-
midium mucronatum (Fr.) Schlecht, *Cornell
University Agricultural Experiment Station Mem-
oir 268, 39 pages, 1945.*
Karla Longree: The Effect of Temperature
and Relative Humidity on the Powdery Mildew of Roses, *Cornell University Agricultural
Experiment Station Bulletin 223, 43 pages, 1939.*
E. W. Lyle: The Blackspot Disease of Roses,
and Its Control Under Greenhouse Conditions, *Cornell University Agricultural Experiment
Station Bulletin 690, 31 pages, 1938.*
W. D. McClellan: Control of Powdery Mildew of Roses in the Greenhouse, *Cornell University Agricultural Experiment Station Bulletin
785, 39 pages, 1942.*

---

*The attention of the reader is directed to
the section of color pictures, in which rose
black spot and some diseases of other ornamentals are illustrated.*

Viruses
on Roses

Philip Brierley

The rose is a leading crop in commercial floriculture. Firms that produce roses under glass usually are
specialists, for those roses require well
lighted and ventilated greenhouses and
higher growing temperatures than
many other flower crops.

Some producers propagate roses by
cuttings, but most greenhouse roses are
grafted or budded on Manetti, a
special understock variety (*Rosa noiset-
tiana* var. *manetti*) that is grown and
propagated chiefly in the Pacific Coast
States and Texas. Manetti stock for
grafting is shipped from nurseries in
Oregon, Washington, the Netherlands,
England, and France to the producers
who do their own grafting in the greenhouse with scions from their own flowering varieties. Nurserymen also bud
Manetti in the field, inserting buds of
varieties from a greenhouse or from
their own field-grown roses.

Buds that are set early in the season
may be forced into growth the same
year by removing the top of the understock. Such plants are marketed in the
fall as started buds. Buds set later in
the season are not forced into growth,
but on removal of the top of the understock at maturity in the fall may be
sold as dormant buds.

The greenhouse producer replaces
some of his flowering plants each year,
generally using his selection of greenhouse varieties budded or grafted on
Manetti. Hybrid tea roses dominate
the greenhouse business, but a few

hybrid perpetuals, ramblers, and baby ramblers, also purchased as budded plants, are grown in pots for Easter and for Mother's Day.

The nurseryman thus has an important role in supplying rose plants for greenhouse production.

Perhaps equally important is his production of roses for garden planting—primarily hybrid teas but also hybrid perpetuals, climbers of the rambler and large-flowered classes, singles, and species roses. Nurseries in New York, Pennsylvania, New Jersey, Texas, California, and other States propagate roses for garden planting. The common understock used for outdoor roses is *Rosa multiflora* and its varieties, but Ragged Robin (Gloire des Rosomanes) is preferred in California. A few types of roses are grown on their own roots. Budded rose plants for the garden are marketed only after one or two seasons of growth in the nursery.

Many diseases afflict roses, both under glass and in the garden. The worst ones are of fungus or bacterial origin. No virus disease of major importance has yet appeared on roses in this country.

Viruses diseases of the mosaic class and rose streak are present here. Rose mosaic was believed to be serious when it was first recognized in the late 1920's. Rose wilt occurs in Australia, and it or a similar one has been reported in Italy. Because reports from Australia and Italy indicate that the virus disease is much more damaging than the ones we already have in this country, roses may not be imported from Australia and Italy to the United States.

ROSE MOSAIC is characterized by yellowish areas in the rose leaflet, usually next to the midrib and feathering away from it. Growth is retarded in the chlorotic—yellowish—patches, and some distortion of the leaflet results. In varieties like Ophelia, Mme. Butterfly, Radiance, Rapture, and Templar, both chlorosis and distortion are conspicuous, and the disease is eas-

ily recognized, although not every leaf shows symptoms. In Better Times, Briarcliff, Columbia, Talisman, and others, the mosaic symptoms are similar but milder and more easily overlooked. In *Rosa odorata*, formerly used to some extent as a greenhouse understock, symptoms are also mild. In Manetti they are mild and erratic.

A second symptom is water marking, an intricate pattern of fine grayish lines in leaf surfaces with little or no distortion. Water marking is the typical expression in Blaze, Conrad Ferdinand Meyer, Duchess of Wellington, Joanna Hill, Kaiserin Auguste Viktoria, Paul's Scarlet Climber, *R. hugonis*, *R. wichuraiana*, Souvenir de Claudius Pernet, Ulrich Brunner, and others. Ring patterns of fine grayish lines also occur.

Roses affected with mosaic are less vigorous than normal plants and production is lower. The degree of inferiority varies with the intensity of the symptoms. In some greenhouse varieties, among them Better Times and Peters' Briarcliff, production seems to be only slightly inferior, and plants with mosaic frequently pass unnoticed.

Soon after rose mosaic was first recognized, observers agreed that no natural spread occurred in greenhouses. Its appearance in new varieties of recent seed origin and the occasional appearance of high percentages of mosaic in nurseries, suggested, however, that natural spread was taking place in the field.

Floyd F. Smith and I made test plantings of healthy roses in Oregon, New York, Virginia, and Maryland, but we failed to detect any natural spread of rose mosaic. No mosaic resulted from 229 transmission tests made by Smith with insects commonly found on roses in Eastern States. The insects in the tests included 42 species in the families Cicadellidae, Cercopidae, Membracidae, Araeopidae, Fulgoridae, Aphiidae, and Coccidae and in the order Homoptera, and one species of thrips (order Thysanoptera). In further experiments, roses were not infected with strawberry crinkle by the strawberry aphid, nor with red raspberry mosaic by the raspberry aphid, nor with aster yellows by the six-spotted leafhopper.

Various methods of grafting and budding serve to transmit rose mosaic, the symptoms appearing 20 to 49 days or longer after such inoculation. No transmission takes place if the bud is removed before tissue union is effected. No evidence of seed transmission was found. We failed to transmit the rose mosaic virus from rose to rose by mechanical means.

Robert W. Fulton at the Wisconsin Agricultural Experiment Station in 1952 transmitted rose mosaic virus by mechanical inoculation from rose to cucumber and cowpea. From cowpea he transmitted it to 25 other plant species in 7 plant families. The virus proved unstable and was extremely difficult to inoculate into rose even from the most favorable source, cowpea.

Floyd Smith and I concluded that simulated natural spread of rose mosaic resulted from the nursery practice of taking cuttings from the tops of the understock of field-budded plants after such tops had been removed to force the inserted buds. By this practice mosaic could be introduced in either understock or budwood and transmitted to additional understocks and top varieties in succeeding years. When new rose varieties were supplied as budwood, the disease appeared in these new sorts and suggested natural spread of mosaic. The weak and erratic expression of mosaic symptoms in Manetti permitted this process to go on undetected, so that natural spread of the disease was inferred. Although the origin of rose mosaic is unknown, such nursery practices very likely account for the distribution of the disease in this country.

A NUMBER OF VARIANTS or distinct mosaic diseases of rose have been reported. They differ from the typical rose mosaic in developing patterns of a brighter yellow, or more severe leaf distortions, or some other characteristic symptom.

Transmission of a chlorotic disorder by grafting from rose to rose was reported by M. Vibert in France as early as 1863. A. Christoff in Bulgaria found a virus of *Rosa gallica* transmissible by grafting to apple and pear and a virus of apple transmissible to *Rosa gallica* and to pear. I. Kovatchevsky also reported a rose virus disease in Bulgaria. C. Blattny found a vein mosaic of *Rosa canina* in Czechoslovakia.

H. Earl Thomas and L. M. Massey found two mosaic diseases of rose in California that differed sufficiently from the typical rose mosaic to be designated as rose mosaics 2 and 3. They also infected rose with the virus of apple mosaic and with another from peach affected with the disease now known as yellow bud mosaic. The diseases were shown to be distinct from each other by distinctive responses in suitable rose test varieties. Their rose mosaic 3 proved infectious to apple.

L. C. Cochran found two roses in California naturally infected with the virus of peach ring spot.

Floyd Smith and I collected five yellow mosaics of rose that differed from the typical mosaic in having brighter and lighter yellow areas. Each of the collections was from a single affected rose—one from a greenhouse and the other four from garden varieties. Comparison of the five collections in five test varieties of roses showed that no two were identical in expression of symptoms, but we tentatively accepted them as strain variants of rose mosaic.

M. Kramer studied rose mosaics in Brazil and assigned one of his collections to rose mosaic 3 of Thomas and Massey and another to our rose yellow mosaic. I. Klášterský in 1949 reported from Czechoslovakia a morphogenic virosis of *Rosa lucida*, *R. rugosa*, and the moss rose Gloire de

Mousseuses. It had abnormal cornet-shaped leaves. Manual inoculation with crushed leaves reproduced those symptoms in *Rosa arvensis* and *R. moyesi*. Klásterský's reports in 1949 and 1951 indicate that the morphogenic virosis generally causes little injury to roses.

I cannot form even a tentative conclusion as to how many rose virus diseases are involved in the several reports I have mentioned. The several workers have made use of different varieties or species of roses as test plants, so that even the reported symptoms cannot be compared. The facts that some (but not all) rose viruses are infectious to apple and pear and that roses can be infected by viruses from apple and from peach show that a number of separate entities are involved. Further study of the interrelationship of the viruses of rosaceous plants is clearly needed. It is a fortunate fact that all the rose viruses known in North America can be transmitted from rose to rose by tissue union only—that is, by budding or grafting, and not by manual methods nor (as far as we know) by insects. In this important respect they are similar to the typical rose mosaic, and should be subject to control by measures effective against the type disease.

Symptoms suggestive of virus disease but never proved to be of virus origin are common in garden roses and particularly in understock varieties. Manetti canes sometimes bear zones of severely dwarfed and crinkled leaves, alternating with zones of nearly normal leaves, a condition called rattlesnake by western nurserymen. Similar zoning appears in the less commonly grown *Rosa odorata*.

The rattlesnake symptoms are far more conspicuous than rose mosaic symptoms in those understocks. Smith and I were unable to get evidence that a virus is involved, for affected Manetti induced no symptoms in hybrid tea roses when grafted or budded into them, and we found no Manetti that did not sometimes develop the rattlesnake symptoms spontaneously. The nature of this abnormality remains unknown, but it is certain that confusion of rattlesnake symptoms with rose mosaic led to high estimates of mosaic prevalence in early surveys. Similarly, some early claims that rose mosaic had lethal effects now appear to have been based on confusion of rose mosaic with the effects of immaturity of the Manetti understock. Such immaturity is now avoided by use of a starch test, which shows when the understock is ripe enough for digging and shipping.

ROSE STREAK was common in the 1930's in the rose species and varieties assembled at Glenn Dale, Md., and Arlington Farm in Virginia by Walter Van Fleet and others in the Department of Agriculture. It was later found in a few plants in a garden in the District of Columbia, in one plant in the New York Botanical Garden, and in a few plants in one district of Texas. Reports of its occurrence elsewhere have not been confirmed; the disease evidently has been confused with cane canker and possibly also with verticillium wilt.

No such disease of roses is known in other countries, but the limited distribution we know of suggests that the streak disease was imported in one or more of the many rose species and varieties assembled from all over the Northern Hemisphere for breeding purposes. Since streak was not recognized as a disease by the plant breeders, it was evidently propagated by budding or grafting and probably sent to a few other areas in named varieties or in understock roses. The disease is now static because it has no natural means of spread in this country and affected plants are seldom propagated.

Some 60 varieties of rose have been found affected with streak. Among them are teas, hybrid teas, hybrid perpetuals, hybrid multifloras, hybrid wichuraianas, hybrid rugosas, hybrid Bengals, Noisettes, Chinas, polyanthas, and the understocks Manetti and multiflora.

Symptoms vary greatly in different types of roses. Most distinctive patterns are brownish rings and brown vein banding in fully expanded leaves, accompanied by brownish or greenish rings in canes, as shown by *Rosa odorata*, Silver Moon, and other roses. Green vein banding patterns persist in old leaves that have otherwise lost their green color and are later prematurely abscised. A yellowish-green vein banding appears in the leaves of some hybrid multifloras, usually accompanied by greenish or brownish rings in the canes. The characteristic symptoms in these systemically infected outdoor roses are expressed in leaves and canes as they approach maturity in the fall. No distinctive effects of streak are recognizable in young leaves or young canes of such plants.

Some hybrid tea roses—Briarcliff, Mme. Butterfly, Ophelia, Radiance— have not been found affected in nature. When such a variety is experimentally infected with streak by budding, a black, dead lesion develops in the bark next to the inserted bud. It soon girdles the cane and kills the bud and all parts distal to it. The virus usually remains localized in the black lesion about the inserted bud, but a secondary lesion of similar appearance may appear in an adjacent rapidly growing shoot. Such lesions are construed as local infections in canes. That symptom has been confused with cane canker and other fungus diseases. The black lesions resemble fungus cankers. They can be eliminated by pruning. The uninvaded parts of the same bush remain free of virus. The streak virus has never been successfully subtransferred from hybrid teas that express this local necrotic reaction. Buds taken from the discolored areas die without uniting with a test variety; buds from adjacent normal tissues unite but carry no virus.

The rose streak virus was not found to be transmissible mechanically. No evidence of transmission by seed was found. An intensive search for insect vectors failed to reveal any insect capable of transmitting the virus. Transmission by budding is uniformly successful if the bud is from a systemically infected rose and if union is accomplished.

Symptoms appear after 18 to 40 days or occasionally longer. As with the rose mosaic virus, transmission fails if the streak-affected bud fails to unite or if it is removed before union has taken place. The rose streak virus invades roots as well as canes and can be recovered from roots by inserting a sliver of root in the cane of a suitable test rose just as a bud would be inserted. When roots are inoculated with the virus, the upward movement of the virus into the canes of the inoculated plant may be delayed 2 years or more. Hybrid teas like Briarcliff or Mme. Butterfly develop the typical local lesions of streak even when previously infected systemically with rose mosaic. That affords some evidence that the viruses of rose mosaic and rose streak are not closely related.

ROSE WILT was first recognized in Australia in 1908. B. J. Grieve began to study it at the University of Melbourne in 1929. The appearance of the disease at first suggested a bacterial disorder, and rose wilt was tentatively attributed to bacteria until Grieve established it as a virosis. It is known in Victoria, New South Wales, South Australia, Tasmania, and in New Zealand. A similar disease occurs in Italy.

Rose wilt is extremely serious in some seasons, but may lapse into milder form for a few years, only to reappear with original virulence. Pernetiana roses, as Golden Emblem and Ville de Paris, seem most susceptible. Hybrid teas are somewhat less susceptible, but rose wilt has appeared in severe form in several, among them Dame Edith Helen, Sunburst, Mme. Abel Chatenay, Columbia, and Etoile de Hollande. Tea roses are relatively resistant; Grieve had not seen definite examples in this class when he wrote about the disease in 1942. No plants other than roses are known to be susceptible to rose wilt.

The first symptoms of rose wilt are downward curling and brittleness of young leaves. Defoliation of young shoots then proceeds from the tip downward. About a day later the young shoot tips become discolored and begin to die back 1 to 2 inches. The rest of the cane then takes on a yellowish-green appearance before it turns brownish black. Leaf buds often remain green after nearby tissues are darkened. Later the whole stem may die back to older wood. The leaf buds at that stage also turn brown and rot away. Apparent recovery may follow: The plants grow normally for a season or two, but eventually the symptoms reappear.

Grieve found gummy deposits in and around the vessels of young affected stems, and necrosis of cortex, medullary rays, and phloem. Later there was swelling of cell walls, with distortion and collapse of phloem elements and the formation of intercellular spaces. In older leaves that persisted on the canes, circular or irregular red-brown lesions sometimes appeared. Parenchyma cells near such necrotic areas were depleted of starch and yellowed and contained gumlike deposits. Spherical or oval intracellular inclusions were present in palisade cells near the areas of necrosis and gum formation.

Unlike the rose viruses known in North America, that of rose wilt is mechanically transmissible from rose to rose. Extracted sap is infectious even after passing a Seitz filter. Transmission by budding succeeded if the bud lived, but many diseased buds died without uniting. Symptoms appeared 10 to 20 days after plants were inoculated. R. Gigante in Italy found the Italian rose virus was transmitted by mechanical inoculation, and four of seven roses exposed to aphids of the genus *Macrosiphum*

became infected. Grieve recorded a single transmission of the rose wilt virus by rose aphids, but he did not claim significance for the single infection. Although no direct comparison of Gigante's rose disease with rose wilt has been made, Grieve has expressed the opinion that the two viruses are the same.

No cure is known for any virus disease of roses. Workers in British Columbia, California, and Indiana attempted to cure roses affected with mosaic diseases with heat treatments, but the viruses were not inactivated at any temperature that rose tissues endured.

Control therefore must rest on choosing only healthy roses for propagation. That would seem to be the effective way, for none of the rose viruses present in this country is known to be transmitted by any means other than by propagation practices. It is hard to select healthy roses, however, because the virus symptoms are often poorly defined, or erratically expressed, or obscured by other diseases or by weather or insect damage. The problem is doubly difficult because most flowering roses are propagated on understocks; unless both understock and scion variety are free of disease, the program is a failure. The flowering roses that supply budwood or scions generally are more easily diagnosed than the understocks. Symptoms are expressed more clearly in greenhouses and there are fewer obscuring factors under glass. There is an advantage, therefore, in choosing budwood and scions from roses grown under favorable greenhouse conditions. Even then it is advisable to mark diseased plants plainly whenever they are detected, lest symptoms be masked or overlooked when budwood is chosen.

Understock roses generally express ill-defined virus symptoms. Grown in the field, they are exposed to many diseases and injuries that obscure the signs of virus. Thus selection of virus-

free understocks by direct inspection
seldom is practicable. Some nurserymen propagate *Rosa multiflora* by seeds,
thus ensuring virus-free understocks,
for the rose viruses are not seed-borne.
But, the Welch variety of *R. multiflora*,
which is prized in Texas for thornless-
ness and for resistance to black spot,
and Manetti, which sets no seed, must
be propagated vegetatively. Floyd
Smith and I suggested indexing such
vegetatively propagated understocks
by budding them into good test varieties, preferably under favorable conditions in greenhouses. The hybrid tea
roses Ophelia, Mme. Butterfly, Rapture, and Radiance express mosaic,
yellow mosaics, and streak. Understock plants that proved virus-free on
such indexing could then be lined out
as a foundation block to supply cuttings for commercial propagation.
Virus-free understocks would afford an
important advantage in that a virus
introduced into the nursery in a diseased bud variety would remain confined to that variety. The mechanism
for contaminating additional varieties
would be lacking.

THE NURSERY practice of utilizing
the tops of field-budded Manetti as a
source of cuttings for the following
season persists even though it affords
little opportunity for detecting rose
viruses and it provides a means of
transmitting them to other plants.
Economic considerations favor this
practice. The tops are a crop byproduct, available in good condition to
supply cuttings at a time when cuttings are in demand. Such cuttings are
available without extra cost.

PHILIP BRIERLEY *is a senior pathologist
in the Bureau of Plant Industry, Soils, and
Agricultural Engineering. He is a native of
New Hampshire and was trained in plant
pathology at the University of Minnesota
and Cornell University. Dr. Brierley has
been with the Department of Agriculture
since 1922 and has studied diseases of Irish
potatoes, onions, and various ornamental
plants.*

Aster Yellows

L. O. Kunkel

Aster yellows is a disease you see
almost everywhere. It causes conspicuous symptoms and affects many different kinds of plants.

It occurs on buckwheat, red clover,
tomato, carrot, lettuce, onion, parsnip,
salsify, and spinach; on such common
weeds as daisy fleabane, dandelion,
horseweed, plantain, ragweed, and
wild lettuce in grasslands, forests, and
waste places; and on such popular
flowers as calendula, Centaurea, China
aster, chrysanthemum, Clarkia, cocks-
comb, coreopsis, cosmos, gaillardia,
marigold, nemesia, petunia, phlox,
Scabiosa, snapdragon, Statice, straw-
flower, and Veronica in gardens—even
penthouse gardens—throughout the
country.

It is exhibited, unintentionally, at
the great flower shows. Not infrequently the Paris daisy that wins first place
in a flower show has aster yellows in
one or more of its branches.

Aster yellows was the first virus disease shown to infect a large number of
species in many different families of
plants. By 1931 I had taken the disease experimentally to 184 species
belonging in 38 families, all of which
were Dicotyledones. Aster yellows
since then has been found to infect
about 300 different species belonging
in 48 families, three of them Mono-
cotyledones and 45 Dicotyledones.
The known host range extends from
the onion, a representative of the
Liliaceae, to the China aster, a repre-

sentative of the Compositae, and thus spans most of the evolutionary range of the seed plants.

SYMPTOMS OF ASTER YELLOWS vary greatly in plants of different ages growing at different rates, in different species, and under different conditions. The chief effects, more or less general in many host species, are stunting, production of numerous slender secondary shoots, chlorosis in foliage, virescence in flowers, sterility, and an upright habit of growth. In the twining plant *Thunbergia alata* the disease destroys the plant's ability to climb.

The earliest symptom in young China aster plants and in plants of many susceptible species is a clearing of veins in immature leaves—usually on one side of one or two leaves. Leaves produced during chronic stages are more or less chlorotic throughout. They are dwarfed and somewhat narrower than comparable leaves on healthy plants. Also, they are sometimes deformed as a result of unequal growth in the two halves. They tend to take an upright position instead of laying down as do leaves of healthy plants. Old leaves may develop a slightly reddish, brownish, or purplish tinge in the late stages. The main stems usually have shortened internodes. Secondary shoots produce an abnormally large number of side branches that are slender and yellowish.

Aster plants affected while young produce no flowers. Plants affected after they have reached an advanced stage of development produce stunted, malformed flowers. Flowers affected after they have started to mature produce seeds of normal size or seeds that are either smaller of larger than normal size. All such seeds are sterile, but seeds from unaffected flowers in the same heads may be normal. Aster yellows virus is not known to be passed in the seeds of any plant.

One of the most striking effects on diseased flowers is phyllody. Stamens and ovules may develop into leafy structures. Buds often are produced in the stigmas of flowers. They give rise to secondary flowers, which in turn may give rise to tertiary flowers by the same process. In that way flower chains are produced. The chains usually consist of only two or three flowers, but occasionally they may be composed of as many as six flowers each. The flower chains frequently tend to turn green.

Aster yellows can be identified by symptoms only if it can be observed in several different kinds of plants. The disease cannot be identified by symptoms alone in any one species, for there are many other diseases of the yellows type that cause like symptoms.

AN INSECT, the leafhopper *Cicadula sexnotata*, later renamed *Macrosteles divisus* and still later, *M. fascifrons*, spreads aster yellows. Other insects that feed on the China aster, including several other leafhoppers, do not spread the disease. Newly hatched aster leafhoppers, even those from parents that carry the virus, are invariably virus-free. They cannot spread the disease until they obtain virus from a diseased plant and, surprising as it may seem, they are never able to transmit immediately after first feeding on such a plant. A rather long period, usually 9 to 14 days, has to elapse between the time when the virus-free insects first feed on a diseased plant and the time when they are first able to transmit. Once this period (which has come to be known as the incubation period of the virus in the insect) is completed, the insect usually is able to transmit continuously as long as it lives without again feeding on a diseased plant.

Strong colonies of the aster leafhopper have been maintained continuously since 1924, when we learned that it spreads the disease. The availability of the insect, its high efficiency as a vector, and its capacity to live and breed on many different species of plants made it suitable for use in studies of virus transmission. The sensitivity of the virus of aster yellows to moderately high temperatures made possible its destruction in whole or in part in both diseased plants and virus-bearing insects without undue harm to either, and thus gave an excellent experimental approach for studies on virus concentration in both plants and insects. Those characteristics of the aster leafhopper and the virus combined to give them a special suitability for use in work on the insect-vector relationship.

The salient features of the relationship between the aster yellows virus and the aster leafhopper consisted in virus specificity for the insect, virus incubation in the insect, and virus retention by the insect. This relationship, which needed to be explained, seemed to parallel a similar relationship between virus and host plant. Although aster yellows virus was not highly specific for the China aster or the periwinkle, it did not infect a majority of species even in the Compositae, the family in which about one-half of the known suscepts belonged. To this limited extent it was specific for the China aster, the periwinkle, and other host plants. The virus was not obtainable from an infected plant immediately after the plant became infected. About 2 weeks, the incubation period, had to elapse between the time the plant received an infective dose and the time the virus could first be obtained from it by the insect vector. Likewise, once a plant became infected, it ordinarily remained infected as long as it lived. These features—specificity for the plant, incubation in the plant, and retention by the plant—were believed to be correlated with multiplication of the virus in the plant. It was natural therefore to suspect that similar features in the virus-insect relationship might result from virus multiplication in the insect even though the virus in the insect caused no visible symptoms.

In searching for evidence in support of this hypothesis or against it, use was made of experiments involving heat inactivation of aster yellows virus in living plants. It had been found that the virus could be destroyed in diseased periwinkle plants and the plants cured by heat treatments at about 104° F. for a certain minimum period (about 12 days), depending on the size of affected plants. If treatments were stopped a bit short of the minimum, the treated plants would recover from the disease and would appear to be cured. Eventually symptoms would reappear, however, and in due course the treated plants become thoroughly diseased.

The time needed for symptoms to reappear in such treated plants varied with the length of treatment. When treatments were relatively short, the time required for reappearance of symptoms was short. When treatments were long but still short of the minimum necessary for cure, the time required for reappearance of symptoms was long. Because cured plants remained healthy indefinitely and no virus could be obtained from them, it was concluded that all of the virus in them had been destroyed by the treatments. Because plants treated for periods too short to cure but long enough to give temporary recovery eventually became as thoroughly diseased as untreated plants, it was concluded that only a portion of the virus present in them at the time of treatment had been destroyed and that the portion not destroyed had multiplied and caused relapse. It was reasoned that, as the amount of virus destroyed would increase and the amount remaining in the plant decrease with length of treatment, it would be expected that the interval preceding relapse would increase with length of treatment, as a small amount of virus remaining in a plant after treatment would require a longer time to reach a given level of concentration than a large amount. If the uninactivated virus in treated plants had not been able to multiply, the plants would not have relapsed.

The heat-treatment experiments with diseased plants suggested that the aster yellows virus in viruliferous insects also might be inactivated by heat. When tests were made it was found that that occurred. Infective insects could be rendered nonviruliferous by heat treatments at about 104° F. for 12 days or longer. Insects rendered nonviruliferous in this way could regain ability to transmit only by being allowed to again feed on a diseased plant. When virus-transmitting insects were heat-treated for periods of 1 to 11 days, they also lost ability to transmit but in these instances the loss was temporary. Such insects always regained ability to transmit without again feeding on a diseased plant but only after a waiting period.

If permanent loss of ability to transmit by infective insects resulted from heat inactivation of all virus in the insects, then the regaining of ability to transmit by insects that were heat-treated for periods only a little shorter than those required to give permanent loss of ability to transmit, and in which we may conclude only a very small amount of uninactivated virus could have remained, must have resulted from virus multiplication in the insects.

The heat-treatment experiments brought strong evidence that the virus of aster yellows multiplied in both the periwinkle plants and in the leafhoppers.

Aster yellows virus has never been transmitted manually by means of plant juices from diseased to healthy plants, but in 1941 L. M. Black showed that it could be transmitted to virus-free aster leafhoppers by needle inoculations with juices from viruliferous leafhoppers. Later he reported in a personal communication that it also could be transmitted to virus-free leafhoppers by needle inoculations with juices from diseased aster plants.

Dr. Black tried to determine whether or not the virus could be maintained indefinitely by means of serial transfers in insects that were never allowed to feed on a susceptible plant, and thus to obtain further evidence by another experimental method as to whether or not the aster yellows virus multiplied in its insect vector. Although some evidence was secured that supported the view that it could be so maintained, technical difficulties prevented him from passing the virus serially through a sufficient number of insect colonies to prove conclusively that it could be kept going indefinitely in this way.

In 1951, however, Karl Maramorosch succeeded in passing aster yellows virus serially by needle inoculations through ten colonies of virus-free aster leafhoppers that were never allowed to feed on a susceptible plant. He estimated that the virus present in the leafhopper juice that served as his original inoculum was diluted about 1 to 10,000 at each transfer and that the virus present in the inoculum at the ninth and tenth transfers, if no multiplication had taken place, would have been diluted to 10^{-36} and 10^{-40}, or many billions of times. But he also showed that the infectivity and presumably the concentration of virus in juices at the ninth transfer was as high as in the juices in the first transfer. He thus confirmed by another method the conclusion that the virus of aster yellows multiplies in the aster leafhopper. That finding is believed to account satisfactorily for the biological relationship long known to exist between aster yellows virus and the aster leafhopper. It also is believed to account for similar relationships between many other plant viruses and their insect vectors.

L. O. KUNKEL *is a plant pathologist who has been doing research on virus infections of plants since 1914, when he joined the Department of Agriculture to work on potato diseases. From 1920 to 1923 he studied virus diseases of sugarcane at the Experiment Station of the Hawaiian Sugar Planter's Association in Honolulu, and from 1923 to 1932 he headed researches on virus diseases at the Boyce Thompson Institute for Plant Research at Yonkers, N. Y. Since 1932 he has continued this work in the Rockefeller Institute for Medical Research, first in Princeton, N. J., and more recently in New York.*

Scab of Apples

G. W. Keitt

Apple scab occurs throughout the world where apples are grown, except in very dry or warm climates. It is most severe in localities with cool, moist springs and summers, as in parts of the north central and northeastern United States and southeastern Canada and northwestern Europe.

In most of the important apple-growing areas, efficient and economical control of scab is one of the chief essentials for successful growing of apples. If scab is severe, crops of the more susceptible varieties may be a total loss unless control measures are applied. Even the best of the control programs now most widely used may fail to give satisfactory results when the disease is very severe or conditions hinder the application of fungicides.

Apple scab is caused by the parasitic fungus, *Venturia inaequalis*. Little is known about the history of the disease before the modern study of fungi and the discovery of their ability to cause diseases of plants. The scab fungus was first reported and named in Sweden in 1819. It was first reported from the United States in 1834. Probably the scab fungus is an age-old parasite that has become an increasingly important agent of disease as the apple has been modified under culture and grown in large plantings.

The fungus attacks the cultivated varieties of apples and crab apples and numerous other species of the genus *Malus*, including the common wild crab apples *M. coronaria* and *M. iowensis*. It is not known to attack plants outside the genus *Malus*. Other species of *Venturia*, however, cause similar scab diseases of plants of genera closely related to *Malus*, such as *Pyrus* (pears) and *Crataegus* (hawthorns).

In most parts of the United States and Canada the scab fungus attacks only the leaves, blossoms, and fruits of the apple plant, but in some cool, moist climates, the young twigs and bud scales also may be infected.

SCAB MAY OCCUR on both surfaces of the leaf blade and on the midrib and petiole. It often appears first on the under surface, because it is first exposed to infection as the buds break and the leaves unfold.

The scab spots—lesions—usually appear first as small, olive-colored areas, which increase in size and may darken with age. They often take on a velvety appearance on account of the abundant production of spores on the ends of short, erect, threadlike branches of the fungus. The earliest lesions are largest, sometimes one-half inch or more in diameter. Later lesions tend to be smaller, because resistance to the disease increases with the age of the leaf.

Some of the spots are fully covered by the fungus growth and have a definite, round margin. Others show a radiating and netlike pattern of fungus growth with a less definite margin. As the leaf attains its full size, the upper surface usually becomes resistant to infection; the midrib remains susceptible somewhat longer than the leaf blade. The under surface usually remains susceptible throughout the season, but the development of the fungus in the mature leaf may be so restricted that the individual lesions are not easily recognized. These late, under-surface infections may be important for development of the fruiting bodies of the fungus that produce ascospores, which start infection in the following spring.

The larger scab spots, especially on the upper surface of the leaf, may become brown, except at the margins.

That happens when the fungus in the middle portions of the spots dies. Sometimes the leaf tissues under the spots are killed. Sometimes the leaf tissues remain alive throughout the season. If infection is abundant, the spots may merge. Severely infected leaves may be shed. As will be seen later, leaf infection is of great importance to overwintering of the fungus and to the development and the control of scab in the following season.

All of the outer parts of the unopened fruit buds are highly susceptible to infection when they become exposed after the cluster buds break. Scab on the calyx and the bud or blossom is similar to the heavier type of scab lesions on the leaves, and the pedicel spots resemble those on the petioles. Bud or blossom infection commonly leads to shedding of the blossoms or to severe infection of the developing fruit.

The fruit is most susceptible when young. Early infections cause the largest lesions and the greatest injury. The scab spots are small and olive-colored when first seen. They enlarge and usually become velvety in appearance during the period of abundant spore production by the fungus.

A very thin cork layer is commonly formed in the apple tissue beneath the fungus, especially when the fruit is young. It may develop to the extent of cutting the fungus off from its source of nourishment; and the older scab spots often become brown and corklike as the fungus dies from the middle and weathers away. Since the corked area cannot expand as rapidly as the surrounding healthy parts of the fruit, cracks frequently occur in the corked parts, and the fruits may become dwarfed or misshapen. Often the scab spots are bordered by a narrow, whitish band, because of loosening of the outermost membrane (cuticle) of the fruit by the growth of the fungus. The more severely affected fruits are shed.

As the fruit approaches maturity, it becomes more resistant and the scab lesions develop very slowly. Infections may occur too late in the season to cause visible lesions by harvesttime. Small, dark scab spots may then develop during the storage period.

Scab spots on the twigs and the bud scales are like those on fruit in storage. Small blisters develop, and rupture of the cuticle exposes the olive-colored growth of the underlying fungus. Often the loosened cuticle forms a whitish ring around the spot.

THE SCAB FUNGUS has two kinds of spores, which are microscopic, seedlike bodies. Either kind can germinate in water on a susceptible part of the apple plant and penetrate the cuticle of the plant by a microscopic, peglike growth. A fungus thread then develops between the cuticle and the cellulose wall of the outer layer of cells of the apple plant. This thread grows and branches and the fungus cells thicken until a solid layer of fungus growth several cells deep may be formed over the area of the lesion.

One kind of spores, called conidia, is produced at the surfaces of the scab spots from short, erect, threadlike branches of the fungus. Conidia may be produced at any time in the growing season, but most abundantly when the fungus is in a vigorous condition in spring and summer. These spores are released when wet and are spread chiefly in water during rains or very heavy dews or fogs. When they are washed off the branches that bear them, some more conidia are quickly produced.

The other kind of spores, ascospores, is produced in the spring in fruiting bodies (perithecia) of the fungus that develop in the dead apple leaves on the ground. These spores are produced in small sacs. During rainy periods, when the leaves containing the perithecia are thoroughly wet, the sacs elongate through an opening in the fruiting body and forcibly discharge their spores into the air.

In most parts of the United States the scab fungus overwinters only in the dead apple leaves on the ground. Ascospores produced in these leaves start the disease in the spring. Conidia produced from scab spots of the current season then continue the spread of the disease. In a few areas where twig infection occurs, conidia from twig lesions, as well as ascospores, can start the disease in the spring.

SPRAYING WITH FUNGICIDES is the most widely used control measure. Development of an efficient spray program requires understanding of the main factors that favor or hinder the development of the disease and influence the effectiveness of spray treatments.

For many years spray programs were started with an application just before the blossoms opened, or even later, because of the mistaken idea that infection by ascospores was not important enough to require earlier treatments. Actually, the number of ascospores produced in the overwintered apple leaves is one of the most important factors in the development of scab epidemics. The prevention of infection by ascospores is a key to scab control.

The abundance of ascospores and the time of their maturity vary with climatic and other conditions. Soon after leaf fall, the scab fungus grows into the dead leaves. The perithecia are produced only in close connection with the scab fungus tissue that was developed in the living leaves; therefore, the amount of living scab fungus in the leaves when they fall has an important bearing on the quantity of ascospores produced.

Cool fall weather, snow cover in winter, and cool, moist springs favor the production and discharge of ascospores. Scarcity of living scab fungus in the leaves when they fall, early disintegration of the fallen leaves, high temperatures when the leaves are moist, and prolonged dry or hot weather limit the ascospore supply.

The mature perithecia will stand hot weather when dry, but soon break down in hot, moist weather. The maturing and discharge of ascospores is favored by alternate periods of wetting and drying in cool weather. In climates with a winter snow cover and moist, cool springs, such as those of Wisconsin and similar northern parts of the apple belt of the United States and Canada, ascospores are ordinarily ripe and ready for discharge during rainy periods by the time the first susceptible parts are exposed in the opening buds. Farther south, the conditions for ascospore production may be less favorable and constant. In Wisconsin and areas with similar climate, ascospore discharges can generally be expected during rainy periods from the time the cluster buds of the apple break in the spring until the year's crop of ascospores is exhausted, which is usually about 2 or 3 weeks after petal fall. L. K. Jones and I, at the Wisconsin Agricultural Experiment Station, found up to 289 ascospores in a cubic foot of orchard air during spring rains. Such concentrations of ascospores can cause abundant infection and greatly increase the difficulty of scab control.

In order to protect against early infection, one has to know the stages of bud unfolding at which infection can first occur.

The first susceptible tissues exposed in the opening cluster buds are the tips of the leaves and of the sepals of the young blossom buds. The time from the breaking of the cluster buds until the leaves have fully expanded is the most critical period for scab development and the most difficult for its control by sprays. The young parts are at their highest susceptibility, their unfolding and expansion from day to day expose unprotected surfaces, and the ascospores are in their greatest supply.

Early infection of the sepals of the blossom buds is important with reference to the development of scab on the fruit and to the protection of the fruit by spray. Conidia of the fungus are produced in great abundance on the infected sepals, where they are in an ideal position for infecting neighboring parts of the young fruits to which the sepals are attached. Most of the severe, one-sided scab infection on fruits was started by conidia from early infections of the sepals.

More than 80 percent of the blossoms in certain Wisconsin orchards were found to have sepal infection in a severe scab year in which the trees had been unprotected by spray at the early delayed-dormant stage. The later sprays successfully controlled scab on fruits that did not have sepal infection, but failed to control it on the sepal-infected fruit. Prevention of sepal infection is one of the most important essentials for the successful control of apple scab.

Temperature and rainfall are important. The scab fungus grows very slowly at temperatures near the freezing point. Its growth increases with increased temperature to a maximum in the range of about 60° to 75° F. Growth ceases at about 85°, but the fungus can stand higher temperatures and resume growth when favorable temperatures occur. Ascospores can be discharged at the temperature of melting ice or any higher temperature that ordinarily occurs during spring rains. Temperatures governing germination and infection by both kinds of spores are about the same as those that govern growth of the fungus. About 13 to 18 hours of wetting is necessary for spores to infect at 40°, but at 70° the minimum wet period that permits infection is about 4 to 6 hours. Germinating spores can survive drying and resume growth and cause infection when wetted again.

Rainy periods favor the development of the perithecia, the distribution of both kinds of spores, and the processes of spore germination and infection. They also favor vigorous tree growth, which is more susceptible to scab than sparse growth, wash off fungicides, and often interfere with fungicidal treatments.

The resistance or susceptibility of apple varieties to scab is important. Very susceptible varieties should have first priority in the control program. They may require special treatments. In most situations it is not necessary to avoid planting susceptible varieties if they are desired for other qualities, as the disease can be controlled by fungicides.

The establishment of varietal resistance is complicated by the fact that different lines of the fungus have different capabilities for infecting various apple varieties. Therefore varieties may be reported as resistant in one area and susceptible in another. The ability of a pathogenic fungus to develop lines that can attack resistant varieties is a common obstacle to the use of resistant varieties of crop plants; however, the search for new and stronger resistance continues and the use of resistant varieties continues to be one of the most valuable methods of plant disease control. Long-time breeding experiments, in which it is sought to introduce into our best apple varieties the high resistance found in some other species of *Malus*, have been started in several places and seem to offer substantial promise for the future.

SCAB CONTROL varies so much with conditions that no single program can be recommended for general use. I give here some of the principles and facts that are basic to a wise choice of control measures. Growers should consult their State agricultural services and learn all they can about the reasons for their control programs as well as the best ways for carrying them out. Though breeding resistant varieties holds promise for the future, spraying with fungicides continues to be the main reliance for control.

The spray programs most widely used depend chiefly on protection of the susceptible parts of the apple plant from infection by the fungus. The protection should desirably begin before the first infection occurs in the spring. It should be kept up by repeated applications as long as there is danger of infection. These requirements present serious problems on account of the number and expense of the treatments, and extensive, competent experimentation in the areas

concerned is the only reliable guide to finding the most practical programs.

The timing and number of the spray treatments are influenced by the spray materials used. Aside from cost, two of the chief considerations in choosing spray materials are efficiency for disease control and the likelihood of causing spray injury. The materials with strongest fungicidal activity generally cause the most spray injury. Indeed, the history of choice of fungicides for apple scab is largely one of retreat from spray injury.

Bordeaux mixture, the first important spray used against this disease, is one of the most efficient protectant fungicides known, but it often causes severe russeting of fruit and injury to the leaves. It was therefore largely replaced by liquid lime-sulfur.

Lime-sulfur is efficient against the fungus, but may cause serious spray injury under some conditions. While it is still used in substantial amounts, especially in the preblossom applications, it is being increasingly replaced by less injurious materials. The wettable sulfurs have been extensively substituted for lime-sulfur, especially in the after-bloom treatments. However, even the wettable sulfurs may cause objectionable spray injury in some situations.

Extensive research is in progress to develop sprays that will control scab efficiently with still less danger of spray injury. Much attention is being given to organic chemical compounds, which seem to offer much promise. It should be recognized that many years of extensive orchard-spraying experiments are necessary in order to assess the practical value of a fungicide for apple scab control. It must stand the test under the range of conditions found from year to year and place to place, and it must be compatible with the insecticides with which it must be mixed.

One of the great deficiencies of any spray program based wholly on protection of the susceptible parts by repeated applications is that, under favorable conditions for scab infections, no economically practical number of treatments would fully protect all the young developing parts. Under favorable conditions for spraying, the bud and fruit parts can be kept protected with a workable degree of efficiency because all the blossom buds are exposed to infection in a short time. New leaves, however, are put forth from day to day for many weeks. Under severe conditions for scab infection, the best practical spray program based wholly on protection will not prevent the fungus from establishing itself in the unprotected leaves in sufficient amount to develop an abundant supply of ascospores the next spring. Furthermore, the infected leaves furnish a source of conidia that constantly threatens further fruit and leaf infection throughout the season. That problem is being attacked from two main approaches.

One approach is through the use of spray materials, especially in early season, that have some value in eradicating the fungus after it infects or in checking the production of conidia if the fungus survives. The lime-sulfur-lead arsenate spray has a considerable value in these respects, and on that account it is extensively used in the prebloom sprays in areas where scab is severe and experience has shown that the spray injury is not too great. Various spray materials, especially organic mercury or other organic compounds, are being developed with the aim of eradicating the scab fungus from early infections, as well as protecting against infection. This approach through use of sprays that have both protectant and eradicant properties is very logical and promising. Substantial progress has been made. The degree of success with which such materials and methods can be developed remains to be seen.

Another approach to this problem is through supplementing the best available spray programs by a direct attack on the scab fungus with an eradicant fungicide. This method is adapted for

situations in which scab occurrence is severe and the best available tree spray programs are uncertain of control or cause too much spray injury. This method has been used extensively by Wisconsin apple growers for nearly 10 years. By means of a special boom a single application of spray is applied to the orchard floor in the spring after the ground is free of surface water and before apple buds break enough to expose susceptible tissue. Commercial preparations containing the sodium salt of dinitro-o-cresol or the triethanolamine salt of dinitro-o-sec.-butylphenol, one-half gallon in 100 gallons of water, are applied under 400 to 600 pounds pressure at the rate of 600 gallons an acre. Such treatments commonly eliminate 95 to 99 percent of the ascospores, with corresponding reduction in ascospore infections. Where this method is used, orchards are not cultivated during the period of ascospore discharge, because cultivation may lessen the effectiveness of the treatment. In Wisconsin this ground spraying has practically eliminated the danger of failure of well-executed spray programs on account of very severe occurrence of scab or because of unavoidable delay of critical applications. It has also made possible the successful use of the milder fungicides, thereby avoiding some serious problems of spray injury.

Perhaps an ideal fungicide for control of apple scab and many other diseases would be one that would penetrate into the susceptible plant tissues, kill or inactivate the fungus or other causal agent in infections that had already occurred, and render the plant immune to further infection for a substantial period of time. A search for such internally active materials has been started. Work in this field is encouraged by the striking successes with internally active substances for combatting infectious diseases of man and animals and insect pests of plants.

Much progress has been made in improving spray machinery and methods. The tendency is towards increased mechanization and the elimination of hand labor. Fixed or automatic spray heads or booms are rapidly replacing hand-operated spray outlets, and extensive research is in progress on spraying with concentrated materials instead of highly diluted fungicides. Dusting continues to be preferred to spraying in some situations, especially where very quick coverage is necessary or ground or weather conditions are more favorable for dusting than spraying. In most cases dusting against apple scab is used as a supplement to spraying, rather than as a complete substitute.

In conclusion, a control program designed for use under very severe conditions of scab occurrence is outlined. It is offered as an illustrative program that has been very successfully used in Wisconsin, rather than as a recommendation for adoption in other States.

The ground spray as outlined in the foregoing.

Prebloom sprays designed primarily to keep the young bud and fruit parts protected from the time they are sufficiently exposed to warrant spraying. Begin after the cluster buds have broken open and the tips of the young blossom buds and leaves have grown out about one-fourth inch and spray at intervals of not more than 7 days. About three prebloom sprays are usually required in Wisconsin, the last of which should come at the open-cluster stage. Liquid lime-sulfur, 1–50, is a standard material. Other fungicides may be substituted.

A spray in bloom 10 days after the last prebloom treatment, applied only if the calyx spray is not due by that time. A mild spray, such as a wettable sulfur or a dithiocarbamate, without an insecticide, is used.

After-bloom sprays designed to keep the fruit protected until harvest. The time and number of treatments vary somewhat with the seasonal conditions. The milder fungicides, such as wettable sulfurs or dithiocarbamates, are used. Ordinarily five or six treatments are given after bloom at about 2-week intervals, beginning with the calyx spray. Without the ground spray, the after-bloom treatments with mild fungicides would usually come at intervals of about 10 days or less, and lime-sulfur might be desirable in the final treatment on the more susceptible varieties to guard against late-season infection and the development of scab in storage.

Insecticides are used in this program as recommended by entomologists and the spray dates are set to meet the needs for control of insects as well as scab.

Excellent spray materials, equipment, and methods are now available, and apple scab control can be assured if they are correctly used. However, there is no substitute for competent planning of each detailed spray program or for timeliness and thoroughness in carrying it out.

G. W. KEITT *is a professor of plant pathology and chairman of the department of plant pathology of the University of Wisconsin.*

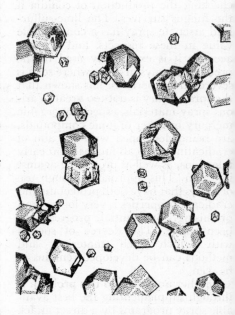

Crystals of tomato bushy stunt virus.

Blotch
of Apples

John C. Dunegan

The fungus *Phyllosticta solitaria* causes blotch, a serious disease of apples.

It has not been found in the far West, but east of the Rocky Mountains it has been observed in all apple sections, from New Jersey west to Nebraska and southward to the southern limits of apple growing. It causes most trouble in southern orchards.

The fungus attacks the leaves, fruit, and the current season's twig growth of the apple tree. The following spring the fruiting bodies—pycnidia—formed on the twig cankers ooze many small, colorless, one-celled spores. Raindrops wash them to the new leaves, fruit, and shoots, where they germinate and start anew the cycle of infection. The spore discharge from the overwintered cankers occurs 3 to 9 weeks after the petals have dropped from the blossoms.

The fruit becomes resistant by the middle of the summer and is seldom infected late in the season, but the young leaves and shoots, especially water sprouts, remain susceptible throughout the growing season. The fungus remains alive in the twig cankers at least 3 years, and each spring produces a new crop of spores that infect the new growth.

Varieties vary in susceptibility. McIntosh, Maiden Blush, and Northwestern Greening are very susceptible. Rome Beauty, Wealthy, Yellow Newton, and Yellow Transparent are moderately susceptible. Delicious,

Golden Delicious, Grimes Golden, Jonathan, Stayman Winesap, and Winesap are quite resistant, but their resistance is only relative and occasionally the fungus can seriously affect them. Ben Davis, once popular in the Midwest, and Oldenburg are extremely susceptible.

Apple seedlings grown for the production of nursery stock can be infected by the blotch fungus. The disease formerly was introduced into new areas in diseased nursery stock. That situation has been improved by spraying the seedlings with fungicides or by growing them in the Pacific Northwest.

Two types of blotch symptoms occur on apple leaves. Tiny white spots (one-sixteenth to one-eighth inch in diameter) form in the blade tissue between the veins; on veins and leaf stems—petioles—the fungus produces elliptical, sunken, tan or buff lesions. Usually only one black dot—the pycnidium or spore case—forms in the center of each white spot. A variable number form in the buff-colored lesions on the veins and petioles.

Often the leaves remain uninfected even though the fruit and twigs show many infections. The white spot phase ordinarily does little damage, but the infection that develops near the base of the petioles frequently defoliates the trees by midsummer. The fungus may grow from the petiole infections into the adjacent twig tissue, causing a canker to form at the leaf scar.

Blotch infections develop on the twigs, water sprouts, and fruit spurs of the current year's growth. They first appear as dark, raised, roughly circular spots, studded with tiny projections caused by the formation of the pycnidia within the shoot tissues. As I mentioned, some of these infections are the result of the fungus passing from the leaf petioles into the twig tissues. Others, particularly those on the stem between the leaf scars, are the result of infections from spores.

The infections from spores are particularly numerous on the succulent, rapidly growing water sprouts. The center of the canker soon becomes slightly sunken and brown to tan. In the second year this central or older part of the canker is surrounded by a dark border of varying width, indicating the extent of the advance of the fungus. Pycnidia are formed in this area. During the third season an additional boundary zone forms. Usually by then the canker becomes irregular and roughened. If the infections are numerous, several cankers may coalesce into roughened, cankered areas several inches long. They may eventually girdle the twigs.

As the fungus does not penetrate deeply into the twig tissues, the lesions are soon separated from the living tissues by a callus layer. The dead tissues finally crack into fragments and are sloughed off as the result of the tensions set up by the normal increase in diameter of the twigs. This process takes time and the roughened scar tissues can be seen encircling the larger twigs and branches for several years after spore production has ceased.

On the fruit the symptoms are quite dissimilar at different stages in their development. The common name of the disease refers to the mottled or blotched appearance of the fruit.

The earliest symptom (but one not frequently seen because it persists so short a time) is the isolated, usually dark-colored and semihemispherical, raised or blisterlike areas, one-eighth inch in diameter, on the young apples. The spots appear in late May or early June and slowly enlarge. Usually they develop fringed margins. By midsummer the spot is slightly raised and dark and has irregular but distinct margins. Frequently the spot at this stage has a starlike appearance. Later several spots may merge, a depression of varying depth and diameter develops, and the fringed margins, so characteristic of the spots in midseason, disappear. If numerous infections are on the apple at the beginning of the season, their subsequent growth and fusion may cause unsightly dark areas, which cover one-half or more of the surface of the apple and completely destroy its market value.

The fungus does not produce a rot of the fruit tissues, because only the outer layers of cells are invaded. Badly infected fruit may crack, usually in three directions from a central point. Secondary fungi then can enter and rot the apple.

The control of apple blotch must have as its ultimate aim the elimination of the twig cankers, for they are the agency by which the fungus perpetuates itself from one season to the next. Spray materials used to inhibit the formation of the cankers also protect the leaves and fruit.

As the cankers can be present on young trees, all trees for new plantings should be thoroughly inspected as they are received from the nursery to be sure the disease is not being introduced at the time the orchard is established. The young trees should be thoroughly inspected again the year after they are planted. Any cankers that escaped the previous inspection can be removed by pruning, if they are in the smaller twigs, or shaved off with a sharp knife, if they are on the larger limbs or on the trunk of the tree.

Max W. Gardner demonstrated in Indiana that the development of the fungus could be retarded in young orchards by those measures. But the procedure is practical only during the first few years in the life of the orchard, for the trees soon get too large to permit the careful inspection needed.

On older trees many cankers can be eliminated by normal pruning operations. Trees that have been neglected for several years must be pruned thoroughly to remove the cankers and permit proper spraying.

Cutting out the cankers on the young trees and thorough pruning of older trees are helpful control measures, but at best they are only supplementary aids. The control of the disease on the leaves and fruit and the elimination of the cankers depend mainly on the use of fungicidal sprays.

During the period of spore discharge from the overwintered cankers, which starts approximately 3 weeks after the petals have dropped and continues for about 6 weeks, the young leaves, fruit, and twigs must be protected from infection. Many field experiments have shown that lime-sulfur solution and the wettable sulfur preparations used to control the apple scab fungus are only partly effective in controlling the blotch fungus. The standard procedure therefore, is to use bordeaux mixture (4–4–100) or ferbam (ferric dimethyl dithiocarbamate) at the rate of 2 pounds in 100 gallons of water. The first spray should be applied 2 weeks after the petals have fallen, followed by three applications at intervals of 2 weeks or only two applications at 3-week intervals.

If properly applied, those sprays will protect the leaves and fruit from blotch infections and prevent new cankers from forming on the current year's growth. Because the cankers formed the preceding season will ooze spores for at least two more seasons, however, the spray program must be carried on for at least three or four seasons. After that the fungus can be kept under control by one or two sprays—with materials at half the strength I recommended—each season.

An objection to the use of bordeaux mixture to control blotch is the injury that is apt to accompany the continued use of a copper-containing spray. In some seasons that injury to leaves might be worse than the injury caused by the blotch fungus. In other seasons the use of a copper spray 2 weeks after the petals have dropped may cause serious russeting of the fruit. Ferbam, therefore, is preferred. On light-colored apples it may leave a dark residue that must be removed, but that is a minor drawback, compared to the injury that may result from the use of bordeaux mixture.

JOHN C. DUNEGAN *is a pathologist in the Bureau of Plant Industry, Soils, and Agricultural Engineering.*

Bitter Rot of Apples

John C. Dunegan

Bitter rot, a destructive disease of apples caused by the fungus *Glomerella cingulata*, has long been feared by growers in Maryland, Virginia, West Virginia, Arkansas, and southern Illinois, Indiana, and Missouri.

An account published in 1870 in the Transactions of the Illinois Horticultural Society said: "Last year the orchard . . . had at least one thousand bushels on and the proprietor did not get a bushel of winter apples. The bitter rot blasts them like the breath of ruin and the promise of spring ends in disappointment and decay. . . ."

Seventy-seven years later, near Centerton, Ark., I found 96 percent of the crop on some trees destroyed by the fungus.

The disease is not entirely unknown in northern orchards, but usually it is unimportant except in seasons when unusual weather favors the development of the fungus on neglected trees.

Temperatures above 70° F. and abundant rain favor the development and spread of the fungus. Bitter rot is distinctly a warm-weather, midsummer disease. The fruit infections rarely appear before the middle of June but continue to develop until early September. Losses vary from year to year but once the fungus becomes firmly established in an orchard, control is difficult.

The bitter rot fungus is a microscopic plant that can live in the tissues of the apple. The fungus filaments—mycelia—penetrate the skin, kill the individual cells of the apple pulp, and cause a breakdown or rot of the tissue.

Small, light-brown, circular spots under the skin of the apple are the first sign of the disease. When the spots are one-half inch or more across, concentric rings of pink pustules appear on their surfaces. The pustules are masses of spores—conidia. As the fungus penetrates more and more of the apple tissue, the area of invaded tissue, originally conical-shaped, becomes enlarged, until finally the entire apple is involved. Sometimes, however, the growth of the fungus is checked and the only effect is a cone-shaped cavity of varying depth, covered by the skin, which has turned dark and papery.

When only one or two infections occur on an apple, the individual spots grow rapidly in favorable weather; the concentric rings of spore masses soon develop, facilitating the spread of the fungus to adjacent fruit.

Occasionally one encounters apples with 500 to 1,000 individual infections. They have a peculiar peppered appearance. The individual spots often remain small and blisterlike. Under those conditions, the fungus does not extend very far into the fruit tissue.

Aside from that unusual symptom, the disease usually is easily identified, especially when the rings of pink spores (which later turn dark brown or black) are present on the fruit. One other common rot of the apple, black rot, is sometimes confused with bitter rot. The black rot fungus, however, causes a less watery type of rot, and, although concentric bands of color are also present on the apple, the fungus never produces concentric rings of spore masses.

Infected apples frequently remain in the trees. As the season advances they shrivel into hard masses called mummies. The fungus can remain alive in them until the following year and then produce spores to infect the new crop of fruit. The removal of the mummies, therefore, is important in control.

The bitter rot fungus also persists from season to season in dead twigs and branches. Sometimes the fungus actually kills the twigs and causes cankers but usually it merely invades tissues weakened or killed by other agencies—the black rot and blotch fungi, the pear blight bacillus, mechanical injuries, and injuries due to low temperatures.

Once established in the dead twig and branch tissues, the fungus survives for several years and is a continuing source of spores to infect the succeeding crops. Frequently the first fruit infections of the season occur in a cone-shaped area below a dead twig producing bitter rot spores. The newly infected apples produce more spores, which spread the fungus through the tree. The cone-shaped pattern of the primary infection is obliterated as the season progresses.

The bitter rot fungus occasionally produces spots on apple leaves, particularly on neglected trees, but that phase of the disease is not important.

Sometimes the fungus forms a different type of fruiting body on the fruit and twig tissues. Numerous sacs (asci), each containing eight spores (ascospores), are formed within a hard, black, spherical case called a perithecium. The ascospores can be seen only through a microscope. They are forcibly ejected from the perithecium and, like the spores produced in the pustules (acervuli), can infect other apples.

Apple varieties vary considerably in susceptibility. Golden Delicious, Jonathan, Yellow Newton, Northwestern Greening, and Grimes Golden generally are more susceptible than Rome Beauty, Stayman Winesap, Delicious, York Imperial, and Winesap. Even normally resistant varieties, however, may be seriously affected in hot, rainy weather. The degree to which different varieties are infected depends largely on climate and their proximity to sources of infection.

I do not mean to imply that every apple tree in the country is constantly threatened with a destructive attack of the fungus. Actually, the fungus spreads very slowly and many orchards remain entirely free from the disease. But when the disease does appear in an orchard, control measures must be promptly instituted lest in a favorable season the fungus runs wild in the orchard and ". . . the promise of spring ends in disappointment and decay. . . ."

The control of the fungus depends on proper orchard sanitation, to remove sources of infection, and the use of effective fungicides, properly applied in a definitely timed schedule to insure thorough coverage.

Persistent cases of bitter rot can be traced at times to the presence of a few infected trees of a susceptible variety remaining in the orchard from an earlier planting. Those old trees must be removed as the first step in control: The value of the fruit they produce is apt to be much less than losses they cause by serving as a reservoir of bitter rot spores that infect the adjacent and more valuable trees.

The removal of mummies from the trees, particularly if the disease has been serious the previous year, and proper pruning to eliminate the dead twigs that harbor the bitter rot fungus are also essential in the control program. In fact, unless those sanitary measures are practiced, the control of the fungus by spraying will be difficult and at times impossible.

Because the first infected apples are rarely noted before the middle of June, the spray program usually starts with an application between June 10 and 15, a second spray is applied July 1, a third application about July 15 to 20, and a fourth application during the first week in August.

During cool, dry seasons the intervals between the spray applications can be increased 7 to 10 days, and only three instead of four applications need be made during the season.

Since all spraying leaves a residue on the fruit which may interfere with its sale, no fruit should be sprayed later than 1 month before its ripening date.

If the bitter rot is rampant in the orchard, it may be necessary to violate that precaution to obtain control of the fungus. Then the fruit must be washed or brushed to remove the spray residues before it is offered for sale or used at home.

It is essential to apply the spray before infections appear on the fruit. In orchards where almost the entire crop has been ruined for several years, it may be necessary (depending on the season) to start spraying earlier than June 15 and apply sprays at intervals of 2 weeks until the fungus is under control. All the spraying operations for bitter rot control must be thorough and every effort should be made to cover the apples by spraying from both sides of the trees.

Bordeaux mixture before 1944 was the only material that had controlled the bitter rot fungus successfully. This spray preparation, consisting of 8 parts of copper sulfate, dissolved in water and added slowly to a suspension of 12 parts of hydrated lime in 100 gallons of water, was effective.

In 1944 scientists found that some of the organic spray materials, particularly Phygon (2,3-dichloro-1, 4-naphthoquinone) and ferbam (ferric dimethyl dithiocarbamate), used at the rate of 1 and 1½ pounds, respectively, to 100 gallons, were equally as effective as bordeaux mixture for the control of the bitter rot fungus.

Later experiments confirmed those results and the organic materials are now used in preference to bordeaux mixture to avoid the chemical injury that was so commonly associated with the use of bordeaux mixture. The number of spray applications required to control the bitter rot fungus remains the same, however, irrespective of the material used in the sprays.

JOHN C. DUNEGAN *is a pathologist in the division of fruit and nut crops and diseases, Bureau of Plant Industry, Soils, and Agricultural Engineering. He is in charge of investigations on the control of diseases of deciduous tree fruits.*

Rust Diseases
of Apple

D. H. Palmiter

Many a fruit-growing district in the East is "a land of red apples and red cedars." In the Midwest where cedars did not occur naturally the pioneers often planted them for windbreaks near orchards. The combination would be felicitous were it not that some fungi require both apples and cedars for their development.

Before our cultivated apples, quince, and other pome fruits were introduced from Europe, three such fungi, natives, infected the leaves or fruit of native crab apples, hawthorn, serviceberry, and sorbus, all members of the rose family. They could not overwinter on those hosts, however, and used the cedar trees *Juniperus virginianae*, *J. scopulorum*, *J. horizontalis*, and *J. communis* as winter hosts.

Since three different fungi are responsible for three different rust diseases of apples, we must know something of their life history and symptoms on both apple and cedar before we can control them.

The best known of the three diseases is cedar-apple rust. It produces yellow lesions on the leaves and fruit of wild and cultivated apples and is caused by the fungus *Gymnosporangium juniperi virginianae*.

A similar disease is hawthorn rust. Its common native host is hawthorn. It also infests apple leaves but not the fruit. It is caused by the fungus *G. globosum*.

The third disease is quince rust. It is destructive on quince. Its native host plants include hawthorn, Amelanchier, and wild apples. It also infects the fruit of some varieties of apple. The fungus is *G. clavipes*.

The three fungi were studied early in the nineteenth century. At first the forms on the cedar and on the apple were considered to be different. By 1886, however, more study showed that the spores produced by the fungus on cedar trees would infect apples and that the spores produced on apples were responsible for new infections on the cedar. The rust diseases cannot spread from cedar to cedar nor from apple to apple but must alternate between the two hosts.

The fungus that causes cedar-apple rust spends almost 2 years of its life cycle on the cedar trees. Cedar leaves are infected between July and April by aeciospores blown from lesions that develop on apple leaves. Small brown galls, called cedar apples, appear during the summer but do not mature until the following spring, when they may be 2 inches in diameter. After a few warm spring rains, about the time apple blossoms are in the pink stage, the galls increase in size and extrude gelatinous tendrils from round depressions on all sides of the galls. The tendrils—long, thin, and bright orange—form a mass several times that of the original brown galls. The tendrils, or horns, consist of many two-celled teliospores, which germinate in the tendrils by producing four sporidia from each of the two cells. All teliospores do not germinate at the same time. With each rain the horns push out farther and expose more spores. When the supply of teliospores is exhausted the galls dry up and may drop. If the twigs bearing the galls are killed, the dead galls often remain hanging on the cedars through the next year.

After the small sporidia are produced, a decrease in humidity causes them to be discharged forcibly into the air. Air currents carry them considerable distances. Viable spores have been collected by airplane traps several miles from redcedars at altitudes up to one-half mile. They may eventually settle on apple leaves or fruit. If a film of moisture is present and the temperature is between 56° and 61° F., the sporidia germinate quickly and penetrate the host tissue in 1 to 3 hours. Little germination occurs at temperatures below 47° or above 85°. Either leaf surface may be infected. Fruit lesions are usually near the blossom end.

The yellow rust spots appear on the upper surface of the apple leaves in 1 to 3 weeks, depending on the temperature and the susceptibility of the variety. As the spots increase in size, a sticky exudate containing pycniospores appears. The true function of this spore stage was not known until 1933, when investigations by J. C. Liu at the University of Wisconsin showed that insects are attracted by this exudate. They carry spores from one rust spot to another and thus fertilize the fungus. Thus it continues growth and completes its life cycle on the apple tree by producing the final spore stage.

After fertilization, the fungus grows through the leaf and produces fruiting bodies, called aecia, on the lower surface of the leaf. Fruit of susceptible apple varieties also may be infected and spores may be produced. Aeciospores are produced in thin-walled tubes. In July and August the spores mature and are released by the splitting of the tube walls. They are carried about by the wind. Those that land on cedar leaves may germinate at once to start galls or may remain dormant until the following spring, when they germinate to infect the new growth. Now that better control methods are available, few spores are produced on orchard trees. Infection of cedar trees is largely from spores produced on wild or seedling apple trees growing near the cedars.

THE LIFE HISTORY of the hawthorn rust fungus is about the same as that of the cedar-apple rust fungus. The galls produced on cedar trees are more irregular in shape than the apple rust galls. The teliospores are extruded as dark-orange, wedge-shaped protrusions during spring rains. Sporidia may be discharged for 2 or 3 days while the galls are drying. Unlike the apple rust galls, they persist and produce spores again another year.

The hawthorn rust fungus does not cause lesions on apple fruit. The lesions on the upper surface of apple leaves are similar to those of the apple rust fungus but smaller. On the lower leaf surface, the two fungi look quite different. With the hawthorn rust the aecia are relatively few in number and are at the center of the lesion and surrounded by a region of orange-colored leaf tissue. The peridial tubes, in which the spores are formed, are persistent and long and spread apart to release the aeciospores. They do not curl back, as do those of the apple rust fungus.

The aeciospores of the hawthorn rust are mature in the fall. The wind distributes them. They do not germinate well until cold weather approaches. Some spores perhaps do not germinate until the following spring, when new galls on the cedars are started. If no apple orchards are nearby or if orchards are well sprayed, aeciospores from infected hawthorn trees may serve to reinfect the cedars.

THE QUINCE RUST fungus infects twigs, branches, or trunks of the cedar, but not the leaves. It produces elongated, swollen, rough cankers, which turn red as the teliospores begin to form in the spring. Jellylike masses of yellowish-orange teliospores later are exuded during the spring rains about the time apple trees are in bloom. The cankers remain active and increase in size year after year unless the twig or branch dies. Spore forms are like (but larger than) those of the other apple rust fungi. Infections of apple leaves result in flecks or abortive lesions. The fruit of many apple varieties may be infected, but few if any aecia are produced on most varieties. The fungus sporulates abundantly on quince and hawthorn fruits and twigs, however. They are covered by a mass of bright-orange tubes, in which the spores are formed. The spores formed on infected quince or hawthorn fruit are then able to reinfect cedar trees.

Many of the apples infected by quince rust drop in June. Those that mature are misshapen and may have dark-green sunken lesions, usually near the blossom end. Some varieties, such as Cortland, tend to crack open. Infection becomes visible 2 or 3 weeks after bloom, and the lesions often appear as dark-green raised areas near the blossom end. As the fruit grows, the diseased parts develop slowly and finally appear as sunken areas. The tissue under the sunken area is hard and extends to the apple core.

MOST OF THE APPLE plantings in the United States before 1850 were seedling trees. No two of them were alike. If disease or insects were unusually harmful to a particular tree, it was considered a weakling and removed or left to its fate. Trees later were propagated by grafting, and named varieties were selected for quality of their fruit. It soon became evident that certain varieties were subject to leaf and fruit infections of the rust.

During that period, about a century ago, Wealthy, Rome Beauty, Winter Banana, Salome, Jonathan, and York Imperial apples became popular as the apple industry expanded rapidly in the Eastern and Central States. But those very varieties were highly susceptible to cedar-apple rust—it is not surprising that trouble developed wherever they were planted near cedar trees or cedar trees were planted near them.

In 1912 the loss in Virginia from rust on apples was estimated to be more than 500,000 dollars. Besides, many trees were greatly weakened and young trees were killed before they reached bearing age. West Virginia reported a loss of 75,000 dollars in one county. Complaints of severe damage from rust diseases were also reported from Iowa, Wisconsin, and New York. Another serious outbreak occurred in 1927 and 1928. Considerable loss of fruit occurred in New York and Iowa.

Rust diseases injure apples in several ways. The infected fruit is reduced in grade, so that most of them are culls. Quince rust tends to cause a high proportion of McIntosh fruit to drop in June, and fruit of Cortland and some other varieties tends to crack. Considerable loss from secondary rots may follow rust infection. Fruit size is reduced by heavy foliage infection, so that even uninfected fruits have little value. Infected trees are greatly weakened by defoliation and the reduction of active leaf surface. As few as 10 rust spots on a leaf may cause leaves of some varieties to fall by midsummer. Such trees may suffer winter injury and often fail to set fruit buds for the following season. Young trees in nursery and orchard may die because of infection and defoliation.

METHODS OF CONTROLLING the diseases were considered even before fungicidal sprays were commonly used. The fact that apple trees can only be infected by the spores produced on cedars suggested the possibility of control by removing the cedars—a simple and practical procedure in places where cedars were not too numerous and belonged to the fruit grower. This method of control was first reported in 1892 following experiments by L. R. Jones. Investigations of the effectiveness and cost of removing cedars were made by H. S. Reed and C. H. Crabill in Virginia between 1910 and 1915. As other methods were less effective or more expensive at that time, the removal of cedars became the commonly recommended control practice. Eight States—Virginia, Arkansas, Kansas, Nebraska, West Virginia, Pennsylvania, New York, and Missouri—passed laws empowering authorities to remove cedars.

In the East, however, many orchards

were in valleys fringed by cedar-bearing hills on which it was impractical to exterminate the cedar. The esthetic value of cedars in some estates and parks outweighed the value of nearby orchards.

Another method of avoiding rust lay in the differences in the susceptibility of different trees to rust. But varieties reported resistant in one place were said to be susceptible in another.

We now know that the cause of that early confusion was lack of understanding that three different fungi were responsible for the rust. Paul R. Miller, of the Department of Agriculture, pointed out in 1939 that varieties like Rome Beauty and Wealthy were susceptible to all three rust fungi; varieties like York, Grimes, Ben Davis, and Jonathan were susceptible to apple and hawthorn rusts but were resistant to quince rust; and Stayman Winesap and Delicious were infected only by quince rust. D. E. Bliss in Iowa in 1933 discovered that strains of the fungi exist—the strains may limit or extend the list of varieties usually considered susceptible to a given species.

The early lack of understanding of the problem meant that progess in the selection and breeding of apples for resistance to rust was slow. Now such work is going ahead full speed. Varieties resistant to all species of rust may be produced some day. We already have some varieties resistant enough to be grown commercially in places where more susceptible kinds would suffer severe damage without special applications of fungicides.

But changing varieties of apples to avoid disease is indeed a slow process. Orchards already planted cannot be changed without great expense even if resistant varieties are available. New varieties must be acceptable to processors and consumers of the fresh fruit before extensive orchard plantings can be recommended.

The use of fungicides to control the diseases was stimulated by the outbreaks of rust early in this century. Bordeaux mixture was generally rec-

ommended then for apple scab and other diseases. Bordeaux gave good control of rust when several properly timed applications were made, but that was expensive and often caused severe injury to the fruit and leaves, especially when frequent applications were made early in the season.

Liquid lime-sulfur, introduced as a fruit fungicide in 1907, was tried on apples in many States. It gave only partial control unless frequent applications were made. Inadequate spray equipment was no doubt a factor. Many spray schedules called for applications at 2-week intervals; more frequent applications were considered to be impractical. Because lime-sulfur proved to be a good scab fungicide, however, and caused less injury than bordeaux on certain varieties, it soon replaced or supplemented bordeaux in many districts.

Wettable sulfur products, tested extensively following the rust epidemics of 1927 and 1928, were found to be commercially feasible in New York when they were applied on a 5-day schedule or timed to precede rainy periods during and following the bloom. But despite all the experimental work on fungicides up to 1940, growers often failed to get good results. The removal of cedar trees near susceptible varieties was still considered the best method of controlling rust diseases in most States.

Of the many fungicides developed between 1940 and 1953 only ferbam has been outstanding for the control of all three forms of rust on apples. It is available for spray purposes as a 76-percent active, dry, wettable powder.

The use of ferbam makes unnecessary the close timing of applications that are necessary when sulfur is used to control rust, because ferric dimethyl dithiocarbamate, the active part of ferbam, is translocated externally and internally to such an extent that new growth is protected. J. M. Hamilton, L. O. Weaver, and I, working at the New York State Agricultural Experiment Station, found that the toxic element in Fermate (ferbam) is taken into the plant in sufficient amounts to give a degree of protection through systemic action, particularly against the cedar-rust fungus. Consequently even a spotty coverage of ferbam controlled rust, whereas a spotty coverage of sulfur failed to control. Ferbam applied to the lower leaf surface prevented infection when the rust spores were placed on the upper leaf surface.

Ferbam (76-percent active) used alone at the rate of 1 or 1.5 pounds to 100 gallons of spray at the pink, petal-fall, and 10-day stages of apple development gave satisfactory control of the rust diseases in New York over a 10-year period. When a combination of wettable sulfur and ferbam was used for control of both scab and rust, one-half the usual amount of each fungicide was used, and an extra application during bloom was made. Because the number and timing of sprays for rust control may vary in different sections of the country, owners of apple trees should follow the recommendations issued by their own county agents or State experiment stations.

The use of 4-percent ferbam dust with sulfur as the diluent, applied before or during rainy periods, has satisfactorily controlled apple rust diseases. Such dusts can be applied quickly. Commercial growers like them particularly when special applications are needed, especially during the bloom period. Ferbam dusts applied by plane have also given good control.

So far no other fungicides (except maybe some other carbamates) have equaled ferbam against rust diseases, but many commercial orchardists for whom rust is not a serious problem use other fungicides, such as wettable sulfur, naphthoquinones, and glyoxalidines. Additional rust protection has been obtained by adding one-half pound of ferbam to each 100 gallons of spray when those materials are used during the period of critical rust infection.

Ferbam has also been used experimentally in combination with the phenyl mercury fungicides and with captan fungicides to control both rust and scab.

IF YOU GROW cedar trees as ornamentals, it is well to protect them from rust—to keep the rust fungi from disfiguring them and to keep the fungi from producing spores that would infect flowering apples or other ornamental plants susceptible to rust.

If you plan to make new plantings of cedars, it is wise to consider using the cultivated varieties of cedar that are resistant to the rust. For twenty years Anthony Berg selected, propagated, and tested redcedar trees for resistance to cedar-apple rust. In 1941 he published his results with a selection from West Virginia that showed outstanding resistance.

In established plantings you can get partial control by spraying the surrounding apple or other susceptible pome trees with ferbam. That will restrict greatly the source of new infection. Commercial orchards sprayed with ferbam produce few rust spores capable of infecting cedars. Many of the cedar infections now come from spores produced on neglected apple trees which, as likely as not, can be removed.

The direct spraying of cedars with bordeaux and sulfur for rust control is done sometimes. The usual procedure is to make one application in July or August to give protection from spores that are discharged in the summer. Another application in late fall or early spring will kill any spores that may remain on the cedars until spring. Such sprays are said to give 80 to 90 percent control.

Spring applications of sulfur, bordeaux, and dinitrocresylate have been used on rust-infected cedars to prevent the cedar galls from producing viable spores. Rush P. Marshall reported in 1941 the results of tests conducted in Connecticut in which one early spring application of bordeaux 180 (a combination of copper sulfate, lime, monocalcium arsenite, zinc arsenite, and fish oil) gave superior control of spore formation and greatly reduced the number of new rust galls on cedar trees.

THUS THREE METHODS of controlling the fungi that cause apple, quince, and hawthorn rusts are available.

In localities where either the cedar or the pomaceous host can be eliminated the remaining host will be unharmed.

Resistant varieties of both host plants are available and are recommended if both plants are to be used in the same area.

For most commercial apple orchards, nurseries, and estates where wild cedar trees are abundant, however, the use of ferbam in sprays or dusts is the most practical means of control.

Susceptible cedars may also be protected by one or two applications of bordeaux 180 in places where it is desirable to prevent damage to the cedars or to reduce the production of spores that would otherwise reinfect pomes.

D. H. PALMITER *has been associated with the New York State Agricultural Experiment Station since 1937. He is a graduate of Oregon State College and received his doctorate in plant pathology at the University of Wisconsin. In New York he has investigated methods of controlling various fruit tree diseases by means of fungicide applications.*

Anthony Berg: A Rust-resistant Red Cedar, *Phytopathology,* volume 30, *pages 876–878, 1940.*

N. J. Giddings and *Anthony Berg:* Apple Rust, *West Virginia University Agricultural Experiment Station Bulletin 154, pages 1–73, 1915.*

L. R. Jones: Apple Rust and Cedar Apples, *Vermont Agricultural Experiment Station Annual Report Number 6, page 83, 1892.*

Paul R. Miller: Pathogenicity, Symptoms, and the Causative Fungi of Three Apple Rusts Compared, *Phytopathology,* volume 29, *pages 801–811, 1939.*

D. H. Palmiter: Three Rust Diseases of Apples and Fungicide Treatments for Their Control, *New York State Agricultural Experiment Station Bulletin 756, pages 1–26, 1952.*

Sooty Blotch and Fly Speck

A. B. Groves

Sooty blotch and fly speck are the common names for two diseases of the apple that can mar the appearance of the fruit.

Sooty blotch appears as sootlike spots or blotches. Fly speck makes dark spots that look somewhat like fly specks. Although the two diseases are not caused by the same fungus (sooty blotch is caused by *Gloeodes pomigena* and fly speck by *Leptothyrium pomi*), they are so commonly found in association and develop freely under the same favorable climatic conditions that they are usually described together.

Sooty blotch is also widely known by the name cloud and less commonly as sooty smudge, sooty spot, and inky spot. It appears as dark-brown to olive-green spots or smudges on the surface of mature pomaceous fruits.

Fly speck appears as well-defined, slightly raised, small, dark spots on the surface. The specks commonly occur in groups, seldom singly. The two diseases cause little or no actual injury to the fruit, but by disfiguring it they lower its market value. They are most troublesome in orchards on low land or in other places where air drainage is poor and the humidity tends to remain high. Both diseases are easily controlled, but the possibility of their occurrence cannot be ignored if blemish-free fruit is to be produced.

Sooty blotch occurs throughout the humid fruit-producing regions of

North America, and has been reported from Great Britain and France. Specimens I received from Australia in 1932 appeared identical with types I then was studying in Virginia. The disease has been observed on wild crab apples in the mountains of West Virginia. Probably the diseases occur more widely than has been reported, but have received less attention than more serious disorders.

The sooty blotch spot on an apple consists of a thin fungal crust, or thallus. Profusely branched and connecting threads of rather thick-walled cells, which are brown to olive green, make up the thallus. It varies from a somewhat uniform thin mycelial mat with indefinite margins to a type with clearly defined margins and heavy aggregations of cells, known as plectenchymal bodies, scattered through it. The plectenchymal bodies may occasionally develop into pycnidia, although they usually fail to develop spores.

The fly speck thallus is dark brown to olive green and is sharply defined. The individual specks are much smaller than an entire sooty blotch spot, the fly speck thallus usually being about 250 to 300 microns in diameter. This is much larger than the individual plectenchymal bodies in a sooty blotch thallus, however. The individual fly speck spots show no connection one with another which is visible to the unaided eye. Microscopic examination reveals the individual specks of one group or colony to be connected by hyaline mycelial strands, however.

A careful examination of numerous sooty blotch specimens reveal differences in the gross morphological appearance of the spots. The variations may be grouped into a few characteristic types. After studying specimens from widely separated sections of the country, I classified them into four groups.

The most common is the ramose, or branched, type. Strong radial or fernlike growth is a common characteristic. Plectenchymal bodies vary from sparse to abundant and tend to be irregular in shape.

Spots of the rimate group, the second most abundant, have roughened cuticle in the infected area. The fungus penetrates the cuticle and grows most abundantly along the minute fissures produced. The heavy aggregations of fungal cells along the fissures are conspicuous enough to be readily detected through a hand lens.

The punctate, the third type, is typified by conspicuous darker dots or specks throughout the spot. The dots, or plectenchymal bodies, although quite conspicuous, are smaller than those of fly speck, and the interconnecting mycelium is plainly visible.

The fourth and least conspicuous type is the fuliginous, or smoky smudge, type. The spots may be rather well defined or with indefinite margins, covering large areas of the fruit. Plectenchymal bodies are characteristically absent under normal conditions although they may form on fruits placed in a moist chamber. The fungal mat is thin and lacks conspicuous growth characters. The fuliginous types may be removed from the surface of the fruit with light scraping, but cannot be wiped off.

Sooty blotch and fly speck occur commonly and are of consequence only on the pomaceous fruits. The only extensive investigation of the natural host range of the sooty blotch fungus was made in 1930 and 1931 by R. C. Baines and M. W. Gardner, of Purdue University. They reproduced the disease on apple fruits through the use of pure cultures from 10 woody plant hosts: Hard, or sugar maple, *Acer saccharum;* the pawpaw, *Asimina triloba;* downy hawthorn, *Crataegus mollis,* leatherwood, *Dirca palustris;* white ash, *Fraxinus americana,* spicebush, *Lindera benzoin;* sycamore, *Platanus occidentalis;* slippery elm, *Ulmus fulva;* willow, *Salix nigra;* bristly greenbriar, *Smilax hispida;* bladdernut, *Staphylea trifolia;* and prickly-ash, *Zanthoxylum americanum.* The cultures were obtained from the fungus found on the young twigs.

Inoculum presumably comes from infected twigs. The greater abundance of spots on the upper side of the fruit and over areas close to the twigs indicates that the twigs are a source of inoculum, rather than fallen fruits from the previous season.

The sooty blotch fungus forms pycnidia abundantly. Conidia are produced less freely. I have found only a few conidia in examining many apparently mature pycnidia on the surface of apple fruits. A. S. Colby, of the University of Illinois, in 1919 reported the conidia to be almost hyaline, one-celled, of varying shape, and measuring 10–20 by 4–7 microns. He also found infection to be spread by single-celled mycelial fragments or chlamydospores.

Baines and Gardner reported spore production within the pycnidia on woody hosts other than apple. They found spore production to be abundant, the spores maturing and discharging in the late spring. The mature spores they found were bicellular.

C. F. Taylor and I. G. Bennett, of the University of West Virginia, made fruit-bagging experiments to determine the time of infection on unsprayed apple trees. They found relatively little fly speck before early July, although infection increased rapidly afterwards. All fruit that was unprotected before mid-July became heavily infected. Little infection occurred on fruits that were exposed only after mid-August—perhaps, therefore, the normal infection period for fly speck lies between early June and mid-August.

The situation with sooty blotch was less clear. Their experiment was divided into two series. In one series many fruits were bagged early in the season and the lots were unbagged at 10-day intervals until late September. In the parallel series lots of fruits were bagged at 10-day intervals after June 22 and allowed to remain bagged for the remainder of the season. Fruit exposed only before June 22 was 36 percent infected with sooty blotch. Fruit

exposed for the rest of the season after that date was 100 percent infected. The amount of infection declined slowly as the period of exposure was shortened. Little infection apparently developed after early September. Their results indicate that infection may occur from mid-June to September.

Sooty blotch has been commonly characterized as a superficial disease: The fungus does not penetrate deeply into the host tissue. The superficial character of the disease cannot be correctly interpreted as being wholly outside the host cells, however.

Evidence of the cuticle-rupturing nature of the fungus is afforded through the manner in which the diseased spots lose moisture more rapidly than the surrounding tissue, and the spots become sunken when fruits are held for a few weeks after harvest. The entire fruit eventually shrivels when it is infected extensively.

Investigations I made in 1932 demonstrated the manner in which the sooty blotch fungus penetrates the cuticle of the host fruit and spreads through the epidermal cells immediately beneath the cuticle. Some types make only scattered penetrations of the cuticle; the main part of the mycelial mat is on the surface of the cuticle. The rimate types proliferated abundantly in the cuticular fissures created until the major part of the invading fungus was within or beneath the epidermal layer.

The sooty blotch fungus may be cultured and grows readily, if slowly, on various media. It is not very easy to isolate the fungus, though, because it is hard to free the thallus of contaminating organisms. Surface sterilization frequently destroys the fungus it is desired to isolate, particularly the fuliginous types. I have readily isolated the fungus by gently swabbing and wiping the diseased surface with sterile water and cotton-tipped swabs, cutting small pieces of diseased tissue out, and placing the tissue on the surface of a plain agar plate. The fungus soon produces a thin, pubescent layer of aerial mycelium. Bits of it are removed with very finely drawn glass needles and transferred to the surface of a plate of nutrient agar. The fungus produces a leathery and markedly heaped-up thallus in culture. The color varies from olive green to deep brown and gray. The submerged mycelium usually appears black. The colonies produce characteristic masses of spores, which at first are salmon pink but later become quite dark in mass. The spores bud freely, and it is difficult to find specimens of uniform size and form. Isolates vary in microscopic appearance, but there appears to be no correlation between these variations and thallus types encountered on the fruit.

Sooty blotch and fly speck never presented a difficult problem in the past. The fungicides commonly used for protection against more serious diseases were normally quite adequate against sooty blotch and fly speck. The diseases have tended to reappear, however, in well-cared-for orchards since the widespread shift from the inorganic insecticides and fungicides to the organic pesticides. The inorganic fungicides formerly used were principally copper salts and had a wide range of fungicidal effectiveness. The organic fungicides have a much more specific character.

Evidence and observation indicate that the reappearance of sooty blotch can be attributed partly to the lesser effectiveness of, or persistence of, the organic fungicides used on apples, and partly to a reduction in late-season spraying made possible because of the reduction in insect problems through the use of DDT and other organic insecticides. Growers have not tended to make summer applications of fungicides alone, spraying only where they considered it necessary also to combat insects.

The sooty blotch which has reappeared in well-sprayed orchards the past few seasons has been of the fulig-

inous type. Whether this indicates a greater resistance of this type to the ferbam and captan fungicides, or to an infection which occurs after the fungicide becomes ineffective and only the fuliginous type develops rapidly enough to become visible before harvest, has not been determined. Fly speck has also reappeared together with the fuliginous type of sooty blotch.

C. F. Taylor conducted extensive control trials on sooty blotch and fly speck. He tested many fungicides and made applications at intervals through the season. He found ferbam to be superior to bordeaux against fly speck but inferior against sooty blotch. Although ferbam applications in late May were the most effective, no application of ferbam was entirely satisfactory. Bordeaux mixture was most effective in mid-July. Sulfur was not a satisfactory fungicide in his tests. The use of sulfur is generally avoided in summer spraying, however, because of its tendency to cause sulfur sunscald when temperatures are high.

That fly speck usually appears earlier than sooty blotch suggests either an earlier time of infection or a more rapid rate of development following infection.

A. B. Groves *is a plant pathologist with the Virginia Agricultural Experiment Station. He has been stationed at the Winchester Fruit Research Laboratory since 1929. His field of specialization includes tree fruit diseases and the problems associated with their control.*

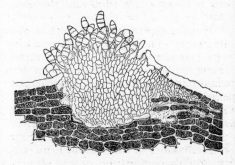

Coryneum pustule on peach.

Powdery Mildew on Apples

Roderick Sprague

Apple powdery mildew, caused by the fungus *Podosphaera leucotricha*, is widely distributed in the United States. It is serious mainly in the far West, notably in the warm, dry valleys of Washington (in the neighborhoods of Wenatchee and Yakima) and Oregon and in some valleys of California.

Many of the old susceptible varieties—Black Ben, Grimes, Spitzenberg, and to some extent Yellow Newtown—have all but disappeared from commercial production in the West and no longer cause problems. Jonathan and Rome Beauty, which are still widely grown, however, are highly susceptible to powdery mildew.

Jonathan is used as a pollinizer for Delicious and Red Delicious. It carries mildew in the mixed orchards. Jonathan is being replaced in the West by less susceptible and more profitable varieties, but its value for juice processing and its recognized merit as a fruit will keep it in continued use for many years. Therefore the control of apple powdery mildew on those useful but susceptible varieties remains an important problem.

Powdery mildew attacks the leaves, twigs, blossoms, and fruit of apples, pears, and sometimes quince, hawthorn, serviceberry, cherries, and prunes. Usually the mildew found on cherries is a closely related species (*P. oxyacanthae*) which is reported now and then on apples.

Powdery mildew first forms off-white or pale-gray, feltlike patches on the margins of leaves, usually on the under side. The fungus then gradually spreads until it covers the whole leaf surface and all the leaves in a terminal cluster. The mildew grows down the twig, which it covers with a gray felt. Dark-gray or black patches later form on the gray felt after the many tiny, globe-shaped winter fruiting bodies of the fungus develop in the summer.

Young infected leaves become somewhat narrowed and folded longitudinally, and their under sides are exposed. Some become curled, crinkled, and stiffened. Many fall off before autumn. Terminals attacked early in the year often fail to survive or have tiny, dried remnants of leaves left on them at harvest. Such twigs and their buds are easily injured in winter. Mildewed terminals tend to enter the winter with open buds. Jonathan is particularly subject to terminal killing because of this inability to close the buds over with bud scales. Because so many terminals are killed or stunted by mildew, the trees are forced to send out twigs from side buds; twig bunching or staghorn growths often result. They deform the tree and reduce its fruiting surface.

Blossom infection sometimes occurs when the fungus overwinters in the dormant blossom bud. Such infection usually causes blighted clusters in which no fruit survives. Because the infected buds emerge late in spring, the chances of widespread seasonal blossom infection are slight. Sometimes young fruits are attacked soon after the blooming period, however. The fruit infection does not last very many weeks but sometimes causes an etching or russeting of the fruit, especially at the calyx end.

Russeting of fruit has been the cause of most of the complaints about loss from mildew. Heavy cullage from fruit russet in 1948 in eastern Washington led the industry to ask for further research of the problem. A great deal of work was done by D. F. Fisher, of the Department of Agriculture, about a quarter of a century ago at Wenatchee. Later E. L. Reeves continued the investigations. Mildew continued to be abundant on susceptible varieties in eastern Washington but very little fruit russeting attributable to powdery mildew was seen between 1948 and 1953. Mildew injury to the fruit in California is not common.

Mildew on such resistant varieties as Delicious or Winesap is usually from infections of the current season. Very little overwinters, except under favorable conditions in thickly planted orchards. A few twigs of Winesaps appear infected in very early spring.

The infection on Delicious from the current-season spores usually starts as obscure marginal lesions. They may show a pale, wine-colored or lavender-tinted border. The leaves usually roll inward. In orchards where Jonathan and Delicious are closely interplanted, 50 percent of the leaf clusters of Delicious sometimes are infected, but the lesions usually are restricted or only a leaf or two in one cluster is diseased.

Mildew appears in the Wenatchee district before blossoming time. It develops rapidly until June. After hot weather comes, the rate of its spread slows down, but the total infection slowly increases until harvest. During severe infestations about 75 percent of unsprayed leaf clusters of Jonathan are infected at harvest. The next spring 10 to 40 percent of the emerging buds show mildew, which arises from overwintering mycelium in the buds.

The severity of the winter determines how many infected buds will survive. The mildew fungus is relatively winter hardy, but severe cold will kill many of the diseased buds and with them the mildew. Mildew is a parasite that cannot survive without its host plant. Trees that are not sprayed for mildew show excessive twig injury and in time will succumb to winter injury.

THE FUNGUS that causes mildew grows on the surface but it sends long suckers (haustoria) into the leaf cells. Perhaps that is why it is hard to kill it with fungicides.

The fungus produces enormous numbers of spores in chains on the fungus threads. Wind carries the spores great distances. The spores require little moisture to germinate—the dew in irrigated orchards is enough to allow the fungus to develop in dry regions.

A survey in Chelan, Douglas, and Okanogan Counties in north central Washington in 1949–1951 showed that mildew was nearly as prevalent in orchards irrigated by rills along the ground as in ones irrigated by sprinklers. There has been a tendency to blame the sprinklers for an increased amount of mildew.

Overhead sprinklers tend to favor mildew in resistant varieties or in some young orchards of Golden Delicious. On susceptible varieties such as Jonathan, the type of irrigation did not appear to have any great influence on mildew although sprinkling at frequent intervals tended to increase mildew.

In Jonathan the mildew is usually worse on the southwest and west sides of the trees and in the treetops. In a tree that shows about 75 percent of the leaf clusters mildewed the tops will usually average about 95 percent mildew.

DR. FISHER mentioned that lime-sulfur sprays to control apple scab would also control mildew. For that reason mildew was seldom serious in a region where scab was serious and an efficient spray program was carried out for scab. Lime-sulfur has been used less and less in the West, and outbreaks of scab have occurred in several places in Washington.

To control mildew in the far West I recommend:

1. Spray with 2.5 percent concentrate 32° Baumé lime-sulfur (2.5 gallons in 100 gallons of water) as the blossoms reach the pink stage, just before blooming; or use dried sodium polysulfide at the rate of 3 pounds to 100 gallons of water.

2. Spray with 2.0 percent lime-sulfur after 75 percent of the petals have fallen; or use 2.5 pounds of the dried sodium polysulfide to 100 gallons of water.

3. Spray with 2 to 4 pounds of wettable sulfur 2 weeks later. Micronized sulfur has given adequate control at 2 pounds to 100 gallons.

In orchards sprayed with lime-sulfur or with sulfur, the mildew is held down to 5 to 20 percent until July. As no summer spraying is safe with sulfur sprays or dusts in the north central area, mildew starts to spread after the last of the sulfur has disappeared from the foliage. By fall mildew may have arisen to 30 percent or even up to 45 percent or more on trees that had been given only two sprays with lime-sulfur at the pink and calyx stages.

Those suggestions as to rates of application are based on the use of spray guns manually operated from power-driven sprayers, either stationary or portable. Most of the growers now are turning to the use of air-blast sprayers with fixed nozzles. Dosages for them are based on amounts of material per acre. The dosages are computed by determining the amount of material used per tree by the old hand spray gun method multiplied by the number of trees per acre, less about 20 percent. The fixed nozzles forced by an air blast give coverage with little or no spray runoff, hence about 20 percent less spray is usually needed. Some of the so-called concentrate sprayers use very fine jets and apply the spray in exceedingly fine droplets at relatively high concentrations of material. Proportionately less water is used per acre. Many factors are involved in determining how much material to use per acre.

In the warm valleys of the far West, sulfur cannot be applied after the first cover spray because of the danger of injury from sulfur shock or of fruit scalding. Usually, however, a second cover spray, using 2 pounds of micronized sulfur, is safe on Jonathan. On Delicious and Stayman Winesap, sulfur is generally not recommended at all. In the cooler parts of the northern areas, lime-sulfur is safe on Delicious if it is applied at the pink and calyx stages only. As mildew is seldom serious on Delicious, the early sprays often are not needed. Because scab has appeared in some places, the program for scab control will fairly well eliminate mildew on Delicious. In a few cases ferbam, 1.5 pounds to 100 gallons of water, can be substituted for sulfur. Ferbam is not overly effective against apple powdery mildew and its effect does not last more than 10 or 12 days.

Many experimental materials have been tested at the Tree Fruit Experiment Station in Wenatchee, Wash., and at the Hood River Experiment Station in Oregon against apple powdery mildew. Few proved to be as efficient as lime-sulfur; those few were too costly or were unobtainable on a commercial scale.

Dusting with sulfur from the ground or from airplanes (60 pounds to the acre) was effective in places where water for sprays was not readily available. Dusting in the early part of the season was less effective than the wet treatments, however.

Pruning sometimes helps check mildew in a young orchard. Mildew in young Golden Delicious tends to be restricted to a few terminals. It is sometimes cheaper to prune them than to spray. If the mildew occurs on most of the twigs, pruning may not be practical, or it may not be wise to give such a shock to the young tree in summer.

Mildew-susceptible varieties should be eliminated if possible. A few susceptible trees in an orchard can cause a considerable increase in mildew in the more resistant varieties even if they are some distance away. If susceptible varieties are planted as an integral part of the orchard, the grower must resort to a spray program.

It is not possible to repress mildew by the use of any of the standard understocks. There is no danger in top-working Jonathan to Delicious, however. The Delicious trees grow and flourish with no increase in mildew although Jonathan sap flows through their branches. Of course, if only part of the tree is top-worked to Delicious, the adjacent Jonathan branches will infect the Delicious branches to some extent because of the abundant spores carried to the resistant Delicious from adjacent Jonathan leaves.

In all future breeding programs aimed at development of better apple varieties, mildew should be considered. Susceptibility to mildew appears to be a dominant trait in Jonathan hybrids. Jonathan-type apples said to be resistant to mildew are available, but widespread trials are needed to prove their commercial value.

RODERICK SPRAGUE *is a pathologist at the Tree Fruit Experiment Station, Wenatchee, Wash. He is a graduate of Washington State College and received the doctor's degree from the University of Cincinnati.*

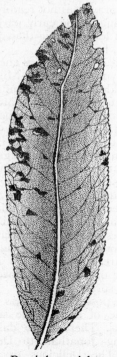

Peach bacterial spot.

Stony Pit of Pears

J. R. Kienholz

Stony pit causes deformity and pitting of pear fruits. A roughened bark condition may accompany the pitting. Narrow yellow places along the veinlets of the younger leaves appear in some varieties. Numerous "stone cells" beneath or surrounding each fruit pit and the hard structure of the fruit give the disease its name.

Research men have known of the existence of stony pit in Beurre Bosc pears in Oregon and Washington since 1919 and in California since 1925. Stony pit also occurs in New Zealand, Canada, England, and probably wherever Bosc pears are grown. Surveys of orchards have disclosed that 1 to 70 of every 100 Bosc trees are affected; 10 to 80 percent of the cull Bosc fruits at the packing houses can be attributed to stony pit.

Stony pit was considered a form of drought spot before 1938, although various cultural practices failed to correct the trouble. Proof that the disease was caused by a virus was obtained in 1938, when previously healthy Bosc and Anjou trees produced pitted fruits after diseased Bosc buds had been inserted in their limbs in 1936. Because most of the commercial loss occurred in the Bosc variety up to 1950 and because the disease was prevalent only in Bosc, we believe that diseased trees originated largely in nursery plantings for which scion wood had been carelessly selected from diseased orchards. Bosc is the only variety known to express complete symptoms of the disease—fruit pitting, an oak-bark condition of the trunk and larger limbs, and a veinlet yellowing of younger leaves.

From 10 days to a month after petal fall, dark-green areas form just under the epidermis of diseased fruit. Lack of growth in those areas and the rapid development of surrounding healthy tissue result in deeply pitted or deformed fruit at maturity. Sometimes a greenish halo surrounds the pit; dark, sunken, circular areas, with raised centers of healthy tissue, may form.

The tissue at the base of the pits generally becomes lifeless. In severely infected fruits a concentration of the darkened spots occurs near or within the grit cell ring. The most striking feature of diseased fruit is the production of numerous sclerenchyma cells (grit cells) beneath or surrounding the pitted areas. Fruits bearing numerous pits become so gnarled and woody they can hardly be cut with a knife.

Sometimes only a few pits, or one, may form on a fruit, or pitting may be shallow and scattered on varieties like Anjou, Hardy, and Old Home. On those varieties the pitting generally is later in developing than on Bosc; occasionally it appears only a month before harvest. Unless other tree symptoms are present, the mild fruit symptoms are easily confused with those caused by the tarnished plant bug (*Lygus pratensis*), boron deficiency, or cork spot.

A natural, angular, bark cracking occurs on healthy pear trees as they mature. A "measled" bark condition is associated with diseased Bosc trees after stony pit has been present in them for several years. Small pimples may appear on the bark of 1- or 2-year-old Bosc twigs. Later in the season or the following year, the epidermis cracks and the underlying tissue collapses. The cracking and shrinking occur in such a way that somewhat concentric, target-canker effects are produced on small limbs. Continued growth and cracking of the limb tissue causes older

limbs to assume a ribbed appearance, sometimes called oak-bark. The trees reaching this stage of the disease have less foliage because the lateral buds fail to grow. Terminal shoots and fruit spurs bear most of the scant leaf surface. Such trees are more subject to winter killing than vigorous trees.

Oak-bark has been found only on scion wood of a top-worked tree. In others the rough bark may be present only on the trunk wood. The virus therefore may be carried in either unit, and although fruit symptoms appear after the second year from transmission of the virus to the healthy unit, bark symptoms appear only after several years of growth or not at all, depending on the varieties involved.

True leaf symptoms consist of narrow, chlorotic areas along the veinlets of the leaves. Varieties expressing this symptom usually begin showing the yellowing in younger leaves about June. The youngest two or three leaves on terminal shoots generally appear healthy, the three to five middle leaves show chlorotic veinlets, and the basal, dark-green leaves again appear healthy. As the middle leaves attain full maturity and take on the dark-green color, the virus symptoms gradually fade. An exception is the Forelle variety, in which leaf symptoms persist throughout the season.

A second, or false, leaf symptom consists of faint or definite mottling, usually toward the edges of the leaves. That may be the result, in diseased trees, of a partial plugging of the transporting tissues, so that leaves cannot obtain enough nutrients or water during critical stages of growth. This leaf symptom is not limited to stony pit trees and is no indication that the stony pit virus is present in the tree.

Each variety reacts differently to the stony pit virus. Bosc exhibits the complete symptoms on fruit, bark and leaves. Winter Nelis shows only fruit symptoms. Vicar of Wakefield expresses only leaf symptoms. Bartlett exhibits no symptom. It is known to carry the virus in a symptomless condition, however, for when healthy Bosc or Anjou are top-worked to infected Bartlett, the virus is transmitted to the scion varieties upon which typical pitting appears in the fruit.

Varieties of pears known to show fruit symptoms are Beurre d'Anjou, Beurre Bedford, Beurre Bosc, Beurre Clairgeau, Buerre Hardy, Cole Winter, Durandeau, Laxton's Superb, Old Home, Packham's Triumph, Patrick Barry, Pitmaston Duchess, Waite, and Winter Nelis.

Definite leaf symptoms have been found on Anjou (rarely), Bosc, Doyenne du Comice, Forelle, Orel, Patten, some seedlings of *Pyrus communis*, and Vicar of Wakefield.

The oak-bark symptoms have appeared only on Bosc, although Anjou and Comice have sometimes formed a targetlike cankering on trunks and scaffold limbs on trees known to have been infected for at least 10 years. It is possible that different strains of the virus exist which may cause mild leaf symptoms or severe fruit pitting on varieties not usually affected.

Graft inoculations have failed to yield definite stony pit symptoms in apples (*Malus sylvestris*, varieties Delicious and Yellow Newtown); flowering quince (*Chaenomeles japonica*); hawthorn (*Crataegus douglasi*); medlar (*Mespilus germanica*); mountain-ash (*Sorbus sitchensis*); quince (*Cydonia oblonga*); rose (*Rosa multiflora*); and serviceberry (*Amelanchier florida*).

CHEMICAL INJECTIONS have been made into diseased pear trees to determine if stony pit symptoms could be relieved. Injections of boric acid, zinc sulfate, copper phosphate, and manganese borate failed to influence the fruit pitting over a period of 3 years. Neither borax nor boric acid applied as sprays or as ground applications alleviated the fruit symptoms.

After symptoms appear the tree remains infected for the rest of its life. The severity of fruit pitting may vary somewhat from season to season, but it never disappears. Occasionally an individual leader branch may bear severely pitted fruits for years, while the other fruit on the tree appears healthy. The virus seems to become more potent in rapidly growing young trees and milder in very old trees that make little terminal growth. Dehorning, or cutting off diseased limbs, is no cure for stony pit. In fact, the fruit and leaf symptoms usually appear in more severe form after such treatment.

Severely infected Bosc trees, with oak-bark symptoms and sparse foilage, should be eliminated from the orchard. as they are no longer profitable. When it was discovered that Bartlett showed no symptoms, even though infected by the stony pit virus, it was suggested this variety might be top-worked to less severely diseased Bosc trees. Many growers followed this suggestion, despite the hazards of leaving diseased but symptomless varieties in the orchard.

S. G. Babson, of Parkdale, Oreg., has top-worked more than 100 pear trees affected with stony pit to the Bartlett variety. In no case have stony pit symptoms appeared in the Bartlett fruits on those trees in 15 seasons. His method of top-working has been to place 50 buds or more in the smaller limbs, eventually retaining only the framework of the diseased trees. To change a variety completely over to Bartlett has sometimes required two additional years of supplemental budding to complete changing limbs missed in the first budding.

Studies of the production of such top-worked trees, made by G. G. Brown, of the Hood River Branch Station of Oregon State College, indicated full production was usually attained during the third or fourth year. The average production of the top-worked trees after the fourth year was higher than unworked Bartlett trees of the same age: Mr. Babson obtained in 4 years what would have taken 12 to 14 years to accomplish by replanting healthy trees. As the trees were bearing full crops during the high-price cycle of the war, the gain was amply justified from an immediate economic standpoint. But because of greater mortality of the trees to winter injury and because a virus reservoir remains in such trees as a source to infect healthy trees in the orchard, the advisability of top-working diseased trees can be seriously questioned as a sound practice in maintaining a productive orchard.

FEW NEW PLANTINGS of Bosc pears have been made in the Pacific Coast States. Many healthy and diseased Bosc trees have been top-grafted to Bartlett. Infections resulting from top-working diseased Bosc to susceptible varieties have occasionally been observed in the varieties Anjou, Hardy, and Winter Nelis. Natural infections on those varieties were largely a curiosity up to 1945. About that year, fruit growers from various districts began calling attention to the pitted fruits on an occasional Anjou pear tree in their orchards. Since Anjou is one of the leading varieties of winter pears grown in the Pacific Coast States, the increase of stony pit on the variety presents a real threat.

Pear trees in three orchards at Hood River have been mapped periodically since 1936. One orchard, planted originally to Bosc pears in 1913, developed considerable stony pit before 1936. Most of the trees were subsequently top-worked to either Anjou or Bartlett. In this top-worked block of trees, 44 percent of the Anjous developed stony pit and 15 percent of the unworked Bosc became diseased. None of the Bartletts top-worked to previously diseased Bosc showed symptoms of stony pit. Severe winter damage in 1948–1949 killed many of the top-worked trees, or parts of them, so that the original orchard contained many interplanted young trees in 1952. An adjacent part of the same orchard, planted originally to Anjous and Bartletts, remained free from stony pit until about 1945. By 1949 eight Anjou trees were diseased; 16 Anjou trees showed stony pit symptoms in 1951. Nine percent of the original Anjous became diseased

after 1945. Chances for new infections in the orchard were above average because of the presence of many diseased trees nearby.

The two other orchards mapped probably represent more usual conditions. Stony pit was not found in the two orchards, which had 858 and 669 pear trees, before 1940. Only one Bosc tree existed in the orchards, and even though it remained healthy until 1950, it was removed. No known source of the stony pit virus is present within one-half mile of the two orchards. In 1949, three trees, or 0.6 percent, of the Anjous had developed stony pit; that increased to 1.7 percent by 1951 in the one orchard. In the second orchard 1.1 percent of the Anjous were diseased in 1949; that increased to 2 percent by 1951.

We know of no insect vector responsible for spreading the stony pit virus, although several suspected species of leafhoppers need to be investigated. The point to be emphasized is that stony pit is now common enough in the Anjou variety that the practice of cutting scion wood from random trees in an orchard presents a hazard in the development of disease-free nursery stock for the pear industry. Nurserymen should select mother trees during the growing season that are known to be free from disease and true to type from which to select their scion wood. Fruit growers should eliminate all virus-infected trees from their orchards whenever it is practical to do so. The chances of infecting healthy trees increases greatly as the virus source becomes more common. A season extremely favorable for the spread of the stony pit virus could be disastrous to the individual grower or to a whole district.

J. R. KIENHOLZ, *a pathologist in the division of fruit and nut crops and diseases of the Bureau of Plant Industry, Soils, and Agricultural Engineering, is a native of Washington. His advanced training was obtained at Washington State, Michigan State, and Oregon State Colleges.*

Scab on the Pear

J. R. Kienholz

Pear scab is a disease of world-wide importance. Fungicides have to be used every year to control it in all but a few arid districts. During seasons favorable for scab infections, losses of 20 to 30 percent of the fruit are not uncommon, and if control measures are neglected, practically all of the fruit may be unmarketable.

The scab fungus (*Venturia pyrina*) may attack the flower parts, fruit, leaves, or young twigs. Wet weather, particularly early in the growing season, is probably the greatest factor in determining the increase or decline of pear scab from year to year. A closely related fungus (*V. inaequalis*) causes apple scab, but it cannot infect pears, and the pear scab fungus cannot infect apples. The observations reported here pertain mainly to the conditions in the Pacific Northwest.

ABOUT THE TIME the petals fall in the spring, dark velvety or sooty spots may appear on young fruits. Infections may occur on the leaves, the fruit stems, the calyx lobes, or even the flower petals. If the fruit stems are attacked, the young fruits are usually weakened and drop. If fruit growth continues, a badly misshapen pear results. The scab spots usually enlarge as the fruit grows until arrested either by hot, dry weather or by fungicidal sprays. Early infections eventually may involve the whole side of a fruit; later infections may result in numerous smaller spots. The central, or older part, of an early scab spot may die and leave a corky or russeted skin area. An olive-brown rim of active fungus tissue often remains alive at the edge of the spot. This tissue may produce new spores and the spores in turn cause numerous new infections during wet weather.

Leaf infections are like those on the fruit, but they usually appear slightly later. They are more common on the lower surface of the leaves than on the upper. Individual spots rarely become more than three-fourths inch in diameter and appear black, because of the compact growth of the fungus. Sometimes the fungus threads radiate in less compact masses to produce a fernlike, irregular scab patch. Single scab spots are common on the leaves. They often envelop the midrib or leaf veins and cause considerable puckering or twisting of the leaf. As the scab spots mature and dry out, they may crack or tear, leaving a jagged, black-rimmed hole in the leaf. Less food is manufactured for the tree by scabby leaves. Numerous infections may cause the leaves to weaken, dry up, and drop prematurely. Continued attacks of the disease will devitalize the trees.

New twig growth on pear trees may be infected at any time during the growing season. Most infections result when rains are frequent. During spring and summer new twig lesions are inconspicuous. They appear merely as small, blisterlike pustules, no larger than a pinhead. Sometimes the fungus remains invisible within the twigs as a latent infection. Occasionally a shallow, spore-producing layer is formed. A corky layer often forms beneath the twig infections and many are sloughed off before autumn, leaving small depressions on the twigs. If the twig infections are not sloughed, the fungus remains dormant in the twigs until the following spring, when renewal of tree growth causes the fungus to become active again. The fungus breaks through the epidermis of the twig, forming a scab pustule. Numerous scab spores mature in the pustules, usually before the blossom clusters separate. The overwintered twig lesions also are generally sloughed off during the growing season, but occasionally a few remain to form spores the next season. Old sloughed lesions may appear in 2- to 5-year-old branches as small crater-like depressions.

THE PEAR SCAB FUNGUS has two distinct stages in its life cycle.

Throughout the growing season the fungus lives as a true parasite within the pear tissue. After primary infections occur in the spring the fungus pushes or breaks through the surface of infected fruit or leaves, and produces summer spores (conidia). These spores are formed in great numbers when weather conditions are suitable. They are dispersed by rain and wind to cause new infections. Each spore, if moisture and temperature are favorable, can develop a tiny germ tube, which may enter the host tissue and cause a new infection. These processes may occur many times during the season and numerous secondary infections may result.

The summer or parasitic stage may also overwinter in infected twigs. Because the spores are generally mature before the pear buds unfold, it is the most important source for primary infections the following spring.

The fungus also overwinters as a saprophyte on the infected leaves that drop in the fall. Thick-walled, flask-shaped, beaked structures, known as perithecia, are formed within the old leaf tissue during the winter. Numerous tiny, saclike organs, called asci, containing eight small, two-celled spores (ascospores), are formed within the perithecia. The ascospores become pale olive green as they approach maturity, about the time the pear buds are unfolding. When moisture and temperature conditions are favorable, they are discharged through the beaks of the perithecia into the air. Air currents carry the spores to the trees, where they may germinate and cause

primary spring infections. Those infections soon produce the summer spores, and secondary infections result when conditions are favorable for the fungus.

Scab spores are disseminated only during moist periods. Continual moisture for 5 to 48 hours is necessary before the spores germinate and infect susceptible pear tissue. If the temperature during the rainy period is about 75° F., a spore may germinate and infect the plant within approximately 4 to 5 hours. At lower temperatures moisture must persist for a longer time, so that at 40°, a wet period of approximately 48 hours is required before infection occurs. After infection has taken place, 12 to 25 days are required before the fungus grows enough to become visible to the naked eye. When scab spots suddenly appear on fruit during dry weather, it must be remembered that the infections occurred during a previous rainy period.

MOST OF THE COMMERCIAL pear varieties commonly grown are susceptible to scab infections. Fruits of Anjou, Bartlett, Comice, Winter Nelis, Easter, Forelle, Seckel, and Flemish Beauty often are severely affected. Bosc fruits are very susceptible in the young stage, but about the time they shed their pubescence they become highly resistant. Frequently a variety only lightly attacked in one district may be the most seriously affected in another. The first spray is generally timed according to pear bud development. Since a pollinizer variety like Easter unfolds its buds earlier than Anjou, the early spray, if timed for the Anjou variety, may allow some infections on exposed Easter buds. If timed for the Easter variety, the spray is too early to be fully effective on the Anjou variety.

Twig infections have never been observed on Bartlett in the Hood River Valley of Oregon. Yet in districts with higher rainfall twig scab is common on the variety. Climatic conditions, fertilizers, pruning practices, soils, cover crops, and other factors all have a part in modifying growth characteristics of pear trees and their susceptibility or resistance to the scab fungus.

The fungus also varies its attack on pears. G. W. Keitt, at the Wisconsin Agricultural Experiment Station, determined in greenhouse tests that at least two strains of the scab fungus exist in Oregon. One strain attacks Bartlett but not Anjou pears. Another infects Anjou but not Bartlett. This condition has been observed under field conditions in Oregon. Probably other strains of the fungus exist in nature, but their relationships have not been definitely demonstrated.

Trees should be well spaced and pruned to give an open type of growth so that proper aeration occurs within the trees and to allow thorough spray coverages to be applied. Eliminating excessive water-sprout growth during the summer is often profitable, because it reduces the chance for additional twig infections. Early spring cultivation, to bury the old infected leaves, will lower the amount of the overwintering fungus, which may cause primary infections. Heavy cover crops often prevent rapid evaporation of moisture in an orchard, thereby extending the infection time for the scab fungus. On the other hand, sprinkling orchards during dry periods has not materially increased the scab problem.

THE SECRET of scab control is to prevent the primary spring infections. Any overwintered twig infections are more important sources of spores that cause primary infections than those developed in overwintering leaves. Most of the twig lesions expose their spore masses by the time the delayed dormant spray is to be applied, although a small number may sporulate after that period. Therefore the lime-sulfur application is delayed as long as possible in order to "burn out" as many twig lesions as possible without causing damage to exposed pear buds. Lime-sulfur will usually cause severe russet on tender-skinned pears when applied in humid districts after the outer bud scales drop, but it is often used later without injury in drier and hotter districts.

Lime-sulfur (a minimum of 6 gallons to 100 gallons of water) is the most effective fungicide for destroying the spore masses in twig lesions. Bordeaux mixture and wettable sulfur do not penetrate under the epidermal covering of the scab pustules and kill only a few of the surface spores. Thorough coverage of the twigs is essential, since the fungicide kills the spores largely by contact.

Some twig infections may not open until after the delayed dormant spray has been applied, and ascospores produced on overwintered leaves usually mature after that period. Thus it is necessary to apply cover sprays to protect new pear growth from scab infections.

The proper fungicide for use as cover sprays depends mostly on the variety grown and partly on climatic conditions. In that respect we can put pears into two general groups: Those intended for cannery use, or varieties upon which a russet skin does not lower the fruit grade; and the tender-skinned, shipping varieties, which require a smooth skin surface to command top market prices.

Varieties in the first group may be sprayed with lime-sulfur at the pink and calyx stages of bud development or, if needed, until hot weather may be expected. Lime-sulfur has an advantage over many others in being an eradicant spray as well as a protective material. It is dangerous to use any sulfur fungicide on pears when temperatures of 90° F. or over may occur, or if an oil spray will be used within 45 days.

Tender-skinned varieties like Comice and Anjou may be severely russeted by sulfur sprays. The fruit set of Anjou has been cut an average of 30 percent by their use. The spray-sensitive varieties are susceptible to injury early in the season or until the young fruits shed their pubescence about the end of June. As lime-sulfur and other potent eradicative fungicides cannot be used on the tender varieties, milder protective fungicides have to be used. Consequently, the spray applications must be well timed and applied thoroughly to realize satisfactory scab control.

Ferbam (ferric dimethyl dithiocarbamate) and ziram (zinc dimethyl dithiocarbamate) are substitutes for the wettable sulfur sprays. They have been used on tender-skinned pears in the Pacific Northwest since 1944. They have given satisfactory scab control when timed properly and applied thoroughly. They are generally used at the rate of 1½ pounds to 100 gallons of water.

FOLLOWING the delayed dormant spray of lime-sulfur, ferbam or ziram as a first cover spray is usually applied at the pink (preblossom) stage of bud development. If the weather is cool and the buds are slow in opening, it may be advisable also to spray at the prepink, or green-bud, stage before the "pink" spray. If primary infections are not prevented at this early period, the protective fungicides will give only partial scab control later.

Bordeaux mixture or prepared copper fungicides may be substituted for ferbam or ziram on Comice pears, but sulfur in any form is extremely injurious on this variety after the delayed dormant period.

Ferbam or ziram is generally applied at the calyx, or petal-fall, period. Additional applications of ferbam or ziram at 15- to 20-day intervals may be advisable if the season is excessively rainy.

Ferbam and ziram are compatible with most of the newer insecticides, but lime, casein spreaders, or other alkaline materials lower their effectiveness against scab. Applications of ferbam, especially if mixed with oil, are not recommended later than 30 days before harvest because of the difficulty in removing the spray residues. Thorough applications of the earlier sprays will usually make late applications unnecessary.

THE SPRAY SCHEDULE to control pear scab should consist of:

1. The delayed dormant, or green-tip, spray. Use 6 to 8 gallons of liquid lime sulfur (32° Baumé) or its equivalent to 100 gallons of water. Maximum control of the twig scab pustules will be obtained if the application is delayed until a few of the outer bud scales are so loose they can be shattered off during the spray operations. Severe injury may result if used after the bud scales have fallen to expose the young pear buds, particularly on Anjou and Comice pears.

2. Preblossom sprays. The first cover spray is applied at the pink, or preblossom, period when seasonal development is normal. If weather is cool and buds are slow in opening, an additional spray should be applied at the prepink, or green-bud, stage. Ferbam or ziram (1½ pounds to 100 gallons of water) should be used on spray-sensitive varieties, or lime-sulfur (2½ gallons to 100 gallons of water) on varieties not injured by sulfur. Bordeaux mixture or prepared copper fungicides may be substituted for ferbam or ziram on Comice pears, but beware of sulfur in any form on this variety after the delayed dormant period.

3. Calyx spray. A spray consisting of ferbam or ziram (1½ pounds to 100 gallons) is generally applied at the calyx, or petal-fall, period. On varieties not sensitive to the action of sulfur, lime-sulfur (2½ gallons to 100 gallons of water) is recommended unless hot weather may be expected.

4. Additional cover sprays. Additional applications of ferbam or ziram at 15- to 20-day intervals may be needed if the season is excessively rainy. Many of the spray materials, except sulfurs, that cause early injury on the spray-sensitive varieties can often be used with safety on them after July. It is too late by then to use them in an efficient scab control program, but

they might find usage in special cases. Copper sprays, while not usually causing russet at this time, will intensify any russet already present on the fruit. When scabby fruits or leaves are present on the trees after midsummer, a late outbreak of scab may appear if heavy dews or late summer rains occur. Ferbam or ziram, at the rate of 1 to 1½ pounds to 100 gallons of water, may be added to the last codling moth spray to protect the fruit from late infections or storage scab. This practice is not recommended generally, since the residues are difficult to remove after late applications, and scab should be controlled by the earlier sprays if they are applied in the proper way.

AFTER PEAR FRUITS are picked from the trees at harvest they are no longer susceptible to scab infections. Clean fruits picked from scabby orchards do often develop new scab spots while in common or cold storage, but they result from late infections in the orchard. If rains occur 10 to 14 days ahead of harvest, fruit infections may become visible shortly after the fruit is placed in storage. If the infections occur only a few days before harvest, however, the appearance of scab spots on the fruit in cold storage may be delayed until December or January. To prevent scab from appearing on stored fruit it is necessary to control the fungus in the orchard.

Visible scab spots enlarge only slightly during the storage life of the fruit, but the occurrence of several scabby spots causes the fruit to be discarded or sold for less value. Scabby pears transpire and lose weight more rapidly than sound pears in storage, but generally less than 1 pound per box difference can be measured after 5 months in cold storage.

J. R. KIENHOLZ *is a pathologist in the Bureau of Plant Industry, Soils, and Agricultural Engineering. He has been stationed at the United States Fruit Disease Laboratory, Hood River, Oreg., since 1931.*

Fire Blight of Pears in California

C. Emlen Scott

Outbreaks of fire blight wiped out the pear orchards in the San Joaquin Valley and southern California at the turn of the century. It threatened the industry in the Sacramento Valley and was found elsewhere in northern California in 1904. M. B. Waite, of the Department of Agriculture, was sent to California to inaugurate control procedures. He demonstrated the method of removing blighted parts by cutting below the point of infection and using a disinfectant on tools and cuts in the tree. The procedure, somewhat modified, has been the only control method available until recent years.

The application of copper compounds in sprays or dusts during the blossom period is now an established practice in most orchards of Bartlett pears in the districts of California where blight flourishes. Nearly all the experience with this preventative procedure is with the Bartlett pear, which accounts for more than 85 percent of the 39,000-odd acres of pears in California.

The successful program of fire blight prevention now in use in many pear orchards in California is based on facts and hypotheses developed by workers in the California Agricultural Experiment Station and elsewhere. In 1934 H. Earl Thomas and P. A. Ark published the results of a study on the relationship of pear nectar concentrations to the fire blight organism. George H. Vansell had pointed out that the sugar concentration of nectar of fruit trees may vary from less than 3 percent to 55 percent, the higher concentration occurring during periods of low humidity and the low concentration of nectar when the atmospheric humidity was near saturation.

The studies of nectar and various sugar solutions showed that the fire blight bacteria ceased to multiply when the sugar concentration exceeded 20 or 30 percent. Thereupon a theory was developed as to the conditions that give rise to an epidemic of fire blight and explain the observed cases of control with copper sprays. The theory was that most of the activity of blossom-visiting insects occurred during warm days and nights when the nectar concentration was too high to permit the organism to multiply. When such periods of insect activity and blight distribution are followed by rain or high humidity, the nectar is diluted sufficiently to permit multiplication of the blight organism and its entry into the floral parts. The pear growers in California have frequently observed that epidemics of fire blight follow that pattern.

The essential aspects of the fire blight situation in California are:

1. Main blossom period. Epidemics of fire blight have one or more waves of infection during this period. It is sporadic, but the most disastrous phase. Under California conditions the blossom period usually lasts 3 weeks or longer. Epidemics originating in this period appear to be almost entirely due to dissemination by insects. Blossom infection from rain-borne inoculum is infrequent and not commercially important.

2. Late blossom period. The Bartlett variety quite regularly produces some blossoms for a month or so after the main blossom period. Late blossoms are not numerous but they are frequently blighted and are a concern to the pear grower. Part of the control program is usually directed toward control of blight in the late blossoms. That can be done in part by adding a copper-containing material to the codling moth or other insecticidal sprays.

3. Shoot infection. Infection of succulent vegetative shoots during the summer occasionally is an additional problem. No direct preventative measures against this type of infection are known. We have not seen serious damage from blight infections originating in shoots in orchards which have not had an abundance of blossom blight.

4. Fruit infection. Direct infection of fruit near harvesttime has occasionally caused damage in orchards in which considerable blight is present. In several orchards where fruit infections developed, insecticidal oil sprays greatly increased the number of blighted fruit. In one orchard in 1943, 10 trees sprayed with an insecticide plus oil had an average of 17 percent blighted fruit per tree. Ten trees in an adjoining row sprayed with the same insecticide without oil had 0.5 percent blighted fruit per tree. All cases of serious loss of fruit brought to our attention have been related to the use of insecticidal oil sprays near harvesttime. There has been no explanation for this fact.

5. Fall blossoms. Defoliation of Bartlett pear trees after harvest by spider mites or by certain spray materials is usually followed by light to heavy production of blossoms. Pear growers are worried when it occurs, because there have been a few cases of serious blight infections in this unseasonable bloom. No investigations have been made of ways to control this phase of fire blight, but it is assumed that sprays or dusts would be as effective as for the normal blossom period.

During the epidemic of blight in El Dorado County in 1945 it was demonstrated that bordeaux mixture consisting of one-half pound each of copper sulfate and lime in 100 gallons of water was as effective as stronger mixtures. Growers have claimed protection from considerably less copper. One careful operator has apparently controlled blight by using 15 pounds an acre per application of a dust containing 4.5 percent copper.

Observations in California pear orchards indicate that the main function—if not the only one—of copper is to prevent growth of the blight organism in nectar. Probably the organism is carried to blossoms by insects when the nectar is too concentrated to permit its growth as well as when the nectar is greater in volume and lower in sugar concentration. When the nectar is sufficiently diluted by rains or high humidity the organism reproduces and invades the flower through the nectaries. The objective therefore is to place a little copper in the nectar before periods of high humidity and to renew the applications as new blossoms open.

Several operators of orchards where blight has been particularly damaging have carried on a program for seven consecutive years which is designed to afford maximum insurance against the disease. Because of the long blossoming periods common in California and the need for preventing blight in the late bloom, the operators may make up to eight applications in addition to adding copper compounds to the sprays for codling moth. Besides bordeaux mixture and copper-lime dust, a number of fixed or proprietary copper materials are used. We have seen no difference in results from sprays or dusts applied by the various types of ground and air equipment provided that there is adequate distribution of the material. Those using a program for maximum feasible protection will make applications at intervals not to exceed 5 or 6 days in "blight weather" and an interval of about 10 days when the weather remains relatively dry.

The number of applications that would give adequate protection could be reduced if it were possible to predict periods of rain or high humidity accurately for the various pear districts. Many growers feel that they cannot make extensive use of weather predictions. They make four to eight special applications solely for blight control. A few growers have been fairly successful in depending on weather predictions and using the airplane or helicopter two or three times in the season for rapid and timely application of a copper dust at critical periods.

Copper compounds are the only chemicals clearly demonstrated by extensive usage to be effective. Since it is generally accepted by pear growers that control can be had with such small amounts of the copper compounds that no appreciable russeting of Bartlett pear fruit results, there has been no serious demand for other chemicals. Sulfur and ferbam have failed to prevent blight.

No unusual amount of russeting has been reported from the use of sprays or dusts which do not exceed 1 pound of metallic copper an acre. Bordeaux mixture, 800 gallons (one-half pound each of copper sulfate and lime in 100 gallons of water, or its equivalent in other copper compounds) contains 1 pound of metallic copper. Less than 800 gallons is usually adequate for a thorough coverage of pear trees at blossom time. With dusting equipment that requires 30 to 40 pounds of dust to cover an acre adequately it is desirable to use a dust that does not exceed 3.5 percent of metallic copper. The commonly used 7 percent copper dusts often cause excessive russeting when applied at 30 to 40 pounds an acre. The 7 percent dusts are used by a few pear growers who have ground or air equipment that gives effective distribution at 10 to 15 pounds an acre.

Experienced growers have learned it pays to remove blossom infections as soon as detected. When blight cutting is delayed until the following fall or winter, the operation is more expensive in terms of labor required and loss of future production because of heavier cutting and the danger of leaving more hold-over infections.

C. EMLEN SCOTT *has been extension plant pathologist in California since 1931. Previously he was assistant plant pathologist in the California Department of Agriculture.*

Phony Peach and Peach Mosaic

A. E. Cavanagh, C. H. Rothe

Phony peach and peach mosaic are virus diseases of peach. The first recorded observation of phony peach was made at Marshallville, Ga., more than 50 years ago. By 1915, the disease had increased to the extent that commercial peach growers in central Georgia were alarmed and J. H. Hale, a grower, asked aid from the Department of Agriculture. He said the disorder seemed to be the most serious menace to the industry ever encountered in that locality.

After preliminary investigations were made, the United States Peach Disease Field Laboratory was established at Fort Valley, Ga., in 1921. The phony peach control project was organized in 1929 shortly after the virus nature and communicability of the disease had been demonstrated by Lee M. Hutchins, of the Department of Agriculture.

The disease that later was known as peach mosaic was brought to the attention of the Department in 1931 by inspectors who were making a survey for the presence of the phony peach disease near Bangs and Clyde, Tex. It later developed that a new peach disease, which proved to be peach mosaic, had attracted the attention of peach growers and pest control officials in Colorado that year. Growers in southern California detected a new peach disease in 1933. It also proved to be mosaic.

Both phony and mosaic produce a symptom complex in peach. Phony-infected trees are dwarfed, have a deep-green color, and present a rather compact appearance in comparison with healthy trees. The internodes are shortened and foliage is flattened. Viewed from a distance, the phony tree has a more or less even outline; a normal tree with long terminal growth presents an irregular outline. Phony trees bloom earlier and come into leaf earlier than normal trees and retain their foliage longer in the fall. Fruit on infected trees is much smaller in size and quantity. Phony weakens but does not kill the tree as do some other virus diseases such as yellows, rosette, little peach, and X-disease.

A chemical test helps to identify phony. Sections of roots or twigs from phony-infected trees show numerous, well distributed, purple spots after 3 to 5 minutes in a solution of methyl alcohol and hydrochloric acid. For general use the solution should be about 15 percent acid. There is no known chemical test as a confirmatory aid in identifying peach mosaic.

Mosaic-infected trees present symptoms that vary with the season, the variety, and the part of the tree affected. The more important symptoms may be classified in five general groups: Color breaking in the blossom petals of the varieties that have large pink blossoms; retardation of foliage development; mottling and deformity of leaves; deformity of fruit; and abnormal twig growth.

Mosaic is transmitted in nature, presumably by insects. It may be transmitted artificially by budding or grafting from any part of the affected tree. Mosaic, like phony, does not kill the tree.

Inspections made in 1929–1952 demonstrated a general distribution of the phony disease in Alabama, southern Arkansas, northern Florida, Georgia, Louisiana, Mississippi, south central South Carolina, and eastern Texas. Local areas of infection were found in Illinois, Kentucky, Missouri, North Carolina, and Tennessee. Isolated cases occurred in Indiana, Maryland, Oklahoma, and Pennsylvania.

Similar surveys in 1935–1952 for mosaic revealed a general infection in Arizona and New Mexico and in parts of central and northeastern Texas; Riverside and San Bernardino Counties, Calif.; Mesa County in Colorado; Bryan County, Okla.; and Grand and Washington Counties in Utah. Localized areas of infection were found in other counties of those States and in southwestern Arkansas.

Both phony and mosaic occurred in 1952 in two States, Arkansas and Texas.

Peach mosaic has been observed in Baja California, Coahuila, and Chihuahua in Mexico.

Nearly 2 million peach trees were made unprofitable by the ravages of phony between 1929 and 1952 and were destroyed. In Georgia more than a million infected trees were destroyed before 1929. In the Southwestern States approximately 300,000 trees are known to have been destroyed because of mosaic infection—evidence that, if phony and mosaic were allowed to go unchecked, the peach industry could not prosper in those areas. The several States in which phony or mosaic are most prevalent and in which control programs are centered produce about two-thirds of the peaches in the United States and a yearly average of 10 million peach nursery trees.

THE ONLY CONTROL thus far devised for both phony and mosaic is the destruction, after inspection, of the infected trees. An obstacle is the incubation period, the time between the initial infection and the development of visible symptoms. The period varies from 14 days to 1 year for mosaic and from 1 to 3 years for phony. Obviously, therefore, when all visibly infected trees are eliminated, there are others which are actually infected but in which the disease is in the incubation period and cannot be detected.

In carrying out this process of elimination, one encounters other complicating factors. Almond, apricot, plum, prune, and certain varieties of peach, for example, are tolerant to the mosaic virus. Some of those hosts, in fact, are completely symptomless. Elimination of those species of *Prunus*, along with the visibly infected peach trees, is therefore necessary in some areas to obtain adequate control. It has also been established that wild plum is a host of the phony virus. Its elimination in orchard areas therefore must be included in an effective control program.

Department investigators in 1948 reported four species of leafhoppers to be vectors of phony. Studies of insecticidal sprays for leafhopper control were started in the hope that they might be another useful weapon against the disease.

Annual inspections have been made of peach trees in the control areas. Infected trees are removed immediately. Mosaic symptoms are more pronounced during the first part of the growing season. Phony manifestations are more evident during the last part. Inspections for mosaic therefore are made from April to August and for phony from June to October, depending on the locality. As an additional aid to control of phony, growers are urged to establish new orchard plantings as far away as possible from old orchards and thickets of wild plum.

The program of phony control was put in operation in 1929 and of mosaic control in 1935. The control project is conducted and financed jointly by the Bureau of Entomology and Plant Quarantine and the pest control agencies of the affected States.

The objectives are to prevent further spread of the diseases by adequate nursery and budwood (mosaic) inspection and quarantine enforcement; to control peach mosaic in the commercial areas; and to suppress and hold the phony disease in check in the commercial area of the generally infected States. The first aim, properly executed, assures the production and shipment of disease-free nursery stock.

The second and third are measures of control in areas where the two diseases have ravaged commercial production of peaches. The operational programs differ somewhat by States to fit local conditions and requirements.

Several factors bear directly on the effectiveness of phony disease control: Abundance of the primary vector, density of peach and plum trees, and ecology. Certain latitudes, elevations, and soil types result in distinct types of agricultural crops and native plants, which have their effect on the abundance of vector population. The disease is most destructive in areas where *Homalodisca triquetra*, the primary vector of phony, is abundant and where peach and plum also are dense. As an example, in the Fort Valley, Ga., area, where phony was first discovered, those conditions favorable for the rapid development of the disease are present, and phony has taken its heaviest toll.

To be effective, control in commercial areas of high incidence must be on an area-wide basis. Experience has demonstrated that inspections made in that way will reduce or retard the annual increase in infection to the extent that peach production continues to be profitable. Annual inspections of only scattered orchards in such areas do not produce the maximum benefit.

In a phony-infected area it is a sound procedure to remove wild plums from a 300-yard zone around a new planting site at least a year before the orchard is set. That will prevent or retard vectors from picking up the disease from infected wild plums and establishing the disease in such new plantings at an early date. New orchards should not be set immediately adjacent to old infected orchards. When an old infected orchard is removed, it is not advisable to reset to peaches immediately because infected vectors may be present. At least a year should elapse between removal and replanting.

By means of chemically testing twigs of wild plums, surveys have been made in 83 counties of 11 States. In making the surveys, 16,104 plum twigs have been tested from 550 locations. The presence of phony was indicated in 611 twigs, an average incidence of 3.8 percent. Phony disease is known to occur generally in wild plums in substantially the same area as it is known to occur in peach. Orchardists in an infected area are requested to remove wild plums from the environs of their orchards as a prerequisite to having their orchards inspected.

The following reductions in disease incidence from the peak years to 1951 indicate the effectiveness of mosaic control: California, 5.78 percent in 1936 to 0.52 percent in 1951 (90 percent reduction); Colorado, 4.43 in 1935 to 0.22 (95 percent reduction); Oklahoma, 2.59 in 1941 to 0.005 (99 percent); Texas, 0.80 in 1937 to 0.04 (95 percent); Utah, 1.60 in 1936 to 0.38 (76 percent).

QUARANTINES regulating the movement of peach and related nursery stock from and within known affected areas have been in effect for both phony and mosaic since the beginning of control operations. Products have been regulated under uniform State quarantines.

The phony quarantine in 1952 had the following requirements: Each nursery in the regulated area producing the regulated products—peach, plum, apricot, nectarine, and almond—shall apply to the State quarantine official for approval of proposed nursery-growing sites on or before August 15 of each year; selected nursery sites shall be at least 300 yards from wild or domesticated plum, one-half mile from phony-infected commercial orchards, and one-half mile from urban areas; the ½-mile environs of the nursery site shall be inspected before October 1, and all phony trees found within such environs shall be removed prior to November 1; and all budding shall be restricted to the slip-bud method.

The mosaic quarantine provides for certification of nurseries when no mosaic infection is found in the nursery stock and when mosaic-infected trees found within a mile of the nursery are removed before May 16 of each year. Because mosaic may be transmitted by means of buds from infected trees, all budwood sources must meet the same requirements as the nursery stock. The California quarantine prohibits movement of nursery stock from the regulated area.

Through the application of inspection and elimination of infected trees over a period of years, substantial reductions in the incidence of both phony and mosaic have been achieved. The practice has resulted in the apparent eradication of phony disease from Illinois, Indiana, Maryland, Oklahoma, and Pennsylvania, and from more than 100 counties in other lightly infected States. Mosaic has apparently been eliminated from 21 counties of the known infected States. All areas in which eradication apparently has been accomplished were lightly affected by the diseases when controls were first applied. In areas of general infection, control has been more difficult, but a persistent application of approved practices has achieved and maintained a sufficiently low level of infection that commercial fruit production has continued to be profitable.

A. E. Cavanagh *is the project leader on the phony peach and peach mosaic control project, with headquarters at Gulfport, Miss. He joined the Department of Agriculture in 1921. Since 1936 he has worked in Atlanta, Ga., Little Rock, Ark., and San Antonio, Tex., in connection with the phony peach and peach mosaic project.*

C. H. Rothe *was born on a ranch in Texas and is a graduate of the Agricultural and Mechanical College of Texas. He joined the Department of Agriculture in 1925 and is now assistant project leader engaged in peach mosaic disease control at Riverside, Calif.*

Brown Rot of Peach

John C. Dunegan

Brown rot has been the scourge of peach growing in the more humid sections of the United States since Colonial times. Sometimes it is called simply *the rot* because it occurs so commonly and affects so adversely the fortunes of all who handle and eat peaches.

Its first symptom on the fruit is a small, brown spot, which rapidly enlarges and soon destroys an entire peach and all peaches near it. Masses of gray spores form on the surface. As the fungus develops best in warm, humid weather, brown rot long was considered merely the aftermath of such conditions. By 1880, however, people realized that rot did not develop solely as the result of the "delicate" nature of the peach but that a fungus caused it.

Now we know also that a common insect, the plum curculio, is implicated in the spread of the brown rot disease. The punctures the insect makes when it feeds and lays eggs furnish ideal points of entry for the spores of brown rot. Although brown rot can be very serious even if the plum curculio is absent, it cannot possibly be controlled during harvest periods of warm, rainy weather if the insect is prevalent in an orchard.

For many years the fungus, *Monilinia fructicola*, was considered to be identical with a brown rot fungus that attacks plums, apples, and pears in Europe. The two are distinct, however. The fungus on peaches, plums, cherries, and (only rarely) apples and pears in the eastern part of the United States is a native of the region. Probably it occurred as a disease of wild plums long before the settlement of the Western Hemisphere.

The European brown rot fungus is now known to be present in California, Washington, and Oregon and in a few scattered localities east of the Rocky Mountains. Its activities are described by E. E. Wilson in another article in this volume (p. 886). I shall discuss only the common brown rot fungus so prevalent in the eastern part of the United States.

The life cycle of the brown rot fungus is a vicious circle: The fungus constantly multiplies its sources of infection so that the disease can become more destructive, given proper weather conditions, each succeeding year. To control the fungus, by interrupting its development at some point, one has to know its life cycle.

As I indicated, brown rot starts as a speck that rapidly enlarges and may involve the whole peach in a few days with a brown, rather firm rot. Masses of spores—conidia—are soon formed on the rotten surface. The spores may be blown by wind, washed or splashed by raindrops, or carried by insects or man to other peaches, which in turn develop the characteristic brown spots and eventually are destroyed. Sometimes the destruction of the fruit can involve one-half or more of the crop in less than a week. Complete destruction of the crop occurs less often now than 50 years ago, but it may still occur during periods of favorable weather in orchards that are poorly cared for.

The fungus completely penetrates the tissues of the peach. The rotten peach left hanging on the tree loses moisture and shrivels. By the end of the growing season it becomes a dry, distorted object that is aptly called a mummy. The peach stone is covered by the tough, leathery remains of the peach cells held in place by the fungus threads (mycelia), which have spread all through the flesh. The skin remains as a covering. Just beneath the skin the fungus threads are closely interwoven and form a hard rind. The mummy can withstand very adverse conditions.

If the infected peach had dropped to the ground immediately instead of drying up in the tree, very likely it would have disintegrated under the action of various molds and bacteria. Only rarely do rotting peaches on the ground form mummies. Once the peach has dried into a mummy, however, it may fall to the ground, but in that condition it is not affected by soil organisms, and many persist for several years.

If the mummy is partly or completely covered by soil, the fungus produces another stage in its life cycle the following spring when the peach blossoms begin to open. Small, brown, goblet-shaped structures—the apothecia—develop from the part of the mummy embedded in the soil and unfold on the surface of the ground.

The apothecia are never formed on mummies lying only on the surface of the ground. Some part of it must be buried in the soil for apothecia to form. The mummy, however, does not have to be intact, as numerous apothecia will develop from buried fragments. That phenomenon will be repeated for several years. In a series of experiments I once made, I observed apothecia produced from the same group of peach mummies for six successive seasons. J. B. Pollock reported finding apothecia in Michigan from plum mummies 10 years old.

The upper surface of the apothecium is the spore-bearing layer. It consists of closely packed vertical sacs—the asci—each containing eight spores (ascospores). The asci are separated from each other by sterile, threadlike structures (paraphyses), so that each sac or ascus stands as a separate entity, with its apex pointing upward.

When the individual spores are mature, the base of the ascus absorbs moisture and the spores are forcibly ejected into the air above the apothecium. There they are swept away by air currents, and some may be carried upward into the peach trees. As the formation of spores takes several days, the discharge of ascospores into the air is more or less continuous. Often a blow on a group of apothecia will bring about the sudden release of a whole group of ascospores, which will be visible for an instant as a smokelike cloud above the apothecia. The number of ascospores discharged into the air in an orchard soon reaches astronomical proportions, but, fortunately, only a few land on the unfolding peach blossoms. The ascospore that happens to lodge on the sticky surface of the pistil of the blossom germinates and sends a mycelial thread down the style into the very small peach, causing the phase of the disease called blossom blight. Having destroyed the young peach, the fungus grows down the stem and into the twig, killing the tissues and forming a stem canker.

Unless the conditions are extremely favorable for the growth of the fungus, the number of blossoms blighted or destroyed by the fungus is not enough to effect materially the size of the peach crop. Blossom blight is an important and serious phase of the brown rot disease, however.

Its importance lies in the fact that the blighted blossoms and the cankers on the twigs soon are covered with masses of spores—conidia—which can infect and blight other blossoms. Moreover, the twig tissue killed by the fungus decomposes into a gummy substance, which oozes to the surface, surrounds the blighted blossom, and prevents it from dropping.

Every time it rains during the rest of the spring, a fresh crop of conidia is produced on the blighted parts. The green peaches are not readily infected by the fungus, but as the peaches start to mature they become extremely susceptible. Conidia formed on nearby blighted blossoms are scattered by the wind and raindrops to the maturing peaches, which soon develop the telltale spots.

Experimental data indicate a correlation between the number of blighted blossoms (that is, the centers of conidia production) and the number of mature peaches infected at harvesttime. The spores can germinate and infect uninjured peaches through the hair sockets—the tiny pits in the skin where the hair develops. Punctures caused by the plum curculio provide additional sites for the spores to germinate and penetrate the flesh of the peach.

Once infection has taken place, conidia begin to develop upon the surface of the peach in a few hours. The appearance of those spores completes the cycle which started the preceding year on a maturing peach that eventually mummified and dropped to the ground: Apothecia produced by the mummy ejected ascospores into the orchard air; the unfolding blossoms were infected; and conidia formed on the blighted parts finally infected the maturing fruit of the new crop.

Several variants in this cycle may occur. In mummied peaches that remained on the tree instead of falling to the ground, apothecia would not be formed. But often conidia are produced on the mummies in the trees the following spring; those spores, like the ascospores, can produce blossom blight. Occasionally the twig cankers formed one season can also produce spore tufts on their surfaces the following spring and may serve as a source of blossom infections. Spore production the second season on twig cankers, however, is rather uncommon in the case of the common American brown rot fungus, M. fructicola. It is common in the far West on twigs infected by the European fungus, M. laxa.

The American brown rot fungus grows best at temperatures between 70° and 80° F. and is killed by a temperature of 127°. It is not killed by exposure to freezing temperatures;

it has been known to produce symptoms of rot in 12 days on peaches held at 36°. Periods of rainy weather encourage infections of blossoms and fruit and the production of spores on the infected parts.

THE FUNGUS would be serious enough if its effects were confined to the orchard. Unfortunately, though, it continues to destroy the fruit after it has been harvested. Conditions that favor the development of brown rot on the maturing fruit also scatter conidia throughout the tree. Some of those spores germinate immediately. Others may not start to grow until after the fruit is picked. In favorable seasons, a grower may deliver what he considers disease-free fruit to shippers, only to learn later that his fruit developed rot in transit and was quite rotten when it reached the market. Moreover, even apparently sound fruit may show brown rot infections and spoil after the housewife has bought it from the grocer. The destructive effects of the fungus are indeed far-reaching—in some seasons it destroys more than 2 million bushels of peaches.

Considerable work has been expended on ways to combat the disease.

Unfortunately the removal of rotted fruit, cankers, and infected twigs cannot be depended upon to control brown rot. These sanitary measures do reduce materially the sources of infection and should be practiced along with pruning and removal (thinning) of fruit to make it feasible to protect the remaining fruit with fungicidal sprays or dusts—the main control procedure.

Before 1907, peach growers used bordeaux mixture, potassium sulfide, and occasionally flowers of sulfur with only indifferent success. W. M. Scott discovered in 1907 that a mixture of sulfur and stone-lime (called self-boiled lime-sulfur) gave effective control of the brown rot fungus.

The discovery was of great importance. The use of sulfur ended the possibility of injury that accompanied the use of bordeaux mixture for brown rot control during the growing season. Although self-boiled lime-sulfur has been replaced by mixtures of sulfur, lime, and a wetting agent, or by finely divided sulfur pastes, elemental sulfur in some form is still the most effective fungicide we know of to combat brown rot.

To control blossom blight, one has to apply sprays every 3 or 4 days during the blossom period. The development of high-capacity, rapid-delivery types of spray machinery has made it feasible to control blossom blight.

Wettable sulfur (6 pounds to 100 gallons), lime-sulfur (1 gallon to 100), ferbam (1½ pounds to 100), and Phygon (2 pounds to 100), are all effective materials to use for blossom blight control if a sufficient number of closely spaced applications are made during the bloom period.

If all the blossoms on a peach tree opened in a day, they could all be protected by a single spray. As the blossom period generally extends 7 to 15 days, however, one has to spray at regular intervals to protect the blossoms as they open.

The control of blossom blight is of such fundamental importance that every peach grower should aim to do so. It is true that in some seasons the lack of rain at harvesttime greatly retards the development of fruit rot and a good crop may be harvested despite the blighting of many blossoms scattered through the trees. But the weather at harvest cannot be foreseen at the beginning of the season—hence the need for the protection given by control of blossom blight.

Experiments over many years have standardized the control procedures after the blossom season. There may be local variations, but the general schedule calls for spraying at petal fall, when most of the shucks have dropped, 2 weeks later, and approximately 1 month before harvest.

Sulfur, 6 to 12 pounds, depending on the composition of the sulfur preparation and its degree of fineness, is added to 100 gallons of water for the sprays. Appropriate amounts of insecticides are added for the combined control of disease and insect pests.

Some growers apply sulfur, lime, and insecticides as dusts instead of as sprays. Properly applied, dusts give adequate control of the fungus and can be applied rapidly to large acreages during critical periods. Frequently the light dusting machines can be used when waterlogged soils make it impossible to move the heavy spray machines through the orchards.

In orchards where blossom blight has not been controlled (particularly in humid sections) additional protection against brown rot results from the application of preharvest dusts or sprays. One may use wettable sulfur, 6 pounds to 100 gallons of water; dilute lime-sulfur, 1 gallon to 100 gallons; or sulfur-lime dusts. The application of the fungicide should start about 3 weeks before harvest and should be repeated at intervals of not more than 7 days until the fruit is picked. Dusting is a particularly advantageous procedure for these preharvest applications, as the entire acreage can be treated rapidly and the dust does not leave an objectional deposit on the fruit.

JOHN C. DUNEGAN *is a principal pathologist in the division of fruit and nut crops and diseases of the Bureau of Plant Industry, Soils, and Agricultural Engineering. He joined the staff in 1921 and until 1945 was engaged in field investigations of fruit diseases in Georgia and Arkansas. In 1945 he assumed leadership of the deciduous tree fruit disease project at the Plant Industry Station, Beltsville, Md.*

_____

The attention of the reader is directed to the section of color photographs, in which appear pictures of peaches infected with brown rot, anthracnose, and bacterial spot. Diseases of apple, pear, citrus fruit, strawberry, grape, and cherry are also illustrated.

Scab or Black Spot on Peach

John C. Dunegan

Peach scab is also called black spot or freckles—apt names because the black spots on a badly infected peach do make it look freckled.

Cladosporium carpophilum, the fungus that causes the disease, occurs throughout the world on peach twigs, leaves, and fruit. In the United States and probably elsewhere fruit trees grown in dry sections are rarely affected, but in more humid sections the fungus is so persistent that growers must undertake control measures every year to protect the fruit. The fungus occasionally attacks plums and cherries but is of little importance on them.

The disease appears on the fruit as small, greenish, circular spots, one-sixteenth to one-eighth inch across, which become visible about the time the fruit is half-grown. The spots usually are most numerous near the stem. At times they cause an excessive dropping of the fruit by killing the stem tissues. The spots slowly increase in size, turning olive green to black and velvety as the result of the mass of dark spores that form on the surface. If the spots are especially numerous, they may coalesce into a crustlike covering over most of the fruit, which interferes with the normal growth of the peach as it matures. Badly infected fruit may crack open to the pit and be destroyed by the brown rot fungus.

On twigs of the current season's growth, the fungus produces many small oval, brown lesions or cankers that may retard the growth of the twigs. Spores produced in the twig lesions the following spring start anew the cycle of fruit, leaf, and twig infections.

Toward the end of the growing season the scab fungus occasionally develops on the lower surface of the leaves as indefinite pale-green or brownish patches scattered irregularly over the leaf blade, midrib, and stem. The leaf infections are of little economic importance because the area involved is not extensive and only negligible defoliation occurs. The infections give the plant pathologist an easy way to get in pure culture an organism that ordinarily is hard to isolate free from contaminations.

The life cycle of the peach scab fungus is simple enough. It consists merely of a series of superficial spots alternating between the twigs (where the fungus overwinters) and the fruit, twigs, and leaves produced the following season. The process is an endless cycle; the fungus always is present on some part of the peach tree. Its very ubiquity would seem to make it difficult to control, and yet, in truth, it is one of the easiest. So readily can the fungus be controlled that the presence of scab spots on peach fruit is an indication of improper spraying procedures. This is one of the diseases where research has shown the way to uniformly satisfactory control year after year.

The secret of the control of the peach scab fungus lies in the proper timing of the spray application. When bordeaux mixture was the only spray material available, few growers made any effort to control the scab fungus—compared to the injury that generally followed the use of this copper spray, the scab disease was the lesser of two evils. The demonstration in 1907 that a mixture of sulfur and lime could be used safely on peach trees made the control of the scab fungus practical. The demonstration in 1917 by G. W. Keitt that 40 to 60 days elapse from the time the spores first infect the peach until the spots become visible furnished the final clue to the problem. Keitt showed that

the fungicide must be applied within 3 to 4 weeks after the petals have dropped if the fruit is to remain scab free. Since the peaches are then very small and show no evidence of scab infections, it took some time to convince peach growers that the control application must be made early in the season. For years now a single application of sulfur as a spray or dust 3 to 4 weeks after the petals have dropped has been the standard procedure. Sulfur is also used in later sprays to protect the fruit from infections of brown rot. The sprays have little effect on scab infection on the fruit, except on late-maturing varieties, but they do prevent some twig lesions as a comparison of sprayed and unsprayed trees shows.

I have to admit that that control program merely prevents infection on the fruit. It does not eradicate the fungus—the new shoots and branches are infected by the end of the growing season and next year's fruit crop must likewise be protected by sprays. As the standard fungicides applied to peaches for scab and brown rot control do reduce the number of twig lesions, a grower could perhaps eliminate the lesions by additional sprays after the fruit is harvested. But that would not be economical, as it is much less expensive to apply one spray early each season to protect the fruit from scab infections than it would be to apply a series of postharvest sprays to prevent overwintering lesions from developing on the twigs.

THE PEACH SCAB FUNGUS is almost unique in the problem it presents: An ever-present fungus is so efficiently controlled by one application of a sulfur fungicide that it is uneconomical to make any attempts to eradicate the fungus.

JOHN C. DUNEGAN, *principal pathologist in the Bureau of Plant Industry, Soils, and Agricultural Engineering, is in charge of investigations of the control of diseases of deciduous fruit trees. He has studied fruit-disease problems in the United States since 1921*

Bacterial Spot of Peach

John C. Dunegan

Under the unwieldy title, "Observations on a Hitherto Unreported Bacterial Disease the Cause of which enters the Plant through Ordinary Stomata," Erwin F. Smith, one of the pioneer plant bacteriologists, described in 1902 a yellow, motile bacterial organism. The bacterium, now called *Xanthomonas pruni*, was found to be the cause of a destructive disease of the Japanese plums in Michigan. Later research in other sections proved that it also attacked the leaves, branches, and the fruit of the peach, almond, apricot, nectarine, and one variety, English Morello, of cultivated cherry.

On all of them, instead of rotting the fruit or wilting the leaves and branches, *Xanthomonas pruni* merely kills small spots of tissue. Bacterial spot is, therefore, an apt name for the disease.

Years ago the organism destroyed the extensive plum industry in Georgia. It is commercially important now on plums in Japan and New Zealand, but in eastern United States it is the peach industry that suffers most from attacks of *X. pruni*. It is not known to occur in the fruit sections west of the Rocky Mountains. Because of its prevalence on peach, I limit this discussion to a description of the disease on that host.

The organism can enter uninjured peach tissues through the normal openings, the stomata, on the under side of the leaves and on the fruit and twigs whenever high humidity or rains occur during the growing season. Entrance through the stomata has been demonstrated repeatedly, in experiments, in the leaves and twigs. It has not been demonstrated experimentally in the fruit, yet it occurs under natural conditions in untold numbers of instances on peaches every season. We do not know whether infection results from the entrance of a single bacterium or whether a number of individual organisms must enter through one opening to set up the cycle of infection within the host tissue.

Once inside the peach leaf, fruit, or twig tissue, the bacteria multiply and fill the spaces normally existing between various cells. The individual cells are cut off from the normal interchange of oxygen, nutrients, and water vapor and are exposed to toxins produced by the bacteria surrounding them.

Likewise it is evident from the microscopic study of young spots on the leaves and fruit that the organism can dissolve the material that forms the boundary zone between the walls of two adjacent cells. As the number of bacteria increases, the individual cells die and are split apart, so that the normal cellular structure is completely disorganized. Eventually the mass of bacteria becomes so great that the outer host tissues are ruptured, and the bacteria ooze to the surface of the leaf, fruit, or twig, spreading over the surface and drying into a thin film. Once this oozing has occurred, there is no further destruction of tissue in this individual spot.

Actual tissue destroyed by the bacterial mass involves only a tiny area. In a typical fruit spot, for example, the area is but a few cells wide and not more than 8 or 10 cells deep. It is, indeed, a microscopic pocket filled with bacteria.

THE DISEASE would be of little commercial importance if the killing of small pockets of cells were the only effect of the bacterial invasion. That destruction of the cells is followed by renewed growth of the surrounding tissues in the fruit. It forms callus tissue, which seals the area destroyed by the bacteria from the surrounding healthy tissue. The subsequent growth of the peach, particularly its rapid increase in diameter as it approaches maturity, sets up a series of strains that result in the development of extensive cracks and roughened areas that make the peach unmerchantable. Actually the injury results from the renewed growth of the tissue, for the callus tissue cannot expand as the peach increases in diameter.

As INFECTIONS of fruit may occur from the beginning of the season until the fruit is harvested, the severity of the injury depends on how early the infection took place. Infections that occur just before harvest, after the fruit has nearly reached its maximum diameter, have little effect on the appearance of the fruit because there are no growth tensions to cause cracking at that late date.

The cycle of disease development on the leaves follows much the same pattern. The leaf spots are generally angular, one-sixteenth to one-eighth inch long, and usually confined to areas between the small veins. Pale green at first, they change to purple and finally to dark brown. As with the fruit, the oozing of the bacteria to the surface of the leaf ends the cycle as far as the individual spot is concerned.

The development of bacterial spots on the leaf is followed not by renewed tissue growth, as on the fruit, but by the dropping out of the disease area. That causes a shot-hole effect. Affected leaves, even though there are only a few spots on them, soon become yellow and fall to the ground. In favorable seasons the trees may be defoliated by midseason. The reason for that is not clearly understood, but presumably it is the result of the toxins the bacteria produce.

Most growers consider the fruit injury the most important phase of the bacterial spot disease. Really, though, it is the constant loss of the leaves (50 to 200 a day) that causes the most damage. The trees are weakened by the defoliation. The buds for the succeeding season also are adversely affected. If the defoliation occurs by midsummer, new growth is stimulated in the fall and the trees enter the winter season in a weakened condition only to succumb to low-temperature injury. So damaging is such premature defoliation that it means success or failure when peach trees have been established on light, sandy soils.

Bacterial lesions on the twigs and branches have little effect on the subsequent growth of the tree; they are on the surface and are soon separated from the surrounding healthy cells by a layer of callus tissue.

They are, however, of vital importance in the life cycle of the bacteria. They are means by which the bacteria survive the winter. In the less humid North Central States the bacteria infect the twigs late in the fall but apparently do not produce visible symptoms until the following spring. Along the Atlantic seaboard typical lesions can be detected on the twigs in the winter.

Regardless of the time the symptoms develop on the twigs, however, all investigators agree that the organism overwinters in the twigs and that bacteria oozing from the overwintered lesions start the cycle of leaf, fruit, and twig infections the succeeding year.

Wind and rain are the main factors in the spread of the organism. If the early spring weather is dry, therefore, the disease may appear merely as cone-shaped areas of infected leaves here and there on the tree. If the early spring is rainy, however, the disease may seem to develop throughout the tree at once.

ONCE primary infections develop in the spring, the subsequent spread of the bacterial organism depends upon an abundance of moisture. The disease thus is much more prevalent during rainy than dry seasons. So necessary is water in the spread of the organism that the disease is more severe on the west side of the trees because the leaves may remain damp with dew later in the morning than those on the east side. Many leaves show a series of spots in a straight line parallel to the long axis of the leaf blade—an indication that a bacteria-laden drop of dew has rolled down the leaf.

Temperature influences the time of the first appearance of the disease in the spring and its subsequent development. The organism grows most luxuriantly in the laboratory at temperatures between 75° and 83° F. In the orchard the disease spreads most rapidly when the temperatures range between 70° and 85°. Within that range the individual spots develop profusely. Bacteria may ooze from them within 7 days, whereas at temperatures below 70° the cycle of development of the individual spots may be prolonged to 20 or 25 days. The growth rate of the bacterial organism is reduced by temperatures above 85°. It ceases to multiply at about 100° but remains alive and can renew its activities when the temperatures drop. In laboratory experiments it has required an exposure of 10 minutes at 124° to kill the organism.

BECAUSE THE DISEASE is more severe on weak trees that are poorly cared for, the first step in control is to induce vigorous growth. In some sections fairly satisfactory commercial control can be obtained merely by pruning, cultivation, and the use of nitrate of soda.

In many orchards on light, sandy soils, however, it is hard to keep the trees growing vigorously, and additional control measures are needed. Many types and combinations of spray materials have been tested. The susceptibility of peach foliage to chemical injuries is an important detail; many bactericides cannot be used because of the excessive injury they cause.

One mixture, a zinc-lime spray, prepared by dissolving 8 pounds of zinc sulfate in 100 gallons of water and then adding 8 pounds of hydrated lime, has been used extensively in many districts. The mixture does not injure peach leaves (except in a few localities along the Atlantic seaboard). Carefully applied, it has given a fair degree of control in most seasons. But this has to be applied at least six times, starting at petal fall and at intervals of 2 weeks thereafter. Moreover, while the zinc-lime spray is compatible with arsenate of lead, it is not compatible with the new organic insecticides that are widely used to control insects in peach orchards.

A SATISFACTORY control for the bacterial spot disease is one of the most urgent needs of the peach industry. Some progress has been made in the development of less susceptible varieties and this may be the final solution to the problem. Pending the development and the commercial adoption of resistant varieties, however, the search must continue for effective spray materials to protect the orchards now in bearing.

The possibility of killing the bacteria in the overwintering twig lesions during the dormant season, when more potent materials may be used on the peach without producing injury, is being investigated in several parts of the country. That is a logical approach to the problem, for the elimination (or at least marked reduction in the number) of overwintering sources of infection would necessarily affect the number of primary infections initiated the following spring.

JOHN C. DUNEGAN *joined the staff of the Bureau of Plant Industry, Soils, and Agricultural Engineering in 1921. He studied the control of peach diseases in Georgia from 1921 to 1928, and from 1928 to 1945 investigated apple and peach diseases in Arkansas. Since 1945 he has been in charge of the investigation of deciduous fruit tree diseases in the United States.*

Anthracnose of Peach

Donald H. Petersen

Peach anthracnose is a "new" disease in southeastern peach orchards. So recent is it that many salient points in its cycle of development remain to be investigated.

It was described in England as early as 1859 on peach fruit and it was known in Japanese orchards, but peach anthracnose did not attain commercial importance in the United States until 1947. Before then only occasional specimens were seen in the eastern peach-growing sections, but in 1947 many affected peaches were found in carloads of fruit shipped to Chicago from Marshallville, Ga. Additional specimens were observed in South Carolina and Georgia in 1948 and 1949. By 1950 the disease had become so serious in Georgia that the crop in some orchards was not harvested and some lots of fruit were rejected at the shipping points because of anthracnose infections. In 1951 very few infected peaches were found in Georgia, but a mild outbreak was noted in some orchards in West Virginia and South Carolina.

The first visible symptom of the disease, which is caused by *Glomerella cingulata*, is one or more tiny, round, brown spots, one-sixteenth to one-eighth inch in diameter, on the surface of the peach. The spots can be confused with the first symptoms of brown rot, caused by *Monilinia fructicola*. Infections of brown rot, however, enlarge rapidly and soon involve the entire peach, whereas anthracnose lesions persist as circular spots.

The circular anthracnose spots slowly enlarge and may eventually attain a diameter of 1 inch. A light-colored depression forms in the center of the spot as the result of the collapse of the underlying tissues rotted by the fungus. Concentric rings of salmon-pink spore masses soon form in the depression and give the spot a distinctive appearance. No other fungus or bacterial pathogen produces on peaches a circular, depressed spot covered with rings of spores. Those symptoms persist even after the infected fruit has dried into a hard, almost shapeless mass. Symptoms of the anthracnose disease are known only on the peach fruit.

Apparently none of the commercial peach varieties grown in Georgia is immune to attacks of the anthracnose fungus. It has been observed on Early Rose, Uneeda, Erly Red Fre, Pearson Hiley, Early Hiley, Hiley, Dixired, Dixigem, Southland, Belle of Georgia, Golden Jubilee, U. S. No. 10, Dixigold, Redhaven, Ambergem, Sullivan Elberta, Halehaven, and Elberta.

The sudden appearance in 1947 of anthracnose on peaches in Georgia and its prevalence until 1951 is hard to explain.

Bitter rot, the analogous disease of apples caused by *G. cingulata*, has been known for many years. Peaches and apples have been grown close together for decades in many sections without any widespread development of the disease on peaches even when nearby apple orchards were seriously affected. Moreover, the peach district of central Georgia, where anthracnose has occurred since 1947, is south of the commercial apple sections; there are so few apple trees in home plantings in central Georgia that the spread of the fungus from apple to peach seems unlikely.

Nevertheless, the fungus destroyed many peaches in this section after 1947. The spores that caused the first infections each season must have come from a source other than the peach. This possibility is limited at present to the initial infections, since it is not known whether the disease spreads from peach to peach after the first infections appear.

The anthracnose disease was not observed in central Georgia before 1947, the first year that blue lupine was grown extensively for seed production in the peach section. That new agricultural practice takes on a special significance when it is realized that the anthracnose fungus also attacks the blue lupine plants and that spores from blue lupine can produce typical anthracnose symptoms on peaches.

Blue lupine had been introduced into Georgia as a winter cover crop in 1942 or so. For that purpose the plants are turned under early in the spring. Starting with a few fields in 1946, a constantly expanding acreage of blue lupine was left to mature seed in 1947 and the succeeding years. Thus, instead of being turned under early in the spring, the lupine plants, with sporulating anthracnose lesions on the stems, leaflets, and seed pods, were left near peach orchards until much later in the season, when peaches were beginning to mature.

In 1950 this possible correlation between lupine plantings and peach anthracnose was studied in 46 blocks of peach trees in 25 commercial orchards. In many of the blocks of trees, the disease was most severe on the fruit of the first few rows of trees adjacent to a field of lupine stubble, the lupine seed having been harvested about the time the first varieties ripen.

Growers who did not have lupine near peach orchards in 1950 escaped injury. In 1949, with lupine near the same orchards, the peaches of the same growers had been damaged by the disease. Anthracnose was found to be more severe in orchards adjacent to fields where lupine was grown for seed than where it was turned under green. Exceptions were noted in places where there was no anthracnose even though orchards were next to fields of lupine.

Severe frosts during the winters of 1950–1951 and 1951–1952 destroyed the commercial plantings of blue lupine in central Georgia. The elimination of one host provided a unique test of the possible relationship between the fungus on blue lupine and peach in central Georgia. Observations throughout the 1951 and 1952 peach harvests revealed only an occasional diseased fruit in the orchards.

The fact that anthracnose spores from blue lupine plants can produce anthracnose of the peach, the correlations observed in the orchards in 1950, and the almost complete absence of the disease on peaches in 1951 and 1952 when the lupine plantings were destroyed by low temperature all indicate that the occurrence and spread of the anthracnose disease of peaches in central Georgia can be attributed to the practice of growing blue lupine for seed in the area. However, the reports of peach anthracnose from areas where lupine is not grown indicates that the complete story is not known. The source of the infective anthracnose spores in these areas has not been determined.

Experiments to protect peaches from anthracnose infections with various fungicides were carried out in 1950 and 1951 but no conclusive results were obtained. Experiments in South Carolina in 1952 indicated that the fungicide N-trichloromethylthiotetrahydrophthalimide (captan) may materially aid in reducing the amount of infected fruit. The number of sprays needed and the frequency of application has not been determined. The tests indicate that sprays applied earlier than 6 weeks before the beginning of harvest were of doubtful value. It is best not to grow blue lupine for seed in fields next to peach orchards.

DONALD H. PETERSEN *is a pathologist in the division of fruit and nut crops and diseases, Bureau of Plant Industry, Soils, and Agricultural Engineering. Since 1950 he has been engaged in a study of peach disease problems in South Carolina in cooperation with the South Carolina Agricultural Experiment Station.*

Cherry Leaf Spot

F. H. Lewis

Cherry leaf spot, caused by the parasitic fungus *Coccomyces hiemalis*, is one of the major factors that determine the cost of producing cherries and the yield and quality of the fruit.

The disease occurs on the sour cherry, *Prunus cerasus*, sweet cherry, *P. avium*, and the mahaleb cherry, *P. mahaleb*, wherever they are grown under conditions that favor the survival of the fungus. That includes our eastern and central producing areas and the more humid areas in the West. Because it has been most serious on sour cherry in the Eastern and Central States, this discussion largely concerns the experimental work on sour cherry in those regions.

The losses are due primarily to the injury the disease does to the leaves, which become yellow and drop. Failure to control leaf spot on sour cherry, with consequent defoliation of the trees before harvest, usually results in a crop of low-quality and unattractive fruit of light-red color. The fruit often is low in soluble solids, including sugars, has a flat, watery taste, and may be unsalable. While such fruit may mean the loss of the crop for a season, that loss is sometimes less important than other losses brought about by the loss of the leaves.

Studies by W. C. Dutton and H. M. Wells, of the Michigan Agricultural Experiment Station, after the early defoliation of unsprayed trees in 1922, showed that trees that had been prematurely defoliated produced fewer blossoms the following year, the flowers were poorly developed and slower in opening, fewer cherries ripened, and the cherries were smaller. Many fruit spurs died, and the crop was greatly reduced on the spurs that survived. By reducing shoot growth and spur development, the defoliation lowered the yield for several years.

Following the worst outbreak of cherry leaf spot on record in the Cumberland-Shenandoah Valley in 1945, thousands of sour cherry trees died and many others had severe injuries.

In Virginia on trees defoliated in May and June of 1945, the average weight of the buds in late summer was 90 milligrams. The buds on trees that had retained their foliage averaged 147 milligrams in weight. The smaller buds did not have enough vitality to survive the winter. All unsprayed trees died. None of the trees died in one orchard where sprays had delayed defoliation 4 weeks or more.

Heavy early defoliation in West Virginia in 1945 stimulated the production of secondary growth on 64 percent of the terminals about 2 weeks after harvest. The secondary leaves were soon lost to leaf spot, and some tertiary growth developed. Following this poor control of leaf spot, an estimated 72 percent of the branches were killed the following winter. Those trees bore almost no fruit in 1946.

Early defoliation in 1945 in Pennsylvania was followed by the death of more than 25,000 trees, besides general killing of shoots, spurs, and branches, and a light crop of poor fruit in 1946. Delay of the first leaf spot spray application until 10 to 12 days after petal fall in one orchard of about 100 acres resulted in general leaf spot infection and death of all of the trees in the orchard worth, at that time, close to $100,000. In no case in the area did an orchard defoliated in June of 1945 escape without severe injury or death during the following winter. Where defoliation was delayed but virtually complete in July within

3 weeks after harvest, severe injury occurred, but most of the trees survived. If leaf spot was controlled until late September the trees were not injured.

In the block of young trees used for experimental spraying in Pennsylvania in 1945, about one-third of the leaves remained on unsprayed trees 1 week before harvest. The increase in trunk size of the trees during that summer was less than half as great as on trees where leaf spot was controlled. No trees died during the following winter. Killing of shoots and spurs was general on the unsprayed trees, and the bloom in 1946 was very light in comparison with adjacent sprayed trees. The 1946 crop of cherries on the trees unsprayed in 1945 remained of poor color until just before harvest. Then they darkened rapidly and unevenly and shriveled and dried during an abnormally short harvest season. The yield in 1946 averaged 36.2 pounds to the tree; 56 percent of the cherries on the trees unsprayed in 1945 graded No. 1. Trees on which leaf spot was controlled best in 1945 had an average of 107 pounds each, 79 percent of which graded No. 1.

Those examples illustrate the fact that the losses from premature defoliation in one year by leaf spot on sour cherries may reduce quantity and quality of fruit for 2 years or more or may weaken a tree so that it cannot survive the following winter. Such severe attacks are not general: The disease usually is kept under fair control.

The losses from premature defoliation by cherry leaf spot on nursery stock of the sour cherry, sweet cherry, and *Prunus mahaleb* are usually caused by failure of many of the buds to grow on the weakened rootstocks and failure of the trees to grow to salable size in a year. Failure to control leaf spot on the rapidly growing seedlings of sweet cherry has been a reason why some eastern nurserymen have been reluctant to propagate sour cherry on rootstocks of sweet cherry.

Little information is available regarding losses from premature defoliation by leaf spot on sweet cherries in the orchard. Orchard trees of sweet cherry commonly are less injured by leaf spot than is the sour cherry. The effects of the disease appear to be like those on sour cherry.

The part of the losses from cherry leaf spot attributable to the cost of the control program varies greatly among the different producing areas. The cost evidently is least in some sections of California and greatest in the sections of the East that have the longest growing season. Some growers spray one or two times; others do so eight or nine times each season, besides cultivating the orchard in the spring. The total cost of the control program often exceeds 75 dollars an acre each year on sour cherries in the Cumberland Valley of south central Pennsylvania. Probably a fair estimate for the Great Lakes districts is 35 to 50 dollars. Those programs also control other diseases and insects. About one-third to two-thirds of the cost could be eliminated if leaf spot were absent.

LEAF SPOT normally appears on sour cherry on the upper surface of the leaf as a small interveinal spot of dying tissue of variable color. The spot rapidly enlarges, becomes brown to purple, and dies from the center outward. The spots are irregular or round and may occur over the entire surface. The individual spots never become large, but they may merge and so kill large areas of the leaf. The appearance of many spots on the leaf usually precedes rapid yellowing and dropping. The spots may separate from the healthy tissue, drop out, and make a shot-hole condition.

The appearance of the spot on the upper surface usually is accompanied or preceded by a pink mass of fungus spores on the lower surface. The mass may be more or less columnar, following its extrusion through a small hole in the leaf surface or it may be a somewhat hemispherical mass, following weathering and drying. It may be absent or difficult to locate after a long period of dry weather or if the fungus in the lesion is killed by a fungicide.

Leaf spot infection on the fruit stems (pedicels) and fruit are unusual and often hard to identify. Such lesions are usually small and brown, without the spore masses of the fungus on them.

The symptoms of leaf spot on other species of cherry are somewhat like those on sour cherry. On sweet cherry, the spots are often larger and more nearly circular in shape than those on sour cherry. The spore masses of the fungus, particularly on sweet cherry seedlings, are often present in large numbers on the upper surface of the leaf. *Prunus mahaleb* has some tendency to show a chlorotic ring around the young lesion, and the dead spots rarely drop out. Other species like the chokecherry, *Prunus virginiana*, are more apt to show shot hole than the sour cherry.

THE FUNGUS that causes leaf spot on sour cherry and sweet cherry in the United States conforms generally with the description of *Coccomyces hiemalis*. Probably the fungus is the only common one on *Prunus mahaleb*.

B. B. Higgins, of the Cornell University Agricultural Experiment Station in New York, in 1913 and 1914 divided the various isolates or collections of *Coccomyces* that he studied into three species based on both morphologic and host-range differences: *Coccomyces hiemalis* on sweet cherry (*Prunus avium*), sour cherry (*P. cerasus*), and pin cherry (*P. pennsylvanica*); *Coccomyces prunophorae* on the plums *Prunus americana*, *P. domestica*, and *P. insititia*; and *Coccomyces lutescens* on the wild black cherry (*Prunus serotina*), the chokecherry (*P. virginiana*), and *Prunus mahaleb*.

G. W. Keitt in Wisconsin in 1918 published the results of more than 1,000 cross-inoculation tests and added others in 1937. He used isolates of *Coccomyces* from all three of the groups of cherries and plums set up by Higgins. In no case did the *Coccomyces* isolate from any two *Prunus* species show exactly the same host relationships. Further, the same isolate commonly infected different hosts with different degrees of severity, varying from slight flecking to abundant production of typical leaf spots. He tentatively grouped the fungi as follows according to the plant from which they were obtained. *Prunus cerasus*, *P. avium*, *P. mahaleb*, and *P. pennsylvanica*; *P. domestica*; *P. virginiana*; and *P. serotina*. *Prunus mahaleb* was susceptible to isolates of all four groups. *P. cerasus* was infected only by isolates from Group 1.

J. B. Mowry, of the Indiana Agricultural Experiment Station, reported in 1951 the inoculation of 66 species, varieties, and hybrids of *Prunus* with single-spore cultures of *Coccomyces*. He added *Prunus fruticosa* to Keitt's Group 1. He obtained infections on sour cherry and *Prunus mahaleb* with the isolate from *P. serotina*, and on both sweet and sour cherry with the isolate from *P. pennsylvanica*. Seedlings of *P. cerasus*, *P. insititia*, *P. mahaleb*, and *P. tenella* were susceptible to most isolates tested. Seedlings of *P. besseyi*, *P. japonica*, *P. pumila*, *P. persica*, *P. salicina*, *P. serotina*, *P. spinosa*, and *P. virginiana* were susceptible to relatively few isolates. Seedlings of *P. glandulosa* and *P. maritima* were resistant to all seven isolates.

While future work may be needed to clear up some aspects of this situation it seems clear that the *Coccomyces* fungi which cause leaf spot on the cultivated cherries, *Prunus cerasus*, *P. avium*, and *P. mahaleb*, form a group which conforms in general with Higgins' description of *Coccomyces hiemalis*. It is evident from the work I have described and that of R. O. Magie in Wisconsin in 1935 that this fungus is able to cause leaf spot on several other *Prunus* species, including the plums, under more or less ideal conditions. No evidence has been found that *C. lutescens* is of any significant importance on cherries. There is no known evidence that the common wild cherries, *P. pennsylvanica* and *P. serotina*, are of any importance as a source of the leaf spot fungus in sour cherry orchards.

Coccomyces hiemalis belongs to the order Phacidiales of a group of fungi referred to as Ascomycetes because they bear the spores of the perfect or sexual stage in a club-shaped organ called an ascus. Dr. Higgins first described it in 1913. He found the perfect stage of the fungus on the leaves of sweet cherry, *P. avium*, and showed that it was the fungus that previously had been called *Cylindrosporium*.

Coccomyces hiemalis passes the winter in the old leaves on the ground as a partly formed, round or somewhat elongated, dark-colored fruit body, which normally extends from the lower to the upper epidermis of the leaf but remains covered above and below by the epidermis.

The fruit body, or stroma, begins to swell toward the lower leaf surface during the first warm days in the spring. Club-shaped asci then form within the stroma. There follows the formation of eight two-celled ascospores within each ascus. As the asci enlarge rapidly within the stroma, the covering of the fruit body is lifted until it ruptures. The ascospores within the asci mature shortly afterwards—normally when the sour cherry is in the pink, or early-bloom, stage of growth. The ascospores are discharged through the end of the ascus in wet weather and are carried upward by wind. If they lodge on a susceptible leaf under favorable conditions, the ascospores germinate and leafspot results in 1 to 2 weeks. Penetration of the leaf by the germ tube from the ascospore occurs through the stomata of the leaf.

After the fungus invades the leaf, a disk-shaped mass of fungus mycelium is formed beneath the epidermis of the leaf. Secondary spores, the conidia, are borne on the surface of this mass. When they have accumulated in sufficient numbers, the epidermis of the leaf is ruptured and the conidia appear in a pink to whitish-pink mass. The

conidia, or summer spores, are borne in large numbers and are spread from leaf to leaf by water. The rapid spread of leaf spot in the summer and fall is usually due to the rapid increase and spread of the fungus by means of repeated generations of conidia throughout the summer and fall.

Besides the regular, or normal, ascospores and conidia, the fungus produces conidia in the overwintering fruit body after the ascospores are discharged in the spring. The conidia cause leaf spot if placed on a susceptible leaf under favorable conditions, but may be of little significance in the normal reproduction of the fungus. The fungus also produces small spores, called microconidia, on the leaves in fall. Their function in the reproduction of the fungus is unknown.

AN APPROACH to the problem of control of a disease of this type is based on the knowledge that we are dealing with two plants, the cherry tree and the fungus *Coccomyces* in this case, both of which have their normal manner of development and sensitivity to various influences. The modern orchard sets up a nearly ideal situation for the reproduction of both plants. Our purpose is to interfere in some way with the reproduction of the fungus without seriously injuring the cherry tree.

A healthy sour cherry blooms while the leaves are still small. The leaves are folded along the midrib while small and begin to unfold during the latter part of the blooming period, usually while the flower petals are falling. The growth of the spur leaves is rapidly completed after petal fall, but growth of new leaves on the terminals continues until midsummer. The leaf spot fungus rarely infects the very young leaves, apparently because the stomata through which the fungus enters the leaf are not mature until about the time the leaf unfolds. Once unfolded, however, the leaves are susceptible to infection throughout the summer and fall.

As the fungus overwinters in the old

leaves on the ground, any factor that reduces the prevalence of the fungus one year will reduce the likelihood of serious trouble with the disease the following spring. Thus few infections one year make it less likely that leaf spot will be a problem the following year. Too much faith in this fact, however, has led to trouble. The fungus often spreads rapidly in the fall and may overwinter at a high population level although it was not a problem earlier in the growing season. Too, if the ascospores are abundant enough to establish the fungus on the tree in the spring, it may spread rapidly in wet season.

In dooryard or garden trees outside of orchard districts, the fungus can be destroyed by raking and burning the old leaves on the ground in fall and winter. That work is not practical in commercial orchards because of the labor involved, but part of the same purpose can be served by disking or plowing the old leaves under before the ascospores mature in the spring or by spraying the old leaves with one or more chemicals that destroy the fungus in them.

Clean cultivation of the orchard would be desirable if the sole aim were the destruction of the leaf spot fungus, but that is often not practical because of the cost, the shortage of labor, and the desirability of maintaining some sort of trashy soil cover in the orchard. A considerable reduction in the population of the fungus can be obtained merely by disking both ways along the tree rows in the orchard.

Good results have been obtained in reducing the production of ascospores in the old leaves on the ground by means of fungicidal ground sprays. The most common spray material used for the purpose has been the sodium salt of dinitro-o-cresol, sold under the trade names of Elgetol and Krenite and used at one-half gallon of the paste to 100 gallons of spray and applied at the rate of about 500 gallons the acre. The mixture seems to have special merit in orchards where cultivation is not feasible, but it has not been generally accepted in commercial practice. The objections to it are usually the extra cash outlay required, the shortage of labor, and inability to reduce safely the number of summer sprays in districts where neighboring growers allow the fungus to overwinter undisturbed.

THE DIFFERENCE in sensitivity of the tree and the leaf spot fungus to the action of chemicals often permits a high degree of control with sprays applied to the tree. Such sprays are now the principal means of control in commercial orchards and nurseries.

The time when the first fungicidal spray is needed depends on the presence of leaves large enough to be susceptible, the presence of mature ascospores of the fungus, the presence of moisture for a sufficient length of time to permit infection, and a temperature at which the fungus will grow.

All those conditions normally are met about the time the flower petals fall, and most spray schedules call for the first application then. That has been satisfactory when the population of the fungus is at a reasonable level and the ascospore-induced infections are few. At times, however, the petals are slow in falling and leaf growth is rapid during late bloom. Such a situation, coupled with a high population of the fungus and wet weather near petal fall, may permit many infections. The application of a spray just as the first flowers opened on sour cherry in Pennsylvania in 1947 reduced the percentage of infected leaves 3 weeks later to 1.9, compared to 24.5 with sprays started at petal fall and 92.7 on trees not sprayed at all.

Contrary situations do occur. Few or no infections may occur until a month or more after petal fall, perhaps because of a scarcity of the fungus.

Following the fungicidal spray at petal fall, additional sprays are applied as needed. On sour cherry that normally means a second spray about 10 days after the first, two sprays in June, and the last just after the fruit is picked in July. More sprays timed at closer intervals and applied before the long rain periods during the season are often needed on rapidly growing nursery trees, on orchard trees growing in areas with a long growing season, and in places where an attempt is to be made to control a high population of the fungus without the use of a copper fungicide. A combination of all these factors has led to the general use of eight or nine sprays each season in south central Pennsylvania.

It is necessary generally to spray sour cherry trees every year regardless of the size of the fruit crop. To newly planted trees the first spray is applied when the first leaves unfold with additional sprays at intervals as needed to keep the new leaves protected.

Workers in the different cherry districts disagree as to the chemicals to be used for control of leaf spot: The severity of leaf spot varies widely among areas, the length of the season over which protection must be provided is different, and the severity of the injury to the tree by the fungicide varies between districts. The effects of the fungicide on the tree, however, usually are different in degree only. Some general statements therefore apply in most cases.

The early work on fungicides for cherry leaf spot was primarily concerned with bordeaux mixture. Many tests of lime-sulfur solution, elemental sulfur preparations, copper compounds, and organic fungicides followed. Most commercial growers now use sulfur on sweet cherries and one of the proprietary copper compounds on sour cherries, although a considerable amount of bordeaux mixture is still used and the organic fungicides are gaining in usage each year.

The choice of a fungicide for use on sour cherries is partly determined by the effect of the fungicide on the tree and fruit. Fungicidal sprays cause various types of leaf and fruit injury such as leaf scorching, leaf spotting, leaf yellowing and dropping, and fruit scald. They also affect leaf size and photosynthetic activity, the size of the fruit, the solids and acid content of the juice, the color of the fruit, the yield, canning quality, and so on. The aim in any control program is to balance the various factors as precisely as possible in order to control the disease with the least injury to the tree and fruit.

Sour cherries of acceptable size commonly run about 100 to 125 fruits a pound. Variations in size of 10 or 15 cherries a pound have been general in Pennsylvania with different fungicides. The solids content of the juice is normally about 14 percent, with 1.5 to 4.0 percent variation common between fungicides. The acid content of the fruit has varied from 0.8 to 1.5 percent with different fungicides. The weight of pits has varied from 6.5 to 8.3 percent of the total fruit weight. The color of the fruit has varied from a very light to a very dark red.

Those characteristics are related in that any fungicide that reduces size of the fruit usually increases the percentage of solids and acid in the fruit and total weight of pits in a ton of fruit. The color of the fruit does not seem to be closely related to the other effects. All the variations are important because one or more of them affects in turn the yield and grade of raw fruit, the amount of waste and yield of cans of fruit the ton of raw fruit at the canning factory, and the attractiveness of the product to the consumer.

The effects of the fungicide on fruit quality and yield are of major importance in commercial cherry growing and canning where differences of 10 or 15 percent may mean the difference between profit and loss. It should be kept in mind, however, that failure to control leaf spot is usually much more serious than the injurious effects of the fungicide applied for its control.

Bordeaux mixture, at a concentration of 2 pounds of copper sulfate and 6 pounds of hydrated spray lime to 100 gallons of water, has been one of the most effective fungicides. Concentrations varying from about 1.5–3–100 to

6–8–100 are now used. It has caused severe leaf injury when used during wet or abnormally dry weather or on foliage on which aphid honeydew was present. It has dwarfed the fruit more than any other treatment. The fruit has been dark red in color with a high content of solids and acid.

The low cost and high degree of effectiveness of bordeaux mixture has made it one of the best materials for control of cherry leaf spot on sour cherries in the nursery, on nonbearing orchard trees where no more than four or five sprays are required, and in the sprays before bloom, at petal fall, and after harvest on bearing trees. It has given satisfactory results when used all through the season on bearing trees in northeastern Wisconsin and comparable conditions. In other areas the use of bordeaux mixture during the period of rapid fruit growth has caused excessive dwarfing of fruit.

The proprietary copper compounds, of which Copoloid, Copper Hydro, Copper A, Cupro-K, and Bordow are examples, have been used at rates of 8 to 12 ounces of actual copper plus 3 pounds of hydrated spray lime in 100 gallons of water. Properly used, any one of them has given fair to good control. As a group, they have been less effective than bordeaux mixture, but they have caused less leaf injury, and the number of leaves remaining on the tree has often been as high with one of them as with bordeaux mixture. They have sometimes been associated with an injury on the fruit that has occurred as a black line around the stem of the fruit and is very objectionable in canned cherries.

The copper compounds have been the most frequently used materials for leaf spot control on sour cherries since about 1940. They have represented a compromise between the older fungicides, bordeaux mixture and lime-sulfur solution, in that they have given less fruit dwarfing than bordeaux mixture and better leaf spot control than lime-sulfur. They still have considerable merit for use in some of the Great Lakes districts where injury by them is at a minimum, and in other areas where small orchards or garden trees do not justify extra labor and expense with a more complicated spray schedule in an effort to obtain maximum crops of perfect fruit. They have not been satisfactory in south central Pennsylvania because of excessive leaf and fruit injury. With the relatively large number of sprays required there for leaf spot control, crop reductions of 10 to 20 percent by a copper fungicide have been frequent in hot, dry harvest seasons.

None of the copper materials may be used on sweet cherries without danger of injury.

FERBAM preparations sold under such trade names as Fermate, Ferradow, and Karbam Black, have been used both alone and with elemental sulfur, usually one of the sulfur pastes. The usual concentration has been 1.5 pounds to 100 gallons of water of a product containing about 75 percent active ingredient. Two pounds has been the minimum effective concentration in Pennsylvania with the sprays started before bloom and continued at 7- to 14-day intervals until harvest. One and one-half pounds has been adequate when used with one of the elemental sulfurs.

Ferbam has not usually caused any visible injury to the tree or reduction in fruit size. The large fruits have been comparatively low in solids content, largely or entirely because of their size, and have been unsatisfactory to some canners because of this.

F. H. LEWIS *is a professor of plant pathology at Pennsylvania State College and pathologist at the Pennsylvania State College Fruit Research Laboratory, Arendtsville, Pa. He is a graduate of Clemson Agricultural and Mechanical College and obtained his doctor's degree in plant pathology from Cornell University in 1943. He has worked on cherry leaf spot and the effects of fungicides on cherry fruit quality in New York and Pennsylvania since 1940.*

201500°—53———46

Two Root Rots of Fruit Trees

H. Earl Thomas, Stephen Wilhelm,
Neil Allan MacLean

A disease known as oak fungus disease, oak root fungus disease, mushroom root rot, shoestring root rot, and armillaria root rot is responsible for large annual losses in most varieties of tree fruits in the western part of the United States.

Fig, persimmon, northern California black walnut, and French pear are the only orchard trees or rootstocks now known that will live a normal life span in the presence of *Armillaria mellea*, the fungus that causes the disease. All other orchard varieties or rootstocks show varying degrees of susceptibility.

Infected trees show—until they are killed—a progressive yellowing and wilting of the foliage and a stunted growth. Some fruit tree species, peach and apricot among them, may be killed within a year or two after planting. Others, such as the myrobalan 29 and Marianna 2624 plums, may live for 10 years or more in the presence of the fungus.

The fungus infects the roots and lower part of the trunk. It is there that a diagnosis of the disease can be made. Infected bark tends to become moist, spongy, and somewhat stringy. At times it will slough off, leaving the wood exposed. The characteristic fans or mycelial plaques are formed in the bark and between the bark and the wood. These fans, of coarse, white or yellowish-white, radiating hyphal strands, are the most characteristic signs that the disease is present.

After fall and winter rains, a second stage in the life cycle of the fungus is to be found at and around the bases of infected trees—the mushroom or toadstool stage. In rainy weather the fungus may produce large numbers of yellow-brown or honey-colored mushrooms, from which we get the names mushroom root rot or toadstool root rot. The mushrooms appear only for a few weeks each year and therefore are not a good year-around sign of the disease.

Other structures of this fungus are the rhizomorphs—rootlike growths of compact fungus strands, dark outside, white inside and somewhat smaller than the lead in a pencil. They spread the fungus from root to root for short distances through the soil and these structures appear to be the only ones which are able to penetrate the roots to start new infections. They are not formed at high temperatures (above 80° F.), a fact that no doubt is related to the scarcity of this root rot in warmer areas. The name shoestring root rot has been derived from them.

Armillaria is very sensitive to drying in or on the soil but can live as a saprophyte on dead woody material in moist soils for many years. It resumes its parasitic activity when trees susceptible to it are planted again. Susceptible roots may become infected by growing into or near an already infected or decayed root and coming into contact with the rhizomorphs. The rhizomorphs invade the roots by means of pressure and dissolving enzymes. The fungus grows through the outer cortex and to a lesser extent the wood of the root to the crown of the plant. The death of a tree follows the killing of the roots and the girdling of the lower trunk. In an orchard in which many trees are infected one finds groups of dead trees in circular areas—evidence of how the fungus spreads outward from a center.

The fungus may be carried into new areas by floodwaters and perhaps infrequently by irrigation and cultivation. But the great majority of infections trace back to earlier cropping to susceptible plants or to the presence of the fungus on native vegetation—notably oak trees—in the case of new land. The fungus does little apparent damage to most native trees and shrubs in natural sites.

The use of resistant rootstocks and soil fumigation help control *Armillaria* in deciduous orchards.

As we have noted, rootstocks differ greatly in susceptibility to *Armillaria*. Only four are very resistant. We list five groups of rootstocks from the very susceptible to the very resistant:

Group 1—almond, peach, apricot; replants may be killed in 1 or 2 years.

Group 2—mahaleb cherry, Morello cherry, quince; susceptible, but somewhat less so than group 1.

Group 3—myrobalan plum, mazzard cherry, apple; unwise to plant in known oak root fungus spot.

Group 4—myrobalan 29, Marianna 2624; selected for greater resistance than ordinary plum roots.

Group 5—fig, persimmon (three species—(*kaki, lotus, virginiana*), French pear, black walnut (*Juglans hindsii*); usually live a normal life span in the presence of the fungus.

Of the many chemicals that have been tested as soil fumigants against *Armillaria*, only one, carbon bisulfide, can be recommended. It does not give complete control, but if it is applied correctly it does give commercial control in lighter soils.

Other chemicals that have been tested may give a better kill of the fungus but are not satisfactory because they do not penetrate deeply enough or they are too expensive. A fungicide to be effective against *Armillaria* has to move to a depth at least of 6 or 7 feet. Carbon bisulfide usually goes only 5 or 6 feet deep in many soils. It is relatively cheap, but it is inflammable, poisonous, and corrosive.

Carbon bisulfide can be applied with a hand applicator or with a power-drawn applicator. The hand applicator is used when only a small space is to be treated. Power-drawn equipment is used when areas of an acre or more are to be treated.

Treatment is usually done in the fall after the crop has been harvested. The soil should be warm and porous. It should have a uniform and low moisture content, but it should not be dry. The dead trees are pulled, all the large roots are dug out, the land is leveled, and the fumigant is injected. When the fungicide is applied with a hand applicator, 2 ounces by weight (1⅝ ounces by volume) of the material are injected at a depth of 6 to 8 inches at points 18 inches apart. The rows are also 18 inches apart and the injections are staggered. Injections should not be made closer than 6 to 8 feet from any living tree (or up to the tree drip) as the material is toxic to living roots. A gallon of carbon bisulfide will treat approximately 180 square feet. To treat a single tree space 24 x 24 feet takes 3⅓ gallons.

The power equipment is in the form of a 3-standard subsoiler with automatic measuring valves. In operation the injector standards are submerged to the desired depth, at which point the pumps automatically begin to dispense the liquid chemical in prescribed dosages.

THE ROOT DISEASE of many plants, particularly fruit trees and vines, caused by the *Dematophora* stage of the fungus *Rosellinia necatrix*, attracted attention in Europe about 1880 and in California much later. The fungus was reported years ago in the eastern part of the United States but does not seem to have become established there.

The disease was first recognized in California in 1929 on apple trees growing in Santa Cruz County. In 1938 it was known in 8 counties and in 1947 in 15—Alameda, Butte, Contra Costa, El Dorado, Monterey, Napa, Orange, Riverside, San Benito, San Bernardino, San Joaquin, San Mateo, Santa Clara, Santa Cruz, and Sonoma. In 11 of them in 1953 the disease was restricted in distribution.

Probably it had been introduced on

nursery stocks. It has been seen in two nurseries in central California. Because the disease is most prevalent in apple and pear orchards in California and most apple and pear seedling stocks before 1920 were imported from Europe, the fungus may have been introduced into California on such stocks.

The above-ground symptoms consist of sparse foliage, slow growth or none at all, wilting of leaves, and death of twigs, branches, and leaves. The dead leaves may remain attached for several months. Sometimes, particularly when moisture and temperature are favorable, the fungus appears for an inch or so above ground on the bark of the dead tree and forms a dark, velvety mat with white-headed spore-bearing structures, called coremia.

The symptoms below ground are more distinctive. In early stages the white, cottony mycelium pervades the cortex, wood, and adjacent soil. Later the fungus may form indefinite plaques within the bark and loosely aggregated strands of associated hyphae. It never attains the well-defined mycelial fans and less commonly seen rhizomorphs produced by the oak root fungus, *Armillaria mellea*. Still later the root is killed, and the surface is often covered by a dark, hard, mycelial mat, from which the coremia and cottony white growth may arise.

Dematophora root rot differs from that caused by *Armillaria* in its erratic distribution within the orchard, in the cottony outgrowth from the root under highly humid conditions, in the absence of a mushroom stage, and in absence of well-defined mycelial fans, or rhizomorphs.

A useful diagnostic feature, when a microscope is available, is a pear-shaped swelling near the end of each cell in the hyphal strands of the fungus. We have not found these in any other fungus associated with apple roots. The mycelium has a remarkable resistance to competing soil micro-organisms and to dryness. It has survived in apple roots in the laboratory for at least 8 years with only occasional watering.

Once established in an orchard, the fungus seems to spread primarily by two means—along and within the roots of infected plants and in fragments of roots, which are sometimes transported by cultural operations. The mycelial growth in soil is usually limited to a few inches from roots or other invaded plant material. Perhaps water spreads the fungus also. No spore form seems to play any part in dissemination of the fungus in California.

To find out which species of deciduous fruit and nut trees are susceptible to attack by the *Dematophora* fungus, tests were made in two naturally infested orchard plots and in large boxes in which plants were grown in artificially infested soil. Much of the work was done by Harold E. Thomas at the University of California College of Agriculture.

The following plants are susceptible: Quince (*Cydonia oblonga*), Black Mission fig (*Ficus carica*), butternut (*Juglans cinerea*), northern California black walnut (*J. hindsii*), eastern black walnut (*J. nigra*), apricot (*Prunus armeniaca*), mazzard cherry (*P. avium*), sand cherry (*P. besseyi*), sour cherry (*P. cerasus*), almond (*P. amygdalis*), peach (*P. persica*), black cherry (*P. serotina*), Siberian crab apple (*Malus baccata*), apple seedlings of Golden Delicious and McIntosh (*Malus pumila*), apple rootstocks known as East Malling I, II, IV, V, VII, and IX, and the pear species *Pyrus betulaefolia*, *P. bretschneideri*, *P. calleryana*, *P. communis*, *P. communis cordata*, *P. regeli*, *P. ovoidea*, *P. amygdaliformis* var. *persica*, *P. phaeocarpa*, *P. serotina*, *P. serrulata*, *P. ussuriensis*.

Other possible rootstocks, especially for apple and pear, are being tested for resistance. The crab apples, *Malus floribunda* and *M. toringoides*, in preliminary tests seem to have considerable resistance but little is known of their suitability as rootstocks for the locally grown apple varieties.

Resistance tests conducted for more than 10 years have revealed two important resistant stocks in the species *Prunus cerasifera* and its hybrids, the myrobalan and the Marianna plums. Selection number 29 of the myrobalan plum and 2624 of the Marianna have proved highly resistant and are good stocks for commercial varieties of plums and apricots. These stocks, especially Marianna 2624, also are resistant to armillaria root rot and to the effects of waterlogging of heavy soils. Replanting affected spots with Marianna 2624 rootstock on which plum or apricot can be grown offers the best promise in situations to which these fruits are adapted.

MANY CHEMICALS have been tested against this fungus in closed cans of soil and several have been tried in orchards. To date no encouragement has come out of these tests.

Every possible precaution should be taken to prevent the spread of the fungus during irrigation or other cultural operations as well as in the movement of nursery stock.

H. EARL THOMAS *is professor of plant pathology in the University of California, and plant pathologist in the California Agricultural Experiment Station at Berkeley.*
He is the author, with H. N. Hansen and Harold E. Thomas of The Connection Between Dematophora necatrix and Rosellinia necatrix, Hilgardia, *volume 10, pages 561-564, 1937, and* Dematophora Root Rot, Phytopathology, *volume 24, page 1145, 1934.*
STEPHEN WILHELM *is assistant professor of plant pathology in the University of California and an assistant plant pathologist in the California Agricultural Experiment Station.*
NEIL ALLAN MACLEAN *was formerly assistant professor of plant pathology at the University of California and assistant plant pathologist in the California Agricultural Experiment Station at Berkeley.*

For further reading the authors suggest Harold E. Thomas' Studies on Armillaria mellea (Vahl) Quel., Infection, Parasitism and Host Resistance, *Journal of Agricultural Research, volume 48, pages 187-218, 1934, and* Identification and Treatment of Armillaria Root Rot, Almond Facts, *March 1942.*

Coryneum Blight of Stone Fruits

E. E. Wilson

Coryneum blight also is called shot hole, corynosis, a peach blight, fruit spot, winter blight, and pustular spot. It is caused by the fungus *Coryneum beijerinckii (Clasterosporium carpophilum)*, which was first noted in France in 1853 and subsequently in North and South America, Africa, Australia, and New Zealand. It has been found in Michigan, Ohio, and many other parts of this country, but it is serious only in the far western States.

Its natural hosts belong to the genus *Prunus.* The peach (*P. persica*), apricot (*P. armeniaca*), nectarine (*P. persica* var. *nectarina*), almond (*P. amygdalus*) and sweet cherry (*P. avium*) are the main ones. Other known hosts are the European plum (*P. domestica*), the wild cherries (*P. serotina, P. virginiana,* and *P. padus*), the cherry-laurel (*P. laurocerasus*), and *P. davidiana.*

Coryneum blight differs in severity on the various stone fruits. For example, it is seldom found on sweet cherries in California, but it is serious on them in the Pacific Northwest.

It attacks dormant leaf buds and blossom buds, blossoms, leaves, fruits, and twigs. In California, the extent to which these structures are affected varies greatly among the four principal hosts. On peaches and nectarines, for example, twigs and dormant buds are severely affected and so are leaves and blossoms at times, but by and large peach fruit are not seriously affected. But on apricots twig infection is rare, the disease being confined largely to dormant buds, leaves, and fruit. On almonds, twig lesions occur but seldom abundantly. Leaf infection is common on almond and sometimes blossom infection is common.

The lesions of coryneum blight at first are small, round purplish-black spots on the surface of the affected part. The lesion seldom is more than 5 millimeters in diameter on fruit, but as the fruit develops the surface of the lesion becomes raised and scurfy. On young leaves the diseased areas may expand rapidly and kill large areas of the blade. If the lesions are on the petiole, the leaf is killed outright. Frequently large numbers of young leaf clusters are killed by lesions that develop on the base of the petioles. On the blades of mature leaves, the affected areas soon are separated from the non-affected tissue by abscission zones and thereupon fall away. Newly formed leaves with only a few lesions will drop, but older leaves commonly remain on the tree despite a number of lesions.

Affected buds are darker in color than unaffected ones. Often, particularly on apricots, they are "varnished" by a thin film of dried gum. The fungus kills the bud by invading apparently between the bud scales and by attacking the twig near the base of the bud. Invasion of the bud is common with all hosts.

On peach and nectarine twigs, the lesions, which at first are small, purplish, raised spots, expand into elongated, necrotic cankers. Many twigs, especially those in the lower part of the tree where much of the best fruit is produced, are killed in late spring and early summer. The disease thereby reduces the bearing surface of the tree for a number of years to come.

The two names of the causal organism reflect the different opinions as to the nature of its fruiting structure. That need not concern us now, but we shall pay close attention to the life cycle of *C. beijerinckii*. Here, too, some disagreement exists regarding the number of fruiting structures. Paul Vuil-

lemin in France reported in 1888 that the fungus has a sexual stage, which he named *Ascospora beijerinckii*. R. Aderhold in Germany, R. E. Smith in California, and Geoffrey Samuel in Australia later studied the fungus carefully, but none found the sexual stage. Apparently, therefore, only one type of propagative structure is regularly produced—a four- to six-celled, ovoid, yellowish conidium, borne on a short stalk (conidiophore), which rises from a simple cushion of fungal cells.

When the conidium drops from the conidiophore to a favorable place, it germinates and produces a germ tube from one or more of its four or five cells. A conidium deposited on a twig or leaf and surrounded by a film of moisture quickly produces a gelatinous sheath about itself. The sheath anchors the conidium to the substrate so that rain does not easily dislodge it. Infection is accomplished by a slender projection from the germ tube, which penetrates the host tissue. On leaves the infection hypha penetrates directly through the cuticle and is seldom if ever found entering stomata. After entry of the infection hypha, the fungus produces mycelium between the walls of the host tissue. From this mycelium loosely packed cushions of hyphal cells then form, emerge to the surface, and give rise to conidia.

Coryneum beijerinckii therefore passes its entire cycle on the tree. Contrary to Vuillemin's belief, the mycelium in leaves that fall to the ground apparently does not play a part in its development. For its perpetuation the fungus depends on the mycelium and conidia that remain alive in the diseased buds and twigs. In California the fungus undergoes a period of unfavorable conditions in summer, when lack of rain and probably high temperatures prevent its development. Throughout this period the conidia inside blighted dormant buds retain their viability, although those on the surface of twig lesions do not. Hence conidia are present and readily available for infection even during the inactive stage of the fungus. After rains begin in autumn, conidia develop on the surface of twig lesions and new conidia develop inside diseased buds. Occasionally the fungus survives in diseased blossoms that remain in the tree.

As I have noted, the incidence of twig and bud infection differs in the four main hosts. Consequently we find that on apricots, which are not subject to twig infection, the diseased dormant buds are the primary inoculum sources; on peaches and nectarines, twigs and buds are equal in importance as inoculum sources; and on almond, blighted spurs are probably more important than blighted buds. Fruit, on the other hand, is not an important source; conidia are seldom produced on fruit lesions.

Winds play a secondary role in disseminating the conidia. Moving air is ineffective in detaching the conidia from the conidiophore; air currents cannot remove the conidia from inside the blighted buds. Water washing over the twigs and buds readily accomplishes this step in dissemination and, in addition, spreads the spores about the tree. Conidia washed downward by rain subject the twigs and buds in the lower part of the tree to much heavier infection than those in the upper part. The dispersal of conidia upward and outward from their sources apparently is accomplished by spattered and wind-blown spore-laden raindrops.

For the infection process no less than for dispersal, the fungus requires the moisture supplied by rain. To germinate and infect the host the conidium must be in a film of water. Consequently no infection occurs during dry weather. Infection is initiated only when the susceptible parts are wet for a long enough time to permit the conidium to germinate and the germ tube to penetrate the host tissue. Once that occurs, the fungus is no longer dependent on the moisture supplied by rain but obtains it from the host. The length of time required for infection, in turn, is influenced by temperature. Our information on the relation between temperature and growth of the fungus is not extensive, but a few general statements are possible regarding infection and development of the lesions. Although temperatures in California in winter are below the optimum for growth (about 72° F.) of the fungus, probably they are seldom so low as to prevent infection and disease development. It should be remembered in this connection that the temperature is usually higher in rainy than in dry winter weather. In fact, the temperature during rainy periods seldom goes lower than 45° but often as high as 60°. We find therefore that infection occurs during the long rains of midwinter. The influence of temperature is evident, however, in the length of time required for infection and the length of the time between infection and the first visible symptom.

To permit infection at the most favorable temperature, the host parts must remain wet for several hours. Temperature below the optimum prolongs the time necessary for the fungus to gain entrance to the host and lengthens the incubation period. In warm spring weather it is not unusual to find lesions developing 5 to 6 days after the rainy period which initiated infection. In winter 15 to 18 days may elapse before lesions can be seen.

Knowing something about the conditions necessary for infection and having a general knowledge of length of incubation periods, we can obtain considerable information from data such as that presented in the chart on page 709. Here is represented by graphs the increase in the number of twig and leaf lesions during the 1935–36 season and the rainfall record for that season. We first note that rains fell in October, November, and early December and a small wave of twig infection was found on December 24.

On the basis of what I said earlier regarding the length of incubation periods, this infection probably was initiated during one or both of the December rains, the last of which ended 12 days before the lesions first became visible. Apparently, therefore, infection was not initiated during the October and November rains, probably because they were too short to permit it. Data obtained in other years support the view that the first autumn rains not uncommonly are too short to permit twig infection, but those rains often initiate abundant leaf infection, which, however, is of little consequence to the tree because the leaves fall shortly thereafter. Further examination of the chart reveals that large numbers of twig lesions developed at two other times during the winter. Each of the developments followed an extended rainy period.

Here again, data obtained in different years have agreed in all major respects. Consequently we can draw some general conclusions from them. First, twig and dormant bud infection in serious amounts is not likely until the longer rains of winter begin. Second, such infection may occur any time during the winter or early spring when rains of sufficient length do occur. This information has been of great value, as we shall see, in formulating a fungicidal control program for the disease.

BECAUSE *Coryneum beijerinckii* survives from one season to the next only in the tree, the elimination of the hold-over sources should aid in controlling the disease. Removal of the diseased twigs at pruning time is both impractical and destructive to the fruiting wood.

Eliminating the conidia in and on the diseased parts by means of chemical sprays so far has proved only partly successful. Several phenol and cresol derivatives, notably sodium dinitro-o-cresolate and sodium pentachlorophenate, destroy a great many of the conidia. Applying them as sprays to the dormant tree has noticeably reduced the incidence of the disease at times. Apparently however, they do not destroy the mycelium of *C. beijerinckii* in diseased twigs, so the fungus soon produces a new supply of conidia.

With peaches, control of coryneum blight by means of a protective spray is highly effective. Professor R. E. Smith in 1906 obtained almost complete suppression of new infection from spraying peach trees with bordeaux mixture, 10–10–100. His program, it is safe to say, prevented the abandonment of peach growing in some parts of California. The program consisted in spraying the trees in November or early December and again in February with the bordeaux preparation. The primary purpose of the later spray was the prevention of leaf curl. Omission of this application became possible after better sprayers were developed.

Dr. Smith demonstrated that effective control depended on the timing of the spray application at the beginning of the winter season. He summarized his findings somewhat as follows: Trees sprayed in December were free from coryneum blight and leaf curl; trees sprayed in January were free from leaf curl but affected somewhat by blight; trees sprayed in February and March were free from leaf curl, but severely affected by blight.

In our work at the California Agricultural Experiment Station the timing of the spray treatment in relation to leaf fall was studied closely. The foliage, of course, interferes with deposition of the spray on the twigs. It is desirable therefore to delay that treatment until the leaves are off the trees. Our results indicated that that can be done if the treatment is not delayed too long. The practice of some growers of spraying any time between leaf fall and late December is not to be recommended because severe twig infection may have preceded the treatment. In fact, a small amount of twig infection may occur before leaf fall. Between 1935 and 1941, for example, tests showed that infection before leaf fall occurred in two seasons out of the six, but in only one season was the amount sufficient to cause appreciable damage to the tree. Apparently, therefore, the practice of spraying soon after leaf fall is a safe one.

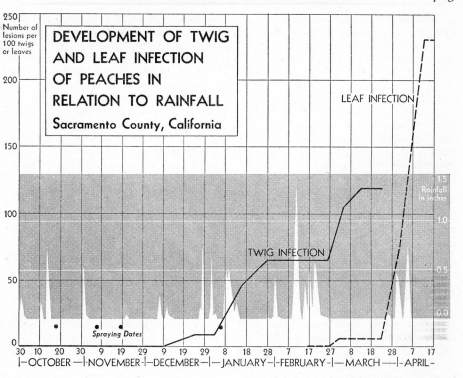

DEVELOPMENT OF TWIG
AND LEAF INFECTION
OF PEACHES IN
RELATION TO RAINFALL
Sacramento County, California

LEAF INFECTION

TWIG INFECTION

Spraying Dates

Rainfall
in inches

Number of
lesions per
100 twigs
or leaves

|—OCTOBER —|-NOVEMBER-|—DECEMBER—|—JANUARY—|-FEBRUARY-|— MARCH ——|-APRIL–

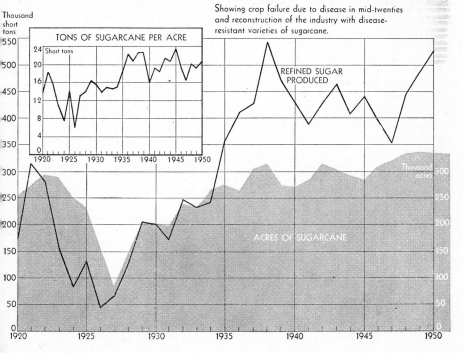

CANE SUGAR PRODUCTION IN THE UNITED STATES 1920–1950

Showing crop failure due to disease in mid-twenties
and reconstruction of the industry with disease-
resistant varieties of sugarcane.

Thousand
short
tons

TONS OF SUGARCANE PER ACRE

Short tons

REFINED SUGAR
PRODUCED

ACRES OF SUGARCANE

Thousand
acres

The single autumn treatment is expected to prevent twig infection throughout the dormant season, when heavy and prolonged rains occur. To be effective over such a long period, the fungicide deposit must have superior weather-resistant qualities. Our experience is that bordeaux mixture meets the requirements admirably—it is toxic to the conidia of *Coryneum beijerinckii* and it has excellent weather resistance as well. One-fourth or more of the copper deposited by bordeaux in autumn often is found on the twigs in spring. Few other fungicides can meet those requirements. A single treatment of lime-sulfur will protect the twigs for a short period but not throughout the winter. Some of the so-called fixed copper fungicides prove satisfactory if their weather resistance is increased by the addition of a sticker. Petroleum spray oil is used for the purpose. To obtain the maximum sticking qualities from such a supplement, the fungicide particles have to be incorporated in the oil phase of the emulsion. A stable oil-in-water emulsion is unsuitable, because the fungicide particles remain in the water phase and are wetted by the oil only after the water has evaporated from the spray deposit on the host. By selecting the proper emulsifier, however, conditions can be made that promote differential wetting of the fungicide particles by the oil.

We have considered so far the control of coryneum blight in peaches only. The procedure for controlling the disease in apricots is similar in that an autumn spray is applied. Its primary object is to prevent the fungus from attacking the dormant buds. Because leaf and fruit infection cause serious losses in apricots, however, it may be necessary to apply another spray in the spring.

Investigations in California and in Australia on the timing of this treatment demonstrated that leaf and fruit infection is prevented by spraying the trees just after the unopened blossoms emerged from the winter buds but before the petals unfolded. At times a second spray soon after petal fall may be necessary but, by and large, the autumn treatment followed by the preblossom treatment is sufficient. As a preblossom treatment is given for the brown rot blossom blight disease in many parts of California, no additional expense is involved in following the two-treatment program.

Early attempts to control coryneum blight in almonds, following the same procedure as for peach, gave indifferent results. It soon became apparent in our tests, however, that coryneum blight on almonds is much less a wintertime disease than suspected. That is to say, twig and dormant bud infection, though present, are not so common as either to destroy appreciable numbers of twigs or to supply abundant conidia for infection. Then, too, infection of dormant buds apparently occurs more frequently in early spring than in winter. In any event, a bordeaux spray treatment just before the blossom buds begin to open materially reduces the number of buds infected. Moreover, such a treatment subsequently reduces the amount of flower and leaf-cluster blighting which can be a serious phase of coryneum blight on almonds. Experience indicated the need for an additional spray to prevent leaf infection in years when rainy weather extended into late spring. This spray is now applied soon after the trees are through blossoming.

The timing of the first treatment was later reexamined and it was decided to forego control of dormant bud infection in favor of more effective prevention of leaf-cluster and flower infection during the blossoming season. The first spray now is applied just after the blossom buds emerge from the winter buds but before petals unfold. A treatment at this stage of host development also aids in preventing brown rot blossom blight disease.

E. E. WILSON *is professor of plant pathology in the University of California at Davis, where he has been engaged in studying fruit diseases since 1929.*

Root Rots in the East

C. N. Clayton

Root rot diseases kill many deciduous fruit trees in orchards in the eastern part of the United States each year. That annual loss of trees in bearing orchards is not particularly spectacular, but the loss of trees is quite important and often is of great concern to orchardists. Since the death of fruit trees from root rot most frequently occurs after they reach bearing age, the loss to the grower includes the investment in growing the tree as well as the potential production of the tree. Besides, the reduced yield of small or low-quality fruit on infected trees markedly increases the cost of production.

Several species of parasitic fungi cause infectious root rot diseases of fruit trees. Some of the diseases, such as the black root rot of apple, caused by *Xylaria mali,* are restricted in distribution to certain areas and a few crops. Others, such as armillaria or mushroom root rot, caused by *Armillaria mellea,* affect many kinds of woody plants in most of the United States as well as many other countries.

The root rot diseases, caused by the several fungus parasites, have similar symptoms on the above-ground parts of the tree. Fruit trees affected with root rot show stunting of leaves and branches and yellowing and wilting of leaves. Death of an affected tree occurs after the bark and cambium of the trunk are killed by a root rot fungus.

On the above-ground symptoms one cannot make a sure diagnosis of root rot because somewhat similar symptoms result from root injury or trunk girdling by insects, rodents, cold, or chemicals. Diagnosis of parasitic root diseases can be made only by examination of the affected roots or of specialized fruiting structures such as sporophores, rhizomorphs, or sclerotia. Without microscopic examination and isolation of the causal fungus, it is often impossible to diagnose the cause of the root rot.

The following root rot diseases of deciduous fruit trees in the Eastern States are discussed here: White root rot of apple, black root rot of apple, and clitocybe root rot.

THE WHITE ROOT ROT OF APPLE is due to a fungus, *Corticium galactinum,* which has been known as a parasite of apple trees for many years. In 1902 an investigator of the Department of Agriculture reported that the fungus was a widely distributed parasite of apple roots in West Virginia, Kentucky, southern Illinois, Arkansas, and Oklahoma. The disease was said to have caused considerable loss to apple growers in those States during the preceding 30 years in orchards set out on newly cleared land. It was suggested that the pathogen was transferred to young apple trees from nearby oak trees. Studies started in 1932 disclosed that white root rot was causing death of many trees in orchards in Virginia, Maryland, Tennessee, Delaware, and Indiana. In North Carolina white root rot has been found on bearing and young apple trees in scattered orchards.

The disease is confined to orchards that were set on newly cleared land or orchards near woods. The pathogen has been found growing abundantly on the roots of blackberry, dewberry, Japanese wineberry, dogwood, sumac, white campion, holly, and kalmia. In 1951 *C. galactinum* caused a root rot of ornamental shrubs and herbaceous perennials of many kinds in one place in Maryland. Included in the list of susceptible plants were species of blue wild indigo, winter jasmine, iris, pearl bush, peony, flowering almond, double flowering plum, spirea, viburnum, and peach.

C. *galactinum* has been reported as causing a root rot of white pine and a decay of firs, western white cedar, and spruce. According to E. A. Burt, of the Missouri Botanical Gardens, the white root rot fungus sporulates on a variety of substrata, including wood of both coniferous and broad-leaved species. L. T. White in Canada gave a revised description of the fungus in 1951 and listed it as occurring from Canada to Texas and westward to the Pacific coast, Europe, West Indies, and Japan.

The fungus appears on the surface of affected apple roots as a white or cream-colored layer of mycelia, which may persist for several years on old apple stumps and roots. The wood under the bark of affected roots often shows characteristic bird's-eye or zonate spots. At times affected roots appear knotted or gnarled. The wood of diseased roots, after being completely rotted, is very soft and light in weight. The pathogen produces spores on an inconspicuous hymenial layer on the surface of roots, on the surface of soil at the base of trees, or in open pockets in the soil. This layer, when it is dry, is white to cream-colored. It is waxy cream to ochraceous buff when it is moist.

During 15 years or more of observations of the disease in apple orchards, J. S. Cooley, of the Department of Agriculture, found that apple trees were frequently attacked at the collar by the white root rot fungus—the fungus apparently did not spread readily through the soil but by spores carried by wind or manual means. Trees died within 2 years after the above-ground parts first showed symptoms of the disease, but trees of all ages may be killed by white root rot.

Dr. Cooley found that trees 37 years old at the start of an experiment in two orchards in Virginia continued to die over an 8-year period, when more than one-half of apple replants in infested soil became infected with the rot. In an orchard in North Carolina young trees planted in sites where trees affected with the rot had been removed were killed within a year.

Cooley and Ross W. Davidson in 1940 reported successful inoculation of the roots of young apple trees with pure cultures of the fungus.

THE BLACK ROOT ROT DISEASE OF APPLE, caused by *Xylaria mali*, occurs in the southeastern and south central parts of the United States—primarily from Maryland to South Carolina west to Arkansas and Illinois. There black root rot is probably the most common and destructive parasitic root rot of apple trees. The fungus attacks oak and probably other deciduous woods. Maple, hackberry, grape, sassafras, and ash have been infected by inoculation, but we do not know whether they are susceptible to infection under natural conditions.

Large, fingerlike fruiting bodies frequently are found at the base of diseased trees. These spore-bearing stromata are at first white and produce many one-celled hyaline spores. Soon they turn black, and by autumn mature ascospores have formed in their surface layer. Another characteristic is that the surface of affected roots is covered with a black, charcoallike stromatic coating. The wood of affected roots becomes brittle; trees in advanced stages of the disease are easily uprooted, for the roots break off easily near the trunk under the strain of uprooting.

The symptoms of black root rot above ground are like those of other serious root disorders. The leaves on diseased trees have a pale-yellow cast. Many lateral buds fail to grow. The terminal growths are short and give the appearance of a thin foliar growth. In later stages one or more of the main branches may die. Others may remain normal, but more commonly death of the whole tree results. Bearing trees in late stages of the disease tend to bear heavily, but the fruits are small and of a poor quality.

The black root rot disease does not kill apple trees so quickly as does the white root rot disease. Although trees of all ages are susceptible, most trees that die from black root rot are at least 10 years old. Affected trees are rarely killed in a single season after the time of infection. The fungus spreads from root to root of an individual tree and within 3 or 4 years after infection a tree may die. Each year a few more trees in an orchard carrying the fungus are affected, so that eventually 25 percent or more of the trees may be killed or removed because of the disease. Where a tree has died or has been removed because of black root rot, the site is undesirable for replanting. Since the length of time the organism may persist in the soil is known to be 16 years or more, replanting would be risking a recurrence of the disease.

The best temperature for the growth of the black root rot fungus and also for infection is near 77° F. No growth occurs above 95° or below 41°. The fungus can penetrate directly through the bark or enter through wounds. Peak infection seems to come in July, because of a lessening of metabolic activity of the roots in midsummer.

The most important source of inoculum is the mycelium in the roots of diseased trees, even though ascospores are produced in great abundance and undoubtedly are carried long distances by wind and other factors. The fungus may survive the death of the host plant by many years and serve as inoculum for infection of replanted apple trees.

A high incidence of black root rot has been found within 2 to 3 years on young apple trees planted in thoroughly infested orchard soils in West Virginia. They tested a large number of clones of Malus species exposed to natural infection and found that none of the clonal stocks or seedling stocks inoculated with Xylaria mali in pure

culture exhibited any promising measure of resistance to the fungus.

Another species of Xylaria, X. polymorpha, has been reported to occur on apple in Virginia, New York, and Georgia. That fungus is not so vigorously parasitic as is X. mali.

IN NORTH CAROLINA I have found armillaria root rot to be the greatest cause of death of peach trees. The disease has also killed apple and peach trees in clay and sandy soils in several other sections of North Carolina. The greatest prevalence of the disease is in orchards planted on newly cleared land. In such locations pieces of wood invaded by the fungus serve as inoculum for infecting roots of fruit crops.

In the Southeastern States another mushroom fungus, Clitocybe tabescens, causes a root rot of pear, peach, apple, and other woody plants. The clitocybe root rot disease is so similar to armillaria root rot in symptoms and its effect upon the plant that positive diagnosis cannot be made without the presence of the mushrooms or cultural studies. One major difference between a mushroom of Clitocybe and Armillaria is that the latter has an annulus or ring on the stipe and the former does not.

Control of root rot diseases of tree fruits in eastern United States depends primarily on the avoidance of the diseases by planting trees in soil that is not harboring the pieces of woody material in which a root rot fungus is present.

Care in removal of diseased trees to avoid spreading inoculum of the root rot fungus from one place to another is necessary. Resistant rootstocks are not known or are not satisfactory for one reason or another. The use of chemical fumigants to kill the fungus in woody material in the soil before planting trees has possibilities.

C. N. CLAYTON *is a plant pathologist at North Carolina State College, Raleigh. He has been engaged in research on diseases of fruit crops in that State since 1945.*

Virus Diseases of Stone Fruits

L. C. Cochran, E. L. Reeves

Stone fruits have been grown in North America for some 300 years, but up to 1930 only five virus diseases were known to affect them.

Peach yellows, the first virus disease known to affect peach, may have been present around Philadelphia as early as 1750. Seven epidemics, the latest in 1920, wiped out orchards in different sections of the country. Little peach, thought to be caused by a strain of the peach yellows virus, became serious in the same geographic area as yellows in the late 1800's and now causes greater losses than yellows. Red suture, believed to be caused by another strain of the peach yellows virus, was first seen about 1910. Rosette and phony disease appeared in southeastern United States at about the same time that little peach appeared farther north. The phony disease has become the most serious virus disease of peach. More than 1,500,000 phony-affected peach trees have been removed from orchards in Georgia alone.

Since 1930, more than 40 new virus diseases have been found in North America on peach, nectarine, plum, sweet cherry, sour cherry, apricot, almond, and many ornamental and wild species of the genus *Prunus*.

It is indeed strange that so many troubles should have come upon us so suddenly. Growers and research men alike are inclined to ask why and from whence they came. They cannot be attributed to any foreign importation,

because apparently only a few of those known in North America have been found in foreign countries and probably these were carried abroad from America. It appears then that most of our stone-fruit viruses are indigenous to North America and have gained access to stocks during the processes of fruit growing.

Peach yellows was recognized soon after peach culture was started in Massachusetts in 1630 or so—indicating that the causal virus was present in other hosts, from which it probably spread to peach. As peach culture spread, peach yellows went along until it reached the limit of the range of the peach yellows vector. Peach yellows may have been carried to areas outside of the vector range in nursery stock, but since yellows eventually kills peach trees and there was no vector to spread the causal virus to other trees, the disease never became established.

Little peach and red suture of peach show relationship to yellows and are generally credited to strains that have arisen from the yellows virus. Rosette, on the contrary, has a different geographic distribution than yellows and has few characters in common with yellows. Rosette appeared on peaches soon after peach culture extended into Georgia, pointing to an indigenous occurrence, possibly on wild plums. The phony disease also appears to have started in Georgia, from where it spread north and west.

Peach mosaic was already widely distributed when it was discovered in 1931. Surveys during the next few years showed it present more than 600 miles south of the border in Mexico and in various localities in the Rio Grande and Colorado River Valleys of the United States. The high incidence in several *Prunus* species in those areas indicates that it may have been present for a long time before it was discovered. Not until it escaped into the areas of intensive culture, where it produced striking effects on peach, was it seen. The distribution indicates that peach mosaic may have been centered in the vicinity of El Paso and was locally spread among the Indian villages in infected plums, which were commonly propagated by transplanting sucker shoots. It was probably introduced into the peach areas of Colorado, Utah, and southern California and Texas in infected nursery stock, which had been grown near infected plums. Sour cherry yellows appears to have been present in orchards for a number of years but was not recognized because of the presence of other disorders which caused leaf casting.

The distribution of X-disease and western X-disease is more difficult to explain. Reports of growers and the extent of occurrence indicate that both had been present in some areas for a long time before they were recognized. The variation in symptom expression in different areas indicates the presence of fairly widely varying forms. When X-disease was first seen it was limited to one locality in Connecticut, but during the next few years it spread rapidly westward in chokecherry and within 15 years was well established in the north central Midwest.

Cherry buckskin was first seen several years before X-disease was recognized on peach, and at that time its occurrence was limited to a small area in the Bay district of central California. It is now recognized that the virus causing cherry buckskin infects peach, with symptoms nearly identical with those of western X-disease. Western X-disease is rapidly becoming widely distributed in the major peach areas of central California. Western X-disease is also widely dispersed in the central valleys of Washington and Oregon east of the Cascade Range, in southern Idaho, and central Utah. The similarity of symptoms on various hosts produced by the viruses causing X-disease and western X-disease of peach, buckskin of cherry, and possibly others points to the possibility that they may have stemmed from a common source.

The origin of many of the diseases, particularly on cherries in the western United States, is something of a mystery. Stone-fruit culture in that area, particularly the nursery business, is still regarded as a relatively young industry. It seems logical that some of the viruses may have been present on native hosts and as fruit crops moved in they spread to fruit trees. The present occurrence of certain diseases with a relatively slow rate of spread would fit well into such a theory. There is good evidence to show that the cherry mottle leaf disease of sweet cherries was present in cherry trees near Wenatchee more than 20 years before it was recognized. It has been shown to be indigenous in native stands of bitter cherry near infected orchards, but spread into commercial orchards was relatively slow before 1930. Diseases with a rapid rate of natural spread, such as albino cherry in southern Oregon and little cherry of the Kootenay Lake area of British Columbia, point to either a new introduction or introduction into a host favorable to an efficient vector.

To postulate the origin of viruses is like trying to account for other kinds of life. There is no evidence to support an origin other than that they have evolved in the same way that other forms have. When they become prevalent in an area it is merely evidence that they have either been introduced into an environment favorable to them or that they were present and the environment has been changed so that it is favorable.

THE ECONOMIC IMPORTANCE of individual virus diseases affecting stone fruits is strikingly variable.

Peach yellows became so extensive in northeastern United States and the Great Lakes States in epidemic eras that it caused peach culture to disappear from certain localities for a time. Phony peach continues to be a serious threat to peach culture, particularly in Georgia and Alabama. Peach mosaic has caused the loss of more than 200,000 peach trees in southwestern United States and remains uncontrolled in many areas. Western X-disease has caused extensive losses in peach orchards in Northwestern States and is responsible for disappearance of peach culture in some localities. Surveys in several States indicate that upwards of one-third of all the sour cherries in the United States are affected with sour cherry yellows. Fruit production on thoroughly diseased sour cherry trees is reduced to 50 percent or less, thus indicating a total crop reduction of at least 15 percent. Interpreted in terms of a crop worth 45 million dollars, sour cherry yellows causes an estimated loss of more than 5 million dollars annually.

Some other virus diseases offer potential threats to stone fruits because of their ability to destroy trees or crops, but are limited in distribution and have caused only locally serious losses. Albino cherry is chiefly responsible for disappearance of cherries from the Rogue River Valley in western Oregon, where it is has spread rapidly through orchards. The disease is limited to that area, which is isolated from the more important cherry-producing areas by mountains. Sour cherry pink fruit, cherry rasp leaf, peach wart, peach yellow bud mosaic, and apricot ring pox are diseases that ruin the commercial value of their hosts and have caused serious local losses, but are still limited in occurrence to local areas.

Cherry twisted leaf, cherry mottle leaf, and cherry necrotic rusty mottle, also of only local occurrence, ruin the value of some horticultural varieties of cherries but cause only partial crop losses to others. In contrast to them is little cherry, a disease affecting sweet cherries in the Kootenay Lake area of British Columbia. Its occurrence was limited to a single orchard when first observed in 1933, but during the next 15 years it spread over an area 100 miles in diameter—despite mountainous barriers, large lakes, and the great distances between orchards.

Little cherry reduces the fruit size to one-half normal size and ruins the flavor, yet causes no tree or leaf symptoms. The rapid rate of spread through the infected area and the serious effects it has on fruit make it a serious threat to sweet cherries in other districts.

A sizable number of virus diseases affecting stone fruits cause only small losses. Some have produced striking effects on a few trees but are limited in occurrence. Others are of wide distribution, but cause only minor effects. Ring spot is nearly universal in some *Prunus* species, particularly cherries, in western United States; after the initial stages of infection, however, damage appears to be limited to a possible reduction in tree vigor. While these viruses are relatively unimportant economically, their presence complicates research.

THE EXPRESSION of virus diseases in plants is usually indicated by development of some consistent off-type or abnormal change in appearance as compared to normal or healthy plants; such abnormal characters are referred to as symptoms. Demonstration that a given symptom is caused by a virus is generally accepted if that symptom is reproducible on a comparable previously healthy plant following some mode of transmission in the absence of any visible pathogen. Since plant viruses are obligate parasites which cannot be cultured outside of their hosts and are generally too small for their presence to be determined with ordinary equipment, it is necessary to depend on the symptoms they produce to indicate their presence and determine their identity.

Symptoms of virus diseases of stone fruits range from effects too mild to be recognized to various kinds of fruit and foliage abnormalities and even death of the affected trees. The most common types of symptoms are those expressed on leaves. In place of the uniform green color of normal leaves, affected ones develop patterns composed of spots, rings, blotches, or streaks of light green, yellow, or shades cf red, brown, or black. Some diseases cause leaves to become uniformly chlorotic or colored. Reduction in size, deformation, death, and shedding of leaves are also common symptoms. Unfruitfulness, failure of fruit to mature or mature at the normal time, and deformation of fruits are common effects of virus diseases. It should be recognized that similar abnormalities are caused by other factors, such as insect injury, chemical spray injury, nutritional disorders, fungus and bacterial diseases, and genetic factors; thus all abnormalities in plants are not indicative of the presence of a virus.

On the basis of symptoms, virus diseases of stone fruits might be divided into groups as follows:

Mosaics: Those that cause chlorotic, mottled, or necrotic patterns in leaves. Diseases in this class are: Peach—peach mosaic, yellow bud mosaic, mottle, ring spot, asteroid spot, necrotic leaf spot, golden-net, calico, and blotch; sweet cherry—mottle leaf, rusty mottle, twisted leaf, rugose mosaic, Lambert mottle, necrotic rusty mottle, tatter leaf, and pinto leaf; sour cherry—necrotic ring spot; plum—line pattern, white spot, and Standard prune constricting mosaic; apricot—ring pox; almond—almond calico.

Yellows: Those that cause a general chlorosis of a part or all of the leaves, sometimes accompanied by defoliation and failure of fruits to mature: Peach—peach yellows, little peach, red suture, peach rosette, and X-disease; sweet cherry—buckskin, albino, little cherry, and small bitter cherry; sour cherry—sour cherry yellows, green ring mottle, pink fruit.

Stunts: Those that cause shortened internodes, resulting in stunted growth, usually accompanied by darker green color: Peach—phony, Muir dwarf, and rosette mosaic; plum—prune dwarf.

Bud failures: Those that are characterized by death and shedding of buds on the past season's growth during the dormant season, without chlorotic or necrotic patterns in leaves: Peach—willow twig; almond—Drake almond bud failure.

Excrescences: Those that cause outgrowths on plant organs: Peach—wart; sweet cherry—rasp leaf.

Cankers: Those that cause necrotic pockets in the bark, resulting as the bark gets old in large cankers: Sweet cherry—black canker; and plum—diamond canker.

MANY OF THE VIRUS DISEASES affecting stone fruits are known to spread in orchards but vary markedly in rate of spread. Insect vectors for four diseases—peach yellows, little peach, phony, and western X-disease—have been determined. It is presumed that spread of the others, which takes place independent of man, is also by insects.

All of the vectors found so far are leafhoppers; all have shown ability, once they have fed on diseased plants and acquired the virus, to retain the virus for a long time. Such vectors are easier to find than those that transfer viruses by mechanical contamination of their mouth parts and lose the virus after one or two feedings.

The ecology of insect vectors is important in the spread of viruses. Those that move about freely, especially if they travel long distances, tend to move viruses in a like manner; those that have few winged individuals tend to spread viruses in a contiguous pattern. The vectors of the phony disease of peach are long-lived, large, and rugged and can move far. Phony spreads in a random pattern; new cases occur often in the far side of an orchard away from the source of infection. In contrast, the yellow bud mosaic disease of peach appears to spread in close colonies. The vector for yellow bud mosaic is not yet known, but it should be an insect with only weak flying habits.

Viruses that affect woody plants have been transmitted experimentally by grafting tissue from the diseased plant onto the healthy plant. For some diseases transmission can be effected with any of the tissues of the diseased plant, but for others it is necessary to select tissues from twigs bearing leaves or fruits that are showing symptoms. The common procedure is to use bud shields or bark shields from the diseased plant and insert them under the bark in a T-cut in the usual manner of budding. Other tissues, such as pieces of fruit, sections of leaves, flower petals, and wood chips, have been successfully used as inoculum for some viruses. Many attempts have been made to transmit stone-fruit viruses with juice expressed from tissues of diseased trees, but none has been successful from diseased to healthy trees.

The ring spot and sour cherry yellows viruses have been shown to pass through seeds of certain species to seedlings. Ring spot was found to pass through 1 to 3 percent of peach seeds and in a higher percentage in mazzard and mahaleb cherry seeds. Sour cherry yellows has been shown to pass through mahaleb cherry seeds. Studies conducted on a number of other viruses, particularly peach mosaic, phony, peach yellows, and western X-disease, have shown that they are not seed-transmitted. Part of the world-wide geographic occurrence of both the ring spot and sour cherry yellows viruses can be attributed to distribution in seeds. If this reasoning can be used, it is further evidence that most of the other virus diseases, which have limited geographic distribution, are not transmitted through seeds of peach or cherry species commonly used for rootstocks.

The INCUBATION PERIOD of a virus disease is generally considered to be the elapsed time between infection and symptom development. The incubation period of some stone-fruit virus diseases is long, but for most others trees infected in the fall develop symptoms during the following grow-

ing season. The length of the incubation period is strongly influenced by the season in which infection occurs. For some diseases, inoculations made early in the spring when trees are breaking dormancy may result in symptom development within 2 or 3 weeks. But, if made after growth has started, symptom development may be greatly delayed and is usually limited to tissues near the inoculation point and the terminals of strong shoots arising near the inoculation points. Symptom development can often be forced by cutting back shoots to near inoculation points and thereby producing sucker shoots. Such new rapid-growing shoots pull the virus into them and develop symptoms.

Some stone-fruit viruses require more than 1 year for development of symptoms. Expression of the phony disease of peach depends on sufficient build-up of the virus in roots and requires 18 months to 3 years. Under field conditions, sour cherry yellows, pink fruit of sour cherry, small bitter cherry, red suture of peach, and others often require more than a year for symptom development. Sweet cherry black canker, peach willow twig, and prune diamond canker do not develop characteristic symptoms on 1-year-old growth; therefore 2 years or more are needed after inoculation for infected growth to develop identifiable symptoms.

Viruses differ in their rate of translocation in infected trees. For most diseases small nursery trees inoculated in the fall are uniformly diseased when growth develops the following year, indicating that the virus has become thoroughly systemic.

On the larger trees, the viruses of stone fruit may require one or more growing seasons to become distributed thoroughly. Other viruses are slow movers in tissue but in time become thoroughly systemic. If rasp leaf virus is introduced into the main stem of a nursery tree in the fall it will usually be expressed only on leaves within a few inches of the inoculation point during the next growing season. Prune dwarf is likewise a slow mover. A few viruses appear rarely to become thoroughly distributed in their hosts.

Normal shoots are common on peach trees infected by yellow bud mosaic or X-disease. Buds taken from them fail to infect healthy trees. If either disease becomes thoroughly distributed in affected peach trees, the trees die. Western X-disease virus appears also to require a long time to become well distributed in affected sweet cherry trees, but rapidly becomes thoroughly systemic when inoculated into chokecherries. Small bitter cherry appears never to affect whole trees and it is common for affected and normal cherries to occur on adjoining spurs or even on the same spur.

THE HOST RANGE of stone-fruit viruses is as variable as the viruses themselves. Some appear to affect a wide variety of hosts and others a relatively few. Some affect all their hosts with the same type and severity of symptoms and others may be ruinous on one horticultural variety and infect another without the production of symptoms. Some infect a wide number of species within the *Prunus* genus and even species outside the genus, yet within a species may infect one horticultural variety but another may be immune. In general, any species of *Prunus*, until it has been proved immune, must be regarded as a possible suspect to a virus that infects a related species.

A few stone-fruit viruses affect species outside the genus *Prunus*. Ring spot has been recovered from naturally infected rose and has been inoculated into apple seedlings. Cucumber and squash have become infected following rubbing with juice containing the ring spot virus. *Kerria japonica*, Japanese Kerria, and rose were experimentally infected with yellow bud mosaic. Carrot, tomato, parsley, and periwinkle were infected with X-disease, and tomato, peri-

winkle, and tobacco were infected with peach rosette by use of dodder, *Cuscuta* species, a parasitic plant that formed a bridge between infected and healthy plants. These results are important because they indicate that some stone-fruit viruses can infect distantly related plants and it is therefore necessary to consider herbaceous plants as possible hosts until they have been proved otherwise.

TO DETERMINE whether a plant is a host of a given virus, one has to demonstrate the presence of the virus in it naturally by indexing it or to inoculate it and then index it.

Indexing is accomplished by grafting tissue from the suspected plant onto one known to develop characteristic symptoms for the virus in question. If the suspected plant is inoculated and no symptoms develop on it, yet the presence of the virus in it is indicated by index tests, the plant is regarded as a symptomless carrier. If symptoms develop on the plant after inoculation, one must ascertain that the inoculum had only one virus in it before the symptoms can be ascribed to the virus for which the host is being tested.

Host-range studies are hampered by the lack of methods for transfer of viruses between hosts which will not intergraft. Some results have been obtained by use of the juice-rubbing technique and by use of dodder to form a bridge between plants through which the viruses can flow.

As we mentioned, for some reason the juice-rubbing method has not been successful for transmitting viruses to woody plants. Also, dodder is known not to transmit some viruses and will not grow on some plants. Insects may be useful to transmit viruses to certain plants which we now have no means of testing.

THE PRESENCE of forms and strains of viruses in plants is evidence that viruses are continually changing. Changes probably take place in the formation of single new virus particles, which will survive and multiply if they have some quality that allows them to compete with the parent virus. One quality seemingly necessary is that of invading host cells, along with or in exclusion of the parent virus. Insects then can pick up the new form and transmit it to a host apart from the parent virus. Sometimes new forms get into growing points of plants and are evident because subsequent growth bears different symptoms from the remainder of the infected plant.

Most of the viruses affecting stone fruits appear to exist in nature in few to many forms or strains. No variants are known for the viruses causing phony peach or peach rosette. Peach rosette kills trees so rapidly that it is entirely possible that variants have not had sufficient time to become segregated. If rosette should infect hosts which it does not kill, variants might become expressed. Peach yellows also kills peach trees, but less rapidly than peach rosette. Little peach and red suture are believed to be caused by strains of the peach yellows virus and may have arisen because of the quality that neither of them kill peach trees as rapidly as yellows. Yellows does not kill plum trees and the little peach and red suture strains may have arisen in plums and spread to peach. Both little peach and red suture appear to be stable strains and can be obtained and identified from orchards at will. Peach mosaic and ring spot, on the other hand, exist in innumerable variants, forming a gradient from one extreme of symptoms so mild that diagnosis is difficult to effects that severely damage the trees. Variations of other features, besides severity, also occur, such as type and amount of mottle, amount of dwarfing, rate of movement of virus through trees, and others. The variations are so numerous that new cultures obtained from naturally infected orchard trees, while they can be fitted into the gradient, cannot be definitely identified with previous cultures.

A number of other stone-fruit virus diseases, such as western X-disease, sweet cherry necrotic rusty mottle and mottle leaf, are known to have variable symptoms, caused by the existence of many virus forms. As evidence accumulates it seems likely that some of the diseases that have been described separately are actually merely expressions of different forms of one virus. Certainly X-disease, western X-disease, and buckskin produce similar symptoms on peach although they produce somewhat different symptoms on sweet cherries in different areas. Lambert mottle and necrotic rusty mottle produce similar symptoms on Lambert cherry but differ on other varieties. Ring spot, as originally described on peach, appears to be very similar to necrotic ring spot described on sour cherry.

The control of virus diseases of stone fruits is complex because of the many variable features of the diseases. Measures applicable and sufficient for one disease may not suffice for another or even for the same disease in another area. Before satisfactory control measures can be recommended, the nature of the disease, its distribution, host range, rate and manner of spread, effect on yield, and other facts should be known. In general, control procedure can be divided into two categories: Prevention by exclusion and (if already present) reduction by removal of diseased trees or application of other procedures that reduce their detrimental effects.

All evidence indicates that viruses, like other forms of life, do not arise out of nowhere but are direct descendants of preexisting forms; therefore procedures that exclude them are the most efficient means of control and should be used wherever practical.

Federal quarantines have been promulgated to prevent entrance of viruses and other pests from foreign sources. State quarantines have been established to prevent movement from infected areas in one State to another part of the same State or into other States. In general, quarantines are efficient only where areas are protected by natural barriers, such as bodies of water, deserts, and mountain ranges. Quarantines have also been used on new diseases or for outbreaks of disease in new areas while studies were being made to determine practical means of control or for slowing down spread while control or eradication was being attempted.

RECOMMENDATIONS for control of established virus diseases of fruit trees have generally been to remove infected trees from orchards. For certain diseases and in certain districts that procedure may still be generally recommended. The question as to whether removal of diseased trees, or roguing, is practical depends on the rate of spread, whether spread is originating in the orchard or from outside sources, how much damage the disease causes, and whether there are resistant host varieties or procedures to protect against infection.

Roguing coupled with isolation, use of disease-free nursery trees, and wild-host-removal programs have been the only practical means of control for some diseases, especially those that spread rapidly and severely damage all varieties of a given host. Those procedures have controlled peach yellows and reduced it from a dire threat to the peach-growing industry to the rank of a minor disease. Isolation in intensively cultivated fruit areas may be hard to achieve and may not be necessary for diseases that spread slowly.

For diseases which are generally distributed, have a rapid rate of spread, and have symptomless hosts or other features that make it impractical to remove diseased trees, other procedures of control have to be developed.

THE USE of resistant or tolerant varieties (varieties which, although infected, are not materially damaged), tolerant or resistant top and rootstock combinations, mild symptom-produc-

ing virus forms to protect against infection by more damaging ones, chemotherapy, and control of vectors are approaches which offer promise as control measures. Heat has been used to kill certain viruses in infected budwood and nursery trees, and certain chemicals have reduced infection by others in experimentally inoculated trees. No treatment with chemicals, spray materials, fertilizers, or other materials has resulted in the cure of virus-diseased fruit trees in the orchard.

There is ample evidence that stonefruit virus diseases have been spread in infected nursery stock. Control procedures in general are ineffective unless such spread is stopped. Nurseryimprovement programs are under way in several States, but because they are concerned with different diseases and different conditions, procedures and specifications which have been developed are variable. There are some general considerations that are regional in scope and there is need for consideration on a regional basis. Nurserymen need the assistance of research, regulatory, and extension men and growers. Growers need the advantages of starting orchards with better stock and can assist much in the problems by working closely in cooperation with those trying to help them.

L. C. COCHRAN *is in charge of investigations of virus diseases of deciduous fruits for the Bureau of Plant Industry, Soils, and Agricultural Engineering. He is a native of Indiana and holds degrees from Purdue University and Michigan State College. Before joining the Department of Agriculture in 1941, he was engaged in investigations of citrus and peach virus diseases at the Citrus Experiment Station of the University of California at Riverside.*

E. L. REEVES *is stationed at the United States Horticultural Laboratory at Wenatchee, Wash., and is a pioneer in investigations of stone-fruit virus diseases occurring in northwestern United States. He was born in Idaho and holds degrees from the University of California and Washington State College.*

Bacterial Canker of Stone Fruits

E. E. Wilson

Bacterial canker, bacterial gummosis, and bacterial sour sap are names given to a disease of stone-fruit trees.

The disease is found in the eastern and midwestern parts of the United States, but it is of major consequence only in the States bordering the Pacific Ocean. Even there it varies in frequency and severity. It is said to be rare in the cherry districts of Oregon east of the Cascade Mountains but is often destructive west of the Cascades. In the Sierra Nevada foothills of central California it is severe on plums but much less severe in the central valleys.

Its names denote its main features. An abnormal oozing of gum from the affected branch suggests the term bacterial gummosis. Gum flow, although common in cherries and apricots, is by no means a constant feature of the disease on them or other stone-fruit trees. Some of the most severe cases in the Sierra Nevada foothills are accompanied by little or no gumming; the exudate, when present, is a watery material that flows from moist, sour-smelling, discolored areas of the bark.

Bacterial canker, on the other hand, is a more appropriate term because the diseased areas on branches are always necrotic lesions or cankers.

The disease affects many parts of the tree, but the most common and most destructive phase is that on the trunks, limbs, and branches. There the pathogen enters the bark and makes circular to elongated, brown, water-soaked or gum-soaked lesions in the bark and outermost sapwood. Branches girdled by the canker may fail to grow in the spring. If they produce leaves and grow for a period, they die the first warm days of summer. The affected bark tissue is brown, gum-impregnated or water-soaked, and sour smelling.

Bacterial canker may kill a tree by girdling the trunk, but it seldom extends below ground. The root systems of trees thus killed not uncommonly develop a number of new shoots within the year.

The second most destructive phase is the blighting of the dormant buds and the subsequent killing of the twigs that produce the buds. Cherry and apricot are particularly susceptible to infection of dormant or partly opened buds. On them the bacteria kill the buds and produce a small canker on the twig at the base of the bud. On some plums, however, extensive invasion of the twigs commonly follows infection.

At times, in California, bacterial canker attacks blossoms of cherry and plum. The flowers die soon after they open. Loss of crop through blossom infection is infrequent, but it may be heavy when it does occur.

In England the disease is said to attack plum and cherry leaves extensively, causing much defoliation, which lowers the vigor of the tree. In California the usual dry weather of late spring and summer minimizes such infection. Occasionally a few trees in an orchard may lose their leaves, but no extensive or recurring outbreaks of leaf infection are experienced. Leaf spotting, when it occurs, is often associated with severe infections of branches. Bacteria washed from such cankers by rain presumably cause infection of the surrounding leaves.

The fruit of the apricot and cherry trees sometimes develop sunken, black lesions bordered by water-soaked margins. The lesions later become even more sunken as the fruit enlarges. Lesions also occur on the fruit stems.

Sudden witherings of the new leafy shoots of Santa Rosa, Wickson, and

Duarte plum varieties have been seen several times in California. That is a common and destructive manifestation of bacterial canker in England, because, once established in green shoots, the disease invades the older twigs. Under our conditions, seldom more than a few terminal shoots are affected and the disease rarely extends from those parts into the older twigs. Moreover, with us the bacteria apparently do not survive in the summer in affected shoots.

THE CORRECT DESIGNATION for the organism causing bacterial canker of stone-fruit trees is now considered to be *Pseudomonas syringae*. For a number of years the pathogen was known either as *Pseudomonas cerasi, Bacterium cerasi,* or *Phytomonas cerasi,* according to the system of classification followed at the time. The changes in the names typify the complications that arise in classification when an organism has a wide range of hosts and has been studied at various times by various persons. At one time or another this organism has been given no less than 12 species names, each one designating it as a pathogen of some particular host or group of hosts. *Pseudomonas syringae* was the first species to receive proof of pathogenicity and an adequate description when, in 1902, C. J. J. Van Hall, of the University of Amsterdam, reported that it produced a blight of lilac.

In the following list, the binomials now considered to be synonymous with *Pseudomonas syringae* and other pertinent data are given: *Bacillus spongiosus,* by R. Aderhold and H. Ruhland on cherry in Germany (1907); *Pseudomonas cerasi,* by F. L. Griffin on cherry in Oregon (1911); *Bacterium citriputeale,* by C. O. Smith on citrus in California (1913); *Bacterium citrarefaciens,* by H. A. Lee on citrus in California (1917); *Pseudomonas hibisci,* by K. Nakata and S. Takimoto, on the hibiscus in Japan (1923); *Pseudomonas vignae,* by M. W. Gardner and J. B. Kendrick on cowpea in Indiana (1923); *Bacterium viridifaciens* by W. B. Tisdale and M. M.

Williamson on lima bean in Wisconsin (1923); *Bacterium trifoliorum,* by L. R. Jones et al. on clover in eastern United States (1923); *Bacterium holci,* by J. B. Kendrick on *Holcus* species and other hosts in Iowa (1926); *Pseudomonas prunicola,* by H. Wormald on cherry, plum, and other hosts in England (1930); *Phytomonas utiformica,* by F. M. Clara on pear in New York (1932).

H. Wormald, in England in 1931, described still another species (*Pseudomonas mors-prunorum*) that causes a canker condition of stone-fruit trees in England. *P. mors-prunorum* retains its species name even though it is admittedly very similar, both culturally and physiologically, to *P. syringae* (*P. prunicola*). One gets the impression that *P. mors-prunorum* most frequently is the cause of severe infection of branches, whereas *P. syringae* most frequently is the cause of infection of leaves and green shoots, but no great consistency is exhibited in these features. No purpose is served by attempting here to distinguish between the symptoms of the two.

PSEUDOMONAS SYRINGAE is encountered in many parts of the world on lilac, most species of stone fruit, pear, apple, citrus, avocado, clover, cowpea, lima bean, common bean, rose, sorghum and related grasses, corn, pearl-millet, foxtail, hibiscus, and forsythia. *Pseudomonas syringae* var. *capsici* has been reported on pepper from Italy.

Of the species of *Prunus* cultivated for their fruit, the apricot (*P. armeniaca*) is probably the most susceptible. Next are the plum (*P. domestica* and *P. salicina*) and the sweet cherry (*P. avium*). The peach (*P. persica*) and nectarine (*P. persica* var. *nectarina*) are on the whole less susceptible than the sweet cherry. The almond (*P. amygdalus*) is only occasionally damaged. The sour cherry (*P. cerasus*) and the duke cherries (hybrids between *P. cerasus* and *P. avium*) are rarely found in California, so little is known about their susceptibility under our conditions. Sour cherries are highly resistant to the disease in Oregon, and the duke cherries are rarely affected.

Of the species of plums used as rootstocks, the Marianna (hybrid between *P. cerasifera* and a native plum) is prone to infection. The myrobalan (*P. cerasifera*) is affected somewhat, but is much more resistant than Marianna. From England have come reports of two resistant rootstocks of plum, the Myrobalan B and Purple Pershore.

Susceptibility among the mazzard cherry (*Prunus avium*) rootstocks varies greatly, because seedlings of both the wild and cultivated sweet cherries are grown for the purpose. One, the vegetatively produced F 12/1, developed at the East Malling Research Station in England, is said to exhibit a high degree of resistance.

The mahaleb cherry (*P. mahaleb*), used quite widely as a rootstock for sweet cherries in California, seems to be resistant to bacterial canker.

Only one selection of *P. cerasus* is grown as a rootstock in California. It is the Stockton morello, which is commonly obtained by planting the root suckers from trees on this root. It appears to be relatively resistant to bacterial canker.

Formerly all rootstocks of peach were seedlings obtained from commercial varieties; Salwey and Lovell were most popular. In one district where bacterial canker is prevalent those varieties appear to be little affected. Two other rootstocks, the Shalil and Stribling's S 37, have come into use because of their resistance to root knot nematode. Their susceptibility to bacterial canker is not known.

Records of tree losses indicate that the common varieties of sweet cherry are susceptible in the following descending order: Lambert, Napoleon (Royal Ann), Bing, Chapman, Lewelling (Black Republican), and Black Tartarian. Lambert is listed as less susceptible than Napoleon or Bing in Oregon. Lambert is listed as very resistant in England.

The plums grown in California belong to two species, *P. domestica* and *P.*

salicina. A few varieties, however, apparently are hybrids between *P. salicina* and other species. The more important varieties exhibit tolerance to the disease in the following increasing order (the letters in parentheses indicate whether the varietal characteristic is predominantly that of *P. salicina* (S) or that of *P. domestica* (D), no attempt being made to distinguish the hybrids): Duarte (S), President (D), Clyman (D), Climax (S), Giant (S), Grand Duke (D), Tragedy (D), Santa Rosa (S), Wickson (S), Burbank (S), Formosa (S), Gaviota (S), Beauty (S), Kelsey (S).

Peach varieties such as the Elberta and its variants, Fay Elberta and Early Elberta, the now rarely planted Phillips Cling, the Halford No. 2, and J. H. Hale not infrequently are affected severely by bacterial canker. Lovell and Early Crawford are less affected by the disease.

Among apricots, the Blenheim, Royal, and Tilton varieties are most commonly planted in California, and all are highly susceptible.

On almond, the disease has been observed on Nonpareil, Ne Plus Ultra, and Texas.

BECAUSE THE BACTERIUM occurs on a wide range of host plants, there is always the possibility that the disease may be introduced into stone-fruit orchards by intercropping with an annual host. Some observations in California suggest that among the tree fruits, at least, some cross infection occurs. On one occasion, blossom infection by *P. syringae* developed in pear trees adjacent to apricot trees with bacterial canker, the incidence of blossom infection on pear being highest in the trees nearest the apricots. Another time, leaf and twig infection developed in late spring on orange trees near pear trees, in which bacterial canker developed in late winter. Upon cross inoculation, the bacteria from the citrus trees readily infected the pear. All indications were that the disease had not been present in the orange trees the year before the outbreak occurred; attempts to culture the bacteria indicate that they do not often survive in affected twigs of such trees. Consequently the evidence pointed to pear trees as the source of inoculum.

The question of where the bacteria survive from one year to the next has been answered differently by different investigators. One investigator in England, for example, failed to obtain viable bacteria from branch cankers after midsummer. Another failed to get viable bacteria from diseased bark in August or September following infection, but obtained them from the outer xylem beneath cankers that had involved the cambial area. The investigator concluded that the bacteria may survive in such deep-seated tissue after they have died in the bark. In California we have evidence that the bacteria remain viable in certain parts of the cankered bark areas. Some of the cankers renew their activity a second year, and the bacteria responsible for the renewed activity are located in the terminal margins of the canker.

All the time the disease is active the bacteria are found in the watery or gummy material that oozes from the canker. The bacteria can be washed about the tree by rain. In that way, probably, the bacteria reach the winter buds and later the blossoms and leaves. Leaf infection occasionally develops in California; when that occurs, the lesions are most abundant below branch cankers. In our climate, however, the diseased areas on leaves soon dry up and drop away; thus they leave no affected tissue in those parts to harbor the bacteria during summer.

ALL WHO HAVE WORKED with bacterial canker in England and America have noted that its period of greatest activity is fall, winter, and spring. The only infection found in summer is that on leaves and green shoots. The progress of the disease through the tissue of the branches occurs only in fall, winter, and spring. If, for example, we introduce the bacteria into the bark of plum branches at various times of the year, we find that only small lesions are produced in September and October and that larger lesions are produced by inoculating any time between late November and mid-April. Inoculations made later in the spring again produce only small lesions.

Another view of the seasonal nature of the disease may be had by comparing the sequence of events in the development of the canker with the dormant and growth periods of the tree. Suppose the canker was initiated by an infection in late autumn. In our climate the affected area expands slowly throughout the colder months of winter, but as temperature rises in spring it increases its rate of expansion and is making the greatest development as the tree begins to grow.

Two types of cankers are recognizable then. One is a well-defined, brown, water-soaked or gum-soaked area of bark with margins that end more or less abruptly in tissue normal in color. The other is an ill-defined area through which extend loosely connected and discontinuous, brownish, water-soaked or gum-soaked bands and streaks that gradually merge with undiscolored tissue at the upper and lower margins. This type of canker is often so extensive and poorly defined that one is not certain whether it was produced by infection at one place or several.

As spring advances and the trees produce leaves, the affected bark changes gradually. The water-soaked condition disappears. The tissues over most of the affected area become dark brown and dry. In the well-defined type of cankers the periphery is clearly marked but in the other type it grades into a series of reddish-brown streaks.

Throughout the summer no further changes are perceptible in the diseased bark, but a roll of new bark tissue develops about the lateral margins of some cankers. Such tissue sometimes extends around the ends of the cankered area.

The following October or November

activity may again be found in some of the cankers. The proportion of cankers renewing their activity a second year varies greatly between years, between varieties of a given stone fruit, and even between orchards. The first indication of activity is a water-soaked discoloration at the terminal margins of the well-defined type of cankers and between the reddish-brown streaks at the upper and lower periphery of the ill-defined type. Under our conditions the water-soaked area expands slowly during the winter and rapidly during spring but again ceases its development in early summer.

RAIN SPREADS the bacteria about the tree and carries them into wounds or natural openings. The importance of moisture to infection is particularly apparent in the development of leaf spotting and green shoot wilt. Once infection is established, however, atmospheric moisture probably has little further influence on the course of the resulting lesion. In the dry summer climate of California, on the other hand, soil moisture apparently affects canker development in one respect at least. During a severe outbreak of bacterial canker some years ago, noticeably fewer plum trees were killed in nonirrigated orchards than in irrigated ones. The nonirrigated trees were infected quite commonly, but the cankers were not so large as those in irrigated trees.

Experiments in the orchard and in soil tanks show that the extension of cankers in the trees is not affected so long as the soil moisture remains between the field capacity and the permanent wilting point. When, however, soil moisture is reduced to the permanent wilting point, canker extension ceases. An orchard soil seldom if ever is deficient in moisture during the height of canker activity in spring, although it will become dry in summer unless some water is supplied by irrigation.

On the other hand, how does drought, coming in late summer when bacterial canker normally is inactive, influence the severity of the disease? A possible answer is that a deficient soil moisture adversely affects the survival of the bacteria in the cankers. A decrease in the survival of the bacteria, in turn, would diminish both the numbers of cankers which become active the following winter and the amount of inoculum available for new infections.

Experiments conducted in California indicate that temperature exerts a great influence on the progress of the disease through the host tissue. Apparently the optimum for canker extension is about 70° to 75° F., which is also optimum for growth and multiplication of *Pseudomonas syringae* in culture media. Consequently the rate of canker extension is less in winter than in autumn and spring, as was noted earlier. Nevertheless, during the coldest periods of the California winter, canker extension may be appreciable on clear days when the sun warms the branches. Under such conditions, canker development on the south side of a branch may exceed that on the north side.

Pseudomonas syringae occurs in many parts of the world, but seriously affects stone-fruit trees only in a few regions. The very fact that the activity of the disease is confined to autumn, winter, and the spring probably is responsible in part for its limited occurrence in regions of low winter temperatures. Conversely, moderate temperatures during those seasons probably are responsible in part for the severity of the disease in England, Australia, and California and Oregon.

As I noted earlier, the tree becomes more susceptible to bacterial canker as it goes into dormancy and less susceptible after growth begins in the spring. Moreover, the period of susceptibility is concurrent with the period during which the host tissue does not respond to the presence of the bacteria. Such responses are of two types, depending on the area affected: That initiated by the vascular cambium when the lesion occurs in the neighborhood of this tissue, and that initiated by a phellogen (so-called cork cambium) when the lesion occurs at other places in the bark.

For example, if the pathogen is introduced into the bark at the cambium in September, it begins to invade the tissue and cause a discolored area above and below the point of inoculation. Before the lesion has reached appreciable size, however, it is buried beneath new xylem tissue produced by nonaffected cambial cells or at least by other undifferentiated cells in the cambial region. Moreover, if the bacteria have invaded the phloem or cortex the lesion is soon isolated from the nonaffected tissue by a phelloderm.

If the bacteria are introduced into the branch late in the autumn, no such host reaction is in evidence. In spring, however, after the tree begins to grow, there is again evidence of healing activity.

Is this healing reaction of the host the factor that confines the activity of the cankers to the dormant season, or does healing merely follow a cessation of canker activity that is caused by some other changes in the host?

Moreover, is there a relation between this healing reaction and resistance to bacterial canker?

The following information bears on the questions as far as conditions in California are concerned: Whereas a periderm layer several cells thick may form along the lateral margins of the lesions in the bark, this layer often does not extend around the upper and lower ends of such lesions. Periderm formation and cessation of canker activity is earliest in varieties that begin to grow earliest in the spring. Among plums, and to some extent among cherries, the most resistant varieties begin to grow earlier than the less resistant varieties. We distinguish here, of course, between resistance to infection and resistance to the progress of the lesion through the tissues after infection. Varieties that exhibit the most vigorous healing around the canker also exhibit the greatest tolerance to the presence of the disease. Such evidence shows healing to be closely correlated with susceptibility of the host, but it does not prove that healing is the determining factor.

An investigator in England has made a close study of the healing phenomenon in the susceptible Giant Prune and in the resistant Warwickshire Drooper plum. She has concluded that though the progress of the pathogen under certain circumstances may be restrained by the phelloderm barrier, there is no significant difference between the resistant and susceptible host with respect to the first development of phellogen in spring. Earlier I had suggested that some change in the tissue destined to become meristematic might precede appearance of the phellogen, and that such a change might deter canker extension. In any event, susceptibility to the disease apparently cannot be explained from the anatomical standpoint alone.

THE RAPID and extensive development of the diffuse type of canker, together with evidence that the bacteria frequently are present only at the center of such cankers, suggests that a toxic effect is exerted beyond the area occupied by the bacteria. In fact, *Pseudomonas syringae* and *P. mors-prunorum* have been found to produce in liquid media a material which injures the bark when it is injected into plum branches. Apparently it is an endotoxin of protein nature. The Giant Prune, which is susceptible to bacterial canker, is more injured by the toxin than the Warwickshire Drooper plum, which is resistant. It may be, therefore, that the amount of toxin released by the bacteria into the tissues of the host determines, in some measure, the effect of the disease on that host.

There is the possibility that injury in advance of bacterial invasion is due in part to a deleterious byproduct produced from the host tissue. Not uncommonly the affected bark tissue of plums contains large numbers of crystals that have the refractive index of calcium oxalate. A number of bacteria have been reported to produce oxalic acid from the fermentation of glucose. That this acid may accumulate in sufficient amounts to cause injury to the host tissue is questionable because it is readily combined with calcium, forming calcium oxalate, which, because of its insolubility, should be relatively noninjurious to the tree tissues.

No marked effect of soil fertility on the disease has been noted. In tests I conducted, peach trees that received an application of ammonium sulfate in spring survived an attack of bacterial canker somewhat better but were no less susceptible to subsequent infection than nonfertilized trees. According to results of trials conducted in England, neither the nitrogen, potassium, nor phosphorus content of the soil affects the susceptibility of plum trees, although applications of lime apparently increased susceptibility.

WE HAVE CONSIDERED the general subject of susceptibility to bacterial canker among species and varieties of *Prunus* and included in the discussion both the fruit-producing and the rootstock types. We shall now consider what happens when the susceptibility characteristics of both types occur in the same tree. First, however, we should note that most of the trees planted in California are produced by inserting a bud from the desired fruit-producing sort into the base of the trunk of the appropriate rootstock. Later the trunk of the rootstock is cut off just above the bud, which, upon growing, produces essentially all of the above-ground part of the tree. Presumably, therefore, the effect of bacterial canker on such trees depends largely on the susceptibility of the overstock, for, as we noted earlier, this disease is almost always confined to the above-ground parts. In fact, to our knowledge, bacterial canker never attacks the roots directly and rarely does the canker extend from the trunk into the roots.

Though much of our information on root involvement came from trees propagated on the usual rootstock, some of it came from seedlings—trees on their own roots. If any difference existed between bud-propagated and seedling trees with respect to root infection it was so slight as to be overlooked. Trees propagated by that method, therefore, should rarely be injured or killed by bacterial canker in the root system. Hence, the statement that the effect of the disease in such trees depends largely on the susceptibility of the overstock seems well founded.

ANOTHER method of propagation is that of grafting the trunk of the rootstock several feet above ground with scions from the desired commercial sort. Cherry trees are commonly propagated in that way in England. For trees so produced, the effect of the disease is determined both by the susceptibility of the understock and the susceptibility of the overstock. Inasmuch as infection of the trunk may result in death of the entire tree, the susceptibility characteristic of the understock is of primary importance in trees propagated in this manner.

Attempts to provide the tree with a resistant trunk have been tried by various persons. M. C. Goldsworthy and R. E. Smith of the California Agricultural Experiment Station found that trees consisting of commercial plum varieties grafted high on myrobalan and Marianna rootstocks survived somewhat longer than trees produced by budding this rootstock near the ground. In a severe outbreak of bacterial canker in 1929, however, many such trees were lost. Later experience with the Marianna selection 2624 shows it to be highly susceptible in the disease. The myrobalan seems much more resistant and one selection, the Myrobalan B, produced in England, is said to afford a satisfactory trunk for susceptible varieties of plum.

Likewise, investigators in England regard the Kentish Bush plum to be a superior understock on which to work the Giant Prune and Victoria plum. Several selections of mazzard, particularly the one designated F 12/1, developed at the East Malling Research Station, are said to afford a resistant trunk for sweet cherry.

We have considerable evidence that the rootstock may influence the susceptibility of the scion. According to investigators at the East Malling Station, England, certain mazzard selections apparently induce susceptibility to canker and leaf spotting in the Bigarreau de Schrencken cherry growing on them, while others tend to increase its relative resistance.

Some years ago I observed a similar phenomenon on Santa Rosa plums. An outbreak of green shoot infection by *Pseudomonas syringae* was much less severe on trees produced by grafting plum scions onto peach trunks 4 or 5 feet from the ground than on trees produced by budding the plum into peach rootstock near the ground. More recently, another investigator in California found evidence that apricots on peach root are less susceptible to bacterial canker than apricots on myrobalan root, whereas apricots on apricot root are intermediate in susceptibility. He also reported that plums top-worked on peach trunks (in these cases the Salwey and Lovell peaches) were more resistant than plums that were top-worked on myrobalan and Marianna trunks.

Needless to say, many questions regarding the effect of rootstock on susceptibility of the scion remain unanswered. One in particular is this: Why, on the same rootstock, do some plum varieties prove less susceptible when top-worked than when budded near the ground? The explanation of this anomalous situation is possibly found in the fact that trees of these plum varieties, when budded near the ground, produce roots from above the bud union and in so doing gradually become established on their own roots. Thereafter, presumably, the susceptibility of the above-ground parts of such trees is no longer modified by the original rootstock.

REMOVAL OF branches infected with bacterial canker has a place in control procedure. If such branches remain in the tree, the bacteria in them will be spread to nearby trees by rain and the cankers will continue to spread into more and more of the tree. Whether the removal of individual cankers is feasible depends upon the number of cankers and their extent. It may be more practical to remove the entire branch than to spend time on the removal of diseased tissue. In any event, such surgical work should be done in the summer when activity of the disease is at its minimum.

We have attempted, without success, to treat affected branches with chemicals for the purpose of killing the bacteria inside the tissue. Zinc chloride, a material formerly employed in treating fire blight cankers, proved to be injurious. Such chemicals as copper nitrate, phenolic compounds, and sodium arsenite were ineffective.

Workers in England have paid considerable attention to control of the disease by spraying. The program adopted for that climate consists of an application of bordeaux, 10–15–100, in autumn for protection of the branches and an application of bordeaux, 6–9–100, in spring for protection of shoots and leaves. Such a program is said to reduce the incidence of bacterial canker materially in the susceptible Bigarreau de Schrencken variety of cherry. A similar program has been recommended in Australia.

For some years, cherry growers report benefits from an application of bordeaux, 16–16–100, after leaf fall in autumn.

E. E. WILSON *is professor of plant pathology in the University of California at Davis where he has been engaged in studying fruit diseases since 1929. His studies of bacterial canker extended over a 9-year period. Dr. Wilson is also on the staff of the California Agricultural Experiment Station.*

The Tristeza Disease of Citrus

T. J. Grant, L. J. Klotz, J. M. Wallace

The sour orange has long been recognized as a desirable rootstock for the propagation of commercial varieties of citrus. It was highly recommended and widely used until the time of the rapid spread of the tristeza disease in South America and the quick decline in California. The presence and threat of the disease and the problem of satisfactory rootstocks in affected areas continue to be of importance to citrus growers in many parts of the world.

Some 40 years ago growers in South Africa learned from experience that the sour orange was a failure as a rootstock under their conditions. In 1924, the unsatisfactory growth of sweet orange on sour orange rootstock in South Africa received some attention and was referred to as rootstock and scion incompatibility. Instances of "incompatibility" of sweet orange on sour orange rootstock were found between 1924 and 1940, and the trouble appeared in Java, Argentina, Uruguay, Brazil, California, Paraguay, and Australia. In Argentina and Uruguay, the disease was referred to as podredumbre de las raicillas. In Brazil Sylvio Moreira referred to it as tristeza, a word that describes the sad appearance of the diseased trees. Tristeza is now the common name for the disease in South America.

The disease, when it was recognized in California, was referred to as quick decline. As this particular type of rootstock problem made its appearance and became important in various parts of the world, many theories were advanced to explain the effects produced—stock-scion incompatibility, soil acidity, various types of nutrient deficiencies, soil toxins, high content of soil moisture, long dry periods, nematode infestations, pathogenic organisms, virus infection, and others.

Indications of the importance of the disease were reported by A. A. Bitancourt, Sylvio Moreira, J. C. Bertelli, and others. Guy Bush, agricultural attaché at the American Embassy in Rio de Janeiro, informed the Department of Agriculture of the importance of the disease and showed visiting citrus growers and scientists from the United States the effects of the disease. He urged that cooperative investigations be undertaken.

Citrus growers in the United States, alarmed by the losses associated with the disease in South America, urged the Department to send someone to study the disease. After consideration of all available information, a virologist, C. W. Bennett, was sent in 1946 to South America. The Instituto Agronomico at Campinas, in São Paulo, Brazil, the center of a diseased region, extended the use of its facilities for carrying out the work in the field and in screenhouses and the assistance of A. S. Costa, a virologist, and Sylvio Moreira, a horticulturist.

H. S. Fawcett and J. M. Wallace, of the Citrus Experiment Station of the University of California at Riverside, reported in 1946 that quick decline had been transmitted by graft inoculation of healthy trees and could therefore be considered to be an infectious disease, caused by a virus. At about the same time M. Meneghini, of the Instituto Biologico in São Paulo, reported the results of tests to demonstrate that the oriental black citrus aphid (*Aphis citricidus*) could transmit tristeza in Brazil—an indication of the virus nature of the disease.

Henry Schneider, of the California Citrus Experiment Station, described the collapse of the phloem, or food-conducting, tissues of the sour orange rootstock of infected trees. His studies in 1946 and 1947 also led to the development of a method of detecting the presence of the disease by means of a microscopic examination of bark tissues at the graft union of the sweet orange on the sour orange rootstock. Symptoms like those of tristeza and quick decline can be found on trees that have been girdled by gophers or have been injured on the bark or roots by one of many agencies. Such trees, however, do not show in their internal bark or phloem tissue the reactions that are characteristic of the virus-infected trees. Thus, the anatomical technique has been helpful in diagnosing the disease and determining its distribution.

C. W. Bennett's and A. S. Costa's investigations confirmed the transmissibility of tristeza by means of the oriental black citrus aphid and demonstrated transmission of the disease by buds. They laid the basis for the cooperative tests of rootstocks that followed.

Fruit growers in South Africa had learned that they could grow commercial citrus when they used their Rough lemon as a rootstock. When the tristeza disease spread through Brazil, Sylvio Moreira, at the Limeira Citrus Experiment Station, noted that the citrus varieties growing on sweet orange and Rangpur lime rootstocks continued to grow normally while the varieties on sour orange rootstock in nearby plantings died or were unthrifty.

The need for more information about the reactions of various rootstock-scion combinations then became evident. Under the direction of Frank Gardner, of the Subtropical Fruit Field Station of the Department of Agriculture at Orlando, Fla., 265 lots of seed, representing many types and varieties of citrus and citrus relatives, were assembled, treated, and forwarded to Brazil.

They and varieties collected in Brazil were studied by A. S. Costa, T. J. Grant, and Sylvio Moreira as rootstocks for several commercial varieties of citrus tops, as tops on sour orange rootstock, and as unbudded seedlings.

Plants in all the investigations were subjected to inoculation. The oriental black citrus aphids were fed on citrus trees carrying the tristeza virus and then transferred and allowed to feed on the plants to be tested. In instances in which plants under study failed to show any response to the first inoculations, the inoculation was repeated two and three times.

On the basis of the test, the rootstocks were classed as nontolerant and tolerant.

The nontolerant rootstocks behave like the sour orange and the inoculated sweet orange tops show disease symptoms. The citrus types in the group include grapefruit, pummelo, shaddock, some acid lemons and limes, some tangelos, and some closely related types of citrus. All, as far as tristeza disease is concerned, are considered unsatisfactory as rootstocks for the usual commercial varieties of citrus and cannot profitably be used as rootstocks in areas where tristeza occurs.

The tolerant rootstocks include the types of citrus that (under the conditions of the tests in Brazil) continued to show no symptoms of disease in the sweet orange tops even though they were inoculated with the tristeza virus. Among them, generally speaking, are the mandarins, such as Cleopatra, some mandarin hybrids as Rangpur lime, the sweet oranges, the trifoliate orange, the Rough lemon, some citrumelos, a few citranges, and some tangelos. The fact that sweet orange tops on these rootstocks continued to grow well despite the tristeza virus showed that these rootstocks tolerated the virus and that they are the most likely to be satisfactory for use in places where tristeza occurs.

The tests of the many citrus types and varieties as tops on sour orange rootstocks showed by the early occurrence of symptoms and decline of the plants that the sweet oranges were easily infected with the tristeza virus by means of the oriental black citrus aphid. The sour orange on sour orange rootstock, on the other hand, was difficult to infect by means of this aphid and most of such plants survived the repeated inoculations. On the basis of time it took for symptoms to show, the degree of tolerance and nontolerance of different citrus types varies greatly.

From the tristeza inoculations of seedlings, it was learned that certain varieties could show disease symptoms on their own roots—among them were varieties of the West Indian lime, grapefruit, some tangelos, pummelos, and some acid lemons. The use of species and varieties of citrus that show symptoms of tristeza as seedlings helped in the study of behavior of different citrus types and in the development of faster methods for detecting the presence of the virus.

Among the interesting and important results of the investigations at the agronomic institute at Campinas were the finding of mild strains of the tristeza virus and the unexpected indication that plants invaded by the mild strains are protected from showing the striking disease symptoms caused by the severe strain of the virus.

The definite proof that there are mild strains of the tristeza virus helps to explain some of the variation of intensity of disease symptoms in orchards. In South America and California some trees decline and die quickly and others linger on for several years with mild symptoms. Those differences, which previously may have been attributed to differences in environment or variety now have to be investigated for relationships of virus strains. The indication that the mild strains may afford protection opens the door to a new field of research.

P. C. J. Oberholzer, I. Mathews, and S. F. Stimie investigated the decline of grapefruit trees in South Africa and concluded that stem pitting of grapefruit was readily perpetuated by budding and was probably of virus nature. Certain aspects of the disease symp-toms bore considerable resemblance to blind pocket psorosis, and they suggested that the disease is caused by a strain or strains of the psorosis virus. Their investigations indicated that the disease was confined largely to the grapefruit scion and that the rootstock did not seem to be of importance, although they thought the latter should be investigated further.

The report of their studies stimulated a series of observations and studies in several parts of the world. A. S. Costa, T. J. Grant, and Sylvio Moreira, after study of their tristeza-inoculated plant material in Brazil, suggested a possible relationship between tristeza and the stem pitting disease of grapefruit in Africa. A. P. D. McClean, of South Africa, pointed out similarities of the stem pitting disease of grapefruit and a disease of lime plants in the Gold Coast. Subsequently he presented further evidence of the similarity of the tristeza disease, the stem pitting disease of grapefruit, and the lime disease. In 1951 J. M. Wallace and R. J. Drake, of California, reported stem pitting of West Indian lime plants affected with quick decline. Thus, again, the combination of cooperative and independent investigation in many parts of the world brings us one step closer to an understanding of the great similarity of these diseases and the varying effects that they have on different citrus types and varieties.

The recognition of the similarity of these diseases is important as it indicates that in the case of grapefruits and limes the use of tolerant rootstocks does not furnish an adequate means of insuring the economic production of these under tristeza disease conditions. The knowledge, however, that there are different strains of the causal virus and the indication from the work in Brazil that infection with milder virus strains protects plants from the severe forms of disease may eventually be employed to produce grapefruit on tolerant rootstocks even in tristeza-affected areas.

The oriental black citrus aphid is recognized in South America and in South Africa as the insect vector of the virus. That aphid is not known to exist in the United States. The results of studies by R. C. Dickson, R. A. Flock, and M. McD. Johnson at the California Citrus Experiment Station indicate that the melon aphid is a vector of the quick decline virus, but apparently is not a particularly efficient carrier of the virus because only a small number of transmissions were obtained in a large number of tests. Prevalence and efficiency of the vectors are major factors in the spread of the disease under field conditions and of interest to all citrus growers, especially in newly affected areas. Much remains to be learned concerning insect vectors and their ability to transmit the mild and severe forms of the causal virus of the disease. In all new areas where the disease is found it is essential to determine the severity of the virus strains present and to test for the presence of insect vectors.

T. J. Grant returned from Brazil in 1951 and undertook the work of testing for presence of the tristeza virus in the citrus areas of Florida. By November of that year the first series of seedlings of West Indian lime test plants were inoculated by means of bottle grafts. Twigs were used from field trees in a state of decline. In February of 1952 the first vein-clearing symptoms on the lime test plants were observed. Subsequently bark samples from other declining field trees were examined by Henry Schneider. His results, plus those from inoculated test plants, showed that a strain of the tristeza, or quick decline, virus was present in Florida. This proof was followed by action of the Florida State Plant Board and Citrus Experiment Station and a system for orchard inspection and testing of suspicious cases was established.

The reaction of the infected lime test plants held under controlled conditions suggests that the strain of the tristeza virus present in Florida is mild compared to the severe virus strain present in Brazil. The individual and scattered groups of infected trees in the Florida orchards suggest that the insect vector is not an efficient carrier of the virus. It is estimated that the mild strain of tristeza virus has been in Florida since 1942 or longer. The reactions of the lime test plants also indicate that frequently under field conditions declining trees are carrying more than just the tristeza virus. It seems likely that with intensive research investigations there eventually will be discovered several new virus diseases of citrus.

After the virus nature of the tristeza and quick decline diseases was recognized, it was soon learned in Brazil and California that the sweet orange tops on sweet orange rootstocks could be carriers of the virus even though they showed no symptoms.

If trees of certain rootstock-scion combinations could carry the causal agent of the disease without showing any visible symptoms, the disease might be carried from affected to disease-free areas. Quarantine officials would have no way of knowing that the apparently healthy plant material harbored a virus that could cause great losses to the citrus industry. This is equally true of the grower who in visiting an orchard and observing a new variety cuts off some budwood to carry home. In so doing he may very well be the means by which the virus is brought into a disease-free area. E. P. DuCharme and L. C. Knorr, sent to Argentina by organizations of citrus growers in Florida and Texas and in cooperation with the Florida State Citrus Experiment Station, reported that the disease very likely reached Argentina between 1927 and 1930 on two large shipments of Rough lemon rooted nursery stock from South Africa.

Nurserymen have no quick test to distinguish between the healthy plants and apparently healthy ones that carry the virus. Eradication of the disease therefore would be difficult. The simple method of removing or destroying only the trees that showed symptoms would be completely inadequate as many of the remaining trees could be symptomless carriers of the causal virus. The formulation of quarantine measures is primarily a local problem, which will have to be given specific attention in each newly affected area.

Although the recommendations as to what to do about the disease in areas already affected must be determined by local conditions, no rootstock found to be nontolerant of the disease should be employed in such areas. The tolerant rootstocks most desirable for a specific region are sometimes known but for horticultural reasons are not necessarily satisfactory in other regions. Hence there is need for rootstock test plantings but in any such test plantings there is a predominant need to be absolutely sure that the budwood employed is free of all transmissible diseases.

Strains of the tristeza, or quick decline, virus are known to be present in citrus orchards in California, Louisiana, and Florida. The interaction of these with other citrus diseases has yet to be investigated thoroughly. That is necessary for the establishment of a sound basis for the continuation of profitable production of citrus; it is especially necessary in the case of grapefruit, in which even the mild tristeza virus strains alone can cause some damage. The first important step in the reduction of losses occasioned by bud-transmissible disease is the establishment of effective methods for bud certification. California and Texas have bud-certification programs, and the organization of one was started in Florida.

T. J. GRANT *is a member of the Bureau of Plant Industry, Soils, and Agricultural Engineering stationed in Orlando, Fla.*

L. J. KLOTZ *is head of the division of plant pathology in the University of California, at Riverside.*

J. M. WALLACE *is a plant pathologist in the Citrus Experiment Station of the University of California.*

Foot Rot of Citrus Trees

L. J. Klotz, J. F. L. Childs

Foot rot, mal di gomma, gummosis, and brown rot gummosis are some of the names given a disease that attacks citrus trees the world over.

Foot rot is as good a name as any—it has priority of usage. Gummosis is a general term for several troubles in which gumming is a symptom. Brown rot gummosis was intended to indicate the causal relationship between the bark disease and brown rot of citrus fruits caused by species of *Phytophthora*. Mal di gomma simply means the gumming sickness, whether caused by *Phytophthora* species or other biological and physiological troubles.

First reported in the Azores in 1834, foot rot quickly spread to Portugal (1845) and other Mediterranean countries. By 1863 it was destroying thousands of citrus trees in Italy and Sicily and had appeared as far away as Australia. It appeared in Florida in 1876 or so and in California about the same time. Between 1834 and 1914 it had spread to virtually every citrus-producing region in the world.

The study of plant diseases was still young but it had made considerable progress by the time foot rot was ravaging the citrus orchards of the Mediterranean region. For example, Charles Moore, who went from Australia to study the foot rot problem in Spain, recognized in 1867 that the disease probably was caused by a fungus parasite. Several fungi and bacteria were falsely accused before it was proved in

1913 that *Phytophthora citrophthora* is the real cause of foot rot. Two other species of *Phytophthora*, *P. parasitica* and *P. palmivora*, were later isolated from foot-rot-like infections of citrus trees. *P. citrophthora* and *P. parasitica* are isolated with about equal frequency from foot-rot lesions in California.

The most widely recognized symptom of foot rot is the presence of diseased bark and the exudation of gum, usually near the soil line. Affected bark first looks dark and water-soaked, and underground in wet soil it may smell fishy or sour. Gum often exudes from diseased bark in sufficient quantity to flow down the trunk. The gum is most noticeable in dry weather because rain dissolves and washes it away. •

Bark lesions usually are more extensive at or below the soil surface, but they may extend 18 inches or more upward. Infected bark is killed through to the wood, which is usually stained brown. In dry weather the dead bark dries, shrinks, and the margins split.

Foot rot may cause severe damage to the below-ground parts of the tree by periodically damaging the smaller permanent roots and the fibrous feeder roots. Under favorable conditions, the small roots are quickly replaced, but damage to the root crown is more serious and permanent. Through the root crown all the sugars and other manufactured food materials must pass on their way from the leaves to the roots. Serious damage to the crown region therefore usually means the death of the tree.

The work of R. E. Smith, L. J. Klotz, and H. S. Fawcett in California, Lillian Fraser in Australia, and Victoria Rosetti in Brazil has given us a fairly complete understanding of the growth relations of the foot rot fungus.

We know, for instance, that the fungus thrives best in damp locations, that free water is necessary for the formation of the swarmspores, and that those spores can swim about like minute tadpoles until they come to rest on some suitable food material (possibly a citrus root) or they die.

We also know that swarmspores are formed in spore sacs, or sporangia, which in turn are formed most readily at temperatures near 75° F., and that a drop in temperature, such as usually follows a thundershower, causes the swarmspores to be released into the water. The fungi are sensitive to heat, *P. citrophthora* being killed, for example, by exposure to temperatures of 112° for 1 minute, 111° for 2 minutes, 110° for 5 minutes, 105° for 90 minutes, 100° for 210 minutes, 98° for 25 hours and 91° for 75 hours.

The acidity of the soil has an important bearing on the survival and virulence of the fungus. Using Rough lemon seedlings grown in pots, Miss Fraser found that the greatest amount of root infection took place in soils between pH 5.4 and 7.5; moderate infection occurred at pH 4.8 to 5.0; and only very slight infection occurred between pH 4.3 and 4.5. The results— obtained in the laboratory—confirmed her observations on the incidence of root decay under field conditions.

Another factor that has an important bearing on the incidence of foot rot is the susceptibility of the host. Even before the cause of the disease was known, growers recognized that foot rot occurred more often and caused more damage on some varieties of citrus trees than on others. That was true in the Mediterranean countries, where sour oranges were grown long before sweet oranges, lemons, or limes were introduced and where effects of the disease on the different varieties of citrus could easily be compared. Charles Moore, an Australian, visited Spain in 1867 and found sour orange used widely as a rootstock because it was known to be resistant to foot rot disease. Because of the general use of the basin method of irrigation, which promotes *Phytophthora* infections of the tree crowns, sour orange is the only rootstock that is acceptable and used in Italy and Sicily.

In 1896 the foot rot problem was studied in Florida and the use of sour orange rootstock was recommended for its control. R. E. Smith in California suggested that considerable immunity could be obtained through using Florida sour orange as a rootstock. At Professor Smith's suggestion, H. S. Fawcett started research on the cause of the disease and in 1913 announced that *Pythiacystis citrophthora*, later named *Phytophthora citrophthora*, was the causal organism.

The discovery of the true cause of foot rot made it possible to study the susceptibility of the many varieties of citrus. L. J. Klotz and H. S. Fawcett in 1930 published the results of a study of the susceptibility of about 100 species and hybrids of citrus. They found that the various species of citrus and citrus relatives could be arranged in descending order of their susceptibility to foot rot as follows: Lemons (*Citrus limon*), limes (*C. aurantifolia*,) pummelos (*C. grandis*), grapefruits (*C. paradisi*), sweet oranges (*C. sinensis*), mandarin oranges (*C. reticulata*), citrons (*C. medica*), sour oranges (*C. aurantium*), kumquats (*Fortunella* species), and trifoliate orange (*Poncirus trifoliata*).

Considerable variation in susceptibility was found among the species in each genus. For example, Imperial grapefruit was found to be no more susceptible than standard sour orange but Pernambuco grapefruit was more susceptible than some of the limes.

The most satisfactory approach to the control of foot rot is through the use of resistant varieties of citrus as rootstocks. Sour orange has been the almost universal choice of rootstock so far as resistance to foot rot is concerned, but the more resistant trifoliate orange is often used in regions where foot rot is unusually severe. In areas where foot rot is not severe, sweet orange and Rough lemon stocks are usually satisfactory if the trees receive proper protective attention. Cleopatra mandarin rootstock is being used to some extent in Florida under similar conditions.

Many factors other than resistance to foot rot enter into the choice of a rootstock. For example, resistance to cold and adaptability to soil type and fruit quality are important. Rough lemon stock is widely used in Florida because of its adaptability to deep, sandy soils but it is only moderately resistant to foot rot and is not very tolerant of cold. The quality of fruit produced over it is not high. Cleopatra mandarin is rather resistant to foot rot and trees on it produce high-quality fruit, but with some scion varieties production is low.

The matter of rootstock selection has been further complicated by tristeza or the threat of tristeza. That disease has been so devastating to trees on sour orange root that sour is now considered an undesirable stock.

It is impossible to state what rootstocks will be most satisfactory from all standpoints, but it is worthwhile to indicate the direction in which progress seems most likely. Sweet orange will probably be used more than in the past, with emphasis on the varieties that are most resistant to foot rot such as Indian River or Jaffa. Mandarin varieties, such as the fairly resistant Cleopatra, doubtless will receive more consideration. Some selections of *Poncirus trifoliata* stock are highly resistant to foot rot, and will probably be used. In addition, *P. trifoliata* is tolerant to tristeza, cold-resistant, and produces high-quality fruit especially on heavy soils.

The second approach to the problem of foot rot control is to provide an environment unfavorable to the growth and survival of the fungus in the soil. That is particularly important when trees must be grown on only moderately resistant stocks.

As the foot rot fungus requires abundant moisture, citrus obviously should not be planted on poorly drained, heavy soils. Drainage should be provided where necessary and irrigation water used sparingly. In areas of heavy rainfall, clean cultivation and trimming up the skirts of the tree promote air circulation and more rapid drying of the top layer of soil.

The root crown is the most critical infection site from the standpoint of loss of the tree. Removing the soil from around the crown roots exposes them to the drying effects of air and sunlight and has been found helpful in combatting foot rot. Excavation is most easily accomplished by directing a jet of water under high pressure against the soil around the crown roots until a basin approximately 6 inches deep and about 4 feet across is washed out. The young tree, on rootstocks moderately susceptible to foot rot, should be set high enough that after the soil settles the top lateral roots are barely covered.

Careful inspection should be made of the crown twice a year during the first 3 years of growth and at least once a year thereafter. Covering the crown and a foot of the lower trunk once a year with a water suspension of a one-package (ready-mixed) bordeaux mixture (a spray-dried product, made to about the consistency of house paint) is a good way to prevent infection. Under experimental conditions in Florida, however, bordeaux mixture and other fungicides have not proved effective unless combined with the method of exposing the root crown plus clean cultivation under the trees.

Manipulation of the soil pH for the purpose of foot rot control is probably not advisable in mineral soils or in areas where the soil reaction is naturally close to pH 7.0. To attempt to lower the soil reaction from 6.0 or 7.0 to 4.5 might cause serious nutritional disturbances. But in areas of high rainfall and in organic soils, the soil reaction is frequently as low as pH 4.0 to 6.0. Under such conditions, the soil reaction can often be maintained at pH 4.5 by the use of suitable amendments and fertilizer. Even on organic soils, however, nutritional problems may develop when the soil is maintained at pH 4.5 or lower. Hence, attempts to control foot rot through altering the soil pH may prove useful in some areas, but should be pursued with caution.

The first step in treatment is to expose the infected bark and wood by excavating the soil if that has not been done. Next, all the diseased bark is removed with a heavy knife and scraper, cutting one-quarter to one-half inch into healthy bark to be sure that all infected tissue is removed. The exposed wood is then covered with a fungicide. Many different fungicidal preparations, such as bordeaux paste, have been used as wound paints and with fairly satisfactory results. However, Avenarius (Red Arrow) carbolineum seems particularly suitable in this instance because it penetrates well into the wood in addition to being an excellent disinfectant and is waterproof for a period of several months. Later the wounds should be painted with a water-emulsified asphalt preparation (obtainable under such names as Tree Seal or De Ka Go), which will make them waterproof indefinitely.

L. J. KLOTZ *is head of the division of plant pathology of the University of California at Riverside.*

J. F. L. CHILDS *is a pathologist at the Subtropical Fruit Field Station of the Bureau of Plant Industry, Soils, and Agricultural Engineering, Orlando, Fla. He has degrees from the University of California.*

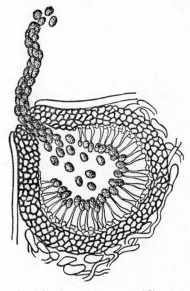

Conidia borne in a pycnidium.

Virus Diseases of Citrus Fruits

J. M. Wallace, T. J. Grant

Psorosis designates a group of diseases of citrus that have certain characteristics in common, notably the symptoms they produce on young leaves. Among them are psorosis A, psorosis B, concave gum, blind pocket, crinkly leaf, and infectious variegation.

No one has been able to reproduce the diseases by isolating fungi or bacteria from diseased plants, but they have been transmitted by means of buds, leaves, and bark tissues. No insect vectors are known for them. Studies in the field indicate that their spread is associated with manmade bud grafts and occasionally by naturally occurring grafts of root tissue. A characteristic symptom on young leaves of affected trees was discovered in 1933 by H. S. Fawcett, who demonstrated by further procedures that the diseases are caused by viruses.

Young-leaf symptoms appear during the growth flushes and vary greatly in extent and degree on individual trees at a given time and between seasonal peaks of greatest growth.

Small, elongated, cleared places, much lighter than the rest of the leaf blade, occur in the region of the veinlets.

They may be numerous and scattered over the entire blade or they may occur on only certain parts of the leaf. At times most leaves of suitable growth show symptoms. At other times relatively few leaves have symptoms. It is not uncommon to find strong symptoms on one leaf and to find none on an adjacent leaf of the same age.

Often some of the small flecks are quite indistinct. Others coalesce to form large blotches. A characteristic pattern known as the zonate, or oak-leaf, pattern is sometimes present. In California that pattern occurs on nearly all leaves of the spring flush of trees affected with the concave gum psorosis. It is seldom found on leaves of later flushes.

The cleared areas gradually disappear as the leaves mature. Large soft leaves frequently show symptoms until they harden or become almost mature. The oak-leaf pattern generally is retained longer than the ordinary flecking or stippling symptom. A careful examination of both sides of the leaves is necessary to distinguish between faint psorosis symptoms and some effects caused by thrips, spider mites, or mechanical injuries. Symptoms are seen most readily when the leaf is shaded from direct sun and viewed with the transmitted light of the sky coming through the blade.

THE YOUNG-LEAF SYMPTOMS associated with concave gum and blind pocket types of psorosis are indistinguishable from those found on trees affected with the other types except that nearly all leaves of the spring flush of trees having concave gum show strong zonate patterns.

The outstanding features of concave gum psorosis are the concavities of various sizes that develop on the trunks and larger limbs. Usually a fairly normal bark covers the surface. Cracking of the bark often occurs in the central part of the concavity or around the margin and gum appears on the surface. Occasionally the bark may scale, but that may be due to the presence of psorosis A in the trees in addition to concave gum. The only symptom in the wood usually is the development of gum immediately under the concavity. As long as the concavities remain few, the trees appear not to be seriously handicapped, but many concavities may cause dwarfing and a decline in growth. Large limbs of affected trees are sometimes slightly twisted and irregular in shape although they do not have the typical concavities.

Blind pocket usually makes concavities deeper and narrower than those of concave gum. A smaller area of wood may be affected, so that the depressions may become very narrow or almost closed. In older lesions the wood under the central part of the blind pocket concavity shows more alteration than in the case of concave gum and is composed of a rather loose wood parenchyma, often impregnated with a waxy or gummy substance. The apparent point of origin is often found quite deep in the wood under the bottom of the pocket. Only rarely is gum exuded to the surface.

The concavities formed on trees affected with either concave gum or blind pocket psorosis cannot always be defined as being that of either one or the other of these types of psorosis. Most of the differences might be explained on the basis of varietal response or growth rate of the affected trees. On citrus varieties such as mandarin (which often produces uneven, fluted, or grooved trunk growth) it is not easy to diagnose the diseases with certainty or to tell which type is present. From a practical standpoint this latter point is of no particular importance. The absence of the zonate pattern on the young leaves of trees suffering from blind pocket indicates that the two types of psorosis are distinct even though they are very probably caused by closely related virus strains.

CRINKLY LEAF, seen mainly on lemons, induces young-leaf symptoms much like those of the other psorosis types. Some of the leaves also become pocketed and warped. Carried to sweet orange, it causes typical young-leaf symptoms and some puckering or cupping of leaves. Sweet orange root-stocks of lemon tops affected by crinkly leaf develop bark symptoms typical of psorosis A. Crinkly leaf disease may result from a mixture of two viruses, one of which is the psorosis A virus and the other a yet unidentified virus. Crinkly leaf may even be a strain of psorosis A. Experimental inoculations with all possible combinations of the other known psorosis types have not produced the crinkly leaf disease. Crinkly leaf is not found as commonly as psorosis A, possibly because the leaf symptoms are so striking on lemon that propagation from diseased trees has been easily avoided by informed nurserymen.

Infectious variegation psorosis is found occasionally on lemons, but is not very important. It has been transmitted by means of buds. On young leaves of lemon, orange, and other citrus it causes symptoms like those of the other psorosis types. On some of the older leaves of lemon, grapefruit, and sour orange, parts of the blades are white or pale yellow. Sometimes the chlorotic or variegated areas are entirely on one side of the midrib. Sometimes they are scattered over the entire blade in no definite pattern. Some leaves near affected ones appear normal. The white or light-yellow color persists on affected leaves and does not disappear, as in the case of the flecking symptom of young leaves. There may also be rather marked distortion of leaves. Fruits on affected lemon trees are sometimes small, misshapen, and bumpy. Some of the symptoms of crinkly leaf are usually associated with infectious variegation. It has not been determined whether infectious variegation is caused by a mixture of virus strains, nor has it been possible to produce the symptoms of infectious variegation by infecting citrus trees with various combinations of the other types of psorosis.

PSOROSIS A and psorosis B cause the bark condition commonly known in California as scaly bark. The psorosis types that cause bark lesions occur the world over and should not be confused with leprosis (which is called scaly bark in Florida, where psorosis also occurs). Sweet orange, grapefruit, and tangerine trees infected with psorosis A or psorosis B commonly develop the typical bark lesions, but lemon and sour orange never show bark symptoms.

Psorosis A and psorosis B seem to be caused by closely related virus strains, differing perhaps only in virulence. Psorosis B produces more harmful effects; besides the young-leaf and bark symptoms, it induces symptoms on old leaves, twigs, and fruits. The persistent symptoms on older or mature leaves consist of circular spots or rings of varying sizes, usually comprised of a yellowish-green central part surrounded by a light-yellow border. As the leaves mature, the under side of the affected area becomes yellowish brown and slightly raised, as though gum had formed in the leaf tissues. Some fruits of trees affected by psorosis B show surface rings bordered by sunken grooves of different sizes and patterns. Young green fruit sometimes has round spots like those on mature leaves. In other cases, especially on grapefruit, large circular grooves, partial rings, or irregular circles occur on the rind and result in a rough, bumpy condition.

On trees infected with psorosis B, the bark of green twigs and small limbs often shows raised, corky areas like those on mature leaves. As the twigs become older, the bark develops reddish-brown areas that split and flake off.

Psorosis B is not often encountered in the field. Because affected trees grow poorly and show striking symptoms early, propagators usually are able to avoid trees with psorosis B.

Psorosis A is the most common type. Infected trees may periodically show transitory leaf symptoms, which often go unnoticed. The bark symptoms are the ones that attract attention—although trees take at least 6 years and up to 20 years or more to produce bark symptoms. Trees infected with psorosis

and showing no bark symptoms are nevertheless carriers of the causal disease agent.

The bark lesions begin as pimples or small scales or flakes of the outer bark, under which the tissue is brown. The scales of outer bark are dry, irregular flakes, one-twelfth to one-eighth inch thick. They loosen and break away from the live bark underneath. The scales occur first on localized areas of the trunk or limbs. As the scaling advances, the deeper layers of the bark become disorganized in growth and some of the tissues become impregnated with gum or gumlike materials. Scaling is more or less continuous and the lesions increase in size. Gum sometimes exudes to the surface of the bark.

SYMPTOMS INDUCED in the wood by psorosis A and psorosis B show no differences except that wood symptoms may appear in the latter in a shorter time after bark lesions develop.

Soon after a bark lesion becomes visible, gum layers begin to be formed in the wood underneath. In some seasons the embryonic layer of woody tissue immediately beneath the cambium is acted upon in some way so that the cells between the medullary rays are forced apart and partly broken down. Those pockets become filled with a colorless, watery, gumlike substance. Normal wood is then laid down for some time before another gum layer develops. The process continues until there are many bands of normal wood alternating with thin layers of gum. The older gum layers become buried deeper in the wood with each successive period of wood growth. The gum hardens as it ages and becomes yellowish brown. Wood staining appears in later stages. At first only small areas of stained wood are present; in the wood under old and well-advanced lesions, all of the wood excepting narrow bands nearer the bark becomes stained. Top deterioration begins after wood staining appears. Impregnation of the wood with gum blocks the vessels through which water moves, and top decline results largely from a shutting off of the water supply.

WE KNOW OF NO INSECTS that carry the psorosis viruses. We have no definite evidence that insects are a factor in their spread. The viruses are rarely, if ever, transmitted through seeds. They cannot be transmitted from diseased to healthy trees by pruning or other cultural practices.

There is only one chief source of infection—the parent tree, from which buds are taken. As with all known virus diseases of plants, transmission occurs and healthy trees become diseased when virus-bearing tissue is grafted to them.

When natural root grafts occur between a diseased and a healthy tree, the healthy tree becomes diseased. Because natural grafting of roots takes place only infrequently, however, the amount of disease from that cause is probably not very great: The use of scions or buds from psorosis-affected trees for top-working old trees or for growing nursery trees accounts for nearly all of the naturally occurring psorosis.

CONTROL OF PSOROSIS lies in prevention. The absence of any significant amount of natural spread of the disease in the field makes prevention effective.

To repeat: Citrus trees grown from healthy budwood parent trees are free of psorosis and remain so except in rare instances of natural root grafting between healthy and diseased trees in an orchard. The long delay in the appearance of bark lesions on affected trees, however, and the inexperience of some workers with trees in detecting young-leaf symptoms have meant the production and sale of diseased trees.

A service was started in 1937 by the California State Department of Agriculture by which prospective parent trees are thoroughly inspected repeatedly for a year or more. Trees considered free from psorosis are registered by the California Department and

their offspring are sold as registered, psorosis-free stock. Nurserymen may choose for themselves whether they wish to grow and sell registered nursery trees, but in California more and more producers of citrus stock are realizing the value of the practice. Since the program was put into operation about 2,000 parent trees have been registered by the citrus nurserymen and growers of the State. A similar program has been put into effect in Texas.

No CURE for psorosis-affected trees is known, but the productive life of trees that have psorosis A can be prolonged by certain procedures.

For many years growers and tree surgeons have been wont to remove the loose, discolored bark lesions by scraping with a specially designed bark scraper. The only injury to the cambium is in small spots where the affected bark extends completely to the cambium. If the trees are carefully inspected each year over their entire framework for new bark lesions, treatment is more effective and takes less work. On trunks and larger limbs the lesion area and a 4-inch surrounding margin of bark should be scraped. Small limbs usually are cut off several inches or a foot below the lower limits of the lesion. A good practice is to reinspect the treated lesions each second year and to scrape again if any more roughening, scaling, or gumming has occurred. The new lesions should be treated then.

The treatment of large old lesions is usually of doubtful value, particularly if there is evidence of staining in the wood or if the top of the tree shows signs of deterioration. Also, if trees show many active lesions over the trunks and limbs, it may be that too much attention and labor will be required to warrant treatment.

A new and satisfactory treatment is to induce bark scaling with chemicals. It consists of brushing the lesions and marginal bark with a 1 percent solution of dinitro-o-cyclohexyl-phenol in kerosene. The solution, known as DN–75, is prepared by the Dow Chemical Co. It is inexpensive and easily applied, but the directions as to its use and application must be carefully followed. Improper use of DN–75 will seriously injure the trees. The chemical, like the scraping treatment, is not a cure. It is merely a way of prolonging the commercial productivity of the tree. It is not recommended for trees that show top deterioration or for trees that already show wood staining under the lesions.

PSOROSIS, primarily the bark-scaling type, psorosis A, is widely distributed over the citrus-growing areas of the United States and elsewhere. Its economic importance varies in individual plantings. In California the percentage of diseased trees may be as high as 75 percent in groves not more than 25 years old.

Data obtained in 1943 and 1944 in a survey conducted in California by the Emergency Plant Disease Survey covered 18 groves—14,320 trees—16 to 50 years old. The percentages of trees with bark symptoms ranged from less than 1 percent to approximately 30 percent. Replants, thought to have been necessary because of psorosis, sometimes ran as high as 15 percent in the older groves. The surveyed groves perhaps represented the average of the California plantings. Many plantings, however, have a much higher percentage of diseased trees than the ones surveyed. Yield estimates in the older groves showed that the affected trees were yielding on the average about one-third less than healthy trees of the same age. As the effect of the disease worsens, the yields drop proportionately. Replanting also represents a loss.

OTHER VIRUS DISEASES of citrus include stubborn disease and exocortis.

Stubborn disease was first called that at East Highlands, Calif., by J. C. Perry, who observed that when affected navel orange trees were topworked with healthy buds of the same variety they were slow or stubborn in their growth and had the same general appearance as the original trees.

H. S. Fawcett demonstrated later that the disease could be transmitted by tissue grafting. From his studies he concluded that the disease was caused by a virus. Further observations by J. C. Johnston, L. J. Klotz, and Dr. Fawcett proved that the "acorn-shaped" or "pink nose" fruits sometimes found on navel trees were also symptoms of stubborn disease. The disease of grapefruit in Arizona and the Coachella Valley of California known as crazy top, blue nose, or blue albedo may be the same malady. It is not known that this type of disease occurs in other citrus areas of the world. The little-leaf disease in Palestine is said to resemble the stubborn disease in California.

Its symptoms on foliage and branches are hard to describe. Large affected trees look like the unproductive "Australian" type of navel. The leaves are shorter, broader, and more upright. Multiple buds and shorter internodes tend to make the trees somewhat bushy. At first there are more leaves than normal, but later in severe cases the leaves become somewhat chlorotic and shed more than on healthy trees. Many twigs die and the trees gradually bear less and less fruit.

Fruits on affected trees are usually fewer in number, more irregular in size, and paler in color. Often more off-bloom fruits are produced. Some of the fruits, even the smaller green ones, may show the characteristic acorn shape. Mature acorn fruits, however, are not always found every year on diseased trees. The rind of the acorn fruit appears normal near the stem end and abruptly becomes thinner and smoother until it is quite thin at the stylar end, which, in navels, often takes on a pinkish color—hence the name pink nose. Grapefruits frequently have a blue color in the albedo of the thin part of the rind. The blue may be visible on the rind surface —hence blue nose.

The disease has not been observed on citrus other than navel orange and grapefruit. There is no definite evidence of natural spread in the field, but lately it has seemed to increase in some older plantings. Because of the suspicion that stubborn disease may be spreading by some natural means from diseased to healthy trees, we recommend that particular attention be given in the selection of budwood parent trees so as to avoid the use of buds from trees that show any suggestion of the disease.

Exocortis, known as scaly butt in Australia, is characterized by a scaling of the bark of trifoliate orange (*Poncirus trifoliata*), a commonly used rootstock for certain citrus. Usually a severe stunting of the scion or top of affected trees occurs. Navel and Valencia orange, grapefruit, and lemon trees grown on trifoliate rootstock commonly show bark shelling of the trifoliate and a stunted top growth, but sometimes trees are stunted without evidence of bark shelling on the rootstock. Studies in Australia suggest that the disease is caused by a virus but that it is typically a bud-union effect. It has not been seen on unworked trifoliate seedlings. In two instances the scaling persisted and enlarged onto sucker growth from the trifoliate rootstock that developed after the navel orange scion was broken off or died back completely. Other experiments indicate that many orange, grapefruit, and lemon trees on other rootstocks carry the virus without showing evidence of its presence. When buds from such trees are propagated to trifoliate rootstock, however, many of the trees grow poorly in the nursery and develop bark symptoms on the rootstock within 4 to 8 years after budding. On the other hand, it has been established that buds from certain orange and grapefruit trees develop normally and probably remain so indefinitely. No lemon trees in Australia have been found to be free of the virus.

Although exocortis has not been of great economic importance in the United States because of the rather limited use of trifoliate orange as a rootstock, it is of interest because of the possibility that some of the new rootstocks that are being developed or selected to replace those that are susceptible to quick decline may prove to be subject to exocortis. In other words: This disease is an additional complication in the program of finding desirable rootstocks for citrus.

We do not know whether the exocortis virus causes any trouble on citrus grown on the commonly used rootstocks other than trifoliate orange. One way to prevent losses therefore is to use rootstock species that are known not to be susceptible. Because of certain merits of trifoliate orange (such as resistance to quick decline, gummosis, nematodes, low temperatures, and possibly drought, as well as its beneficial influence on yields and fruit quality), however, it has been a preferred rootstock in some areas. Where it is used as a rootstock, the scion bud to be grown on it should be selected from trees on trifoliate rootstock that are 10 years old or older and show no evidence of stunting or bark shelling on the rootstock. We believe that such a practice will result in healthy trees, because we have no definite evidence that trifoliate seedlings carry the virus of exocortis or that there is any natural spread from diseased trees to healthy trees in the orchard.

J. M. WALLACE *is a plant pathologist in the Citrus Experiment Station of the University of California at Riverside.*

T. J. GRANT, *principal pathologist at the Subtropical Fruit Field Station, Orlando, Fla., spent 3 years in Brazil on tristeza disease investigations. Before that he was agricultural attaché of the American embassies in Nicaragua, Costa Rica, and Panama. He has been concerned with tropical agriculture and has worked in the Department of Agriculture for more than 17 years. He has degrees from the University of Massachusetts and the University of Wisconsin.*

Virus Diseases of Grapevines

W. B. Hewitt

A killer of grapevines, Pierce's disease has twice threatened to destroy the vineyards of California, once between 1884 and 1900 and again between 1935 and 1941. In the earlier days, the disease was known by various names—mysterious disease, vine plague, Anaheim disease, and California vine disease.

It first started taking its toll of the vineyards of southern California near Anaheim and Pomona during the growing season of 1884. It spread to other sections of Los Angeles and Orange Counties and thence into San Diego, Riverside, San Bernardino, Ventura, and Santa Barbara Counties. It destroyed more than 35,000 acres of excellent vineyards. Actual losses were more extensive than just the vineyards; local wineries had to close down.

There were no records of Pierce's disease in the San Joaquin Valley during the early epidemic. Growers recalled its first appearance in the valley near Poplar in Tulare County in 1917. It was reported in the same county near Woodlake in 1921, and in other parts of the county in 1927 and 1931. Reports of the disease had become fairly numerous by 1934, and indicated its spread into Kern and Fresno Counties. By 1935 it was increasing rapidly throughout the San Joaquin Valley. Its continued development over the next 4 years indicated that another epidemic had erupted in the center of California's table-grape and raisin industry. By 1940 the disease had developed in nearly all of the grape-growing regions of the State except the Livermore and Martinez areas of Alameda and Contra Costa Counties.

The incidence of disease reached a peak of nearly 6 percent of 300,000 acres of vines in 1941. Losses ranged from only a few vines to the complete destruction of some vineyards and even entire vineyard districts. The disease declined rapidly after 1941 to less than one-half of one percent in 1946. Since then the number of diseased vines in the San Joaquin Valley has varied but has remained low.

The occurrence of diseased vines in individual vineyards, in districts, and in the entire San Joaquin Valley followed a rather consistent pattern. At first diseased vines were widely scattered and irregularly distributed. Later they became concentrated in more localized areas, not apparently associated with environment, soil, or cultural practices. Large numbers of diseased vines were found in vineyards adjacent to irrigated pastures and alfalfa plantings and in areas where such plantings were extensive.

In San Bernardino, Riverside, and San Diego Counties in southern California, the spread of Pierce's disease followed a pattern similar to that in the San Joaquin Valley, but the losses were relatively light. In the north-coast counties, Pierce's disease was most prevalent in vineyards adjacent to brush lands and along stream banks with abundant native cover. In some parts of the Napa Valley, the disease has continued to destroy many vines annually, though the losses have not been nearly so great as they were between 1940 and 1943.

In addition to California, Pierce's disease was found in a Thompson Seedless vineyard near Carrizo Springs, Tex., in 1941–1942. This virus is reported to be the cause of grape degeneration in Florida. A similar disease has been reported in Argentina.

The symptoms of Pierce's disease in grapevines are contingent on the variety and the locality in California. The variations, however, are in the rate and degree to which symptoms show, and not in the symptom pattern. In the hot interior valleys symptoms show earlier in the season and are usually more pronounced than in the coastal regions.

Scalding and burning of the leaves, the first symptoms, may develop any time after mid-June. Leaf scalding is characterized by a sudden drying of a part of the leaf while it is still green. Tissue around the margins and the tip of the large veins dries up and later turns brown. The size of the scalded areas varies from a fraction to as much as half the leaf surface. Leaf burning, usually preceded by yellowing of the tissue before it dries and turns brown, starts about the margins and progresses, often in concentric zones, toward the base of the leaf at the point of attachment of the petiole. In newly diseased vines, these symptoms frequently show on only one cane or on the canes growing from one arm or side of the vine. As the season advances the amount of leaf burning increases. Severely affected leaves drop, leaving the petiole attached to the cane.

Fruit on canes that show leaf symptoms early may be dwarfed and later wither and dry. If it is late in the season before leaf scalding occurs, the fruit may prematurely color before withering and drying.

The second and later seasons of the disease are characterized by delayed growth in the spring, followed by dwarfing of affected parts of the vines. The first four to eight leaves on the shoots growing from affected parts of diseased vines often show interveinal chlorosis or mottling and deformity. Mottling is more intense in the first leaf and becomes less with each successive one formed on a shoot. As the season advances, the leaves on these vines in the second year of disease will show scalding and burning and will drop from the vine. Some canes in severely affected vines may die back

from the tips. Much of the fruit withers and dries before harvest. Canes fail to mature evenly and have irregular patches of green bark in portions that should mature to a normal brown.

Death of the root system of diseased vines follows closely the decline of the top. Roots of vines in early stages of the disease appear normal. But as the disease advances the wood tissue in the roots discolors, and they die back progressively from the tips to the vine trunk.

Diseased vines may live only a few months or as long as 5 years. Young, vigorously growing vines seldom live more than one season after they become diseased. Older and less healthy vines live longer. Diseased vines usually live longer in the cooler coastal regions than in the interior valleys.

THE CAUSE of Pierce's disease is a virus that has a wide range of hosts and is spread naturally to grapevines by several species of leafhoppers. The virus has been experimentally transmitted to healthy grapevines by grafting pieces of roots, canes, and trunks of diseased vines to healthy ones. It has also been experimentally transmitted from many other host plants to grapes by several species of sharpshooter leafhoppers. The virus does not transmit by juice transfer from diseased to healthy vines or by shears, knives, and common vineyard implements. Cuttings taken from diseased vines and infected nursery stock will carry the virus.

The incubation period before symptoms of Pierce's disease appear in grapevines after inoculation by grafting or insects is 8 weeks to 15 months, depending somewhat on the time of year inoculations were made. Young vines grown continuously in glass houses usually showed symptoms 8 to 15 weeks after inoculation. Old vines in the vineyard inoculated between May and August usually developed symptoms the same season; those inoculated in September or later rarely showed symptoms before the following July.

VECTORS OF THE VIRUS are sharp-shooter leafhoppers and spittle insects; 20 species of leafhoppers and 4 species and 6 varieties of spittle insects are known to be able to transmit the virus to grapevines. Norman W. Frazier and J. H. Freitag, in experimental studies at the University of California Agricultural Experiment Station, Berkeley, found three insects, the green sharp-shooter, *Draeculacephala minerva;* the redheaded sharpshooter, *Carneocephala fulgida;* and the blue-green sharp-shooter, *Hordina circellata* to be the most important vectors of the Pierce's disease virus to grapes in California. Other leafhoppers reported to be vectors are: *Carneocephala triguttata, Cuerna occidentalis, C. yuccae, Draeculacephala californica, D. noveboracensis, D. crassicornis, Friscanus friscanus, Graphocephala cythura, Helochara delta, Homalodisca liturata, Neokolla gothica, N. confluens, N. heiroglyphica, Pagaronia triunata, P. 13-punctata, P. furcata,* and *P. confusa.*

H. H. P. Severin, also working at the California Agricultural Experiment Station in Berkeley, reported the following species of spittlebugs capable of transmitting the virus to grapevines: *Aphrophora angulata, A. permutata, Clastoptera brunnea, Philaenus leucophthalmus, P. pallidus, P. fabricii, P. marginellus, P. spumarius,* and *P. impressus.* The grape leafhopper, *Erythroneura elegantala,* does not spread the virus.

The green, the redheaded, and the blue-green sharpshooters, the three most important spreaders of Pierce's disease to California grapevines, are commonly found in the vineyards. The other species of insect vectors have rarely or never been found in vine-yards, but occur on various wild host plants of the virus. The green and red-headed sharpshooters are the principal vectors of the virus in the interior valleys, and the blue-green sharpshooter in the coastal areas.

Life histories, host ranges, and habits of the three important vectors were worked out by Mr. Frazier at Berkeley. The green sharpshooter is widely distributed and occurs in most of the principal grape-growing districts of the State. It frequents grassy areas of bogs, stream banks, irrigation ditches, and areas wet from faulty irrigation. Very large populations have been observed in the grass of permanent pastures, in thinning stands of alfalfa that contain grasses, in young grainfields, orchard cover crops, lawns, and in the grass along roadsides and ditches. Green sharpshooters may also be found in grass in vineyards, especially areas of the vineyards where irrigation water is allowed to accumulate.

Host plants of this insect are numerous; in fact, it has been found on more than 130 species of plants, although it prefers grasses for both feeding and reproduction. Some of the common food and breeding grasses are ripgut brome, *Bromus rigidus;* Bermuda-grass, *Cynodon dactylon;* hairy crabgrass, *Digitaria sanguinalis;* barnyard grass, *Echinochloa crusgalli;* foxtail fescue, *Festuca megalura;* Italian ryegrass, *Lolium multiflorum;* darnel, *L. temulentum;* annual bluegrass, *Poa annua;* and yellow bristlegrass, *Setaria glauca.* Other important host plants include Johnsongrass, *Holcus halepensis;* toad rush, *Juncus bufonius;* redmaids, *Calandrinia menziesii;* neck-weed, *Veronica peregrina;* and cocklebur, *Xanthium canadense.* Grapevines are not favored hosts of the green sharpshooter, but the insects have been observed feeding on the succulent tips of shoots and canes. The spread of Pierce's disease virus to grapevines by the green sharpshooter apparently occurs during such feeding.

The life history of the green sharpshooter includes three generations a year in the San Joaquin Valley. The insects overwinter primarily in the adult stage, but a few nymphs have also been observed to live through the winter. The overwintering adults begin to lay eggs in the latter part of February. The first-generation adults mature late in April. Second-generation adults mature about the last of June, and the third-generation adults about the first of August. The generations usually overlap and are somewhat later in the northern than in the southern part of the valley.

The green sharpshooters do not migrate in large numbers. They move instead into or through an area by infiltration of small numbers of adults over extended periods of time. On warm summer evenings the flight activity begins about sunset and continues for an hour or so. In the fall and winter their movement is slow and is limited to the warm periods.

Redheaded sharpshooters have been found in all of the main grape-growing districts north of Corona, especially in the San Joaquin Valley. This vector prefers to feed and breed in a sparse, open growth of grass and weeds. It has been found commonly in grassy areas along stream banks and irrigation canals, about the margins of dense plant growth, and even along roadsides.

Hosts of the redheaded sharpshooter include more than 75 species of mostly annual plants. Bermuda-grass, *Cynodon dactylon*, however, is probably one of its most important food and breeding plants. Other important host plants include hairy crabgrass, *Digitaria sanguinalis;* saltgrass, *Distichlis stricta;* foxtail fescue, *Festuca megalura;* redmaids, *Calandrinia menziesii;* common purslane, *Portulaca oleracea;* redstem filaree, *Erodium cicutarium;* and puncturevine, *Tribulus terrestris.*

The grapevine is not a favored host of redheaded sharpshooters and they do not reproduce on the plant. The spread of Pierce's disease to grapes by this insect probably occurs during times of incidental feeding.

The life history of the redheaded sharpshooter includes four generations in Fresno and Tulare Counties. They overwinter as adults. First-generation adults develop about the middle of April; second-generation adults, in early June; the third, about the first of August; and the fourth, near the middle of September.

Movements of the redheaded sharpshooter are limited to localized areas. The adults are relatively active but do not have migratory flights. They move about individually rather than in mass. Flights occur in the warm summer evenings for about an hour or more after sunset.

Blue-green sharpshooters, the most important vectors of Pierce's disease in the vineyards of the coast counties, are common in the coastal fog belts of California. They have also been found feeding on brush and brambles along stream banks in the interior valleys. Unlike the green and redheaded sharpshooters, they feed mostly on trees, vines, perennial shrubs, and weeds. They have many hosts—more than 150 species of plants. Some of the more frequent ones are willow, *Salix;* nettle, *Urtica gracilis;* blackberry, *Rubus vitifolius;* European grape, *Vitis vinifera;* California grape, *Vitis californica;* blue elderberry, *Sambucus glauca;* and California mugwort, *Artemisia vulgaris.*

Grapevines are a favored host of the blue-green sharpshooter for feeding and breeding. Populations of more than 500 adults and nymphs have been found on a single grapevine. Adults move into the vineyards as new growth starts in the spring. They may stay on grapevines until late fall. Many adults leave the vineyards, however, when new growth ceases in the vines and move to other host plants. Studies of the life history and movements of the blue-green sharpshooter have not been completed, but evidence indicates limited migratory movement.

MANY HOST PLANTS may be carriers of the virus which causes Pierce's disease of grapevines. Mr. Freitag, who worked out the host range of the virus at the experiment station in Berkeley, reported 111 species in 41 families of plants as carriers—among them grasses, clovers, many weeds, brambles, grapevines, shrubs, and even trees.

Alfalfa is one of the more important crop plants affected by this virus, which produces in it the disease known as dwarf. Alfalfa plants that have the dwarf disease seldom live more than a few months, and the average life of alfalfa stands in many sections of California has been reduced to only 2 or 3 years. The alfalfa dwarf disease was first described and proved to be transmissible by J. L. Weimer, of the Department of Agriculture, during research undertaken in cooperation with the California Agricultural Experiment Station at Davis. The name dwarf adequately describes the general appearance of diseased alfalfa plants. After each cutting, the diseased plants are slower in growth. The stems are short and the leaves small. Fewer buds are formed. The number of stems decreases. Dwarfed plants are usually late to bloom or fail to bloom altogether, and are generally darker in color than normal plants. Roots of diseased plants show yellowing in the woody tissues. In the early stages, the yellow discoloration may involve only a small portion of the outer ring of xylem tissue; as the disease advances, the entire woody part of the root becomes discolored. The bark shows no effects of the disease, however.

Dwarf-resistant varieties of alfalfa have been developed by Byron R. Houston and Ernest H. Stanford at the station at Davis and are available for planting.

Other host plants that show symptoms of Pierce's disease virus, according to Freitag, are the snowberry plant, *Symphoricarpos albus;* four species of sweetclover, Hubam sweetclover, *Melilotus alba annua;* white sweetclover, *M. alba;* yellow sweetclover, *M. officinalis;* and sourclover, *M. indica.* Symptoms of the virus in the clover species include slight dwarfing of plants, yellowing and burning about the margins of leaves, and premature dropping of leaflets. The snowberry was found very susceptible when inoculated by blue-green sharpshooters. The leaves became chlorotic, and burned about the margins, then dried. Finally the entire plant died.

Plant species found to be naturally infected with Pierce's disease virus, as proved by recovery of the virus by the insect vectors, are:

Graminae, grass family: Wild oats, *Avena fatua;* ripgut brome, *Bromus rigidus;* Bermuda-grass, *Cynodon dactylon;* hairy crabgrass, *Digitaria sanguinalis;* barnyard grass, *Echinochloa crusgalli;* Italian ryegrass, *Lolium multiflorum;* Dallisgrass, *Paspalum dilatatum;* annual bluegrass, *Poa annua.*

Salicaceae, willow family: Willow, *Salix* species.

Urticaceae, nettle family: Nettle, *Urtica gracilis* var. *holosericea.*

Polygonaceae, buckwheat family: Ladysthumb, *Polygonum persicaria;* curly dock, *Rumex crispus.*

Chenopodiaceae, saltbush family: Mexican tea, *Chenopodium ambrosioides.*

Saxifragaceae, saxifrage family: *Escallonia montevidensis; Hydrangea paniculata.*

Rosaceae, rose family: California wild rose, *Rosa californica;* California blackberry, *Rubus vitifolius.*

Leguminosae, pea family: Sydney golden wattle, *Acacia longifolia;* Scotch broom, *Cytisus scoparius;* bur-clover, *Medicago hispida;* sweetclover, *Melilotus* species; Ladino clover, *Trifolium repens* f. *giganteum.*

Anacardiaceae, sumac family: Poison-oak, *Rhus diversiloba.*

Vitaceae, vine family: Boston ivy, *Parthenocissus tricuspidata;* California wild grape, *Vitis californica.*

Myrtaceae, myrtle family: Australian brush-cherry, *Eugenia myrtifolia.*

Onagraceae, evening-primrose family: Fuchsia, *Fuchsia magellanica.*

Oleaceae, ash family: Foothill ash, *Fraxinus dipetala.*

Verbenaceae, vervain family: Pigeon-berry, *Duranta repens.*

Labiatae, mint family: Sweet marjoram, *Majorana hortensis;* garden balm, *Melissa officinalis;* rosemary, *Rosmarinus officinalis.*

Scrophulariaceae, figwort family: Speedwell, *Veronica* species.

Capriofoliaceae, honeysuckle family: Blue elder, *Sambucus caerulea.*

Compositae, sunflower family: California mugwort, *Artemisia vulgaris* var. *heterophylla;* coyote brush, *Baccharis pilularis.*

PLANT SPECIES experimentally infected with Pierce's disease virus, as proved by recovery of the virus by the insect vectors, are:

Graminae, grass family: Wild oats, *Avena fatua;* rescue grass, *Bromus catharticus;* ripgut brome, *B. rigidus;* Russian bromegrass, *Bromus* species; Bermudagrass, *Cynodon dactylon;* hairy crabgrass, *Digitaria sanguinalis;* barnyard grass, *Echinochloa crusgalli;* diffuse lovegrass, *Eragrostis diffusa;* foxtail fescue, *Festuca megalura;* Johnsongrass, *Holcus halepensis;* Sudangrass, *H. sudanensis;* common foxtail, *Hordeum murinum;* barley, *H. vulgare;* Italian ryegrass, *Lolium multiflorum;* darnel, *L. temulentum;* Dallisgrass, *Paspalum dilatatum;* Kikuyugrass, *Pennisetum clanedestimum;* Mediterranean canarygrass, *Phalaris minor;* gnawed canarygrass, *P. paradoxa;* timothy, *Phleum pratense;* annual bluegrass, *Poa annua;* yellow bristlegrass, *Setaria glauca.*

Cyperaceae, sedge family: Yellow nutgrass, *Cyperus esculentus.*

Cannaceae, canna family: *Canna* species.

Urticaceae, nettle family: Nettle, *Urtica gracilis* var. *holosericea.*

Polygonaceae, buckwheat family: Black bindweed, *Polygonum convolvulus;* ladysthumb, *P. persicaria;* rhubarb, *Rheum rhaponticum;* curly dock, *Rumex crispus.*

Chenopodiaceae, goosefoot family: Mexican tea, *Chenopodium ambrosioides.*

Resedaceae, mignonette family: Common mignonette, *Reseda odorata.*

Pittosporaceae, pittosporum family: Karo, *Pittosporum crassifolium.*

Rosaceae, rose family: Toyon or Christmas berry, *Photinia arbutifolia;* cotoneaster, *Cotoneaster rotundifolia* var. *lanata;* California blackberry, *Rubus vitifolius.*

Leguminosae, pea family: Scotch broom, *Cytisus scoparius;* pea, *Lathyrus cicera;* pea, *L. clymenum;* grass pea, *L. sativa;* white melilot, *Melilotus alba;*

Hubam clover, *M. alba* var. *annua;* sourclover, *M. indica;* yellow sweetclover, *M. officinalis;* strawberry clover, *Trifolium fragiferum;* alsike clover, *T. hybridum;* crimson clover, *T. incarnatum;* redclover, *T. pratense;* white clover, *T. repens;* Ladino clover, *T. repens* f. *giganteum;* vetch, *Vicia articulata.*

Geraniaceae, geranium family: Redstem filaree, *Erodium cicutarium;* fish geranium, *Pelargonium hortorum.*

Vitaceae, vine family: Boston ivy, *Parthenocissus tricuspidata.*

Myrtaceae, myrtle family: Australian brush cherry, *Eugenia myrtifolia.*

Onagraceae, evening-primrose family: Willowherb, *Epilobium californicum;* panicled willowherb, *E. paniculatum;* godetia, *Godetia grandiflora;* evening-primrose, *Oenothera hookeri.*

Araliaceae, aralia family: Variegated ivy, *Hedera helix.*

Umbelliferae, parsley family: Short white carrot, *Daucus carota* var. *sativa;* water parsley, *Oenanthe sarmentosa.*

Oleaceae, olive family: Lilac, *Syringa vulgaris.*

Apocynaceae, dogbane family: Periwinkle, *Vinca major.*

Boraginaceae, borage family: Buckthorn weed, *Amsinckia douglasiana.*

Labiatae, mint family: Mint, *Mentha* species.

Rubiaceae, madder family: *Coprosma baueri.*

Caprifoliaceae, honeysuckle family: Japanese honeysuckle, *Lonicera japonica;* blue elder, *Sambucus caerulea;* snowberry, *Symphoricarpos albus.*

Compositae, sunflower family: California mugwort, *Artemisia vulgaris* var. *heterophylla;* China aster, *Callistephus chinensis;* annual burweed, *Franseria acanthicarpa;* prickly lettuce, *Lactuca serriola;* prickly sowthistle, *Sonchus asper;* cocklebur, *Xanthium canadense.*

In feeding, sharpshooter leafhoppers seek the xylem tissue of plants, as was shown by Katherine Esau, Byron R. Houston, and I, at the California Agricultural Experiment Station at Davis. Seventy percent of the feeding punctures that touched the xylem were found to pass through the phloem tissue. The feeding punctures often branched in several directions in the plant tissue.

Experiments with the green and blue-green sharpshooters have shown that the insects transmit Pierce's disease virus to grapes only when they feed in the xylem tissue. Viruliferous insects fed only on strips of phloem tissue did not transmit the virus to grapevines. Parts of diseased grapevine containing bark and wood and wood tissue free of bark grafted into healthy vines transmitted the virus. Pieces of bark tissue alone did not transmit the virus, however.

The studies showed that the virus causing Pierce's disease is apparently limited to the xylem (wood). As the parenchyma cells in the wood are the only living cells in the tissue, the virus probably develops in those cells. The insect vectors, in searching for water-conducting vessels in the wood, probably feed on the contents of some parenchyma cells and pick up the virus in that way. They probably transmit the virus also in the process of feeding in the xylem tissue.

A COMPARATIVE STUDY OF TISSUES of healthy and diseased grapevines made by Miss Esau at Davis showed that the anatomical changes induced by Pierce's disease occurred in the wood, bark, and leaf mesophyll. Gum formation and subsequent excessive development of tyloses in the wood were found to be the primary effects of the virus. Gum was formed in all types of cells in the wood of young and old vines. In young vines inoculated through a single leaf by sharpshooters, plugging of the vessels with gum occurred even before external symptoms and became more pronounced with the passing of time. The first internal symptoms were observed in tissues collected 24 days, and the first external symptoms 55 days, after inoculation. The studies indicated that the virus moved downward as well as upward in the vine from the inoculated leaf and that mostly the movement was relatively slow.

Tyloses occurred in the vessels of all sizes. There were more in the diseased wood than in the healthy. They were not always associated with gum. Healthy Emperor grapevines had few tyloses in the vessels of the current season's wood. The numbers increased with the age of the wood. In diseased tissue from the same variety, the number of vessels with tyloses was much higher, and their frequency occurred in the reverse order—they decreased with the age of the wood.

THE OCCLUSIONS of gum and tyloses were sufficient to account for the acute water-shortage symptoms of leaf scalding and burning so characteristic of the disease. More plugging of the water-conducting vessels was observed in the two varieties Emperor and Palomino, which decline rapidly with the disease, than in the more tolerant varieties, Carignane and Petite Sirah.

About July each year the axes of the grapevine ripen. The brown color of maturing canes of healthy grapevines follows the normal development of new cork inside the primary phloem fibers and in the phloem of older parts of the vine. Canes of diseased vines mature irregularly, with patches of green bark in the brown canes. Cork fails to form under these green patches and in patches of bark in older parts of vines. The areas also have little or no starch in the cells.

RAINFALL HAS HAD a profound influence on the development of epidemics of Pierce's disease. A close positive correlation exists between periods of rainfall above normal and the incidence of Pierce's disease. The disease has developed and spread rapidly during successive years of heavy rainfall. In Anaheim, Calif., from 1878 to 1883, rainfall was 34.7 percent below normal and there are no records of diseased vines. The seasons of 1883 and 1884 were unusually wet; rainfall was 226 percent above normal. Many vines died of Pierce's disease in 1884 and 1885. The disease was less severe during the next two drier seasons, but in 1888–1891, when the rainfall was 50.7 percent above normal, the disease increased very rapidly and spread through most of southern California.

Pierce's disease apparently was present in the central San Joaquin Valley before 1935, but few cases were reported. The wettest period on record for the region was 1935–1941, when the rainfall averaged 54.9 percent above normal. The number of new cases of Pierce's disease increased rapidly through 1941, but dropped to a low point the next 6 years, when the average rainfall was 6.2 percent below normal.

In the central coastal counties, the relation of rainfall to the spread of Pierce's disease was as definite as in the interior, but a lag of 1 to 3 years occurred in the building up of the disease.

Periods of heavy rainfall are favorable for continued and succulent growth of host plants of vectors. Grasses, the favored host plants of the redheaded and green sharpshooters, can grow later in the summer and provide food and breeding plants for larger populations.

THE CONTROL of Pierce's disease by the systematic removal of diseased vines appeared in the early investigations to be a practical approach to the problem. Diseased vines, a source of the virus, would be removed, and healthy stock would be replanted in their place.

Test plots of about 10 acres each were first established in Tulare County in 1937 and later in Fresno County. Diseased vines were mapped and removed twice each season. Rogued and nonrogued plots were compared for more than 10 years. The distribution of diseased vines was similar in both rogued and nonrogued plots. Diseased vines were usually scattered over the plot, although one or more plots each season would have large numbers of diseased vines in places. When those concentrated numbers of diseased vines recurred in subsequent seasons, they were usually in different sections of the vineyard plot. The infections that occurred one season did not usually appear to have any definite relation to those occurring in the next. By 1942 the results of the studies indicated that roguing small 10-acre blocks had no effect upon the incidence of disease. Plots that were rogued and had the diseased and missing vines replanted to healthy stock, however, had more complete stands of vines and were in better production than were nonrogued vineyards.

In the spring of 1943, the University of California Agricultural Experiment Station established two large plots in Tulare County. The purpose was to test further roguing, to study vector populations in relation to disease spread and occurrence, to test possible vector-control practices, and to try various control measures for the disease itself.

One plot in a typical vineyard area near Woodlake, Calif., consisted of nearly 1,000 acres, of which 793 were in vineyard. The plot area also included home yards, irrigated and dry pastures, two small dairies, alfalfa, peaches and other stone-fruit trees, citrus, and waste land. The second plot, near Lindsay, consisted of 240 acres of vineyard, surrounded by several different crops and dry, uncultivated land. More than 338,700 vines were examined twice each season between 1943 and 1947, once in June and once in September. All diseased vines were recorded and destroyed by sawing off close to the ground.

Results of the studies showed that the spread of Pierce's disease in the plot areas was similar to that in other vineyards outside the plots. The incidence of disease in the valley, however, was declining rapidly each season. The occurrence of diseased vines in the plots was not related to previous season's infections and was apparently independent of cultural or control practices. There was no evidence of spread from diseased vines in the plot to other vines. Pierce's disease spread into the plot from outside, and there was no evidence of a greater concentration of diseased vines about the margins than elsewhere in the plots.

The total populations of vectors, as sampled by sweeping with nets at intervals through the growing season, showed a positive correlation with the incidence of disease in areas of about 100 acres or more, but not so in smaller areas. There was no apparent difference in the number of diseased vines in plot areas with a grass cover crop after mid-July, a normal practice in many irrigated vineyards of the valley, and in those where weeds had been killed by cultivation and oil sprays.

Observations on the feeding habits of green and redheaded sharpshooters indicated that they feed only occasionally on vines, and then primarily on canes that had grown to the ground among the grass. But in experiments where the shoots were kept on 7-foot trellises, the vines actually developed a little higher percentage of disease than in adjacent plots of control vines where the shoots were allowed to grow to the ground.

Attempts to control Pierce's disease by controlling the vectors with chemical sprays or dusts have failed to show any decrease in the incidence of disease. Although experiments in control have given mostly negative results, a great deal of knowledge about the disease—its hosts, vectors, and manner of spread—has been accumulated. The disease is no longer a mystery.

THREE OTHER VIRUS DISEASES of grapevines have been spread into some new plantings in California by vineyardists who choose their propagating wood indiscriminately.

The diseases are commonly known as white Emperor, vine mosaic, and fanleaf. They have become increasingly important as old plantings are being replaced on phylloxera-resistant stocks and as new plantings increase. White Emperor is a disease of the variety Emperor, a late red table grape grown mostly in Fresno, Tulare, and Kern Counties. Vine mosaic and fanleaf have developed primarily in varieties of wine grape.

WHITE EMPEROR, the grape that will not color, has no market value for table grapes and very little value as culls for making alcohol. Normal Emperor fruit colors to a bright red, and the clusters of grapes are very attractive. To meet specific market standards, the fruit must be sweet and must color to a minimum standard.

Vineyardists have been concerned by the fact that fruit on certain individual Emperor vines does not color properly by harvesttime. Symptoms show in the fruit and leaves. At maturity, the fruit of diseased vines is usually low in sugar and may vary in color from a pale greenish yellow to pink. Early in the season, leaves of diseased vines are darker and thicker than normal. They are wrinkled along the vines and curled down around the margins. As they age they become reddish to bronze in color, and the rolling at the margins becomes very prominent. The tissue between the five large veins gradually turns yellow as if sunscorched, while that adjacent to the veins becomes reddish brown.

The disease has been studied by H. P. Olmo, at Davis, and A. D. Rizzi, of the California Agricultural Extension Service. They reported that individual "white" vines would continue to produce white grapes and "red" vines to produce red fruit over a period of years, and that progeny vines would produce white or red fruit respectively. Harmon and Snyder of the Department of Agriculture, working in Fresno, showed in carefully mapped vineyard plots that over a 10-year period white Emperor did not spread.

The cause of the disease of Emperor grapevines is probably a virus. Harmon and Snyder showed by some intergrafting experiments that the white type of Emperor carries an infectious factor that will transmit to red Emperors and cause them to turn white.

VINE MOSAIC, first reported in California in 1945, occurs in many of the vineyards in the northern part of the State. Only one vineyard in southern California is known to have the disease. This form of mosaic, called panachure in France, has been reported in several European countries—Portugal, France, Spain, Switzerland, Italy, and Czechoslovakia—and South Africa. Reports of grape disorders mention two mosaic diseases—white mosaic, which is called vine mosaic in California, and true mosaic, which has not been found in California.

Bright-yellow leaves on the spring growth is an outstanding symptom of the California form of vine mosaic. Some of the yellow leaves turn white; as they age they burn about the margins and dry up. Others develop some green color. Later-formed leaves may show different kinds and degrees of mottling or may appear normal. Chlorosis and mottling in many yellow and cream-colored patterns are usually present in leaves of diseased vines most of the growing season. The cream-colored areas occur in bands about the large leaf veins, in irregular blotches, or in speckles as if splattered over the leaf surface. A light-green mottling often develops in young leaves and disappears as the leaves age. In some leaves chlorosis appears to have leaked out of the veins into the surrounding tissue. Varieties such as Pinot Blanc, Sauvignon Blanc, French Colombard, and Folle Blanche fail to set fruit. Sometimes the blossoms shell after bloom or set mostly seedless berries.

Mosaic is caused by a virus that is easily transmitted from diseased to healthy vines by grafting. We have little evidence to indicate that the disease spreads in the field.

FANLEAF WAS FIRST recognized in the variety Pinot Chardonnay in Santa Clara Valley in 1948. It has since been found in several new and some old vineyards of a number of varieties. The disease is known in several European countries under different names—in France, dégénérescence infectieuse; in Italy, arricciamento and roncet; and in Portugal, urticado. The disease also occurs in Germany, Switzerland, and Sicily.

Symptoms generally characteristic of fanleaf are a gradual dwarfing of the vine; early-season dwarfing of shoots; deformity of shoots and leaves; mottling of leaves on early-season shoot growth; and shelling of flowers from the clusters, or the setting of mostly seedless berries. Internodes on early-season growth fail to elongate. Later growth tends to zigzag at the nodes as the the shoots lengthen. Some of the nodes have two or more buds and are enlarged. The leaves on young shoots stand upright along the axes and do not open out as early as do leaves on normal vines. Leaves are variously deformed. On the young shoots they show mottling. The petiolar sinuses, normally narrow, open and spread out, and the margins straighten or even bend upward in deformed leaves. The angle of sinus opening sometimes has exceeded more than 200 degrees. The five main veins of the leaf become gathered together toward the midrib, like a partly closed fan. That symptom suggests the name fanleaf. Marginal sinuses may be opened deeply so that the leaves appear tattered; or they may be closed, and the leaves lopsided.

Fanleaf is also caused by a virus that is transmitted by grafting. It does not appear to spread naturally in the vineyards of California.

THE CONTROL of all three of these diseases—white Emperor, vine mosaic, and fanleaf—can be accomplished by the careful selection of healthy propagating wood of both the rootstock and the scion varieties. There is no cure for diseased vines. Healthy stock should be replanted in their place.

W. B. HEWITT *completed his graduate studies at the University of California in the fall of 1936. Since then he has been teaching plant pathology in the College of Agriculture in the same institution.*

Ills of the American Bunch Grapes

Alvin J. Braun

The American bunch grapes and muscadine grapes are grown almost exclusively in the eastern United States because the climate there is unfavorable for the commercial production of most of the European varieties. The American bunch grapes are either the selections from natural crosses or hybrids produced by crossing native species with the vinifera, or European, grape.

The principal eastern grape-producing States are New York, Ohio, Michigan, and Pennsylvania. In New York State, which produces about one-third of the grapes grown in the Eastern States, the value of the grape crop and grape products was about 13 million dollars in 1952.

The bunch grapes are used mainly for unfermented grape juice, wine, jelly, and fresh fruit. The Concord has been the leading variety for a long time, but interest has grown in varieties suitable for making champagnes and high-quality wines. For that purpose the Catawba and Delaware varieties are most generally grown now. The introduction of promising French hybrids may change preferences as to varieties in the next few decades.

Diseases have been largely responsible for limiting the areas of commercial production. Black rot was primarily the cause of the abandonment of large acreages in the East in the early 1900's. Downy mildew,

powdery mildew, dead arm, anthracnose, and crown gall have made extensive control measures necessary in some localities.

Diseases of the American bunch grapes generally are harder to control in the Southern States, presumably because of the prevailing high temperatures, high humidity, abundant rainfall, and longer growing season. The weather conditions greatly influence the occurrence and severity of the diseases, even in a locality. Consequently the danger always exists that diseases that have caused only minor loss may develop in epidemic proportions. As a general rule, however, each variety in any given region has its own specific diseases for which control measures must be considered.

The selection of a vineyard site with adequate air drainage is highly important in reducing the possibility of serious disease losses. The removal of badly affected parts of the vine at the time of pruning and general vineyard sanitation make attempts to control disease more effective. Practices that make conditions less favorable for the development of the overwintering stages and spore dissemination may be considered as measures to supplement the recommended spray program.

In vineyards where disease losses are apt to be serious when no spraying is done, the benefits from properly applied treatments are greater than their cost. If the losses are sporadic and minor, it is doubtful whether the expense of the full schedule of treatments is returned through increased yields. The decision to apply control measures, therefore, depends on a knowledge of the history of disease losses on a particular variety in a given locality.

Although dusting for disease control has been considered less effective than spraying, experiments in New York vineyards from 1946 through 1952 indicate that dusting with especially adapted dust applicators might be entirely satisfactory against some dis-

ILLS OF THE AMERICAN BUNCH GRAPES 755

eases if the applications are properly timed. In several of the tests, good to excellent control of black rot, downy mildew, and powdery mildew was also obtained with concentrate sprays (using 25 gallons to an acre) where an air blast was employed to carry the fine mist to the vines. The investigations were still in the developmental stage in 1953.

BLACK ROT, caused by *Guignardia bidwellii*, is the most widely distributed and the most destructive disease of grapes east of the Rocky Mountains. It is especially prevalent in the more humid sections and is particularly destructive in the Southern States and along the Gulf coast. Environmental conditions in the Pacific coast grape-producing areas apparently are not conducive to the establishment of black rot. It does not seem possible that an occasional source of infection would not have been carried into the area on early imports of grape stock from the East. Black rot is probably indigenous to North America. All vinifera varieties and most of the widely grown American-type bunch grapes are susceptible to it.

Among the more susceptible varieties commonly grown in the East are Catawba, Concord, Dutchess, and Niagara. Part or complete resistance to black rot is found in Campbell Early, Clinton, Delaware, Diamond, Eaton, Elvira, Fredonia, Ives, Missouri Riesling, Moore Early, Portland, Worden.

The fungus is capable of infecting all green parts of the vines, including leaf blades, petioles, tendrils, shoots, blossoms, and fruits. The fruit infections are the most damaging. In most instances they represent the only damage of economic importance to the crop. Most infection occurs on the younger developing plant parts, but fruit infection may continue until harvest, especially in vineyards where early-season infections are numerous and where weather conditions favorable for spore dispersal and germination occur late in the season.

The foliage infections appear as tiny, more or less circular spots. The spots are reddish brown and are usually encircled by a ring of yellow tissue. Through the coalescence of many spots, large areas of the leaf may become affected. Pycnidia develop in the spots, and within a short time pycnidiospores are formed. The lesions on the shoots, petioles, and tendrils are usually longer than those formed on the leaves.

On the fruits the lesions first appear as minute tan-colored spots. The lesions rapidly increase in size. After a few days the entire berry is rotted. Pycnidia develop, and the berry soon turns black, shrivels, and becomes mummified. Pycnidiospores produced on the affected parts are exuded in moist weather. They infect other susceptible parts of the vine when moisture and temperature favorable for spore germination occur. Late in the season immature perithecia develop in the mummies. They develop asci during the winter. In the spring they discharge mature ascospores capable of infecting the developing leaves and shoots. There is evidence that early-season infections might also result from pycnidiospores developed in the lesions on overwintered canes, tendrils, or other parts.

When periods of rainfall or persisting dew are frequent before bloom, infections may become numerous on the vegetative parts of the vine. Then 25 percent or more of the berries may become infected in a single infection period during or shortly after the bloom period. As moisture is needed for the expulsion and germination of the spores, the disease is more destructive in seasons of heavy rainfall.

Black rot can be effectively controlled by three or four applications of ferbam (1½ pounds in 100 gallons of water) or bordeaux mixture (4 pounds each of copper sulfate and hydrated spray lime in 100 gallons of water). In vineyards where conditions favor the early-season development of lesions on the vegetative parts, the first application should be made when the new shoots are 18 to 24 inches long. Applications immediately before bloom and immediately after bloom are especially important in preventing infection of the developing berries. Under most conditions an additional application 7 to 14 days after bloom, depending on the weather, is required to protect the rapidly enlarging berries from infection.

Investigations at the New York State Agricultural Experiment Station from 1945 through 1951 indicate that certain modifications of the previously recommended control practices are advisable: Four properly timed applications to alternate sides of the row were as effective as three applications applied to both sides. The experiments also demonstrated that thorough coverage of the berries with the fungicide is not essential.

Ferbam, besides being more effective than bordeaux mixture or any of the other fungicides tested, caused no injury to the vines and under certain conditions stimulated growth of the vines and the yield. On the other hand, bordeaux frequently injured the foliage so that vine growth and yield were lower. Three ferbam sprays applied at a reduced concentration of 1–100 gave excellent control in several trials under conditions where 50 percent or more of the berries rotted in the check plot.

The addition of various spreaders and stickers to the sprays did not increase the effectiveness of ferbam. When the spray coverage in the tests was less thorough, the addition of the adjuvants actually reduced the effectiveness of ferbam. Ferbam 1½–100 is generally recommended for the control of black rot under average conditions when 100 to 150 gallons of spray are applied. When a lower application rate is employed or in places where black rot is unusually difficult to control, more might be necessary.

DOWNY MILDEW, caused by *Plasmopara viticola*, is common in most eastern grape-growing areas. The fungus thrives best during cool, moist weather. Therefore it is most destructive in the northern areas.

Downy mildew may cause a rot of the bunches on most of the American bunch varieties commonly grown in the Eastern States. Downy mildew fruit rot has seldom been observed on Concord and Delaware. Foliage infection, sometimes resulting in partial or complete defoliation, occurs in most varieties. The foliage of Delaware and some vinifera hybrids is extremely susceptible to infection; in cool, moist weather, complete defoliation may occur before the crop ripens. Early defoliation may retard ripening to the extent of making the crop of little or no commercial value and renders the vine more subject to winter injury.

When the weather is favorable, primary infection usually occurs just before bloom, but in some seasons in the Northern States the first infections may not become evident until 3 or 4 weeks after bloom.

New infections first become apparent on the upper surface of leaves as water-soaked places, which soon become light-yellow, roughly circular spots. The spots merge with the surrounding green tissue without any distinct line between diseased and healthy tissues. The spots enlarge and usually form irregular lesions. The centers of the lesions become brown in a few days. A downy white growth of branching conidiophores develops on the under surface of the leaf lesions in periods of frequent rainfall and high humidity. The conidia spread the disease to other parts of the vine through the summer whenever weather conditions favorable for spore dispersal and germination prevail.

Oospores, the overwintering stage of the fungus, are produced in the intercellular spaces of the affected parts. These spores remain dormant until the following spring, when they are set free by the disintegration of the diseased tissues in which they were formed. Only oospores that have been subjected to freezing temperatures can germinate. The oospores germinate by the production of short unbranched promycelia, which bear large sporangia. Each sporangium releases swarmspores capable of producing the primary infections on the vines when moisture and temperature are favorable.

The infected clusters may exhibit various kinds of symptoms, depending on the stage of maturity at the time of infection. Fruits infected shortly after the blossom period remain small and soon become covered with the downy white fungus growth bearing conidiophores. Berries infected later in the season discolor gradually because of the disintegration of the internal tissues. Dark, sunken areas may develop on the surface of the decaying berry. The berries on some varieties, infected just before attaining full size, become hard and leathery and develop a reddish coloration, which makes the fruit look like a miniature red apple. In some localities this symptom has given rise to the name of apple rot. Considerable fruit loss may also result from infection and subsequent withering of the cluster stem, which prevents further development of berries on the distal part of the cluster.

Bordeaux mixture is still the most widely used fungicide for downy mildew. The concentration of the mixture and the number of applications required for satisfactory control depend on the susceptibility of the variety and the severity of infection likely to occur in a given locality. In vineyards in New York, three applications of bordeaux mixture, 4–4–100, are satisfactory for control under most conditions. The sprays should be applied immediately before bloom, immediately after bloom, and 7 to 10 days later. On varieties extremely susceptible to foliage infection an additional application when the fruit is about half-grown may be necessary to prevent infection of the newly developed leaf area, especially if the disease is already established on other parts of the vine. When bordeaux mixture is used, the addition of a spreader or spreader-sticker does not increase control. Tests in New York vineyards indicate that the applications to control the fruit-rot phase need not be so thorough as we once considered necessary if the applications are timed properly in relation to the bloom period. Fixed-copper fungicides with lime added (4 pounds of lime for each pound of metallic copper) are somewhat less effective than bordeaux mixture of an equivalent concentration of copper. The fixed-copper materials are less injurious than bordeaux mixture and are preferable in vineyards where high rates of application are necessary for the thorough coverage required for effective control of certain insects.

POWDERY MILDEW, caused by *Uncinula necator*, is present in most grape-growing areas of the Eastern States. In the Pacific Coast States it is considerably more destructive; when temperature and humidity are favorable it is capable of destroying the entire crop of vinifera grapes in unsprayed vineyards. In the East the fungus primarily attacks the foliage and cluster stems; it appears on the berries only in unusually favorable seasons.

Powdery mildew infection appears as a superficial, grayish-white growth on the shoots, tendrils, cluster stems, berries, petioles, and upper surfaces of the leaf blades. This powdery fungus growth can be rubbed off with the fingers; then the discolored epidermis is exposed. Conidia, produced in abundance on the surface of the feltlike fungus growth, spread the disease to other parts of the vine. Brownish-black perithecia, formed on the surface of the infected areas, constitute the overwintering stage of the fungus.

Unlike black rot and downy mildew, this disease is favored by periods of low rainfall and only moderately high relative humidity (between 70 and 80 percent).

Powdery mildew is controlled in the East by the copper fungicides applied for black rot or downy mildew. When ferbam is used in the early sprays for the control of black rot or when powdery mildew is the only disease requiring control, the application of a copper-containing fungicide 2 or 3 weeks after bloom and again about 2 weeks later is effective. Bordeaux mixture, 2–4–100, or an equivalent concentration of a fixed copper and lime, is adequate under most conditions, because the disease is relatively easy to control on grapes. Sulfur sprays or dusts recommended for the control of powdery mildew on the west coast produce marked injury to the foliage of the bunch grapes growing in the Eastern States.

DEAD ARM, caused by *Cryptosporella viticola*, is responsible for recurring losses in many vineyards in the Northeast, where vineyards in which 10 to 20 percent of the vines show harmful effects from dead arm are not uncommon. The disease has also been reported on the Pacific coast.

Its most prominent and destructive effect is the dead arm that gives the disease its name. In June and July the foliage on the shoots from affected canes, or arms, that have not been killed by the disease is yellowed, dwarfed, crimped, and ragged at the margin. Such abnormal conditions are the result of a canker on the arm or on the trunk below the point of attachment of the arm. A dry rot in the woody part of the trunk spreads in both directions from the canker. As the canker enlarges each year, other arms may become similarly affected. If they are not removed, the entire vine above the canker eventually dies. As the season progresses, many of the affected leaves drop from the vine and the remaining leaves develop a normal green color. The healthy foliage and shoots from unaffected parts of the vine and from adjacent vines soon cover up the affected growth and thus make it difficult to detect diseased vines in midsummer. On the green shoots, petioles, cluster stems, and tendrils, small reddish-brown lesions develop from infections of the current season. In years favorable for late-season infections, lesions on the cluster stem may become sufficiently numerous to be instrumental in causing berries to drop from the cluster stem. The following spring the lesions appear on the canes as brownish-red elevations or as longitudinal cracks, from which stringy fibers of host tissue are exposed.

The fruit may be infected in some seasons. The rot is like that produced by the black rot organism. The affected berries become dark gray, shrivel, and produce mummies with surface pustules. The color is not so black as that of black rot, the shriveling is less convolute, and the pustules are slightly larger and less numerous.

Conidia are formed in pycnidia, which develop in the lesions on the shoots, arms, and trunks. In the spring shortly after the buds open, the pycnidia swell and exude long tendrils of spores. Most of the spores are dispersed early in the season, but production of spores may continue throughout the summer.

Under conditions favorable for germination, the spores infect the tender, succulent growth. Trunk and arm cankers may result from infections in pruning cuts and other wounds. Pycnidia are usually not developed on the current season's growth. Shoot lesions in most years therefore are most prevalent on the first 12 or 18 inches of cane growth. Although the causal organism has been shown to produce perithecia, the perfect stage is rare and probably is not important in perpetuating the fungus.

The control measures suggested for dead arm are the systematic removal of affected parts of the diseased vines and early-season spraying to prevent new infections. Care should be taken to prevent carrying the fungus to healthy vines on pruning equipment that might have become contaminated when used to cut through cankers on other trunks. Pruning cuts should be made at least 6 inches beyond the lower margin of the infection in order to make certain that the affected part is entirely removed. Early applications of bordeaux mixture have been recommended to supplement the control of dead arm. Three applications of ferbam, timed for the control of black rot, had no appreciable effect on the late-season infections that were unusually abundant in New York vineyards in 1950.

CROWN GALL, caused by *Agrobacterium tumefaciens*, may attack grape roots, trunks, and canes. It is common in most grape-producing areas, but it seldom does serious damage. European varieties and hybrids are generally more susceptible than the American varieties. In New York the Isabella is the only variety that has shown extreme susceptibility to the crown gall organism, although galls of considerable size have also been observed on other varieties, including Concord.

The galls may occur on any of the woody parts of the vine but usually are most abundant on the basal part of the trunk. The galls on the roots are more or less spherical and are usually found near the ground line.

The control of crown gall on grapes is essentially the same as recommended for its control on other woody plants. Badly infested land should not be used for cultivation of the varieties known to be extremely susceptible. Care should be taken to avoid planting stock that shows evidence of galls on the roots or canes. Large galls that are present on the upper parts of the trunks or on the arms can be removed by pruning the arm or trunk some distance below the affected tissue or by renewing the vine by means of a shoot from the base of the vine. Removal of the old wood of the vine as soon as the trunk begins to show a gnarled appearance is considered effective in reducing the incidence of trunk infections.

ANTHRACNOSE, caused by *Elsinoë ampelina*, is found on some grape varieties in the Eastern States, but usually is considered of minor importance in the North. Outbreaks are local and usually sporadic. The most susceptible varieties are Champion, Catawba, Campbell Early, Diamond, Norton, and Salem. The Concord, Delaware, Moore Early, and Niagara have been reported to be resistant.

The disease appears on the leaves as small, irregular, dark-brown, sunken spots, with dark margins. The spots on the fruits are usually larger, more sunken, and gray. Their margins are darker than the centers and give them a characteristic appearance from which the name "bird's-eye rot" was derived. Lesions also develop on the shoots, petioles, tendrils, and cluster stems like those of anthracnose on raspberries.

Frequently two or more lesions on the berries unite and cause the fruit to become dry and wrinkled. Shoot lesions may coalesce and cause the death of the terminal portion of the shoot.

Conidia are produced on the surface of the infections of the current season and also on the surface of lesions on overwintered parts of the vine. Those spores can spread the disease during most of the growing season. The perfect stage of the fungus develops during the winter in ascocarps present in the old cankers. The ascocarps are much like those of the raspberry anthracnose organism, *Elsinoë veneta*.

The control of anthracnose depends on spraying and on the removal of the more seriously affected parts of the vine at the time of pruning. Research men have recommended a delayed dormant application of 10 gallons of liquid lime-sulfur in 100 gallons of water followed by four or five applications of bordeaux mixture (8–8–100) when the new shoots are 7 to 8 inches long, just before bloom, immediately after bloom, 7 to 10 days later, and at the time when the berries are about half-grown. The applications of ferbam recommended for the control of the black rot might also control anthracnose.

OTHER DISEASES—generally localized or appearing only in some seasons—include bitter rot (caused by *Melanconium fuligineum*), ripe rot (*Glomerella cingulata*), cotton root rot (*Phymatotrichum onmivorum*), armillaria root rot (*Armillaria mellea*), measles (cause unknown), and verticillium wilt (*Verticillium albo-atrum*). A number of other fungi have been observed on grape foliage but their effect on the vines is usually negligible.

ALVIN J. BRAUN *holds degrees from the University of Chicago, University of Wisconsin, and Oregon State College. His early experience with the diseases of small fruits was as research assistant, from 1938 to 1942, at the Oregon Agricultural Experiment Station. From 1943 to 1945 he was with the Guayule Research Project at Salinas, Calif., and the Emergency Plant Disease Prevention Project in Ohio. Since 1945 he has been in charge of investigations of diseases of small fruits at the New York State Agricultural Experiment Station at Geneva, where he is an associate professor in the division of plant pathology.*

Selected bibliography:
Alvin J. Braun: Some Effects of Fermate and Bordeaux Sprays on Concord Grapes (*Abstract*), Phytopathology, volume 39, page 3, 1949; Control of Black Rot and Downy Mildew of Grapes With Concentrate Sprays, Dry Dusts and Wet Dusts, (*Abstract*), Phytopathology, volume 42, page 5, 1952.
Leslie C. Coleman: The Dead Arm Disease of Grapes in Ontario, Scientific Agriculture, volume 8, pages 281–315, 1928.
J. B. Demaree and G. W. Still: Control of Grape Diseases and Insects in Eastern United States, U. S. D. A. Farmers' Bulletin 1893, 36 pages, 1951.
C. T. Gregory: Studies on Plasmopara viticola, International Congress Viticulture Report 1915, pages 126–150, 1916.
Donald Reddick: The Black Rot Disease of Grapes, New York (Cornell) State Agricultural Experiment Station Bulletin 293, pages 289–364, 1911; Dead Arm Disease of Grapes, New York (Geneva) State Agricultural Experiment Station Bulletin 389, pages 463–490, 1914; Powdery Mildew of Grapes and Its Control in the United States, with F. F. Gladwin, International Congress Viticulture Report 1915, pages 117–125, 1916.

Red Stele Disease of Strawberry

W. F. Jeffers, D. H. Scott

Considerable interest always attends the first occurrence of a serious plant disease. Sometimes it can be traced to plants introduced from a foreign country. Sometimes there is some other ready explanation. Often, however, the origin of a new disease remains a mystery.

One such is the red stele disease of strawberry. It is caused by *Phytophthora fragariae*. It was reported officially in Illinois in 1935 and in Maryland and California in 1936, but it had been seen in all three States a few years earlier.

How such a serious new disease could appear almost simultaneously in locations so far apart is truly perplexing. There was no evidence of introduction of diseased strawberries from other countries, and it seems unlikely that red stele was spread from one location to the others.

The first report of red stele in the world is similarly perplexing. It suddenly appeared in Scotland about 1920. Its origin is unknown. Perhaps the fungus causing it had been present in some other part of the world for centuries without causing noticeable damage and when it reached Scotland and the United States it found very susceptible varieties and favorable conditions.

Another possibility is that the pathogen developed suddenly through hybridization of other fungi or by mutation.

Its name is descriptive. Its main diagnostic symptom is a red discoloration of the central vascular cylinder—the stele—of strawberry roots. The redness, most evident in early stages of infection, can be found when other evidence is lacking that plants are diseased.

Soon after primary infection, the stele turns reddish while the rest of the root tissue looks normal. The red stele fungus is closely followed by secondary organisms. The roots die from the tip upwards and become brown. That color masks the reddened stele, but usually there is some extension of the red color upward from the dead tissue. In late stages of infection, diseased roots may be so badly rotted that there is little evidence of red stele. Lateral roots and minute rootlets are also invaded and are killed back to the primary root. The so-called rat-tail symptom results when the upper section of primary roots is still white while the lower portion is blackened. Sometimes there may be several separate infections on a root.

Foliage symptoms of red stele appear after active growth begins in the spring. If the season is dry, infected strawberry plants may die before blossoming. If rainfall is heavy, however, little above-ground evidence of the disease may be apparent until fruit begins to develop. Plants growing in poorly drained soil usually show foliage effects later than those in well-drained soil.

The first above-ground symptom is a slight off-color in the leaves—usually a dull bluish green instead of the normal light green of the young leaves. Soon the leaves of badly affected plants begin to turn red and are noticeably wilted. The entire plant may die within a few days—a promising planting of strawberries might suddenly become a total loss.

Red stele commonly causes plants to be severely stunted and discolored without killing them. Such plants produce only a few small, worthless fruit. Poorly drained places in a large field may contain stunted or dead plants while the rest of the planting is healthy. Many growers therefore have thought poor drainage is the direct cause of red stele. Unless the causal fungus is present, however, the disease cannot develop. The fact is that strawberries are very resistant to direct damage from poor drainage—they prefer soils with a good supply of moisture.

Affected plants that do not die in spring often recover in summer. Rotted roots disintegrate and new ones are produced, so an examination of the roots then will disclose little or no evidence of red stele. The disease usually becomes active the following spring, however, and the plants will again become infected.

As the red stele organism is active only during cool spring weather and the reddened stele becomes obliterated later in the season, positive diagnosis can best be made in March and April—a fact of great moment to growers, nurserymen, and regulatory officials who want to get disease-free planting stock. A careful inspection of strawberry fields in spring makes it possible to determine whether the red stele disease is present and to get a clue to the potential fruit production of a planting.

In the few years since its discovery, red stele has become in many localities the most serious disease affecting strawberries. It is especially serious in Maryland, Michigan, Illinois, New Jersey, Oregon, and Washington.

At first it was hard to isolate the fungus that causes red stele, but it was accomplished by scientists in the Department of Agriculture and in England. Since strawberries belong to the genus *Fragaria*, the fungus was named *Phytophthora fragariae*.

The fungus can live for many years in fertile soil even if strawberries are not present. Once a field becomes infested, therefore, it is usually useless for further production of susceptible varieties of strawberries.

The fungus spreads through the soil by microscopic swimming cells known as zoospores. These spores require high soil moisture and therefore the fungus is of serious importance primarily in moist or poorly drained areas. The swimming bodies infect roots of strawberry plants and kill the water-conducting tissue (stele), causing it to turn red. Such interference with the water supply naturally causes the plant to wilt and to become stunted or to die. The degree of injury depends primarily on the number of roots affected on a plant. To a lesser extent the amount of soil moisture may affect the degree of injury resulting from red stele.

Flood water and drainage water can carry the zoospores over fairly long distances and thus infect other fields of strawberries. The disease can also be spread from field to field by transportation of soil on machinery, cattle, and such. However, most long-distance spread of the red stele disease is through use of infected planting stock. It is not unusual for a strawberry grower to spread red stele unwittingly through his neighborhood by giving infected plants to his friends. So it is essential that nurserymen and all others who distribute plants obtain special inspection service to be certain that the plants are free of red stele.

The fungus causing red stele is most active during cool, wet weather. Most infection occurs at soil temperatures of 32° to 55° F. Therefore, in most strawberry-growing areas this is the late winter or early spring period. During the summer the fungus becomes inactive and withstands hot summer weather by formation of another type of spore, the oospore. It also is microscopic and has a thickened wall, which enables it to withstand adverse conditions. These spores enable the fungus to remain in soil for many years.

Several strains of *Phytophthora fragariae* exist. They differ in their ability to infect different varieties of strawberry—a variety resistant to red stele in one area may be susceptible in another area or the reverse may be true. Consequently, confusion has arisen concerning resistance of straw-

berries to the red stele disease. Fortunately new varieties having resistance to several races are being developed. It is advisable to test small plantings of various resistant varieties before making extensive plantings.

SOON AFTER RED STELE was discovered in the United States, it was learned that extensive acreages devoted to strawberries were contaminated. No economically feasible field-control methods were available, and research workers began immediately to test varieties for resistance.

Aberdeen, an American variety, was the only one out of the many tested that was completely resistant to the disease. Aberdeen is too soft, too variable in quality, and too subject to leaf scorch to be an acceptable commercial variety, however, so breeding work was begun in 1937 by the Department of Agriculture to originate commercial varieties of strawberries resistant to red stele.

The principal objective in the breeding work has been to develop resistant commercial varieties for different seasons and different regions of the country. More recently the objectives have been expanded to include resistance to at least two races of the red stele fungus and for varieties adapted to both frozen-pack and fresh-market use. Studies on inheritance of resistance to the disease have been conducted in conjunction with the practical phase of originating new varieties.

Some seedlings that were planted never were evaluated because various unfavorable conditions occurred before the plants fruited. About 350,000 seedlings have been examined for resistance to red stele and for desirable fruit characteristics. Hundreds of selections were made but nearly all were discarded because of undesirable fruit characters, particularly softness. Many selections have been tested extensively both by institutions and private individuals, but relatively few resistant varieties have been introduced for commercial use.

The extent of the work is indicated in the following figures of crosses of strawberry plants made at the Maryland and Oregon stations in cooperation with Department of Agriculture and the number of seedlings grown for red stele resistance:

CROSSES USED

Year	Maryland	Oregon
1938	55	.....
1939	59	.....
1940	15	.....
1941	29	.....
1942	3	.....
1943	8	26
1944	48	25
1945	16	26
1946	14	33
1947	14	31
1948	16	22
1949	14	28
1950	13	19
1951	17	26
1952	8	3
Total	329	239

SEEDLINGS GROWN

Year	Maryland	Oregon
1938	2,034	.....
1939	4,996	.....
1940	4,493	.....
1941	13,000	.....
1942	4,000	.....
1943	5,200	6,178
1944	33,818	9,424
1945	21,000	9,561
1946	46,200	14,713
1947	12,085	16,631
1948	23,030	17,537
1949	26,724	19,966
1950	21,262	10,862
1951	25,140	7,397
1952	21,900	10,380
Total	264,882	122,649

Among the varieties resistant to red stele in the United States, with their parentage, the year introduced, and the estimated commercial acreage planted to them in 1952, are:

Aberdeen, a chance seedling, introduced in 1919, not grown commercially.

Fairland, a cross of Aberdeen and Fairfax, introduced in 1947, grown on 500 acres.

Pathfinder, a cross of Howard 17 and Aberdeen, 1938, on 25 acres.

Redcrop, a cross of Aberdeen and Fairfax, 1949, 300 acres.

Sparkle, a cross of Fairfax and Aberdeen, 1943, 1,500 acres.

Temple, a cross of Aberdeen and Fairfax, 1943, 2,500 acres.

Vermilion, a cross of Redstar and Pathfinder, 1950, 50 acres.

The development of resistant varieties has eliminated an important hazard to strawberries grown in infested soils. Of much significance here is the fact that the best soils for strawberries are often well suited for development of the red stele disease. In some States many hundreds of acres of land especially suitable for this crop were made useless for profitable production.

Breeding for resistant varieties is far from completed. Earlier and later maturing varieties than those now available are needed, and larger, firmer-fruited sorts for all seasons would be welcome additions. Varieties adapted to different strawberry regions are still to be obtained.

The plant breeders must now take into account in their work the newly discovered fact that races of *Phytophthora fragariae* exist. All of the present named varieties of strawberries in the United States are susceptible to a new race—race S— of the fungus. In Great Britain five and possibly more races exist.

Tests have indicated that a few unnamed selections are resistant to both known races of the causal fungus. They have been obtained from crosses between U.S.-3374 or Md.-683 as one parent, and Fairland or Temple as the other parent. Both U.S.-3374 and Md.-683 have Scottish selections as one parent (CC-18 and BK-46, respectively) and it is presumed that their resistance to race S was inherited from those ancestors, which were introduced because of their resistance to red stele in Scotland.

Because red stele only rarely affects varieties such as Fairland, Temple, and Sparkle, it is assumed that race S is not widespread and may not become the serious problem that the common race (race A) has been. It is expected that new varieties resistant to both known races of the red stele fungus will be available soon. Since red stele is caused by a soil-borne organism, it cannot spread as rapidly as wheat rusts and other diseases caused by wind-borne fungi. Strawberry breeders and growers have little reason to fear a sudden widespread destruction of their resistant varieties by new races of *Phytophthora fragariae.*

Inheritance studies for resistance to race S have been conducted under conditions highly favorable to severe infection of plants by the pathogen.

Md.–683 or U.S.–3374 when selfed or crossed with Aberdeen or any other varieties susceptible to race S produced seedlings of which 20 to 25 percent were highly resistant to race S. Progeny of the cross between Md.–683 and U.S.–3374 (both parents resistant) yielded more resistant seedlings than crosses involving one susceptible parent. Resistance is partly dominant and is governed by a number of genes. Field studies on inheritance of resistance to race A have indicated that resistance as obtained from Aberdeen is also partly dominant.

During the first few years that seedlings and selections were tested for resistance to red stele, elimination of susceptible material was done in fields naturally infested with the pathogen. Results were often inconsistent because of variable soil moisture conditions and irregular distribution of the disease. Soil infested with the red stele organism has been used more recently in greenhouse benches and has given very satisfactory results. Raised greenhouse benches, about 6 inches deep, are lined with a heavy, watertight material

with an overlap in the bottom of the bed for restricted drainage. The infested soil, taken from fields where plants have shown serious infection, is put in the benches to within 2 inches of the top. Enough steamed and composted soil is added nearly to the top. Some space is left to make watering easier. Between late August and October, seedlings are transplanted from seed flats directly into test benches. They are spaced about 2 inches apart. Good growing conditions are maintained until about the end of November.

Usually by that time the roots have extended to the bottom of the benches and the crowns are about one-fourth to one-half inch in diameter. Heavy, frequent watering is then begun and a temperature of about 45° to 55° F. is maintained. Conducting the test during the winter provides the cool temperature necessary for uniform infection of plants by the organism. Infection occurs quickly under favorable conditions and the major part of the root systems of susceptible plants is destroyed within 2 months after exposure to cool temperatures is begun. Frequent watering of the beds is an important factor in raising the degree and uniformity of infection.

Breeding for red stele resistance was being conducted in 1953 by the agricultural experiment stations of Illinois, Michigan, Maryland, and Oregon. The only program known to be active abroad was at the West of Scotland Agricultural College at Auchincruive, Scotland. Testing of strawberry varieties and selections for resistance to new races was under way in England by C. J. Hickman at the University of Birmingham and in this country at the University of Maryland and the nearby Plant Industry Station at Beltsville.

In the past few years the presence of the virus in strawberries has added another aspect to the work—that of maintaining stocks resistant to red stele in a virus-free condition. That has been accomplished with some success through isolation of plantings and a thorough aphid-control program by the use of parathion dust. Most, if not all, of the selections to be exchanged for testing in the future will be virus free. Unless a source of immunity to virus can be found in strawberries, however, virus infection probably always will be a hazard in the breeding work.

Reports of differences in varietal susceptibility show definitely that races of *P. fragariae* exist in several States and it is especially urgent that breeders, regulatory officials, and others concerned with movement of strawberry plants over long distances be careful to prevent shipment of infected plants.

STRAWBERRY growers who do not have the red stele fungus in their land should be especially careful to prevent its introduction through the use of infected planting stock. Growers in all but the southernmost States should learn to recognize the red stele disease and be certain that they use only disease-free stock. If red stele is in the immediate area, care should be taken to prevent the contamination of uninfested land.

Once land is infested with the red stele fungus the main control measure consists of resistant varieties. There are a number of good varieties which will make perfect growth where susceptible varieties are a total loss. They may not meet all of the many specific requirements of various areas, however.

W. F. JEFFERS *is professor of plant pathology at the University of Maryland. Since 1939 he has been active in research and extension work dealing with the nature and control of red stele disease of strawberries.*

D. H. SCOTT *is senior geneticist in the division of fruits and nuts, Bureau of Plant Industry, Soils, and Agricultural Engineering at Beltsville, Md. He obtained his doctor's degree at the University of Maryland in 1949. His special field of work is breeding strawberries, blueberries, and other small fruit.*

201500°—53——50

Virus Diseases of the Strawberry

Harold E. Thomas, C. P. Marcus, Jr.

Strawberries are subject to several types of virus diseases. Some of the diseases are of little importance to the crop, but others have seriously interfered with production.

Those of the yellows type had the widest distribution and greatest importance in 1953. They have spread rapidly to practically every strawberry section of the country. In the Pacific Northwest, before yellows appeared, the crinkle disease did great damage. As yellows moved through the area, the two diseases became so closely associated that it was hard to tell one from the other. The combination of the two undoubtedly accentuates the hazard of virus to the strawberry industry there.

If one is to identify accurately a virus disease of strawberry in the field, the symptoms must be clear and definite. But the symptoms often are masked by high or low temperatures, conditions of growth, and peculiarities of the variety. Some other means of identification must be resorted to.

Methods of indexing to susceptible varieties or species, termed indicator plants, often can be used to identify a virus. The insect vector that normally transmits the disease in the field from the diseased to the healthy plant can be used to transmit virus to indicator plants. The grafting technique is employed to graft a stolon—runner—of the plant being tested to a stolon of the indicator plant. The use of indicator plants has advanced greatly our understanding and classification of strawberry viruses. They enable us to separate and recombine virus entities in a disease complex. They also can help us determine the presence or absence of virus diseases in stocks of commercial varieties. The indicator plant most commonly used is the wild strawberry *Fragaria vesca*, which grows wild in or around wooded areas.

Investigators have used various selections of *F. vesca*. The one most widely used is a clone selected by R. V. Harris of East Malling, England. In California a closely related species, *F. bracteata*, has been used, along with local clonal selections of *F. vesca*. Any variety or species that distinguishes the virus may be selected as an indicator, but an advantage lies in the use by all investigators of clones of similar type to permit accurate comparison of results.

DISEASE COMPLEXES in the United States formed by the combination of virus entities were demonstrated through the investigations of Norman Frazier and Harold E. Thomas, of the California Agricultural Experiment Station, and later by J. B. Demaree and C. P. Marcus at the Plant Industry Station at Beltsville, Md. They found that the yellows type of diseases are combinations of at least two virus components. We use the term "yellows type of diseases" in plural form to emphasize that this disease complex has various combinations.

The components obtained from the virus-diseased plants when transmitted to indicator plants fall into broad categories or types in the indicator, but each type shows considerable variation. When these variations combine in nature to produce the disease as observed in the field, it is assumed that the variety of symptoms produced is the result of the varying nature of the components that go to make up the complexes. Climatic conditions affect the symptoms of the disease, but the variation in the components in the complex is thought to be of greater importance.

EVEN A SINGLE VARIETY of strawberry can show a wide range of virus disease symptoms. That fact and the still greater range of symptoms shown among varieties has caused confusion in attempts to classify the diseases. In other words: The description of a disease in only one susceptible variety is inadequate for general diagnosis in all varieties. Some other means of identification must be used and this is where the indicator plant becomes helpful and necessary. By indexing the diseased plant to the indicator the type of disease can usually be determined.

The symptoms produced in the indicator are so different from those in the variety under test, however, that the description of the disease in the susceptible variety corresponds little with the symptoms produced in the indicator. Therefore a different set of symptoms to describe the two will undoubtedly be necessary. The logical answer to the problem of describing a disease may well rest in the description of the symptoms caused by the entities as they affect the indicator plants and the enumeration of these entities that are resolved from the disease complex. Investigations have not advanced to the point that this type of description is generally possible, but it may well form the basis for future classifications. This type of classification would make it necessary for workers to use a single clone of the indicator, or a specified combination of indicators. These, like varieties, vary to some extent in the symptoms expressed and the degree.

Diseases of the yellows type, the worst of the virus ailments of strawberries, cause a loss of vigor and a marked stunting. Symptoms are cupping, usually upward, of the leaves, a yellowing of leaf borders, and dwarfing of petioles and blades. Stunting is common in all varieties.

Investigators in the California Agricultural Experiment Station, the Department of Agriculture, the Oregon Agricultural Experiment Station, and the University of British Columbia have demonstrated the presence of two entities in the yellows disease complex, as expressed in indicator plants of *Fragaria vesca*. One causes a mottle type of symptom, which in *F. vesca* produces small, dark-green, wrinkled leaves, streaked or spotted with yellow. The leaflets vary in size and shape, and often one is extremely small or absent. The entire plant is dwarfed and weak. Thin stolons—if any at all—form. Dwarfing and some leaf spotting may be the only symptom in milder attacks. The second component of the yellows disease causes moderate stunting and a mild uniform yellowing of the *F. vesca* plant. No leaf symptom is evident other than yellowing, reduction in size, and occasionally slight puckering or cupping. Fewer stolons are produced.

Another virus that may be related to the yellows type of diseases is found mainly in the eastern United States. Dr. Demaree and Mr. Marcus, who identified it, named it type 2 virus. In *F. vesca* it causes small, yellowish-green leaves that have a smooth, normal shape and uniform leaflets. The petioles of young runner plants of the infected indicator are much shorter than normal and curve downward. Consequently for several weeks the under sides of the leaflets show from above, but eventually resume an upright position; many buds grow from the base stem and make multicrowned, dwarfed plants.

Single infection in most cultivated varieties with any one of the three viruses causes only minor effects or none at all. The effects of several together may be entirely different.

In the grouping of virus troubles the stunt disease falls with the yellows type because of the stunting effect that it causes. Leaf petioles attain one-half to two-thirds of normal length but remain upright. No yellowing occurs,

but the upper leaf surface has an unusual flat, dull appearance. Cupping of leaves, upward or downward, is common.

THE CRINKLE TYPE of diseases is second in economic importance. They occur mainly in the Pacific Northwest. Their chief symptom in cultivated varieties is a crinkling or wrinkling of the leaves. Small, yellowish, pinpoint spots start in the developing leaves and expand somewhat as the leaves grow. The result is a flecked appearance. The faster growth of the healthy tissue around the spots causes a crinkled surface. In the severe form, veins are partly cleared so that the plant gets a somewhat yellowed look. Small sectors in the leaves, narrowing from the margin inward, may become yellow and translucent. There is some reduction in vigor and production of fruit. Some varieties show only the pinpoint mottle spots. Only limited analyses with indicator plants have been reported for this type, but research workers have described mild and severe forms in a single variety. Perhaps, therefore, combinations of virus components do occur.

THE WITCHES'-BROOM DISEASE is in a third and minor group of viruses that affect the strawberry. Its main symptom is the long, upright, stiff, spindly leaf petiole, whose leaflets are much smaller than normal and tend to arch downward. The crowns multiply to give the plant a bushy, broomlike appearance. The amount of brooming varies with the variety. The shortness of the internodes between runner plants allows the plants to set close to the mother and heightens the bushy appearance of the clone. Because growers can easily tell the conspicuous symptoms, the trouble has been eliminated in most places.

LEAF ROLL is quite distinct from the other virus groups. The downward rolling of the leaflets, its main symptom, is most pronounced in the basal part. In bad cases, opposite margins of leaflets may touch or overlap to form a tube. The leaf petioles are taller and spindlier and the leaflets smaller and narrower than normal. The leaf surface is ruffled and rugose. The color is pale green. Irregular yellowed areas vary in size. The leaf symptoms do not show in *Fragaria vesca* when grafts are made. All showed virus type 2 in the indicator— perhaps that virus is a component of a leaf roll complex or merely was present in addition to leaf roll.

The disease is of little economic importance.

STRAWBERRY GROWERS are always searching for the best and most productive stock. Freedom from diseases, particularly virus diseases, is essential. Mostly, careful inspection of the plants only was used as a basis for determining freedom from virus. That is not enough: Virus elements might be in the stock without showing symptoms. Such stock, infected with other components of the disease, degenerates and yields less.

Indexing helps overcome the difficulty. The indexing usually is done in a greenhouse where all plants (but particularly the indicator) can be sprayed or fumigated and protected from outside contamination by vectors. The growth cycle of both the plants to be indexed and the indicators should be correlated to produce stolons of approximately the same age at time of grafting. The best unions are obtained when relatively young tissues are grafted. Hardened and unpliable stolon tissue seldom unites in a graft. Instances occur when the plant to be indexed fails to form stolons and a young petiole or flower stem must be substituted. This may be a less convenient graft but satisfactory if a union is obtained. In-arching, the grafting method most widely used, involves the cutting of tongues in opposite directions on the stolons being grafted and inserting the tongues together. The grafts are

then bound with tape. The time required for transmission of the disease to the indicator depends largely on the time of year the graft is made. From late spring to fall, when light intensity, day length, and temperature are most satisfactory, virus symptoms will show in *F. vesca* indicators in 2 or 3 weeks. Grafts made in the winter take up to 2 months for symptoms of virus to appear. Some components take longer to show in the indicators than others.

Indexing also can furnish evidence as to the amount of virus contamination in a given field, area, or section, or in any specific variety. It can reveal the types of viruses to be found in various parts of the country or the State. Indexing can be used to determine the presence of virus in wild strawberries growing near virus-free planting stock The wild stock, if contaminated, should be eliminated to reduce the hazard of reinfection in the planting stock.

ONCE A SOURCE of virus-free stock is found, it must be kept healthy. Different methods have been employed to fit local circumstances and varying situations. Isolation of the stock from the vicinity of other strawberries is essential. We know little about other hosts of the viruses, but very likely other agricultural crops harbor them. Further study may locate them. Because wild relatives of the strawberry might be reservoirs of virus, they have to be avoided when virus-free stocks are planted. The control of insect vectors is essential.

Some States have undertaken certification of stock to guarantee its purity and freedom from diseases, particularly virus troubles. Not all programs have been successful. Some failures occurred because of inability to verify the presence or absence of virus disease by careful inspection without recourse to indexing.

The California Department of Agriculture has initiated a system of certification in which indexing and isolation are employed. Planting stock of cooperating nurseries is isolated from general agriculture. Mother-plant beds are maintained under clonal separation. Plants of the progeny of each mother plant are indexed. The entire clone, if it is clean, is transferred to a mother-row propagation. Random indexing of that row is done, and if no virus is found the stock is released for field propagation. Certification is provided the following year for the stock that develops therefrom.

An experimental program for the production of virus-free strawberries has also been started in Oregon, Washington, and Idaho. Indexing is done to find virus-free plants to be used as base stock, which is grown under isolation or in screenhouses to produce foundation stock. The foundation stock is isolated and dusted to prevent reinfection with virus. From it comes the plants that are to be certified as being virus-free.

THE STRAWBERRY APHID, *Capitophorus fragaefolii*, carries strawberry yellows, witches'-broom, and crinkle. The aphid is widely distributed in the Pacific Coast States but is rare elsewhere in this country.

Capitophorus minor and an unnamed species of the same genus are found frequently in strawberry fields in the Eastern States. These two species of aphids have readily transmitted both of the eastern types of viruses to *Fragaria vesca* under controlled conditions. It seems likely that they spread the viruses in the field.

Five species of aphids—*Myzophis rosarum, Macrosiphum pelargonii, Myzus ornatus, Myzus solani,* and *Myzus porosus*—can transmit the viruses, but less readily than *Capitophorus fragaefolii,* the common strawberry aphid in the West.

Winged forms of the insects, capable of migrating considerable distances, are responsible for most of the spread. Very likely the wingless forms can spread only a little virus from one planting to another, but considerable migration of wingless aphids within a

planting has been observed at a season when winged forms were absent.

Winged forms of *Capitophorus fragaefolii* in the colder parts of the United States appear soon after strawberry blossoms begin to open and continue to be in evidence throughout the harvest season. Later in the summer, when temperatures are high, the number of aphids declines. This aphid can overwinter in its mature wingless state. The severity of winter weather has a bearing on the number of aphids that survive. In milder climates, as in California, winged forms appear in early fall and wingless aphids occur abundantly throughout the winter months. The population is low during the warm summer period. A species of *Capitophorus,* common in the East, has a similar life history to that of *C. fragaefolii* there, but its winged forms have been observed in the fall as well as spring.

Since aphids spread strawberry viruses, their control or suppression will reduce the incidence of disease. The best time to attempt to control the insects is when the winged forms appear. The control of aphids in a partly infected field will prevent the spread of virus throughout the field. New plantings can be kept free of virus if the aphid vectors are controlled. Parathion, tetraethyl pyrophosphate, and the gamma isomer of benzene hexachloride, applied as 1-percent dust, are effective.

HAROLD E. THOMAS *received a doctor's degree from the University of California in 1928. From that time until 1945 he was associated with the California Agricultural Experiment Station, where he worked on the diseases and breeding of small fruits. In 1945 he became associated with the Strawberry Institute of California, of which he is now director.*

C. P. MARCUS, JR., *has been a plant pathologist with the Department of Agriculture at Beltsville, Md., since 1950. His work has concerned the virus diseases and the production of virus-free stocks of commercial varieties of strawberries.*

Diseases of Berries in the West

Folke Johnson

Raspberries and blackberries bring in about 10 million dollars a year to growers in the Pacific Coast States of California, Oregon, and Washington.

Diseases often are of great importance in so large an industry. They differ somewhat, according to locality and crop. California is concerned mostly with the trailing blackberries, Boysen, Logan, Nectar, and Young. Black and red raspberries are more important in Oregon. In Washington the leaders are red raspberries and the Cutleaf Evergreen blackberry.

The varieties of red raspberries produced commercially in Oregon and Washington are somewhat different. Production in Washington is almost limited to the Washington variety, but there are a few fields of Tahoma and Willamette. Oregon has a large acreage in Cuthbert in addition to Washington and Willamette raspberries.

A well-drained soil is needed for growing red raspberries. Silt loam or silty clay-loam soils even on moderate slopes are avoided because their water-holding capacity is often great enough to suffocate the roots. Sandy or porous soils with fairly heavy subsoil, where free water during the rainy season remains in the root zone for long periods, have the same effect. The choice soils are those of good texture, as loams or sandy loams, where excess water drains off or percolates away from the roots.

Root suffocation by water, one of the severest of problems in maintaining healthy plants, is referred to as wet feet. The symptoms are best described as a general decline in plant growth. On affected plants the lateral branches produced in the spring on the fruiting canes often are less than 12 inches long; normally they are at least 36 inches. The leaves are smaller, bronzed or yellow, and lack the bright green of healthy leaves. Usually all the canes in a hill are affected. The plants may die in dry hot weather or may linger on and produce a few weak canes, about 2 to 4 feet long, for the next season's crop. They remain unthrifty and finally succumb. A healthy plant annually produces 8 to 12 or more young, vigorous canes 8 to 10 feet or more high. Sometimes when the root system has been killed during the rainy season, only weak, short laterals an inch or two long are produced with small, undeveloped leaves, which soon wither and die. New canes fail to develop and the plant succumbs. The fruit from affected hills is greatly reduced in size, number, and quality. If the plants are dying when the fruit is ripening, it shrivels up, turns a dark red, and has little flavor. The fruit is crumbly and hard to pick.

Root suffocation is noticed mostly in late spring or early summer in the lowest places in the field. All plants in such locations are thus affected and a field may be spotted with dead or weakened plants, while in the higher levels the canes are normal. Symptoms of root suffocation do not generally appear until the second or third summer after planting, although older plants may also become affected, particularly after an unusually wet season.

The only known control is to provide better drainage. Replanting with new stock is not practical, because the new plants also will become affected. All commercially grown raspberries, such as Washington, Willamette, and Cuthbert, are susceptible. Newburgh tolerates the condition but is not grown extensively in the West. There is indication of tolerance or resistance among new hybrids, but they require further testing for other qualities before they can be recommended.

WHEN FIRST INTRODUCED in 1938, the Washington was resistant to western yellow rust, caused by *Phragmidium rubi-idaei*, which had plagued other varieties. In 1944, however, a new strain of the rust fungus infected the Washington variety. It has since become widespread in Washington and Oregon.

The most obvious symptom is the yellow flecks or pustules on the upper surface of the leaves in early spring. Light-orange pustules break out 2 or 3 weeks later on the under leaf surface, on the canes, or on leaf petioles. Sometimes they almost cover the leaves and cause them to die prematurely. The yellow or light-orange pustules contain numerous spores, which are carried about by wind currents or splashing raindrops. New infections arise all summer. In favorable weather all the plants in a field become infected. Severe infection means defoliation, and lesions produced on the canes weaken them so they break easily during subsequent cultural practices. The pustules and cane lesions turn dark and become black in late summer and early fall.

Another kind of spore remains over winter on the canes, fallen leaves, plant debris, fence posts, soil—anything. Those spores do not germinate until early the next spring, when new infections arise on the young unfolding leaves in the form of inconspicuous, pin-point, orange blisters. Those are followed by the yellow stage on the upper leaf surface and the life cycle has been completed.

Experiments by E. K. Vaughan, of Oregon State College, and me, demonstrated that a delayed dormant spray application to the canes when the buds have begun to unfold, usually in late March or early April, will check the disease. Several fungicides, such as bordeaux mixture, lime-sulfur, ferbam, Phygon-XL, Elgetol, and Cop-O-Zinc, have given effective control. They do not eradicate the disease but reduce it

so that no great damage results before the crop is harvested. Of the newer varieties, Willamette and Tahoma are resistant. Prompt removal and burning of the old fruiting canes in the fall aids in reducing the spore load for infections the following year.

ANTHRACNOSE, caused by the fungus *Elsinoë veneta*, is present to some extent each season. It is worse on black raspberries than on the commercially grown red varieties. The disease is recognized in early spring on the lower parts of young canes by the appearance of round to elliptic sunken spots, one-eighth to one-fourth inch or more in diameter. Those lesions have light-gray centers with purple margins, are somewhat depressed in the centers, and may become so numerous as to impair the movement of water and nutrients through the canes. Similar spots, but smaller, may be present on the leaves and even on the fruit.

The spray schedule against yellow rust will usually suffice to hold in check anthracnose on red raspberries. Often an additional spray is required, especially in the black varieties. Several proprietary materials have given good results if applied when the current season's canes are 8 to 12 inches tall.

GREEN MOSAIC, a virus disease, is most prevalent on the Cuthbert raspberry. The effect on the plants is a gradual loss of vigor, reduced yields, and lower quality of fruit. Such plants are more easily winter-killed than are healthy ones. The outstanding symptom is a mottling of dark- and light-green areas on the foliage; the dark-green blisters are intermingled with the light-green areas near the veins. Such leaves are deformed and smaller than healthy foliage. Mottling is more evident on the young leaves near the cane tips. It is more pronounced in early summer than later in the season, when the symptoms become masked.

Mosaic may be introduced into a field by planting diseased nursery stock. Once established, it spreads rapidly by the feeding activities of aphids, *Amphorophora rubi*, which move about from diseased to healthy plants. Studies by L. K. Jones and Karl Baur, formerly of the State College of Washington, showed that in one field the number of infected plants increased from 9.5 percent to 51 percent in 2 years. They also showed that careful roguing was an important means of holding the disease in check.

The Washington, Tahoma, and Willamette varieties have shown symptoms of being infected with a virus disease called ring spot. The disease has closely followed the appearance in 1947 of aphids on those varieties. Ring spot was present throughout western Oregon and Washington in 1953. The main characteristic is the presence of circular, light-green rings bordering nearly normal green tissue. The rings are about one-fourth to one-half inch in diameter. It is not unusual to find ring spot and a mosaic mottle on the same canes, in which the former symptoms are present on the young leaves and mosaic on the older. Thus far no apparent stunting or loss of vigor has been associated with the disease.

Another symptom often observed on Cuthbert and other red varieties is a mild mottle, or flecking, of small, light-yellow areas scattered over the leaves. The flecks are more abundant on the older leaves of new growth. The symptoms disappear in hot weather and reappear when lower temperatures prevail. Experiments conducted by G. H. Huber, formerly of the Western Washington Experiment Station, demonstrated the virus nature of the symptoms. He refers to the disease as mild mosaic.

The virus may be transmitted by grafting tissue from diseased to healthy plants, and the large raspberry aphid, *Amphorophora rubi*, is the natural vector in the fields.

When the virus is transmitted from red raspberries to Cumberland and other varieties of black raspberry, by grafting or aphids, severe symptoms develop. The first effect is the appearance of water-soaked areas or streaks at the tips of the new canes. The streaks later become purple, and the tips bend downward and usually die. The lateral branches also show this discoloration, followed by tip dieback. Sometimes during high temperatures, when the cane tips have not been killed, growth is retarded and there is produced a rosette of branches and leaves, followed by near-normal growth. Leaf mottle, characterized by light- and dark-green areas scattered over the leaves, is associated with cane tip necrosis. As in red raspberries, the mottle becomes masked with high temperatures but reappears on the same plants during cool weather. Growth of affected plants is greatly retarded, and the fruiting laterals are shorter than on healthy canes.

The virus has been recovered from six red varieties, Antwerp, Cuthbert, Latham, Lloyd George, Marlboro, and Newburgh, but not from Washington or Tahoma. Of 11 black raspberry varieties (besides the wild species *Rubus leucodermis*) tested for susceptibility by using aphids as vectors, all were found susceptible by showing typical symptoms of cane tip, dieback, and mosaic.

THE TERM BLACKBERRIES includes the trailing forms that often are referred to as dewberries. In California dewberries are grown on about 6,000 acres. Most extensively grown are Boysen, Logan, Nectar, and Young, all believed to be derived at least in part from the wild Pacific coast dewberry, *Rubus ursinus*. Some of those varieties are grown in western Oregon but are of minor importance in Washington. In Oregon and Washington the Cutleaf Evergreen blackberry, *R. laciniatus*, is important. Recently introduced varieties from Oregon are Cascade, Chehalem, and Pacific, which also are derivates of *R. ursinus*.

Verticillium wilt is one of the worst diseases of trailing blackberries in California and Oregon. Stephen Wilhelm and H. Earl Thomas, of the

University of California, found symptoms first appearing when the new shoots produced in the spring are 1 to 2 feet tall. The canes droop and wilt, and the lower foliage becomes yellow. The yellowed areas begin at the distal parts of leaflets and progress inward between the veins. Later they turn brown and become necrotic. The lowest leaves of severely affected plants fall off in early spring, leaving only a tuft of small, green leaves at the tips of the canes. Leaf killing is aggravated by an abrupt onset of hot weather following a cool spell. All young shoots in a hill are not usually affected, as those produced in warm weather escape infection and grow normally as long as such weather lasts. They may show light symptoms in autumn. After the dormant season, some of these apparently healthy canes die; the necrosis progresses from the tips downward to the roots. The following year others may produce normal leaves and fruit. If prolonged high temperatures follow cool weather, entire plants may be killed at harvesttime.

Verticillium wilt is caused by the fungus *Verticillium albo-atrum*, which is present in the soil. Dr. Wilhelm found that the organism tolerates both heavy clay loams and sandy loams and can exist either in an alkaline soil with a reaction of pH 8.5 or one as acid as pH 4.5.

Certain clones of the wild Pacific coast trailing blackberry, *R. ursinus*, and the commercial dewberry varieties, Boysen, Young, and Nectar, are highly susceptible to infection by *Verticillium*. Varieties of black and red raspberries also become infected with the organism. The late Dr. S. M. Zeller, of Oregon State College, however, discovered that in the latter group the Cuthbert variety is tolerant of the disease even though infected. Other resistant or immune species and varieties include clones of the wild trailing blackberry, Logan, Mammoth, Chehalem, Himalaya, and the Cutleaf Evergreen.

Once established in a field verticillium wilt is hard to eradicate or con-trol. Susceptible crops should not be planted in *Verticillium*-infested soil. Only disease-free stock should be used in establishing new fields and any plants that subsequently show the wilt symptoms should be removed promptly with the root systems and burned. That is practical only when fewer than 5 percent of the plants are diseased.

Blackberries are also subject to other disorders of fungus origin. One, leaf and cane spot, caused by *Septoria rubi*, is mostly present on the dewberries in the Willamette Valley of Oregon and in parts of Idaho. Sometimes it is serious in the commercial berry-growing regions of coastal California. The fungus spores are spread from diseased to healthy tissue primarily by splashing water.

A major symptom on the leaves is small, light-colored spots, bordered with red or purple, about one-eighth inch in diameter. The spots also are present on the canes and may become so numerous as to cause premature defoliation and death of the fruiting canes. The plants are not killed but continue to produce new shoots, which become infected later in the season. The overwintering lesions on the canes become brown. In Oregon a spray of lime-sulfur in February or March is recommended for control. In California a second application with zineb is required in the early-blossom stage.

A closely related and serious disease is found on Cutleaf Evergreen blackberries in western Washington. Only the fruiting canes show symptoms of small, black, circular spots, which begin to appear in December. They enlarge, several lesions coalesce, and it is not unusual to find the base of the canes discolored black for several feet. The fruiting canes become girdled, and by March the entire cane growth may be killed. The new spring shoots show no symptoms until the following winter. In Washington the best control is a spray application with ferbam or Phygon-XL in mid-June or early July. At that time the young shoots are trellised, usually beneath the fruiting canes, and the spray thoroughly covers this new growth, protecting it from infection.

The Cutleaf Evergreen blackberry in the Pacific Northwest is also affected with cane and leaf rust caused by *Kuehneola uredinis*. George W. Fischer and I found the disease widespread in western Washington in 1949. Cane and leaf rust makes its first appearance in late spring or early summer, when large, lemon-yellow lesions are produced. They split open the bark of the overwintered canes. Later in the summer, minute, yellow pustules are present on the lower leaf surfaces and sometimes on the fruit. In autumn the leaf pustules become buff-colored from the formation of another spore form. How the rust overwinters has not been determined definitely. Susceptible varieties include also the Broadleaf form, two unnamed hybrids, and Chehalem. Some clones of the wild trailing blackberry, *R. ursinus*, are also infected. Nine commonly grown varieties of dewberry, besides Himalaya, and two numbered hybrids were found to be immune. No definite control program has been developed for the disease.

Stamen blight, *Hapalosphaeria deformans*, another disease found mainly in the Pacific Northwest, can cause serious losses to the fruit of Boysen, Young, and Cutleaf Evergreen blackberries. Occasionally it has been found on *R. ursinus*. Stamen blight is most easily detected when the flowers open. Then the anthers of the blooms are transformed into gray, moldy masses of spores. The stigmas, which are not infected, function normally; when some are pollinized by insects with pollen from healthy blossoms, a deformed fruit results with only a few normal drupelets. It is not known definitely when infection takes place, but it likely occurs during early spring from spores produced in the flowers the previous year and carried over winter in the buds. No conclusive control program has been developed, but a lime-sulfur solution with water sprayed on the canes in August has resulted in about 60 percent control.

Two bacterial diseases of blackberries are important in the West— cane gall and crown gall, caused by *Agrobacterium rubi* and *A. tumefaciens*, respectively. In symptoms they are somewhat alike with the appearance of rough, warty outgrowths. In the former the enlargements are primarily present on the canes, which are split open. The knobby outgrowths in crown gall are confined mostly in the crowns and on the roots. *A. rubi* infects plants of the genus *Rubus;* while *A. tumefaciens* also infects fruit trees, vegetables, and ornamentals.

Experiments by L. C. Coleman, of the Dominion Laboratory of Plant Pathology, Saanichton, B. C., showed that the horsebean, *Vicia faba*, could be used as a differential host, for it is susceptible to infection by the cane gall organism but not by the crown gall bacterium. Severe infection devitalizes the plants.

The organisms readily contaminate the soil in which they can persist without susceptible plants for several years. All blackberries and dewberries are susceptible to infection by both organisms, as are black and red raspberries, but raspberries appear to have more resistance than the other brambles.

Pruning out and burning infected canes as soon as symptoms appear offers some degree of control. New plantings should be established on noncontaminated soil with disease-free stock. Introducing soil from a contaminated field into noninfested areas by cultivation implements or other means should be avoided.

DWARF is the most important virus disease in the trailing blackberries. It generally is present in the three Pacific Coast States and is important to the Loganberry industry.

Plants affected with dwarf take on a yellowed hue. The canes are much shorter and three or more buds are produced in the leaf axils where only one is normally present. The canes are spindly at first and in later years become stout, stiff, and unnaturally upright. The leaves are mottled with irregular bronzed and light-green splotches and are smaller than healthy foliage. Considerable leaf distortion by crinkling and puckering of the tissue between the veins is noticeable.

The Phenomenal and Logan varieties are most susceptible to dwarf, although the thornless Logan is reported somewhat tolerant to the disease in California. The wild *Rubus ursinus* is infected and serves as a reservoir from which the virus can spread to commercial fields. The aphid *Capitophorus tetrarhodus* is a vector of the virus in Oregon, but the means whereby the spread is effected in California is unknown. Dwarf has not been found occurring naturally in the Boysen, Nectar, and Young varieties.

An unusual malformation of the Thornless Logan, referred to as purple stunt, has been observed in western Oregon by E. K. Vaughan, of Oregon State College. The disease is minor, but it deserves attention because if it should become generally established in the Logan fields great losses may result. Purple stunt is characterized by severe stunting. The canes seldom reach a length of more than a few inches and remain purple throughout the season. Death of affected plants is the usual result.

As with most virus diseases in other crop plants, there is no control once a plant has become infected. If stunt is not too prevalent in a field, diseased plants should be rogued out and burned. Disease-free stock should be used when establishing a new planting.

Control of the insect carriers is an important and effective method for reducing spread of viruses in the fields.

FOLKE JOHNSON *is a plant pathologist at the Western Washington Experiment Station of the State College of Washington. He was reared in the Pacific Northwest. Dr. Johnson is a graduate of that institution; before returning there in 1943, he spent 4 years investigating virus diseases of plants at the Rockefeller Institute for Medical Research and Ohio State University.*

Diseases of Berries in the East

W. F. Jeffers

Growers of raspberries, blackberries, and dewberries usually appreciate the severe losses that diseases may cause but often they are not aware of the ten percenters—the less severe ailments that may make the difference between a profitable crop and an unprofitable crop.

With the present high cost of production and premium prices for high-quality berries, it is more essential than ever before that growers follow sound disease-control practices. Just as they make careful plans for fertilizing, pruning, and harvesting, they should take steps to prevent and stop diseases before it is too late. The alert grower of bramble crops learns to identify the diseases in order to insure profitable production.

MOSAIC is the most widespread and common virus disease of raspberries, yet so many symptoms and effects are associated with mosaic that it is hard to describe properly.

Apparently several different but related viruses can cause mosaic. Plants infected with a mixture of mosaic viruses usually show symptoms different from those infected with only one.

Two main types of mosaic diseases occur on raspberry. Green mosaic causes a mottled pattern of light and dark green areas in infected leaves. Yellow mosaic causes bright-yellow discoloration of part or entire leaves. Both attack black and red raspberries.

Control measures for them are about the same.

Black raspberries generally respond to mosaic infection by a gradual reduction in growth and fruit production. Leaves are smaller in size, usually misshapen, and mottled. Severe infection may cause considerable puckering of leaf tissue between the veins so that blisterlike spots are formed. The entire plant may be severely stunted, and fruit will be small, dry, and nearly tasteless.

New canes often are somewhat stunted and have brittle tips. Leaves on infected canes often are bunched near the tip because of compacting of the new growth. Infected plants may produce fair crops of fruit for a few seasons after planting, but after that they are usually of little value.

The causal virus permeates roots, stems, and leaves. Therefore even though tip layers might appear healthy they will later develop symptoms of mosaic. In some districts symptoms of mosaic are masked by hot summer temperatures; leaves formed then may appear normal, but during cool weather later in the season mosaic is again easily seen. Sometimes the effect of mosaic is so mild that the plants are little damaged, but when the plants are grafted to healthy plants of another variety the new plant may become severely diseased.

Black raspberries may be infected with a type of mosaic that makes the leaves yellowish green and much smaller. Infected plants usually are stunted and produce poor fruit.

Mosaic infection in red raspberries usually results in yellowish-green discoloration of the leaves and general stunting of the plant. Often leaflets are malformed and blisterlike places are produced between the veins. Leaves formed late in the summer sometimes show small yellow spots on the upper surface. High summer temperatures may mask the symptoms. Infected plants gradually decline in vigor and ability to bear good fruit.

The use of the disease-free planting stock is of primary importance in control of mosaic. Growers who have disease-free plants of good commercial varieties should try to keep them so and use such stock or reliable certified stock for new plantings.

New plantings should be at least 500 feet away from other fields of brambles. Wild or escaped raspberries in the vicinity should be destroyed.

Because only an aphid that feeds primarily on raspberries can spread raspberry mosaic, new plantings should be far enough from other brambles to be protected from this weak-flying insect. A suitable insecticide can be used to kill aphids in the bramble patch.

New plantings should be examined several times during the first growing season and infected plants should be removed. Aphids that are present should be killed before the plants are carried out of the field. Otherwise they might spread mosaic to other plants.

Most black raspberries are very susceptible to mosaic. Some varieties of red raspberries are less severely affected than others and should be grown if mosaic is a serious problem. Indian Summer, Lloyd George, Antwerp, Herbert, Marcy, and Newburgh are among the varieties that are poor hosts for the aphid vector (*Amphorophora rubi*). Therefore they usually are not affected by mosaic. Latham is often infected with mosaic, but usually it is less severely injured than Cuthbert, Taylor, Chief, June, and others.

MILD STREAK is the most serious disease of black raspberries in some places. A virus trouble, it does not kill plants but causes them to produce poor fruit. The disease has become serious in Maryland. It is also bad in other parts of the East, but because of its apparent mild effect on the plant it often is not recognized as a disease. Red raspberries are not affected by the streak viruses.

Streak diseases get their name from the discolored stripes on canes of black raspberries. The intensity of the streaking varies from faint, dull lines to bright, purplish ones. Severe streak causes a more drastic purple marking, which sometimes may cause much of the stem tissue to turn bluish. Mildly infected plants generally make good growth and live as long as healthy plants, but severe streak causes stunting and often kills plants within a year or two after infection.

THE FRUIT of infected plants looks dull, somewhat shrunken, and dry—healthy fruit is bright and plump. Fruit from diseased plants is smaller than healthy fruit and shatters more readily—a serious loss of quality and quantity that means lower returns to the grower.

Leaves of plants affected with mild streak often curl downward early in the season. Lower leaves of affected canes may die later in the summer and remain hanging on the stalk. Tips of new canes often are somewhat more curved than healthy tips. Clearing of the veins of lower leaves also may occur in streak-affected plants.

All or only a few canes in a hill may be streaked. In the Cumberland variety, cane streaks usually appear as dull, gray discolorations resembling areas where the normal bloom has been rubbed away. Later in the season the markings may become slightly reddened, but by fall they generally cannot be detected. Cane symptoms first become apparent soon after new growth begins in the spring. In the variety Naples the streaks are greenish brown. In Logan they are usually more of a violet or purple.

Fruiting laterals do not generally show symptoms of streak as well as new canes do, but some seasons they may clearly show the typical streaking.

One should remember that at times other than the fruiting season plants affected with mild streak may appear quite healthy to persons unfamiliar with the disease. Growers unknowingly may thus use infected tip layers in setting new plantings.

In striking contrast to mild streak, severe streak has a drastic effect on the plant. It causes new canes to be stunted and blue in color and to have curved, misshapen leaves. Such plants are usually noticeable and are removed by the grower or else they die within a year or two. Mild streak is by far the most serious of the two streak diseases, for infected plants live many years and are difficult to detect. Thus a planting can become badly diseased within a few years and produce nothing but poor fruit. Growers are reluctant to remove plants that appear healthy and continue to care for a badly diseased planting year after year in the hope that the quality of the fruit will improve.

THE USE of disease-free planting stock is of basic importance in controlling mild and severe streak. There is generally not much danger of severe streak in commercial planting stock as it is readily detected. Because mild streak is so hard to recognize, however, there is difficulty in certifying for freedom from the disease. Mild streak fortunately is not widespread and healthy plants can be had. Growers should learn to recognize the disease and obtain planting stock from areas where the disease does not occur. Careful inspection of fields at fruiting time will disclose the presence of disease, and healthy fields can be selected for planting stock. Recently infected plants cannot be recognized because symptoms usually take several weeks before they appear; therefore planting stock should not be taken from a field showing any amount of mild streak.

Selection of an isolated planting site is important in control of streak diseases. No vector has been proved to spread mild streak, but quite likely an insect is responsible. New plantings at least 500 yards from other raspberries generally can be kept free of the disease, while infection may build up rapidly in plantings next to raspberries. Mild streak occurs frequently when blackberries grow near raspberries. The two crops should therefore be separated. All wild or escaped brambles near raspberry plantings should be destroyed.

If a few streak-infected plants are present in a planting, they should be burned in place or covered with a burlap sack before being removed. That is necessary to prevent possible spread of a streak by insects from plants that would be carried through the patch.

VERTICILLIUM WILT, or blue stem, of raspberry is caused by a fungus (*Verticillium albo-atrum*) that lives in soil. The same fungus attacks tomato, potato, pepper, eggplant, blackberry, maple, barberry, common daisy, groundsel, pigweed, and other plants.

Because the fungus can attack part of a raspberry plant or the entire root system, the disease causes varying degrees of injury. Plants usually are not killed in a single season, but infection becomes increasingly severe for several years until the entire plant is killed. The main reason is that raspberries make many canes, which act almost as separate plants.

First symptoms of wilt appear in early summer, when the lower leaves of new canes, instead of being in prime condition, turn yellow and die. Soon other leaves begin to wilt and the cane turns blue, wilts, and dies. The blue color may involve the entire stem or may be in the form of one or more blue stripes extending up the stem. Several new canes may be affected or in more severe cases the fruiting wood may likewise wilt and die. Infected fruiting canes may fail to mature properly, and small, dry fruit results.

A characteristic symptom is evident when the lower stem or roots of a recently wilted plant are cut. Such parts will show a distinct brown discoloration of the woody tissues. Roots may be killed and rotted by the disease.

Verticillium wilt causes much more damage to black raspberries than to red raspberries. Severely infected fields of black caps have been observed adjoining fields of red raspberries that showed no evidence of infection. Wilt is more apt to cause severe losses in heavy or poorly drained soil. Conditions for infection can occur even on rather steep hillsides if the soil is moist. Very likely the fungus follows natural drainage flows in fields.

The basic measure for the prevention of verticillium wilt is the use of healthy plants in noninfested soil. Great care is necessary in selecting planting stock, for young plants may be infected without showing symptoms. Therefore, if wilt is present in a field it is best not to use new plants from the general vicinity of the infected area. Use of dependable certified stock is a wise precaution, for once the wilt fungus is introduced into a new area it readily becomes established and can exist in the soil for several years even if no raspberries are present.

New planting sites should be selected from land that has not recently been planted to raspberries, blackberries, potatoes, tomato, or any other crop highly susceptible to wilt. Infested soil should be planted to grains, legumes, or other nonsusceptible crops for at least 3 years before being again planted to raspberries. A common practice in some places is to plant tomatoes or potatoes between rows of young raspberry plants. That procedure is not recommended, for those crops are apt to introduce the wilt fungus.

Removal of the infected plants is a sound precautionary measure if only a small percentage of the planting is affected. If diseased canes and roots are left in the soil, however, the fungus develops sclerotia, which can withstand unfavorable conditions, germinate, and produce mycelium that will infect new plants. The soil in the infected areas might well be thoroughly drenched with formaldehyde (1 part in 50 parts of water) or a 1-1,000 solution of bichloride of mercury. A drench containing any standard copper fungicide could also be used. After a month or more, new plants could be placed in such treated areas.

Special care should be taken to avoid transfer of wilt-infested soil through the planting or to healthy fields. Cultivating equipment and drainage water may spread the causal organism.

Most varieties of black raspberries are susceptible to verticillium wilt. Red raspberries generally are more resistant, but some varieties have a greater degree of resistance than others. Cuthbert and Syracuse are highly resistant. Latham is a little less resistant. Most blackberries are not severely affected by the disease. Therefore if wilt is a limiting factor in production of raspberries, some possibility exists that satisfactory resistant varieties may be available. Further work is needed to develop wilt-resistant black raspberries.

ANTHRACNOSE is the most common of the many diseases of raspberries. The fungus *Elsinoë veneta* causes it. Anthracnose occurs in Europe, Canada, Australia, and nearly all sections of the United States.

Black raspberries are most severely affected. Red raspberries, purple raspberries, blackberries, and other brambles also are susceptible.

Its most evident effect is cane infection. Circular, reddish-brown sunken spots up to one-fourth inch across are formed on young shoots of black caps. So many infections may be present on a young cane that the entire surface, especially near the tip, is discolored, roughened, and stunted. In cases of such severe infection the entire cane or the infected area may die. The spots enlarge as the canes grow and may reach a diameter of almost one-half inch, although they are commonly about half that size. Mature spots tend to be circular and have a purple margin with a gray center. Sometimes the cane may crack if deep lesions are present.

Anthracnose also affects the lateral branches and can result in a stunted growth and poor formation of buds, which affects the following crop.

Cane infections on red raspberries are usually smaller and do not penetrate so deeply. Some swelling may occur around the infected area. Gray discoloration of the bark of red raspberries appears to be one phase of the disease.

Leaves of black raspberries may also be infected with the anthracnose fungus. Early in the season many small yellowish spots may be present, but later they enlarge up to one-eighth inch and are light-colored, with reddish margins. Many small lesions may be so closely grouped that an area of the leaf will be roughened. Late in the season infected tissues may fall away from the leaf so that a shot-hole effect results. Main veins on the leaf may also show small lesions.

Anthracnose may cause varying degrees of damage to fruit of black raspberry. In the Eastern States it does not seem to cause much damage to fruit of red raspberries. Individual drupelets or larger areas of the fruit may remain reddish and hard as the fruit matures and may cause it to be misshapen.

Severe infection results in small, red, hard, worthless fruit. Infection of primary and secondary fruit pedicels may interfere with normal development and result in small, brown, dry fruit or improperly ripened fruit. Often that symptom is not associated with the anthracnose disease and is attributed to other causes.

An important prevention is to use disease-free plants in setting new plantings. Tip layers of black raspberries or young plants of red raspberries may have a small amount of infection, which is difficult to detect. Such planting stock should be carefully examined, and badly diseased plants should be discarded. The above-ground part of the stem— handle—of black caps should be removed. Those stems are often left attached to the roots as a guide for cultivation purposes, but if they are infected the fungus will readily spread to new shoots. The upper part of red raspberry plants can be dipped in a solution containing ferbam at the rate of one-half pound to 25 gallons of water.

Wild or escaped raspberries or blackberries surrounding the new planting should be removed if possible. They often are diseased, and the fungus may spread to the new field. For control of anthracnose as well as other diseases it is recommended that new plantings be at least 100 yards from old plantings.

Fungicides giving excellent control of anthracnose have been developed and are in common use on raspberries in place of lime-sulfur and bordeaux mixture. If applied properly so as to replenish spray deposits washed away by rain, good control of anthracnose can be obtained. Details are given in the spray schedule for raspberries.

Clean cultivation aids in the control of anthracnose for it allows better air circulation and penetration of sunlight into the planting. Since the anthracnose fungus is favored by moist, shady conditions, weed control, proper plant spacing, pruning, and avoidance of excessive use of fertilizers are important in retarding development and spread of disease. An important precaution in selecting a new planting site is to avoid places where air drainage is poor and where dews are unusually heavy.

Old fruiting canes should be removed and burned as soon after harvest as possible. Any new growth that shows heavy anthracnose infection should also be pruned out and burned at that time. That is important, for the causal fungus overwinters only in cane infections.

The Quillen variety of black raspberry is said to be resistant to anthracnose although it is not widely grown. Among red raspberries Cuthbert, Ranere (St. Regis), and Turner usually are not severely injured.

SPUR BLIGHT is particularly injurious to red raspberries, but black raspberries are not generally affected by this disease. Spur blight, caused by the fungus *Didymella applanata*, occurs in most sections where red raspberries are grown in the eastern United States. In recent years it has increased considerably in severity.

Reddish-brown areas on the stem around buds is its common symptom. Buds forming at affected places are killed or so weakened that they produce little or no fruit. During the summer the infected spot enlarges until much of the lower cane may be darkened. Often such affected places may begin at the crown and extend several inches up the stem. Leaves may be killed and entire stalks may die or be severely weakened. Infected areas become dotted with small, brown fungus pycnidia, which rupture through the bark. These bodies produce spores, which can cause new infection during warm weather. In late summer or fall the infected areas turn silvery gray and show many small, black fungus structures. This phase of the pathogen is the main means by which it survives the winter; in favorable spring weather these perithecia discharge ascospores, which cause primary infection.

Providing good air drainage and entrance of sunlight in a planting is highly important in preventing spur blight. The causal fungus is most active in shady plantings where humidity is high. Some control of those factors can be had by increasing planting distances, using fertilizer moderately, pruning properly, and eliminating weeds in and around the planting.

Old fruiting canes and infected canes should be removed and burned soon after harvest. Since the pathogen overwinters in diseased canes, this is an essential feature for control of spur blight.

Use of fungicides is necessary if spur blight is a serious problem. A dormant spray of lime-sulfur or one of the dinitro compounds, followed by several summer applications of ferbam, should give adequate control. As all infected wood is not eliminated by pruning, fungicides are needed to prevent infection of new growth by spores of the pathogen.

LEAF SPOT, caused by the fungus *Septoria rubi*, attacks raspberries in warmer sections in the Eastern States. Red raspberries are usually more seriously affected than black raspberries.

Leaf damage usually is not evident until warm summer weather. Small brown or purple spots first are noticeable on lower leaves of fruiting canes. Later they appear on new canes and then gradually involve all the foliage. The spots usually are brown and about one-eighth inch across. Affected tissue dies and falls away, so that leaves have many small, ragged holes. Badly affected leaves usually fall off. By late summer complete defoliation may result. Such destruction of leaf tissue weakens plants, so that fruit production is greatly reduced and growth retarded. Weakened plants are more subject to winter injury and other adverse conditions. After a few years of severe leaf spot, a planting is usually worthless for commercial production. Cane symptoms consist of dark-brown, roundish spots about one-eighth inch in diameter.

Varieties differ greatly in resistance to leaf spot. St. Regis is grown in some warm sections primarily because of its freedom from the disease. Plant breeders probably will be able to develop resistant varieties.

Use of fungicides according to the general spray program given later will help control leaf spot.

Sanitation practices directed toward the destruction of diseased leaves is helpful.

PLANTS AFFECTED WITH ORANGE RUST are easily detected. Lower leaf surfaces become covered with a bright-orange, powdery mass of spores in early summer. The spores are produced by the fungus *Gymnoconia interstitialis*, which causes the disease on black raspberries and other brambles. Red raspberries are not affected by orange rust, although on them another fungus causes a minor disease known as autumn rust.

Orange rust does not kill affected plants but causes them to be stunted and weakened to such an extent that they produce little or no fruit. Badly diseased plants will often produce many spindly shoots instead of the few sturdy canes normally formed. The infected canes usually have few or no spines and the foliage is pale green and stunted or misshapen. After leaves pass the orange rust stage, they often dry up and fall to the ground. The remaining foliage may appear relatively normal, but the fungus occurs throughout most of the roots, stems, and other parts of diseased plants and remains active even though plants appear healthy.

From the orange spores (aeciospores) produced in early summer, small brown spots develop later on the lower side of leaves of black raspberry. The spots produce another type of fungus spore (teliospore), which infects cane tips that are in the process of rooting. Such tip layers show no evidence of infection until the following season, when the leaves become pale and malformed before production of the orange rust stage.

Of first importance in preventing the disease is the use of rust-free planting stock—infected plants remain diseased until they die.

Rust-infected wild brambles near a planting site are a constant threat to nearby black raspberries. Therefore if such diseased plants cannot be removed it is best not to plant black raspberries. It is often possible to destroy wild brambles by burning or chemicals.

As soon as rust appears in a planting, the diseased plants should be removed by digging out the roots. If rust spores are present, however, the plant should first be burned or otherwise treated to prevent further spread of the fungus.

AMONG OTHER DISEASES of raspberry are some that generally are of minor importance but at times can cause serious losses.

Cane blight, a fungus trouble, often is associated with plants that have been weakened by winter injury or other causes. Fruiting canes may die before harvest or lateral stems may die or be so severely stunted as to produce only worthless fruit. This disease probably is important primarily because of other factors which weaken plants and predispose them to attack by the cane blight fungus.

Powdery mildew can at times cause severe foliage damage especially in warm regions and in dense, shaded plantings. Red raspberries are much more susceptible than blacks.

Crown gall has often caused damage to raspberries, but if disease-free stock is used there is usually little loss from it. During recent years its severity has decreased by strict nursery inspection.

Fruit rot can be a problem when wet weather prevails at harvesttime. Several fungi may be involved, but if a spray program, as outlined later, is followed until shortly before fruit ripens the disease should be largely prevented.

DISEASES OF BLACKBERRIES AND DEWBERRIES include anthracnose, which is caused by the same fungus that causes anthracnose of raspberries. Cane symptoms, similar to those on raspberry, consist of gray spots with a purplish-brown margin. The lesions may be so numerous as to affect large areas and may seriously weaken the canes.

Leucretia dewberries are very susceptible to anthracnose and in the Southern States all above-ground parts of the plant may be affected. Direct fruit infection often causes great loss. Green fruit may show rough, dry spots, which do not ripen and result in misshapen, worthless fruit. In some cases dewberries may be so seriously affected that they are shrunken, brown, and dry.

Of primary importance in the control of anthracnose is to cut and burn wild and escaped brambles near a planting. Removal and burning of fruiting canes and badly diseased new growth is important in obtaining adequate control of anthracnose. In southern areas where all growth is removed after harvest there is an excellent opportunity to help prevent this disease by carefully raking and burning all the canes and leaves. Spraying with a recommended fungicide is necessary in areas where anthracnose is severe and susceptible varieties are grown. Several applications of bordeaux mixture (4–4–50) have been recommended in Southern States. The spray schedule outlined for raspberries should give adequate control.

DOUBLE BLOSSOM, a disease of blackberries and dewberries, is caused by a fungus (*Cercosporella rubi*). Buds become infected and produce bunches of slender branches, which are known as witches'-brooms. Sometimes such abnormal branches may be a foot or more in length, but they often form a dense matted mass of compacted leaves which do not extend more than a few inches from the stem. Diseased flower buds are larger than healthy buds. Upon opening, the petals are twisted and misshapen and often are pink.

Infection by the double blossom fungus greatly lowers fruit production and results in weakened plants, which are very unsightly. The disease is more common in the South than in the North. Raspberries are not known to be affected by double blossom.

Control of double blossom is obtained by removing and burning infected canes and blossom clusters. In the South the disease on Leucretia dewberries is controlled by removal and burning of all growth as soon as harvest is completed. New growth formed during the rest of the growing season usually is free of infection.

Orange rust on the blackberry has

symptoms similar to those on black raspberry—notably the bright-orange, powdery spore masses on the under side of leaves.

Eldorado, Snyder, Evergreen (Black Diamond), and Lawton blackberries and Lucretia dewberries are resistant to orange rust.

Control measures given for this disease on black raspberry are adequate for blackberries and dewberries.

DISEASE CONTROL PROGRAM for raspberries and blackberries:

Use disease-free planting stock.

Plant in well-drained, fertile soil not recently grown to any bramble crop and preferably not to potatoes, tomatoes, peppers, or eggplant. Do not interplant with any of those crops.

Locate new plantings as far away as practical from other brambles.

Remove wild or escaped brambles surrounding the planting and continue to keep them as completely eradicated as is practical.

Space plants far enough apart so that the mature planting will not be crowded. Make provision for space for spray equipment to be moved through planting without damaging plants.

Use recommended varieties known to be resistant to disease.

Remove virus-diseased plants as soon as they are observed.

Follow recommended practices for control of aphids and other insect pests of raspberry.

Do not stimulate excessive new growth by too much fertilizer.

Keep weeds under control in and around the planting.

Follow a spray program recommended by your State authorities. A spray schedule that should give good control of most fungus diseases of raspberry and which is adapted to most eastern areas is as follows:

Delayed dormant. Apply at time buds begin to break and before leaves are one-eighth inch long. Use 2 gallons of concentrated liquid lime-sulfur or 1 pint Elgetol or 1 quart Krenite in 25 gallons of water. Lime-sulfur at this dormant concentration (1 part to 12 parts of water) will readily injure actively growing foliage. Elgetol and Krenite can likewise kill foliage if improperly used.

New cane spray. Apply when new canes are 6 to 12 inches high. Use one-half pound ferbam in 25 gallons of water. (Ferbam is the common name of the chemical ingredient of such trade products as Fermate, Karbam Black, and Ferrodow.)

Preblossom. Apply when blossom buds begin to swell but before they open. Use one-half pound of ferbam in 25 gallons of water.

After blossom. Apply as soon as the blossom period is over. Use one-half pound ferbam in 25 gallons of water.

Fruit spray. Apply about 1 week before harvest begins. Use one-half pound ferbam in 25 gallons of water.

After harvest. Apply as soon as possible after harvest. Use one-half pound ferbam in 25 gallons of water. If possible all fruiting canes should be removed soon after harvest and new canes tied up. Then the after-harvest spray can be applied without much difficulty. Otherwise this spray is difficult to apply due to rank cane growth but should be applied even if fruiting canes are not removed until later.

Use only recommended materials and in the recommended concentrations. Raspberry foliage can be readily damaged by improper materials or excess dosages. Apply with a good sprayer, preferably a power-driven model that delivers at least 100 pounds pressure. Spray thoroughly, covering all surfaces of canes. Do not mix fungicides with insecticides unless it is known that the materials are compatible. Reliable spreader-sticker compounds will often greatly increase the effectiveness of fungicides.

W. F. JEFFERS *is professor of plant pathology in the University of Maryland. He received the doctor's degree there in 1939 and since then has been active in research and extension work dealing with control of diseases of strawberries and raspberries.*

The Cultivated Highbush Blueberry

Austin C. Goheen

Our cultivated highbush blueberries are mostly hybrids and selected wild plants of *Vaccinium australe* and *V. corymbosum*, the native blueberries of eastern North America. A few are hybrids between the species *V. australe* and *V. lamarckii*, the lowbush blueberry that forms the bulk of the wild blueberry crop that is harvested in Maine.

When the commercial cultivation of blueberries was first started, and the fields were small and isolated, and the plants remained relatively free from disease—blueberries, in fact, were hailed as one crop without serious disease problems. But that happy condition no longer prevails. Modern plantings, in large fields of genetically similar bushes, are subject to considerable damage from several disease-producing agencies. The most serious diseases are stunt, mummy berry, botrytis blight, powdery mildew, and stem canker.

STUNT, a virus disease of the yellows type, is prevalent in New Jersey and North Carolina. Entire fields may become so badly diseased that little or no crop is produced. The disease also occurs in Massachusetts, New York, Michigan, Maryland, and eastern Canada. It occurs in wild highbush blueberries in New Jersey.

In nature it is transmitted by the leafhopper, *Scaphytopius magdalensis*. It can also be spread in diseased cuttings and nursery stock. In experiments it

has been transmitted in diseased buds and grafting wood. We know from tests that dodder, a parasitic seed plant, can transmit the disease from blueberry plants to other blueberry plants and to *Vinca rosea*, but such transmission has not been observed under natural conditions. Inoculating healthy plants with the juices of diseased plants has not transmitted the disease. Stunt is not spread in the field by pruning knives or other mechanical methods.

Its symptoms are variable, differing with variety, time of year, stage of growth, and age of infection. Stunt dwarfs the bush, reduces the size of the leaves, and causes an abnormal coloring of the leaves. The fruit on bushes that have been infected for a number of years are inferior in size and quality. Diseased bushes eventually fail to set fruit.

The most marked symptom is found in the terminal leaves of young shoots, which in spring and early summer develop pale-green or yellowish margins. Often they are cupped. By holding the leaves perpendicular, one can see a pattern like a Christmas tree: The midrib and lateral veins remain dark green and the pale colors extend inward in the areas between the lateral veins. In late summer the interveinal areas redden brilliantly before healthy plants show any normal red fall coloring. Then the Christmas tree pattern is very striking. Leaf symptoms vary with variety. Rubel shows the spring symptoms throughout the season. Infected Rancocas bushes exhibit only late-summer symptoms. Bushes infected for some time frequently do not show the leaf symptoms.

Stunt was first observed in New Jersey in 1926. In 1942 R. B. Wilcox, of the Department of Agriculture, described the trouble as of virus origin. In 1945 C. A. Doehlert, of the New Jersey Agricultural Experiment Station, found that the disease could be transmitted by mixed colonies of leafhoppers. Subsequently P. E. Marucci and W. E. Tomlinson, Jr., of the same station, proved that the vector was either *S. magdalensis* or *S. verecundus*, two similar insects that are widely distributed on ericaceous plants in swamps of eastern North America. M. T. Hutchinson, also of the New Jersey station, found that *S. verecundus* does not occur in appreciable numbers in the cultivated blueberry fields although it is common in nearby cranberry bogs. *S. magdalensis* therefore seems to be the principal vector for stunt virus.

No variety is immune to stunt. Rancocas appears to be tolerant to the virus. Plantings of Rancocas in badly infected fields have continued to produce crops of berries long after the disease has destroyed other varieties.

Three control practices are each partly successful. Prompt removal of plants that show stunt symptoms reduces the reservoir of diseased plants that the leafhopper may feed on. In districts where the disease occurs sporadically this practice is effective.

In areas where the disease is bad and the leafhopper is abundant, roguing alone is not successful. Here the second practice, control of the leafhopper, is necessary. Four applications of DDT or methoxychlor (3 pounds in 100 gallons of water) have greatly reduced the numbers of leafhoppers in tests in New Jersey but have never completely destroyed them. Roguing and insect control together are the best control procedures for use in New Jersey and North Carolina.

Use of disease-free plants in setting new fields is the third practice. Rigid specifications have been set up for the certification of healthy plants in New Jersey. But even with certified plants, new fields in New Jersey and North Carolina should be rogued and the leafhoppers controlled.

The ultimate control of stunt in areas where the vector is abundant seems to rest on the development of immune varieties or elimination of sources of the disease. No truly immune varieties were available in 1953. A number of wild species and varieties of blueberries have been put under test in New Jersey in the hope that among them an immune plant might be found to form the basis of a breeding program whose objective would be the development of resistance to stunt.

MUMMY BERRY, a fungus disease, is widespread in commercial blueberry fields in eastern North America. In the northern zones it sometimes destroys the crop of some varieties. In the Pacific Northwest and in North Carolina it is rare on the cultivated blueberry but more or less abundant on other blueberry species.

The causal fungus, *Monilinia urnula*, has a complicated life cycle. From harvest in early summer until the blueberry buds open the following spring, the fungus is found on the ground under the bushes in the form of mummies. The mummies are compact masses of fungus tissues that formed in infected berries the previous season. In early spring, when the blueberry buds start to open, the fungus renews its development, and mummy cups—the apothecia—are produced from the old mummies. Along the inner surface of the mummy cup sexual spores, or ascospores, of the fungus are produced in profusion. The ascospores, released during periods of rainy, cool weather, are carried by wind to the young flower and leaf buds. Ascospores landing on the moist surfaces of the young buds grow into the young leaf and flower bud tissues. After about a week the infections become apparent as necrotic areas on the petioles and along the midveins of the leaves in spur infections or at the base of the flowers in cluster infections. The infected spurs and clusters soon die, and conidia of the fungus are formed along the central axes of the spurs or clusters. The conidia are carried by wind or by insects to the stigmas of open flowers. The young berries become infected and develop into new mummies, which carry the fungus through the summer and the following winter.

Weather conditions are important. In early spring the mummies must have moisture before apothecia and ascospores are produced. Primary infection of the spurs and clusters depends on wet weather at the time the buds are beginning to open. Secondary infection of the flowers depends on weather conditions that affect dispersal of the conidia. Differences in spring weather may explain the differences in the amount of damage done by mummy berry in different years. A cool, wet spring favors the outbreak of an epiphytotic.

Mummy berry was first identified in 1832 in Russia on the wild European lingberry, *Vaccinium vitis-idaea*. It was first discovered in North America on various wild blueberries in Michigan in 1898 by B. O. Longyear, of the Michigan Agricultural Experiment Station. He described the life cycle of the fungus essentially as we know it today.

Varieties differ considerably in susceptibility. June and Rancocas are blighted more severely by primary infections than are Weymouth, Cabot, and Stanley. There are also differences in the amount of secondary infection with different varieties.

It can be controlled at the time of primary infection in the spring. The young blueberry buds can be protected from infection through the use of ziram fungicide applied as a heavy spray over all the surfaces of the bushes, or the spores of the fungus can be destroyed before they blow to the bushes through the mechanical or chemical destruction of the mummy cups. Protection with ziram is more effective than destruction of the cups because the wind can blow spores to the bushes from distant sources. In order to obtain control, treatments must be applied just before the release of the spores from the cups. In New Jersey this usually occurs during the first or second week in April.

BOTRYTIS BLIGHT is widespread in areas where blueberries are grown, but it often is overlooked because it is confused with mummy berry. It destroys the fruit when whole flower clusters are blighted at blossom time, when individual green berries become infected and rot, or when berries become infected at harvesttime and rot during marketing or in cold storage. The fungus can develop on stored berries at temperatures only slightly above freezing.

The disease attacks a variety of species. It is most severe in places where the weather is cool and wet when the blueberries are maturing and the bushes are producing new growth. The disease organism has been isolated from dead blueberry tips gathered in Washington, Michigan, Maryland, New Jersey, New York, Massachusetts, and Maine.

The cause is the common gray mold fungus, *Botrytis cinerea*. Besides producing blueberry fruit rots and tip blights, it occasionally produces leaf spots. It is abundant on such debris as fallen corollas, insect-damaged berries, and mummy lesions on or under the bush. Its production of spores reaches a peak during the period just after blossoming. After the weather becomes warm and dry in the summer, sporulation occurs only for short periods following rains. The fungus has been isolated from dead blueberry tips at all times during the year. In the spring the first sporulation of the fungus is observed on the dead tips.

The blight was one of the first diseases reported on commercial blueberries but no investigations of methods to control the disease were undertaken until 1949. No control method has been found for the disease.

POWDERY MILDEW is widely distributed on cultivated and wild blueberries in eastern North America. It is not normally widespread on blueberry leaves until midsummer after the crop is harvested. For that reason it is not generally controlled in cultivated blueberry fields. Undoubtedly considerable damage results to the blueberry from the early defoliation that it causes in susceptible varieties, but the damage is hard to evaluate. On the lowbush blueberries, which are extensively harvested in Maine, it is one of the worst fungus disorders.

It is caused by the fungus *Microsphaera penicillata*, which occurs on a number of different plants. Probably blueberry strains of the fungus are confined in their host range to *Vaccinium* species and other closely related plants, but no cross-inoculation work with the organism has been done.

The fungus grows only on the surface of living blueberry leaves. In late summer the web of fungus growth on the surface of the blueberry leaf produces tiny, dark-brown, round bodies—cleistothecia—which fall to the ground with the leaves and carry the fungus over winter. Within them, in asci, the sexual spores of the fungus are produced. In spring, when the ascospores are mature, the cleistothecia rupture and release the ascospores into the air. Wind may carry them to young leaves of the blueberry. If conditions are favorable, the spores germinate and initiate small spots on the leaf surfaces. In late spring and early summer the spots remain so small that they are generally overlooked by the casual observer. The fungus continues to develop slowly, however, and when the infection is well established on susceptible varieties about the middle of the summer, a powdery layer of summer spores, or conidia, is produced on the leaf spots. These spores spread the fungus rapidly to uninfected areas. On susceptible varieties the fungus may cover the entire leaf surface. In late summer the infected areas produce a new mass of cleistothecia, which repeat the cycle for the following season.

The susceptibility of different varieties and selections to the disease varies considerably. Some are badly infected,

others have scarcely a single infected leaf. No variety is immune to the disease although some resistant ones do not become infected until the middle of October. Most of the named varieties that have been introduced by the Department of Agriculture since 1940 are highly resistant. Jersey, which is planted most extensively in New Jersey is very susceptible. Cabot and Pioneer, which are most susceptible to the disease, are being replaced with newer varieties that have superior horticultural qualities and resistance to powdery mildew.

The disease can be controlled by dusting or spraying. On the lowbush blueberries in Maine, applications of copper-lime dust (25 pounds of monohydrated copper sulfate mixed with 75 pounds of hydrated lime) at the time of blossom drop and again 10 days later will check the disease. The dust should be applied at the rate of 40 pounds to the acre to be effective.

On cultivated blueberries, cover sprays with wettable sulfur (3 pounds in 50 gallons of water) or bordeaux mixture (4 pounds copper sulfate and 4 pounds hydrated lime made to 50 gallons of spray with water) at the end of blossoming give good control. Either material should be applied at the rate of 300 gallons an acre to be effective.

STEM CANKER is injurious on cultivated and wild highbush blueberries and the wild rabbiteye blueberry in the southeastern United States. It has also been found on cultivated bushes in a few places in New Jersey.

It is caused by *Physalospora corticus*, a fungus that lives on the living bark of the blueberry and produces cankers on the twigs and stems. Both sexual and asexual spores are produced on the surface of the cankers over a long period during the growing season. In wet weather, spores are liberated to uninfected parts of the bush or may be blown to nearby bushes.

If weather favors infection and the spores land on susceptible blueberry tissue, a new canker will form; it appears as a reddish, conical swelling, which does not enlarge the first season. Thereafter it swells gradually. After a few years it may girdle and kill the stem. The use of infected cutting wood or rooted cuttings to establish new fields may carry the disease great distances.

Symptoms vary with the susceptibility of the infected bushes. Sometimes the fungus may penetrate the bark and make big cankers with deep cracks and fissures on the main stem of the plant. On less susceptible varieties the cankers are less extensive, they are not swollen, and they may form only on side branches.

Varieties differ in susceptibility. Only a few varieties—Angola, Wolcott, Murphy, Scammell, Atlantic, Ivanhoe, Jersey, Rubel, and Rancocas—are resistant enough to remain in commercial use in North Carolina.

Stem canker was first observed in North Carolina in 1938. Some fields then were already heavily infected. The disease was observed in New Jersey in 1951.

It is hard to control in North Carolina. Fungicides have been ineffective because the fungus produces spores over a long period during the season. Roguing or removal of infected bushes is of little value because the disease may become reestablished from the wild. Resistant varieties, such as Murphy, Wolcott, and Angola, offer the only possible control. In New Jersey, where the disease does not occur in the wild, the eradication of individual cankers or entire infected bushes probably would eliminate the disease.

SEVERAL OTHER DISEASES have been reported on blueberries in North America and Europe. Most are local or serious mainly on *Vaccinium* species other than the cultivated highbush blueberry.

Witches'-broom, or stem rust, is caused by the fungus *Pucciniastrum goeppertianum*, a heteroecious rust with fir, *Abies* species, as the alternate host. It occurs on cultivated and wild blueberries in New England and on wild bluberries in many places. It produces several short, swollen twigs on infected bushes, which are crowded on a small area near the point of infection. Heavily infected bushes produce no fruit. Possibly the disease can be controlled by removing all the true fir trees from the vicinity of the blueberry field. Pruning the infections from bushes might also be of some value.

Leaf rust is caused by the fungus *Pucciniastrum myrtilli*, another heteroecious rust with hemlock, *Tsuga*, as the alternate host. It normally occurs on various blueberry species only in areas where hemlock trees are present. In some seasons it occurs in severe outbreaks in cultivated fields far removed from the alternate host. The fungus can evidently be spread rapidly by uredospores after an infection is once established. The fungus produces small, irregular, dark-brown spots on the leaves. The spots may become numerous later in the season and cause early defoliation. No control is known for the disease on cultivated highbush blueberries, but copper-lime dusts applied at the time of blossom drop, followed by an additional application 10 days later, have been effective in controlling the disease on lowbush blueberries in Maine. This is the same treatment that is used against powdery mildew.

Several leaf-spot diseases have been reported on blueberries in North Carolina and other parts of the Southeast. The most important is double spot, caused by the fungus *Dothichiza caroliniana*. The disease occasionally causes severe defoliation in North Carolina and must be controlled by spraying with bordeaux mixture.

Crown gall of blueberries is caused by the bacterium *Agrobacterium tumefaciens*, which produces galls on many other plants. It is found on highbush blueberries in New York, New Jersey, Michigan, Washington, and British Columbia. It occurs on plants in the field, in nurseries, and in cutting beds.

It produces swollen galls along the stems and small twigs and occasionally at the base of the canes near the ground. The galls are irregular and of various sizes. Often the gall involves the entire circumference of the branch and affected branches and twigs die. In Washington certain varieties and selections are badly infected, while plants of a different selection in adjacent rows may be healthy. Although various other host plants become infected when inoculated by bacteria isolated from blueberry galls, the blueberry strain of the crown gall organism appears to be best adapted to the blueberry. The disease is probably spread in the field or nursery when plants are pruned or when softwood cuttings are made. No attempts have been made to control the disease in blueberry fields.

Tip blights of blueberries occasionally are common. They are probably caused by winter injury, excessive soil moisture, or other environmental factors that weaken the bush. Frequently stem tips of bushes, weakened by other causes, are infected by weakly parasitic fungi. *Diaporthe* (*Phomopsis*) *vaccinii* is reported to be a cause of tip blight in North Carolina, New Jersey, and New England. That fungus is not often encountered, however, and is only one of a number of fungi that may be found in blighted tips. In Washington *Diaporthe vaccinii* occurs as a saprophyte on dead blueberry tips.

AUSTIN C. GOHEEN, *a native of Washington State, received his undergraduate training at the Western Washington College of Education and the University of Washington and his graduate training at the State College of Washington. He has been with the Bureau of Plant Industry, Soils, and Agricultural Engineering since 1950. He has worked on blueberry and cranberry diseases in New Jersey in cooperation with the New Jersey Agricultural Experiment Station. He was transferred to the Plant Industry Station at Beltsville in 1953.*

Disorders of Cranberries

Herbert F. Bergman

Fruit rots cause an annual loss of 10 to 15 percent in our crop of cranberries, which are grown extensively in Massachusetts, Wisconsin, and New Jersey and less widely in Washington, Oregon, Maine, and Rhode Island. The value of the crop is 10 million to 20 million dollars a year.

Two or three decades ago the losses went as high as 25 percent, but they have been reduced by changes in cultural practices, improvements in fungicides, greater efficiency in handling and storing, and the development of the canning industry, which offers an immediate and profitable outlet for the berries that—although sound at harvest—probably would develop excessive decay if they were stored and shipped as fresh fruit.

Directly affecting the abundance of rot are the amount and frequency of rain and the temperature and humidity. Humidity and temperature (to a lesser extent) are affected by local conditions. A local condition that bears on humidity is the density of vine growth. Excessive growth prevents the evaporation of water among and under the vines after rain, fog, or dew. Thus the atmosphere may remain saturated or nearly saturated for hours after the air and soil surface under the thinner vines have dried. Poor drainage also keeps the soil wet and makes a high humidity under the vines.

The application of nitrogenous fertilizers, late holding of the winter flood (particularly holding until July or holding late in successive years), sanding too frequently, or too heavy applications of sand on bogs with dense vine growth promote excessive growth especially on bogs with peat or muck bottom. Excessive use of water (such as too frequent flooding and holding water high in the ditches) also tends to increase the amount of rot because the surface of the soil is kept wet and the humidity of the air under the vines is increased.

To find out the relationship between weather in Massachusetts and the ability of cranberries to remain in good condition, extensive studies were made by Dr. Neil E. Stevens, formerly of the Department of Agriculture. He began the work with Dr. C. L. Shear in 1915. Although he worked on all phases of investigation pertaining to cranberries, his chief interests were weather in relation to keeping quality, the occurrence and spread of the false blossom disease, and the effect of acidity or alkalinity of flooding water on the productivity of cranberry vines. Dr. Shear, also of the Department of Agriculture, went to New Jersey in 1901, at the request of the American Cranberry Growers' Association, and began studies which were continued until 1907. He made extensive observations in the field, collected specimens in New Jersey and Massachusetts, and made laboratory studies of the various diseases of cranberries. He also conducted experiments in New Jersey on methods of controlling fruit rot. As a result of the work, most of the present knowledge as to the identity and life histories of the fungi causing fruit rot as well as of those causing diseases of the vines was obtained.

Records over a long period show that the keeping quality of berries from individual bogs and from an entire region varies greatly from year to year.

An apparent correlation was found in Massachusetts and New Jersey between exceptionally large crops and unusually poor keeping quality. Keeping quality was correlated with rain-fall, but the correlation between keeping quality and the number of rainy days in July and August, when the fruit is developing, was closer than the correlation between keeping quality and total amount of rain. The amount of rain in September has no bearing on keeping quality.

The correlation between keeping quality and temperatures during May and June was very close. The basis used in comparing temperatures in different years was the total of "day degrees" above 50° F. Fifty was subtracted from the mean temperature of each day and the remainders were added together. Fifty was chosen as a base point because many fungi begin active growth on cranberries at about that temperature.

During the years of the study, an unusual amount of rot occurred in berries of the Early Black variety whenever the May and June temperatures were unusually high. Moreover, those were the only years in which an unusual amount of decay is known to have occurred in Early Black. In years in which May and June temperatures were lower than normal, the keeping quality of Early Black was better.

Early Black and Howes, the oldest of the cultivated varieties, are the principal ones grown in Massachusetts, where about 65 percent of the entire crop of the United States is produced. McFarlin is grown to a limited extent. Early Black and Howes are grown extensively in New Jersey. The principal variety in Wisconsin is Searles, and McFarlin is next in importance. McFarlin is the most important variety in Washington and Oregon, but Searles also is grown to a considerable extent.

The keeping quality of berries of the Howes variety also was poor in all years in which that of Early Black was poor. The keeping quality of Howes, however, is less definitely correlated with temperature during the growing season than that of Early Black.

Field observations indicate that in determining the keeping quality of the general crop, temperatures during May and June are the most important; distribution of rainfall and temperatures during July and August come next; and the size of the crop, third.

The keeping quality of cranberry crops in Massachusetts and New Jersey vary to some extent independently of each other, although it has been observed that when the keeping quality of the crop in either State has been conspicuously poor that of the crop in the other State also has been below normal.

The keeping quality of the cranberry crops of Wisconsin and of the Washington-Oregon areas also varies from year to year, depending on weather conditions during the growing season. In the Washington-Oregon areas rainy weather during the picking season is apparently the most important factor in determining the amount of rot that will occur.

EIGHT SPECIES of fungi are known to be important causes of fruit rot: *Guignardia vaccinii, Acanthorhyncus vaccinii, Glomerella vaccinii, Godronia cassandrae, Diaporthe vaccinii, Sporonema oxycocci, Pestalotia vaccinii,* and *Ceuthospora lunata.*

The rots caused by most of them are practically the same in external appearance. The fungi causing them can be identified only by making cultures from the rotten berries and identifying the fungi in the cultures.

The fungi grow, in culture, at widely varying rates at different temperatures. *Godronia* and *Sporonema* grow slightly at 32° F., and grow most rapidly at about 59° and 68°, respectively. *Diaporthe, Glomerella,* and *Guignardia* begin to grow between 35° and 40°, and their rate of growth increases rapidly above 50°. They grow well at temperatures between 59° and 86° and make their best growth at 82°, 77°, and 77°, respectively. *Acanthorhyncus,* however, begins to grow only at temperatures of 60° to 70° and makes its best growth at about 85°.

Because temperatures in New Jersey during the growing season are higher than in other cranberry-growing regions, field rot occurs on the bogs more abundantly there and often has caused the loss of 50 to 75 percent of the crop in unsprayed bogs. Many bogs in New Jersey, however, produce berries of good keeping quality; most of the rot there is due to fungi that grow best at high temperatures. *Guignardia* is the most important; *Acanthorhyncus* is next; a small part is caused by *Glomerella.*

Temperatures during the growing season in Massachusetts usually are high enough to permit the development of field rot. It usually occurs, however, only on a few bogs, but on them sometimes causes the loss of 15 to 40 percent of the crop. In years when conditions are more favorable for rot, it is found on a greater number of bogs and becomes more serious on the few bogs where it occurs yearly.

When field rot occurs, *Glomerella* generally is the principal cause, particularly in early varieties. Some seasons, however, the temperatures may be higher or lower than normal, and are higher on some bogs than on others. In years in which temperatures during the growing season are above normal, and because of differences in local conditions on some bogs, or parts of them, *Guignardia, Sporonema,* and *Diaporthe* are sometimes more important as causes of rot than *Glomerella. Acanthorhyncus* very rarely occurs on Massachusetts bogs.

Field rot is negligible in Wisconsin. It occurs only occasionally in Washington and Oregon. Most of the rot there is caused by *Godronia* and occurs during storage. In Wisconsin, *Godronia* is the only fungus that causes more than a negligible amount of rot, but in Washington and Oregon a considerable part of it is caused by *Ceuthospora.* Occasionally serious loss due to field rot caused by the cottonball fungus, *Sclerotinia oxycocci,* occurs.

The crucial period seems to be near and during flowering, when the fungi causing fruit rot gain entrance into the berries. The fungi apparently are always present on bogs although not always in sufficient numbers to cause a noticeable amount of rot.

Mature fruiting bodies, ready to discharge spores, often are found on old leaves, stems, and dried berries on bogs in Massachusetts within 2 weeks after the winter flood has been drawn off and are abundantly present in May and June. The fruiting bodies discharge spores during and after rain and periods of fog and when the vines are wet with dew. Wind and water may carry the spores to blossoms and leaves. Whenever enough moisture is present, the spores germinate; germ tubes from them grow into the ovaries of flowers and cause rot later.

Spores may also be carried to the leaves where they germinate, the germ tubes entering the leaves, where the fungus continues to grow and later forms fruiting bodies on the surface. Spores are discharged from the fruiting bodies before and during the flowering period of the following year to initiate infection for that season.

THE USE OF FUNGICIDES greatly reduces the amount of rot before and after harvest. Spraying is most necessary in New Jersey and has been generally practiced there since the early 1900's. Spraying has been necessary on only comparatively few bogs in Massachusetts. Spraying generally is not necessary in Wisconsin. In Washington and Oregon, the weather during harvest has a much greater influence on the amount of rot than spraying does.

Most generally used in New Jersey until 1945 was bordeaux mixture 8–8–100, with 2 pounds of rosin fish-oil soap added. Four or five applications of the spray were made. A 10–4–100 bordeaux, with 1 pound of rosin fish-oil soap, has been used in Massachusetts. Only two applications are necessary, one at the beginning of the blossoming period and the second near the end.

Since 1945 an organic fungicide, ferbam (ferric dimethyl dithiocarbamate), has been used extensively in New Jersey and to a considerable extent in Massachusetts. It has largely replaced bordeaux.

Berries picked when they are dry keep better than those picked wet. The practice of water raking, which is extensive in Wisconsin, often increases the amount of rot that develops after harvest. The amount of rot in water-raked berries that remain wet for some time after they are picked is decidedly greater than in those dried promptly, and the amount of rot in the latter is greater than in those picked dry. That is true also in Washington and Oregon, where, in years when autumn rains begin before the berries are harvested, the berries have to be picked wet.

Bruising, even when relatively slight, causes a great amount of rot in berries during storage and marketing. Bruising occurs when the berries are picked, screened, and packed. Much of it can be avoided by care in harvesting and later handling.

Berries in storage must be kept at a low temperature and be well ventilated to reduce loss by rot. During the early part of the picking season in New Jersey and in Massachusetts, the berries often are warm when picked. They should be cooled as quickly as possible in storage. Berries keep best when stored at about 35° F. Extensive sterile breakdown occurs in berries stored at 30° to 32°.

Storage tests with cranberries in an atmosphere containing up to 10 percent carbon dioxide showed that an increase in the carbon dioxide content was injurious rather than beneficial. In an atmosphere with a carbon dioxide content even as low as 2.5 percent, the loss was greater than in normal ventilated storage.

Fungus diseases of leaves and stems often are conspicuous and sometimes locally serious, but they have never been known to be of great commercial importance. The disease known as rose bloom causes the buds in the axils of the old leaves to grow out as abnormal lateral shoots bearing greatly enlarged, rose-colored leaves. The disease was most abundant in Massachusetts and was found to some extent almost every year before 1945, but since then there have been no serious outbreaks, possibly because of changes in cultural practices. Rose bloom is occasionally abundant in Washington and Oregon.

A disease known as fairy ring caused by a fungus of the mushroom type occurs frequently in Massachusetts and New Jersey. The fungus makes a dense underground growth that kills the vines in a zone 3 to 4 feet wide where the fungus is active. After the fungus has killed the vines over an area 8 to 10 feet in diameter, the middle again becomes covered with healthy vines thus forming a ring.

Another disease that causes a rot, known as hard rot, and causes a tip blight of vines occurs frequently in Wisconsin, and is sometimes locally serious in Washington and Oregon. It also occurs occasionally in Massachusetts but is much less important there than in the other areas.

FALSE BLOSSOM was prevalent on three varieties in Wisconsin by 1906. The disease was first found in Massachusetts in 1914 and in New Jersey in 1915, and was general in those States by 1924. Apparently the disease was carried there in infected vines from Wisconsin.

The disease gets its name from the abnormal character of the flowers, which, instead of hanging downward, become erect and have enlarged, greenish, and somewhat leaflike calyx lobes. The petals are shorter, broader, and reddish or greenish. The stamens and pistils are more or less malformed. No fruit is produced.

By 1928 false blossom threatened to wipe out the cranberry industry in Wisconsin, Massachusetts, and New Jersey. It caused a reduction in the crop in Wisconsin and a downward trend in production in New Jersey,

which began about 1924 and was strikingly evident by 1932. Many bogs in Massachusetts also were seriously affected.

Irene Dobrosky, a research worker in New Jersey, proved in 1927 that false blossom is caused by a virus carried by the blunt-nosed leafhopper. Earlier investigators had believed it was due to a disturbance in nutrition.

Dr. L. O. Kunkel, of the Boyce Thompson Institute, had suggested in 1924 that leafhoppers might be the carriers. A survey in 1925 and 1926 had shown that only one genus of leafhopper occurred in the regions in which false blossom was abundant and that it was not present in Washington and Oregon, where false blossom was found not to spread.

No cultivated varieties of cranberries are free from false blossom, but they vary in susceptibility. Howes is very susceptible. Shaw's Success, a variety not commonly grown, is the most resistant. Early Black and McFarlin are intermediate. The resistance is not an actual resistance that is due to opposition offered by the plant to infection by the disease. It is due, rather, to a difference in the preference of leafhoppers to feed on the different varieties.

The Department of Agriculture began a breeding program in 1929 to develop good, resistant varieties. Crosses in which one or both parents were known to be somewhat resistant to false blossom were made in Wisconsin and Massachusetts. From the crosses 10,685 seedlings have been grown. From a cross made at the New Jersey Agricultural Experiment Station 112 other seedlings have been grown. Forty of the more promising seedlings, including six from the New Jersey crosses, were selected in 1940. In addition 182 other selections were made in 1945, making a total of 222 seedlings selected for a second test.

A selective feeding test—a "cafeteria test" for leafhoppers—to ascertain susceptibility to false blossom was made in 1945 on 362 seedlings selected in

1944. In the test leafhoppers that spread the disease were allowed a choice of different varieties on which to feed. Since the attractiveness of different varieties to leafhoppers seemed to be correlated with the rate of spread of the disease on those varieties in the field, the method was valuable in evaluating the probable resistance of the seedlings. Seedlings with the poorest ratings in the test were discarded, and 93 were included among the 182 selected in 1945 for a second test.

The 40 selections made in 1940 were planted in rod-square plots in New Jersey in 1941. Selections were made from them in 1945 and again in 1949. From the latter, three were named— Beckwith, Stevens, and Wilcox. Plans for their distribution to growers in Massachusetts, New Jersey, and Wisconsin have been made so they can be tested on a large scale.

Further tests of the 40 selections of 1940, the 93 selections of 1945, and some others were started in Massachusetts, New Jersey, and Wisconsin, in the hope that new, healthier, and better varieties can be developed.

A PHYSIOLOGICAL DISEASE is one that injures or kills any part of a plant, without involving a fungus or other parasitic organism, or any disturbance of the normal growth or behavior of a plant. Such injury to flower buds and growing tips of cranberry vines, often severe enough to cause their death, was observed in 1919 as a result of flooding bogs in June to control insects. The most serious injury of this kind to cranberries is caused by winter flooding.

Cranberry bogs usually are flooded in winter as a protection against winterkilling. The practice often hurts crop production. When submerged for a long time, cranberry vines may be so injured that their yield the following summer is reduced or destroyed.

The possibility that the injury might be due to a lack of oxygen in the flooding water was suggested by the fact that its lack caused injury to buds, flowers, and growing tips of vines in June flooding. Winter-flooding water often contains little or no oxygen. Injury occurs only on bogs on which the oxygen content of the water was very low at some time during the winter.

Investigations in Massachusetts proved that forms of injury not previously recognized as such are caused by a lack of oxygen during the winter. Observations in New Jersey showed that serious injury from winter flooding occurs there also.

Injury resulting from a lack of oxygen in the water during the winter-flooding period varies greatly in severity. In the most extreme cases it causes the death of some of the stems, leaves, and buds. Other forms of injury are loss of leaves of the preceding season (leaf drop), death of the terminal (fruit) buds, death of small areas of leaf tissue in embryonic leaves within the terminal bud, retardation in the development of the new growth of the uprights from the terminal buds, death of some or all the flower buds, failure of the flowers to set fruit, failure of the fruits to grow to mature size, and reduction in the size of mature fruits.

The occurrence and degree of injury are determined primarily by the relation between the amount of dissolved oxygen in the water and the amount of oxygen required by the cranberry vines.

Water in contact with the air normally contains oxygen in solution. The greatest amount of oxygen that water can hold in solution at 32° F. is about 14 parts per million, at 40° about 12.4, and at 50° about 11.

The oxygen content of the water of the flooded bog tends to remain uniform at a given temperature because of the action of diffusion, convection, and wind. Wind sets the surface water in motion and causes it to mix with water below. The stronger the wind, the faster the mixing proceeds and the greater the depth to which it extends.

Two physiological processes, respiration and photosynthesis, carried on by plants and other living organisms, often cause great variations in the oxygen content of the water. Mosses, algae, and other plants, besides the vines, grow in the bogs. Besides, bacteria and other micro-organisms exist in organic matter on the surface of bog soils and in the soil itself.

Respiration releases chemical energy mainly by the oxidation of carbohydrates. The energy is used for the performance of the physiological processes necessary to maintain life and goes on in every living cell. The process requires oxygen, and carbon dioxide is given off.

The oxygen used in respiration by the cranberry vines and other plants on a flooded bog is taken from that in solution in the water and the oxygen given off in photosynthesis goes into solution in it. Consequently, respiration reduces the amount of dissolved oxygen and photosynthesis increases it.

The oxygen content of water on winter-flooded bogs not covered with ice usually undergoes only relatively small, brief changes, as there is nearly always enough wind to cause mixing, so that the water is kept at or near its oxygen capacity.

On winter-flooded bogs covered by ice, circulation of the water by wind is prevented. The oxygen content of the water is then determined by the relative rate of oxygen consumption by the cranberry vines and the other organisms, as compared with the rate of liberation of oxygen in photosynthesis, mainly in the cranberry vines themselves. Since respiration goes on continuously, while photosynthesis occurs only in light, the oxygen content of the water increases or decreases at a rate proportional to the amount by which the oxygen given off in photosynthesis is greater or less than that used in respiration. Light, therefore, becomes the controlling factor in determining the oxygen content of the water on an ice-covered bog.

The amount of light received by the cranberry vines in water under ice depends primarily on the degree and duration of cloudiness, the thickness of the ice, the inclusion of snow in the ice, and the presence or absence of a snow cover.

Snow on the ice is the most important factor in causing a reduction in the oxygen content of water on winter-flooded bogs, since by excluding light, it prevents the liberation of oxygen in photosynthesis. The inclusion of snow in the ice may sometimes cause almost as great a reduction in the oxygen content of the water under ice as does snow on the ice.

The amount of oxygen required by vines frozen into the ice probably becomes negligible at the low temperature of ice in cold weather. It is always less than that required by vines in water under the ice. That may be an important factor in determining the probability of injury from oxygen deficiency and in determining the severity of injury when an oxygen deficiency occurs. Numerous observations have shown that shallowly flooded vines, which are frozen into the ice during the winter, produce larger crops and bear more regularly than those deeply flooded.

Different parts of the plant vary greatly in their oxygen requirement. The more active the part, the more oxygen it requires. The most active parts of cranberry vines in their winter condition are the flower buds, young leaves, and the growing point of the stem within the terminal buds. They are the first to be injured or killed, therefore, when the oxygen content of the water reaches a low level. The old leaves are much less active. The stems are least active and accordingly are injured only under extreme conditions of oxygen deficiency.

Injury occurs only when the oxygen content of the water reaches a level at which the oxygen requirement of the more active parts of the cranberry vines cannot be supplied. Evidence indicates that this level is about 5.7 parts per million, since injury occurs when the oxygen content of the water reaches that level and remains there for a day or two. The injury is more severe at a lower oxygen content or for a greater length of time. Usually the oxygen content of the water falls to that level only when there are several inches of snow on the ice, but it may do so in very cloudy weather when there is little or no snow on the ice, but much snow is included in it.

Injury from oxygen deficiency on winter-flooded bogs may be greatly reduced or prevented by changes in the flooding practice. Bogs are often flooded too deeply or for too long a time. Bogs should be flooded for as short a time as weather permits and should be flooded as shallowly as possible. Shallowly flooded vines are soon frozen into the ice when ice forms and then are injured less. On bogs that are much out of grade, some parts must be deeply flooded if the higher parts are covered. Then it usually would be better (in Massachusetts and New Jersey) to flood the bog shallowly and run the risk of some winterkilling on the higher parts. Moreover, the loss in yield as a result of oxygen deficiency injury to vines in water under ice on deeply flooded parts of a bog in most years and on most bogs is much greater than the loss from winterkilling on parts of the bog not flooded.

When the water supply is ample, bogs may be flooded in the usual way. Then after 5 to 6 inches of ice have formed, if the oxygen content of the water drops to near 5.7 parts per million, the water should be drawn out from under the ice. As long as ice remains, the bog need not be reflooded, but as soon as the ice melts from any considerable part of the bog it should again be flooded. This procedure has been used with success in Wisconsin and has been used on many bogs in Massachusetts when winters were cold enough to make ice of the desired thickness.

HERBERT F. BERGMAN *has degrees from Kansas State College and the University of Minnesota. He joined the Bureau of Plant Industry, Soils, and Agricultural Engineering in 1917.*

Problems in Growing Pecans

John R. Cole

Several fungus diseases affect pecans. One of them, scab, is considered one of the major obstacles in pecan production and causes losses of millions of dollars to the industry annually.

The scab fungus was first found on leaves of the mocker hickory nut near Cobden, Ill., in 1882. Six years later it was found on leaves of the pecan near St. Martinsville, La. At that time growing of pecans was confined mostly to native trees in Illinois, Indiana, Tennessee, Texas, Louisiana, Oklahoma, Arkansas, and Mississippi. The first orchards were planted in Louisiana and Mississippi about 1880. By 1900 several large orchards had been planted in Georgia and Florida and orchard plantings had increased in the Southwestern States. Now the industry is extensive in the Southeast as well as the Southwest.

On the leaves, shoots, and nuts of susceptible varieties, the fungus causes premature defoliation and mummified nuts. Severely infected nuts may drop prematurely or they may die and remain attached to the shoots for an indefinite period. The scab disease is perpetuated from the old lesions. Because growing tissue only is susceptible, both foliage and nuts become immune to scab at maturity.

Pecan scab has been reported in every State where the crop is grown, but the disease causes most damage in localities where rainfall is frequent and high humidity prevails.

Most varieties are susceptible to scab, but only in sections where the fungus thrives. Infection depends on the presence of a strain or race of the fungus capable of attacking the variety grown. Susceptible varieties may appear immune for a limited time in isolated orchards or even over extensive areas and later succumb to the disease when a suitable physiological strain of the causal organism develops or is introduced and becomes established. The various strains are becoming more uniformly distributed in areas where weather conditions favor the development and spread of the fungus.

Sanitary measures and spraying are essential for effective control of scab. Old shucks and leaf stems should be knocked off before the trees begin to leaf out in the spring. The removal of low limbs that prevent plowing near trees will aid in scab control by letting in sunlight, permit better air circulation, and so allow leaves and nuts to dry quickly after heavy dews or rains. The limbs may be removed by pruning or pasturing with livestock, especially cattle.

A large number of fungicides, including various strengths of bordeaux mixture, insoluble copper compounds, iron, and wettable sulfurs have been used in experimental work for the control of pecan scab. M. B. Waite, of the Department of Agriculture, did pioneer work on the disease in 1909. He found that of all the materials tested, postpollination spray applications of a home-made high-lime bordeaux mixture gave the best control of scab. I used the mixture for some years with varying success. Later J. R. Large and I tested a prepollination spray program and changed the formula from high-lime to low-lime bordeaux. More recently we have found that ziram and zineb, when preceded by prepollination applications of low-lime bordeaux mixture, give good results. They control scab, improve the condition of the foliage, and often reduce infestation of black aphids.

Timing and thoroughness of the spray applications are important. Sometimes weather conditions make it impossible to spray at the proper time to prevent early infection on the young nuts, but when that does occur and the later applications are properly applied to the trees, secondary infection can be prevented and good nuts produced. The big handicap is the cost, which limits economic control to the most favorably located orchards.

THE WORST FOLIAGE DISEASES on pecans are downy spot, brown leaf spot, pecan leaf blotch, vein spot, and liver spot. They always cause some injury to pecans in many localities. Occasionally they are a limiting factor in nut production. When pecan trees are defoliated prematurely, the nuts fail to fill and mature properly. Also, new foliage often develops, uses up food material that should be stored in the trees for the following year's crop, and prevents a set of nuts that year.

Foliage diseases usually occur in trees that are crowded or are otherwise growing under unfavorable conditions. Sometimes they may cause about as much economic damage as scab because healthy leaves are essential to the production of good crops.

A good orchard-management program that keeps the trees in a vigorous condition and the proper spacing of trees so they can take advantage of sunlight will keep down losses from foliage diseases.

Sprays to control scab will also control foliage diseases. In orchards that do not need sprays for scab, one or two applications of bordeaux mixture, ziram, or zineb will usually control the leaf diseases.

COTTON ROOT ROT is caused by a soil-inhabiting fungus and is present in Texas and other States westward to the Pacific coast. It attacks many crops. It is common in cotton and alfalfa fields and has killed pecan trees in Texas and Arizona. The disease is most active during the summer, when the fungus invades the roots and eventually causes their death. Injury to the roots reduces the moisture supply and the leaves dry out. The symptoms may occur within a few days. They may be prolonged over one or more seasons; then part or all of the foliage may be chlorotic and sparse. We know of no practical control of the root rot disease. Growers are advised not to plant pecans in soil infested with the root rot fungus, especially where cotton or alfalfa have been grown.

CROWN GALL is a bacterial disease of pecan trees in both nursery and the orchard. On trees of bearing age the disease is confined mostly to the roots and base of the tree trunk, but occasionally lateral roots also are affected. Wartlike, somewhat fragile growths, a few inches to a foot or more in diameter, are its distinguishing characteristics. Sometimes the growths extend several inches above the ground line. Because of their fragility, the galls often are broken off the roots and become scattered on top of the soil when the orchard is being cultivated.

To control crown gall, it is important to avoid using infected nursery stock, which should be destroyed, preferably by burning at the time of digging. It is suggested that the galls be removed from infected orchard trees and the wounds painted with a mixture of 1 part creosote to 3 parts coal tar. Close cultivation of diseased trees should be avoided.

A DISEASE, named bunch on account of its characteristic symptoms, was first found in 1932 on trees growing in the Red River Valley near Shreveport, La. Its economic importance has not been established. Its distinguishing symptom is the broomlike formation of branches and shoots, which may appear on small or large lateral branches and on sucker growth. In advanced cases, clusters of willowy sprouts may develop directly from the trunk or large main limbs.

The disease may appear in the lower, central, or topmost parts of the tree and then spread to the adjacent branches until the entire tree becomes diseased. We have no record of trees actually dying from the disease, but in several instances the trees were so severely diseased that the growers destroyed them.

Bunch disease is quite similar in appearance to the bunch diseases of Persian, Japanese, and native species of walnut and to black locust, all of which are caused by viruses. Furthermore, it has at least one characteristic of the phony peach disease in that phony trees usually foliate several days in advance of normal trees. In this respect bunch is also similar to peach yellows.

The geographical range known in 1953 extended east into Mississippi along the Mississippi River; west to Austin, Texas; north beyond Wewoka, Okla.; and south to Alexandria, La.

Susceptible varieties include Mahan, Schley, Burkett, Mobile, Success, Centennial, Pabst, Van Deman, Russell, and Moneymaker. The Stuart apparently is highly resistant or is a symptomless carrier of the disease. Several diseased native seedling trees have been top-worked to Stuart and the scions have remained healthy for several years.

Bunch disease appears to be infectious, but no parasite has been found associated with diseased growth.

Little is definitely known about the control of bunch disease. Control measures therefore can only be suggested. It is sound practice to avoid the use of bud or scion wood from diseased trees for propagation. The use of diseased pecan and water hickory trees as stocks should be avoided in working over native stands to standard varieties. To avoid the possible spread of the disease to valuable stands of pecan trees, diseased pecan and water hickory trees growing wild near orchards should be destroyed, and care taken to prevent the survival of sprouts. The pruning out of the diseased branches in lightly affected trees (the cut being made some distance back from any signs of the disease) may eradicate the disease from a tree. Once a lateral branch is affected back to the trunk or main part of a tree, there is little hope of preventing its gradual spread through the whole tree.

PECAN ROSETTE, a nutritional disease, is caused by an inadequate amount of available zinc in the soil to provide the tree with its requirements for growth and nut production. J. J. Skinner and J. B. Demaree, while conducting tests for rosette control in southern Georgia in 1922, were able to bring badly rosetted trees that were growing on soils low in organic matter back to normal by growing and turning under two green manure crops each year. Chemical fertilizers, as used in the experiment, had no influence in increasing or decreasing rosette. A decade later, several research men, working on pecans in Louisiana and Arizona and in California on apple, pear, peach, plum, cherry, and walnut trees and grape vines, discovered independently that zinc applied to the trees or vines by soil applications, dips, or sprays to the leaves, or by other means effected a control or cure of the disease known as rosette or littleleaf.

In its early stage, pecan rosette shows a yellow mottling and crinkling of leaves in the tops of the trees. As the disease progresses, the symptoms appear on the leaves of the lower branches. In advanced stages the leaves become dwarfed, the internodes of the terminal shoots are shortened, and gradually the twigs and branches in the tops of the trees die.

Severely rosetted trees usually do not produce and may become so weakened that they die from attacks of borers or from other causes. Rosette alone, however, has never been known to kill pecan trees.

A varietal resistance or susceptibility seems to exist. Stuart is the most susceptible. In most localities Moneymaker usually is quite resistant.

Rosette may be corrected by applying a solution of zinc sulfate as a spray to the trees or the dry salt to the soil; the method of application is determined largely by soil conditions. Soil applications are not practical in orchards where trees are growing on neutral or alkaline soils; then spraying is necessary. Spraying is satisfactory regardless of the soil condition.

Three spray applications of a solution consisting of 2 pounds of zinc sulfate, analyzing approximately 36 percent zinc and added to 100 gallons of water, will overcome rosette if it is present in the mild form. The first application should be made as soon after pollination as possible. Two further applications should be made at intervals of 3 to 4 weeks. That schedule should be followed annually until all signs of the disease have been eliminated. Then observations should be made regularly for the first signs of its recurrence—it is likely to reappear at any time.

On heavy calcareous soils, where spray applications are not practical, A. O. Alben and H. E. Hammer reported in 1944 that some compost comprising zinc sulfate, manure, and sulfur, and applied in furrows in rather large amounts and plowed under, would overcome rosette in about 2 years.

Zinc sulfate applied to the acid soil where pecans are growing will produce more satisfactory results than spray applications because its effect lasts longer. The zinc sulfate should be broadcast evenly from near the trunk to beyond the limb spread. The rate of application is determined largely by severity of the disease, nature of the soil, and size of the trees. The normal recommendation in Southeastern States is 10 pounds to a tree, applied annually until all signs of rosette have been eliminated from the tree.

Winter injury is usually found on young, vigorous, late-growing pecan trees or those that were defoliated in summer and put out a new crop of leaves late in the season. Older trees, especially those that have received heavy applications of nitrogen, which tends to keep them in a vegetative condition late in the season, may be severely injured by sudden freezes.

The symptoms are dead or dying trees in early summer. Vigorous sprouts grow up later from the roots. Close examination will show that the trunks of the trees have been damaged near the ground. The affected tree usually foliates and grows normally in the spring, but the leaves wither and the tree suddenly dies as soon as hot weather begins. Shot-hole borers and other insects are sometimes present, but their damage is of a secondary nature. A cut through the bark into the cambium layer near the ground discloses the "sour-sap" and discolored wood.

Young trees should be fertilized only in early spring and should not be cultivated later than midsummer, except at the time of planting winter cover crops in the fall when the trees are approaching dormancy.

Injury from sunscald is sometimes confused with winter injury. The symptoms are dead or cankerous areas, usually on the southwest side of the trees or on the tops of larger branches.

One of the best methods of control is to head the young trees as close to the ground as practicable. Lower limbs should not be pruned until the trees have advanced several growing seasons.

JOHN R. COLE, *a plant pathologist, is in charge of pecan disease control at the United States Pecan Field Laboratory, Albany, Ga. He became affiliated with the Department in 1924 and began pecan disease control work at Thomasville, Ga. He was later transferred to Lafayette and Shreveport, La., where he was in charge of pecan disease investigations in the southwestern United States.*

Filberts and Persian Walnuts

Paul W. Miller

The Persian, or English, walnut (*Juglans regia*) is prey to several diseases that harm its growth and reduce the quality and yield of nuts. Some, called parasitic diseases, are caused by micro-organisms that live as parasites on the host plant. Other disorders, known as nonparasitic diseases, result from unfavorable weather conditions, unsuitable soil, or deficiency or excess of one or more mineral elements in the soil.

Bacterial blight of walnuts, caused by *Xanthomonas juglandis*, is of greater economic importance than all other diseases of walnuts together. Its prevalence and destructiveness vary from year to year. It is usually much worse in the foggy coastal districts of the Pacific coast than in inland localities. More than 50 percent of the crop in unsprayed orchards has been lost in years of epidemic outbreaks.

The leaves, nut, catkins, buds, and shoots of current growth are attacked. The disease first appears in the spring on the young leaves as small, reddish-brown spots at the margins or in the tissues between the veins. On the stems the disease causes black, slightly depressed spots, which often girdle the shoots and cause them to die back. Young leaf and catkin buds turn dark brown or black and die. It is most serious and destructive on the nuts, on which it causes black spots of varying size.

The causal organism lives over from

one year to the next primarily in diseased buds and to a lesser extent in hold-over cankers on twigs of the previous year's growth. The bacteria are disseminated principally by raindrops from hold-over sources of infection. The bacteria enter the tissues of the current growth through pores (stomata). Long and frequent rains just before and during blossoming and for about 2 weeks thereafter may bring serious outbreaks, as the nuts are most susceptible then. Infections that occur after the nuts are about three-fourths grown are of little economic importance because they seldom reach the shell. Infected pollen grains from diseased catkins also sometimes distribute bacteria.

The blight can be controlled by timely and thorough applications of certain copper compounds.

Any one of the following spray materials, properly applied, is effective: (1) Bordeaux 4–2–100 (or 6–3–100 in exceptionally wet districts). A summer oil emulsion, at the rate of 1 pint of oil emulsion to every 100 gallons of bordeaux mixture should be added to prebloom applications to reduce the severity of leaf injury in the event that conditions favor its development. (2) Yellow cuprous oxide (Yellow Cuprocide) at the rate of 1 pound in 100 gallons of water (1½–100 in exceptionally wet districts). (3) Tetra-copper-calcium oxychloride (Copper A Compound) at the rate of 2 pounds in 100 gallons of water (3 pounds to 100 in exceptionally wet districts).

Any one of the following dust formulations is effective if enough timely treatments are applied: (1) Copper-lime-sulfur-oil dust composed of 15 percent monohydrated copper sulfate, 30 percent hydrated lime, 10 percent dusting sulfur, 39½ percent talc, 2 percent bentonite, 2 percent diatomaceous earth, and 1½ percent light mineral oil. (2) Yellow cuprous oxide-sulfur dust composed of 5 percent yellow cuprous oxide, 15 percent dusting sulfur, 78 percent talc, and 2 percent diatomaceous earth.

If the walnut orchard is interplanted with filberts, the sulfur should be omitted from the formulas I have given, as it sometimes is toxic to filbert foliage. The following dust mixtures are recommended in a mixed orchard of walnuts and filberts: (1) 15 percent monohydrated copper sulfate, 30 percent hydrated lime, 49½ percent talc, 2 percent bentonite, 2 percent diatomaceous earth, and 1½ percent light mineral oil. (2) 5 percent yellow cuprous oxide, 93 percent talc, and 2 percent diatomaceous earth.

The number of spray applications needed to control the disease satisfactorily varies with the season. In years when the rainfall is sparse during the infection period, one properly timed application will control it. If the rains are heavy and frequent during this period, as many as three properly timed applications are required to control the disease satisfactorily. Since it is impossible to predict the weather during the infection period, the wisest course is to apply the maximum number of applications, which should be made in (a) the early preblossom stage; (b) the late preblossom stage; and (c) the early postblossom stage of pistillate flower development.

Four to six dust applications will be needed to control walnut blight, depending on the amount of rainfall during the critical period for infection. In years when the rainfall is light during the infection period, four properly timed applications will control the disease. In seasons of heavy rainfall during this period, as many as six properly spaced applications are required. The safest course is to apply six applications every year, at approximately 7-day intervals, beginning in the early preblossom stage.

CROWN ROT is caused by the fungus *Phytophthora cactorum*, a "water mold" that thrives best under wet conditions.

Crown rot attacks the bark below the ground line and produces dark-brown or black, irregular cankers or decayed areas at the crown. The infected areas are soft or spongy and usually are confined to the bark. The wood is not attacked, although the disease may discolor it inwards a short space. A black fluid often accumulates in cavities in the cambial region and eventually finds its way to the surface. In more advanced stages the disease extends outward on the lateral roots and kills the taproot. The cankers usually stop at the graft union but occasionally extend into the trunk beyond the union.

The first indication of infection in the above-ground parts of the tree is usually a somewhat stunted appearance, accompanied by sparse, yellowish-green foliage and poor twig growth. The affected trees often set an unusually heavy crop of nuts. In more advanced cases, the trees appear drought-stricken in midsummer, the leaves turn yellow, wither, or drop prematurely; the twigs and smaller branches die back. The tree generally succumbs the following year.

The disease occurs most frequently on trees located in poorly drained or wet soils or in soils where excessive flood irrigation is practiced.

The most effective method of control is to grow walnuts that are grafted on Persian or Paradox hybrid rootstocks.

In orchards of trees grafted on susceptible roots, it is best to expose the crown and basal parts of the main roots to the sunshine and air. That can be done by digging a hole about 18 inches wide and 1 to 2 feet deep around the base of the tree. Leaves and other material should be kept out of the trench so that the crown will be kept dry. Irrigation water should never be permitted to come closer than 4 feet from the tree. The crowns should be exposed when the disease is first noted.

In regions of cold winters it is advisable to cover up the crowns before cold weather begins; cold injury may otherwise result.

Sometimes one can control the disease when the lesions are still small or localized by cutting out the infected areas. The wounds should be disin-

fected with bichloride of mercury 1–1,000, and then covered with bordeaux-linseed oil paint or some other good wound dressing that contains a fungicide.

BRANCH WILT is caused by the fungus *Hendersonula toruloidea* (*Exosporina fawcetti*).

Its first manifestation is a sudden wilting of the leaves on some branches in midsummer or late summer. The disease usually appears first on the smaller twigs and branches, but later may involve large limbs. It may appear in any part of the tree, though it is more common on the south or southwest sides. All leaves on an affected branch wilt at once and then dry to a brownish color but remain attached to the branches until late winter. The bark and wood of the wilted limbs are dark brown or almost black. Similar dead areas may also be found on branches not yet wilted. The discolored areas, or cankers, commonly occur on the upper side of the branch and are frequently centered around sunburned areas or injuries made by harvesting hooks or poles. The discoloration in the wood is caused by a dark-brown deposit, which fills the cells and prevents the normal upward flow of water to the leaves.

A noticeable feature is the loosening and sloughing away of the outer layer of corky bark over the diseased areas. A dark-brown or black powdery deposit is then exposed. The deposit is composed of numerous, dark-brown spores of the causal fungus which are disseminated by wind and rain.

The varieties of walnuts most commonly affected are Franquette and Mayette. Meylan, Eureka, Blackmer, Payne, and Concord varieties also have been found affected. Concord is the most resistant.

Since a lack of vigor increases susceptibility to the disease, trees should be kept in as healthy a condition as possible by proper fertilization, adequate irrigation, and proper culture. All diseased branches should be removed as soon as they are discovered. When diseased branches are removed, the cut should be made well back of the most advanced margins of the affected areas. All wounds should be covered with a good wound dressing such as bordeaux-linseed oil paint. One should try not to injure the branches with harvesting hooks and poles. Experiments indicate that bordeaux mixture (10-10-100) applied after leaf fall helps prevent infection.

MELAXUMA (black sap) is caused by the fungus *Dothiorella gregaria*. It attacks the twigs, branches, and trunk, and generally produces an inky-black liquid, which oozes out of the surface of infected areas. The bark beneath is discolored. It eventually dies and forms a slightly sunken canker.

All cankers on the larger limbs and trunk should be cut out. All of the discolored bark and some of healthy bark around the advanced margins also should be removed. The wounds thus made should be disinfected with bichloride of mercury, 1-1,000, and subsequently painted with bordeaux paste or paint.

BLOTCH is caused by the fungus *Gnomonia leptostyla* (*Marssonia juglandis*). It attacks the leaves, young shoots, and nuts. On the leaves, it produces roundish, reddish-brown spots, that have grayish-brown centers and are up to three-fourths inch in diameter. On the stems of shoots of current growth, the lesions appear as oval to irregularly circular, sunken, light-grayish-brown, dead areas, which have dark, reddish-brown margins.

Blotch is most serious and destructive on the nuts. On them it causes depressed, circular to irregularly circular, dead spots in the husk. They are not quite so large as those on the leaves. Very young nuts that are infected do not develop normally and drop to the ground prematurely. The disease may reduce the yield greatly when it is exceptionally severe.

The fungus overwinters in old infected leaves and nuts on the ground and in cankers on twigs of the preceding year's growth. During rainy periods in the spring, the spores (ascospores) are forcibly ejected from fruiting bodies of another type (perithecia), which develop in the old diseased leaves and nuts and are carried by air currents to the new growth, where they induce primary infection. Spores produced in fruiting bodies in old lesions on twigs are also a source of primary infection. Successive generations of summer spores borne in primary and secondary lesions subsequently spread the disease.

Walnut blotch attacks the eastern black walnut (*J. nigra*), the Hinds black walnut, and the Persian walnut. In the Eastern States it is also found on the butternut (*J. cinerea*). It is rare on the Persian walnut on the Pacific coast; it has been reported only on a few seedlings near Bellingham, Wash.

Timely spraying with bordeaux mixture will control the disease on the butternut. The spray applications should be made when (a) the leaves are unfolding, (b) they are full-sized, and (c) about 2 weeks after the second application.

The same or a similar spray program may be effective on Persian walnuts. Plowing under the old infected leaves on the ground before the spores are shed in the spring also is advised.

RING SPOT is caused by the fungus *Ascochyta juglandis*. It causes round, brown spots, one-eighth inch to 1 inch in diameter, in the leaf tissues between the veins. Its most distinguishing feature is the ringed, targetlike ridges in the affected areas. The lesions may merge and involve still larger areas.

The fungus apparently overwinters primarily in old infected leaves on the ground, from which the spores are spread during rainy periods in the spring.

Ring spot is of minor economic importance. It does not significantly reduce the functional leaf areas or cause premature defoliation. It is rarely seen in orchards sprayed with bordeaux mixture for the control of walnut blight—an indication that the walnut blight control program will also control ring spot.

THE BLACK-LINE (girdle) disorder of grafted walnuts is first marked by poor growth of the shoots and premature yellowing and shedding of the leaves of a part or all of the tree. Death usually follows in 3 to 5 years after the first symptoms are noted in the top of the tree. The decline and eventual death of the tree is caused by a breakdown or separation of the conductive tissues at the graft union.

The first internal evidence of the disorder is the appearance of small, water-soaked, chocolate-colored places in the bark at the point of the union. Later the spots spread horizontally. Often two or more of them coalesce and penetrate the wood. Only a few inches of the circumference of the new tissues at the point of the union may be affected at first, but eventually a narrow, corky, nonconductive layer extends around the tree and cuts off the transfer of water and minerals, so that the tree dies. Black-line occurs in both limb-grafted and crown-grafted trees.

The disorder has been found in the Pacific Northwest only in the Franquette variety grafted on black walnut rootstocks (*J. hindsii, J. nigra*, or their hybrids). A number of other commercial varieties, including Payne, Concord, Mayette, and Eureka, grafted on black walnut rootstocks, have been found affected in California. It has never been found or reported in Persian walnuts grafted on seedling Persian walnut rootstocks in California or Oregon.

The exact cause of black-line is not known. Apparently it is not of parasitic origin, as no parasite has been found to be constantly associated with its occurrence. One theory is that it is due to delayed incompatibility between stock and scion; the fact that it is found only in Persian walnuts grafted on black walnut rootstocks supports that theory. There appears to be a relationship in California between the time of bearing and the time of development of black-line. The early-bearing varieties, such as the Payne, are affected earlier in the life of the tree—an indication that it is either heavy production or the slowing down of growth, or both, that is associated with the development of black-line.

No satisfactory method for the control of black-line is known. Inarching the black walnut suckers coming from the rootstock into the Persian top has been attempted, but so far without any degree of success. Persian seedling walnuts have been planted around the trees and attempts made to inarch them into the trunks of the affected trees, but the results have not been very successful.

Seedlings of the Franquette and other varieties of Persian walnut are used as rootstocks instead of Hinds black walnut by certain nurserymen in order to avoid the disorder. That should result in control as the disorder has so far never been found in Franquettes grafted on Persian walnut rootstocks.

SOME DISEASES attack both Persian walnuts and filberts.

Crown gall is due to the bacterial organism, *Agrobacterium tumefaciens*. It causes galls or overgrowths generally at the collar or root crown but occasionally on the trunk, branches, and lateral roots. The galls appear at the collar or root crown as large, dark-brown or black enlargements with roughened, convoluted surfaces. They may be on only one side of the tree or they may extend around the circumference of the crown or collar. The galls, hard and woody, increase in size from year to year and persist for many years.

The causal organism gains access to the tissues only through wounds. If never penetrates an unbroken surface. The bacteria multiply in the tissues near the surface. With the sloughing off of the outer parts of the gall, many bacteria are discharged into the soil, where they live for a long time.

The incidence of crown gall in an orchard is associated largely with cultural practices. In orchards where the trees are relatively shallow-rooted and deep plowing or disking is done, the trees have more galls on the lateral roots than where shallow plowing or disking is carried on.

The overgrowths or swellings that often occur just below the graft union on Persian walnuts grafted on Hinds black walnut or Paradox hybrids should not be confused with the crown gall disease. Such overgrowths are not pathological but occur because the rootstocks grow faster than the Persian walnut top.

Crown gall can be controlled by surgery (in early stages of infection only) or by painting the galls with a chemical mixture consisting of 20 percent sodium dinitro cresylate (Elgetol) and 80 percent methyl alcohol (methanol). (If only 30 percent Elgetol is available, the mixture should consist of 1 part of Elgetol to 6½ parts of methanol.)

All nursery stock should be carefully inspected before planting and any trees that have galls or suspicious-looking overgrowths should be discarded.

Care should be taken in cultivating the orchard not to injure the collar, crown, or root system, since the presence of any wounds increases the possibility of infection.

Mushroom root rot on Persian walnuts and filberts is caused by the fungus *Armillaria mellea*, whose fruiting bodies consist of honey-colored or light brown "toadstools" or mushrooms, which often appear in clusters about the base of infected areas, generally in October or November. Whether they develop depends on the weather and the extent of the decay.

Mushroom root rot attacks the roots, the root crown, and basal part of the tree trunk. The first sign of affliction is usually poor growth of the shoots, attended by a premature dropping of the

leaves. Only a part of a tree corresponding to the side of the root system first attacked by the fungus may be affected at first. Two to five years generally elapse before the tree finally dies. If the root crown or main roots of an infected tree are uncovered, dark brown or black, rootlike structures, about the thickness of a pencil lead, will usually be found clinging tightly to the surface or just under the bark. The structures, known as rhizomorphs, are a sign of the disease. They resemble roots somewhat but branch in a different way. Rhizomorphs may be absent if conditions are unfavorable for their development.

If the root of an infected tree is cut open, a white or tan fungus growth will be found scattered through the tissues. Frequently a concentration of the fungus mycelium occurs in the cambial region (the region between the wood and the bark), where it appears as a soft, tender, white or tan, fan-shaped, flat fungus growth. The white mycelium is never found on the surface of the root but is always buried within the tissues. The fungus extends into the wood, causing it to decay and become soft and spongy. The infected tissues have a sharp, mushroomlike smell. Eventually the root crown or collar of the tree is completely invaded and the tree dies as a result of starvation due to girdling.

The disease is at first restricted to certain areas of the orchard. The areas keep enlarging by the annual death of more and more trees around the periphery until the whole orchard may become infected.

The causal fungus may be brought into a planting on infected nursery stock or it may be native in the soil where it previously lived on the roots of such trees as oaks, willows, and firs. When the land was cleared, there were left behind infected roots, which serve as a source of infection for susceptible plants subsequently planted on the land. The fungus can live for many years on old, rotten pieces of root.

The pathogen is spread from one

spot or one tree to another by fungus rhizomorphs, which grow through the soil by contaminated running water or possibly cultivating tools.

The fungus produces fruiting structures, commonly called toadstools, if conditions are favorable. The toadstools produce spores, which germinate and produce the vegetative part of the fungus (mycelium). The fungus first develops as a saprophyte that feeds on rotting roots, dead tree stumps, or decaying vegetation in the soil. After a time, rhizomorphs are produced. The rhizomorphs push their way through the soil and gain access to the plant or root through wounds made during cultivation or by borers, mice, and such. They may also penetrate through the epidermis directly by means of a germ tube and infect the living tissues.

The pathogen, once established in the soil, is hard to control. Generally the disease is not noticed until a considerable part of the root system or root crown is involved. If the disease is discovered while the lesions are still small and localized, it is sometimes possible to save the tree by cutting out all the infected areas and painting the wounds with a good disinfectant such as an alcoholic solution of bichloride of mercury (1 part bichloride of mercury, 250 parts of denatured alcohol, 750 parts of water).

The treated roots should be left exposed to the sun and air for a month or so after treatment to permit them to dry out thoroughly.

When walnuts and filberts are growing in soil known to be contaminated with the mushroom root rot fungus, it is wise to throw the soil back from the crown and main roots of all trees, which should be left exposed to the air and sunshine during the summer months to slow up progress of the disease. This practice is also helpful in preventing new infections—but the exposed parts should be covered with soil before winter, or cold injury may result.

Since the root rot fungus spreads through the soil and thus contaminates more and more land and kills more and more trees, it is desirable to restrict its spread as much as possible and to hold it at least within the area already contaminated. Trenching around the contaminated area has been recommended to keep the fungus from spreading. Experiments in California, however, indicate that that is not a satisfactory way to prevent the spread of the fungus unless the trench is at least 6 feet deep and left continuously open; in most instances that is not practical, because it interferes with cultivation and because keeping the trench open is difficult.

The most effective method for the control of mushroom root rot would be to plant walnuts grafted on resistant rootstocks. The eastern black walnut is reported to be highly resistant to mushroom root rot. For many years Hinds black walnut was believed to be highly resistant, but *Armillaria mellea* has been found on its roots in California and Oregon.

The discovery of the fungus in black walnut roots makes it inadvisable to recommend without reservation Persian walnuts grafted on Hinds black walnut roots for land contaminated with the mushroom root rot fungus. Using Hinds black walnut as a stock will not necessarily guarantee freedom from mushroom root rot.

It is possible to kill the fungus in the soil by treatment with powerful soil disinfectants, among the most effective of which are carbon disulfide and chloropicrin. Carbon disulfide is preferable as it is less dangerous to use and not so costly. The method used in applying carbon disulfide is to inject 2 ounces by weight (⅜ ounce liquid measure) of the material in holes 8 inches deep and spaced on an equilateral triangle 18 inches apart each way. The holes must be plugged immediately after application for the gas fumes to be effective. The 2-ounce dose is enough to kill the fungus to a depth of 5 or 6 feet. Since the gas produced is heavier than air, the liquid should not be applied at too great a depth; otherwise, satisfactory kill of the fungus will not be had at the surface of the ground. For light, sandy soils, the depth of application should be about 8 to 10 inches; in heavy soil types, not more than 6 to 8 inches. Carbon disulfide is highly inflammable and should be handled carefully. All living trees and other vegetation, as well as the fungus in the treated area, are killed, but the fumes soon disperse, and the area can eventually be replanted. All infected trees should be taken out before the soil is treated.

All the affected soil area must be thoroughly treated if the spread of the fungus is to be stopped. Treatment of the hole made in the removal of a diseased tree is not enough. The exact determination of the extent to which the fungus has penetrated the soil is difficult. For safety, consequently, the treatment should be extended beyond the probable limits of fungus distribution. Sometimes it may be necessary to sacrifice apparently healthy trees around the area to exceed the apparent limits of contamination.

Walnut and filbert orchards should not be planted on newly cleared land where infected native oak trees formerly stood. Care should also be taken not to injure the basal part of the trunk or the main roots of walnut trees during cultivation, for such wounds increase the chance of infection by providing an easy avenue of entry for the fungus into the tissues.

FILBERT bacterial blight, caused by *Xanthomonas corylina*, is the most destructive parasitic disease of the filbert. It is present in practically all filbert orchards in Oregon and Washington. Its prevalence and destructiveness vary with the season. It causes considerable damage in years of heavy rainfall in fall and winter.

The organism attacks the buds, leaves, branches, and trunk. Occasionally it attacks the nuts, but seldom does it invade the roots.

The disease manifests itself as small, angular or round, pale yellowish-green water-soaked spots in the blades of the leaves. The lesions later turn reddish brown.

The first evidence of infection of the stems of shoots of the current season's growth consists of dark-green, water-soaked areas in the bark. They later turn reddish brown. The lesions often encircle the stems and cause the leaves on the distal parts to turn brown and die. The dead leaves generally cling to the girdled stems for some time and look as though they had been killed by fire.

One- and two-year-old twigs are also attacked and killed. Infection of such twigs takes place indirectly through wounds or by invasion of the bacteria from blighted buds and diseased shoots of the current season's growth. The lesions frequently girdle and kill the twigs. Twig infection is of considerable economic importance, because many of the killed twigs are potential nut bearers.

The formation of cankers on the tree trunk is the most serious aspect of the disease, especially when they girdle and kill the trees, as often happens in orchards up to 4 years old. The trunk is seldom infected after the fourth year, but many buds and nut-bearing twigs in the tops of older trees are attacked and killed.

The original source of infection is diseased nursery stock, from which it is spread by cultural operations and rain. Shears or knives used in pruning or suckering may be readily contaminated with the bacteria by accidentally cutting through an active canker. Unless a disinfectant is used on the tools, the germs are carried to adjoining trees, where other centers of infection may be established.

While bacterial blight can and does attack healthy, vigorous trees, the damage is accentuated when the trees have been weakened or injured by sunscald, cold, drought, improper drainage, or other adverse factors. The tissues of devitalized or injured trees offer much less resistance to infection and the subsequent extension of the diseased areas than do those of strong, vigorous trees. It is therefore important that the trees be kept healthy and vigorous to lessen the damage in the event of infection.

Tree losses from blight traceable to contaminated tools can be prevented by sterilizing the tools with a good germicide, such as a 95-percent solution of methyl alcohol (methanol). The use of such a sterilizing agent on the tools is particularly advisable when suckering and pruning young trees, 1 to 4 years old, as lesions on the trunks during that period frequently girdle and kill the trees.

The incidence of bud and twig blight due to bacterial blight can be reduced in both young and old orchards by timely spraying with bordeaux mixture (6–3–100). The addition of a commercial wetting and sticking agent, such as Dupont spreader-sticker, to bordeaux mixture will increase its effectiveness. In a normal season one application of bordeaux mixture, made in August before the first fall rain, is generally enough to give good control. In seasons of heavy rainfall in fall and winter, supplementary applications in late fall when the leaves are about three-fourths off the tree and in the early spring when the leaf buds are breaking open are necessary to hold the disease in check.

It is possible to combine in one mixture the spray materials recommended for the control of bacterial blight with that recommended for control of the filbert worm and thus save time and labor required to make separate applications. This combination spray consists of bordeaux mixture (6–3–100) plus lead arsenate, 3 pounds in 100 gallons of mixture. To this should be added an efficient, compatible spreader-sticker, such as Dupont spreader-sticker. In preparing this combination spray, the bordeaux mixture should always be made up first, then lead arsenate and the spreader-sticker added in that order. This spray material should be applied after the moths

of the filbert worm begin to lay eggs but before any eggs hatch. In a normal season in the Pacific Northwest, the first moths generally emerge in early July and continue doing so for a month or more.

The filbert is very susceptible to wood and heart rots caused by a variety of wood-rotting fungi.

Those organisms cause a rotting and decay of the heartwood and sapwood. The disease generally begins around pruning cuts and other injuries and works its way back into healthy tissues. Most of the organisms causing wood rots gain access to the tissues through injuries from pruning, careless cultivation, cold injury, sunscald, windstorms, and ice storms. Stubs of branches left in pruning are one of the common avenues of entry.

All wounds one-half inch or more in diameter, particularly if made in the fall or winter, should be painted at once with a paste made by mixing equal parts of a commercial dry bordeaux mixture and water. Later, after the wound has dried out and started to heal, a semipermanent wound dressing containing a fungicide, such as bordeaux-linseed oil paint, should be applied to the surface to prevent the entrance of bacteria and fungi.

All large pruning cuts should be made close to the main branch or body of the tree to expedite healing. In removing limbs, care should also be taken not to tear the bark. This danger will be avoided if the branch is cut nearly half through from the under side first and then finished off from above.

PAUL W. MILLER, *a graduate of the Universities of Kentucky and Wisconsin, is a plant pathologist in the Bureau of Plant Industry, Soils, and Agricultural Engineering. He joined the Department of Agriculture in 1929 after being an instructor in plant pathology and research assistant at the University of Wisconsin. Dr. Miller has conducted research on the diseases of apples, vegetable seeds, strawberries, walnuts, and filberts.*

after

harvest

Market Diseases Caused by Fungi

G. B. Ramsey, M. A. Smith

The diseases of the fresh fruits and vegetables caused by fungi during the various phases of the marketing process are due either to contamination and infection that occur during the growing season or to infections through injuries incidental to harvesting, processing, packing, and transporting the produce.

Like all living things, fruits and vegetables are subject to disease and death when invaded by certain kinds of organisms. Of the thousands of fungi found everywhere in the air, soil, and water and on living and dead plants, some invade normal tissues and cause decay, some cause trouble only when injuries open the way for them to enter, and some do not cause damage under any circumstances.

More than 100 fungus diseases may cause decay and blemishes in commercial shipments of fruit. More than 150 cause serious losses in vegetable shipments during transit and marketing. Some crops have as many as 40 different diseases that might cause serious, costly damage by the time the produce reaches the consumer.

The amount of damage and loss from disease varies greatly with the commodity, the kind of disease, the growing conditions, and the handling conditions.

Because the cost of harvesting, grading, packing, and shipping most fruits and vegetables exceeds the value of the commodity itself at the shipping point, it behooves all hands to have all fresh fruits and vegetables graded, packed, and handled carefully and shipped by approved methods so they bring a suitable price and the loss of valuable food during the marketing process is reduced.

BLACK ROT of banana is caused by the fungus *Endoconidiophora paradoxa*. It is present wherever bananas are grown. It enters the bunches through the tips and butts of the stalks when the fruit is harvested. Severe infection may cause 10 to 25 percent of the fruit to drop from the bunches during ripening and marketing.

The evidence of infection on green fruit is the small black areas at the end of the fruit near the point of attachment to the cushion. The cushions and the main stalk may also show similar discolorations, but little or no growth of the fungus occurs on the surface of the fruit.

The green fruit on arrival at the terminal markets is placed in ripening rooms, where temperatures of 60° to 70° F. and a high relative humidity are maintained—conditions ideal for the development of black rot. When the yellow color begins to develop in the fruit, the infected areas become brown. They have slightly water-soaked borders. A fine growth of the fungus appears over infected fruits and stalks. As the fungus continues to invade the peel of the fruit from the point of attachment to the cushion, the peel turns brown or black. The fungus usually does not invade the edible part of the fruit, but the discoloration of the peel may lower its salability.

Control of black rot depends mainly on the prevention of infection of butts and tips of stalks at harvesttime.

BLUE MOLD ROT, caused by the fungus *Penicillium expansum*, destroys many apples in transit, storage, and market. It occurs on all varieties of apples in all parts of the country.

Blue mold is not important as an orchard disease but when rainfall is abundant and humidity is high, the fungus may be present on fallen fruits and on mashed or overripe fruit in the packing house. The spores on them infect fruit in storage and in the packing shed.

The fungus enters the fruits through skin breaks or lenticels. The decay first appears as soft, watery, light brown or yellow spots, which vary in size and may occur on any part of the fruit. The spots are shallow at first but quickly go deeper. Eventually the decay may involve a third or more of the fruit. Within a few days after decay develops, a white surface growth of the fungus appears. It later becomes bluish green when large numbers of spores are produced. Affected fruit has a musty odor when decay is well advanced and spore production is heavy. The decayed flesh has a musty taste.

Important factors in the control of blue mold are careful handling during picking and packing, packing house sanitation, precooling, and prompt storage at 30° to 32° F. Temperatures in transit should not exceed 45°.

BROWN ROT, caused by the fungus *Monilinia fructicola*, attacks peaches, plums, apricots, and cherries in transit, storage, and market. In the orchard the disease may occur on leaves, blossoms, fruits, twigs, and limbs.

On peaches, plums, and apricots, brown rot first appears as small, circular, light-brown spots, which may enlarge so rapidly as to bring about extensive decay in 24 hours if the temperature is between 60° and 70° and the humidity is high. In its early stages on cherries the decayed areas are light brown, but as the disease progresses the margin of the decayed area fades into the normal flesh color, leaving no distinct line separating diseased from healthy tissue. The skin covering the rotted spot remains firmly attached to the tissue beneath. The decayed areas at no stage are sunken, and the flesh remains fairly firm.

As the decay progresses, yellowish-gray masses of the fungus may develop on the surface. They contain millions of spores, which can start the disease on other fruits. Later the skin turns dark brown or black, and the decay extends to the seed.

Peaches harvested from orchards in which brown rot is present are usually contaminated with the spores. When temperature and humidity are favorable, spores may germinate and penetrate the uninjured skin of the fruit or enter through mechanical injuries that occurred in the orchard or during packing operations. Once infection is established, the disease may spread from one fruit to another by contact.

Usually moisture is sufficient in carloads of peaches for spores of the brown rot fungus to germinate and for the fungus to grow in already infected fruit. New infections are almost entirely prevented by temperatures that are below 50°. The maintenance of proper temperatures in refrigeration is therefore important in retarding development of brown rot.

Fruit with a temperature of 85° loaded into a refrigerator car iced to capacity may take 36 to 48 hours to be cooled below 50°. That is enough time for decay to become established. Precooling peaches for 4 to 6 hours to reduce the temperature to 50° is a good way to retard decay in transit.

In standard refrigerator cars brown rot often is more prevalent at the top of the load than at the bottom because the higher temperatures at the top hasten its development. Usually that is not true in modern refrigerator cars equipped with fans that provide forced air circulation and keep the temperature more uniform throughout the load. The fans, built under the floor racks near the ice bunkers in the ends of the cars, draw the warm air from the body of the car into the bottom of the bunker and force the cold air from the bunkers over the top of the load.

Sprays or dusts containing sulfur are commonly used to control brown rot in the orchard. Large peach-packing centers commonly apply sulfur dust during the grading operation. Other fungicides have been used for post-harvest treatments of peaches, but further research is needed to determine their effectiveness in reducing brown rot in transit and on the market.

BULL'S-EYE ROT is a form of decay found in apples and pears from the Pacific Northwest and British Columbia. Six different rots have the bull's-eye appearance.

The most common bull's-eye rots on both apples and pears in the market are caused by the fungi *Neofabraea perennans* and *N. malicorticis*. From the cankers that the fungi make on twigs and branches, spores may be washed by rain to the apples or pears below. Infection of fruit occurs through lenticels. The diseases develop slowly in the fruit and do not become apparent until after it has been in storage several months. Apparently the fungi cannot spread from one fruit to another.

The decay caused by *Neofabraea perennans* usually is centered around lenticels. It is moderately firm, cream- or tan-colored, slightly sunken, and round. It has brown borders. The surface of the rotten place often is covered with creamy-white spore masses.

Careful spraying with bordeaux mixture is the best way to control the diseases in the orchard. Removing diseased limbs and cankers is another effective control measure.

The rot caused by the fungus *Phialophora malorum* is sometimes grouped with the bull's-eye rots. It occurs in the Pacific Northwest and has been found on fruit in the Midwest and East. The rot is fairly firm and usually occurs around the lenticels as small, shallow, roundish, light-brown spots. Infected places on the fruits may join into large spots. There is usually no evidence of fungus growth or spores on infected fruit. The disease does not spread from one fruit to another.

No satisfactory measures for its control have been developed.

GRAY MOLD, caused by the fungus *Botrytis cinerea*, is a serious disease of pears in storage. The fungus, widely distributed, is found on discarded fruit and other debris in orchards and packing houses. The decay it causes is fairly firm. In advanced stages the fruit often has a sour odor.

Infection occurs most often at the stem end but may take place through skin breaks on any part of the fruit. The skin of affected fruits is at first slate gray, and usually there is a sharp line of demarcation between the diseased and healthy tissue. As the decay progresses the fungus may grow on the surface of the fruit. Later many spores are produced that can germinate and cause new infections.

The fungus can grow from one fruit to another by direct contact and even penetrate ordinary paper wrappers. Fruits so infected often cling together to form "nests." A nest often can be traced to a single decayed pear in a box.

The disease develops rapidly at temperatures between 50° and 60° and will even continue to produce decay at the usual cold-storage temperature of 32°.

Prompt cooling of the fruit and proper temperatures during transit and storage reduce the severity of the disease. The most practical method of preventing the spread of decay from one fruit to another in boxes is the use of copper-treated wrappers.

FUSARIUM ROTS often cause considerable losses during transportation and marketing of vegetables. Many species of the fungus are common in soils suitable for growing vegetable crops. Consequently most vegetables are contaminated by *Fusarium* when harvested even though they may not be infected. Some of the most destructive rots that occur during transit and storage result from infections of open wounds or bruises made during harvesting, packing, or transportation. The decays caused by *Fusarium* generally are most important on root crops, tubers, and bulbs, but tomatoes, cucumbers, and melons are also affected.

Some of the most serious losses of stored potatoes are due to infection of the stem end of the tubers by *Fusarium* while they are in the soil, through wounds made during the harvesting and handling of the crop, and following such diseases as late blight tuber rot. In some seasons it is not uncommon to find 10 percent or more of a lot of potatoes affected with fusarium tuber rot after being in storage a few months. The decay is fairly moist and light brown at first and becomes darker brown and somewhat dry with age. When the decayed areas reach a diameter of an inch or more they usually become sunken, the skin is wrinkled, and here and there small tufts of white, pink, or yellowish mold appear. After long storage periods, some of the tubers may be almost completely rotten. Hollow places in some of them are lined with white, pink, or yellow mold.

Care in harvesting and handling to avoid injuries to the tubers and close grading at shipping time will do much to reduce loss by fusarium rot.

Serious loss of onions during transit, storage, and marketing is often due to rot caused by species of *Fusarium*. Infections usually occur through the root system or through injuries made during harvesting and handling.

Onions with visible decay are discarded at packing time, but those with only slight infections are difficult to grade out. They and the onions with wound infections cause much trouble in storage and transit. The decay produced by *Fusarium* is yellowish brown and moist at first but later becomes spongy. A white or pink mold develops in and on the larger decayed places. Badly injured onions and those showing signs of decay should not be stored. If they are shipped they should be used immediately.

The fusarium decays of melons

usually are the result of infection through the stem or bloom end, but the fungus can enter any injured spot. The decay is moist at first but later becomes spongy. Often a conspicuous growth of white or pink mold appears. As the causal organisms grow best at 75° to 80°, the practice of precooling and shipping melons under good refrigeration is effective in checking the development of the decay during transit and marketing.

Tomatoes, peppers, cucumbers, and other kinds of vegetables that grow near or on the surface of the soil often become affected by fusarium decay at places injured by tools and insects and at spots where other diseases have opened the way for invasion. The decay is usually less serious than the fusarium rots of other crops.

GRAY MOLD ROT, caused by *Botrytis cinerea*, is often the cause of considerable loss during transportation, storage, and marketing of many vegetables. It is particularly damaging to some crops grown in foggy, wet weather and moderate temperatures. The causal fungus produces an immense number of spores on the infected plants. The wind-borne spores that alight on the moist surface of a susceptible vegetable germinate and invade the tissues and cause the discolorations and breakdown that we call decay. Infections may also occur through wounds made during harvesting and packing. Then the injured tissue furnishes the moisture that enables the spores to germinate. Once the fungus is within the plant tissues, it cannot be completely controlled because the organism will continue to grow even at temperatures as low as 32° F.

Transit temperatures between 40° and 50° ordinarily found in refrigerated shipments of many vegetables check the development of gray mold rot briefly but do not control it. When the vegetables reach the market and are taken out of refrigeration, the decay develops rapidly.

During long storage periods, gray mold spreads by contact to other plants within the packages. On green vegetables such as artichokes, tomatoes, peppers, peas, and leafy plants, the first sign of gray mold rot is a small, greenish-tan or brown water-soaked spot with an indefinite grayish margin that merges into the healthy tissue. In green tomatoes and peppers, infection usually starts at or near the stem and the decay spreads rapidly over the shoulders and sides of the fruits. Infections may occur anywhere on them. If there is no break in the skin, large decayed areas may be produced without any evidence of surface mold, but at injuries a fine white mold is produced; it later turns grayish brown when spores are produced. The characteristic decay and the grayish-brown, granular spore masses usually serve to identify this disease.

Gray mold rot is a serious cause of losses of storage onions. The fungus is generally inconspicuous in the field, but enough spores may be produced on a few diseased plants to infect large numbers of bulbs during harvest in wet seasons if the necks are not well cured before the onions are stored. Infections of the neck of the bulbs that are not evident when the onions are stored gradually develop into a grayish-brown decay that may involve half the bulb within a month or so. Careful curing in the field or by artificial means is the best control measure.

Gray mold rot also causes considerable damage to stored carrots, parsnips, and similar root crops. It usually affects only the topped roots in storage and is seldom encountered in fresh bunched vegetables. Spores from dead and dying plants contaminate the roots at harvest. Most of the infections occur at the crown where the tissues are injured by topping or through wounds on the sides of the roots. The decay is light brown and water-soaked at first. Later it is somewhat spongy and darker brown. Affected areas usually have a fine white surface mold, which becomes grayish brown as the spores are formed. Once infection has occurred, the decay will continue to progress in cold storage at 32°, but the rate of decay will be retarded. Root crops suspected of having gray mold infection should be inspected periodically in storage.

LATE BLIGHT of potatoes and tomatoes is serious when moist, moderately cool weather prevails for some time during the growing season. It sometimes destroys a large part of the potato and tomato crops throughout the world. In Aroostook County, Maine, where the seriousness of this disease is well understood, an average loss of about 16 percent of the potatoes in storage was reported one season, although growers spent more than a million dollars to spray potatoes to control late blight.

The causal fungus, *Phytophthora infestans*, seems always to be waiting for favorable weather conditions to start an epidemic. Besides being a serious field disease, it causes great loss of potatoes and tomatoes during transportation, storage, and marketing. When rain, fog, or heavy dew keeps the plants wet immediately before and during harvesting, great numbers of spores are produced on the leaves. They contaminate the potato tubers and tomato fruits.

Affected potato tubers may show brown spots of various size anywhere on their surfaces. On late potatoes the decayed areas are firm to leathery and have fairly definite margins. Even after several months of storage the decay seldom penetrates into the tubers more than one-fourth inch. The brown or chocolate-colored decay greatly reduces the marketability of the potatoes. It also opens the way for secondary infection by species of *Fusarium*, which often cause a complete breakdown of the affected tubers during storage. In early or southern-grown potatoes, infections of late blight produce a reddish-brown decay, which sometimes penetrates the tubers to a depth of one-half inch. That in itself causes serious losses in transit

because inconspicuous lesions overlooked at packing time continue to enlarge. To make matters worse, bacterial soft rot often follows in the blight-affected tubers. The result is that a high percentage of the potatoes is a total loss by the time they reach the market.

The disease originates each season from infected tubers used for seed, from volunteer plants that develop from diseased tubers left in the field, or from plants growing on cull piles that have been allowed to remain in or near the field. The amount of late blight infection can be reduced greatly by carefully disposing of the cull potatoes or by killing the sprouts from cull potatoes by burning or weed-killing chemicals.

Late blight may be satisfactorily controlled in most seasons by the use of thorough spray programs, but sometimes the weather is so favorable for development of the disease that satisfactory control cannot be obtained. When the potato plants are infected, a marked degree of control of tuber rot can be had by killing the plants with chemicals or by other means a week or two before the potatoes are harvested and stored.

In one experiment in which the potatoes were harvested and stored when part of the foliage was green and infected with late blight, there was a loss of 48 percent of the tubers in storage; potatoes harvested from the same field after the foliage had been killed developed only 4 percent of late blight tuber rot in storage.

The development of late blight tuber rot in potatoes is influenced greatly by the storage temperatures. Even when tubers are harvested from green plants that show late blight, a great reduction in storage loss may be obtained by storing the potatoes immediately after harvesting at 32° to 36° F. for about 60 days. Tubers harvested and stored immediately at 50° or above may be expected to show about three times as much decay as similar potatoes stored at 32° to 36°.

Most of the tomatoes shipped to distant markets are harvested in the mature green stage so that they will carry without excessive mechanical injury. They ripen during transit or in ripening rooms at the receiving markets. During epidemics of late blight, great numbers of spores from the tomato plants contaminate the fruit at the stem scar and at wounds made during harvesting and packing. Infections and decay that occur while the fruit is still on the plant are usually visible when the fruit is being packed, and affected tomatoes can be sorted out. Infections that occur just before or during harvesting are not visible, however. Sometimes 25 to 50 percent or more of the fruit from diseased vines is lost in transit and during marketing because of decay that results from such invisible infections.

As it takes 3 to 5 days for visible decay to develop after infection, it would be impossible to harvest tomatoes from blighted vines without running a great chance that much of the fruit will rot during transit. The amount of late blight rot that develops in tomatoes during transit varies with the severity of the vine infections and the weather conditions at harvesttime. Tomatoes picked from dry vines after 3 or 4 days of dry, warm weather are much less likely to rot in transit than those picked from the same vines after a few days of foggy or rainy weather. The moist condition of the vines favors the production of spores by the fungus and also favors their germination and infection of the fruit.

The first visible sign of late blight rot in tomatoes is a small, greenish-brown, water-soaked place, usually at the edge of the stem scar. As the decayed spot gets larger, it changes from greenish brown to brown. Often a rusty-brown, irregular line develops between the diseased and healthy tissue.

The fungus penetrates the walls into the seed cavity of the tomato and causes a complete breakdown of the fruit. Usually there is no visible surface growth of the fungus unless the weather is very humid. Then a white mold may appear over some of the larger lesions and in the stem cavity. The rate the decay develops varies with the temperature, but in the usual shipping conditions the fungus can make good growth. Tomatoes that reveal no decay when harvested may show decayed spots, one-half inch to 1½ inches in diameter, after only 6 days in transit. The only way to avoid the development of late blight rot in tomatoes in transit is to stop harvesting fruit from blighted plants during wet weather. Satisfactory control of late blight in tomato fields may be had by thorough spray programs; that in turn will reduce the losses in transit and in the ripening rooms.

IN THE WATERMELON-PRODUCING regions of the Southern States, stem-end rot often causes more decay of the fruit during transit and marketing than all other diseases combined. It is caused by a fungus, *Diplodia*, which lives on decaying plant debris and affects many crops in the Southern States.

It may be inconspicuous on melons during the growing season. Often no trouble is suspected until a report is received from the market that shows that a number of melons have decayed during transit. Nearly all of the decay occurs at the stem end because the fungus requires some kind of a wound, such as the cut stem, to enable it to enter the fruit. When melons are harvested, the cut stem bleeds rather freely; consequently when airborne spores alight on the moist tissue, germination and infection take place. The fungus passes quickly through the stem into the flesh of the fruit, and the decay progresses rapidly throughout the melon.

The first indication of stem-end rot is a brownish discoloration, shriveling, and softening of the stem. After decay progresses to the flesh, the rind tissues about the stem become water-soaked, greenish brown, and somewhat soft. In advanced stages of decay, the affected tissues of the melon become dark brown, sometimes almost black, and there is a surface growth of dark-gray mold. With age, the area about the stem attachment becomes wrinkled. There is an extensive development of black pustules, the spore-bearing bodies of the fungus.

Melons that seem free of infection when harvested may show stem-end rot extending 3 to 5 inches into the end of the fruits by the time they reach the market. It is impossible to grade out all contaminated fruits at the time of shipment because the decay is not evident then. An effective control of stem-end rot is obtained by leaving long stems on the melons when they are harvested in the fields, then recutting the stem when the melons are placed in the car, and painting the cut surface immediately with a copper sulfate paste. Before this treatment was developed, as many as half of the melons in some cars were lost on account of stem-end rot.

WATERY SOFT ROT, caused by the fungus *Sclerotinia sclerotiorum*, is a destructive disease of practically all kinds of vegetable crops. The fungus inhabits the soil to some extent in all vegetable-growing regions.

Watery soft rot is likely to be prevalent in crops grown in damp soils during moderately cool seasons. Plants that become infected in the field may survive and produce a marketable crop, but they harbor the fungus and serious decay often develops while the plants are in transit, storage, and at the market.

The causal organism is particularly damaging because it can grow at the temperatures ordinarily used during transit. It may continue to grow in cold storage at temperatures as low as 32° F. Wounds are not necessary for infection by it and consequently, when a few infected vegetables are enclosed in a package for shipping, it may spread from one plant to another.

All vegetables in the package may decay. In green beans and peas the fungus frequently spreads from one pod to another, so that by the time the commodity reaches the market there may be a large nest of decayed pods, held together by the prolific growth of the white, cottony mold characteristic of the fungus. This type of spread of watery soft rot also occurs commonly in crates of celery.

The decay is typically a soft, watery breakdown, which has no definite odor other than the characteristic odor of the juices that have been liberated from the plant tissue. In green vegetables like beans, peas, lettuce, celery, and cabbage, the decay is tan or brown, water-soaked, and soft. In root crops like carrots, turnips, parsnips, and sweetpotatoes, the decay is yellow or brown, water-soaked, and moderately soft. In advanced stages hard, black, oval resting bodies, the sclerotia, are produced.

No satisfactory control measure is known other than carefully sorting the diseased vegetables at the time of packing and shipping. Commodities harvested from fields known to be severely infected should be marketed as soon as possible. Vegetables known to be slightly infected may be held in cold storage at 32° for a few weeks, but even then the disease will continue to make some progress. They should therefore be marketed promptly.

G. B. RAMSEY *is a pathologist in charge of the Market Disease Laboratory in Chicago. He holds degrees from Indiana University and the University of Chicago. Dr. Ramsey joined the Department of Agriculture in 1919 after serving as assistant pathologist and extension pathologist in Maine.*

M. A. SMITH *holds degrees from Kansas State College, Iowa State College, and the University of Illinois. He joined the Department of Agriculture in 1931, and has conducted research on the storage, transit, and market diseases of fruits and vegetables at the Market Disease Laboratory since 1942.*

The Diseases Bacteria Cause

Wilson L. Smith, Jr., B. A. Friedman

Diseases caused by bacteria are responsible for a large share of the spoilage of fresh fruits and vegetables in storage or during marketing.

Losses from infection by the soft rot group of bacteria are especially important. They attack nearly all vegetables and on each may cause a serious decay within a few hours. They do not cause decay of tree fruits.

Of lesser importance are bacteria that cause leaf, stem, and fruit spotting and internal discoloration and decay. Both tree fruits and vegetables are affected by bacterial diseases of this type. Though the infected areas are usually limited in size and depth and may be trimmed out without serious waste, the spots make the produce unattractive, form places for invasion by other organisms, and cause serious inconvenience and added expense in preparing the produce for use.

The bacteria that cause postharvest diseases of vegetables and fruits belong to five of the six genera of bacteria that cause plant diseases. In the soft rot group are species of the genera *Pseudomonas*, *Erwinia*, and *Bacillus*. Members of the genera *Pseudomonas*, *Xanthomonas*, *Erwinia*, and *Corynebacterium* are responsible for the necrotic lesions on leaves, stems, and fruits, and internal discolorations and decay.

As the two groups differ widely in the symptoms they produce and the plants they attack, we discuss them separately.

Bacteria that produce soft rot are most common on vegetables that have either a succulent, tender type of growth or fleshy storage tissues. Among the first are such leafy vegetables as lettuce, endive, and spinach; stem or stalk types, like asparagus and celery; and the leafy tops of root crops like carrots and radishes. In the second group are potatoes, carrots, radishes, parsnips, beets, and turnips.

The soft rots are well known because of the losses in white potatoes during transit and marketing. Often 1 to 2 percent of the sacks in a car or truck contain potatoes that are affected with bacterial soft rot. Losses of 5 to 10 percent are not uncommon. The appearance of one "wet sack" in a load indicates soft rot infection to the inspector or purchasing agent, and a reduction in the price of the entire load often follows. A 7-year study of railroad car inspection reports for New York City disclosed that losses due to decay of vegetables was 3.8 percent. Bacterial soft rot alone was responsible for 38 percent of the decay and was found on all of the 31 vegetables inspected, except corn and sweetpotatoes.

The first complete account of any bacterial soft rot and its causal organism was one concerning carrots by L. R. Jones in 1901. He named the causal organism *Bacterium carotovorum*. Later the name was changed to *Erwinia carotovora*. Since then soft rots of many of the vegetables have been attributed wrongly to *E. carotovora*, although other species of bacteria were to blame. At least two other species of the genus *Erwinia—E. atroseptica* and *E. aroideae*—cause soft rot of vegetables.

A number of species of the genus *Pseudomonas* have been described as the cause of soft rot. Among them are *P. solanacearum* on potatoes, *P. marginalis*, and *P. viridilividum* on lettuce and endive, and *P. alliicola* and *P. cepacia* on onions. Three species of the genus *Bacillus—B. polymyxa*, *B. subtilis*, and *B. megatherium*—cause extensive soft rot of potatoes. Each of the species has been reported to infect many different vegetables, and soft rot of vegetables after harvest may be caused by bacteria other than *Erwinia carotovora*. Sometimes it may be caused by a combination of several species.

Soft rot starts on leaves, stems, and seed pods as small, water-soaked, translucent spots, which later may become muddy green or greasy. Rapid softening and disintegration of the diseased tissue follows. Within 20 to 48 hours the entire structure may become a wet, slimy mass.

The first symptom of soft rot on root crops is a water-soaked appearance of the affected tissue. The diseased parts later disintegrate into a mushy mass of disorganized cells, which slough off, while the rest of the root remains firm. The bacteria may invade the plant at the crown and the decay may extend deep into the root through the innermost cells while the outer tissues remain apparently healthy.

The first symptoms on tubers often are a dark or black discoloration of the surface and a somewhat blistered appearance of the skin. The affected tissues are usually cream-colored, soft, and not watery. They are separated by a distinct boundary from the sound tissues so that, if pressed, the mushy tissue squirts from the tuber. Often the outer surface of the tubers appears healthy while the inner part is a mass of rotting cells. Upon exposure to air, the infected tissues may turn tan, gray, or dark brown. Infection may occur first at the lenticels, which at first are water-soaked and swollen. The tissue underneath is generally firm. Unless the potatoes are exposed to high temperatures, the infected area often dries up. Infected tubers have little smell until the infected tissues collapse. Then a foul odor may develop because of bacteria that live on the decomposing tissue.

THE COMPLEX NATURE of soft rot is indicated by the following summary of the symptoms of soft rot caused by different bacteria on several kinds of vegetables.

Potato

Erwinia carotovora: Rot at lenticels or at injuries. Internal rot usually cream or light-tan color.

Erwinia atroseptica: Rot usually starting at stem end but sometimes at injuries, black and sunken, sometimes dry. May progress through heart of tuber. Internal rot brown to black-brown color.

Bacillus polymyxa, B. subtilis, and *B. megatherium:* Usually starts at injuries and extends to heart of tuber. Internal rot dark brown to black, or grayish cast.

Pseudomonas solanacearum: Causes depression at point of stem attachment. Gray-brown discoloration at the surface and moist brown discoloration of water-conducting system. Entire inner tissue of potato may become soft and brown.

Lettuce, Chicory, Escarole, Endive

Erwinia carotovora: Inner leaves of head at first have a greasy water-soaked appearance. Later infected areas turn dark brown and become slimy.

Pseudomonas viridilividium: Outer leaves spotted or darkened. Center of head at first firm but later soft rot develops.

Pseudomonas marginalis: Starts as greasy water-soaked spot that later turns greenish to reddish brown. The infected tissues are soft and slimy and rapidly disintegrate into a foul odorous mass.

Onions

Erwinia carotovora: Affected tissue glossy or water-soaked, later mushy. Generally starts at neck, often confined to central scales. Foul odor.

Pseudomonas alliicola: Inner scales water-soaked and soft. Not unlike frost injury. Bulb appears sound from outside.

Pseudomonas cepacia: Outer scales yellow and slimy. Inner scales not affected. Upper portion of bulb shrinks and skin slips off.

Tomato

Erwinia aroideae: Skin water-soaked, light-colored, greasy translucent, blistered with mass of gas and decomposing cells. Decay progresses rapidly.

Erwinia carotovora: Rot on ripe fruit brownish, often limited to slowly spreading circular lesion.

Erwinia atroseptica: Lesions on ripe fruit dark and water-soaked, and spreading medium rapidly. Medium gas formation and only slight blistering. May be firm.

Celery

Erwinia carotovora: Affected lesions water-soaked and softened. Infected areas turn brown and mushy, but epidermis remains intact. Decay may affect crown, leaf stalks, and leaflets.

Melons

Erwinia aroideae: Decay usually on under side of fruit. Skin shrunken but usually nearly intact. Bacterial ooze through skin. Internal infection forms irregular funnel-shaped decayed section extending into the cavity. Entire inner portion becomes soft and outer tissues may collapse.

THE SOFT ROT bacteria grow and cause infection over a wide temperature range. *Erwinia carotovora* and *E. atroseptica* grow at temperatures from about 35° to about 89° F. *E. aroideae* grows at temperatures up to 105°. The optimum temperatures for growth and infection by the three organisms are 77°, 78°, and 95°, respectively. The soft rot bacteria of the genus *Pseudomonas* grow at temperatures from about 41° to about 102°, with an optimum around 86°. Growth of soft rot bacteria in the genus *Bacillus* is scant or absent below 55° and greatest at slightly above 89°. One species within this group, *B. subtilis*, will grow at 122° and *B. polymyxa* and *B. megatherium* at temperatures above 105°. At the lower temperatures, therefore, infection by

bacterial species in the genera *Erwinia* and *Pseudomonas* is most probable. At higher temperatures soft rot would more likely be caused by species of *Bacillus*. Although soft rot may occur over a wide temperature range the highest percentage is apt to develop within the range of 69° to 89°, where most of the bacterial species that cause soft rot grow well.

Organisms that cause soft rot live for long periods in the soil and may infect plants before they are removed from the field. Contaminated water in large washing vats resulting from washing infected produce is also a source of infection. Infection of many vegetables may occur in trimming, as cutting knives transmit the bacteria from diseased to healthy plants.

Standing water in the field when the plants are approaching maturity, injury from exposure to sun and wind on hot, dry days, and mechanical injuries during harvesting, grading, and packing may form places for bacterial invasion and favor development of soft rot.

Soft rot often is not evident at the time of storage or when the produce is shipped to market, but in order to delay the possible development of the disease it is customary to use low temperatures during storage or transit. During short storage periods or in transit, temperatures below 50° will delay the appearance of soft rot symptoms. For longer storage periods, temperatures approaching 32° are recommended for leafy vegetables and root crops and 40° for potatoes. It is highly important to keep moisture from condensing on the produce.

Standing moisture facilitates invasion by soft rot bacteria. If the temperatures fluctuate above 32°, infection and decay follow rapidly. Low temperatures do not prevent bacterial infection, but they delay development of decay and are the common (and possibly the best) way to preserve fresh produce. Soft rot often develops rapidly, however, after the produce has been removed from refrigerated storage. Such produce should be consumed or processed as soon as possible after removal from cold storage.

Good control of bacterial soft rots may be obtained by care in sorting and packaging the produce. Spreading of infection is retarded by use of sterilized trimming knives, eliminating and disposing of diseased produce before it comes in contact with healthy material, sorting out injured or bruised produce, and careful handling to avoid causing mechanical injuries. Curing potatoes at moderate temperatures and high humidity before storing or shipping allows the injured surfaces of the tubers to "cork over"; the "cork layer" prevents the entrance of most bacterial pathogens.

THE BACTERIAL DISEASES that cause spotting and wilting are most important during the growing period, but sometimes they continue to develop after harvest and cause damage in storage or at the market. The wilt diseases cause discoloration of the internal tissues and are often not discovered until the vegetable is cut when it is prepared for food. The symptoms of the more important of these diseases are:

Tomato

Bacterial spot (caused by *Xanthomonas vesicatoria*): Spots on mature green fruit are brownish-black, elevated, scabby areas, one-eighth to one-fourth inch in diameter, with feathered or irregular margins. Old spots are sunken, gray, or bleached and the affected skin is dry, paperlike, and ragged. Spots are superficial and do not develop into soft rot.

Bacterial speck (*Pseudomonas tomato*): Causes dark brown, slightly raised specks, one thirty-second to one-sixteenth inch in diameter, with definite margins. Spots are superficial and decay does not follow.

Bacterial canker (*Corynebacterium michiganense*): Spots on mature green fruit are light brown to brown, slightly raised circular areas, about one-sixteenth to one-eighth inch in diameter. They are surrounded by a characteristic white halo. Spots are superficial and do not develop into soft rot.

Beans

Common blight (*Xanthomonas phaseoli*) and halo blight (*Pseudomonas phaseolicola*): Cause circular to irregular-shaped, watery or greasy-appearing spots on the pods. The margin of the common blight spots becomes almost brick red as the spots become older. A yellowish crust of bacterial ooze is sometimes evident on the common blight spots and a grayish-white crust on the halo blight spots.

Peas

Bacterial blight (*Pseudomonas pisi*): Pod spots in the early stages are small and water-soaked. In more advanced stages they are larger, slightly sunken, greasy, or water-soaked, irregular-shaped, and have gray or grayish-brown centers.

Cucumbers

Bacterial spot (*Pseudomonas lachrymans*): Spots on cucumbers start as minute, circular, water-soaked areas. Later the affected tissues dry and crack and the centers of the spots become sunken and chalky white in color. A gummy exudate is sometimes present on the spots. A breakdown and soft rot frequently follow.

Cauliflower and Cabbage

Leaf spot (*Pseudomonas maculicola*): Leaf spots are water-soaked at first and then become brownish or purplish gray. They coalesce and become elongated as they enlarge and give the leaf a ragged appearance. Spots on the cauliflower head are small, gray to brown, and affect both the epidermis and deeper tissues. Later develops into soft rot.

Black rot (*Xanthomonas campestris*): Causes yellowing of the leaves and blackening of the veins. Leaves shed from stalk. Often followed by soft rot.

Celery

Bacterial blight (*Pseudomonas apii*): Causes numerous small irregular-shaped spots on the leaflets. Spots are yellow at first, but later are rusty brown with a yellow border or halo.

Stone fruits

Bacterial spot (*Xanthomonas pruni*): Fruit spots at first are small, circular, and light brown. Later they enlarge, darken, dry out, and crack. A viscid, yellowish, gummy exudate is sometimes present on the lesions.

Lemon

Black pit (*Xanthomonas citri*): Fruit spots are sunken, roughly circular, one-fourth to one-half inch in diameter, brown at first and later black. The white part of the peel beneath the pits collapses and turns light brown to reddish brown.

Potato

Ring rot (*Corynebacterium sepedonicum*): Causes odorless decay that is confined at first to vicinity of vascular ring of the potato. Affected tissues are cream-colored to pale lemon yellow and have a soft cheesy texture. Starts at stolon attachment and progresses through vascular system to the eyes. Causes characteristic cracking that extends into the vascular ring. Soft rot frequently follows.

Brown rot (*Pseudomonas solanacearum*): May cause a slight depression at the stolon attachment. Sometimes shows as a grayish discolored patch on surface of potato. Causes moist brown discoloration and soft softening of the vascular ring. A gray sticky bacterial ooze often exudes from the vascular tissue. Later the interior becomes soft

brown and only the shell of the potato holds it together.

Fruits and vegetables affected with bacterial spot and wilt diseases at harvest should be carefully graded and sorted to eliminate all that show symptoms of disease and then should be refrigerated promptly to retard development on the apparently sound produce. They should be used as promptly as possible after they are removed from the refrigerated storage.

WILSON L. SMITH, JR., *is a pathologist in the division of handling, transportation, and storage, Bureau of Plant Industry, Soils, and Agricultural Engineering, at Beltsville, Md. He has higher degrees from the University of Maryland and Cornell University. His major research studies have concerned bacterial diseases of plants.*

B. A. FRIEDMAN *is a pathologist at the Market Pathology Laboratory of the division of handling, transportation, and storage of horticultural crops in New York City. He obtained his doctorate in bacteriology at New York University.*

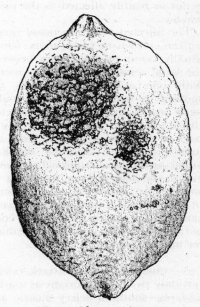

Blue mold rot on lemon.

Postharvest Virus Diseases

Lacy P. McColloch

Virus diseases are widespread and affect many food crops, but the ones that produce marks or blemishes on otherwise marketable fruits and vegetables are fewer than those that attack the plants in the field.

CABBAGE MOSAIC is occasionally found on vegetables in the market, but usually it is not serious. It became generally prevalent in southeastern Wisconsin in 1934. Similar diseases have since been reported in California and Washington. The cabbage head is not so readily affected as the plant leaves.

The affected head has many small, sunken, brown or black spots, which usually occur on the tissues between the large veins. The spots may merge with one another. Sometimes the spotting is confined to a few outer head leaves, but it may be scattered throughout the head. Often only a part of the head is affected from exterior to center. Spotting develops either as the head approaches maturity in the field or later in transit or storage. An indication of the disease in stored heads is the untimely separation of the leaves from the core. Seriously affected heads are worthless for market.

A NUMBER of viruses attack celery, but only two are important as market diseases—southern celery mosaic and western celery mosaic. Southern celery mosaic is confined largely to Florida, but a similar disease has been reported from several other States. Affected plants appear stunted and the leaves are yellowed and mottled. As growth continues, however, the new shoots are only faintly mottled, and that is usually unnoticed after blanching. The leafstalks often show brownish or buff-colored, sunken, water-soaked spots, and may eventually become brown and shriveled. Seriously affected bunches are worthless, but plants showing only moderate mottling of the leaves are marketable.

Western celery mosaic is the most serious virus disease of celery grown in California. Rust-colored spots and streaks appear on the upper surface of older leaves. The stalks are unaffected. As the blemishes are confined to the upper leaves, which are removed in preparation for market, losses are less serious than if the stalks of the celery were affected.

MOSAIC, one of the most serious diseases of cucumbers, may occur anywhere that they are grown—in greenhouse and field. The mosaic virus causes a mottling of the fruits and sometimes prevents the development of the normal green color. Other symptoms are wartlike protuberances, distortion, and stunting of the fruits. The most severely affected fruits are eliminated in grading and packing. Mottled fruits are less attractive than normal ones, but are salable.

SPOTTED WILT, a virus disease of lettuce, has become increasingly important in some of the coastal districts of California. It is more prevalent in the late-summer and early-fall crops than in others. Spotted wilt has not been found in the Imperial Valley of California or in Arizona.

Typical symptoms of spotted wilt on head lettuce are the presence of brown, sunken streaks and spots, especially on the lower part of the midrib. Any of the leaves, however, including the heart leaves, may be affected. The leaves often show some curvature of the basal attachment. Seriously affected heads are worthless.

GARDEN PEAS are attacked by a number of viruses in the field. Two are important factors in the quality of marketed peas.

Mosaic is the most serious virus disease of peas in the market. It may occur wherever peas are grown, but the tall varieties grown in California and Washington for market are more susceptible than the varieties grown mainly for canning. American Wonder, Perfection, Canners Gem, Dwarf White Sugar, Little Marvel, Wisconsin Early Sweet, and Surprise are among the varieties that are resistant to the common mosaic.

The virus affects the pods and causes distortion, mottling, and sometimes dark-green ridges, between which are sunken, yellowish-green areas. Affected pods are poorly filled. Seeds are more yellow than normal. Affected pods do not change very much during transit. The mosaic condition detracts from their appearance and may lower the quality.

The spotted wilt virus affects peas less often than the mosaic virus, but it may occur wherever the insect vector that spreads it is found. Pea pods affected with it may have characteristics similar to those of mosaic, but generally the pods show spots of irregular brown patterns with concentric markings. The pods may also be stunted, distorted, and collapsed. The condition may become somewhat worse during transit, but the disease was present when the peas were shipped.

THE PRINCIPAL VIRUS DISEASES affecting peppers on the market are tobacco mosaic, tobacco etch, and certain strains of cucumber mosaic. Some of them occur together in the same plant and make identification difficult.

Pepper pods that have a spotted, lumpy, or ring-marked surface probably have a virus disease.

A yellow strain of tobacco mosaic virus that causes a spotting of pepper pods is widespread and may affect peppers wherever they are grown. The spotted appearance is due to cream-colored spots and streaks, which occur in the green-colored tissues of the pod. The cream-colored areas are not sunken. The spotted appearance is present when the peppers are shipped and does not increase in transit. Affected peppers are unattractive, but unless they are very seriously spotted they would not be discarded on the market.

When the tobacco etch virus occurs alone, it causes little or no markings of the pepper fruits. When it occurs in combination with the tobacco mosaic virus, the complex causes serious damage to affected pods. The disease appears first as round, granular spots, which appear submerged as seen through the normal waxy coating of the fruits. The tissues surrounding the spots collapse later and dry out, causing the spots to appear as raised lumps. Only one side of the pod is usually affected. Affected pods may change during transit and appear much worse than when packed. Seriously affected pods are a total loss.

The common cucumber mosaic virus is widespread, but it causes little damage in pepper pods. A strain of the virus that causes a ring spot on pepper pods is becoming increasingly important in peppers on the market, however. Ring spot makes round markings of various sizes on the pod. The smallest spots involve all the tissues within the ring. They may retain the green color after the rest of the pod is red or they may appear reddish, but paler than the normal red tissues. Large spots have a circular, greenish-brown ring, which outlines the spots. The tissues within the ring usually have normal color but gradually become raised, because of the collapsing of the affected tissues that form the ring. Pods are affected when shipped, but may change during transit and appear worse on arrival. Seriously affected pods are worthless.

OF THE MANY virus diseases that affect potato plants in the field, net necrosis and tuber necrosis virus are most likely to be found on marketed potatoes.

Net necrosis is a name applied to a disorder of tubers produced by plants affected by the leaf roll virus. The virus enters the tuber at the stem end and kills the strands that conduct food and water. The brown color of the network of killed strands makes the netted appearance. The appearance varies, however, with the angle at which the tuber is cut and may appear as dots or streaks. The netted appearance is best brought out if one pares the potato lengthwise. The discoloration may extend throughout the tuber or only a short distance at the stem end.

Often infected potatoes do not show net necrosis at harvest, but the condition develops in storage or transit if the temperature is favorable. At the optimum temperature for development, 50° F., a maximum amount of net necrosis develops in 90 days.

The development of net necrosis in tubers of the Green Mountain variety can be prevented largely by holding freshly dug potatoes at 70° for 60 days or at 32° to 36° for 30 to 60 days. Chippewa, Katahdin, and other new varieties, although subject to leaf roll, do not develop net necrosis.

Tuber necrosis is caused by the same virus that causes alfalfa mosaic. It is a relatively new disease of potatoes. It was reported first in 1946 and has become increasingly important since then. It has caused serious loss in the White Rose potatoes, the principal variety grown in California, and has also been found in the Pontiac variety.

Necrosis in the tuber starts at the stem end in the tissues just under the skin. At that stage the skin over the necrotic areas becomes purplish to silver. The diseased areas continue to enlarge and may eventually extend into all tissues. Discolored areas often occur as pockets. The necrotic tissues frequently develop in rings or spiral patterns. Affected tissues are deep brown

and dry and are corky or mealy. In seriously affected potatoes the surface over necrotic areas becomes dry, cracked, and sunken. The sunken areas in the skin may be irregular or in the form of rings or half moons.

Necrosis is usually present at harvest, but often deepens and spreads in storage. Occasionally potatoes that appear sound at digging time become severely affected after 6 weeks of storage. All varieties tested (Netted Gem, Pontiac, Mohawk, Chippewa, Teton, and Houma) have been found susceptible.

BEAN PLANTS are subject to a number of viruses that dwarf and disfigure them, interfere with their normal function, and reduce the yield. They generally are classed as mosaics. Greasy pod, southern bean mosaic, pod mottle, and pod-distorting mosaic produce symptoms on the pods that detract from their appearance. They are most likely to be seen on the market.

Symptoms on beans affected by viruses vary with the severity of the disease. A mottled appearance, typical of symptoms of certain viruses, may result from irregular areas of dark green, which appear water-soaked in contrast to the grayish green of the normal areas on the same pod. Pods that are mottled, malformed, or lumpy and have many irregular, sunken areas generally may be suspected of having a virus disease.

Greasy pod is caused by a strain of the common bean mosaic virus. The pods are most severely affected when temperatures are high. The disease is marked by the shiny or greasy appearance of the pods. Topcrop, Rival, Contender, Tenderlong 15, and Improved Tendergreen are resistant to common bean mosaic.

Southern bean mosaic was first reported in Louisiana, but is now known to occur in Illinois, California, Maryland, Georgia, Mississippi, and other States. It has become more and more serious. Affected pods are strongly mottled and malformed. No fully resistant variety has been found.

Pod mottle virus produces symptoms much like those produced by southern bean mosaic virus, but the two diseases are distinct. The pod mottle virus was first found in South Carolina in 1945. Little is known about its distribution or economic importance. Affected pods are strongly mottled. The surface may appear roughened or irregularly sunken. Many of the popular varieties of green-podded bush and pole snap beans are resistant. Some varieties of the green-podded bush type, such as Full Measure, Landreth Stringless, Green Pod, Longreen, Plentiful, and Tendergreen, are susceptible, however.

The pod-distorting mosaic virus is a strain of yellow bean mosaic. It also affects sweetclover, red clover, and gladiolus. Beans may become infected if grown near those plants if they are carrying the virus. The affected pods are distorted and malformed. The surface is lumpy and irregular and has many sunken areas. No variety is resistant to yellow bean mosaic, but the disease is seldom found in the Southern States.

INTERNAL CORK, a virus disease of sweetpotatoes, was first reported in South Carolina in 1944. It occurs in Georgia, North Carolina, Virginia, Tennessee, Mississippi, Maryland, Louisiana, Alabama, and Texas.

It causes serious losses in some places, but because of its obscure nature it is probably often overlooked in the commercial sale of sweetpotatoes. It causes hard, brown or nearly black, corky spots in the flesh of the roots. The corky spots do not appear on the surface. To find them one has to cut the roots, preferably in thin transverse slices. The corky spots may appear singly or in groups anywhere in the flesh. Occasionally a group of spots merge into a large, dark, corky area. The only external evidence of the disease is an occasional pit or sunken place in the surface over a corky spot. If affected roots are cut and the spots exposed to the air, the color fades to a medium brown. If they are exposed

for several days, the drying and shrinking of the healthy tissues cause the corky spots to appear raised. Seriously affected roots are unsatisfactory for food because the corky spots remain firm and are bitter.

TOMATO PLANTS and fruits are affected by several viruses and may be affected by more than one virus at the same time. Virus diseases may occur anywhere that tomatoes are grown. All varieties are susceptible. Virus diseases most frequently found on tomatoes in the market are tomato mosaic, double-virus streak, and spotted wilt.

Fruits affected by certain strains of the mosaic virus show a pattern of mottled color, which is retained after they are ripened. That detracts from their appearance and causes wastage through paring because the affected parts do not ripen thoroughly. The fruits are not necessarily a total loss, however, and the disease does not make them more subject to decay. The mottled pattern caused by tomato mosaic is entirely on the surface. Affected areas do not collapse, become sunken, or turn brown. The most typical diseased fruits as seen in a market are green with cream-colored marks radiating from the stem scar over the shoulder area. Those marks may be continuous streaks or may be broken up by small areas of green tissues. The margin between the green and cream-colored areas is usually distinct. When affected tomatoes ripen, the green portion becomes red, but the cream-colored areas turn yellow, so that the mottled appearance remains. Shoulder markings are the most typical symptoms, but the mottled places also may extend over any part of the fruit. Mosaic-affected fruits that are found on the market were affected when shipped; the only change that occurs in transit is the change in color.

Fruits affected with double-virus streak have many small, irregular, or angular spots anywhere on the surface. Glossy at first, they turn brown and usually are slightly sunken. The spots often merge into larger, irregular, brown ones. Sinking and discoloration of the affected areas increases with time and can be expected to become more conspicuous in transit. Fruits showing the disease are unattractive. The most seriously affected ones may be a total loss.

The virus disease known as spotted wilt has caused serious losses in some sections of California and Oregon because of the presence there of a damaging strain of the virus. The disease also occurs in Texas and in some of the east North Central and Atlantic States, but generally it does not cause serious losses there. Affected fruits in the market usually show several or many ring patterns, often with a mottled condition, which is due to the lack of normal ripening in the surrounding tissues. The ring appearance is due to a slight sinking and shriveling of the tissues around the margin of the affected area which causes the center of the ring to appear raised. The affected areas may be practically normal in color or may appear bronzed or reddish brown.

STONY PIT, a virus disease of pears, may occur anywhere pears are grown. Commercially important losses, however, appear to be confined to the Pacific coast area. The Bosc variety is most subject to stony pit, but the disease also affects Anjou, Winter Nelis, Hardy, and Forelle.

In affected fruit, masses of stone cells occur in the flesh of pears at the bottoms of dimplelike depressions. The lumps of stone cells are so hard that it is almost impossible to cut them. When the pitting is severe and the pits are numerous, fruits may be greatly distorted. Seriously affected fruits are worthless. Fruits that are only slightly pitted, however, are often marketed.

LACY P. McCOLLOCH *is a pathologist of the Bureau of Plant Industry, Soils, and Agricultural Engineering.*

Injuries From Chilling and Freezing

Lacy P. McColloch

Fresh fruits and vegetables are kept cool on their way to market so as to slow down the processes that cause their overripeness and decay. Refrigeration is the foundation of the big industry that makes it possible for us to have fresh produce the year around.

But some commodities that are subjected too long to low temperatures are so injured or weakened that their physiological processes are impaired or slowed to the point of inability to function, and decay becomes far more extensive than normal.

The fruits and vegetables that require high temperatures for growth generally are the ones most subject to injury by chilling or low temperature. Among them are bananas, citrus fruits, cucurbits, eggplant, peppers, potatoes, sweetpotatoes, and tomatoes. In handling them one has to remember that each has its own requirements or limitation as to the temperatures at which it can be held safely.

Chilling injury, which differs from freezing injury, results from holding a commodity at low ($32°$ to $50°$ F.) but not freezing temperatures for enough time to impair its life processes. The effect is not well understood, but it appears that the tissues, unable to carry on normal metabolism, gradually become weakened. Chilling injury therefore is relatively slow.

Freezing injury results when ice crystals form in the tissues of fruits or vegetables. It usually occurs if they are subjected to temperatures corresponding to their freezing points or lower. Freezing injury may take place in a few hours and in spots or throughout the commodity. Tissues injured by freezing generally look as if they were soaked in water.

Chilling injury often is not apparent at the time fruits and vegetables are removed from low temperatures but becomes evident several days later. The symptoms are more noticeable in some commodities than in others. It is hard to diagnose chilling injury definitely because clear-cut symptoms are absent.

BANANAS are highly sensitive to unfavorably low temperatures. Injury so severe as to make them unsalable may occur if they are held at 45° F. or below in still air for 12 hours. The upper limits of temperatures that may cause chilling injury are not sharply defined, but the lowest temperature at which bananas should be held is 56°.

Ripe fruits are slightly more susceptible than green fruits. Chilling injury is confined mainly to the peel, in which some of the surface cells are killed. Severely chilled green fruits may have dark-green, water-soaked specks or nearly the entire surface may be dark. The latex exudes little or not at all in chilled green bananas when they are broken. It is clear, rather than milky or cloudy. That condition, however, is not a definite indication of chilling—it also is characteristic of bananas that are beginning to ripen. If chilled to a lesser degree, green fruits develop a dull, smoky appearance on ripening, rather than a bright-yellow color.

Chilling injury does not become apparent on ripe fruits unless they are held at low temperatures a long time. The characteristic dull appearance soon develops, however, when chilled ripe fruits are removed to higher temperatures.

One has to know a good deal about bananas to recognize chilling injury, especially in green fruits, because factors other than chilling may cause a similar appearance.

CITRUS FRUITS are not chilled to the point of injury during the normal transportation period, but may be injured in storage if unfavorably low temperatures prevail. Storage may be necessary for citrus fruits in order to spread the marketing period. Because the demand for lemons is greatest in warm weather, a large part of that crop is stored for a while.

The storage behavior of citrus fruits is influenced by their degree of maturity and their inherent differences. The storage temperatures recommended, however, are those found most desirable for most of them. Low-temperature injury results in the development of various disorders, some of which are common to all citrus while others are specific for certain kinds.

Grapefruit stored at 32° to 40° F. for 2 or 3 months might suffer pitting, watery breakdown, scald, and browning of the oil glands. The pits in the rind are a type of low-temperature injury that may occur in all citrus fruits. Pitting is especially serious if grapefruits are stored for 2 months or more at 32° to 40°. The pits may occur anywhere on the surface and often are numerous. Occasionally the collapsed tissues appear bleached, but usually they are darker than the healthy rind. Pits developed on fruits stored at 32° are smaller than those on fruits stored at 36° and 40°.

Watery breakdown may develop in any citrus fruit stored at low temperatures for 2 or 3 months. Grapefruit picked late in the season are more susceptible than fruits picked earlier. Affected fruits are soft, spongy, and water-soaked in both peel and flesh and look as if they had been frozen. Affected fruits develop a fermented odor when they are held at room temperature.

Scald involves a superficial and fairly uniform browning of large areas of the rind. Affected areas at first are firm, but in severe cases the surface becomes spongy and soft and resembles an early stage of watery breakdown.

Another type of browning is confined entirely to the oil glands. It usually occurs at 32° and 36° F. Affected glands close together give the appearance of mass discoloration. Actually the discoloration is confined to the oil glands and the surrounding tissues are only slightly discolored.

Lemons also are subject to pitting, watery breakdown, and scald. The handling and storage problems of lemons are quite different, however, from those of grapefruit or oranges. Because lemons can be picked at a more immature stage than grapefruit and oranges, they can be held at a higher storage temperature for the 3 months needed to carry the winter and spring crop to summer.

Lemons stored at 58° F. until ready to ship will escape the disorders I mentioned. Even at that temperature, however, lemons are somewhat subject to a browning of the membranes—a disorder known as membranous stain, which cannot be detected until the fruits are cut. It is greatly increased by storing lemons at 40°. If lemons are stored after reaching the market at temperatures of 32° to 40° for 60 to 90 days, low-temperature disorders may be expected to develop. For short-term storage (2 to 4 weeks) in the market, 32° is perhaps the most desirable temperature for lemons because membranous stain does not occur then and other injuries do not become serious in that period if the fruits have not previously been stored at a low temperature.

Pitting, brown stain, and watery breakdown usually develop if oranges are stored at low temperatures for a long time. Such disorders can be avoided if the storage period is shortened and fruits with longer storage-life expectancy are selected.

Pitting is worse on early and midseason varieties of Florida oranges than on late-maturing varieties. The variety Pineapple is one of the most susceptible. The variety Valencia is quite resistant to pitting and other low-temperature disorders. Valencia oranges can be stored at 32° to 34°, but the storage period should not exceed 12 weeks.

Brown stain is characterized by a superficial and fairly uniform browning of a large area of the rind. Like watery breakdown of grapefruit, it usually develops in certain varieties of oranges stored at 32° for 2 months or longer. None of the low-temperature disorders has been serious in Florida-grown Valencias stored at 32° for 8 to 12 weeks.

SWEETPOTATOES are much more subject to chilling injury than is generally thought. Noncured sweetpotatoes are more susceptible than cured ones. Subjecting noncured roots to temperatures of 50° or below for only a few days may seriously affect their storage life. Although no variety should be held at low temperatures, the varieties differ in their sensitivity to low temperatures. The Jersey group—Big Stem Jersey, Little Stem Jersey, Orange Little Stem, Maryland Golden—is most seriously affected by cold. Second to this group is Nancy Hall. Porto Rico is the most resistant.

Chilling injury of sweetpotatoes does not become evident immediately after exposure to low temperatures. Noncured roots subjected to 40° or below during transit or on the market may develop surface pits in 2 or 3 weeks. Roots stored at 50° show evidence of cold injury after 5 months in storage. Increased decay is the best indication of such injury. The most typical symptom in the Jersey group is a type of spongy breakdown and brown discoloration of the inner tissues. After the same period of storage at 50°, the Nancy Hall variety develops a dull cast, and discoloration develops usually at the stem end. Because fungi attack the weakened tissues, the condition soon appears as typical end rot. Chilled sweetpotatoes are poor keepers in storage, and losses continue during wholesale and retail handling. The consumer may make selections that are free from decay, but be unaware of the internal condition until after the roots are cooked. Hard areas, pithy breakdown, or a darkened condition of the cooked flesh indicate that sweetpotatoes were stored at temperatures that were too low.

Freshly dug sweetpotatoes that are to be marketed promptly without curing should not be subjected to temperatures below $50°$. Roots that are to be stored should be promptly cured at $85°$ and the subsequent storage temperatures should be maintained between $55°$ and $60°$.

TOMATOES may suffer chilling injury in the field while they are on the vine, while they are in transit, or after they reach the market. The conditions during the normal transit period from shipping point to market generally do not lead to chilling injury, but some cars arrive at the markets each year in which the fruits have been chilled. Unless the fruits are injured to the point of physiological breakdown, the symptoms of chilling injury on tomatoes are not clearly evident. As a result much confusion exists and litigation over losses occurs each year.

Tomatoes may be considered as having been chilled when their physiological processes have been so impaired that ripening does not take place when the fruits are placed at temperatures that are normally favorable for ripening. Chilling injury ordinarily cannot be detected at the time tomatoes are removed from cars with low temperatures. The injury usually does not become apparent until the fruits have been in the ripening room 2 or 3 days. At that time tomatoes that have been seriously chilled have a dull, lifeless, picklelike appearance and feel rubbery to the touch. The internal symptoms are a watery (but not mushy) appearance of the tissues and a slightly fermented odor.

Alternaria rot around the stem scar and as numerous small lesions over the surface of a high percentage of the tomatoes in the ripening room usually accompanies chilling injury and is an indication that the fruits have been chilled. Fruits that are less chilled show little sign of physiological injury while in the ripening room.

Tomatoes may be held at temperatures of $32°$ to $40°$ for 3 to 5 days and still ripen satisfactorily with little or no increase in decay. Tomatoes held for 6 to 8 days will ripen satisfactorily as to color, but may show an increase in decay in proportion to the length of exposure. Tomatoes are definitely weakened by holding at those low temperatures for 9 to 12 days. Ripening is unsatisfactory and decay is extensive. Tomatoes are so weakened by holding at $32°$ to $40°$ for 17 to 21 days that the entire lot usually becomes lifeless and rots without ripening. Chilling injury develops more slowly at $45°$ than at $32°$ or $40°$, but tomatoes should not be held at $45°$ for more than 3 to 5 days.

Ordinarily the field heat in the tomatoes when loaded is such that several days are required to cool the load to desirable temperatures, even by refrigeration. Fruits near the bottom bunker of the car, however, cool rapidly and may arrive on the market with a pulp temperature of $36°$ to $40°$ if the car was moved under bunker icing. Under normal conditions, if the transit period does not exceed 6 days, the tomatoes would be at such low temperatures for only 2 to 4 days, and those conditions are not sufficient to cause chilling injury.

If, however, the transit period exceeds 10 days and the load is refrigerated, there is danger of chilling injury to the tomatoes near the bottom of the bunker. If the tomatoes have been exposed to temperatures of $40°$ or below in the field for a week or more before harvesting, or stored at $40°$ to $45°$ for a week before shipping, and are refrigerated in transit, or if the car is iced and left on track at the market, the fruits may be at low temperatures for a long enough time to become chilled.

Refrigerated cars that are diverted from one prospective market to another are likely to become chilled because of the longer time in transit. Chilling injury is particularly likely in shipments made when the outdoor temperatures are low. Heavy icing at that time is undesirable. Tomatoes shipped to northern markets in winter may even need heater service to protect them against chilling injury as well as freezing.

Although tomatoes can withstand low, but not freezing, temperatures for 3 to 5 days without suffering injury, it is not advisable for the fruit temperature to be lower than 50° during transit. This recommendation is made because of the uncertainty of the previous treatment of the tomatoes and also the uncertainty of how the load may be handled before the tomatoes are ripened.

LACY P. MCCOLLOCH, *a plant pathologist, joined the Department of Agriculture in 1928. His investigations have dealt primarily with storage diseases of fruits and vegetables, particularly the handling, transportation, and ripening of mature green tomatoes as relating to quality and decay. He was trained at the University of Arkansas.*

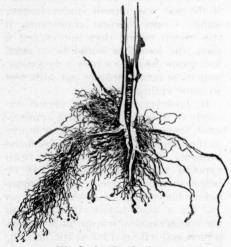

Black shank of tobacco.

Physiological Disorders

T. R. Wright

Diseases of fruits and vegetables caused by adverse environmental conditions during growth in fields or orchards or during harvest, storage, and marketing are called physiological diseases.

One important cause of a number of physiological disorders is suboxidation, or anaerobic respiration. The first part of this chapter is devoted to symptoms of suboxidation on a number of commodities; the latter section is devoted to the description of miscellaneous disorders.

Fruits and vegetables are living organisms. If their supply of oxygen is greatly reduced or withheld during postharvest handling they are likely to smother with progressive death of various parts of their tissues. Off-odors and off-flavors accompany the smothering of tissues, and the tissues become susceptible to decay because of weakening and death of cells.

Potato black heart may occur in the field during excessively hot weather in waterlogged soils because the tubers cannot get enough oxygen to supply the respiratory demands at high temperatures under those conditions. It may occur in potatoes in transit when the car temperatures are allowed to go over 90° F., or in storage houses where bins are so large that the middle of piles receive insufficient ventilation. Flues through the piles and the false floors and walls with which newer storage houses are being equipped provide enough aeration to alleviate this trouble in most cases.

Excessive temperatures may induce black heart in storage by increasing the rate of respiration of tubers to such an extent that the oxygen within the tissues is used up more rapidly than it can be replenished. Black heart is externally visible only in the most serious cases. It appears then as moist areas, purplish at first and later changing to deep brown or black. Tissues of the central part of the tuber become dark gray, purplish, or black. The affected tissues, clearly delineated from healthy areas, are firm or leathery. They may dry out and separate to form cavities.

Snap beans are subject to surface blemishes of a chestnut-brown color, called russeting. Both green pod and wax pod varieties are affected. The lesions are of various sizes and shapes, but most often occur as parallel diagonal streaks. They resemble those of sunscald but occur on both sides of the pod. Although the cause of this defect has not been definitely established, similar symptoms may be produced by holding the beans in a moist, warm environment without ventilation. Russeting may develop during long periods in transit.

Lemons are affected sometimes by a disorder called albedo browning in which the albedo, the white spongy inner part of the rind, becomes discolored. It may be intense enough to show through the skin as a diffused browning that varies from a barely discernible blemish to quite extensive browning. The disorder is aggravated by storage at 32° and poor ventilation.

Cranberries are subject to smothering when carbon dioxide accumulates and oxygen is depleted in overcrowded storage rooms or in tight containers. The disorder usually affects berries near the center of containers and is associated with large amounts of decay. Affected berries lose their crispness and bright color, become dull red, and have a leathery texture.

Apple brown heart is a brown discoloration of the flesh of apples held for long periods in atmospheres containing high concentrations of carbon dioxide gas. The disorder has been particularly troublesome in ships exporting Australian apples to England. It may occur also when apples are held in sealed containers or are heavily coated with waxes that interfere with normal air exchange.

Packaging of consumer units of fresh fruits and vegetables in sealed transparent films has caused some suboxidation problems. The films differ in permeability to oxygen, carbon dioxide, and water vapor, and the different kinds of fruits and vegetables vary in their tolerance to atmospheres low in oxygen and high in carbon dioxide. In general it has been found advisable to use either unsealed or perforated packages in order to avoid suboxidation troubles.

Other functional disorders besides those caused by suboxidation develop in storage or transit, often without apparent cause.

Apple scald is a serious physiological disease of some apple varieties. It is a superficial browning that may become visible in storage or, more likely, after storage while the fruits are being marketed. Usually only the skin tissue is affected, the flesh remaining edible, but in serious cases the trouble may extend into the flesh. Then decay fungi readily invade the disrupted tissue.

Apple scald is usually associated with immaturity at harvest. Low storage temperatures do not reduce scald but retard its development. In fact, the disorder usually does not appear on susceptible fruits stored at 32° until after their removal to higher temperatures. Delay in storing the fruit is not conducive to scald development if enough ventilation is provided. The actual cause of scald, while associated with fruit volatiles, is still unknown.

Humidity, low oxygen levels, and excess carbon dioxide do not affect the incidence of scald. Early investigators tried a large number of absorbents for removing the gases given off by apples, but only those known to have an affinity for esters offered any degree of scald control. The best results were had with fats and oils, such as creamery butter, tallow, mineral oil, and neat's-foot oil. The most practical control was obtained by wrapping the fruit with paper wraps impregnated with mineral oil. Nearly as effective control of scald was obtained by scattering shredded oil-impregnated paper throughout the apple pack.

The development of oiled wraps made possible further investigation of scald. The most critical period in the postharvest life of apples was found to begin with picking and to extend 6 to 8 weeks. The scald-producing processes were most active and the control measures effective only when applied during that period.

Oiled wraps are being used throughout the world to control scald. The wraps are impregnated with about 15 percent by weight of tasteless, odorless, mineral oil. When shredded oiled paper is used a minimum of one-half pound for each bushel of apples is recommended for satisfactory results.

Oiled paper, however, will not entirely prevent scald. Extremely susceptible varieties, such as Arkansas (Black Twig), develop the disorder despite oiled paper but to a lesser extent. Susceptible varieties picked immature or held in poorly ventilated common or cold storages through the critical 6 to 8 weeks after harvest are so susceptible that oiled paper is of little benefit.

Charcoal air filters are used in some storage rooms to remove volatile products of respiration of the fruit. The air in the room is passed through the filters approximately three times an hour. Although scald is reduced by this air purification, it is generally controlled more effectively and economically with oiled wraps.

Apple bitter pit is an example of a physiological disorder that starts in the orchard but becomes important in storage. It causes nearly round, sunken spots one-eighth to one-fourth inch in diameter on the surface of the fruits and necrotic, corky areas in the flesh. Affected tissue may be bitter. The spots are usually brownish but may vary from gray green to reddish brown on the blush side of fruits. Bitter pit is associated with irregularities in moisture and nutritional requirements, particularly just before harvest. Australian investigators have suggested that the pits arise as the result of uneven conversion of starch to sugar bringing about unbalanced osmotic relationships between cells. The cells that remain starch-filled are subject to desiccation, collapse, and discoloration. Picking fruit when mature and prompt cold storage help keep damage at a minimum.

Jonathan spot of apples, which is a skin disease, appears during storage almost entirely on apples of the Jonathan variety. Its cause is unknown. The round spots are blackish on the blush side and greenish brown on the pale side of the fruit and have sharply defined borders. The lesions range from pin-point size to three-eighths inch in diameter. During storage the spots may increase in size and merge. Secondary decay fungi often are found in the spots. Jonathan spot develops as the acidity of the fruits decreases with the approach of maturity. Storing the fruit in atmospheres containing carbon dioxide prevents it. The spotting may be avoided largely by picking at an early stage of maturity and storing promptly at $32°$ F. Delays after harvest and common storage at temperatures above $40°$ allow ripening to progress and favor spot development.

Apple soft scald and soggy breakdown appropriately belong in a discussion of low-temperature injuries, but in the storage of apples the two disorders are peculiar in that certain precautions will permit storage at temperatures as low as $31°$ that otherwise might cause disastrous losses. Apples affected by soft scald look as though they had been rolled over a hot stove. The margins of the stripes or spots of dead, scalded skin are sharply defined. The underlying flesh becomes brown and dry. The dead skin is often invaded by rot-producing fungi, usually species of *Alternaria*, which cause the lesions to darken or become black. Varieties most commonly affected by soft scald are Jonathan, Rome Beauty, McIntosh, and Golden Delicious. It is less common on Delicious and Winesap. Soggy breakdown is similar in nature and cause, but it occurs as islands or bands of brown flesh, which often are not visible externally.

Soft scald and soggy breakdown never appear in apples stored at temperatures above 38°. They occur most commonly when susceptible varieties are picked at an advanced stage of maturity or are permitted to ripen after picking before being placed in cold storage. Apples picked at the proper stage of maturity and stored the same day at 31° rarely are affected. Storage at 34° to 36° for 4 to 6 weeks before lowering the temperature to 31° generally controls the disease in susceptible apples. Holding Jonathan apples in an atmosphere containing 25 percent carbon dioxide gas for 24 hours before storage at 31° is an effective preventative of soft scald.

Anjou pear scald is similar to apple scald both in its appearance and in the susceptibility of fruits harvested before they are fully mature. It also is subject to control with oiled-paper wraps. Anjou scald appears as a dark-brown surface discoloration, which affects only the appearance of the fruits. The flesh remains edible. Anjou scald usually develops on fruits stored past February 1, but does not appear until they have been removed from cold storage to warmer temperatures to ripen. In the first 24 hours of ripening the disorder may affect all the pears in a lot, particularly if the wraps are removed when the pears are placed in the warm room.

Anjou scald was noticed by Henry Hartman of the Oregon Agricultural Experiment Station as early as 1928. At about the same time J. S. Cooley and J. H. Crenshaw, then of the Department of Agriculture, stationed at Hood River, Oreg., were attempting to control gray mold (*Botrytis cinerea*) decay of Anjou pears with copper-impregnated wraps. The treatment was partially successful, but wraps so treated were too brittle for practical use. To remedy that, the manufacturers added about 18 percent by weight of the type of oil that had been used for several years in apple wraps.

The copper wraps first developed were effective in controlling both the botrytis decay and scald but caused fruit injury under certain conditions. Later Hartman, and his co-workers, developed a wrap which could be used safely, that contained 1.5 percent basic copper—calculated as actual copper—and 17 percent light, tasteless, and odorless mineral oil. The modified wrap controlled both gray mold decay and Anjou scald without fruit injury. It is in general use in the Anjou pear districts in the Pacific Northwest.

Common pear scald, distinct from Anjou scald, occurs on Bartlett, Bosc, and other commercial varieties. At first it causes a brown or black discoloration of the skin. It progresses rapidly into the flesh at moderate or high temperatures. In late stages the skin easily sloughs off. The taste and odor of affected fruit are disagreeable even before discoloration appears. Like apple scald, pear scald is worse on immature fruit and under poorly ventilated conditions, but unlike apple scald it is not controlled by oiled paper. Scald develops on Bartlett pears in 30 to 35 days at 43° F. and in 70 to 80 days at 36°, but usually not at all at 31° during the maximum 90-day storage period of this variety. It usually does not develop on other commercial varieties until near the end of the maximum storage period.

Onions are subject to a breakdown of such importance in storage that it is often miscalled storage breakdown although the disease also may occur in the field. It is characterized by a grayish, water-soaked appearance of the outer two or three fleshy scales of the bulb similar to freezing injury. Storage breakdown differs from freezing injury in that interior scales are not involved, and the disorder is not continuous around the bulb. Storage temperatures near 32° and relative humidity at about 65 percent are less favorable to development than higher temperatures and humidities.

Citrus fruits also are subject to a number of physiological disorders. Pitting of grapefruit and of midseason and late oranges usually does not develop until after 4 to 6 weeks in storage. The disorder appears as sunken spots in the rind. They are pinkish at first on grapefruit and later become brownish on both grapefruit and oranges. Pits are generally one-fourth to one-half inch in diameter when they occur singly, but several may merge to form pits up to 2 inches in diameter. The flesh under the larger pits often has a tainted flavor, becomes soft, and is susceptible to fungus decay.

The Pineapple variety of oranges is often severely affected with pitting, even during comparatively short periods in transit. Some doubt exists in the case of Valencia oranges as to whether pitting is distinct from aging or they are both the result of the same unknown cause. Valencia oranges that are shipped under refrigeration are not likely to develop pitting or aging symptoms until several days after unloading. Low relative humidity in storage or in transit and storage temperatures of 36° to 40° seem to favor the disorder.

Membranous stain of lemons occurs in fruits harvested during cool, damp weather. When the fruits are cut open, it can be seen as a browning of the membranes between the segments. At times the browning may extend to the core tissues or to the pulpy tissue inside the rind.

Pitting of lemons, a low temperature disorder, and red blotch, a physio-logical field disease which seldom is a problem in storage, may be grouped with membranous stain as being favored by storage at 32° to 40°. Maintenance of storage temperatures at 55° to 58° reduces loss from the disorders and also retards decay, which makes serious inroads at higher temperatures.

Stylar-end breakdown of Tahiti (Persian) limes in some years becomes the most important transit disease of limes of advanced maturity from Florida. It appears as a grayish-tan, water-soaked spot at the base of the tip of the fruit. The area may enlarge rapidly to include as much as one-half of the lime. The affected rind remains firm but darkens and becomes sunken below the adjacent unaffected skin.

Perishable commodities from the different parts of the country are marketed during precise seasons of the year. Within the limits of each season, experienced receivers have little trouble with breakdown disorders in fruits and vegetables from reliable shippers. Careless harvest practice, whereby fruit is allowed to become overmature before harvest or is delayed in the field or orchard before it is placed in cold storage, and poor storage and shipping operations, which allow temperatures in cold storage or common storage to become higher than those recommended for maximum keeping quality or permit transit delays under unfavorable conditions, all may drastically shorten the marketing life of fruits or vegetables. Produce that has been mishandled is likely to degenerate before the end of the normal marketing season, and care is needed to detect such fruit and divert it from ordinary trade channels. Retailers often display fruits too long under far from ideal conditions which bring on physiological deterioration and thus cause unnecessary losses to themselves and consumers.

T. R. WRIGHT *is a pathologist in the Horticultural Field Laboratory of the Department of Agriculture, Wenatchee, Wash.*

Mechanical and Chemical Injuries

G. B. Ramsey

Mechanical and chemical injuries during the grading, processing, packing, and shipping of fresh fruits and vegetables may sometimes be mistaken for diseases. They often open the way for decay-producing organisms that otherwise would not be able to invade sound produce.

All fresh fruits and vegetables are contaminated to some extent by thousands of spores and fragments of mold of various fungi that are present in the soil, water, air, field boxes, and grading bins. Whether the organisms will cause infection and decay often depends on the presence of wounds or other injuries, the types of organisms present, and temperature conditions. Although not all contaminating organisms cause decay, some do, and consequently the safest procedure is to harvest, pack, and ship all produce as carefully as possible to avoid injuries that might open the way for infections.

Among the most common mechanical injuries in the preparation and marketing of fruit are bruises, cuts, and stem punctures made at harvesttime, and nail, splinter, and sand injuries from field boxes and grading bins. Bruises, cuts, and splits also occur during shipment to markets when the containers are loaded improperly, the freight cars receive rough handling in the switching yards, and the containers are being unloaded and hauled to the warehouse or market.

In harvesting it is necessary to make fresh wounds when the fruits and vegetables are cut or pulled from the plants. Nevertheless, it is advisable to harvest, handle, and pack with care to avoid making injuries any more extensive than necessary. Vegetables and fruits are often seriously cut and bruised when containers with high bulge packs are lidded. Tight packs are desirable, but unnecessary pressure should be avoided.

Commodities like potatoes and onions are subject to mechanical injuries during harvesting and packing. They also are sometimes severely bruised and split during transit if protective pads are not used over the floor racks of the car. Severely injured stock in the bottom layer of bags must be sorted out and sold at a discount or discarded even if the wounds have not become infected.

Because of the difficulty of making a tight load of watermelons that will remain in place during transit, watermelons are probably more seriously damaged by splits and bruises than any other kind of produce. Rhizopus rot, yeasts, and other fungi often follow the injuries because the melons are not shipped under refrigeration. Careful loading with an adequate bedding of straw or similar material on the floor and padding on the ends and sides of the cars help reduce the damage.

Chemical injuries of fruits and vegetables during transit and storage are often caused by accidental exposure to some toxic gas; by chemicals used improperly for the control of decay, for washing, and other kinds of processing; or by accidental contact with chemicals in storage or in transit.

The most important chemical injuries found on produce in the market are caused by acid, ammonia, arsenic, nitrogen trichloride, and sulfur dioxide. Less serious injuries sometimes occur when the produce comes in contact with chemicals left in the freight cars. However, chemicals such as salt, fertilizers, coal tar, and oil products that used to cause injuries are seldom hauled now in cars used for shipping fruits and vegetables and injuries of this kind are seldom encountered. Potatoes and watermelons are the products that most frequently suffer chemical injuries from car contamination. Often the injuries thought to be caused by chemicals are found to be merely bruises on the commodities in contact with the floor and sides of the car, but occasionally the flattened areas on potatoes and melons are so soft, flabby, and discolored as to indicate the penetration of some chemical.

When it is necessary to wash apples to remove spray residue, the best results are had by using hydrochloric acid in the bath. The treatment sometimes injures the fruit unless the proper strength of acid is used. Acid injury on apples may appear anywhere on the fruit where drops of acid water have evaporated. The affected skin is bleached and somewhat softened; after it becomes dry, it often shows slight cracks. That injury can be seen a few days after the apples are washed. It can be prevented by paying special attention to the concentration of the bath and by thorough rinsing after the acid bath.

Ammonia injury occurs most commonly in apples, pears, peaches, plums, and onions when the gas accidentally escapes from cold-storage refrigerating or precooling systems into the cars or storage rooms. Very little of the gas produces decided color changes in the pigments of the skins of fruits and vegetables, especially the red and yellow ones.

The gas enters apples and pears most readily through lenticels or through breaks in the skin. The alkaline reaction of the chemical with the color pigments causes brown or black discolorations of red tissues and dark-brown discolorations of yellow tissues. The color changes take place almost immediately on exposure to ammonia and are permanent except when—rarely—the natural acids neutralize the alkali and some of the natural color returns. This sometimes happens in apples and pears, but usually the lenticels remain more brownish black than normal.

Ammonia injury to peaches appears as brown blotches of various sizes over the fruit. On plums the brownish to black discolorations are usually localized in spots. Heavy concentrations of the gas make the affected areas uniformly brown and affect the tissue under the skin. Even slight ammonia injury makes peaches unmarketable. The injury to peaches and plums occurs most frequently when the fruit is accidentally exposed to ammonia while being precooled in cars before shipment.

Ammonia injury of onions usually occurs in storage rooms. Even slight leaks in the ammonia system will eventually cause severe discoloration of red, yellow, and brown onions. On exposure to ammonia, the dry outer scales of red onions become greenish black or black; those of yellow and brown onions become dark brown as if they had been scorched. White onions show only a greenish-yellow discoloration of the outer dry scales. The discoloration of onions usually is limited to the outer scales, but the blemished appearance lowers marketability. In severe cases the outer fleshy scales of the bulbs become greenish yellow and water-soaked.

Arsenical injury may come about when apples have a heavy coating of arsenical spray residue and are allowed to remain wet for several hours before washing. It may also be produced if old washing solutions in which dissolved arsenic has accumulated are used and when the fruit has not been properly rinsed after washing. Soluble arsenic generally accumulates in the stem basin or calyx cavity and causes a burning of the skin and death of the tissue immediately underneath. The dark-brown or black and slightly sunken spots spoil the appearance of the fruit and often open the way for decay-producing organisms.

Nitrogen trichloride is used for fumigating citrus, melons, tomatoes, and other produce to reduce decay during transit and marketing. Generally it causes no injury but occasionally improper use results in some damage. The injury usually appears as sunken, tan or brown borders about the stem end and at wounds, which allow the gas to penetrate into the inner tissues. The injury is somewhat like that caused by sulfur dioxide, but the affected areas are usually darker brown and not so deeply sunken.

Sulfur dioxide sometimes injures produce when there is a leak in refrigerating systems that employ the gas. A conspicuous bleaching and sinking of the tissues occurs where the gas enters.

Sulfur dioxide is used also to stop the development of molds during transit and storage of California grapes. The gas is applied in the cars of grapes after they are loaded at the shipping point and periodically while the fruit is in storage. Occasionally the concentration of sulfur dioxide gets too high and injury occurs—chiefly a bleaching of the pigment in the skin at the stem end. Strong concentrations may practically decolorize even heavily pigmented fruits or kill the skin over the entire fruit. Severely affected fruit may also become moist because of the bleeding of the juices through the dead skin. In grapes, discoloration usually is most prominent about the stem attachment. The bleached skin and injured tissues underneath may eventually dry out and form craters about the stem. A slight bleaching around the stem, however, is not serious.

Although sulfur dioxide has never been recommended for controlling decay in tomatoes, cars of tomatoes badly injured by this gas have been received in the markets. Green tomatoes apparently are very susceptible to the gas.

G. B. RAMSEY, *a graduate of Indiana University and the University of Chicago, is a pathologist in charge of the Market Disease Laboratory in Chicago. He joined the Department in 1919 after serving as assistant pathologist and extension pathologist in Maine.*

Cuts, Bruises, and Spoilage

T. R. Wright, Edwin Smith

Fruits and vegetables, being tender, bruise easily and then spoil quickly—as every housewife knows who sorts apples, pears, peaches, bananas in the grocery as a matter of course to avoid taking spoiled ones home.

Between tree and retail bin—before the housewife inflicts her own bruises on them with thumbnail and fingers as she sorts them—apples might have to go through quite a bombardment of heavy blows when packages are roughly handled during storage, car loading, transit, and delivery to retail stores.

Pears, before softening, are more resistant to bruise injuries than most other deciduous fruits. Their market value is lowered greatly, though, by skin injuries that resemble bruises but actually are caused by friction. That type of blemish, sometimes called "belt burn," occurs during packing and handling. Pears withstand normal handling without showing blemishes when they are packed immediately after picking. As they age in storage, however, the skin becomes less resistant and the degree of disfigurement from a like amount of friction increases progressively during successive weeks of storage.

At a temperature of 31° F., Anjou pears may be stored for a month before packing without showing excessive abrasion blemishes, but longer delays are not advisable. In packing, paraffin-coated chip-board liners will protect pears from friction against the box sides. Pears are extremely sensitive to abrasions after they ripen, and if they are not handled with great care when they are being placed in retail displays, unattractive blemishes are certain to appear.

Defacement of peaches from bruising follows excessive pressure in the package or from rough handling and jostling of the package after the peaches have softened. Severe bruising of peaches in baskets frequently occurs at the bottom of the package (because of the weight of the fruit above) or at the top of the package (from lid pressure in overfilled baskets). The extent of the bruising is related to the ripeness of the peaches when they are shipped.

Loss from the bruises on peaches to be used for processing is extensive. Fruit is wasted; extra labor is needed to trim bruised spots; yield of Fancy grade halves is lowered when trimming makes the fruit good only for slices. To avoid such losses, growers must pick canning peaches so that the fruit is mature but not soft. Studies showed that the number of fruits severely bruised was four times greater when mixed firm and ripe peaches were sized than when firm peaches only were sized. When mature but firm fruits, sized 24 hours after picking, were processed, 1.26 pounds of trimmings per 500 peaches were removed, as against 4.04 pounds of trimmings from peaches that were sized 5 days after picking.

Spoilage due to excessive bruising extends also to seemingly more durable products such as potatoes. "Transit bruising" is apparent on the surface of potatoes and is caused largely by pressure of the tubers against the floors or walls in cars or trucks. The use of excelsior pads on floor racks in the cars have more than paid for their cost in reduced spoilage of that type, and care in loading to prevent shifting of sacks against side walls will avoid bruising from that source.

Cracks or "shatter bruises" follow heavy impacts when potatoes are handled while turgid and may cause serious damage in some places at harvest. It also becomes a problem when attempts are made to grade and sack potatoes after storage at low temperatures without a warm-up period. Potatoes warmed to a range of 35° to 50° F. in the bins before passing over the grader remain free of cracks; 50 percent of those that have not been warmed may have fresh cracks. Such damage may extend quite deeply into the flesh and cause more extensive damage than is apparent on the surface.

The careful adaptation and adjustment of the potato digger to immediate field and crop conditions is especially important in preventing digger cuts and "feathering." The tender skin of early potatoes is easily scuffed to cause feathering, and, wherever soil conditions make it possible, the digger chains should not employ kickers or eccentrics. Eccentrics, if they are used, should be set for the minimum throw necessary to remove the soil.

If the tissues exposed by feathering are allowed to dry rapidly they fail to cork over normally. Shriveling and a brown discoloration result. The unsightly appearance from the discoloration and the withering of seriously affected potatoes greatly lower their market value—losses that can be largely avoided by protecting the freshly dug potatoes from drying by picking up promptly after digging, using tightly woven bags, and covering with tarpaulins during hauling.

Internal black spot of potatoes, a blackening of the internal tissues, may follow bruising. The disorder usually is most pronounced just beneath the skin. Potatoes grown in regions where internal black spot is a serious problem should receive special care in handling to avoid mechanical injuries.

Waste due to mishandling is not confined to those fruits and vegetables that must be thrown away at the store or at home because of their bruised appearance and poor quality.

Cuts and bruises furnish an entry for fungi and bacteria that cause rots during storage or shipment and result in much greater waste than that due to bruising alone. Spoilage from rots following cuts and bruises affects even products such as oranges, lemons, and grapefruit on which surface bruises do not show readily.

A research project of the Department of Agriculture was started in 1903 to study the decay of California oranges while in transit to eastern markets. Losses from decay at that time were estimated to be as great as 1,500,000 dollars annually. The rots were ascribed to two species of blue mold, *Penicillium glaucum* and *P. digitatum*—fungi that were considered saprophytic or incapable of penetrating healthy, living tissue. It was observed that rot that was just starting was in the area where the skin had been previously injured by a cut or an abrasion.

The observations were followed by a series of laboratory studies by Mrs. Flora W. Patterson, a Department of Agriculture mycologist, who found that the blue mold fungus could not penetrate the epidermis of a sound orange even under conditions most favorable for its growth. It was thus evident that preventing injuries would reduce decay by blue mold.

G. Harold Powell and associates in the Department of Agriculture investigated the extent of mechanical injuries to oranges during harvesting and packing and their relationship to decay. He published his findings in a circular issued February 27, 1905. He found that as much as 35 percent of the fruit from some growers was mechanically injured and that some pickers injured 50 to 75 percent of the oranges they picked. The number of injured oranges in 10 packing houses varied from 4.2 to 22.7 percent. Twenty-five to 30 percent of the fruit from one association that had the reputation of producing fruit of the poorest carrying quality was found to be injured before shipment. Shipping tests disclosed that apparently sound fruit packed by the association showed an average of only 1.8 percent decay upon arrival in New York, compared to 26.9 percent in mechanically injured fruit.

The findings resulted in real progress in reducing bruises and decay after they were brought to the attention of orange growers. Before that time 15.8 percent of the fruit from one large corporation was mechanically injured. Subsequently the injuries were reduced generally to less than 2 percent. Harvesting methods were revolutionized, packing-house equipment was redesigned, and measures to control insects in the groves were changed in order to eliminate mechanical injuries to the fruit before it was shipped.

That early work profoundly influenced the citrus industry in California and was the forerunner of many studies on the importance of careful handling to reduce spoilage of fruits and vegetables. In the decade after 1907 extensive experiments demonstrated the importance of careful handling in harvesting oranges in Florida, grapes in California, and sweet cherries, red raspberries, and Italian prunes in the Pacific Northwest.

No special investigations had been conducted with apples relative to the effect of careful handling in lessening rot invasions before 1917, when H. J. Ramsey and his associates, in writing a Department bulletin on "The Handling and Storage of Apples in the Pacific Northwest," cautioned growers about the need to prevent skin injuries to avoid the serious storage decay of apples caused by blue mold. In the light of recent pathological studies with apples it is interesting to note that although they believed the blue mold fungus incapable of infecting an uninjured, healthy fruit they pointed out that "a microscopic break in the skin of an apple is sufficiently large to afford entrance to the decay fungus."

It was generally believed that *Penicillium expansum*, the organism that causes blue mold decay in apples, would not penetrate the unbroken skin of a healthy fruit until F. D. Heald, of Washington State College, reported in 1932 that an examination of apples in commercial storages showed entrance through lenticels more frequently than through skin ruptures.

Harley English, of the Department of Agriculture, later discovered that blue mold entered apples through true lenticels and also through minute lenticel-like openings, the nature of some of which was obscure. English and his associates also observed that many lenticel infections occurred in bruised areas and thought it probable that localized pressure ruptured cells in the lenticel basins and thereby increased susceptibility. The observations changed the conception of infection and the procedures for preventing blue mold (which is by far the most important rot of apples) because previously it was the common belief that prevention of stem punctures or other visible skin breaks during harvest and packing would largely avoid infections by blue mold.

The apples thus far observed to have blue mold infections at lenticels had all been subjected to commercial handling at harvest. Interest centered in how much the bruising due to commercial handling had contributed to the vulnerability of apples with apparently sound skin. This interest was intensified in 1947 and 1948 by the large number of bruises found on commercially handled apples in the Pacific Northwest. Slight bruises on red apples are not very noticeable and are largely ignored by the apple industry. However such bruises might be the cause of the microscopic injuries concerning which Ramsey and his associates cautioned in 1917.

In experiments we conducted in 1947, apples at different stages of maturity were picked and handled carefully so as to be as free from bruises as possible. On the bruise-free apples, bruises of two intensities were produced. Some bruised fruits were then dipped in a bath containing blue mold spores to determine the relationship of the bruises to blue mold infections. On the 431 apples with 762 bruises that were not dipped in the bath only one infection occurred, but 450 infections occurred among the 858 bruises of the 419 apples that were dipped. From this it is apparent that bruises do not greatly increase infection if the apples are protected from contamination.

In commercial practice, apples receive many bruises just before or after passing through washing solutions, which usually are contaminated with fungus spores from other apples. When there were two bruises per fruit on apples that were dipped in contaminated water, the average number of infections per 100 fruits was 48, but there were only 5.9 infections per 100 apples that were unbruised. Nearly three times the number of infections were found at severe bruises as at slight ones and more than five times as many in bruises on large apples than in bruises on small apples. Large apples that had been picked at an advanced stage of maturity and severely bruised had the greatest number of infections—an average of 103 infections in each 100 bruises.

Experiments in 1948 showed that apples that had been bruised when withdrawn from cold storage at intervals during the winter became increasingly susceptible to blue mold infection as they ripened. Bruises made at the time of harvest, however, lost much of their earlier vulnerability to the blue mold organism when exposure to the spore-bearing bath was postponed until after various periods in storage. Experiments in 1949 showed that blue mold developed in 20 to 58 percent of the bruises in apples dipped in a spore bath immediately after they were bruised, as against only 2.5, 0, and 0 percent when apples were held in cold storage 3, 7, and 14 days, respectively, between the times of bruising and exposure to the spore-contaminated solutions.

Those findings—that blue mold infection may occur through the apparently unbroken skin at bruises—are important to the industry because of the number of bruises caused during the washing and packing operations. In studies of apple bruising between harvest and distribution to retail stores it was found that many of the smaller bruises were caused during washing and packing either just before or immediately after immersion in washing solutions that may be heavily contaminated with blue mold spores. In certain instances all the apples were bruised; individual fruits showed 30 to 50 small bruises or dents.

Faulty operation and maintenance of packing-house machinery often are to blame for extensive bruising. Washing and packing equipment is often operated to handle from 400 to 450 bushels an hour instead of the rated capacity of 300 to 350 bushels an hour. Excessive bruising results. Often little is done to reduce the force of impact of fruit with machinery parts, particularly at the point where the apples are dumped onto the equipment and at points of transfer from one part of the machine to another.

Many rot-producing fungi can become established without a skin injury, but some cause decay in fruits and vegetables much earlier because of injuries from careless handling. Noteworthy among them are *Botrytis cinerea* and species of *Rhizopus*, which are responsible for enormous losses.

Rots caused by bacteria that enter through injuries are especially serious in some vegetables. Outstanding is bacterial soft rot, caused by *Erwinia carotovora* and other species. The organisms infect potato tubers chiefly through injuries and cause more extensive spoilage in the early and intermediate crops than any other factor. New potatoes exposed to excessive field temperatures during harvest often have surface temperatures of 109° to 122° and higher. Such surface temperatures are possible whenever air temperatures in the shade range from 90° to 95°. Potato tissues that have

reached 109° to 113° are likely to develop soft rot.

In areas where hot weather prevails during harvest, it is advisable to dig and pick up the potatoes early in the morning or in the evening. Digging, sacking, and trucking should be so coordinated that freshly dug tubers are not allowed to lie exposed on the ground more than 15 minutes before being sacked, loaded, and moved to shelter. Ventilation and temperatures below 70° are essential during storage and transit to restrict growth of bacterial soft rot.

T. R. WRIGHT *is a pathologist in the Bureau of Plant Industry, Soils, and Agricultural Engineering, United States Department of Agriculture, at Wenatchee, Wash. He is a graduate of Pennsylvania State College and did graduate study at the University of Minnesota.*

EDWIN SMITH *was head of the Wenatchee laboratory of the division of handling, transportation, and storage of horticultural crops from 1932 until his retirement in 1952. He has conducted research on the handling, transportation, and storage of apples and other fruits in Canada and England as well as in the United States.*

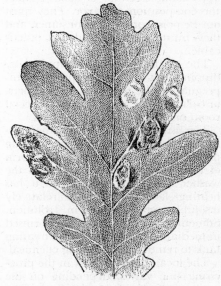

Leaf blister on white oak.

Using Chemicals
To Stop
Spoilage

J. R. Winston, H. B. Johnson,
E. M. Harvey

Chemical treatments are applied after harvest to reduce the decay of some kinds of fruits and vegetables during storage, transit, and marketing.

The treatments are directed against fungi and bacteria that contaminate the produce during harvesting, grading, and packing and against weakly parasitic organisms that do not become active until after harvest.

Suitable treatments for harvested fruits and vegetables must quickly kill or retard the development of the decay fungi. They must not injure the fruit or vegetable. They must not leave an objectionable residue or odor or affect the composition or flavor. They must not be poisonous to the consumer, and they must be economical and practicable.

The treatments may be applied by dipping in a wash tank; spraying; impregnating the wrappers, crate liners, or cartons; and fumigating in a special room or in the car or truck.

The usual method is to pass the commodity through a bath. The treating tank may be on the receiving platform of the packing house or between the washer and drier. Sometimes it has heating facilities to keep relatively insoluble compounds in solution. Sometimes the commodity is rinsed immediately upon leaving the treating tank to remove the adhering chemical.

The location of the tank in the processing line varies, depending on the mode of action of the chemicals. The chemical may be a nonvolatile, slow-acting compound, such as the soluble borates; a slowly volatile compound, such as soluble phenolic compounds; or a readily volatile compound, such as chlorine.

The soluble borates—borax, boric acid, a mixture of the two, and the more soluble sodium metaborate—generally are applied in 5-percent solutions. All have been widely used on oranges, grapefruit, and tangerines. The compounds are effective against green mold if the application is made before the infections have become deep-seated. The borates are also used to check stem-end rot in Florida citrus, but their effectiveness diminishes as the fruit ripens.

The borates are slow-acting. Treatment is best made soon after the fruit reaches the packing house. But usually the fruit is not treated until near the end of the packing house process, when it passes through a tank located between the washer and drier. After treatment (but before the fruit enters the drier), it is rinsed with water to remove excess boron compounds, which tend to gum up the machinery and leave an unsightly residue on the fruit. This short treatment, followed by rinsing, does not permit the toxicant to remain on the fruit for more than a minute or two. For best results, it should be left on the fruit for several hours. Since borax-treated fruit is especially apt to wilt, it is waxed after treatment.

A borax wash has also been used to a limited extent to control black rot on sweetpotatoes and decay in cantaloups. In California, sodium carbonate or soda ash, 1.25 to 2 percent, is preferred to borax for use on lemons.

Sodium ortho-phenylphenate has advantages over borax for the treatment of citrus fruits in Florida. It acts quickly and can check decay in citrus even when the application is delayed until several days after harvest, as is likely to be the case when citrus is degreened with ethylene before being packed. Without the aid of a safener,

---

however, it is apt to cause rind injury at normal room temperatures even when it is rinsed off immediately. Even with a safener it may cause rind injury if the temperature of the treating bath is more than lukewarm. Formaldehyde added to a water solution of the phenate or to a water-wax emulsion containing that chemical lessens the injury, but because formaldehyde evaporates quickly its safening effect is only temporary. Hexamine is a formaldehyde-ammonia reaction product with a faint odor of formaldehyde. Added to the phenate solution it practically eliminates rind injury if the temperature of the treating bath is not too high.

The sodium ortho-phenylphenate treatment is commonly applied by dipping the fruit either momentarily or for about 2 minutes in a tank containing a 1 to 1.25 percent concentration of the chemical. It is followed by a fresh-water rinse. The chemical also may be dissolved in the water phase of the wax emulsion which serves as a moderately effective safener, and applied as a flood spray. No rinse is used when the sodium ortho-phenylphenate is applied with the wax.

Sodium chloro-2-phenylphenate, a related compound, has been used to control several kinds of decay on apples and pears in the Northwest. It may be used in the washing tanks at a concentration of 0.6 percent, followed by a fresh-water rinse. Or it may be used in the rinse water at a concentration of 0.4 percent. Washing or rinsing the fruit with the chemical reduces decay, but the treatment is not entirely satisfactory; the fumes irritate the eyes, nose, and throat and contact with the bare skin may cause dermatitis.

Chlorine washes are extensively used for fruits and vegetables. We have little information on how much they reduce decay. Chlorine probably prevents the build-up of decay organisms in wash water and cooling water and so reduces the chance of infection—particularly in packing sheds where dip or soaking tanks are used or where the wash water is used more than once.

Several chlorine compounds are well adapted for treating water used in the packing operations. Sodium hypochlorite is used at concentrations of 3,000 parts per million of available chlorine for tomatoes and 6,000 p. p. m. for citrus. The produce is immersed in the solution for at least 2 minutes. A new sodium hypochlorite treatment for potatoes uses a solution buffered to an acidity of 5.5 to 6.0 pH and a concentration of 100 p. p. m. of chlorine. The immersion period is only 15 seconds. Sodium hypochlorite is also used in conjunction with refrigerated water in flood-type machines for precooling bulk or packed produce. The concentration of chlorine then is 70 to 100 p. p. m. The precooling time averages about 20 to 30 minutes. This combination of chemical treatment with effective precooling is used for produce which requires rapid cooling before loading such as asparagus, celery, corn, peaches, and sweet cherries.

Chlorinated amines are sometimes used at concentrations of 40 to 300 p. p. m. and a reaction of pH 4.0 to 6.5 in wash tanks, rinse water, and cooling tanks. Solutions of this form of chlorine are more stable than sodium hypochlorite solution, and the chlorine is not lost through oxidation of organic matter. The treatment has been used successfully on many kinds of vegetables. It cannot be used on lettuce. It has been used on all kinds of citrus fruits in Texas.

J. R. WINSTON *is in charge of investigations of handling, transportation, storage, and market diseases of citrus fruits and vegetables at the Horticultural Field Laboratory at Orlando, Fla.*

E. M. HARVEY *is in charge of handling, transportation, and storage investigations of citrus and subtropical fruits at the Horticultural Field Laboratory, Pomona, Calif.*

H. B. JOHNSON *is in charge of handling, transportation, and market disease investigations at the Horticultural Field Laboratory at Harlingen, Tex.*

The Values of Fumigants

John M. Harvey, W. T. Pentzer

An advantage of using gaseous fungicides is that they can be much more uniformly dispersed over the treated product than can a liquid or a dust. They also can be applied after packing and loading commodities into a storage room or other enclosed space.

The requirements of an ideal gas to control diseases are that it kill the disease organism but not injure the commodity, leave no residue that is harmful to health, not be explosive or inflammable or otherwise hazardous, be effective in low concentrations and short periods of treatment, be noncorrosive to equipment, and be moderate in cost and readily available.

Such an ideal gas has not been found, but gases with some of those properties are effective in reducing postharvest diseases of numerous commodities.

SULFUR DIOXIDE is used mainly as a fumigant to control decay in stored grapes. Some varieties of California grapes are stored for several months at 30° or 31° F. and 87 to 92 percent relative humidity and are fumigated periodically with sulfur dioxide.

A prevalent postharvest disease of grapes, gray mold rot, is caused by the fungus *Botrytis cinerea*. Some years it has caused 40 percent rot in grapes stored without fumigation. The organism, widespread in nature, attacks different fruits and vegetables. At first the fungus grows just under the surface of the berry and causes the skin to separate from the underlying tissues. The name "slip skin" is applied to this stage of decay. Later the whole berry softens. In the late stages of decay the berries are covered by a gray growth of mycelium and spores of the fungus, which form the typical gray mold rot. The fungus often grows from one berry to another to form a nest of moldy berries.

The amount of gray mold in storage grapes depends largely on the weather before harvest. Rains and long periods of humid weather favor the development of gray mold in the fruit. Although the organism grows best at about 77° F., it also can grow enough at 30° to cause serious decay.

The present techniques for applying sulfur dioxide to grapes were developed over a period of many years. A. J. Winkler and H. E. Jacob, of the California Agricultural Experiment Station at Davis, in 1925 published the results of a study in which they found that at concentrations of 2 to 3 percent sulfur dioxide is absorbed very rapidly. Warm grapes absorb sulfur dioxide faster than cold grapes, mature grapes absorb less sulfur dioxide than immature ones, and injured grapes absorb more sulfur dioxide than sound grapes.

Varieties of vinifera grapes differ greatly in their rate of absorption of sulfur dioxide and in the amounts of the gas that are injurious. In the United States extensive use of sulfur dioxide for grapes is restricted to California, as most varieties grown in the eastern part of the country are highly susceptible to injury by the fumigant.

The extent of the injury is not apparent until grapes are removed from storage and held under market conditions. The cap stems and stems of the grape are affected most. They become yellow or bleached—a desirable "injury" because it keeps the stems from drying to their normal dark brown or black color, a condition which lessens the attractiveness of the bunch.

A more serious injury may occur on the berries, however. It becomes ap-

parent on colored varieties as a bleaching of the tissue near the cap stem or
any injured spot and on green varieties as a yellowing of the tissue. Those
injured areas may become sunken, and
the grapes often look dull and lifeless.
Severely injured berries turn brown
and flaccid and are unsalable. They
have a sulfurous flavor. With modern
procedures for fumigation with sulfur
dioxide serious injury is seldom found
in stored grapes.

The sulfur dioxide absorbed during
treatment is quickly dissipated from
the tissues of the grape. Malaga grapes
that contained 16 parts per million of
sulfur dioxide immediately after treatment have practically none after 5
days. Emperor grapes that contain 13
p. p. m. after treatment contain less
than 1 p. p. m. after 14 days of storage
at 32° F. in the sawdust lug pack.

Therefore protection from mold by
fumigation with sulfur dioxide is only
temporary—additional treatments or
retention of small concentrations of the
fumigant is necessary to prevent later
decay. Some mold spores survive fumigation and may cause infection after
the effects of the gas wear off. Besides,
the fumigation does not kill infections
inside the berry but merely inhibits
growth of the fungus.

Several precautions have to be taken.
The gas is an irritant and a poison in
the concentrations used for grapes. It
can cause serious injury or death to
animals and human beings, and care
should be taken to avoid exposure.

Grapes are quite tolerant of the
fumigant in the concentrations used,
but some other commodities may be
ruined by the gas. Other products
therefore should be removed from
storage rooms where grapes are being
fumigated. Leakage to adjacent rooms
that contain other produce should be
avoided. Sulfur dioxide has a corrosive
action on metal. Exposed metal surfaces should be covered with protective
paints.

The gas is applied commonly to
grapes in storage from weighed
amounts of liquid sulfur dioxide in

cylinders. The cylinders are heated in
a water bath outside the storage room.
The volatilized sulfur dioxide is piped
into the room, where fans disperse it.
The usual procedure is to gas grapes
while warm with an initial concentration of 1.0 percent sulfur dioxide for 20
to 25 minutes. Then come applications
every 7 or 10 days of about 0.25 percent concentrations of the gas for 20 to
25 minutes in the cold-storage rooms.
The gas may be exhausted from the
room through vents or by passing it
through a water spray.

This is the way to calculate the
amount of sulfur dioxide needed for
0.25 percent concentration: The total
capacity of the room is calculated.
From that figure is subtracted the
space occupied by the grapes, which
will be roughly equivalent to one-half
cubic foot per lug, when air voids
between grapes are taken into account.
Since 1 pound of sulfur dioxide is
equivalent to 5.5 cubic feet of gas at
32° F., the free space (cubic feet) in the
room multiplied by 0.25 percent divided by 5.5 will give the pounds of
gas needed. Or: Free space times
(0.0025 divided by 5.5) equals the
pounds of gas needed.

Sulfur dioxide also can be applied to
grapes as sodium bisulfite, added to
the packages. It breaks down slowly in
storage and reacts with moisture to
release small amounts of sulfur dioxide
into the air—a characteristic that
makes the treatment particularly good
in situations in which the fruit is held
for a considerable period and cannot
be regassed by the conventional
method. Sodium bisulfite is used
mostly for grapes packed in sawdust.
Five grams of the powdered chemical
are mixed with the amount of sawdust
required to fill the spaces around the
grapes packed in a chest or lug. The
material should be distributed evenly.
It should not be used if the grapes or
sawdust are wet. It should not be used
in conjunction with other means of
sulfur dioxide refumigation in storage.

Commercial fumigation of grapes
has been successful, but injury to the

grapes has not been completely eliminated. Therefore the aim of research is to find the point at which minimum injury coincides with adequate control of decay—even though a storage room may include several varieties that were harvested at different times and therefore vary in susceptibility to decay and injury. The recommended treatment must be broad enough to cover diverse lots of grapes and conditions.

NITROGEN TRICHLORIDE has been used chiefly as a fumigant for stored citrus fruit. It has been used sometimes on cantaloups, tomatoes, peppers, asparagus, and onions. It does not control decay adequately in grapes and causes an undesirable pitting and discoloration of the stems. It is formed by the reaction of chlorine with ammonium chloride.

It is highly explosive and toxic. To be used safely, it must be greatly diluted in air and generated in special equipment at the time of use. The gas is fed into storage rooms where fans mix it thoroughly with the atmosphere. Only trained persons should use it.

Long exposures to the gas or excessive concentrations may cause injury to citrus fruit. Unusually high concentrations may occur in parts of storage rooms that have poor circulation of air. The result is sunken and browned areas around wounds in the fruit.

Citrus fruits are subject to the attacks of numerous decay organisms during storage. Blue contact mold (*Penicillium italicum*) and green mold (*P. digitatum*) are the most common types. Stem-end rot of citrus caused by *Phomopsis citri* and *Diplodia natalensis* is serious in the Gulf States but of minor significance on fruit grown in California.

Many citrus fruits, if they are stored at temperatures near freezing, become subject to physiologic disorders. Fungicidal materials have to be used therefore to control rot-producing organisms.

In studies conducted at the Citrus Experiment Station at Riverside, Calif.,

L. J. Klotz found that nitrogen trichloride was effective in the control of blue mold and green mold rot of citrus.

Since the gas is effective only against spores on the surface of fruit and not against mycelium within the rind, he recommended that the fruit be gassed soon after picking, before decay starts. When oranges were to be stored for long periods, he recommended one to three exposures of 3 hours each to 8 milligrams of nitrogen trichloride per cubic foot at intervals of 3 to 4 days at the beginning of the storage period. Reinfection was prevented by subsequent weekly gassings. Decay of fruit stored 3 to 4 weeks was reduced 50 to 75 percent by treating with nitrogen trichloride. The recommended concentrations of nitrogen trichloride, the duration of the gassing treatment, and the interval of gassing vary with the tightness of the storage room and the ease with which the gas can be passed through the packed fruit. Specific treatments therefore must be determined for individual storage rooms.

Lemons are much more sensitive to nitrogen trichloride than oranges. Low concentrations of gas at frequent intervals will reduce the amount of decay. Storage rooms for lemons are gassed with concentrations of 1 to 4 milligrams of nitrogen trichloride per cubic foot for 4 hours 3 to 7 times a week, depending on the condition of the fruit.

A. Lloyd Ryall, of the Bureau of Plant Industry, Soils, and Agricultural Engineering, and G. H. Godfrey, of the Texas Agricultural Experiment Station, found that nitrogen trichloride is effective against stem-end rot as well as blue mold and green mold rot of Eureka lemons in Texas. Lemons treated with 0.003 parts per million of nitrogen trichloride for 4 hours at 48-hour intervals developed only 13 percent decay in 2 weeks. Untreated lemons developed 70 percent decay. Even greater control of decay was achieved if the lemons were dipped in a sodium metaborate solution before gassing with nitrogen trichloride.

Cantaloups usually are stored only

during transit and the time they are in wholesale and retail markets. Even during that short period, however, cantaloups are subject to the attack of numerous decay organisms—alternaria rot (*Alternaria* species), cladosporium rot (*Cladosporium cucumerinum*), fusarium rot (*Fusarium* species), and rhizopus soft rot (*Rhizopus nigricans* and other species).

Most of the common decay organisms of cantaloups flourish at 70° or above. Refrigeration usually controls them. *Cladosporium cucumerinum* has the lowest temperature range and is most commonly found on cantaloups held at low temperatures.

J. S. Wiant, of the Market Disease Laboratory in New York, learned that at storage temperatures of 32°–34° very little growth of mold occurs. California melons, however, spend a large part of the postharvest period in transit, where temperatures rarely are that low. They usually are shipped to New York at temperatures ranging from 40° to 50° F. Although decay organisms are inhibited at those temperatures, decay can develop. Various kinds of fungicidal treatments therefore supplement refrigeration.

Nitrogen trichloride has been used commercially to fumigate cantaloups loaded in refrigerator cars destined for transcontinental shipment. Research workers at the United States Plant Industry Station in Fresno, Calif., found that treatment of cantaloups for 4 to 5 hours with nitrogen trichloride at a concentration of 11 to 15 milligrams per cubic foot reduced decay about one-half over untreated checks during a 6-day storage period at 65° F. Melons treated with 17–25 milligrams of nitrogen trichloride for 5 or 6 hours showed only one-third as much rot as untreated melons after 12 days in transit and 2 to 4 days in the market. Even in concentrations as high as 29 to 30 milligrams of nitrogen trichloride, the only injury to the melons was a slight greening of the sutures.

The use of nitrogen trichloride has been discontinued in the melon-grow-

ing districts of California since the practice of top-icing has come into use. The rapid cooling achieved by top-icing generally gives satisfactory control of decay and provides physiological advantages (slowing of the ripening process) not obtained by using a fumigant at warmer temperatures.

D. E. Pryor, of the Wallace Tiernan Co., reported that decay of tomatoes and peppers can be reduced by fumigating with concentrations of 5–12 milligrams of nitrogen trichloride per cubic foot for 4-hour periods. Excessively high concentrations of the gas may cause sunken stem scars in tomatoes and bleached stems in peppers.

THE EPOXIDES, ethylene oxide and propylene oxide, have come into wide use as fumigants for unsulfured dried fruits and spices. L. H. James, of the University of Maryland, reported that treatment with ethylene oxide reduced the mold content of spices by 99 percent and greatly extended the storage period. Since spices are used extensively in making sausage, freeing them of contaminants indirectly reduces spoilage of the sausage. Rita Whelton, H. J. Phaff, and E. M. Mrak, of the University of California, and C. D. Fisher, of the Dried Fruit Association of California, reported in 1946 that spoilage of prunes, figs, dates, and raisins by bacteria, yeasts, and molds was controlled by epoxides. Those materials do not, however, control decay in fresh fruit and may cause serious injury.

Ethylene oxide is about five times more effective than propylene oxide in controlling spoilage organisms. The application of a given amount of a 15-percent solution of ethylene oxide accomplishes the same degree of control as the same amount of 100 percent propylene oxide. Under normal conditions of atmospheric pressure, ethylene oxide changes from the liquid to gaseous state at 51°, while propylene oxide remains in the liquid state up to 95°. Mixing liquid epoxides with a solvent, such as isopropyl formate, raises the boiling point and allows the material to be handled more easily.

Since air mixtures of epoxides are highly explosive, they are often applied in the presence of an inert gas, such as carbon dioxide. Epoxides are poisonous to humans and are especially dangerous when low concentrations are present for long periods. Propylene oxide has the undesirable property of acting as a solvent for inks on packaging materials. Ethylene oxide, therefore, is the more commonly used of the two epoxides.

Ethylene oxide leaves practically no residue on the products that are treated with it. Properly applied, the gas kills all organisms in the treated fruit and prevents spoilage over extended periods unless recontamination occurs. The gas therefore is particularly adaptable to package fumigation. Measured amounts of the chemical in the liquid state are applied just before sealing the individual packages of dried fruit. Such materials as aluminum foil and moistureproof, heat-sealing cellophane are used for packaging, so that the gas will be held long enough to be effective. The time lapse between the application of the fumigant and the sealing of the package is a critical point in the operation, as the fumigant may be lost rapidly by volatilization.

The application of ethylene oxide to the package is a common practice with figs, prunes, dates, and raisins. Figs also may be treated by gassing in the storage room. The oxygen in the room is replaced with the inert gas, carbon dioxide, as a precaution against explosion, and ethylene oxide is introduced at the rate of 12 pounds per 1,000 cubic feet of space. The fruit is fumigated for 15 hours. Figs are usually wrapped within 1 hour after removal from the fumigated storage room to reduce the chance of recontamination.

Only trained operators should apply epoxides, because care and skill are needed to get satisfactory control of spoilage and to prevent accidents from explosion or poisoning.

FORMALDEHYDE GAS is used extensively as a means of fumigating empty sweetpotato storage houses. The gas is generated by mixing a water solution of formaldehyde (formalin) with potassium permanganate. For each 1,000 cubic feet of space in the storage room, 3 pints of formalin are mixed with 23 ounces of potassium permanganate in a container whose volume is about 10 times that of the formalin used in it.

Before mixing the two chemicals, the room should be thoroughly cleaned and tightly closed except for an exit door. The operator should be able to get away quickly after mixing the materials. As formaldehyde is highly irritating and poisonous, he should use goggles and gloves when he prepares for fumigation. After 24 hours, the room should be opened and ventilated for 2 weeks before being used for storage. A storage house should not be fumigated when sweetpotatoes are in it.

H. T. Cook and T. J. Nugent determined the effectiveness of formaldehyde gas on spores of *Rhizopus nigricans* and *Ceratostomella fimbriata*. They found that the amount of gas recommended for fumigation of storages was about four times that required to kill the spores of the fungi in 24 hours. Fumigation tests for shorter periods indicated that the fungi were dead after 2 hours.

Formaldehyde gas has also been used with some success to reduce decay in stored fruit crops. S. J. DuPlessis, in South Africa, applied the gas to storage grapes. He used the same method for generating the gas as we described, but he varied the amounts of formalin and potassium permanganate to give different concentrations of gas. He obtained control of gray mold rot (caused by *Botrytis cinerea*) of Henab Turki grapes by fumigating with 2-percent to 6-percent concentrations of formaldehyde gas, but found that concentrations of 4 percent and more caused injury when applied for 2 hours. A 4-percent concentration of formaldehyde gas, applied for 1 hour before packing, reduced decay after 10 to 12 days in storage from 5.60 percent in the check to only 0.13 percent in treated grapes. Injurious concentrations of formaldehyde cause small, brown, sunken spots to develop around breaks in the skin or around the cap stems of the berries. The flavor of the grapes is not adversely affected. Different varieties of grapes vary in their susceptibility to injury.

In California we reduced decay in grapes without injury by applying a 6 percent formalin spray to the excelsior in a package of grapes, but found the treatment to be inferior to fumigation with sulfur dioxide.

SULFUR DUST applied to peaches when they are graded reduces the amount of brown rot. The sulfur in association with plants is believed to release hydrogen sulfide slowly and inhibit the growth of some decay organisms. M. A. Smith, of the Bureau of Plant Industry, Soils, and Agricultural Engineering, inoculated peaches with spores of the brown rot fungus, *Sclerotinia fructicola*, and dusted them with sulfur. The peaches were kept for 12 days at temperatures ranging from 40° to 85° F. At the end of 12 days, he discovered that sulfur had controlled brown rot in the fruit held at 40°, 45°, and 55°, but not above 64°.

DIPHENYL has been used extensively in the citrus industry to control blue mold, green mold, and stem-end rot. It is a crystalline substance, which may be dissolved in various solvents and impregnated into paper wraps, pads, or box liners used to enclose packed commodities. Diphenyl vapors are slowly released from such materials and reduce the action of decay organisms. A storage test conducted in Palestine showed that oranges wrapped in diphenyl wraps and stored for 18 weeks had only 2 percent of decay, while those in untreated wraps were a total loss. Research workers found that diphenyl controlled decay of lemons in Texas and both oranges and grapefruit in Florida.

G. B. Ramsey, M. A. Smith, and B. C. Heiberg, of the Department of Agriculture Market Disease Laboratory in Chicago, learned that diphenyl vapor inhibits vegetative growth and prevents the production and germination of spores of certain citrus decay fungi. The fumigant thus aids in preventing spread of the molds from decayed fruit to healthy fruit by contact and also by inoculation with spores. The degree of inhibition of growth varied with specific fungi. The most common citrus decay organisms are quite sensitive to diphenyl vapor. The vapor does not kill them, however, for they resume growth when the fumigant is removed.

Many commodities are adversely effected by diphenyl vapor. J. M. Rattray found that South African grapes developed an off-flavor and and turned brown in the presence of ortho-phenyl-phenol, a derivative of diphenyl. W. T. Pentzer and W. R. Barger obtained similar results with Emperor grapes in California. Diphenyl cannot be used with apples, pears, bananas, tomatoes, and cucumbers, because they take up the odor of the chemical. Citrus takes up small amounts of diphenyl in the rind but the flesh is not affected.

IODINE, like diphenyl, is applied to wraps or liners used in packaging and acts as a volatile inhibitor of decay organisms. The packaging material is dipped in an alcoholic solution of iodine and potassium iodide of the desired concentration, dried, and stored in airtight containers until used. R. G. Tomkins, in England, found that iodine wraps reduced decay of oranges caused by *Penicillium digitatum*. He found, however, that iodine was so volatile that it lost its fungicidal effect rather rapidly. It stains the packaging materials an unsightly brown and injures some varieties of fruit.

DuPlessis learned that iodized wraps were effective in reducing the gray mold of grapes. After 10 days in storage treated grapes showed 19.9 percent infection of *Botrytis*, while untreated grapes showed 42 percent. Wraps treated with 1 percent iodine and 2 percent potassium iodide reduced *Botrytis* infection to 1.41–7.04 percent, compared with 12.27 percent in the check. The treatment did not impair the flavor.

In California iodized wraps reduced decay to one-fourth that of untreated grapes. The treatment caused no injury to the fruit, but the control was inferior to that obtained with sulfur dioxide.

MODIFICATION OF ATMOSPHERES in storage rooms by increasing the amount of carbon dioxide (CO_2) and reducing the oxygen content slows down the respiration of the commodity being treated and (sometimes) the organisms of decay. Carbon dioxide does not act as a fumigant. It does not kill disease organisms but only inhibits them. After removal from such modified atmospheres the organisms resume normal growth.

Carbon dioxide has been used with considerable success as a supplement to refrigeration of commodities that are subject to physiologic disturbances at near freezing temperatures. An outstanding example is the storage of New York-grown McIntosh apples at 40° in atmospheres of 5 percent carbon dioxide and 2 percent oxygen. Control of decay comparable to that obtained at lower temperatures is achieved by this treatment without undesirable browning of the flesh.

Charles Brooks and others in the Bureau of Plant Industry, Soils, and Agricultural Engineering found that peaches, apricots, strawberries, and red raspberries were quite sensitive to injury by carbon dioxide. Only slight injury was observed when plums, cherries, blackberries, blueberries, black raspberries, currants, pears, apples, and oranges were treated. Grapes, peas, sweet corn, and carrots were especially resistant to injury by carbon dioxide. Injury from excessive exposure to carbon dioxide was evidenced

by a loss of aroma and flavor or even by the development of fermentation.

Carbon dioxide also has been used to treat fruits and vegetables in loaded refrigerator cars. Applied immediately after loading, the gas is as effective in controlling decay as is rapid cooling to 32°. To obtain the desired results, 800 to 1,000 pounds of solid carbon dioxide are used initially. Carbon dioxide is particularly effective in controlling decay of cherries caused by species of *Rhizopus*, *Monilia*, and *Penicillium*. At 45°, an atmosphere containing 25 percent carbon dioxide controls fungus decay of sweet cherries and also has a favorable effect on the firmness, brightness, and freshness of the fruit. Bing and Lambert cherries tolerate concentrations up to 40 percent when stored for 12 days at 60° or 20 days at 45°.

Carbon dioxide may be introduced into storage room atmospheres in several ways. Simply sealing the room will cause carbon dioxide to accumulate as a result of respiration by the stored commodity. It may be released from cylinders of the compressed gas. It may be obtained by the "melting" of solid carbon dioxide (dry ice). The use of the gas is limited because many storage rooms and refrigerator cars are not sufficiently airtight to retain the gas over extended periods.

JOHN M. HARVEY *is a plant pathologist in the Bureau of Plant Industry, Soils, and Agricultural Engineering at Fresno, Calif. After receiving his doctor's degree at the University of California in 1950, he joined the field laboratory of the Department at Fresno, Calif., where he specializes in the plant diseases associated with the handling, transportation, and storage of horticultural crops.*

W. T. PENTZER *joined the Department of Agriculture as a junior marketing specialist in 1926. From 1929 to 1949 he was in charge of the field laboratory at Fresno, where much of the research on sulfur dioxide fumigation of grapes was conducted. Since 1949 he has been head of the division of handling, transportation, and storage of horticultural crops at Beltsville, Md.*

Oak Wilt, a New Threat

Theodore W. Bretz

Oak wilt is a serious threat to our noble oaks, the lovely trees that since Colonial days have meant much to the economy and development of this country, account for one-third of the hardwood saw timber stand in eastern United States, and are highly valued as ornamentals and as sources of food for wildlife.

Oak wilt has received increasing attention since 1940 because of the damage it has caused in shade oaks and wood-lot and forest oaks in Iowa, Wisconsin, and Minnesota. Since 1947, it has been found in several other Midwestern and Appalachian States from Pennsylvania to North Carolina. It is infectious and destructive, and many foresters, arborists, conservationists, and plant pathologists are concerned about it.

We do not know how long it has been in the United States. An epidemic dying of oak, observed in southern Wisconsin and southern Minnesota 40 years ago, was ascribed to various causes—adverse climatic conditions, insects, and other diseases. But investigators of the Wisconsin Agricultural Experiment Station and the Department of Agriculture established the fungus nature of oak wilt in 1942, and it seems probable that the disease may have been responsible for at least some of the earlier mortality of oaks in that area.

Until the summer of 1949, oak wilt was known only in Wisconsin, Minne-

852 YEARBOOK OF AGRICULTURE 1953

sota, Iowa, Illinois, and east central Missouri. In 1949, forest pathologists found it in the northern Ozark region of southern Missouri and in northwestern Indiana.

Funds obtained from the Forest Pest Control Act and the Arkansas Resources and Development Commission financed a limited survey by Federal forest pathologists in 1950, mainly in the Ozark Mountains. Low-flying airplanes were used to locate suspected infected trees in the forests. Ground crews then examined the suspected trees and collected specimens for laboratory confirmation of the field diagnosis. As a result of that work, the oak wilt was found to be widely scattered in southern Missouri and in northern Arkansas. Other workers found the disease in a few isolated locations in Kansas, Nebraska, Ohio, and Pennsylvania.

Airplane scouting for oak wilt has proved to be satisfactory, fast, and economical. An aerial observer's most effective survey for wilt is limited to about one-quarter mile. Two observers in a plane can usually survey a strip one-half mile wide through the forest. A third member of a crew can greatly speed the work by keeping the position located at all times on a map and indicating on it the location of suspected trees seen by the observers. Landmarks can also be noted that will be useful to a ground crew who may later visit the area to collect specimens for laboratory culturing.

The development of the aerial-scouting technique to locate oak wilt and the discovery of the disease in the Appalachians brought greatly expanded survey activities in 1951. Federal, State, and private organizations participated in the surveys, and their efforts disclosed the presence of the disease over much of our hardwood area. Besides the States I mentioned, oak wilt was found in Michigan, West Virginia, Kentucky, Tennessee, Virginia, Maryland, and North Carolina.

Oak wilt was not found in any additional States in 1952. It was found in many new locations throughout its range, however, with a notable increase in the number of known infection centers in Ohio and in Pennsylvania west of the Susquehanna River.

OAK WILT PRODUCES noticeable and characteristic leaf symptoms, which vary somewhat with the species affected. The diseased trees are most conspicuous from mid-June to mid-September. In species belonging to the red and black oak group, symptoms usually appear first in the top of the tree and at the ends of the lateral branches and progress rapidly downward and inward through the entire crown. The leaves first become dull or pale green, curl upward, and become stiff. They turn yellow or bronze from the apex and margins inward.

The blade tissue next to the petiole is the last to turn brown. Affected leaves may fall from the tree at any stage of symptom development. Defoliation may be slight or nearly complete. Some leaves may remain on the tree to the end of the season and a few may even persist until the following summer. Sometimes sucker growth, in the form of dense clusters of large, succulent leaves, develops on the trunk and larger branches before an infected tree dies. The bark of wilt-killed trees loosens rather rapidly and by the end of the second year following death may begin to shed from the bole.

In white and bur oaks the leaf symptoms are often much more localized. Usually the entire tree does not wilt at once. Individual branches in any part of the crown may develop leaf symptoms, while leaves on the unaffected parts of the tree remain green. The affected leaves may be tan or dark green and look water-soaked. They tend to remain on the branches after they die. The killing of individual branches over a period of years results in stagheading. A brown or black discoloration in the outer sapwood just under the bark is sometimes present in the twigs and branches of infected trees. When one peels back the bark he can see a diffuse brownish discoloration or longitudinal streaks. In cross section it appears as a brown ring or circle of dark-colored spots just under the bark.

The symptoms are sufficiently distinctive so that a diagnosis can usually be made in the field. We know of no other disease of oak with those symptoms or effects. For accurate identification, however, particularly in areas in which the disease has not previously been known, laboratory isolation of the causal fungus from diseased specimens is advisable.

The oak wilt fungus is closely related to the fungi that cause the Dutch elm disease and the canker stain disease of the London planetree, and is a near relative of the important blue stain fungi of forest products. It was described and named *Chalara quercina* by Berch W. Henry in 1944. Later, having discovered new facts regarding its life history, I reclassified and named it *Endoconidiophora fagacearum*.

All species of oak thus far subjected to infection under natural conditions or by artificial inoculation have proved susceptible to oak wilt. They include the following species native to the region in which oak wilt occurs— white (*Quercus alba*), swamp white (*Q. bicolor*), northern red (*Q. borealis*), eastern red (*Q. borealis maxima*), scarlet (*Q. coccinea*), northern pin or Hill's yellow (*Q. ellipsoidalis*), southern red or Spanish (*Q. falcata*), swamp red (*Q. falcata* var. *pagodaefolia*), shingle (*Q. imbricaria*), bur (*Q. macrocarpa*), blackjack (*Q. marilandica*), chestnut (*Q. montana*), chinquapin (*Q. muehlenbergii*), water (*Q. nigra* and *Q. nigra* f. *hemisphaerica*), pin (*Q. palustris*), willow (*Q. phellos*), basket or swamp chestnut (*Q. prinus*), post (*Q. stellata*), Shumard (*Q. shumardii*), and black (*Q. velutina*).

Turkey (*Q. laevis*), laurel (*Q. laurifolia*), Texas red (*Q. shumardii* var. *texana*), and live (*Q. virginiana*) oaks from the Gulf Coast, Gambel (*Q. gambelii*) and Oregon white (*Q. garryana*) oaks from the west coast, cork (*Q. suber*) and English (*Q. robur*) oaks from Europe, and sawtooth (*Q. acutissima*) and Daimyo (*Q. dentata*) oaks from Asia developed typical symptoms of oak wilt when they were artificially inoculated with the fungus.

In nature, species of the red and black oak group usually die the same season that they first show symptoms, often within a few weeks after the first symptoms appear. When symptoms first appear late in the season, however, diseased trees may survive the winter. The following spring sparse, dwarfed, and short-lived foliage develops. Species of the white oak group die more slowly. Bur oaks have been reported to lose all their leaves and die in a single season. The relative susceptibility to the disease of many of the species when growing in their natural environment has not yet been determined. Such information can be obtained only by observation of the behavior of the disease in nature.

Trees closely related to oaks are also known to be susceptible to the disease. Naturally infected Chinese chestnuts (*Castanea mollissima*) have been found and it has been shown by artificial inoculation that the American chestnut (*C. dentata*), European chestnut (*C. sativa*), tanoak (*Lithocarpus densiflorus*), and bush chinquapin (*Castanopsis sempervirens*) are susceptible to oak wilt in the greenhouse.

Experimental evidence indicates that the oak wilt fungus can infect only through wounds that penetrate the bark of the tree. Once established, the fungus multiplies rapidly and is distributed widely in the sapwood of the tree by the time the symptoms first appear. That may happen within 3 weeks after inoculation. A direct and early response of the host to the infection is the plugging of the water-conducting vessels in the sapwood. That response may be actuated by a toxin, which the fungus may produce and which alone will induce wilt symptoms. The obstructions that form in the water-conducting tubes in the sapwood may limit the water supply available to the leaves, and the shortage may contribute to the development of the leaf symptoms. No important plugging of the roots of diseased trees has been observed, and it has been demonstrated that the fungus can move from diseased to nearby healthy oaks through natural root grafts.

Natural root grafting is common in stands of red and black oaks. The grafts provide a highway through which the fungus can pass from tree to tree. Such spread probably accounts for the somewhat radial manner in which the disease extends from an initially infected individual. Progress of the disease in that way is slow. Bur and white oaks in mixed stands often remain unaffected even after the population of red and black oaks has been largely wiped out. A probable explanation might lie in the infrequency of root grafting between different oak species. Root grafts from bur to bur and white to white are reported to be uncommon.

How oak wilt spreads over distances greater than those we can attribute to natural root grafting is not known. Such above-ground spread does occur, but how far from old centers of disease the fungus may be carried in a single passage has not been determined. By aerial surveys oak wilt has been located many miles from any other known center of infection. Such trees often are the dominant or codominant trees in the stand.

Infection by wind-blown spores may possibly occur but appears to be relatively unimportant, even though the fungus has been found to sporulate abundantly under the loosened bark of some wilt-killed trees. If such spread did occur, a much more definite pattern of distribution of the disease within a given area and a much greater mortality in our oak population would be expected than has been the case. Some other agent or agents

of dissemination appear more likely. The discovery that the fungus possesses a spore form (ascospores) admirably suited to transmission by insects or birds, because of its sticky nature, may provide a clue to the mystery of long-distance spread. The ascospore form, which develops only when two compatible strains of the fungus are brought together, has been observed beneath loosening bark of trees killed by oak wilt. The frequency with which it occurs in nature and whether it may develop on other tree parts or other host plants remain to be determined.

THE SPREAD OF THE DISEASE in local areas can be retarded by interrupting the movement of the fungus from diseased to healthy trees through root grafts. In situations in which individual trees are of little value, this may be most readily accomplished by poisoning the healthy trees around the perimeter of diseased trees. A 50-foot buffer zone of killed trees around the infection center is recommended.

Among street, lawn, and park trees, mechanical severance of roots connecting diseased and healthy trees may be more desirable. That may be done by trenching or (in some types of soil) by the use of an especially designed, tractor-drawn knife blade. A cut 30 inches deep is believed sufficient to sever all connecting roots between trees. The effectiveness of the method depends largely upon the promptness with which the root cutting is done after the disease is detected. Root severance should not be delayed more than 3 weeks after the first symptoms appear.

To what extent standing, wilt-killed trees may remain a source of infection is unknown. As the fungus may sporulate under the loosened bark of wilt-killed trees and has been isolated from trees almost a year after death, disposal of such trees by burning or sawing them into lumber and burning the slabs and brush seems to be advisable as a supplementary practice.

We have begun experiments to get more exact information on the danger of leaving oaks that are poisoned and, if they are a danger, on other methods of making certain that they cannot serve as sources of disease. Since wilt symptoms on white and bur oaks may be limited to a few isolated branches, careful and rigorous pruning of all wilting branches has been reported to prolong the life of an occasional tree.

The development of measures (other than the sanitation of known infection centers) for the control of long-distance, above-ground spread of oak wilt will probably await the discovery of the means of such spread. In many regions, however, oak wilt is not yet firmly established and the number of infection centers are few and small. Prompt elimination of those centers might prevent serious spread of the disease.

The fungus will kill small oak trees, but whether the disease may be spread through shipment of nursery-size trees is not known. There is but little evidence with regard to the hazard dimensional lumber may present in the spread of the disease. However, the fungus has not been isolated from heartwood. Kiln drying should kill the fungus if it were present in sapwood. The fungus is reported to have survived for almost a year in logs with bark on them.

Although the disease is widely scattered through much of our commercially important timber in the Ozarks and Appalachians, the percentage of trees infected is low and no significant losses have occurred. But oak wilt is capable of much destruction; should an efficient vector for the fungus appear, it could become a catastrophe. Research on all aspects of the disease has been started and we hope that a control of this menace can be found.

THEODORE W. BRETZ, *a pathologist in the division of forest pathology, Bureau of Plant Industry, Soils, and Agricultural Engineering, is in charge of the division's investigations of oak wilt, conducted in cooperation with the Missouri Agricultural Experiment Station, at Columbia.*

Littleleaf in Pines in the Southeast

W. A. Campbell, Otis L. Copeland, Jr., George H. Hepting

Littleleaf, a disease of shortleaf (*Pinus echinata*) and loblolly (*P. taeda*) pines, was first observed in Alabama in 1934. The early symptoms are a yellowing of the foliage and a reduction in growth. Shoot growth and needle length become greatly reduced as the disease progresses, and often the affected trees produce an abundant crop of small cones. Trees with advanced symptoms are conspicuous because of their short, yellow needles, which are confined to the ends of the branches. The disease rarely affects trees younger than 20 years of age and is most prevalent in stands that are 30 to 50 years old.

Littleleaf occurs in varying amounts in Mississippi, Alabama, Georgia, South Carolina, North Carolina, Virginia, and Tennessee. The littleleaf belt, from Virginia to Mississippi, embraces approximately 30 million acres, of which over half is in forests. Areas of abundant littleleaf cover about 5 million acres of this forest land. But even in areas of greatest abundance, littleleaf is not uniformly distributed throughout stands of shortleaf pine. Age of stand, soil conditions, and degree of erosion are important factors in the distribution of the disease. Stands with severe littleleaf may be found close to healthy stands. The spotty occurrence of littleleaf in many areas and often the relative lack of the disease in nearby stands are generally determined by soil relationships.

A survey made in 1947 in South Carolina disclosed that 118 million board feet of shortleaf pine were recently dead or in the advanced stages of the disease. That means that about 39 million board feet would die each year, because trees in the advanced stages have a life expectancy of less than 3 years. It has been estimated for the South as a whole that littleleaf kills nearly 200 million board feet of shortleaf pine and 20 million board feet of loblolly pine each year. In addition, more than 250,000 cords of pine in the 6–8-inch age classes are annually killed by the disease.

Not all expected mortality can be considered as loss, because much salvage cutting of diseased trees before death is done in areas affected by littleleaf. Diseased trees may live 10 or more years from the onset of symptoms, but they do not increase materially in size. Another type of indirect loss arises from the accelerated conversion of pine stands to hardwoods, which takes place as trees are killed by littleleaf.

The symptoms of littleleaf develop largely from the gradual killing of the fine roots by the parasitic fungus *Phytophthora cinnamomi* and probably to a lesser extent from other causes. New root ends and very young roots are most susceptible to invasion by the fungus. The gradual loss of the fine roots interferes especially with the absorption of nitrogen, and leads to a slow cessation of growth, yellowing of the foliage, and premature death.

The fungus, widely distributed in the soils of the Southeast, occurs in soils in the Coastal Plain and elsewhere where littleleaf is absent. Its ability to attack roots severely depends to a great extent on soil type and condition. Experimental work has shown that root infection is limited in sandy soils, more common in loams, and severe in silts and clays. As the fungus requires abundant moisture to produce the motile spores that cause infection, root damage increases as the subsoils become more poorly drained. The relationship between internal drainage of the soil and root infection helps to explain why the disease is confined to the heavier soils of the Piedmont and related areas.

A person needs to understand the dependence of the root parasite on certain soil conditions in order to develop plans for the management of littleleaf areas. The disease does not normally spread directly from diseased trees to healthy trees. The fungus is already present in most southeastern pine soils and the development of littleleaf is conditioned almost entirely by soil factors that cannot be changed materially except possibly over long periods of time.

Early studies suggested that severe littleleaf was associated with frequent burning, poor pine sites, soil erosion, and steep slopes. Then in 1948, on the Calhoun Experimental Forest near Union, S. C., on various soil associations, the severity of littleleaf was found to increase as internal drainage of the soil became poorer. This discovery stimulated a more extensive study of the relationship of soils to the disease throughout the littleleaf region of the southern Piedmont in 1949. Forest vegetation, soil characteristics, and severity of disease were analyzed in the search for factors associated with the disease. The analysis disclosed that although disease severity may vary from site to site on any one particular kind of soil, the average severity follows a fairly regular relationship to the internal drainage condition of a particular soil series. Internal drainage is defined as the quality of a soil that permits the downward flow of excess water through it. Soil texture, structure, porosity, height of water table, and other factors influence it. Soils with poor internal drainage thus are usually more nearly saturated with water and less well aerated for long periods. In such soils pines develop poor root systems and infections by root fungi are favored.

Although more than 30 factors of soil, vegetation, or fungus have been studied in relationship to littleleaf, only internal drainage and the degree of soil erosion are significantly correlated with the disease severity.

In Piedmont soil groups a striking relationship exists between the internal drainage of soils and the occurrence of littleleaf. In Durham, Alamance, Cecil, Georgeville, Davidson, Lockhart, Lloyd, and Nason soils with excellent to good internal drainage the percentage of diseased shortleaf pine was 3.9. On Louisa, Madison, Appling, and Helena soils with good to poor internal drainage it was 12.1 percent. On Cataula, Mecklenburg, Grange, Vance, Tatum, Herndon, Manteo, and Wilkes soils with generally poor internal drainage 25.5 percent of the trees had the disease.

Although pine stands as young as 20 years of age may be affected, most of those that become diseased first show symptoms when they are 30 to 50 years old. In general, the younger the age of an attacked stand, the more severe the effect will be—obviously, greater loss will result in the stands that show disease at an early age, because most of the diseased trees that should be salvaged will be too small to market except as pulpwood. Stands contracting the disease when they are older often produce a sizable volume of saw timber.

The first problem in dealing with littleleaf stands is that of properly spacing cuttings to minimize the loss of merchantable timber. Suggested intervals for harvesting are based on the amount of disease in the stand and the rate of deterioration of affected trees.

On the basis that littleleaf trees live for an average of 7 years following the onset of symptoms and trees in advanced stages less than 3 years, the following cutting rules are advised for stands that are readily accessible: Where only an occasional shortleaf pine shows littleleaf, cuts can be light and spaced at least 10 years apart. When 10 to 25 percent of the trees show unmistakable littleleaf, cut on at least a 7-year cutting cycle, cutting all diseased or suspected trees at each cut. Where more than 25 percent of the trees show littleleaf, cut all shortleaf pine as soon as merchantable.

With the harvesting of the present littleleaf stands, the question arises as to the future prospects for shortleaf pine on the same sites. Because the disease is associated with soil conditions that cannot be greatly changed except over long periods, succeeding crops of shortleaf pine may be expected to fail at the same or an even earlier age. As many of those sites provide satisfactory yields of pulpwood however, they may be managed on short rotations without undue interference from the disease.

Soil improvement has been suggested as one way to combat littleleaf. That can be accomplished by encouraging hardwoods, especially such species as dogwood, yellow-poplar, and hickory, which are known to improve soils. Hardwoods are more effective than pine in building humus. Practically all hardwoods return more nitrogen, calcium, and other elements to the soil than pine; the eventual change to a greater proportion of broadleaved species in littleleaf areas may serve to reduce the incidence of disease by lowering the number of trees that are susceptible to attack and also by providing more favorable growth conditions for the existing pine. Any effect on pine would be on future stands, however, and the older individuals now occupying the site could scarcely be expected to benefit immediately by conversion to hardwood.

Loblolly pine on severe littleleaf sites is approximately one-third as susceptible as shortleaf and should, therefore, be favored wherever possible. Other pines, such as Virginia, pitch, or longleaf, should also be encouraged where feasible in order to build up the percentage of resistant or immune species.

W. A. CAMPBELL *is a senior pathologist,* OTIS L. COPELAND, JR., *a soil scientist, and* GEORGE H. HEPTING, *a principal pathologist, in the division of forest pathology, Bureau of Plant Industry, Soils, and Agricultural Engineering. All have had years of experience with the littleleaf disease. Their studies of the disease have been made in cooperation with the Forest Service and several State agencies.*

Ailments of House Plants

Freeman A. Weiss

House plants, being creatures of a sheltered environment, may be spared some of the tribulations of pests, diseases, and occasional hardships of nature to which plants growing in the open are often exposed. They are not immune, however, to those afflictions.

Indeed, their indoor environment, which one might presume to be altogether beneficent, is really the cause of most of their ills. The statement seems a little contradictory when one considers how well most plants flourish in a greenhouse. Let us examine for a moment the actual conditions of the environment in which house plants are expected to thrive.

The distribution of light in an average living room is very uneven—greatly different from the even lighting under the open sky. We are impressed with this when we try to make photographs indoors without using supplementary illumination and get pictures with extremely bright highlights and deep shadows. To be sure, we put our house plants, except the very shade-tolerant sorts, in our best lighted windows. But even a single thickness of glass may reduce the intensity of outdoor light by one-half. With storm windows, screens, and curtains besides, the light intensity inside a window may be a tenth or less of that outside. Furthermore, the light near a window is strongly one-sided, and it often undergoes extreme and rapid variation as the sun is obscured by clouds, trees, or buildings. Thus the light may be too strong at times, too weak at others, and always from the side, never overhead as under a bright sky. The artificial light we provide for our own convenience usually benefits house plants but little, as it is turned on only during hours of darkness outdoors and is very spotty. The indoor light we customarily read by is but a fortieth or less as strong as outdoor light on an average bright day.

All those adverse light conditions are accentuated during the short and often dark days of winter, when we cherish our house plants most and want them to flourish and bloom.

Humidity—atmospheric moisture—is so variable that hardly any generalization holds very well, except that as a rule the air inside our houses is much drier than that outdoors, especially in winter when we are using artificial heat. The humidity outdoors ranges generally from about 30 percent to 100 percent of saturation, which means that the air contains from about one-third to the full quantity of water vapor it can hold at any given temperature. Indoors, it is likely to be 30 percent or less most of the time—very much lower in dry regions under winter conditions. The humidifying devices sometimes used on heating equipment seldom raise the humidity more than 10 to 20 percent. Thus the upper range of humidity we can maintain in our living rooms corresponds to only the lower part of the outdoor range. Furthermore, the humidity indoors is constantly low because we artificially keep the temperature fairly uniform in our living rooms, whereas outdoors the humidity increases at night as the temperature characteristically falls. It often reaches saturation, in fact, as shown by the deposition of dew or, in cold weather, of frost.

Some horticultural writers (doubtless middle-aged males!) have urged a return to olden times when the teakettle simmered all day on the cook stove and the family washing was done in open washtubs or boilers and the damp clothes were hung in an ante-room to dry—all of which tended to keep the humidity up to the level preferred by plants. But that, of course, is impracticable.

The daily rise of temperature and its fall at night, together with the concomitant decline and ascent of the humidity, I have already mentioned as characteristic of the outdoor environment. Further, the temperature indoors varies but little, at least in houses and apartments with automatic heat control. It is undoubtedly beneficial to plants to experience a drop in temperature at night—it is their resting period after working all day in the light. Greenhouse managers regularly let the temperature fall at night as much as 10 to 20 degrees. They do so not merely to produce a corresponding increase of humidity, although it does have that effect. The lowering of temperature at night may profoundly affect the growth habits of a plant and perhaps its flowering or fruiting. Those responses are relics of its behavior when it grew outdoors. Some house-grown plants also are benefited by this daily temperature change.

Plants growing in the open ground normally "forage" for water and minerals by sending their roots as deep or far as possible to reach those vital supplies. The soil is a more or less constant reservoir of moisture; the loss from the surface layer by evaporation and plant growth is compensated by a gradual rise from deeper levels. When heavy rains fall, the excess water runs off to lower levels or soaks into the subsoil beyond the immediate range of plant roots. Rain water and water from melting snow are practically free of dissolved minerals. In its passage through the soil, the water dissolves and washes away excess salts and harmful products of fermentations that occur in the organic components of the soil. The alternate fall and rise of soil water causes a corresponding movement of air into and from the soil, and that aeration is important to the health of plant roots.

Pot-grown plants, especially those in impervious plastic containers now much in favor, are at a disadvantage in most of these respects, in comparison with those growing in the open. The quantity of soil is strictly limited. Root growth is limited correspondingly. The soil rapidly becomes water-soaked and just as quickly dries out. There is little chance for natural purifying processes through drainage and aeration. The high mineral content of many city water supplies and the necessity for frequent watering lead to an accumulation of lime and other chemicals in the soil of potted plants. The accumulations are often injurious and difficult to remove.

THIS RECITAL of the adverse factors of house-plant culture might make it seem something of a miracle that such plants ever flourish indoors. Many fine specimens, excellent in foliage and flower, testify to the contrary. I exaggerated unfavorable features purposely just to emphasize the fact of their existence. To the extent that the deficiencies of the indoor plant environment, in such respects as light, humidity, temperature, and water, are corrected so as to approach the favorable conditions of the open ground and air, so will the health of house plants be promoted.

That means good light, as uniform as such a variable factor can be made, supplemented if necessary by artificial illumination. It means providing the nearest possible approach to favorable humidity by placing the pots in shallow saucers filled with water or resting them on trays containing moist pebbles, vermiculite, or other clean, water-absorbent material. Plants kept in very dry rooms should be enclosed, if practicable, in a glass or cellophane-covered case, provided with a moist floor. Extremes of temperature must be avoided, especially a constant excess: House plants will generally flourish best at day temperatures not over 70° F., dropping 5 to 10° at night. Watering should preferably be periodic and regular, with moderate wetness alternating with moderate dryness. Except for occasional drenches, which should be followed by prompt drying, to cleanse the foliage of dust and grime, heavy watering and likewise extreme drying are to be avoided. The water should always be near the temperature of the air or, if applied to the foliage, slightly warmer. It goes without saying that house plants must be protected against illuminating gas, especially that produced from coal, and from exposure to other atmospheric contaminants, like the fumes from coal or oil stoves.

VARIOUS biological agents also may injure house plants. We are here concerned only with the parasitic microorganisms—chiefly fungi and bacteria, but also nematodes and the submicroscopic viruses. The grosser parasites and enemies—insects and mites—as pests of house plants, have been treated in the 1952 Yearbook, *Insects*, which should be consulted for information on their recognition and control. Attention is directed particularly to the chapter, "Insect Pests of Flowers and Shrubs," pages 640–651 in *Insects*.

One could easily make an impressive list of the parasitic diseases that have been recorded at some time or place on indoor plants, but it would be discouraging rather than helpful to the plant grower. Fortunately the diseases that occur at all commonly are few, and principally of three types:

A. Diseases that primarily attack underground parts and are due to soil-borne organisms: Damping-off and root rot, caused by fungi (*Pythium, Rhizoctonia*); crown rot, caused by fungi (*Pythium, Rhizoctonia, Botrytis, Fusarium,* and *Phytophthora*); bulb rot, caused by bacteria and various fungi; crown gall, caused by bacteria; wilt, caused by fungi (*Fusarium, Verticillium*); root knot, caused by nematodes (*Meloidogyne,* formerly called *Heterodera*).

B. Diseases that primarily attack above-ground parts and are caused by airborne organisms: Anthracnose (leaf and stem spots and rots), caused by fungi (*Colletotrichum, Gloeosporium*); leaf spots and blotches, caused by various fungi and sometimes bacteria or leaf-infesting nematodes; stem cankers and dieback, caused by fungi (*Diplodia, Fusarium, Phomopsis,* and others); stem galls, caused by bacteria and sometimes fungi; gray mold shoot blight and bud rot, caused by a fungus (*Botrytis*); mildew, caused by fungi (*Erysiphe, Microsphaera*); sooty mold, caused by fungi (commonly *Capnodium,* following aphid and scale infestation); false smut, caused by a fungus (*Graphiola*).

C. Systemic diseases, which affect the whole plant: Mosaic, ring spot, spotted wilt, and yellows, caused by viruses; chlorosis, caused by nutritional deficiencies.

THE IMPORTANCE of the division into soil-borne diseases and airborne diseases lies in the fact that the former are controllable mainly or only by soil disinfection, either by heat or by chemicals. As a rule those diseases are less influenced by environmental factors, such as temperature and humidity, than are the diseases of foliage. If the soil is initially contaminated with the causal organisms or becomes contaminated from introducing infected plants, there is no lasting remedy other than a complete change of soil or soil disinfection.

The diseases of Group B, on the other hand, are influenced greatly by the environment. For the most part they attack house plants only when some environmental or cultural factor is at fault. For example, the shoot blight and bud rot caused by the gray mold, *Botrytis,* typically occurs only when plants are chilled or are wet frequently and not properly ventilated. Lack of light and excessive humidity, even if only transitory, also favor the disease, which may attack very suddenly. Exposure to moderately warm temperature, with better light and ventilation, and with less frequent or copious watering, will usually check it at once. Avoidance of wetting the leaves when watering, or making sure that the foliage dries promptly thereafter, by setting the plants in a well-lighted and ventilated place (but not in bright sunlight or in a cold draft) will avoid most leaf spots, whether caused by fungi, bacteria, or nematodes. In fact, from the standpoint of house plants, the one good feature of the dry atmosphere in our living rooms is that it gives these leaf diseases almost no opportunity to start.

Mildew, a disease characterized by dirty-white, powdery patches on the foliage, young shoots, and flowers, is also associated with excessive humidity and lack of ventilation. Actual wetting or washing the foliage, followed by prompt drying, checks it, however, and better ventilation and a temporary rise of temperature will usually eliminate it.

There is not much occasion to use fungicidal sprays on house plants, as most of the foliage diseases can be controlled by readjustment of the environment, and the root rots and wilts are not amenable to control by external applications. The control of insect pests, on the other hand, often requires spraying or dusting, but with materials designed for killing insects, most of which have little effect on fungi and bacteria. Occasion may arise when one can use, with benefit to house plants, certain mild fungicidal sprays, such as ferbam, wettable sulfur, or the slightly soluble "fixed" copper compounds, in concentrations considerably lower than those recommended for outdoor plants under summer conditions. Such occasions seldom occur with ordinary house plants under average home conditions.

Soil treatment to destroy disease-inducing organisms is often important in house-plant culture, and heating is not only the most adaptable method for this purpose but is also the most effective.

Heat treatments of the proper intensity and duration can destroy all kinds of soil-borne pests—fungi, bacteria, nematodes, and insects. They leave no persistent toxic residues in the soil, as chemical treatments sometimes do. Soil that is to be heat-treated should first be prepared as if for planting, should be loose, free of lumps and coarse debris, and slightly moist. It can be spread in a pan, about 2 inches deep, and baked in an oven at 200 degrees for 1 hour. Another method is to place it in pots, which are either heated in a pressure cooker or placed on a rack above boiling water in a covered receptacle such as a kettle or wash boiler. The heating time for different sizes of pots by the pressure-cooker method, with the valve set at 10 pounds pressure, should be: 3-inch, 10 minutes; 4-inch, 15 minutes; 6-inch, 30 minutes. If boiling water, without pressure, is used, those intervals should be doubled.

After treatment, the soil should be stirred and well aired for several days to a week before replanting. With large soil masses, especially if heavily manured or fertilized, it is advisable to spread the soil in a layer and wet it down once or twice during the drying period, in order to remove toxic compounds that are produced in the soil by heating. Of course, one must be careful to avoid recontaminating the soil by contact with dirty surfaces or utensils, or replanting to diseased plants.

EXAMPLES of common maladies of house plants:

African-violet. The worst affliction is root knot, especially when complicated (as it often is) with fungus root rot and crown rot. Although not an infallible remedy, the propagation of new plants from leaf cuttings (which should be started in vermiculite, peat moss, or water, then transplanted to heat-treated soil) will usually eliminate this trouble. Gray mold (*Botrytis*) bud rot and mildew may attack plants that are chilled, overwatered, or kept in dull light and not sufficiently ventilated.

Aloe. Root rot caused by *Pythium* and *Rhizoctonia* may be troublesome if the plants are overwatered or are grown in heavy soil without proper drainage.

Asparagus-fern. The most prevalent ailment is shedding of the needlelike leaves as a result of too dry and too warm an atmosphere. Root knot caused by nematodes and a stem canker and wilt of fungus origin also may attack this plant; the remedy for this is to repot in new or heat-treated soil of light texture and provide good drainage.

Begonia. A victim of numerous diseases: Root knot, crown gall, bacterial leaf spot, nematode leaf spot, and gray mold bud and shoot rot; also oedema, a nonparasitic localized swelling of leaf tissue, followed by collapse and death in spots, and caused by excessive wetness of soil and dull light. Overwatering, frequent wetting of foliage, and lack of ventilation are the principal contributing factors in the foliage diseases; change or disinfection of soil is the remedy for the root troubles.

Cactus. Rotting of underground parts by fungi and bacterial leaf spot or rot of the tops are the commonest troubles. These dry-soil plants must be watered sparingly and uniformly, never soaked.

Calla. Bacterial soft rot and phytophthora rot of the rootstock or "bulb" are the worst enemies; both may be carried on these parts or in the soil. Affected plants are very difficult to cure. One must start with healthy rootstocks, planted in disease-free soil. Callas may also carry systemically the spotted wilt virus; affected plants are poorly colored and are weak growers. As there is no cure, they should be discarded.

"Chinese evergreens" (*Aglaonema, Dieffenbachia, Philodendron*). These are usually trouble-free plants, but may suffer from leaf spotting caused by bacteria or anthracnose fungi if the foliage is wet frequently and stays wet too long. Chilling may also damage them.

Ferns. Most house ferns are tolerant of a dry atmosphere but they prefer a soil that is uniformly slightly moist; extremes of wetting and drying are detrimental. Excessive wetting of foliage may induce leaf nematode attack and gray mold shoot rot. Scale insects are especially troublesome. One should not mistake the fern's own spore receptacles on the under surface or margin of the leaves for a rust or other fungus.

Fuchsia. Root knot and gray mold bud rot are the commonest maladies. Control methods are indicated under other headings, e. g., Begonia.

Gardenia. Very susceptible to root knot. Bud drop usually results from too sudden change of temperature, especially chilling, or from too dry an atmosphere. Overwatering and poor drainage are contributing factors, and may also promote stem canker. Chlorosis, a loss of green color or yellowing of the leaves, usually indicates a deficiency of certain mineral elements, as iron or magnesium, in the soil. It is most likely to occur in neutral or alkaline soils. It may also result from damage to the root system by overwatering or disease. The nutritional deficiency can be remedied by careful use of houseplant fertilizers, acidification of the soil with sulfur, or adding a pinch of iron sulfate to each pot.

Geranium (*Pelargonium*). Requires good light to bloom during the winter, and the plants become sluggish in weak light and short days, then are easily damaged by overwatering. Oedema (see under Begonia), gray mold rot, and stem rot may ensue.

Heliotrope. The common diseases are root knot and gray mold rot of buds and shoots.

Kalanchoë and other succulent (fleshy-leaved) plants, as *Crassula* and *Sedum.* Root and crown rot caused by fungi, crown gall by bacteria, are the commonest troubles; sometimes anthracnose on leaves and stems. These plants should be watered sparingly and given good light.

Oleander. Bacterial knot on stems, and anthracnose on leaves, may attack these plants occasionally. Scale insects are troublesome, and their attack may be followed by sooty mold.

Palms. Chilling must be avoided; may be liberally watered if the soil is

well drained. A false smut, characterized by dark scablike spots with powdery brown or yellow centers, may
occur on the leaves, especially of
Phoenix (date palm). Heart rot or
black scorch may attack the base of
the fronds if the plants are in heavy
soil and are overwatered. Sooty mold,
following insect attack, may develop
on leaves in a damp atmosphere.

Peperomia. A virus ring spot is the
commonest disease.

Poinsettia. Yellowing and dropping of
leaves is usually a symptom of chilling,
or may be due to weak light and overwatering. Root knot and bacterial
canker are the principal parasitic
diseases.

Rubberplant (Ficus elastica). Anthracnose on leaves and stems is of common
occurrence, probably often as a sequel
to chilling and too frequent wetting.
Also subject to root knot, and sometimes injured by bacterial gall (crown
gall) on stems.

FREEMAN A. WEISS *is curator of the
American Type Culture Collection, 2029 M
Street, N. W., Washington, D. C. He
holds degrees from the University of
Minnesota and Cornell University. From
1920 to 1950 he was a plant pathologist in
the Bureau of Plant Industry, Soils, and
Agricultural Engineering and worked on
the diseases of potatoes, ornamental bulbs,
azaleas, roses, and other ornamentals.*

Bacterial blight of cotton.

Herbs and Other Special Crops

C. A. Thomas

Several hundred varieties and species of plants are put to specialized
uses by man. Many are cultivated in
a limited way and on a now-and-then
basis according to demand.

This miscellaneous botanical assort-
ment often is referred to collectively
as special crops because the plants are
not known to many people. Usually
only a few growers are favorably situ-
ated to cultivate one or more of them,
and usually a single location is suited
only to a few of them. They are not
unimportant, however, and their areas
of production may be expanded when
their end uses expand and when varieties adapted to other localities are
available.

Among the special crops are herbs
and condiments, as peppermint, spearmint, sage, caraway, thyme, marjoram, and coriander, which yield fla-
voring compounds. Plants yielding
compounds of medicinal use are another important group. Among them
are digitalis, belladonna, poppy, and
ergot, which contain alkaloids or glu-
cosides. Sumac and canaigre are
sources of tannin. Several species of
plants yield compounds that have insecticidal value. Seeds of castor bean,
safflower, sesame, and perilla contain
oils of use for food or industry.

The diseases affecting the special
crops are similar to and as diverse as
those affecting other crops. Root rots,
wilts, leaf spots, blights, and other
diseases are common among them.

Numerous viruses and species of fungi and bacteria are among the agents causing diseases.

A knowledge of the general cultural methods, values, and size and location of the areas of production of these crops is necessary for a clear understanding of their diseases and methods of control.

The production of many of the special crops requires considerable labor, special methods of handling, and often special equipment. Several of the crops must be planted, weeded, harvested, and processed by hand. The amount of labor involved is usually the limiting factor of production for any one grower. Special drying, grinding, or distilling equipment may be required by the grower to prepare his product for market. We thus find many of the special crops being produced year after year by the same few growers who possess the necessary skill, labor, and equipment. Certain perennial crops, like peppermint and spearmint, are usually grown for several years on the same land to avoid replanting costs. Crop rotation then is at a minimum. Persons interested in special crops as a side line or hobby usually follow no rotation practice.

Contrary to popular opinion, the culture of many special crops is not a highly profitable enterprise on a long-time basis. Except in times when imports are cut off or seriously reduced, many of our botanical drugs, condiments, and oils are imported from Europe, Asia, or the Tropics at extremely low costs.

Collections of wild plants are adequate to meet the demand for several plants of specialized use and a few hundred acres suffice for most of the cultivated species. The industrial uses of products of peppermint and spearmint, safflower, and castor bean, however, require the production from several thousand acres.

A considerable amount of seed and planting stock of many special crops are brought into the United States from time to time from foreign countries.

Such imports result from efforts to establish production of crops not native to the United States and to find sources of germ plasm for improvement of crops now in production. The imports often result in the introduction of new disease organisms, which are a source of trouble for the grower.

The use of fungicides, particularly for controlling foliage diseases where several applications are involved, or expensive soil fumigants for controlling soil-borne organisms is not economically feasible for the low-value crops. Fungicidal residues cannot be tolerated in the case of certain medicinal plants, such as digitalis, where the foliage may be used directly as a medicinal compound.

It is often possible to grow the crops in sections where diseases are least troublesome since production in most cases is on a limited scale.

Certain pathogens may be excluded or eradicated by special seed, plant, or soil treatments. Such measures are sometimes effective with the special crops because of the isolated nature of the plantings. Proper cultural practices and treatment of seed are usually helpful.

The use of resistant varieties, if they are available, is often the best or only method of control. Their development, however, is difficult, time consuming, and sometimes impossible.

OF THE MINT DISEASES, let us consider first the verticillium wilt of peppermint. Peppermint, *Mentha piperita*, is cultivated in the United States primarily for its essential oil, which is used to flavor chewing gum, dentifrices, and candy. It also is used in pharmaceutical preparations. The crop is grown in this country in two areas, Indiana and Michigan, and Oregon and Washington. The highest level of production was obtained in 1947, when 1,502,000 pounds of oil of an approximate farm value of 10 million dollars were produced on 47,018 acres.

Peppermint is a shallow-rooted, soil-depleting, long-day plant, which rarely produces viable seed because of its sterility. Propagation is accomplished in the spring by transplanting runners and rhizomes pulled or dug from the soil and by transplanting shoots, which are pulled up with some adhering roots. Peppermint is cultivated as a row crop the first year after planting. The row mint is plowed 4 to 6 inches deep in the late fall of the first year. In subsequent years the mint is allowed to spread over the field and produce a solid stand, called meadow mint. The same planting of mint may be maintained for several years, but it is usually unprofitable to keep a field longer than 2 or 3 years.

Wilt, caused by *Verticillium albo-atrum* var. *menthae*, is probably the most serious disease of peppermint in the United States. It was identified in Michigan in 1924, but undoubtedly it was present before then. It has been most destructive in Michigan and Indiana, but it has been reported also in Oregon and Washington. The disease in Michigan has been one of the major factors responsible for the reduction of peppermint acreage from more than 21,000 in 1941 to less than 10,000 in 1951.

The wilt causes a direct loss by reducing the yield of oil. Infected plants may be killed, stunted, or defoliated. They are weakened and less able to overwinter. Thin stands of mint often are the result.

All species of the genus *Mentha* tested have been found to be susceptible to the wilt disease. Peppermint is one of the most susceptible species. Several varieties of spearmint are more resistant. The organism causing the mint wilt disease is rather specific for mint. Only one or two plants that are not species or varieties of *Mentha* are susceptible.

The most characteristic symptoms of wilt in peppermint and spearmint are asymmetrical growth of the leaves dwarfing, chloranemia, or a bronze to purple coloration of the leaves, wilting, and the development of cankers on the stems and rhizomes.

The causal organism is primarily a vascular-invading fungus pathogen that may survive in soil for several years even in the absence of mint. The fungus may invade young roots of the plants directly through epidermal cells or through wounds. Once inside, the mycelium may become systemic in the vascular system. The exact method by which the organism causes wilting and the development of the other symptoms is not completely understood. Mechanical plugging of the water-conducting elements is not considered wholly responsible. Toxins probably are involved.

High soil moisture at a soil temperature of approximately 79° F. is considered likeliest for maximum infection. Development of the disease following infection is favored by high soil temperature and low soil moisture. Wilt is most severe during hot, dry seasons. Ample soil moisture for infection is presumably present in the early part of most seasons.

Several factors were responsible for the development of the wilt disease in the Midwest to such proportions that culture of peppermint was abandoned in many areas considered to be most suitable for peppermint growing and the production of high-quality oil.

The intensive culture of the plant in a limited area along with the practice of growing mint 2 or 3 years or more on the same land without rotation were undoubtedly conducive to a build-up of the organism in the soil. The fungus was easily distributed over the area on planting stock from infested fields and no real effort was made to exclude the organism from new fields by obtaining planting stock from disease-free plants.

Wilt has not become a serious disease of peppermint in Oregon and Washington. The presence of the disease there is easily explained, because the industry there was started with plants obtained from the Midwest. The fact that wilt has not developed to any extent in the Pacific Northwest, where mint culture is more intensive than in the Midwest, may indicate that environmental conditions are of primary importance in development of the disease.

Eradication of the verticillium wilt organism in the soil by fungicides or soil fumigants is not a promising method of control. Maintenance of soil moisture at proper levels, crop rotation, and avoidance of root injury are helpful in reducing injury from wilt. The use of a wilt-resistant type of peppermint appears to be the most satisfactory method of control.

It is possible to select wilt-resistant types from hybrids produced by crossing *M. piperita* with the wilt-resistant *M. crispa*. Some selections made at Michigan State College are reported to yield considerably more oil than *M. piperita*, to be very resistant under average conditions, and to be similar in quality to natural peppermint.

The manufacturers of chewing gum and candy demand peppermint oil of the highest quality because the sale of their products depends upon flavor. They are reluctant to accept oil from any source other than *M. piperita* for fear of changing the flavor of their products. Until such time as the manufacturers are convinced that the oil from any disease-resistant type of mint exactly duplicates that of *M. piperita*, or until the supply of peppermint oil is exceedingly critical because of diseases, it is unlikely that any type of mint other than the one now being used will be accepted as a commercial source of oil.

RUST, caused by *Puccinia menthae*, has been recognized as a disease of spearmint for many years. The organism produces yellow or brown pustules on the stems, leaves, and petioles in spring or early summer. Later in the season the pustules turn darker brown. The disease reduces the yield of oil because affected leaves produce less oil and often are killed before harvest.

Dusting with sulfur or spraying with bordeaux mixture and early cutting of heavily infested fields have been recommended as control practices. Certain fungicides, such as the dithiocarbamates, are not suitable for controlling mint rust since the residue on the leaves decomposes when the mint is steam-distilled to obtain the oil. Decomposition of the residue results in the production of carbon disulfide, which is highly toxic and may impair the flavor of the oil.

Rust infection of peppermint became serious in Oregon in 1950. Before then, peppermint plantings in the Midwest and Northwest were not damaged by rust. Peppermint was considered either highly resistant or immune to the strain of rust that attacks spearmint. It now appears that a new strain of rust has developed.

DIGITALIS PURPUREA is the main source of the drug digitalis in the United States, and it is the principal species collected and cultivated. There has been interest in other species, however, as sources of compounds of medicinal value. In 1946, a small acreage of *D. lanata* developed in Pennsylvania, but plantings were nearly a complete loss in 1948 because of anthracnose.

Anthracnose of digitalis is caused by a fungus, *Colletotrichum fuscum*, which produces tiny, purplish-brown, circular or angular spots on the leaf surfaces and sunken, fusiform lesions on veins and petioles. The organism is carried on the seed. It causes a damping-off disease of seedlings. It fruits on affected seedlings and is easily spread in the seedbed to healthy plants. Infection becomes severe by late summer. Affected plants are killed or stunted before the herb is ready to be harvested. The disease is favored by warm, wet weather. In the field it is spread mainly by splashing rain drops.

All species of *Digitalis* tested are susceptible. *D. lanata* is the most susceptible. *D. purpurea* is fairly resistant.

Observations over a period of years showed that plantings of *Digitalis* species made with disease-free seed remained free of the disease throughout the season. It thus appeared that if the organism on the *D. lanata* seed could be completely killed it would be possible to produce a disease-free crop. A hot-water treatment (131° F. for 15 minutes) of the seed gave complete control of the organism. Isolated plantings of *D. lanata* made with seed treated with hot water remained free of the disease. Commercial production of this drug crop is again possible.

The control of the disease through the use of disease-free seed is possible because the acreage is small and the plantings can be isolated from other plantings of *Digitalis* that might be affected with the disease. Although the organism may persist for a year or two on debris, it is easy to find land on which *Digitalis* has never been grown. The spores of the fungus are not carried for long distances by the wind. The organism is apparently not common on weeds or other farm crops.

CASTOR OIL, obtained from the seed of the castor bean plant, *Ricinus communis*, has a variety of uses—as a medicinal compound, lubricant, drying oil in paints, lacquers, and varnishes, and for hydraulic fluids, linoleum, oilcloth, soap, printing ink, leather, and textiles. Cultivation of castor beans has been attempted several times in the United States. Before 1900 some production occurred in the Midwest. During both the World Wars, attempts were made to produce beans in this country.

Improvements in varieties, methods, and machinery for harvesting the beans and a renewed demand for a local supply caused growers to devote approximately 80,000 acres to castor beans in 1951. It is estimated that several hundred thousand acres will be needed to meet our industrial requirements.

Castor beans are susceptible to a number of diseases. More than 150 different organisms are known to be pathogenic on the plant. Most occur in areas of high rainfall, such as the Southeast. There, the leaf spots and capsule molds can cause such severe losses that production may not be profitable. In the more arid sections of the Southwest the damage caused by these troubles is usually negligible. That is one of the factors responsible for locating the present plantings of castor beans in Oklahoma and Texas and the irrigated valleys of Arizona and southern California.

Castor beans are not entirely free of diseases there, however. Seedling diseases and troubles caused by soil-borne organisms are present. Research workers have undertaken studies of their prevalence, losses, effect of environmental conditions and cultural practices, and possible controls.

SAFFLOWER, *Carthamus tinctorius*, is a member of the thistle family. It has been grown since ancient times in Europe, Africa, and Asia, where the seed is used for poultry feed and as a source of oil for food and soap. The development of safflower as an oilseed crop in the United States since 1940 has been mainly for a source of drying oil for paint.

Safflower was first introduced and tested in the United States in the 1920's by the Department of Agriculture. The varieties tested then were not particularly suitable for production here because of their low yield and low oil content. Some 20 years later workers at the University of Nebraska began a program for improvement of varieties. The outcome of their work was the development of high-yielding, high-oil types. About 100,000 acres of safflower were grown in 1950 in the western part of the Great Plains and California.

Leaf and bud diseases are so serious in areas of high rainfall and high humidity that production of the crop is unprofitable. Although diseases are less serious in more arid sections, where the crop is better adapted, certain ones are nevertheless troublesome.

Root rot, caused by *Phytophthora drechsleri*, has caused considerable damage to safflower in every State where the crop has been grown. Most of the plantings in the Imperial Valley of California were severely damaged in 1950. The organism is soil-borne and widely distributed. High soil moisture favors the disease. Some varieties of safflower are very susceptible, but others are resistant. Root rot has been most damaging where susceptible varieties have been grown under irrigation and in poorly drained dry-land fields. The use of resistant varieties promises to give satisfactory control.

Rust, caused by *Puccinia carthami*, is another serious disease of safflower. The organism is unique among the rusts in that it is seed-borne. This fact probably accounts for the presence of the disease in the United States. Rust has been known to occur on safflower in Europe and Asia for many years. It undoubtedly was introduced into this country on seed. Rust has become widely distributed in the Great Plains and California since 1950.

Safflower rust is important both as a seedling disease and a leaf trouble. Rust spores carried on the seed or present in the soil may germinate and infect the cotyledons and hypocotyl of seedlings. Hypocotyl infections usually girdle and kill the seedling with a resulting loss in stand. Treatment of seed with fungicides helps improve stands by killing the rust spores.

Rust and some other leaf diseases of safflower might be controlled by applications of fungicides to the foliage. The low dollar return per acre for the crop, however, would make such a practice economically questionable. Many of the leaf and bud diseases are not serious in arid sections.

Troubles like rust and root rot are best controlled by the use of resistant varieties. Sources of resistance to each of the diseases are available to plant breeders among selections of present varieties or foreign introductions.

SESAME, *Sesamum indicum*, has been cultivated in foreign countries for many centuries. The seeds of the plant contain one of the finest edible oils

known. Commercial production has not developed in the United States chiefly because the available varieties shatter their seed when ripe. Hand harvest therefore is necessary. Plant breeders are hopeful of developing nonshattering types. If their goal is accomplished, we undoubtedly shall see production started in this country.

Sesame is known to be susceptible to several diseases. One bacterial and two fungus leaf spot diseases, as well as wilts, root rots and stem rots, and virus diseases are present in experimental plantings. Some of the troubles are seed-borne.

Sesame is a warm-weather crop. It seems best adapted to the southern part of the country. When and if the crop is cultivated there, the net return in dollars per acre may not be high. It thus will be a profitable crop only for growers who can obtain the highest yields with the minimum expense and who are located in areas where diseases are least troublesome. It may be possible to control some of the diseases through exclusion of the causal organisms by special seed treatments or by using seed only from disease-free fields. Other troubles will have to be controlled by such other means as the use of resistant varieties, which may be developed.

The first objectives of the plant pathologist in studying a crop like sesame are the same as for any new crop. He must determine what the diseases are, their relative importance in terms of both direct and indirect losses, the identity of the causal agents, means of distribution, sources of inoculum, effect of environmental conditions on disease development, and sources of disease resistance. Only after a knowledge of these is obtained can he proceed to formulate programs aimed at control.

C. A. THOMAS, *a pathologist in the division of tobacco, medicinal, and special crops at the Plant Industry Station, Beltsville, Md., joined the Department of Agriculture in 1948.*

Wilt, Rust, and Pasmo of Flax

H. H. Flor

Growers of flax have to contend with wilt and rust nearly all the time. So do the plant breeders who try to develop better varieties of flax.

The early wilt-resistant selections, North Dakota Resistant No. 114, Frontier, Chippewa, Winona, and Linota, gave way to Redwing, Buda, and Bison, which had greater resistance to wilt and were less susceptible to rust. Bison became popular during the droughty 1930's but was so heavily damaged by rust in 1940, 1941, and 1942, when rainfall was heavier, that it was replaced by rust-resistant varieties.

About 65 percent of the flax acreage in southeastern North Dakota in 1943 was Viking, one of the rust-resistant varieties that replaced Bison. Viking is susceptible to the pasmo disease, however, and was so heavily damaged that in 1944 the acreage sown to flax was drastically curtailed and Viking comprised less than 5 percent of that sown.

Koto, developed as a rust-resistant replacement for Bison, was free from rust during several years of testing in nurseries throughout the flax-producing area of the North Central States, but was heavily attacked by previously unknown races while it was being increased for distribution.

For more than 30 years Newland was resistant to rust in North America, but Dakota and Renew, varieties that carry the Newland gene for rust resistance, were attacked in 1948 by new races of rust in the Red River Valley of Minnesota and North Dakota.

The new rusts spread rapidly. They caused heavy damage in 1949 and 1950. Rust was widespread in 1951 and reduced the farm income from flax by approximately 10 million dollars in Minnesota, North Dakota, and South Dakota. Because of drought and the use of resistant varieties, losses from rust in 1952 were less than one-tenth those of 1951.

Probably because of wilt, flax has been considered a "new land" crop. Our center of production advanced with the frontier until it reached Minnesota, North Dakota, and South Dakota successively. Flax did better on newly broken land than other crops, but yields went down and often failed when flax was grown for more than a year on the same land.

H. L. Bolley, at the North Dakota Agricultural Experiment Station, determined in 1901 that the failure was caused by a parasitic fungus, which he described and named *Fusarium lini*. The fungus spreads through infected plants, soil, and seed. Once established in a soil, it may persist for 25 years or more.

WILT attacks flax plants at all stages of growth. The roots of seedlings may rot and the plants damp-off. More mature plants may quickly wilt and die. They may be stunted, their leaves may turn yellow and drop off, or they may merely ripen prematurely. The primary stem may die; new, apparently healthy, stems may develop at the first node. Nearly mature plants often have a brown infected streak that extends up one side of the stem and stands out from the healthy green part.

Resistance to flax wilt is not complete. On wilt-sick soil some wilt usually develops in all varieties, even the most resistant. The amount of wilt developing on the same plot varies greatly from year to year. A variety may wilt every year at one station and be consistently resistant at another. In some varieties, plants that show symptoms of wilt die quickly and the surviving plants continue vigorous growth and produce a good crop. In other varieties, few plants succumb, but nearly all are stunted, unthrifty, and produce little seed.

Bolley used the principle of survival of the fittest to select wilt-resistant varieties. On the thoroughly wilt-sick flax plot at the North Dakota Agricultural Experiment Station, he planted lots of flax from many sources and obtained wilt-resistant varieties from the surviving plants. The seed-flax industry in the United States undoubtedly was saved by the breeding of wilt-resistant varieties at the North Dakota and Minnesota experiment stations. Today most of the soils in the North Central States are so heavily infested that only wilt-resistant varieties can be grown successfully.

Flax wilt is most destructive in warm, dry seasons. The flax plant grows best in cool weather, but the wilt fungus thrives at high temperatures. W. H. Tisdale, working at the Wisconsin Agricultural Experiment Station, found that wilt did not develop at soil temperatures below 60° F. and that temperatures between 75° and 82° were most favorable for wilt.

At the Minnesota station, W. E. Broadfoot and N. E. Borlaug have shown that *Fusarium lini* is composed of many races. The races differ in cultural characteristics, pathogenicity on flax varieties, temperature requirements, and compatibility. A variety may be resistant to one race but susceptible to another race.

Antagonism exists between some races. Dr. Borlaug observed less wilt in a variety inoculated with a mixture of two races than when that variety was inoculated with either race alone. That raises the question as to the importance of antagonism between races under field conditions and the role of the other soil micro-organisms in development of wilt.

The "running out" of varieties often is due to a shift in the physiologic race population of the pathogen. The first wilt-resistant varieties, Frontier, North Dakota Resistant No. 114, Chippewa, Winona, and Linota, now wilt severely on the experimental wilt-sick soils at the Minnesota and North Dakota stations and show considerable wilt on some farm soils. Those varieties were highly resistant when they were introduced. When they were released, the races that attacked them probably comprised such a small portion of the population as to cause little damage. The races later built up on the congenial host until they became abundant enough to produce damage.

The wilt-resistant varieties now grown may follow the same downward path. Many of them were developed from hybrids with Bison, however. Bison—and hybrids in which Bison was the wilt-resistant parent—have been grown on wilt-sick Plot 30 at the North Dakota Agricultural Experiment Station since 1925. Since 1930, races to which Bison is susceptible in pure culture tests have been obtained from plants grown on the plot; the wilt resistance of Bison apparently has not changed in that time.

The nature of wilt resistance has not been adequately explained. Dr. Tisdale found that the fungus, on entering resistant plants, stimulated cork formation in cells of adjacent tissues and so isolated the infection. The fungus may sometimes be isolated from aboveground parts of apparently healthy plants, however, so there may be other types of resistance.

Studies on the inheritance of resistance to wilt in flax suggest that multiple hereditary factors are involved. The hereditary behavior is hard to determine because we have no way of differentiating between normal wilting in resistant strains and in susceptible segregates.

Nearly all the flax in the North Central States consists of varieties that have been distributed since 1940. Extensive breeding of flax is being done at experiment stations at St. Paul, Minn.; Fargo, N. Dak.; Ottawa, Ontario; Saskatoon, Saskatchewan; and Winnipeg, Manitoba.

Hybrid material is tested on a wilt-sick plot that has been developed at each station. Wide variations exist in the amount of wilt and the vigor of growth of the variety on the different wilt-sick plots, but all tests seem rigorous enough to meet the farmers' requirements. Even Royal, Renew, Crystal, Rocket, and Victory—varieties that wilt severely on the wilt-sick plots at St. Paul and Fargo—are seldom damaged by wilt in commercial fields. On some farm soils cropped rather frequently to flax, considerable wilt develops in those varieties in hot, dry seasons, but loss due to wilt since 1940 has been small. Bison, Koto, Sheyenne, and Redwood have been highly wilt-resistant.

FLAX RUST occurs in nearly all important flax areas. It attacks only flax. In mild climates it may live over from one crop year to the next on wild or volunteer flax. In colder climates it overwinters on stubble and straw left in the field and on bits of straw in uncleaned seed.

The life history of the flax rust fungus, *Melampsora lini*, is complex. In the North Central States, infection starts each year with the germination of the overwintering teliospores. They are thick-walled spores formed in a palisade layer in the brownish-black crusts on vegetative parts of maturing flax plants. The germ tube of each teliospore usually bears four minute spores (sporidia), which infect the leaves and stems of flax and produce the rather inconspicuous pycnial stage.

The pycnium—the sexual stage of the rust—develops into an aecium bearing aeciospores if it is fertilized by pycniospores from a pycnium of opposite sex. Insects, water droplets, and wind may carry the pycniospores— the sperms. Aeciospore infection gives rise to a uredium. The aecial and uredial pustules look alike. They are

slightly raised and covered with innumerable orange-colored spores. It is these pustules that give the name "rust" to the disease. Under favorable conditions the uredial generation is repeated about every 10 days, and there is a rapid build-up of inoculum.

Rust reduces the yield of seed and lowers the quality of linen and paper made from the fiber. Reduction in seed yield is roughly proportional to the area of plant tissue infected. Rusted plants use water inefficiently. The rust fungus uses food material that otherwise would be available for seed development. The pedicels, which bear the bolls, are frequently girdled in severe infections, and the bolls fail to develop or they break off or the plants may be killed prematurely. Fibers are weakened at the point where stem infections occur and break during processing. The black fungus crusts adhere to the fiber and cause flaws in the cloth and paper made from it.

The use of resistant varieties has been the best means of controlling rust. Varieties resistant in one region may be susceptible in another, however. All the varieties that are immune or resistant in North America are susceptible to races occurring in South America. Bison, susceptible to all races in Europe, North America, and South America, is immune in New South Wales, Australia. Bombay, highly susceptible in New South Wales, possesses the only gene known to condition immunity to all South American races.

The variable reaction of varieties in different regions and the succession of varieties developed for rust resistance that have succumbed to new races or to alterations in the prevalence of races emphasize the need for constant study of physiologic specialization in the fungus.

A series of differentials was developed by testing the reaction to rust of all varieties in the Flax Classification Nursery of the United States Department of Agriculture. The varieties in the nursery had been chosen for diverse type and origin from a world-wide collection of flax. Fourteen races of rust were differentiated in 1935 by the reaction of eight varieties. Three more varieties were added later in order to identify South American races, and five were added to identify hybrids between North American and South American races.

At the North Dakota Agricultural Experiment Station we have studied the inheritance of pathogenicity in the flax rust fungus, the inheritance of resistance in flax varieties, and the interaction of genes for virulence in the pathogen with those for resistance in the host.

Virulence has been recessive in all crosses thus far studied, except on one variety, Williston Brown. Thus the first-generation cross of two races, which between them attacked 15 of the 16 varieties used to differentiate races, attacked only the three that were susceptible to both parent races.

From 133 second-generation cultures of this cross 64 races were identified, 62 of which had not been isolated previously. None of the progeny attacked all the varieties that were susceptible to both parent races, but we got no indication of any inherent relation between the genes for virulence that would prevent the occurrence of such a race.

Resistance to rust in flax has been inherited as a dominant character. Most of the rust-resistant genes lie in three chromosomes. The genes in two of the chromosomes seem to be allelic. Some crossing-over has been observed between some genes in the third. The number of genes in each differential varies from one to four.

Most of the genes for rust resistance in flax are sharply differential, conditioning either high resistance or susceptibility. Some are intermediate, however, with considerable variability both to different races and to environmental changes. Twenty-two different rust-conditioning genes have been isolated from the 16 differentials, and eight additional genes were isolated from other flax varieties. Other varieties are being tested to secure additional sources of rust resistance.

There appears to be also a gene for gene relationship between virulence in the pathogen and resistance in the host. Races attacking a large number of varieties are able to do so because they are homozygous for a large number of recessive genes. A variety is resistant to all races not possessing the specific gene for virulence on it. Varieties with two or more resistant genes are resistant to all races not possessing the two or more specific genes for virulence on them. A differential with two resistant genes cannot differentiate between races attacking neither or either of its resistant genes.

Koto, a variety developed as a rust-resistant replacement for Bison, derived its rust resistance from Morye, one of the rust differential-host varieties. Koto was free from rust during several years of nursery tests in several localities in the North Central States. When released for field increase, however, it rusted heavily, indicating that races attacking it were present but had escaped detection. This was confirmed in subsequent investigations, which showed that (besides Morye) another differential, Tammes' Pale Blue, also carried the Koto gene but that races attacking Koto could not be detected because of a second gene in Tammes' Pale Blue and the three genes in Morye that condition resistance to North American races.

The primary aim of such studies is to facilitate the development and maintenance of disease-resistant varieties. To promote the objective, the flax rust differential-host list of varieties has been revised. Each of the new differentials possesses a single gene for rust reaction to North American races and shows sharp differences in reaction. The 18 new differential lines include seven that have been highly resistant or immune from all North American races, three that possess genes conditioning resistance to some

North American races in varieties now in production, and eight that have differentiated races of flax rust throughout the world most satisfactorily. Thus, physiologic race tests with the new differentials will give the flax breeder a more accurate picture of the virulence of the races with which he must contend and of their distribution and prevalence. If the genes in the differentials serve as sources of resistance, the occurrence of single genes in each promotes an early discovery of changes in race pathogenicity and avoids the masking of virulent races by multiple rust-conditioning genes.

Each line possessing a different rust-conditioning gene has been back-crossed to Bison with the goal of getting lines that combine the agronomic type, wilt resistance, and pasmo tolerance of Bison with each source of rust resistance. Such lines will serve as testers for determining rust races present and as a reservoir of desirable breeding material. They also should facilitate the development of new rust-resistant varieties if the varieties now being grown are attacked by new races.

PASMO, caused by *Septoria linicola*, was first identified in Argentina in 1911. It was found in North America in 1916. Now it occurs in nearly all important flax-growing areas.

Pasmo, primarily a disease of mature tissues, attacks all vegetative parts of the flax plant. On the leaves the lesions are more or less circular, greenish yellow at first, and dark brown in later stages. On the stems the lesions are somewhat elongated. Later they spread up and down and around the stem. As the disease progresses, the stem lesions coalesce, bolls and pedicels become infected, and the entire plant turns dark brown and ripens prematurely. Leaf and stem lesions are dotted with small, dark, flasklike pycnidia, which bear the spores. During wet periods the spores ooze through a pore at the tip of the ripe pycnidium and are spread by wind, rain, and animals.

The disease may be carried from one region to another by spores adhering to the seed or on pieces of infected straw in unclean seed. In regions where it is established, it overwinters chiefly on infected straw and stubble of the previous year.

Pasmo usually does not become severe until the flax crop is approaching maturity. Then the yield of seed may not be reduced seriously.

Pasmo may be very destructive when conditions are exceptionally favorable for its development. Long warm and humid periods, especially when storms cause the flax to lodge, favor the development of pasmo. In southeastern North Dakota in 1943, Viking flax was killed prematurely on thousands of acres. Flax has been heavily damaged by pasmo in Texas in wet seasons.

Although no variety is classed as resistant to pasmo, appreciable differences in susceptibility exist. Viking (B. Golden) and most of the Argentine-type flaxes are highly susceptible. Redwing, Rocket, Royal, and Victory are susceptible. B5128, Bison, Buda, Dakota, Koto, Redwood, and Sheyenne are moderately susceptible. Crystal, Marine, and Minerva show considerable tolerance under field conditions.

No control measures assure against loss from pasmo. Losses may be kept at a minimum by growing the less susceptible varieties, rotating crops, destroying overwintering inoculum on the straw and stubble of the preceding year's crop, and treating seed with a suitable fungicide.

H. H. FLOR *is a plant pathologist with the division of cereal crops and diseases, Bureau of Plant Industry, Soils, and Agricultural Engineering. Since 1931 he has been engaged in the study of flax diseases in cooperation with the North Dakota Agricultural Experiment Station at Fargo. He is a graduate of the University of Minnesota.*

Diseases of Muscadine Grapes

E. S. Luttrell

The muscadine grape (*Vitis rotundifolia*) is a species native to the southeastern United States. Several varieties of commercial importance have been developed from it. It is grown in most of the Cotton Belt in place of bunch grapes, which generally are unsuccessful in the region. The crop is used mainly for wine making and can be used for fresh juice, jellies, and frozen products. It is also sold as fresh fruit in local markets.

Black rot is its most common disease. It occurs on stems, leaves, flower clusters, and berries and is present throughout the growing season. It produces circular, reddish-brown spots on the leaves, black cankers on the stems and flower clusters, occasional blighting of the young stem tips and flower clusters, and brown or black scabs and cankers on the berries.

Infection of the foliage usually is rather heavy, but little defoliation occurs except on a few varieties of minor importance. The scabs and cankers on the berries may lower their quality but usually are responsible for losses of only a very small fraction of the crop. Some varieties are highly resistant or immune to berry infection.

Black rot is caused by the fungus *Guignardia bidwellii*, the same species that causes black rot of bunch grapes. However, the fungus on muscadine grapes represents a distinct physiologic form, which does not infect bunch grapes. The fungus produces conidia in tiny, spherical, black pycnidia, which are formed abundantly in the dead tissue of the spots and cankers during the growing season. Ascospores produced in perithecia on the overwintered fallen leaves are chiefly responsible for the primary infection of the vegetative parts in early spring. The fungus also may survive the winter in the pycnidial stage in cankers on the stems and fallen berries.

The only other disease of any importance on the foliage is angular leaf spot, which is caused by the fungus *Mycosphaerella angulata*. It produces many small, angular, black spots, which are especially conspicuous on the lower surface of the leaf. Heavily infected leaves turn yellow and die. Infection is heavy on all varieties and considerable premature defoliation may result. In the Georgia Piedmont, however, angular leaf spot usually appears late in the season after the berries are mature. Probably it does not greatly affect the yield. In other sections it may develop earlier and be of greater importance.

The most serious diseases of muscadine grapes are the berry rots, of which bitter rot is the most important. The cause is *Melanconium fuligineum*, the same fungus that causes bitter rot of bunch grapes. Only the conidial stage of the fungus has been found. It may overwinter in that stage on berry mummies and dead pedicels. Bitter rot appears on only a few of the young green berries but spreads rapidly through the vineyard as the berries approach maturity. The berries are affected with a soft rot, which usually starts at the pedicel and spreads uniformly until the whole berry is involved. The surface soon becomes covered with a crust of black acervuli, from which the conidia may be rubbed in slimy, black masses. The entire berry finally shrivels to a hard, dry, black mummy. The mummies may cling to the vines, but usually the berries drop in the early stages of the rot. Many berries shrivel slightly and drop from the vines before they show any symptoms of rot. They drop singly or in small clusters clinging to shriveled pedicels. Apparently pedicel blight is merely another aspect of the bitter rot disease, the fungus spreading through the pedicels and branches of the peduncle from berry to berry or blighting the pedicels and causing the berries to drop before they are themselves invaded. Bitter rot usually is responsible for the drop of more than 60 percent of the berries that fall from the vines.

The only other berry rot of consequence, besides bitter rot and black rot, is macrophoma ripe rot. The causal fungus can be induced to develop a perfect stage, which belongs in *Botryosphaeria ribis*. But only the conidial stage, which would be placed in the form genus *Macrophoma*, is found on muscadine grapes. The fungus can overwinter in this stage on infected berries. The first symptoms are small, circular, slightly sunken, tan or brown spots on the surface of the berry. From the spots a brown rot extends irregularly over the berry, and the infected tissue becomes dotted with the black pycnidia of the fungus. The berry may shrivel but does not form a mummy.

Some degree of control of these diseases is doubtless had through such cultural practices as fertilization, pruning, and vineyard sanitation. Resistance to black rot and macrophoma ripe rot exists in some varieties. Although these berry rots are not important enough to make resistance to them a primary consideration in selecting a variety for planting, resistance could be incorporated in new, higher yielding varieties.

No spray schedule has been recommended specifically for muscadine grapes.

E. S. LUTTRELL *is plant pathologist at the Georgia Agricultural Experiment Station, a position he has held since 1942, except for 2 years when he was assistant professor of botany in the University of Missouri.*

Diseases of the Avocado

George A. Zentmyer

The fruit of various species of *Persea*, a genus native to Mexico, Guatemala, and other Central American and South American countries, has been used for food by the inhabitants of those countries for centuries. Selections from those wild trees, of varied fruiting habits, have resulted in the development of the cultivated avocado trees of California, Florida, and Texas.

Avocado trees were introduced into California in the latter half of the nineteenth century, but the principal development of the industry in California and Florida has taken place since 1930. The industry is of even more recent origin in Texas.

A number of diseases of varying severity affect the roots, trunk, branches, leaves, and fruit of the avocado tree. The diseases are caused primarily by fungi, although one virus disease is known. Several troubles are the result of deficiencies or excesses of certain elements used by the trees.

PHYTOPHTHORA ROOT ROT is the most serious problem in avocado culture in California, where it used to be known as "decline." Root rot of avocado also occurs in Costa Rica, Florida, Peru, South Africa, Honduras, Puerto Rico, Mexico, and Texas. The disease has been of little consequence in Florida, although it seems to be on the increase. Root rot was first noted in 1950 in Texas.

Two factors are involved—the soil

fungus *Phytophthora cinnamomi* and wet soil conditions brought about by poor drainage.

The causal fungus was first identified by R. D. Rands in 1922 on cinnamon trees in Sumatra and was first reported on avocado by C. M. Tucker in Puerto Rico in 1928. *P. cinnamomi* since has been found on an increasingly large number of plants, including pine, pineapple, heather, camellia, rhododendron, cinchona, chestnut, peach, yew, a number of deciduous and coniferous nursery trees, and Lawson cypress. V. A. Wager reported the isolation of *P. cinnamomi* from avocado roots in California in 1942.

Root rot increased greatly in California between 1940 and 1953. By 1953 it was estimated that 2,500 acres had been affected, or approximately 175,000 trees, including trees that either had died or were in various stages of disease.

Root rot occurs in California on two main soil types—heavy soils and soils having a permeable surface horizon of relatively shallow depth underlain by an impervious layer of clay or rock. In either case drainage is impeded and moisture conditions favorable for development of *Phytophthora cinnamomi* may occur. In other areas where root rot is found, and on other crops, it is also a disease of heavy or poorly drained soils. On well-drained soils the fungus rarely causes damage.

A gradual deterioration sets in of the above-ground parts of the tree affected with root rot. The general appearance indicates root destruction. Early symptoms include a lighter green color than is normal for leaves, a tendency for leaves to wilt in the presence of an amply moist soil, and a lack of new growth. As the disease progresses, branches die back, many leaves are shed, newly formed leaves are generally small and yellowish green, and fruit does not reach normal size. Frequently an abnormally heavy set of fruit happens soon after symptoms of the disease first appear—evidently a reflection of the fact that much of the root system is rotted and food material has accumulated in the top.

The gradual decline in vigor and productivity of the tree usually goes on for several years, although occasionally the deterioration is more rapid. Many of the small feeder roots on affected trees are blackened, brittle, and dead; healthy roots are difficult to find.

The causal fungus is one of the "water molds." It thus needs wet soil conditions for its best development and for production of its two spore stages, swimming spores (zoospores) and resistant spores (oospores). The fungus thrives at moderate temperatures, making no growth below 50° F. nor above 90° F.

No adequate control measures have yet been found for the disease. At the University of California Citrus Experiment Station, investigations have been started on several aspects of control, including soil fumigation, soil fungicides, soil amendments, resistant rootstocks, crop rotations, and irrigation.

In years when rainfall is not excessive, careful irrigation can do much to retard the progress of the disease and prolong the life of affected trees. It has been observed that water use is markedly reduced in trees affected with root rot, evidently because of the destruction of the small feeder roots. Hence, if all trees in a grove, healthy and diseased alike, are given the same amount of water in one irrigation, water will accumulate in the soil around the diseased trees and accentuate the disease situation. To correct this, the soil-moisture conditions around each diseased tree must be determined at the time of irrigation, and individual trees should be irrigated on the basis of water use. This can be done effectively only where groves are irrigated with low sprinklers. Any condition contributing to the development of excessively wet soil conditions is favorable to progress of the root rot disease; hence particular care should be taken to avoid the occurrence of excess water in the grove.

Soil fumigation has various possible applications to the problem. Research in California has shown that several fumigants, such as chloropicrin at 30 to 40 gallons to the acre and D–D mixture at 100 to 150 gallons an acre, will kill *Phytophthora cinnamomi* in soil. Field fumigation, however, has usually resulted in good growth of replants for a period of only 2 to 4 years, followed by recurrence of the disease. These plots were in areas of widespread infection; recurrence of the disease probably resulted from reinvasion of the treated locations by the fungus. The response of the resistant oospores to fumigants is not known, and there is a possibility that some of the reinfection came from germination of those spores. Fumigation may be useful under certain conditions, as in treating nursery soil or in eliminating the fungus from small isolated spots of infection in the grove.

In tests with soil fungicides, the organic fungicide nabam (disodium ethylene bisdithiocarbamate) has been found to be effective in killing *Phytophthora cinnamomi* in the soil. Research on this treatment is in its preliminary phases, but materials of this type have possibilities for application to various hosts of the fungus, as they are less injurious to higher plants than the common soil fumigants. Soil applications of alfalfa meal (ground stems and leaves) have also been shown in many cases to have some beneficial effect on diseased trees in California; this is attributed to the great increase in saprophytic fungi and bacteria in the soil resulting from these applications, and the possible antibiotic action of some of these micro-organisms against *P. cinnamomi*.

Phytophthora cinnamomi is very sensitive to drying of the soil. Air-drying a light loam to 1 percent moisture has resulted in kill of the fungus and excellent growth of replants in greenhouse experiments. In irrigated groves the spread of the fungus through the soil may be retarded by maintaining a dry, nonirrigated zone at the edge of an area where the disease is present. It may also be possible to make use of this principle in eliminating the fungus from nursery soil where trees are grown in large tar-paper pots.

The method of control that has the most possibility of success in the long run is the development of a rootstock that is resistant to root rot. Tests of 22 varieties of avocado seedlings, including Guatemalan, West Indian, and Mexican types, in California have shown all are similar in susceptibility. Other species of *Persea* from Mexico and Central America are being tested.

Inoculations with *Phytophthora cinnamomi* and limited field observations indicate that persimmon, cherimoya, macadamia nut, and citrus trees are either resistant or immune to root rot. These crops are possibilities for use in replanting areas where avocado trees have been removed because of root rot, at least in California. Other types of subtropical plants may be more adaptable in other regions. The principle of crop rotation is an old and valuable one in control of root rots of annual crops, and may have similar value in controlling avocado root rot.

It should be emphasized that little or no avocado root rot occurs on well-drained soils. A preventive measure, with respect to future plantings, is to plant only clean nursery stock on well-drained soils. Obviously, this is not a remedy for the problem in the case of the thousands of trees already planted on poorly drained soil. Nor does it take into account the fact that in some areas, because of the frost hazard, the best land for avocado plantings is hillside land, where the soil is often heavy or shallow.

Development of a rootstock that is resistant to the disease, that is compatible with present scion material, and that possesses no obvious disadvantages with respect to production or other diseases may ultimately solve the problem. Meanwhile, present measures to permit living with the disease include careful irrigation practices, drying the soil, replanting with resistant crops, and possibly use of temporarily alleviating measures, such as application of alfalfa meal or soil fungicides.

VERTICILLIUM WILT of avocado trees has been known as such since 1948, when I isolated the soil fungus *Verticillium albo-atrum* from affected trees and demonstrated the pathogenicity of the fungus to the avocado. Occasional reports during the previous 15 or 20 years in California and Florida had described sudden wilting and collapse of isolated trees in well-drained soils. In California the trouble was termed collapse, asphyxiation, or apoplexy and was thought to be the result of exclusion of oxygen from the soil, brought about by sudden saturation of the soil with water. It is possible that lack of oxygen could cause such symptoms, but since 1948 *V. albo-atrum* has been invariably isolated from trees with these symptoms in California.

Avocado trees affected with verticillium wilt show symptoms similar to those that develop on other woody hosts. The symptoms include a sudden wilting of all the leaves on a part of a tree, or on the entire tree, and the rapid death of the leaves. The leaves turn brown and remain attached to the branches for a long time. Typical brown streaks may be seen in the wood, when the bark is peeled from branches or roots of affected trees. Within a few months after the initial collapse of the tree, vigorous new shoots may appear, and within 1 to 2 years the trees may recover completely. Occasionally trees die from the disease, and occasionally the disease may recur in a given tree. Most of the affected trees observed in California have recovered completely and have shown no further symptoms. Similar observations have been reported in Florida.

Several suggestions as to control can be made. Use of land that has been planted to a susceptible crop should be avoided, and susceptible crops should not be interplanted after the land has been planted to avocados. Other plants affected by the fungus include tomato, pepper, eggplant, berries, apricot, potato, and a number of flower crops.

Severe pruning of diseased trees immediately after first symptoms of the disease appear may speed recovery. Avocado trees that are or have been affected with verticillium wilt should not be used as sources of budwood. It is possible that the disease may be transmitted in budwood, as with verticillium wilt of rose.

SUN BLOTCH, the only known virus disease of avocado, was first described in California in 1928. Its virus nature was established by W. T. Horne in 1931. It is of common occurrence in California, but has been observed only a few times in Florida.

Typical symptoms are a yellow streaking of the green stems and branches and a yellow-to-red streak on the fruit. On fruit that remains green at maturity, the streak is yellow. On fruit that turns black or purple at maturity, the streak is usually red. A slight deformation and vein chlorosis may occur in the leaves, but the stem and fruit symptoms are the most common. Affected trees tend to have a recumbent, willowy type of growth, and some may be stunted. A checking of bark on mature branches and trunks is often associated with the disease, but it has not been definitely established that this is a symptom of the disease.

Sun blotch is readily transmitted through budwood or graft wood. It is possible that the disease may also be transmitted through the seed, although this has not been proved under controlled, insectproof conditions. The disease has been observed occasionally on young seedling avocado trees growing under conditions in which it is unlikely that insect transmission could be involved.

Control measures include careful selection of disease-free scion and seed sources and the removal of all seedlings showing sun blotch symptoms, as well as of all off-type seedlings, from nursery plantings.

CANKERS of roots, trunks, or branches of avocado trees may be caused by several organisms. *Phytophthora cactorum* and *P. cinnamomi* are the two fungi most commonly involved in California in cankers of the lower trunk and rootstock. Artificial inoculations show that *P. citrophthora*, the fungus that causes brown rot of lemon fruits and brown rot gummosis of citrus trees, is capable of invading avocado trunks. A canker of minor importance on branches and trunks is caused by the fungus *Botryosphaeria ribis*.

Symptoms in the top of the tree vary from gradual loss of vigor and chlorosis of leaves to sudden death of the entire top. Examination of the trunk usually reveals a darkening of the bark and an exudation of powdery white material from the affected bark. When the bark in the cankered area is cut into, it is found to be brown in color and to have a noticeably sour odor. The brown discoloration often extends into the wood as well. On many trees the trunk is not completely girdled, but the canker may extend up the trunk several feet from the ground. A similar trouble known as collar rot has been reported from Florida.

If detected in a sufficiently early stage, cankers can be controlled by cutting out infected tissue and painting the treated area with a fungicidal paint such as bordeaux paste. In California the Guatemalan varieties of avocado appear to be more susceptible than other varieties to these cankers. It is therefore desirable to bud these varieties high and to avoid covering the bud union with soil in low-budded trees.

DOTHIORELLA ROT, the most important rot of avocado fruit in California, is caused by the fungus *Botryosphaeria ribis* (imperfect stage: *Dothiorella gregaria*). The disease is a serious problem on the Fuerte variety in plantings near the coast. In inland areas it is of relatively little importance. The fungus is commonly present on dead wood, dead leaf tips, and debris. It enters the fruit sometime before harvesting. After entering the fruit, it lies dormant, and rot does not develop until the fruit begins to soften, by which time it has reached the consumer. The fact that there is no method of detecting fruit that will develop this rot and culling it out in the packing house creates a difficult marketing problem.

This rot commonly appears first as small, brown, or purplish-brown spots on the green fruit surface. The spots gradually enlarge until much of the surface may be involved. In early stages there is little involvement of the flesh. As the disease progresses, however, the fungus invades the flesh and causes a brown discoloration and an offensive odor. Occasionally the fungus induces a stem-end rot. It may also invade fruit pedicels, causing the fruit to drop. In Florida the fungi *Diplodia* and *Phomopsis* are also involved in stem-end rot of fruit.

The following control measures are effective in reducing or eliminating this fruit rot: Removal of dead wood and dead leaf tissue from trees to reduce sources of fungus inoculum; use of all possible measures to reduce tipburn of leaves; use of low rather than overhead sprinklers; picking of fruit before it reaches the peak of maturity, as it is not so severely affected in early season; and spraying trees.

Research in the 1930's indicated that 8–8–100 bordeaux mixture plus 6 pounds of wettable sulfur gave good control. It has been shown since then that Crag Fungicide 658 (1.5 pounds to 100 gallons), bordeaux 6–6–100, Cuprocide (2 pounds to 100 gallons), and zineb (2 pounds to 100 gallons) are effective in controlling the fruit rot. If rainfall is relatively light, as during the period from 1948 to 1951 in California, two sprays give good control, the first in mid-September and the second in early November.

CERCOSPORA SPOT OR BLOTCH, caused by *Cercospora purpurea*, is the most important disease of avocado in Florida. Lesions on fruit appear as small, scattered, brown, slightly sunken spots that have a definite outline but irregular shape. Grayish spore-bearing structures of the fungus appear on the spots in humid weather. These fruit spots, which are one-eighth to one-fourth inch in diameter, later develop cracks or fissures, which permit the entry of other fungi that cause fruit decay. The *Cercospora* fungus also causes small angular spots on leaves.

Research in Florida has demonstrated that the disease can be controlled by two or three copper sprays, the first between May 1 and May 15, the second not more than a month later, and the third a month after the second. The third is usually necessary only for varieties that mature in winter or early spring. G. D. Ruehle has shown that 6–6–100 bordeaux or 4–4–100 bordeaux (the latter where annual spraying is practiced), or wettable cuprous oxide (1.5 pounds to 100 gallons), or copper A (4 pounds to 100 gallons), or basic copper sulfate (3 pounds to 100 gallons) are equally satisfactory.

SCAB, the next most important disease of avocado in Florida, is caused by the fungus *Sphaceloma perseae*, which attacks both foliage and fruit. This fungus causes corky, raised, brownish, oval-shaped spots on the fruit. As the spots become older they may coalesce and give the fruit a russetted appearance. They may develop cracks that permit entry of other fruit-rotting organisms. Scabby, deforming lesions are also formed on leaves, leaf petioles, and twigs. The disease can be controlled by spraying with 6–6–100 bordeaux or 1.5–100 wettable cuprous oxide, using the same schedule as the one for blotch; very susceptible varieties need additional early applications.

There is considerable variation in susceptibility of the different varieties of avocado to this disease. Lula is listed as very susceptible; Hall, Taylor, and Booth 7 and 8 moderately susceptible; and Fuchsia, Pollock, Booth 1, Waldin, Itzamna, Linda, and Collinson quite resistant.

A THIRD COMMON DISEASE of avocado fruit in Florida, but one causing less damage than the blotch or scab, is anthracnose, or black spot, caused by *Colletotrichum gloeosporioides*. This disease is characterized by sunken black spots on the fruit, the spots being nearly circular in outline and one-fourth to one-half inch in diameter. As the fruit ripens, the fungus invades the flesh to a greater degree until most of the fruit is rotted. The fungus is unable to enter unwounded fruit. It usually becomes established in lesions caused by *Cercospora* or *Sphaceloma*. Where spray applications are made to control cercospora blotch or scab, no additional sprays are necessary to control anthracnose.

POWDERY MILDEW (*Oidium* species; perfect stage unknown) occasionally is found in Florida on foliage in nurseries or on young trees growing in shaded, damp locations. When young trees are affected, tender tips of shoots may be killed back. Dark-green discolorations may appear on the leaves, which show the characteristic white, powdery mildew growth on the lower side. Control may be obtained with lime-sulfur or sulfur dusts if the problem becomes acute.

NONPARASITIC DISEASES brought about either by deficiencies or excesses of certain elements occasionally are found on the avocado.

One of the most common is zinc deficiency, which results in a little-leaf condition, mottling of the leaves, and often a deforming of the fruit. If the deficiency is prolonged, the branches may die back. Best results for control in both California and Florida have been obtained with sprays. Either zinc sulfate and hydrated lime (5 pounds of $ZnSO_4$ and

2.5 pounds of lime to 100 gallons of water) or zinc oxide (2 pounds to 100 gallons) may be used. For severe cases in Florida, twice the indicated dosage of zinc sulfate and lime is recommended. Sprays should be applied soon after new growth appears.

Iron deficiency occasionally occurs in California, primarily in trees on calcareous soils. It is characterized by yellowing of the major portion of the leaf, with the veins remaining green. Little change is caused in fruit size or shape or in leaf size. Soil applications of sulfur and similar acidifying materials have generally been only moderately successful. Reduction in water applications to trees in the problem soils has usually resulted in a lessening of the chlorosis.

Copper deficiency has been reported in Florida on young avocado trees. Symptoms include development of S-shaped shoots and lateral branches, premature defoliation, a multiple-bud condition, and dieback. This trouble is usually corrected by soil or spray applications of copper sulfate.

The presence of excess chlorides in soil or irrigation water is the primary cause of tipburn of leaves in California. Tipburn causes a considerable reduction of green-leaf area, with consequent weakening of the tree. The dead areas are also commonly invaded by fungi such as *Botryosphaeria ribis*, which then spread to the fruit. Control of tipburn is difficult unless water with a lower chloride content is available to use in leaching the soil.

GEORGE A. ZENTMYER *is associate plant pathologist in the University of California Agricultural Experiment Station at Riverside, where he is engaged in research on diseases of the avocado and other subtropical plants and on fungicides. He has also worked on diseases of forest trees on the west coast, and on chemotherapy for control of the Dutch elm disease and other vascular diseases at the Connecticut Agricultural Experiment Station.*

Ethylene From Diseased Plants

C. E. Williamson, A. W. Dimock

A number of symptoms of some fungus, bacterial, and virus diseases of plants are similar to those that develop on plants exposed to ethylene gas, the colorless, inflammable C_2H_4.

Those common symptoms include epinasty, or downward bending of leaves; yellowing; excessive overgrowths; retardation of growth; and premature dropping of leaves, flowers, and fruits. The development of such symptoms suggests the possibility that the diseased plant tissue may produce ethylene.

The role of ethylene gas in inducing various physiological responses in plants has been the subject of investigation for more than 50 years. The earliest recorded observation was made in Germany in 1864 on the toxic effects of illuminating gas on trees. The identification in 1901 of ethylene as the cause of the observed physiological effects of illuminating gas led to the accumulation of a large volume of information on the morphological, anatomical, and biochemical responses of plants to ethylene.

The citrus industry in California established the practice of degreening lemons with the products of incomplete combustion from kerosene stoves or the exhaust gases of internal combustion engines. In 1924 ethylene was identified as the constituent responsible for the loss of the green color.

Our present-day concept of fruit

ripening, especially the sharp rise in respiratory rate with ripening—termed the climacteric—was developed in England from studies of apples in storage. The fundamental effect of ethylene is to initiate the climacteric rise in respiration. Emanations from ripening fruit will stimulate the onset of the climacteric in green fruit. The active emanation from ripening apples was identified by chemical analysis as ethylene in 1934. Subsequently, in all cases of physiologically active emanations investigated chemically, the active substance evolved has been shown to be ethylene. That is now so well established that the demonstration of a physiologically active emanation by any of the bioassay methods is a strong indication that ethylene is present in the gases evolved. In fact, F. E. Denny and Lawrence P. Miller, of the Boyce Thompson Institute, wrote in 1935: ". . . Any evidence that some other chemical is the principal factor must be accompanied by proof that ethylene was not present as an impurity in amounts sufficient to give a concentration of at least 1 part of ethylene in 20 million of air." For chemical identification, at least 25 to 100 parts per million by volume of ethylene is necessary. Where only small quantities of plant material are available or the amount of ethylene is extremely small, the chemical methods are useless. Bioassay methods thus become of paramount importance.

THE RESPONSE of various plant parts has been used to demonstrate the production of physiologically active emanations by plant tissues, especially by ripening fruit. Inhibition of sprouting of potato, inhibition of seed germination, and epinasty of sunflower, potato, and tomato leaves have all been used to detect ethylene. However, the triple response of etiolated pea seedlings, defined as a decrease in rate of growth in length and a swelling and horizontal placing of the region

growing while exposed to ethylene, is the only bioassay method that readily yields quantitative results. The triple response has been demonstrated repeatedly to have distinctive qualitative and quantitative characteristics for different concentrations of gas. Etiolated Alaska pea seedlings are extremely sensitive and will respond to as little as 0.025 to 0.05 part ethylene per million of air. The triple response of etiolated pea seedlings has had widespread use since 1944.

Many species of fungi growing in culture on an artificial medium of one sort or another have been tested for the production of an active emanation. *Rhizopus nigricans*, baker's yeast, *Diaporthe citri*, *Diplodia natalensis*, *Alternaria citri*, *Penicillium italicum*, *Sclerotinia sclerotiorum*, *Aspergillus niger*, *Oospora* species, *Alternaria* species, *Diplocarpon rosae*, *Cryptostictis caudata*, *Mycosphaerella ligulicola*, *Alternaria zinniae*, and *Histoplasma capsulatum* (a pathogen affecting man) failed to give a positive response by bioassay methods. *Penicillium digitatum*, on the other hand, has been shown repeatedly to produce ethylene in abundance from a culture medium. *Blastomyces dermatitidis* and *B. braziliensis*, causal agents of blastomycosis, a lung disease of man, also produce ethylene from a synthetic medium.

The earliest report of an active emanation from healthy tissues is credited to a Captain Selfe, who observed that the gases from oranges packed in the hold of a ship were apt to cause premature ripening of bananas. His observations were verified in the laboratory by H. H. Cousins, who in 1910 reported: "It was shown, however, by direct trial that the emanations from oranges stored in a chamber were found to have the effect of bringing about a premature ripening of bananas if these gases were passed through a chamber laden with this fruit."

Similar observations made by the United Fruit Company before 1917 showed that some bananas ripened more rapidly than the bulk of a shipment and this ripening tended to occur in pockets. The ripe pocket often acted as a starting point for the ripening of an entire bin of bananas. The ripe pocket was not caused by heat or carbon dioxide accumulation, although there seemed to be a direct correlation between respiration rate and accelerated ripening. A United Fruit Company chemist in 1923 reported the presence of an unknown gas in the respiration products of ripe bananas which caused accelerated ripening of green bananas.

In 1932 the volatile substances from ripe apples and pears were observed to inhibit the normal sprout development of potatoes. Healthy immature apple fruits were demonstrated in 1935 to produce ethylene in small amounts. When immature fruits were placed in closed containers, the accumulated volatile substances induced the climacteric, but similar fruits ventilated by a continuous stream of pure air did not ripen. Apparently a threshold value for the stimulating dose exists below which no effect is produced.

Denny and Miller reported a long list of plant tissues that produced an active emanation, as indicated by epinasty of potato leaves. The list included a wide variety of fruits and vegetables and the flowers, leaves, stems, seeds, and roots of other plants. Elmer Hansen, working with pears in storage in 1942, studied the relationship between ethylene production and respiration and observed that ethylene production was either greatly retarded or inhibited under anaerobic conditions, although little difference in the amount of carbon dioxide produced under aerobic and anaerobic conditions was obtained. Ethylene produced by Comice pears increased steadily from 0.11 milliliter per kilogram per 24 hours at 0° C. to 0.19 at 10°, to 0.44 at 20°, then dropped to 0.33 at 30°, and ceased at 40°.

Investigators had observed as early as 1936 that the volatile combustible matter produced by orange fruits increased rapidly when the fruits became infected with Penicillium digitatum. Because the amount of combustible volatiles produced by P. digitatum growing on agar was very small, the rapid increase in amount of volatile combustible matter that occurs with the onset of fungal attack was assumed to be due to injury to the fruit and not to byproducts of the fungus. Similarly other workers found that when Golden Delicious apples in the postclimacteric state became infected with Penicillium and Botrytis, a rapid rise in the amount of volatile compounds occurred. No tests were made to determine the presence of ethylene in these cases.

The emanations of citrus fruits infected with Penicillium digitatum, Diaporthe citri, Alternaria citri, or Diplodia natalensis have been found to induce epinasty of the test plant leaves more quickly than the emanations of sound fruits. It was found also that the emanations of lemons infected with green mold, Penicillium digitatum, caused a rapid yellowing of green lemons and a shedding of the stem ends. The effects seemed to be due to ethylene. The emanations over a 24-hour period from a single lemon infected with P. digitatum contain approximately 0.064 milliliter of ethylene.

Recognition of the facts that diseased tissues produce considerably more ethylene than do healthy tissues and that a number of symptoms of common plant diseases are strikingly similar to the responses of healthy plants to exposure to ethylene gas led to the hypothesis that the symptoms of certain plant diseases may be caused by increased ethylene production. The rapid yellow coloration and early abscission of leaves infected by certain pathogens certainly suggest the action of a substance such as ethylene.

Two diseases characterized by such symptoms are the black spot of rose and the shot hole of cherry, caused by Diplocarpon rosae and Coccomyces hiemalis, respectively. An investigation was undertaken by C. E. Williamson to determine whether diseased tissues produced increased amounts of ethylene and, if so, to correlate the symptoms of the disease with the quantity of ethylene produced.

Different amounts of ethylene were indeed found to be produced by the different diseases, the amount apparently depending upon the pathogen involved. Large amounts of ethylene were produced by rose leaves infected with *Diplocarpon rosae*, cherry leaves infected with *Coccomyces hiemalis*, and chrysanthemum flowers infected with *Mycosphaerella ligulicola*. Somewhat less ethylene was produced by chrysanthemum flowers infected with *Botrytis cinerea* and rose leaves infected with *Cryptosporella umbrina*. A still smaller quantity, though significantly larger than that produced by healthy tissue, was produced by rose leaves infected with *Sphaceloma rosarum* and carnation foliage infected with *Alternaria dianthi*. In the other diseases studied, the infected tissue produced little more ethylene than did the comparable healthy tissue. Bean leaves infected with the halo blight bacterium, *Pseudomonas phaseolicola*, did not produce ethylene in a detectable quantity. In the black spot disease of rose ethylene production is at a maximum while the infected leaf is green, decreases as the leaf becomes yellow, and ceases when the leaf becomes brown. In those experiments, healthy leaves generally produced small quantities of ethylene, the amount depending to some extent upon the species of plant.

Plants infected with certain viruses were found by A. Frank Ross and Williamson to produce different amounts of ethylene. Large amounts of ethylene were produced by *Physalis floridana* plants infected with potato virus Y, provided the temperature of the greenhouse was such as to permit the development of local lesions and consequent necrosis or death of the tissues involved. Other viruses that produce local lesions on inoculated leaves were employed. They included

tobacco mosaic virus (*Marmor tabaci*) on *Nicotiana glutinosa*, *Datura stramonium*, and *Phaseolus vulgaris* var. Scotia; alfalfa mosaic virus (*Marmor medicaginis*) on *Phaseolus vulgaris* var. Scotia; tobacco ring spot virus (*Annulus tabaci*) on *Nicotiana tabacum* var. Turkish; and potato virus X (*Annulus dubius*) on *Gomphrena globosa* and *Nicotiana tabacum* var. Turkish.

Except for tobacco mosaic virus in leaves of Scotia bean and potato virus X in Turkish tobacco leaves, the diseased leaves produced greater amounts of ethylene than did corresponding healthy leaves. Those two failures apparently were not due to peculiarities of the plants, as healthy controls produced detectable amounts of ethylene and leaves of these same plants infected with other viruses produced large amounts of ethylene. In general, the amount of ethylene produced was roughly proportional to the extent of necrosis.

Leaves of Better Times rose infested with the two-spotted spider mite, *Tetranychus bimaculatus*, produced considerably more ethylene than comparable healthy leaves. Leaves of *Physalis floridana* and of *Nicotiana tabacum* with necrotic lesions induced by copper sulfate also produced ethylene, but in slightly smaller amounts than did comparable leaves with lesions induced by viruses. Healthy leaves shredded with a sharp knife just before testing generally produced more ethylene than did uninjured leaves, but the increased quantity varied with the species of plant. These results indicate that ethylene is a product of injured or dying cells rather than the cause of the necrosis that occurs.

The fungus diseases investigated appear to belong in three categories. With some diseases, such as those caused by the obligate parasites, relatively little ethylene is produced; with certain others, such as black spot of rose and shot hole of cherry, caused by facultative saprophytes, relatively large amounts of ethylene are produced. Between those extremes is a large group of diseases with which intermediate quantities of ethylene are produced. Observations of diseases in this category indicate that in some cases slow yellowing and eventual abscission may occur. In each of the five diseases of roses that were studied, there was a positive correlation between the degree of yellowing and defoliation and the amount of ethylene produced. Only with black spot was there rapid defoliation and production of large amounts of ethylene. The anthracnose and the brown canker diseases may result in some yellowing and possibly abscission and production of a moderate amount of ethylene. With the rust and the powdery mildew diseases there was little or no yellowing or abscission and only negligible amounts of ethylene were produced. It appears, then, that the large amount of ethylene produced with certain diseases is the cause of the rapid yellowing and early abscission of infected leaves.

Flowers as well as foliage may be affected by ethylene from diseased tissues. In experiments reported by Dimock and Baker in 1950, it was shown that flower drop ("shelling") of snapdragons and calceolarias and closing of the blooms ("sleepiness") of carnations could be caused by the enclosure of diseased tissues with normal healthy snapdragon, calceolaria, or carnation flowers. In these tests, chrysanthemum flowers infected with the chrysanthemum ray blight fungus, *Mycosphaerella liguli-cola*, or with *Botrytis cinerea* were used as ethylene sources.

In other experiments, conducted by C. W. Fischer, Jr., and J. R. Keller in 1951, brominated activated charcoal enclosed in sealed containers with flowers was highly effective both in controlling growth of molds and in preventing ethylene damage to the blossoms. In those tests, chrysanthemum flowers infected with *M. ligulicola* and carnation blooms infected with *B. cinerea* were used as sources of ethylene. The brominated

activated charcoal was not effective unless it was in close proximity to the blooms, but not touching them.

SINCE HEALTHY CELLS normally produce a small amount of ethylene, there would seem to be a minimum threshold concentration which must be exceeded if the toxic effects of ethylene are to occur. Investigations at Cornell University of storage of flowers have demonstrated that if certain ethylene-sensitive healthy flowers are stored in airtight containers enough ethylene is produced to cause self-injury. With most healthy tissues, ethylene production is slow, and, unless confined, dissipation into the atmosphere is sufficiently rapid to prevent accumulation of ethylene within plant tissues in toxic quantities.

Stimulated ethylene production appears to be associated with aging, diseased, or dying cells. In such cells the normal respiratory cycle may be partially disrupted to produce ethylene in abnormal quantities. Necrosis or death of cells does not seem to be the entire answer, although in experiments where phytotoxic chemicals were used there was a positive correlation between the degree of necrosis and the quantity of ethylene produced. Where injury to the surface layer of plant cells occurs, as by feeding of spider mites, a large number of cells are affected but necrosis is not readily evident.

The observed relationship between temperature and ethylene production, and the decrease in ethylene production to near-zero under anaerobic conditions have direct application to storage of cut flowers. Recent work at Cornell University on low-temperature storage of flowers demonstrated that for most flowers the length of the storage period and the quality of the flower after removal from storage was directly related to temperature and to type of storage pack. The best results were obtained with temperatures near 0° C. (32° F.)

and with a nearly airtight pack or container.

For prepackaged flowers or for flowers stored in water in a moderately tight cold room, the potential damage that can be done if ethylene-producing diseased material is included is serious. Observations have indicated that once a blossom is injured by ethylene it immediately becomes more liable to attack by *Botrytis*. Thus a chain-reaction type of response is initiated that will lead to more ethylene production and thus to more injury.

The observed effects of ethylene produced by diseased plant tissues emphasize the desirability of either near-perfect control or complete elimination of plant disease. If adequate disease control is maintained in field or greenhouse and in the storage room, one of the important factors in successful long-term storage of cut flowers is reduced to negligible proportions.

C. E. WILLIAMSON, *assistant professor of plant pathology in Cornell University, is a native of Indiana. His work with diseases of ornamental plants began at Cornell in 1937. His studies on ethylene effects began with the demonstration of stimulated ethylene production by rose leaves affected with black spot. He is a graduate of Wabash College and Cornell University.*

A. W. DIMOCK, *professor of plant pathology in Cornell University, has specialized in diseases affecting ornamental crops for many years. His interest in ethylene effects was a natural consequence of his close association with Dr. Williamson during his studies on ethylene production by diseased plant tissues and with Dr. C. W. Fischer, Jr., during his studies on effects of ethylene on cut flowers in storage.*

For further reference:

A. W. Dimock and Kenneth F. Baker: Ethylene Produced by Diseased Tissues Injures Cut Flowers, *Florists Review*, volume 106, No. 2754, pages 27–29, 1950.

C. E. Williamson: Ethylene, a Metabolic Product of Diseased or Injured Plants, *Phytopathology*, volume 40, pages 205–208, 1950.

Apricot and Almond Brown Rot

E. E. Wilson

Probably nowhere else in the world are stone fruits grown in such variety and number as in the three States that border the Pacific Ocean. There are grown the edible varieties of peaches, nectarines, apricots, the three types of cherries, plums, prunes, and almonds. There, too, are produced the numerous other species of stone fruits that are utilized as rootstocks for the edible sorts. The orchards in the region are composed not of a few trees of miscellaneous kinds grown in the back yards of scattered farm homes but many trees of the same kind in contiguous blocks extending over hundreds of acres. One entire locality may be given over to cherries, peaches, or prunes; another may be planted only to apricots and peaches; and another to almonds and peaches.

The foundation stocks of all these stone fruits were introduced into the the region. Some came from the Orient and others from Europe; some were introduced first into eastern United States and later brought west; others came directly from their foreign home.

With the establishment of the fruit industry in the Pacific coast region came disease problems: The frequent shipments of nursery stock and other propagative material provided ample opportunity for introduction of diseases. Once introduced, the diseases found large numbers of hosts to affect.

Typical of the maladies occurring on stone-fruit trees in this region are the two brown rot diseases. One of them, which I shall call apricot brown rot for convenience, was introduced from Europe. The other, which I shall call peach brown rot, apparently was native to the eastern part of the United States and developed there on the wild species of stone fruits. Whether it occurred on the Pacific coast before the fruit industry was established or was introduced later is uncertain.

The two diseases, formerly thought to be different manifestations of one malady, are produced by two closely related fungi. The one causing apricot brown rot is *Monolinia (Sclerotinia) laxa.* The cause of peach brown rot is *Monolinia (Sclerotinia) fructicola.*

The latter fungus and the disease it causes are discussed by John C. Dunegan in another article in this volume. Consequently I shall confine my discussion largely to the apricot form.

This fungus, which is common in England and on the European Continent, was found in Oregon in 1915 and subsequently in Washington, British Columbia, and California. It is more common in California than the peach fungus. Outside of the Pacific coast region, however, it is known to occur only in a few localities in Wisconsin and Michigan.

If one reads the early accounts of brown rot in California, one is led to the conclusion that the apricot fungus occurred there long before the peach fungus. Most of those accounts deal with brown rot in the apricot and mention certain characteristics, which we recognize as those of the apricot fungus. Both here and abroad, for example, the apricot fungus is noted for its preference for the apricot. The two German investigators who described and named it mentioned this feature. Another marked characteristic is its propensity for blighting blossoms and twigs. In California at least, the amount of fruit rotting it produces is secondary in importance to the amount of blossoms and twigs destroyed. The peach fungus, on the other hand, seldom occurs on apricot and is distinctively a fruit-rotting organism. Its activity in blossoms and twigs is much less pronounced than that of the apricot fungus.

IN CERTAIN RESPECTS the two fungi closely resemble each other. In the form and structure of their parasitic stage on the hosts, they are indistinguishable. Taken from the host and grown on certain artificial culture media, however, they exhibit certain differences. Nevertheless, for a long time most investigators considered such differences merely the normal variations of a single fungus species. Some still believe that they should not be called different species but should be regarded as variant forms of the same species. Whether they be two species or two forms need not concern us here; the important thing is that they behave differently with respect to disease production and host preferences. Consequently when one is present there arises a particular type of disease problem on a particular group of hosts. When the other is present there arises another type of disease problem on another set of hosts.

To illustrate how the introduction of the apricot fungus into California has affected the lot of the apricot grower, we might consider the situation in the Santa Clara Valley, which lies just south of San Francisco Bay. This valley is extensively planted to apricot, the only other stone fruit in comparable amount being the prune. The peach fungus is occasionally found there on the prunes and peaches. The apricot fungus, on the other hand, is widespread among apricot orchards and, if not controlled, causes serious damage. Consequently, each year one or more applications of a fungicide are required to hold it in check. Were it not for this fungus, therefore, the need for fungicides in the apricot orchards of this valley would be comparatively slight, since coryneum blight, the disease on which great amounts of fungicides are expended in other parts of the State, is not prevalent there.

HAVING COMPARED the two brown rot fungi, I shall now discuss in more detail the activity of *Monolinia laxa*, the apricot species. First, however, a word should be said about the other stone-fruit hosts of this fungus. The almond has already been mentioned as one, the others are the sour cherry, the plum, and the prune. Next, a word about susceptibility among the different varieties of these stone fruits.

Well over three-fourths of the apricots grown in California are of the varieties Blenheim and Royal, both of which are highly susceptible to blossom infection by the apricot fungus. The next most important variety, Tilton, is moderately susceptible but nevertheless is abundantly infected at times.

Investigations at the California Agricultural Experiment Station revealed some interesting effects of parentage on the susceptibility of apricot hybrids. Regardless of the susceptibility of the other member of the cross, the resistant St. Ambroise, Moorpark, and Tilton varieties apparently transmit to their progeny a large degree of resistance.

The principal almond varieties in California are Drake, IXL, Ne Plus Ultra, Nonpareil, Peerless, and Texas. Of these, the Drake is by far the most susceptible to brown rot blossom blighting. The Ne Plus Ultra and IXL are moderately susceptible. The other three varieties are highly resistant. A relatively new variety, the Jordanolo, which resulted from crossing Nonpareil with Harriett, is quite susceptible. Apparently, therefore, this almond hybrid, unlike the apricot hybrids I mentioned, did not inherit resistance from its resistant parent, the Nonpareil. Instead it inherited the susceptible qualities of the Harriett.

Among the 10 most important shipping plums, the Santa Rosa and Wickson are the most susceptible to brown rot blossom blight. Only occasionally are plum fruits affected. Of the prune varieties, the Burton is very susceptible to blossom infection; the French (Agen) is moderately susceptible; and Imperial, Robe de Sergeant, and Sugar are resistant. In the past, most of the brown rot of prune fruit in California has been caused by *Monolinia fructicola*.

Aside from the fact that the Early Richmond and Montmorency varieties of sour cherry are known to be affected, there is little information on this host.

LET US NOW follow the life cycle of the apricot fungus through one season. In spring the fungus enters the blossoms when they emerge from between the scales of the winter buds. It grows rapidly through the blossoms and down into the supporting twigs. Soon after the blossoms wither, the fungus produces small ash-gray masses of conidia on them. Usually the conidia perform no further function, but occasionally they may cause infection of some of the fruit as it ripens. Mr. Dunegan described how the peach fungus produces spores of a second type in the infected fruit that falls to the ground. The apricot fungus has been known to produce this stage in Europe but has not been found to do so in America. Therefore the rotted apricot fruit that falls to the ground is not a source of infection the following spring. Fruits that hang in the tree, on the other hand, harbor the fungus over the winter and in spring produce masses of conidia. Because of the sporadic occurrence of fruit rot, such fruit are relatively unimportant in California as a source of infection.

The most important sources of infection in California are the blighted blossoms and twigs, in which structures the fungus mycelium remains alive but quiescent during the hot, dry summers. After the winter rains begin, it starts a slow development. At numerous places beneath the corky outer bark the mycelium produces small compact masses by growth and segmentation. These small knots of fungus tissue, the sporodochia, or conidium-bearing structures, gradually enlarge and push up through the overlying bark to the surface. Even before the structures emerge the conidia are being produced on them. The first sporodochia appear on the twigs in early spring and continue to appear for

6 weeks or more, developing in greatest numbers just before the blossoming period. Thus even before the buds open in the spring, many strategically located sources are ready to supply conidia for blossom infection.

TEMPERATURE AND MOISTURE affect both the earliness and the amount of sporodochial development. In seasons when rains begin early in the fall and thereafter occur at frequent intervals, sporodochia may appear first in late December and continue to appear for 6 or 8 weeks, so by the time the trees blossom a very large number are present. In seasons when winter rainfall is deficient, however, they may not begin to appear until late January and then in small numbers. Low temperature, particularly during late winter, likewise delays their appearance and reduces their numbers.

The amount of conidia that results from the infection of one blossom is extraordinarily great, because the blossoms and the blighted twig as well bear the sporodochia. Not uncommonly 30 or more of those structures develop on a single twig. Since each sporodochium produces hundreds of conidia, many thousands of the spores arise from a single infection. Multiplying this by the hundreds of infections in a tree, one has some conception of the prodigious numbers available for blossom infection.

Conidia are washed from the sporodochia and to the flowers beneath by rain. They are also liberated from the sporodochia by air currents; being very small, they are readily carried long distances by the wind. As the air carries them through the tops of the trees, they are deposited on twigs, branches, and blossoms. Under favorable conditions they germinate and produce a slender infection strand, which penetrates into the blossom tissue, thereby completing the life cycle of the fungus.

SINCE THE BROWN ROT disease of apricots and almonds is predominantly a disease of the blossoms, we are concerned with the conditions that favor infection of those parts. If the conidia of the fungus are present, the disease will develop whenever the blossoms reach an infectible stage and the proper weather conditions prevail. As long as the blossom parts are protected by the scales of the winter buds, they are not accessible to the conidia of the fungus. They become accessible and consequently infectible as soon as they emerge from the bud. They reach a stage of greatest susceptibility when they are fully expanded and gradually become less susceptible as the petals fall and the young fruit start to grow.

Regarding the effect of weather conditions on the disease, it is known that the fungus grows most rapidly at a temperature of about 68° F., but will cause blossom infection at a temperature as low as 41° or as high as 86°. After it enters the blossom and is not so directly exposed to outside conditions, it develops rapidly even though outside air temperatures may be below the range at which it grows best.

Because the conidia will germinate only in the presence of moisture, little if any infection occurs when the weather is dry. A rain lasting only a few hours, however, will permit infection if the temperature is near the optimum for growth of the fungus. If temperature is below the optimum, a longer moist period is required for infection. The combined influence of temperature and moisture, in large measure, is responsible for the year-to-year fluctuations in the severity of the disease.

WHAT MEANS can be employed to control the disease? Let us recall that the disease can develop only if the fungus is present in the orchard or a nearby orchard, if the blossoms have reached an infectible stage, and if temperature and moisture are favorable for infection. Since no way is known to modify the temperature and moisture conditions in such a way as to prevent infection or prevent the blossoms from becoming susceptible to infection, the only approach by which we might control the disease is that of destroying the fungus or its conidia before they can initiate the disease. One way to do that is to cover the blossoms with a chemical that will kill the conidia that fall upon them.

We know that the blossoms become infectible as soon as they emerge from between the scales of the winter buds and remain so until after the petals fall. We must therefore give them a protective covering of a fungicide as soon as they emerge. Many field trials were necessary before it was learned just when to apply the spray, because the emergence and opening of the blossom is a progressive thing. The tip of the unopened blossom first appears, and as the stem elongates it is pushed out of the bud. Experiments conducted by a number of investigators showed that spraying before the blossoms emerged reduced infection to some extent but not enough to be of practical value. Spraying after the blossoms had emerged completely and the petals were unfolding often proved too late. Spraying just after the blossoms emerged gave the most satisfactory results. Even better control could be expected if the application was followed by another after the petals began to unfold. On the whole, such a schedule proves satisfactory once the grower becomes experienced in judging flower-bud development and in the mechanics of applying the spray. Nevertheless, even a two-application schedule proves inadequate in some years.

The most common cause of unsatisfactory results from spraying is a delay in giving the first treatment. Often rainy or windy weather at the time the spray should be applied interferes with spraying operations, and the fungus gains entrance to the blossoms. Once that occurs, spraying will not prevent the disease from developing. Such difficulties led to the development of another control method which does not require such critical timing of the spray treatments.

Monolinia laxa, it will be recalled, produces only one type of reproductive structure, the conidia. They develop in the tree on blighted twigs and blossoms and on the fruit, which the fungus occasionally attacks and which remains on the tree until spring. Early investigators recognized the desirability of eliminating the conidia and recommended that all blighted twigs and rotted fruit be removed when the trees are pruned in winter. Removal of the numerous blighted twigs proved impractical, however.

Chemical sprays to eliminate the conidia were developed. Monocalcium arsenite proves particularly effective for the purpose. When applied to dormant trees in mid-January, the compound destroys the conidium-bearing mats (sporodochia) present when the spray is applied and prevents their further development by killing the mycelium inside the twigs. One application of a preparation, containing 3 pounds of monocalcium arsenite to 100 gallons of water, commonly reduces sporodochial development 95 to 98 percent and results in a decrease in blossom infection.

Since 1940 or so, growers in several localities have employed this treatment on apricots with comparatively little injury to the trees.

Some safety measures must be observed, however: Give the treatment only after the trees are completely dormant; in California the spray is applied from mid-January up to the time the flower buds begin to swell. Delay the treatment at least 2 weeks after the trees are pruned, or, better still, spray before pruning. Do not add spray oils to the preparation and avoid their use after the monocalcium arsenite treatment is given. It is probably unwise to give the treatment to trees in a low state of vegetative vigor. Yellowing of leaves accompanied by defoliation followed the application of monocalcium arsenite in the winter in one orchard.

Monocalcium arsenite is extremely poisonous and great care must be taken to avoid breathing or swallowing it.

ALTHOUGH monocalcium arsenite preparation does not materially injure the principal apricot varieties or the Santa Rosa and Wickson plums, it injures all almonds and some prunes. Consequently less injurious eradicative fungicides have been sought. Of about 75 other compounds that were tested, the sodium salts of the chlorophenols (particularly pentachlorophenol) eliminated the conidia most effectively. Sodium pentachlorophenate is destructive to the conidia present on the twigs when it is applied but is not highly effective in preventing their further development. Being very soluble, moreover, it is sometimes washed from the twigs by rain before its maximum effect on the conidia has been exerted. Under proper conditions, however, it destroys much of the conidial inoculum. That in turn results in a significant decrease in the amount of blossom infection. Neither the eradicative nor the protective treatment alone satisfactorily controls the disease under all conditions. A combined eradicative-protective program is much more effective.

The protective fungicides most widely used against the disease in California are the copper-containing materials, bordeaux mixture and the fixed coppers. Sulfur fungicides, although relatively effective under favorable conditions, cannot be used on apricots because of the "sulfur sickness" they produce in the tree. The newer types of fungicides, many of which are complex organic compounds, are being tested. Some show promise, but further tests are needed to evaluate their effectiveness.

E. E. WILSON *is professor of plant pathology in the University of California at Davis, where he has been engaged in studies of fruit diseases since 1929.*

Mr. Dunegan's discussion of peach brown rot appears on page 684.

Some Important Diseases of Coffee

Frederick L. Wellman

It has been commonly said that coffee (*Coffea arabica*) is a tree practically free from disease. Actually, the coffee plant is subject to more than 40 diseases—ailments due to lack of minor elements, virus troubles, mild bacterial infections of roots and fruits, and attacks by fungi and parasitic flowering plants. A century of effort has been expended on agronomic and horticultural problems in coffee, but only in the past 50 years has intensive work been done on its diseases.

In 1952 the Office of Foreign Agricultural Relations (now the Foreign Agricultural Service) of the Department of Agriculture sent a mission to study coffee diseases in all parts of the world. The mission was sponsored by the Point IV program and financed by the Institute of Inter-American Affairs. Information gathered on the trip has been incorporated into this chapter, which is based primarily on study and experience in Latin America.

COFFEE RUST, also called the oriental leaf disease, is by all odds the most serious disease of coffee. It does not occur in the Western Hemisphere, maybe just by pure luck. There are two species of rust: The classic *Hemileia vastatrix*, which is so destructive and is found in most of the coffee regions of Africa, the Near East, India, Asia, and the Pacific Islands, and *H. coffeicola*, an equally dangerous rust but still confined to the Cameroons of West

Africa and the nearby island of São Tomé. This discussion deals with the first species.

Ceylon, once one of the world's greatest coffee-producing countries, has had to become an exporter of tea when its coffee crops failed because of rust. The disease was first discovered in Ceylon in 1867. Between 1879 and 1893, after it had become well established, exports of coffee dropped to less than 7 percent of former shipments. In the Philippines in 1891 rust cut the harvest 35 percent. In Java, too, rust practically wiped out the coffee plantations, and the planters turned to hevea rubber as a substitute crop.

The first symptoms are small, yellowish, translucent, oily spots on the leaves. They expand into rather large, round spots and early show a powdery coating of spores on the under surface. As the spores mature, the spots gradually turn bright orange to red. With age the lesions become brown and surrounded with a yellow rusted band. Defoliation occurs to such an extent that many trees retain only two or three pairs of leaves on their branches where they might ordinarily have 15 or 20. Such affected trees are stunted, cannot produce, and usually die after a few years.

The disease was not present in 1953 in the Western Hemisphere. It was brought to Puerto Rico in 1903 but prompt and drastic action by O. W. Barrett, the horticulturist there who also dealt with pathology, destroyed all diseased material. He saved untold wealth for the coffee industry in the American Tropics and for centers of world trade.

In some eastern countries, notably the French Cameroon, Kenya, and Tanganyika in Africa, and in the states of Mysore and Coorg and in the Nilgiri Hills of southern India, growers control the rust by two or three annual spray applications of bordeaux mixture. The sprays are put on just before the heavy monsoon rains begin and again in the short dry spell that intervenes before the light monsoon rains

fall. Sometimes a third spray is used after the light rains end. In countries that have extremely dry seasons, few rust spores are produced in these periods. Likewise little new leaf surface is developed by the coffee trees. When rains begin, both the parasite and the coffee take on new life, but by well-timed sprays the planters plan to keep about 70 percent of their coffee foliage free from rust infections.

Where the seasons are not so well defined, such as in Ceylon, Java, Malaya, and the Philippines, weekly or monthly sprayings are needed to control rust. They increase tremendously the cost of growing coffee. Some plantations in some of those countries have been moved to high altitudes, where cool temperatures reduce the inherent producing capacity of the coffee tree but do permit it to grow with less trouble from the rust.

Spores of the rust are long-lived, withstand drying and other vicissitudes, and may be easily transported on live plants or as invisible dust from one country to another. Quarantines have been instituted, and many research workers in the western Tropics have repeated warnings of the danger. All varieties of coffee grown commercially in the Americas are highly susceptible to *Hemileia*. Increasing transportation between East and West by air as well as by sea multiply the hazards of reintroducing the disease and establishing it this time on western shores.

For more than a half century it has been known that highly tolerant and rust-resistant types of coffee exist. Those better strains, one after another, have been brought to afflicted areas in the Orient. There, at first, they were grown with success, only to succumb later to the rust. Beginning some 30 years ago intensive study was devoted to the phenomenon in India. It was learned that the rust, like others, had biologic races, which attacked new coffee varieties that had been selected for their resistance to the old populations of rust. Moreover, the races were probably the result of mutations, as no one has ever been able to discover an alternate host relationship, which ordinarily is fruitful in producing new races of rust.

Coffee breeders have been able to secure trees with enough resistance in them to be—in time—the basis for developing improved and acceptable coffee types that will grow well in the presence of rust. Through the work of the mission that studied the rust in the Eastern Hemisphere, seeds from all the rust-resistant coffees, and many more, have been obtained for growing in the Americas. After careful disinfection and other prophylactic measures to assure freedom from all diseases and insects, these new coffees are now growing in the Western Hemisphere. They are insurance against the time that the rust comes to this part of the world—if it does.

THE AMERICAN LEAF SPOT is recognized as the most serious disease of coffee in the Occident. It was discovered and studied by N. Saenz in Colombia in 1876. He sent herbarium species from Colombia and Costa Rica to Europe for identification. The causal fungus, *Mycena citricolor* (*Omphalia flavida*), is an inhabitant of wet mountains and woodlands and has a phenomenally wide range of wild hosts, from which it has spread to coffee. Its attack has been particularly severe because coffee culture has been concentrated in cool, moist mountain regions. It may cause losses of 75 percent or more of the crop in some districts. In Costa Rica it takes an annual toll of about 20 percent of the crop. It occurs in all leading coffee countries of the Americas.

The first symptom is a small, dark area on a leaf. In the center of the spot is a yellow infection body. The tiny lesion grows into a round, grayish spot. On the spot are produced a number of fine, yellowish, hairlike stalks, which at one time are tipped with a large, pear-shaped fruiting body. The infection body is not always present in field material but is large enough to be seen with the unaided eye. It is readily detached by water and carried by splashing droplets of rain—practically the only means of distribution. The disease progresses slowly in coffee plantations. Wide roadways, rows of closely set banana plants, thick hedges of old shade trees, and narrow fields of annual crops are barriers against its movement. Rarely in nature does the fungus produce the characteristic brilliant-yellow, miniature mushrooms. They bear few spores. Some bear none at all.

The large infection bodies carry the disease from plant to plant. They cause excessive defoliation and fruit drop. They also attack flowers and green stems and produce lesions on fruits. The trees finally die if serious infection continues. Because the fungus has a comparatively narrow temperature range, the disease is more severe in cool highland areas and does not occur in warm places at low altitudes. It grows fairly well under conditions as cool as 54° F.; well at 61° to 75°, reaching an optimum at 75°; and poorly at 83°. At 86° to 90° it stops growing.

The disease thus far is confined to the Americas. With care it can probably be kept from spreading to the oriental Tropics. The disease can be restrained somewhat in countries of its origin if the coffee is grown at warm, low altitudes, and if the dense protecting shade trees are thinned by severe pruning.

Spraying with bordeaux mixture has been recommended. Tests of other fungicides have been started. It is ordinarily considered that costs of materials, employment of untrained labor, and difficulties of terrain make adequate and regular spray applications practically impossible.

Several years of research under Point IV in cooperative stations by the Office of Foreign Agricultural Relations have resulted in developing a control that does not employ spray methods but is accomplished by removing leaves. During the first 2 weeks of the rainy season, diseased trees are stripped of all leaves, flowers, and fruits, which fall to the ground, carrying the inoculum with them. There the fungus is destroyed by natural means—by insects, slugs, and bacterial action—before the 6 weeks elapse that are required for new leaves to appear on the denuded trees. The current crop is sacrificed, of course, but the larger harvests in the following years compensate for the destruction of the one poor crop. If careful watch is maintained and reinfected trees are defoliated as soon as they are found in the old treated area, the disease apparently may be kept in check indefinitely.

DIEBACK, or anthracnose, caused by the fungus *Colletotrichum coffeanum*, is common in all countries where coffee is grown. It apparently causes injuries at irregular times to seedlings in the seedbed and nursery, to old bearing trees, and to new supplies transplanted in the field. In the places where it has been studied, the fungus has been found to be present on all trees. Losses are hard to measure, because the disease is still not well understood, but the trouble doubtless cuts substantially into profits year after year.

First symptoms of anthracnose are the dark lesions, usually large, which appear on seedling leaves. On weakened or older plants leaf lesions of anthracnose often spread into the stem tissues to which the leaves are attached. Those parts are killed, and the blackened dieback spreads down into branches and stems. When conditions of moisture and temperature favor the disease, it produces profuse masses of sticky spores. The spores are spread by rains, insects, and other means. A variable interval elapses between the period of inoculation with fungus spores and the visible appearance of disease symptoms. Latent infections, which involve the presence of the organism in apparently healthy plants, may therefore occur. Intensive dieback of stems often is found that is unrelated to *Colletotrichum* infection under conditions adverse to tree growth. In

Africa and India dieback is often due to plant exhaustion, following heavy crops. That is true also to some extent in tropical America. Instances are encountered in which the condition known as dieback results as a complex of both widespread infection by the causal fungus and from unfavorable growth conditions or physiological disturbances of infected plants.

The infective dieback disease appears to be more common during the warm, dry season, for the optimum temperature for growth of the *Colletotrichum* is about 83° F. It grows at temperatures up to 90° but is inhibited at 97°. Fair development occurs at a temperature as low as 61°.

Anthracnose alone or with accompanying dieback apparently may occur in all regions where coffee can grow. No wholly satisfactory control is known for it. The fact that dead branches are replaced by new growth tends to allay the fears of growers or pathologists and means that interest lags in developing intensive control measures.

Disease-resistant strains are badly needed. Varieties of coffee have been found in east and central Africa that are highly tolerant to anthracnose dieback. They are being tested in Africa and have been introduced into Latin America for further study. It seems that the use of resistant plants is a promising way to combat it.

Cooperative projects have been started to study spray treatments in Costa Rica. Of several fungicides tested, Fermate was found to be best to keep seedbed and nursery plants free from anthracnose. It also keeps young field transplants free from infective dieback until they are well established in the plantation.

THE COFFEE BERRY DISEASE is a comparatively new disease of coffee. It has been found in Africa, the Belgian Congo, and Kenya. It has apparently increased in severity in the past few years. It is due to a specialized race of the anthracnose organism, *Colletotrichum coffeanum* var. *virulans*, that is peculiarly adapted to infecting fruits. The first symptoms are small, brownish spots, which become glazed, enlarge, and finally get a pinkish color. It is common on coffee grown at higher elevations, where as much as 50 percent of a crop may be destroyed. Its life history is not wholly understood.

Considerable work has been done on methods of control since 1950. The use of sprays has been studied but has given no results of practical value. Some varieties are more resistant than others. Research workers hope to breed varieties of higher degrees of resistance and to introduce that resistance into the regular commercial lines of coffee in the severely diseased regions.

THE THREAD BLIGHT DISEASE, also known as black rot in the Orient is reported in many countries in both hemispheres. Often it is localized in occurrence, but it can cause considerable losses. This is especially true in parts of south India, central Costa Rica, and like regions. It weakens trees and intensifies colletotrichum dieback.

This tropical fungus—*Pellicularia koleroga*—occurs in moist regions and is one of a typical group of thread producers. It occurs in part as thick, traveling threads, tightly glued along the under sides of branches. A thread that reaches a leaf petiole sends out a side shoot to follow it. A broad, tissuelike pellicle is formed on the under side of the leaf by fanlike growths of the fungus hyphae. During this period of apparently superficial attack, the fungus can be torn from the host surfaces, but affected leaves darken, wither, and die.

If the fungus is left undisturbed, petioles of diseased leaves are loosened from branches but are held attached by fungus strings, which permit the leaves to hang swinging in the air like small, black rags. When moist weather comes, the surface of the fungus pellicle on under parts of leaves becomes powdery with spore-bearing bodies.

No thorough study has been made of the temperatures at which sporulation occurs, but vegetative growth of the fungus is good at temperatures ranging from 75° F. to 90°, with greatest development at 83°. It grows poorly at 54° and is completely inhibited at 97°. Much research remains to be done on this parasite and its life history.

Different changes in plantation culture have been tried in order to combat the disease. Clean culture, fertilizing, variations in shade, and defoliation methods have had little effect. It was quickly eliminated in Africa and eastern lands where bordeaux spray was applied to control rust. After many years without black rot, as rust-resistant varieties have been introduced in parts of India and coffee has not been sprayed for rust control, thread blight has again returned with serious consequences. Spraying of individual trees with bordeaux mixture in Central America has given good results. The newer copper sprays have been found to be of equal value. The copper compounds often are injurious to coffee foliage, but that disadvantage is outweighed by the effectiveness of the compound against thread blight.

FRUIT SPOT, or brown eye leaf spot, is a bothersome, common, fruit- and leaf-spotting disease. Its causal organism was named *Cercospora coffeicola* in 1881. It is found on coffee the world over but is not severe in much of the Orient. It is of greater economic importance in Latin America than is ordinarily admitted. Defoliation actually is one of its worst effects. It produces severe decay on the fruit.

Fruit infections result in a characteristic black dry rot. The pathogen is seed-borne. The leaf spots are large; usually only a few occur on a leaf, although one on a leaf is often enough to cause it to drop. The spots have been confused with the American leaf spot, but they are quite different. Cercospora spots have wide brown edges and a light center, with black specks. The disease seems to occur under a wide range of conditions and may be especially severe in nurseries. It grows fairly well even at temperatures less than 54° F. and is relatively good in growth from 61° to 90°. The greatest growth is at 75° to 83°. It grows weakly at 97°. The disease is more severe in coffee exposed to the sun than in well-shaded coffee.

A common and sound way of reducing the disease is to develop a canopy of shade over the plantation. Proper attention to soil protection and adequate moisture content seem to have good effects. No effective fungicide has been found.

ROSELLINIA ROOT ROT is one of several root rots to which coffee is susceptible. The fungus that causes the most trouble is *Rosellinia bunodes*, which is found in both hemispheres. Compared with some of the serious leaf parasites, this disease causes almost negligible losses, but the death of occasional trees may cause so much concern among growers that they attach greater importance to the disease than actual economic losses justify.

The planter first notices a diseased tree by its slightly yellowed and grayish-green leaves, which soon wilt and turn black when the tree dies. The base of the trunk of such a tree usually has bark that is slightly roughened just above the ground and is tightly appressed to the wood below. Dead roots that have been dead long enough are dark, with a hairy, black growth under the bark—a condition that extends up the tree trunk. The bark in those parts has black spots and streaks in the wood. Usually when one tree dies the one next to it will succumb somewhat later.

The cause is an apparently weak-growing fungus, whose growth habits provide a key to control measures. Diseased areas may be isolated by digging a trench around them and throwing the soil that is dug from the trench in towards the disease center. Some planters do not follow this practice but simply replant. Replanting is done even in trenched-in areas. As trees die, it is best to dig them immedi-

ately and remove all large roots from the soil. A wide, deep hole should be left open for 6 or 12 months. Afterwards it may be filled in and replanted with a healthy seedling, which often grows without contracting the disease. At times, however, that treatment fails, and digging must be repeated, with a longer interval between removal of the diseased seedling and replanting with a new seedling. In regions where the disease is believed to be common, jungle land is cleared for coffee with unusual care to remove stumps and large roots of wild trees. Corn or another crop is grown on the land for 2 years before it is made into coffee plantings. The practice seems to help against early infections of rosellinia root rot.

THERE ARE several other root-attacking fungi—other species of *Rosellinia* and species of *Fomes*, *Pellicularia*, and *Ganoderma*. They all cause much the same symptoms as described for *Rosellinia bunodes*. Another root rot, *Armillaria mellea*, as it occurs in Tanganyika causes a curious splitting of roots, trunks, and larger stems, and leaves the bark hanging more or less loose in strips. All root rots are handled as *Rosellinia* is.

FREDERICK L. WELLMAN *since 1943 has been agriculturist and consultant in plant pathology for the Office of Foreign Agricultural Relations of the Department of Agriculture. He spent more than 4 years on El Salvador as a pathologist and worked in coffee. He is now stationed as chief agriculturist at the Inter-American Institute of Agricultural Sciences, Turrialba, Costa Rica, where since 1947 he has devoted himself to a study of diseases of tropical plants, particularly coffee. He was once employed for 2 years as a pathologist for a commercial concern in Central America, and from 1930 to 1943 served as a pathologist in the Bureau of Plant Industry, Soils, and Agricultural Engineering. Dr. Wellman participated in the mission sponsored by the Point IV program in 1952 to study coffee diseases in all parts of the world.*

Glossary

Compiled by
Catherine F. George

ACERVULUS (ah-*sir*-vu-lus) One of many types of fruiting bodies produced by fungi. It is a shallow, saucer-shaped, depressed structure consisting of a layer of stalklike filaments (called conidiophores) that bear at their tips nonsexual spores (conidia) in a cushionlike mass. As the acervulus expands it ruptures the cell layers of the host plant, thus exposing its surface and permitting the spores to be set free. Plural: ACERVULI.

AECIUM (*ee*-see-um) A cuplike spore-producing structure developed by rust fungi. The spores produced in it (AECIOSPORES) can infect the same host on which they are formed but generally infect a different, unrelated one—for example, the aeciospores of stem rust of wheat are formed on barberry and carry the infection to wheat.

AGAR A gelatinlike substance extracted from a seaweed. It is an ingredient used in making culture media to study the growth characteristics of micro-organisms.

ALLELOMORPH (a-*lel*-o-morf) Either of a pair of contrasting genes, or characters, such as roughness and smoothness, occupying the corresponding position in a pair of chromosomes. Adjective: ALLELIC, ALLELOMORPHIC; noun: ALLELOMORPHISM.

ALTERNATE HOST One of two kinds of plants upon which a parasitic fungus must develop to complete its life cycle. For example: The fungus that causes black stem rust of wheat parasitizes wheat and barberry and if deprived of either host cannot complete its life cycle. An aid in the control of rust on wheat, therefore, is to eradicate all barberry bushes in the locality.

AMPHIDIPLOID (am-fe-*dip*-loid) A combination resulting from the hybrization of two species that contains the total chromosome complement—all the characteristics—of both parents.

ANTIBIOSIS (an-te-by-*o*-sis) Antagonism between two organisms, particularly microorganisms in soil, to the detriment of one of them. Antibiosis is used to control some soil fungi (such as the one that causes Texas root rot) by adding to the soil organic materials that encourage the growth of the antibiotic organisms at the expense of the pathogen.

ANTIBODY A chemical substance in the host that opposes the action of parasites, their products, or foreign materials.

ANTHRACNOSE Any disease caused by fungi that produce nonsexual spores in the type of fruiting body called an acervulus. Anthracnose usually is characterized by ulcerlike areas on the host.

APOTHECIUM (ap-o-*thee*-see-um) A disk-, saucer-, or cup-shaped fungus structure whose inner surface is lined with saclike membranes called asci, which contain spores called ascospores. Apothecia are found seated on or in the host or raised on a stalk. Some apothecia are barely visible to the eye; others are several inches in length or diameter. Usually they are more or less fleshy. The ascospores sometimes are set free by simultaneous explosion of the asci within the apothecium.

APPRESSORIUM (ap-re-*sor*-e-um) A suckerlike structure, usually disk-shaped, at the tip of a filament (hyphae) of some parasitic fungi by which the fungus adheres to the host plant. A peg, formed at the center of the appressorium, penetrates the host tissue.

ASCOMYCETES (ass-ko-my-*see*-teez) One of the major groups of fungi, characterized by the production of spores within an oval or tubular membranous sac called an ASCUS. The cells of the ascus divide to form the spores (usually eight), which are called ASCOSPORES. The asci (*ass*-see) of some fungi form a layer over the surface of a part of the host plant. Asci of other fungi are contained in fruiting bodies, of which there are two types—perithecia and apothecia. Yeasts, molds, mildews, and truffles belong to the group and may be referred to as ascomycetes (ass-co-my-*seetz*).

BACTERIOPHAGE A viruslike bacteria-destroying agent.

BACTERIUM A one-celled, microscopic organism which is a low form of plant life. The cell, which may be spherical (coccus type), rod-shaped (bacillus type), or spiral and cylindrical (spirillum type), may occur singly or in colonies or long chains, but each is considered an individual unit. Some have tiny filaments (flagella) that enable them to swim through a liquid. Bacteria are widely distributed in air, water, soil, bodies of living animals and plants, and dead organic matter. Lacking the green coloring matter, chlorophyll, they cannot manufacture their own food from carbon dioxide and water and must get it already prepared from other sources. Some live off dead matter and keep the earth from becoming a junk yard of plant and animal remains. Many live in the bodies of animals or in plants and thereby cause disease. The ones that cause plant diseases are usually of the rod-shaped type. They enter plants through a natural opening, such as a water pore, or through a wound. Once inside they multiply simply by dividing in two, and migrate among the cells of the plant. They may kill the cells or cause cancerous development of them.

BASIDIOMYCETES (ba-sid-i-o-my-*see*-teez) One of the major groups of higher fungi characterized by the production of sexual spores (BASIDIOSPORES) on a club-shaped filament called the BASIDIUM. Typically four basidiospores are formed on each basidium. Except for that characteristic, the fungi belonging to the group (such as rusts, smuts, and mushrooms) differ widely in structure and habits. In rust and smut fungi the basidium is called the promycelium and the basidiospores, the sporidia. A member of the group may be referred to as a basidiomycete (ba-sid-i-o-my-*seet*).

BIOTYPE A group of micro-organisms that have the same genetic characteristics; a subdivision of a race of fungi. See PHYSIOLOGICAL RACE.

BLASTING Causing failure to produce fruit or seeds.

BLIGHT A general term used to describe symptoms of plant disease which may include spotting, sudden wilting, or death of leaves, flowers, stems, or entire plants.

BORDEAUX 4–2–100 The figures following the name of this fungicide indicate the amounts of copper sulfate, hydrated lime, and water to be mixed. In this case, 4 pounds of copper sulfate and 2 pounds of lime in 100 gallons of water.

CAEOMA (see-*oh*-ma) A spore-producing structure of rust fungi similar to an aecium but commonly surrounded with fungus filaments rather than a definite wall; also a genus of the rust fungi.

CALYX (*kay*-liks) The outer group of floral leaves of a plant, often smaller and green in color as contrasted to the inner, more showy part, the corolla.

CAMBIUM LAYER A soft layer, strip, or cylinder of living cells which divide to form new tissues of the plant. The layer ordinarily extends over the plant body except at the growing tips.

CANKER A definite diseased area, usually on woody stems.

CARRIER A plant or animal bearing internally an infectious agent of disease, although it shows no marked symptoms of it. A carrier plant can be a source of infection to other plants or animals. An insect contaminated externally with an infectious agent is sometimes called a carrier.

CAUSAL ORGANISM The organism that produces a given disease.

CELL The structural and functional unit of all plant and animal life. It consists of a small mass of protoplasm, the substance which constitutes living matter, and a denser smaller body, the nucleus, and is surrounded by a membranous tissue, the cell membrane or cell wall. Living organisms may have one cell (bacteria) or billions (man).

CENTIGRADE THERMOMETER A thermometer on the scale of which the interval between the freezing and boiling points of water is divided into 100 parts or degrees. To change degrees centigrade to degrees Fahrenheit multiply by nine-fifths and add 32.

CERTIFICATION OF SEED Seed production and marketing under control to maintain varietal purity and freedom from seed-borne pests.

CHEMOTHERAPY (kem-o-*ther*-a-pee) The treatment of disease by chemicals that work internally.

CHLAMYDOSPORE (*klam*-e-doe-spore) A rounded, nonsexual spore (formed by direct transformation of certain cells of a fungus filament or of an entire filament) which has a thick wall that favors its survival in soil or plant debris.

CHLOROPHYLL The green compound found in leaves and other plant parts by means of which the plant converts water and carbon dioxide of the air into food through the energy of the sunlight in a process called photosynthesis.

CHLOROSIS Yellowness of normally green tissues due to partial failure of chlorophyll to develop. Many diseases cause chlorosis and frequently the pattern of the chlorotic area helps diagnose the disease.

CLEISTOTHECIUM (kly-sto-*thee*-see-um) A minute, black fruiting body of some fungi consisting of a surrounding wall completely enclosing one or more saclike membranes (asci) in which spores (ascospores) are produced. Under pressure of the developing asci the cleistothecium bursts, liberating the ascospores by forcible discharge.

CLONE A group of plants derived from a single plant by means of vegetative propagation such as the rooting of cuttings or slips, budding, or grafting. Every member of a clone has the same heredity, so that under uniform environment a group of plants from a single clone is quite uniform. Compare STRAIN.

COLLENCHYMA (ko-*leng*-ki-ma) The tissue in elongating soft stems and certain other parts of plants which helps support the plant.

CONIDIUM (ko-*nid*-e-um) A fungus spore formed by being pinched off or cut off from the tip of a specialized, erect, aerial filament (hypha) called a CONIDIOPHORE. Conidia have various shapes and sizes. They are sometimes called summer spores because they are produced in abundance during the growing season. Usually they are wind-borne, but some are washed away by rain or drop to the ground where they may be moved about by man, animals, machinery, or water.

COREMIUM (ko-*ree*-me-um) A cluster of erect fungus filaments (hyphae) which are joined together to form a column and which bear nonsexual spores (conidia).

CORIACEOUS (ko-ree-*a*-shus) Tough, leatherlike.

COROLLA (ko-*rol*-a) The petals of a flower collectively; the inner part of the floral leaves of the plant, usually more delicate and brightly colored than the outer part, the calyx.

CORTEX The portion of the stem or root of vascular plants external to the vascular tissue. Adjective: CORTICAL.

COTYLEDON (kot-e-*lee*-dun) The first leaf produced when a seed germinates.

CULTURE To grow a crop; to grow fungi or bacteria on a prepared food material, such as agar or broth (the CULTURE MEDIUM). The entire process of obtaining an organism on prepared media is often called CULTURING.

CYTOPLASM (*si*-toe-plazm) The substance (protoplasm) of a cell exclusive of the nucleus and cell wall.

DAMPING-OFF A disease of seeds or young seedlings caused by fungi. The disease is most evident in young seedlings that topple over and die just after they emerge from the soil (postemergence damping-off). Two other types of damping-off are often mistaken for poor seed rather than disease: Germination failure, in which a seed is invaded in the early stages of germination and fails to sprout; and preemergence damping-off, in which the young seedling is attacked before it pushes its way through the surface of the soil.

DIATOMACEOUS EARTH A whitish powder used as an absorbent in the manufacture of explosives, for filtering, for insulating, or as an abrasive in soap.

DIEBACK Death of branches or shoots beginning at their tips and moving back toward the trunk or stem.

DIPLOID (*dip*-loid) Having a double (2N) number of chromosomes. Compare HAPLOID.

DISEASE A condition in which any part of a living organism is abnormal; the condition of a plant that is being continuously affected by some factor that interferes with the normal activity of the plant's cells or organs. Injury, in contrast, results from a momentary damage.

DISINFECTANT Any material that kills micro-organisms.

DISINFESTANT An agent that removes or inactivates plant pests.

DISSEMINATION The spread of infectious material. Infectious agents causing plant disease are disseminated by wind, water, insects, man, animals, and machinery.

DISTAL Remote from the point of attachment or origin; away from the center of the body.

EMBRYO (*em*-bree-o) A young plant in its beginning, usually contained in a seed or surrounded by protective tissue.

-ENCHYMA (*eng*-ki-ma) A suffix denoting type of cell tissue. Examples are collenchyma, plectenchyma, sclerenchyma.

ENDOSPERM Nutritive tissue formed within the seed of plants and on which the embryo feeds while germinating.

ENZYME (*en*-zim) A natural chemical, produced by plant and animal cells, that brings about changes in organic substances by influencing processes such as ripening, fermentation, or digestion. Some of the bacteria that cause plant diseases produce enzymes which cause some of the cells of the plant to grow more rapidly resulting in the formation of galls or tumors.

EPIDERMIS (ep-i-*der*-mis) The outermost layer of cells of a leaf or other plant part.

EPINASTY (*ep*-i-nas-tee) An abnormal downward curving growth or movement of a leaf resulting from more rapid growth of cells on the upper than on the lower side of the leaf stalk.

EPIPHYTE (*ep*-i-fight) A plant that grows upon another plant (or on a building or telegraph wire), which it uses as a mechanical support but not as a source of food. Some (such as Spanish-moss) may harm the plants they grow on, however, by excluding light or smothering them. Most orchids are epiphytes.

EPIPHYTOTIC (ep-i-fy-*tot*-ik) The sudden and destructive development of a plant disease, usually involving an extensive area. It corresponds to an epidemic of a human disease and the two words are used interchangeably by plant pathologists.

ESCAPE Pertaining to a plant which, in a given population of a species or variety of plants in which a disease is prevalent, remains free from disease although it possesses no natural inherent resistance to the disease. Sometimes plants escape attack because of the way they grow; for example, an early-maturing plant escapes late-season diseases. That kind of escape is called klendusity.

ETIOLATION (ee-tee-o-*lay*-shun) Yellowing of plants due to lack of light.

EXUDATE (*ex*-you-date) Any material or substance formed inside a plant and discharged through a natural opening or an injury; particularly a liquid discharge from diseased tissues. The presence of an exudate and its nature aid in diagnosis.

F_1 The first-generation offspring resulting from a given mating. F_2—second generation, etc.

FACTOR The causative agent transmitted from parent to offspring and determining the development in the offspring of a certain hereditary character; a gene.

FACULTATIVE PARASITE (*fak*-ul-ta-tiv) An organism that can grow either on living or dead organic matter. Compare OBLIGATE.

FASCIATION (fash-e-*ay*-shun) A distortion of a plant caused by an injury to the cells of the bud or by an infection which results in flattened and sometimes spirally curved shoots. The plant may look as if several of its stems were fused.

FILIFORM (*fil*-i-form) Threadlike in shape.

FLAGELLUM (fla-*jel*-um) A tiny, whiplike filament of a cell which enables the cell to swim through a liquid. Plural: FLAGELLA; adjective: FLAGELLATED.

FRUCTIFICATION (fruk-ti-fi-*kay*-shun) (1) Production of spores by fungi. (2) The structure in or on which spores are formed.

FRUITING BODY A complex fungus structure that contains or bears spores and from which they are disseminated. The most important types are apothecia, perithecia, conidiophores, coremia, sporangia, pycnia or spermogonia, aecia, pycnidia, acervuli, and sporodochia.

FUMIGANT A liquid or solid substance that forms vapors which destroy pathogens, insects, etc. Fumigants are usually used in soils or in closed structures such as warehouses.

FUNGI IMPERFECTI (*fun*-jye im-per-*fek*-tee) Imperfect fungi; one of the major groups of the fungi, for which no sexual production of spores is known. The group serves as a catchall: When the sexual stage of a fungus is discovered, the fungus is transferred to one of the three other groups of fungi, depending upon the characteristics of the sexual stage.

FUNGICIDE (*fun*-ji-side) A chemical that kills or inhibits fungi. Bordeaux mixture, lime-sulfur, and ferbam are fungicides.

FUNGUS (*fung*-gus) A low form of plant life which, lacking chlorophyll and being incapable of manufacturing its own food, lives off dead or living plant or animal matter. The body of a fungus consists of delicate threads known as hyphae, many of which form branched systems called mycelia. The mycelia, which may form inside or on the surface of the host, have different branching habits and structures which help to identify the fungus. In fungi (*fun*-jye) growth takes place at the ends of the hyphae. Many fungi multiply by forming spores at the ends of, within, or on specialized hyphae. The spores are tiny, microscopic bodies that function like the seeds of higher plants and are carried by wind, water, insects, man, animals, or machinery. A spore landing on a plant under the proper conditions can produce a new fungus body. Many fungi produce both sexual and nonsexual spores. The manner of production of the sexually formed spores is the basis of classification of fungi into three of their main groups, Phycomycetes, Ascomycetes, Basidiomycetes; in the Fungi Imperfecti, sexually produced spores have not been found. Spores are not known for some fungi, which are classified in a fifth group, the Mycelia Sterilia.

GALL A pronounced localized swelling; an outgrowth, often more or less spherical, of unorganized cells.

GAMETE (*gam*-eet) A matured sex cell.

GENE The unit of inheritance that is transmitted from parent to offspring and controls the development in the offspring of a characteristic of the parent; a factor.

GERM TUBE The threadlike filament

(hypha) produced by a fungus spore when it begins to grow. It may grow into a plant through a natural opening or a wound or force its way through unbroken epidermis. In parasitic fungi it is also called an infection thread. It grows and gives off branches which form the body of the "new" fungus.

GERMICIDE A substance that kills micro-organisms.

GERMINATION The beginning of growth.

GLUME (gloom) A small, dry, light leaf next to the flower of a grass.

GRAFT INDEXING A procedure used to determine the presence or absence of a virus in a plant. The plant is grafted to another plant that is known to show symptoms if affected by the disease in question. The method is used to detect the presence of viruses that are not readily transmitted mechanically.

GRAM-NEGATIVE Not being stained by the crystal violet dye (GRAM STAIN) used in a method of classifying bacteria. Bacteria that retain the stain are GRAM-POSITIVE.

GUTTATION (guh-*tay*-shun) The normal, physiological process of plants of exuding moisture from an uncut surface; the forcing out of cell sap on a free surface.

GYNOPHORE (*iyn*-o-fore) The stalk which bears the pistils of a flower.

HAPLOID (*hap*-loid) Single in appearance or arrangement; specifically, having the basic (or N) number of chromosomes for the species. Compare DIPLOID.

HAUSTORIUM (hos-*tor*-e-um) (1) A special filament (hypha) of a fungus that penetrates the cells of the host plant and absorbs food from them. (2) A rootlike absorbing organ connecting a parasitic seed plant to the food-conducting system of its host.

HETEROECIOUS (het-er-*ee*-shus) Pertaining to the rust fungi: Passing through the various stages of the life cycle on more than one kind of host. Compare MONOECIOUS.

HETEROZYGOTE (het-er-o-*zye*-gote) An organism to which its two parents have contributed unlike genes with respect to any given contrasting pair of chromosomes (for example, one parent contributes the characteristic of tallness, the other, shortness) and which produces two kinds of germ cells with respect to the characteristics.

HILUM (*high*-lum) (1) A small depression of a cell in which the flagella (the whiplike filament that enables the cell to swim through a liquid) is inserted. (2) A small depression of an organ, such as a seed, which usually marks the point at which the organ was attached to its base.

HOST The plant which is invaded or parasitized by a disease-producing agent and from which the parasite obtains its sustenance. The HOST RANGE of a parasite is the various kinds of plants that may be affected by it.

HOST INDEXING A procedure to determine whether a given plant is a carrier of a virus disease. Material is taken from one plant and transferred to another plant that will develop characteristic symptoms if affected by the virus disease in question.

HYALINE (*high*-a-linn) Clear, transparent, without color.

HYDATHODE (*high*-da-thode) A plant gland that exudes fluids; a water pore. Hydathodes are often present at the edge or tip of a leaf.

HYDROGEN-ION CONCENTRATION A measure of the acidity of a chemical in solution. The greater the concentration of hydrogen ions (atoms of hydrogen with positive charges), the more acid the solution is. The hydrogen-ion concentration is expressed in terms of the pH of the solution. See pH.

HYPERPLASIA (high-pur-*play*-zhi-a) Abnormal increase in the number of cells resulting in the formation of galls or tumors.

HYPERTROPHY (high-*pur*-tro-fee) Abnormal increase in the size of an organ or tissue brought about by enlargement of the component cells or by increased cell division or both.

HYPHA (*high*-fa) One of the threadlike strands, or filaments, that constitute the body (mycelium) of a fungus. It may be divided into cells by cross walls (septate) or be one elongated cell with several nuclei (nonseptate), coarse or fine, aerial or submerged, stiff or flexible, and exhibit different types of branching. Some hyphae (*high*-fee) are specialized for producing spores or for penetrating host tissues.

HYPOCOTYL (high-po-*kot*-il) A part of an embryo plant in the seed; the first stem of a plant.

IMMUNITY The ability of a plant to remain free from a disease by virtue of inherent properties of the plant (as distinct from escape). An immune plant is exempt from disease. Physical properties of the plant (such as a tough outer wall, the nature of natural openings, hairiness, and waxy coating of stems) and chemicals produced by the plant account for immunity. A plant may be said to be immune *to* or immune *from* a given disease.

IMPERFECT STAGE The period of life of a fungus during which spores are produced nonsexually. Compare PERFECT STAGE.

INCUBATION (1) The period of time between inoculation of a plant by a disease-producing agent and the appearance of symptoms. The period varies from a few hours with some fungi to as long as a year or more. Although there are no symptoms, the fungus is active during this stage—the spore germinates and sends its germ tube into the cells of the plant. (2) Maintaining inoculated plants or pathogens in an environment favorable for disease development.

INDEXING Determining the presence of disease. See GRAFT INDEXING; HOST INDEXING.

INFECT To become established in a parasitic relationship with a host plant.

INFECTION THREAD The germ tube of a fungus; the specialized filament developed by a germinating spore which penetrates host tissue.

INFEST To be present in numbers. The presence of disease in a population of plants or of pathogens where they can produce disease (as in soil or on seed surfaces) is an INFESTATION. Infestation should not be confused with infection, which can be applied only to living, diseased plants or animals.

INFLORESCENCE A flower cluster; the general arrangement and disposition of the flowers on an axis; the mode of development of the flowers.

INOCULATE To bring infectious material (the INOCULUM) in contact with a host plant.

INTUMESCENCE A blister formed by cells that have burst from sudden water excess after dry periods.

INVASION Growth or movement of an infectious agent into a plant and its establishment in it.

KLENDUSITY (klen-*doo*-se-tee) Ability of an otherwise susceptible variety of plant to escape infection because of the way it grows. For example, early-maturing plants escape late-season diseases.

LAMELLA (la-*mell*-a) Any thin or plate-like structure. Plural: LAMELLAE (la-*mell*-ee).

LEMMA (*lem*-a) The lower of the two leaves enclosing the flower in grasses.

LESION (*lee*-zhun) A localized spot of diseased tissue. Spots, cankers, blisters, scabs are lesions.

LIFE CYCLE, LIFE HISTORY The complete succession of events in the life of an organism.

LIGNIFICATION The formation of lignin in cell walls through the transformation or impregnation of elements of the wall. Cellulose and lignin form wood.

LOCAL INFECTION Infection involving only a limited part of a plant.

MACRO- A combining form meaning large.

MECHANICAL INOCULATION An experimental method of transmitting plant viruses, fungi, or bacteria from plant to plant. In the case of a virus, sap extracted from a diseased plant is rubbed over leaves of the test plant. Generally the method is more effective if the rubbed leaves have been previously dusted with fine abrasive powder, such as carborundum.

MEIOSIS (my-*o*-sis) The process of the division of chromosomes and their reduction in sexual cells to one-half the number found in vegetative cells of a plant.

METABOLISM (meh-*tab*-o-lizm) The chemical changes occurring in living organisms by which energy is provided for vital processes and activities and new material is assimilated to repair the waste.

MICRO- A combining form meaning small or, in the name of an instrument, enlarging (microscope).

MICRON (*my*-kron) A unit of length in the metric system which corresponds to 0.000039 inch. It is the usual unit for measuring spores, bacteria, and other microscopic objects.

MILDEW A plant disease in which the causal fungus forms a coating over the surface of plant parts; or the fungus causing such a disease. The coating, which is a mycelial growth, is usually thin and whitish. There are two types of mildew—downy and powdery.

MILLIMETER A measure of length in the metric system which corresponds to 0.03937 inch.

MOLD Any fungus that produces a superficial, often woolly growth on various types of organic matter; or the growth itself. Molds occur most often on damp and decaying matter.

MONOECIOUS (mo-*nee*-shus) (1) Pertaining to a plant: Having both male and female reproductive organs on the same individual. (2) Pertaining to a fungus, particularly a rust fungus: Having all stages of its life cycle on a single species of plant. Compare: HETEROECIOUS.

MOSAIC A plant disease caused by a virus and generally characterized by irregular light and dark green areas in the leaves.

MOTTLE An irregular pattern of light and dark areas.

MUMMY A dried, shriveled fruit, the result of some fungus diseases such as brown rot. The mummy may hang on the tree or fall to the ground where it survives the winter and is the source of reinfection in spring.

MUSHROOM A conspicuous, fleshy fungus, particularly a gill fungus. The part above ground is the reproductive part of the fungus; the vegetative mycelium is commonly concealed. The word has been applied to an edible form of such a fungus, but more properly it applies to all fruiting bodies, whether edible, poisonous, tough, unpalatable, or leathery.

MUTATE To change. MUTATION is a sudden variation in one or more characteristics of an organism which marks the offspring as different from its parent stock. The offspring is called a MUTANT.

MUTUALISTIC A term applied to a mutually beneficial relationship between organisms.

MYCELIUM (my-*see*-le-um) The vegetative body of a fungus; an aggregate of many filaments (hyphae) of the fungus commonly interwoven into a more or less feltlike mass. The mycelia of various fungi show great variation in appearance and structure.

MYCOLOGY (my-*kol*-o-jee) The science dealing with fungi.

MYCORHIZA (my-co-*ree*-za) A mutually beneficial relationship of roots with fungi. Some trees cannot grow normally without the presence of MYCORHIZAL fungi.

NECROSIS (neh-*kro*-sis) Death. Adjective: NECROTIC.

NEMATOCIDE (*nem*-a-to-side) a chemical that kills nematodes.

NEMATODE (*nem*-a-tode) A roundworm having a tubular body with a mouth and well-developed alimentary canal. Nematodes live free in moist earth, water, or decaying matter or as parasites of animals and plants. The body wall is muscular making it possible for the body to be knotted, curved, or bent. The nematodes that cause plant disease pierce the cells of a plant with a stylet and suck up the juices.

NODULE A lump, knot, or tubercle.

NUCLEUS (*new*-klee-us) The central, dense part of a cell in which the chromosomes are distributed.

OBLIGATE Necessary; obliged. An obligate parasite is an organism that can live only on living matter. Compare FACULTATIVE PARASITE.

OOSPORE (*oh*-oh-spore) A spore (produced by downy mildew and related fungi) formed by the fertilization of a large, passive female cell (OOGONIUM—oh-oh-*go*-ne-um) by a small, active male cell.

PALEA (*pay*-le-a) The upper of two leaves which enclose the flower in grasses.

PARAPHYSIS (pah-*raff*-e-sis) A sterile filament present in the sporeforming structures of some fungi.

PARASITE An organism that obtains its nutrients wholly or in part from another living organism.

PARENCHYMA (pa-*reng*-ki-ma) Plant tissue composed of thin-walled cells of essentially equal diameters. It forms much of the bulk of many plants parts such as the pulp of fruits and the central cells of leaves. Adjective: PARENCHYMATOUS (pa-reng-*kim*-a-tus).

PATHOGEN Any organism capable of causing disease. Adjective: PATHOGENIC; noun: PATHOGENICITY.

PATHOGENESIS The part of the life of a disease-producing organism when it is directly associated with a living host. Compare SAPROGENESIS.

PATHOLOGY The science of disease.

PEDICLE, PEDICEL (*ped*-eh-kil, *ped*-eh-sel) Any slender stalk; especially one that supports a fruiting or spore-bearing organ.

PEDUNCLE (pee-*dung*-kil) The stem that bears a flower or flower cluster.

PERFECT STAGE The period of life of a fungus during which spores are produced sexually. Compare IMPERFECT STAGE.

PERITHECIUM (per-e-*thee*-see-um) A flask-like fungus fruiting body that contains sac-like membranes (asci) in which spores (ascospores) are produced. The spores are expelled or otherwise released through the opening at the top.

PESTICIDE Any agent that destroys pests, such as a fungicide, insecticide, nematocide, etc.

PETIOLE (*pet*-e-ole) The stalk of a leaf.

PETRI PLATE OR DISH (*peet*-ree) A shallow, covered dish of thin glass used in growing bacteria and fungi in the laboratory.

pH A symbol of a scale used to designate the relative acidity of a solution. The scale ranges from 1 to 14. pH 7.0, the midpoint, represents a neutral solution. Numbers less than 7 indicate increasing acidity; those more than 7, increasing alkalinity.

PHLOEM (*flow*-em) Tissue in plants through which foods are transported from leaves to roots. Compare XYLEM.

-PHORE A suffix meaning a supporting stalk.

PHOTOSYNTHESIS The complicated process by which green plants make organic substance (sugar) from water and carbon dioxide of the air through the energy of sunlight.

PHYCOMYCETES (figh-co-my-*see*-teez) One of the major groups of fungi, which may consist of one cell or have filaments (hyphae) with few or no cross walls and which reproduce sexually by the union of two sex cells.

PHYLLODY (*fill*-o-dee) The change of floral to foliage leaves. A PHYLLODE is a flat expanded leaf stem replacing the blade of a foliage leaf.

PHYSIOLOGIC RACE A subdivision of a species of fungus based on its ability to infect a selected variety of its host plant. Race 15B of wheat stem rust is an example. Frequently after a new variety of a plant has been bred for resistance to a species of fungus, the fungus in turn develops a new race which attacks the variety at will.

-PHYTE A suffix denoting a plant of special habitat or characteristic. Examples: Epiphyte, spermatophyte.

PHYTO- A combining form meaning plant. Examples: Phytopathology, phytobiology.

PISTIL The female, or ovule-bearing, organ of a seed plant. Adjective: PISTILLATE.

PLECTENCHYMA (plek-*teng*-ki-ma) A tissuelike mass of closely packed fungus filaments (hyphae). Adjective: PLECTENCHYMA-TOUS (plek-teng-*kim*-a-tus).

PLUMULE (*ploo*-myoole) The first bud of a plant when a seed germinates.

PRIMARY INFECTION The first infection by a pathogen after it has gone through a resting, or dormant, period. Compare SECONDARY INFECTION.

PROMYCELIUM (pro-my-*see*-le-um) The short, club-shaped filament of a fungus that bears spores called sporidia; the basidium of smuts and rusts.

PROTOPLASM (*pro*-to-plazm) The basic substance of which all living matter is made. It is a grayish, semitransparent, sticky substance, within which physical, chemical, and electrical changes are constantly taking place.

PUBESCENCE (pyoo-*bes*-sens) An outer covering of soft, short hairs or down, as on the surfaces of leaves and stems; also the state of being so covered.

PUSTULE A pimplelike or blisterlike structure.

PYCNIDIUM (pik-*nid*-e-um) A flasklike, fungus fruiting body containing nonsexual spores (PYCNIDIOSPORES). It is formed on the surface or more or less embedded in the tissue of the host and often opens by a pore. The pycnidiospores are commonly extruded in mass or in long coils through the pore.

PYCNIUM (*pik*-nee-um) A small, flask-shaped fruiting body of a rust fungus; also called a spermogonium. It contains minute, bacterialike spores called PYCNIOSPORES or spermatia, and filaments that extend out through the mouth of the pycnium (receptive hyphae). A pycnium and its contents are one of two sexes and a pycniospore of one sex must reach the receptive hypha of the other sex for fertilization (which ultimately results in the production of aecia) to take place. The pycnium exudes a sweetish nectar with the spores, which attracts insects. They visit one pycnia after another and thus aid in fertilization much as bees pollinate flowers.

RACE See PHYSIOLOGIC RACE.

RACHIS (*ray*-kiss) Any of various axial structures, such as the elongated axis of a flower cluster or the extension of the leaf stalk of a compound leaf which bears the leaflets.

RADICLE (*rad*-e-kil) A rootlet; the first stem of a plant or both the first stem and the root.

RESISTANCE Ability of a plant to remain relatively unaffected by disease because of inherent properties it possesses. A plant may be slightly, moderately, or highly resistant.

RESTING SPORE A spore, often thick-walled, that can remain alive in a dormant condition for some length of time, later germinating and, in pathogenic fungi, initiating infection.

RHIZOMORPH (*rye*-zoe-morf) A ropelike

strand of a fungus, formed by the joining of fungus filaments (hyphae) into a bundle, by which the fungus makes its way for considerable distances through the soil or along or under the bark of woody plants or elsewhere.

RHIZOSPHERE (*rye*-zoe-sfeer) The area immediately surrounding the roots of a plant.

ROGUE To remove undesired individual plants from a planting.

RUGOSE (rue-*gose*) Rough. The term is used as a part of the name of a virus disease characterized by warty, roughened, or severely crinkled leaves or other plant parts. Noun: RUGOSITY.

RUSSET Brownish roughened areas on the skin of fruit resulting from diseases, insects, or spray injuries that cause abnormal production of cork.

RUST A disease caused by a rust fungus; or the fungus itself. The life cycle of a rust fungus may involve up to five types of spores. Some rusts parasitize only one species of plant during their lives (monoecious) or two species (heteroecious). A rust that is heteroecious and has five types of spores is the stem rust of wheat. The five spore types are the red *uredospores*, which spread the rust from grain plant to grain plant, the dark *teliospores*, which infect nothing but remain on straw or stubble, resisting winter temperatures, and germinate in spring to produce the *basidiospores*, which carry rust to barberry, infect it, germinate, and produce *pycniospores*, which fuse sexually to produce *aeciospores*, which infect the grain plant.

SAPROPHYTE (*sap*-roe-fight) An organism that feeds on dead organic matter. Adjective: SAPROPHYTIC. Compare PARASITE.

SAPROGENESIS (sap-roe-*jen*-e-sis) The part of the life of a disease-producing organism in which it is not directly associated with a living host. Compare PATHOGENESIS.

SCAB A roughened, crustlike, diseased area on the surface of a plant part; also the disease in which scab is a symptom.

SCION (*sigh*-un) A detached shoot (or another part of a plant that consists of more than one bud) which may be propagated; specifically, such a part removed from its place of growth and prepared for grafting.

SCLERENCHYMA (sklee-*reng*-ki-ma) Plant tissue that has hard, thickened cell walls. Stone cells in fruits are SCLERENCHYMATOUS (sklee-reng-*kim*-a-tus).

SCLEROTIUM (sklee-*roe*-she-um) A hard, compact, rounded mass of fungus filaments

(hyphae) which usually serves as a resting body to carry the fungus through unfavorable weather. Some fungi can survive for many years in soil, plant refuse, or seed by means of sclerotia. They vary in size from those that are microscopic to some that are several inches in diameter.

SECONDARY INFECTION Infection resulting from the spread of infectious material which has been produced following a primary infection (the first infection by a disease-producing organism after a resting period) or from other secondary infections without an intervening inactive period.

SETA (*see*-ta) A bristle on or in some fungus fruiting bodies; a bristlelike protuberance from a spore. Plural: SETAE.

SEPTATE (*sep*-tate) Divided into cells or compartments by cross walls (SEPTAE). Used to describe fungus filaments (hyphae).

SHOT HOLE A symptom of disease in which small roundish fragments drop out of the leaves so that the leaves look as though they had been riddled by shot.

SMUT A disease caused by a smut fungus; or the fungus itself. It is characterized by resting spores called chlamydospores, which generally accumulate in black, powdery masses (sori) and germinate to produce either a fruiting body called a promycelium or a germ tube, and the budding of the secondary spores (sporidia or basidiospores) to make yeastlike forms. The black spore masses may break up into a fine dustlike powder readily scattered by wind (loose smut) or remain firm and more or less covered (covered or kernel smut).

SOIL STERILIZATION The process of treating soil so as to kill living things in it.

SORUS (*sore*-us) A fungus fruiting body in which spores are produced in mass; a mass or cluster of spores borne on short stalks, particularly in the rust and smut fungi. Plural: SORI (*sore*-ee).

SPERMOGONIUM (sperm-o-*go*-ne-um) A flask-shaped or depressed receptacle in which SPERMATIA (male sex cells) are produced. It is also called a pycnium and the spores, pycniospores.

SPORANGIUM (spoe-*ran*-je-um) A fungus fruiting body that produces nonsexual spores (SPORANGIOSPORES) within a more or less spherical wall. The structure that supports the sporangium is called a SPORANGIOPHORE.

SPORE The one- to many-celled reproductive unit of a fungus which corresponds to a seed in plants; also the thick-walled resting stage of a bacterium. Fungus spores may be formed by sexual reproduction or vegetatively. Some, called resting spores, have thick walls that enable them to survive unfavorable weather. Some spores are very light in weight so that they can be blown about by wind; others fall to the ground and are moved about by water, man, animals, insects, and machinery. When conditions are favorable the spore is capable of germinating and producing a new fungus body.

SPORIDIUM (spoe-*rid*-e-um) A spore produced on a fruiting body called a promycelium; the basidiospore of rust and smut fungi.

SPORODOCHIUM (spor-o-*doe*-ki-um) A bundle of fungus filaments (conidiophores) that bear nonsexual spores (conidia). It is similar to an acervulus, but is formed on a cushionlike structure which breaks through the host tissue.

SPOROPHORE (*spor*-o-fore) A fungus structure that produces or supports spores.

SPORULATION The process of producing spores.

SPOT A definite diseased area.

STAMEN (*stay*-men) The male reproductive organ of a flower. Adjective: STAMINATE.

STELE (steel, *stee*-le) The central cylinder in the stems and roots of vascular plants.

STIPULE (*stip*-yule) One of the pair of appendages borne at the base of the leaf in many plants.

STOLON (*stoe*-len) A creeping, trailing, or reclining stem or runner which may produce roots or new stems and become an independent plant.

STOMA (*stoe*-ma) A minute opening in a leaf or stem; a pore. Plural: STOMATA.

STRAIN (1) In seed-producing plants: A group derived from seed of common ancestry but differing from others of the species or variety by one or more special characteristics, such as vigor or disease resistance. A strain differs from a clone in that a clone is produced by vegetative propagation, not by seeds. (2) In plant viruses, bacteria, and fungi: A subgroup within a species differing in virulence, symptom production, or to some extent in host range from the rest of the species; more properly called a race.

STROMA (*stroe*-ma) A mass of fungus filaments (hyphae), sometimes including their host tissues, that contains or bears spores. STROMATA often form flat crusts.

SUBSTRATE The substance or object on which an organism lives and from which it gets nourishment.

SUMMER SPORE A fungus spore that germinates without resting and is associated with the rapid increase and spread of the fungus during a favorable season.

SUSCEPT Any plant liable to infection by a given disease-producing agent.

SUSCEPTIBILITY Lacking inherent ability to resist disease.

SWARMSPORE A fungus spore capable of independent movement; a zoospore.

SYMBIOSIS (sim-by-*o*-sis) A mutually beneficial association of two or more organisms.

SYMPTOM Any reaction of a host plant to disease. Usually it refers to visible reactions.

SYSTEMIC Pertaining to a disease in which an infection leads to general spread throughout the plant body.

TAPROOT A primary root of a plant. It grows vertically downward giving off small lateral roots.

TELIUM (*tee*-le-um) The fruiting body of a rust fungus in which spores (TELIOSPORES) that are of a resting type are formed. Telia are often formed in late summer or near the end of the growing season.

THERMAL INACTIVATION POINT The upper temperature limit at which death of an organism occurs after a selected interval of time, usually 10 minutes.

TOLERANCE The degree of endurance of a plant to the effects of adverse conditions, chemicals, or parasites. A tolerant plant is capable of sustaining a disease without serious injury or crop loss.

TOXIN A poison formed by an organism. Adjective: TOXIC; noun: TOXICITY.

TYLOSIS (tye-*loe*-sis) A cell outgrowth into the cavity of a water-conducting (xylem) vessel which plugs the vessel. Plural: TYLOSES; adjective: TYLOSE.

UMBEL The arrangement of flowers arising from a common stalk forming a more or less flattened or rounded cluster.

UREDIUM (you-*ree*-de-um) A fruiting body of a rust fungus in which the red summer spores (UREDOSPORES) of the fungus are produced. It comprises a group of spore-bearing filaments crowded together on which masses of spores are formed. The uredospores

WIDENING DISTRIBUTION OF OAK WILT IN THE UNITED STATES

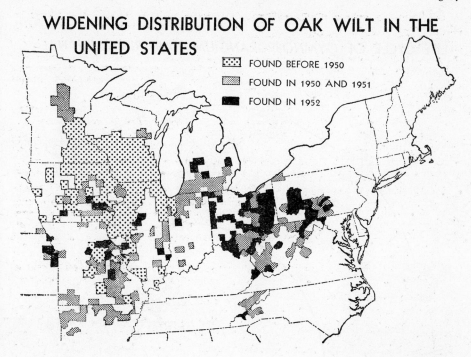

FOUND BEFORE 1950

FOUND IN 1950 AND 1951

FOUND IN 1952

spread rust from grain plant to grain plant.

VASCULAR Pertaining to the tissues of plants that conduct fluids. See PHLOEM; XYLEM.

VECTOR An agent that transmits disease.

VEIN BANDING A symptom of a virus disease in which the regions along the veins are darker green than the tissue between the veins.

VIRESCENCE (veer-*ess*-ense) Becoming green.

VIRULENCE (*veer*-you-lence) Relative ability to cause disease.

VIRULIFEROUS (veer-you-*lif*-er-us) Containing a virus. It usually pertains to an insect which carries a virus internally and can infect a plant with it.

VIRUS (*vye*-rus) An infectious agent too small to be seen with a compound microscope. It is not yet settled whether viruses are living organisms, because they have characteristics of both the living and nonliving worlds. The definition that is generally accepted is that they are large, high-molecular-weight protein bodies capable of multiplying and acting like living organisms when they are in living tissue.

WILT Loss of freshness and drooping of leaves of plants due to inadequate water supply or excessive transpiration or to a vascular disease which interferes with utilization of water by a plant or to a toxin produced by an organism.

WITCHES'-BROOM A symptom of disease in which there is an abnormal brushlike development of many weak shoots.

XYLEM (*zye*-lem) Tissue in plants through which water is conveyed up the stem from the roots and which furnishes mechanical support of the plant. Compare PHLOEM.

YELLOWS A disease (caused by a fungus or a virus) characterized by yellowing and stunting of the affected plants. The viruses that cause yellows diseases generally have not been transmitted mechanically but can be passed from plant to plant either by insects or by budding or grafting or both.

ZOOSPORANGIUM (zoe-o-spor-*an*-je-um) A fruiting body of fungi which produces spores (ZOOSPORES or swarmspores) that are capable of swimming.

ZYGOSPORE (*zye*-go-spore) The resting spore of a fungus formed from the union of similar sex cells.

LIFE CYCLE OF GYMNOSPORANGIUM JUNIPERI-VIRGINIANAE

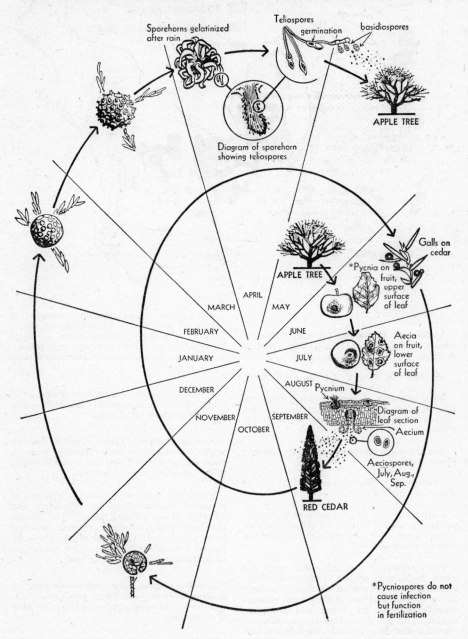

Index

Aagrano, 136
Aamodt, O. S., cited 111
ABBOTT, E. V.:
 Red Rot of Sugarcane, 536–539
 Rots, Blights, and Leaf Diseases
  of Sorgo, 524–526
 Sugarcane Diseases, 526–535
Abutilon virus, 17, 25
Acanthorhyncus vaccinii, 791–792
Acervulus, 507, 897
Acid residues in soil, 101
Actinomyces scabies, 169
Adaptation, defined, 45
Aderhold, R., cited, 706
Aeciospores, defined, 897
Aecium, 507, 897
Africa, 15, 331, 333, 386, 387, 389,
 453, 527, 705
African-violet, diseases, 861
Agar, defined, 897
Aglaonema, leaf spot, 862
Agrobacterium
 rubi, 774
 tumefaciens, 68–72, 187, 188,
  522, 759, 774, 788–789, 804
Agropyron mosaic, 356
Agrox, 135
Air pollution, 94
Alabama, 241, 293, 294, 295, 296,
 297, 303, 306, 307, 311, 318,
 370, 448, 449, 450, 451, 452,
 578, 581, 606, 681, 825, 855
Albedo browning, lemons, 831
Alben, A. O., cited, 799
Albino cherry, 715, 716, 717
Albrecht, W. A., cited, 108
Albugo occidentalis, 477
Albumin, effect on resistance, 171
Alaska, 627
Alfalfa, 95, 100, 228–237
 alsike clover mosaic virus, 230
 bacterial wilt, 230–231
 bacterial stem blight, 231–232
 black stem, 197
 crown and root rot, 234–236
 crown and stem rot, 197
 crown rot, 197, 235
 crown wart, 228, 232
 dodder, 76
 downy mildew, 197, 232
 dwarf, 24, 197, 229, 358, 747
 leaf rust, 234
 leaf spots, 197, 233–234, plate vii
 meadow nematode, 237
 mosaic virus, 20, 227, 230, 884

Alfalfa—Continued
 pea aphid, 197
 pea mottle virus, 230
 resistance in, 196–197
 root knot, 237
 root rot, 197, 235, 236
 rust, 197
 seed, 136, 142, 146, 148
 spring black stem, 232–233
 stem blight and crown rot, 197
 stem nematode, 236–237
 summer black stem, 233
 target spot, plate vii
 wilt, 196–197
 winter injury, 228–229
 witches'-broom, 229–230
 yellow leaf blotch, 197, 234
 yellow virus, 197
Alkali-grass, rust, 278
Allard, H. A., cited, 181
Allelomorph, defined, 897
Allison, C. C., cited, 61
ALLISON, J. LEWIS: Legumes in the
 South, 248–253
Almond
 armillaria root rot, 703
 bacterial canker, 723, 724
 brown rot, 886–891
 bud failure, 153, 154, 717
 calico, 717
 coryneum blight, 705 ff.
 dematophora root rot, 704
Aloe, root rot, 861–862
Alsike clover
 bacterial leaf spot, 225
 cercospora leaf and stem spot,
  224–225
 mosaic, 227, 230
 northern anthracnose, 220–221
 rust, 226
 sclerotinia crown and stem rot,
  218–219
 sooty blotch, 225–226
 virus diseases, 227 .
Alstatt, George E., cited, 356
Alternaria, 238, 847, 882
 blight, carrots, 474–475
 citri, 882, 883
 cucumerina, 210, 501
 dauci, 474–475
 dianthi, 585–586, 884
 leaf blight, muskmelons, 210,
  501
 leaf spot
  soybean, 238

Alternaria—Continued
 leaf spot—Continued
  tomato, 455, 456, 457, 461,
   464, 465, plate xxvi
 porri, 211
 rot, cantaloup, 847
 solani, 215, 455, 456, 457–458,
  463, 465, 505
 stem canker, tomato, 464, 465
 tenuis, 315
 zinniae, 882
Alternate host, defined, 897
Alyceclover, root knot, 252
American
 elm, phloem necrosis, 200
 leaf spot, coffee, 893–894
 pea streak, clover, 227
American Phytopathological Society, 305
AMES, RALPH W.: Infectious Diseases of Carnation, 583–592
Ammonia injury, 836
Amphidiploid, defined, 897
Anderson, C. J., cited, 616
Anderson, C. L., cited, 568
Angell, H. R., cited, 171
Anguina
 agrostis, 273–274
 tritici, 81, 133
Angular leaf spot
 cotton, 11, 12, 141, 316–317
 cucumber, 486
 Muscadine grapes, 874
 tobacco, 108
Anjou pear scald, 833
Annulus
 dubius, 440, 884
 tabaci, 884
Antagonism in fungicides, 143
Anther mold, 228, 273–274
Anther smut, carnation, 586
Anthracnose
 avocado, 880
 bean, 44, 151, 170, 171, 208,
  393, 497
 black walnut, 206
 blackberry, 782
 blue lupine, 199, 250, 684
 bur-clover, 251
 coffee, 894
 cotton, 84, 86, 91, 141, 303–
  306, 312–314, plate iv
 crimson clover, plate vii
 cucumber, 485–486, 499–500,
  plate xxvii
 cucurbits, 485–486
 dallisgrass, 259
 defined, 897
 digitalis, 866–867
 flax, 44, 141
 grape, 202, 754, 759–760
 grasses, 286
 house plants, 860, 862, 863
 Johnsongrass, 260–261, 370–371,
  plate ix
 leaf, sorgo, 207
 lima bean, plate xxv
 northern, red clover, 197, 220
 oats, 140, 194
 pea, 401

England, 86, 105, 109, 225, 272, 326, 472, 481, 497, 569, 570, 575, 599, 612, 622, 625, 631, 633, 670, 722, 724, 726, 728, 729, 766, 849
Entyloma, 282
  oryzae, 159
Environmental injuries, 94–100
Enzyme, defined, 899
Epichloe typhina, 256
Epidermis, defined, 899
Epinasty, defined, 899–900
Epiphyte, defined, 900
Epiphytotic, defined, 900
Epoxides, fumigation with, 847–848
Equipment to apply fungicides, 119
Ergot, 9, 9, 173, 280, plate xxxi
  cereals, 345–346
  forage crops, 272, 274–276
  rye, 7, 63, 66, 345–346
Erwinia
  amylovora, 201, 203
  aroideae, 492, 817, 819
  atroseptica, 150, 187, 438, 474, 817, 818, 819
  carotovora, 186, 417, 419, 474, 492, 817, 818, 819, 841
  phytophthora, 213
  tracheiphila, 210, 485
Erysiphe, 860
  cichoracearum, 210, 211, 488–489, 501–502, 592
  graminis, 46, 109, 193, 196, 253–254
    avenae, 195
  polygoni, 197–198, 199, 208, 212, 226, 249, 401, 497, plate vi
Escape, defined, 166, 900
Escarole, soft rot, 818
Ethylene from diseased plants, 881–886
Ethylene dibromide, 129
Ethylene oxide, 847–848
Etiolation, defined, 900
European field elm, 200
Evans, R. I., cited, 434
Exanthema, citrus, 96
Exocortis, citrus, 157, 743
Exosporina fawcetti, 802–803
Exudate, defined, 900
Eyespot
  grasses, 270
  mosaic oats, 353
  pearlmillet, 262
  sugarcane, 531, 533
  timothy, 265
Ezekiel, W. N., cited, 172

F₁, defined, 900
Factor, defined, 900
Factory gases, injuries from, 95
Facultative parasites, 28, 900
Fading out, grasses, 290, 291
Fairy ring
  cranberry, 793
  grasses, 290–291, plate xix
  spot, carnation, 584

False blossom, cranberry, 8, 201–202, 789, 793–794
False loose smut, barley, 61, 139
False smut, 257–258, 860, 862
Falsetoadflax, 73
Fanleaf, grapes, 752, 753
Fasciation, 900
  sweet pea, 11–12
Fawcett, H. S., cited, 730, 735, 738, 742
Federal Rust Laboratory, 40
Feed and food grains, 321–392
Fendler three-awn grass, 255
Fermate, 136
Fernow, Karl H., cited, 149
Ferns, diseases, 862
Fertilizer, 101, 103
Fescue, 256
  grass seed nematode disease, 273–274
  rusts, 278, 279
  smuts, 282, 283
Fiber crops, resistance in, 196
Field pea
  black stem, 248
  leaf blotch, 248–249
  powdery mildew, 249
  winter, 142, 199, 249
Field rot, cranberry, 791
Fig(s), 152
  armillaria root rot, 702, 703
  dematophora root rot, 704
  fumigation, 847–848
Fiji disease, sugarcane, 528, 535
Filberts
  and Persian walnuts, 800–808
  bacterial blight, 205, 807–808
  labrella leaf spot, 205
  mushroom root rot, 805–807
  wood rots, 808
Fire blight, 4, 10, 11, 12, 13, 63, 65–66
  apple, 201
  pear, 8, 203, 678–680
Filiform, defined, 900
Fischer, C. W., Jr., cited, 885
FISCHER, GEORGE W.:
  Smuts That Parasitize Grasses, 280–284
  Some of the 125 Rusts of Grasses, 276–280
Fisher, C. D., cited, 847
Fisher, D. F., cited, 667
Flag smut, 196, 283, 364–365
Flagellum, defined, 900
Flax, 100, 135, 141
  anthracnose, 44, 441
  asterocystis, 196
  browning and stem break, 141
  dodder, 76
  fiber, resistance in, 196
  grain, resistance in, 206
  pasmo, 141, 869, 873
  rust, 59, 196, 206, 869, 871
  wilt, 178, 196, 206, 869–871
Flax Classification Nursery, 871
FLOR, H. H., 59
  Wilt, Rust, and Pasmo of Flax, 869–873

Florida, 90, 97, 108, 121, 122, 123, 124, 159, 163, 181, 241, 357, 370, 378, 381, 382, 395, 398, 408, 411, 414, 415, 417, 448, 451, 452, 463, 531, 541, 544, 550, 555, 561, 601, 606, 610, 681, 731, 734, 736, 796, 839, 842, 875
Flowers, 136
  storage, 885–886
  See also Ornamentals *and specific kinds*
Fluorine, 95
Fly speck, apple, 663–666
Foex, G., cited, 174
Foliage blight, trefoil, 253
Fomes, 896
Food and feed grains, 321–392
Foot rot
  cereals, 105, 323
  citrus trees, 734–737
Forage crops
  anther mold, 273–274
  blind seed disease, 272–273
  ergot, 272, 274–276
  grass seed nematode disease, 272, 273–274
  northern, 262–267
  resistance in, 196–200
  seed certification, 146–148
  seed diseases, 272–276
  seed treatment, 142, 145
Forecasting weather and disease, 92
Foreign Agricultural Service, 891
Forest trees, resistance in, 200–201
Formaldehyde gas, 848–849
Formosa, 528
Fort, Charles A., cited, 522
Foundation Seed Project, 147
Foxtail millet, 257, 271, 370
Fractilinea, 359
France, 115, 171, 174, 234, 275, 569, 572, 625, 636, 638, 664, 705, 753
Fraser, Lillian, cited, 735
Frazier, N. W., cited, 356, 746, 766
Freeman, E. M., cited, 166
Freitag, J. H., cited, 746
FRIEDMAN, B. A.: Diseases Bacteria Cause, 817–821
FRINK, PAUL R.: Inspection of Imported Plants, 159–161
Frogeye, soybean, 200, 238, 240–241, 246, plate iv
Frost, effect on plants, 94–95
Fructification, defined, 900
Fruit(s), 11, 646–808
  chemical treatments, 842–843
  injuries, 95, 826–830, 837–841
  crown gall, 69
  fungicides for, 117–118
  physiological disorders, 830
  postharvest
    bacterial diseases, 817, 821
    fungus diseases, 809–812
    virus diseases, 822, 826
  resistance in, 201–203
  suboxidation, 830–831

919

International Code of Botanical Nomenclature, 34
International Crop Improvement Association, 146
Intumescence, defined, 902
Invasion, defined, 30, 902
Iodine in wraps, 849
Iowa, 103, 184, 239, 240, 246, 322, 326, 341, 342, 348, 350, 353, 356, 365, 378, 385, 509, 660, 661, 723, 851
Iran, 237
Ireland, potato famine, 5–6
Iris bulbs, nematodes in, 621–624, plate xx
Iron, 96, 99
Italian Prune leaf spot and sparse leaf, 153
Italy, 161, 171, 225, 637, 641, 723, 753

Jackson, A. B., cited, 576
Jacob, H. E., cited, 844
Jacob, J., cited 617
Jacobson, H. G. M., cited, 108
Jagger, Ivan C., cited, 423
James, L. H., cited, 847
Japan, 159, 265, 333, 359, 368, 575, 690, 723
Java, 16, 181, 527, 531, 536, 892
Java black rot, 446, 447
JEFFERS, W. F.:
Diseases of Berries in the East, 775–783
Red Stele Disease of Strawberry, 760–765
Jenkins, W. A., cited, 450
Johnson, A. G., cited, 355
JOHNSON, FOLKE, 352
Diseases of Berries in the West, 770–775
JOHNSON, H. B.: Using Chemicals To Stop Spoilage, 842–843
JOHNSON, HOWARD W.:
Bacteria, Fungi, and Viruses on Soybeans, 238–247
Leaf Diseases of Grasses in the South, 259–262
Johnson, Maxwell O., cited, 126
Johnsongrass, 368–377
anthracnose, 260–261, 370–371, plate ix
bacterial spot, 260, 370
bacterial streak, 260, 370
bacterial stripe, 259–260
covered kernel smut, 372–373
gray leaf spot, 261, 372
leaf blight, 260
leaf spot, 260
loose kernel smut, 373
rough spot, 261, 370
rust, 261, 372
sooty stripe, 261, 372
target spot, 260, 372
zonate leaf spot, 261, 371–372
Jonathan spot, apple, 832
JONES, FRED R.: Sources of Healthier Alfalfa, 228–237

JONES, HENRY A.:
Some Sources of Resistance in Crop Plants, 192–216
Jones, L. K., cited, 649
Jones, L. R., cited, 178, 186, 426, 434, 574, 660, 817
Juniper, mistletoe, 75

Kabatiella caulivora, 197, 220
Kafir, covered kernel smut, 137
Kalanchoë, diseases, 862
Kale, 100
blackleg, 428–429
Kansas, 48, 58, 105, 231, 233, 255, 287, 330, 337, 341, 348, 350, 353, 354, 355, 357, 361, 364, 372, 385, 509, 660, 852
Kassanis, B., cited, 111
KEITT, G. W., 55, 58, 689, 697
Scab of Apples, 646–652
Keller, J. R., cited, 596, 599, 885
Kendrick, J. B., cited, 244
Kentucky, 84, 108, 109, 222, 223, 237, 239, 259, 340, 383, 540, 543, 551, 681, 711, 852
Kentucky bluegrass, 37, 272, 287
crown or foot rot, 271
leaf spot, 266, 289, plate xix
septoria leaf blotch, 266–267
Kernkamp, M. F., cited, 45, 57
KIENHOLZ, J. R.:
Scab on the Pear, 674–678
Stony Pit of Pears, 670–673
King, C. J., cited, 318
Kiplinger, D. C., cited, 615
Klendusity, defined, 902
KLOTZ, L. J., 409, 735
Foot Rot of Citrus Trees, 734–737
Tristeza Disease of Citrus, 730–734
Knight, R. L., cited, 310
Knorr, L. C., cited, 733
Knot, olive, 11–12
Koch, Robert, cited, 15
Koehler, Benjamin, cited, 352
Kohlrabi, blackleg, 428–429
Kotila, John E., cited, 187
Krakover, L. J., cited, 187, 223
KREITLOW, KERMIT W.:
Ailments of Clover, 217–227
Northern Forage Grasses, 262–267
Kudzu, diseases, 252–253
Kuehneola uredinis, 774
Kumquats, foot rot, 736
KUNKEL, L. O., 356, 475, 574, 599, 793
Aster Yellows, 642–645

L–224, 136
Labrella coryli, 205
Labrella leaf spot, filbert, 205
Ladino clover, 100, 217 ff.
anther mold, 273–274
curvularia leaf spot, 224
leaf spot, plate vi
pseudoplea leaf spot, 225
sclerotinia crown and stem rot, 218–219

Ladino clover—Continued
See also White clover
LAMBERT, EDMUND B.: Diseases of the Common Mushroom, 478–482
Lambert mottle, sweet cherry, 154, 717, 720
Lamella, defined, 902
Lance nematode, 621
Lande, H. H., cited, 48
Langford, M. H., cited, 55
Large, J. R., cited, 797
Larmer, F. G., cited, 190
Larson, R. H., cited, 428, 433
Late blight
celery, 209, 408, 409, 410–412, 498–499
potato, 5–6, 12, 29, 44, 49, 84, 86, 89–90, 92–93, 149, 166, 169, 213, 435–437, 503–504, 814–815
tomato, 90, 92, 215, 455, 456–457, 458, 460, 461, 463, 464, 465, 494, 508, 814–815
Late leaf spot, peanut, 449–450
Late raspberry rust, 203
Latent mosaic potato, 22, 214, 440, 504
LEACH, J. G., 170
Bacteria, Fungi, and Insects, 63–67
Leaf and
cane rust, blackberry, 774
glume spot, grasses, 256
head blights, cereals, 344–349
pod spot, pea, 151
Leaf anthracnose, sorgo, 207
Leaf blight(s)
corn, 380–385, plate iii
melons, 166
sorghum, 260, 371
sorgo, 525
sudangrass, 204, 260, 371, plate ix
Leaf blister on white oak, 841
Leaf blotch
field pea, 248–249
pecan, 797
Leaf curl, 17, plate xviii
Leaf disease(s)
coffee, 169
of grasses in the South, 259–262
of range grasses, 253–258
sorgo, 524–526
Leaf mildews, 112
Leaf mold, tomato, 215, 495, 506
Leaf nematode disease, 592, 593
Leaf roll
potatoes, 23, 26, 150, 214, 440, 441, 442, 443, 504
strawberry, 767–768
Leaf rust, 112
alfalfa, 234
barley, 53, 193, 329, 332–333, 335
blueberry, 788
bluegrass, 279
corn, 110
grain, 1–2, 5, 6
grasses, 278–279

Leaf rust—Continued
oats, 110
rye, 110, 279, 329, 335
wheat, 53, 86, 92, 101, 110, 171, 196, 278-279, 329, 332-333, 337, 339, 340, plate i
wheatgrass, 204, 278
Leaf scald
grasses, 237, 259, 263-264, plate viii
sugarcane, 531, 532, 534, 535
Leaf scorch, 203, 511
Leaf smut
grasses, 204, 282-283
rice, 159
Leaf spot(s)
alfalfa, 197, 233-234, plate vii
and blight, rye, 348
and crown rot, Bermuda-grass, 287
and sparse leaf, Italian prune, 153
blackberry, 201, 773-774
buffalograss, 205
cabbage, 820
carpetgrass, 259
cauliflower, 820
cereals, 348
cherry, 695-701, plate xvi
clover, 187
cotton, 315-317
crotalaria, 252
Dallisgrass, 259
grasses, 257
house plants, 860, 862
Kentucky bluegrass, 266, 289, plate xix
Ladino clover, plate vi
millet, plate ix
mountain brome, 264
orchardgrass, 264-265, plate viii
peanut, 172, 212, 449-450, plate xxix
pearlmillet, 262
raspberry, 203, 781
smooth brome, plate viii
strawberry, 203
sudangrass, 260
sweetclover, 198, 224-225
velvetbeans, 252
Leaf streak, orchardgrass, 204
Leafhoppers, 22, 23-24
aster, 643-645
LeClerg, Erwin L.: Making Sure of Healthy Seed, 146-151
Leding, A. R., cited, 302
Leek. See Onion
Lefebvre, C. L., 358
How To Keep Turf Grass Healthy, 285-291
Legumes, 11, 12, 96, 98
and grasses, 217-291
in the South, 248-253
seed, 135, 142, 147
southern, resistance in, 199
Lemma, defined, 902
Lemons
albedo browning, 831
black pit, 821

Lemons—Continued
blue mold, 821, 846, 849
chilling injury, 828
crinkly leaf, 739
degreening, 881
emanations, 883
exocortis, 743
foot rot, 735, 736
fumigation, 846, 849
green mold, 846, 849, 883
infectious variegation, 739
membranous stain, 828, 834
pitting, 828, 834
psorosis, 740
red blotch, 834
scald, 828
septoria spot, plate xviii
sour orange scab, plate xviii
stem-end rot, 846, 849
treating bath, 842
triteza, 732
watery breakdown, 828
Lespedeza, 148
dodder, 251
powdery mildew, 199, 251
sericea, 253
southern blight, 251
Leptosphaeria
avenaria, 195
herpotrichoides, 323
sacchari, 531
Leptothyrium pomi, 663-666
Lesion, defined, 902
Lettuce, 95, 142, 417-425, 816
aster yellows, 421-422, 508
bacterial soft rot, 817, 818, plate xxvi
big vein, 22, 422-423
botrytis blight, 419
brown blight, 210, 423
damping-off, 417-418
downy mildew, 143, 210, 419-420, 500-501
gray mold, 419
mosaic, 18, 19, 210, 420-421, 508
powdery mildew, 210
premature yellowing, 425
redheart, 424
resistance in, 210, 500-501
rib blight, 425, plate xxvii
sclerotinia drop, 418-419
seed decay, 417-418
seedling blight, 417-418
slime or bacterial rot, 419
spotted wilt, 822-823
tipburn, 210, 423-424, 425, 501
Leukel, R. W.:
Four Enemies of Sorghum Crops, 368-377
Treating Seeds to Prevent Diseases, 134-145
Levine, M. N., cited, 46, 53
Lewis, F. H.: Cherry Leaf Spot, 695-701
Leyendecker, P. J., cited, 302
Leytosan, 135
Life cycle, defined, 902
Light, effect on disease, 14

Lightning, 94
Lignification, defined, 902
Lily
botrytis blight, 611, 613-614
bulbs, nematodes, 621-624
bulbs, treatment, 136
scorch, 614-617
Lily-of-the-valley, 160-161
Lima bean(s), 142, 393-400
anthracnose, plate xxv
downy mildew, 92, 210, 393, 400, 498, plate xxv
mosaic, 210
nematodes, 498
resistance in, 210, 497-498
scab, 408
See also Beans
Limber, Donald P.: The Inspection of Imported Plants, 159-161
Lime-sulfur, introduction, 116
Limes
citrus canker, plate xviii
foot rot, 735, 736
sour orange scab, plate xviii
stem pitting, 732
stylar-end breakdown, 834
Lin, K. H., cited, 409
Line pattern, plum, 154, 717
Linford, M. B., cited, 353
Link, K. P., cited, 171, 188
Linn, M. B., cited, 421
Linnaeus, 74
Little cherry, 715, 716, 717
Little peach, 153, 714, 717, 720
Littleleaf in pines in the Southeast, 855-857
Liu, J. C., cited, 659
Liver spot, pecan, 797
Loblolly pine, littleleaf, 855-857
Local infection, defined, 902
Lodgepole pine, dwarfmistletoe, 76
Loegering, W. Q., cited, 48, 59
Long smut, sorghum, 61
Longyear, B. O., cited, 786
Loomis, H. F., cited, 318
Loose kernel smut, 60, 61, 373
Loose smut
barley, 43, 137, 139, 170, 193, 282, 366, 367-368
oats, 43, 52, 60, 61, 360, 365
wheat, 43, 137, 139, 196, 282, 367-368
Losses from diseases, 1-9
Louisiana, 16, 52, 58, 104, 181, 241, 244, 293, 298, 305, 311, 318, 319, 320, 370, 431, 433, 500, 505, 525, 527, 528, 532, 536, 578, 581, 681, 796, 825
Lovegrass, 272
Lovett, H. C., cited, 319
Lowbush blueberry, 787, 788
Lu, Shih I., cited, 54
Lucas, G. B., cited, 52
Lutman, B. F., cited, 169
Luttrell, E. S.: Diseases of Muscadine Grapes, 874-875
Lykkens, S. T., cited, 342

924

926

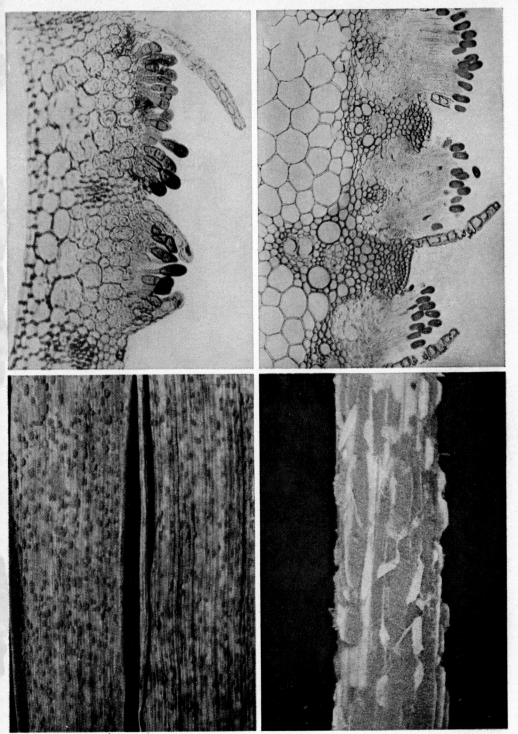

Upper left: Section of wheat stem rust pustule with spores in the wintering stage. Upper right: Section of a pustule of wheat stem rust with red, summer-stage spores. Lower left: Wheat leaves infected with the summer stage of the leaf rust fungus. Lower right: Wheat stem infected with the red or summer stage of stem rust fungus.

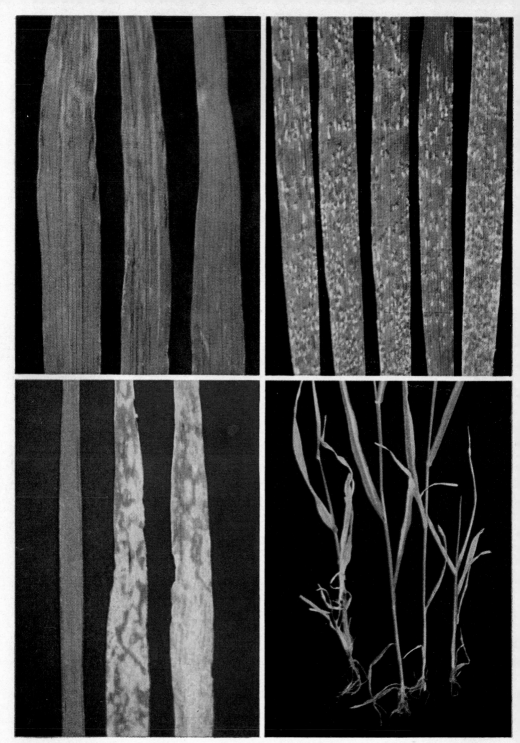

Upper left: Healthy and diseased barley leaves infected with the bacterial blight organism. Upper right: Leaves of oat infected with the red or summer stage of the crown rust fungus. Lower left: Healthy and powdery mildew infected barley leaves. Lower right: Symptoms of Victoria blight, a serious fungus disease of oat plants.

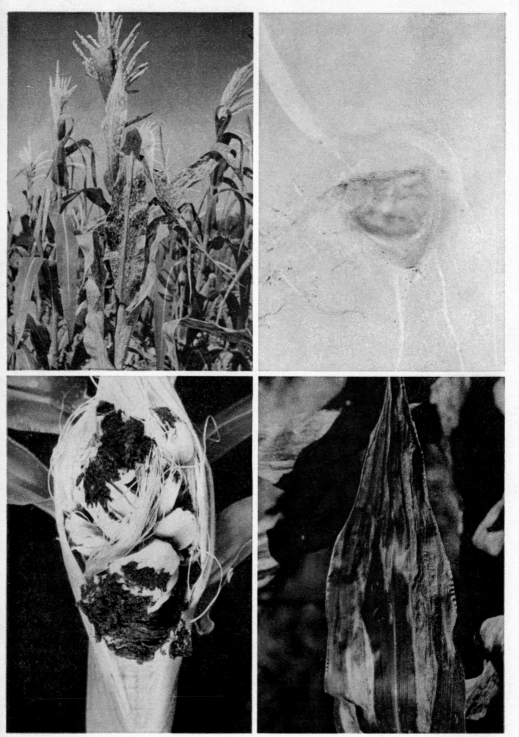

Upper left: Corn with the southern leaf blight, caused by *Helminthosporium maydis*. Upper right: Stunted corn seedling with mycelium of the fungus *Gibberella zeae* on it. Lower left: Common corn smut, caused by *Ustilago maydis*. Lower right: In the North the fungus *Helminthosporium turcicum* causes a serious blight of corn leaves.

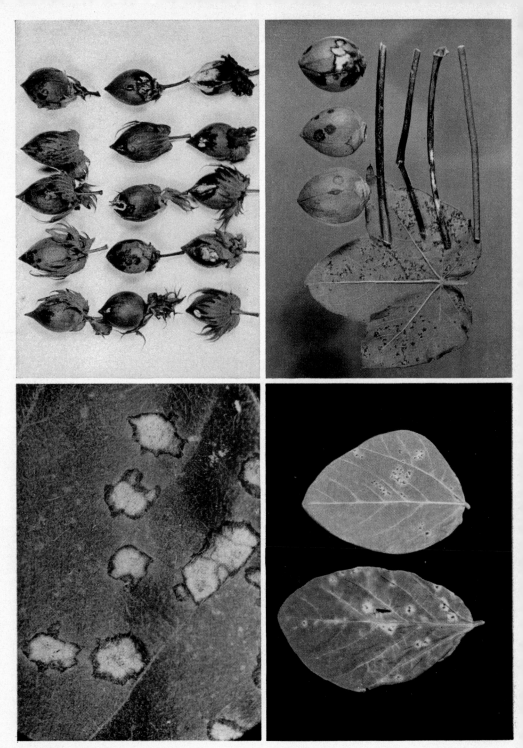

Upper left: Cotton anthracnose, here shown on bolls, reduces yields and discolors lint. Upper right: Symptoms of bacterial blight of cotton on stems, leaves, and bolls. Lower left: Enlarged lesions of the frogeye fungus on soybean. Lower right: Lower and upper surfaces of soybean leaves affected with bacterial blight.

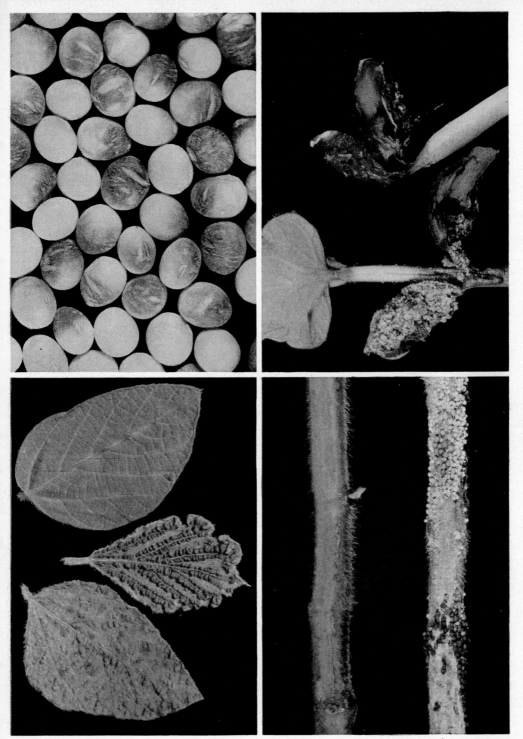

Upper left: Purple stain caused by a fungus on seeds of soybean. Upper right: The purple stain disease on soybean seedlings that developed from infected seed. Lower left: A healthy soybean leaf (top) and leaves beneath infected with virus. Lower right: Fruiting bodies of southern blight fungus attached to a dead stem of soybean.

Upper left: Leaves of healthy (upper) and virus-infected (lower) red clover. Upper right: Leaves of red clover infected with powdery mildew (*Erysiphe polygoni*). Lower left: Leaf spot of Ladino white clover, caused by the fungus *Cercospora zebrina*. Lower right: Stems of red clover discolored by the spring black stem fungus.

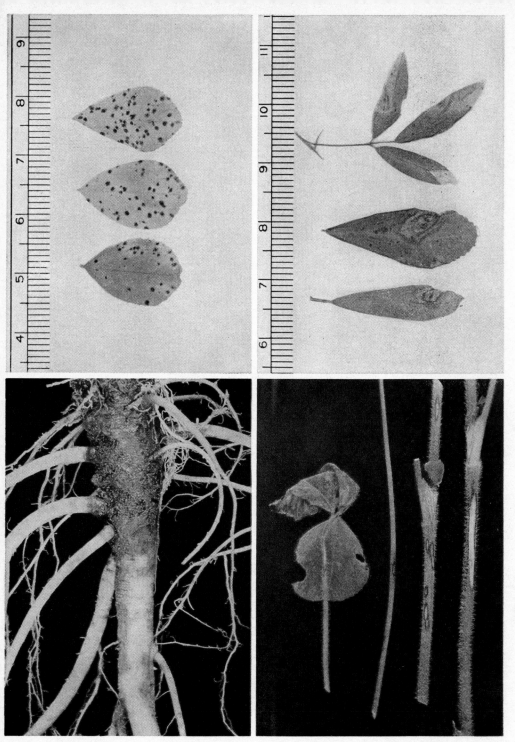

Upper left: Leaflets of alfalfa infected with the common leaf spot (*Pseudopeziza medicaginis*). Upper right: Target spot (*Pleospora herbarum*) on leaves of alfalfa. Lower left: A taproot of red clover showing discoloration caused by root rot fungi. Lower right: Cankers of the northern anthracnose fungus on crimson clover.

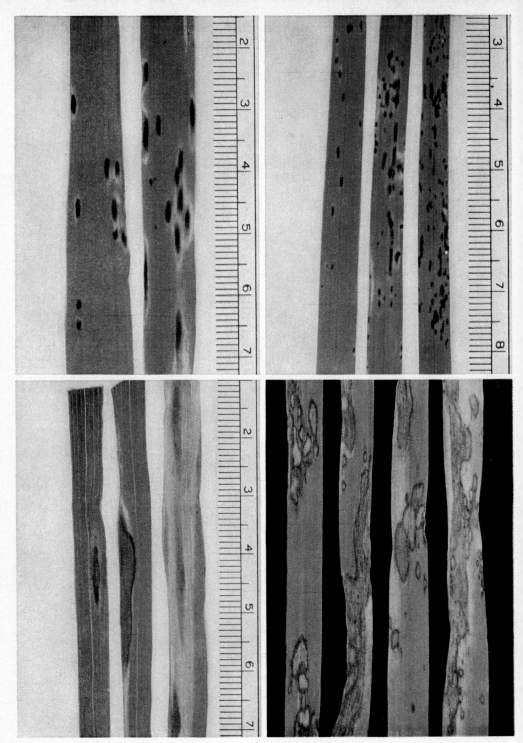

Upper left: Spots on leaves of smooth brome attacked by the fungus *Helminthosporium bromi*. Upper right: Orchardgrass infected by the leaf spot fungus *Stagonospora maculata*. Lower left: Blotching due to a bacterial disease on leaves of smooth brome. Lower right: Leaf infection on smooth brome caused by the scald fungus.

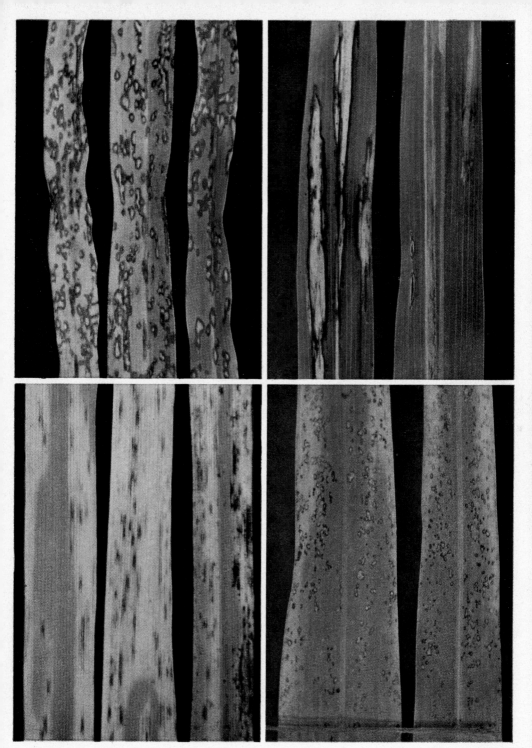

Upper left: Anthracnose (*Colletotrichum graminicola*) on leaves of Johnsongrass. Upper right: Sweet Sudan (tan spots) and common Sudan (red spots) infected by the leaf blight fungus. Lower left: Net blotch on tall fescue. Lower right: Leaves of Starr (wide) and common (narrower) millet affected with cercospora leaf spot.

Upper left: Discoloration of the inner bark, characteristic of elm phloem necrosis. Upper right: Brown needles on western white pine are a symptom of the pole blight. Lower left: Wilting and discolored leaves are symptoms of deadly oak wilt disease. Lower right: A chestnut blight canker, the foreign destroyer of American chestnuts.

Upper left: Eutypella canker of maple, typical of stem infections of forest trees. Upper right: Fruiting bodies of *Polyporus sulphureus,* one of the wood-decay fungi. Lower left: A fruiting body of *Hydnum erinaceous,* one cause of decay in hardwoods. Lower right: Exobasidium fungus gall on azalea, prominent but usually unimportant.

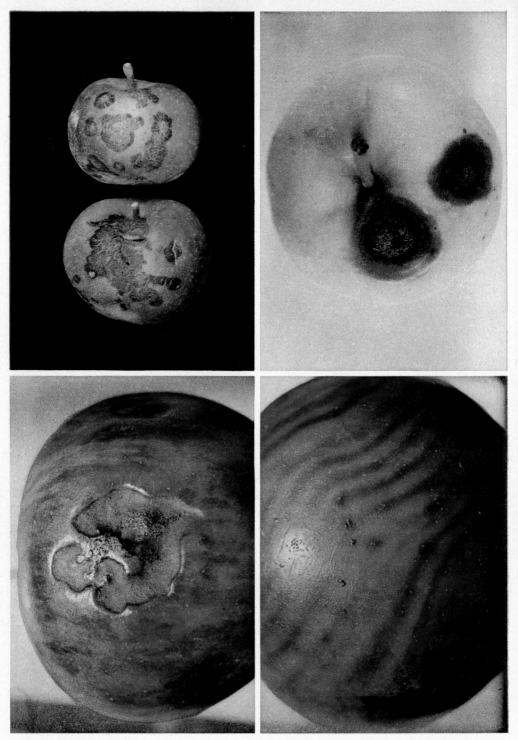

Upper left: Apple scab, a common disease rendering the fruit worthless for market. Upper right: Bitter rot can destroy the entire apple crop within a few days. Lower left: Apple blotch, a midsummer disease, makes characteristic spots on fruits. Lower right: Black rot, a secondary fungus, is common on the fruit at harvesttime.

Upper left: Mosaic, a virus disease of the apple tree. Upper right: The scab fungus forms dark-brown, moldlike patches of fungus growth on apple leaves. Lower left: Spots, caused by rust infections, on apple leaves. Lower right: Rust galls on cedar trees expand in the spring, forming orange masses covered with rust spores.

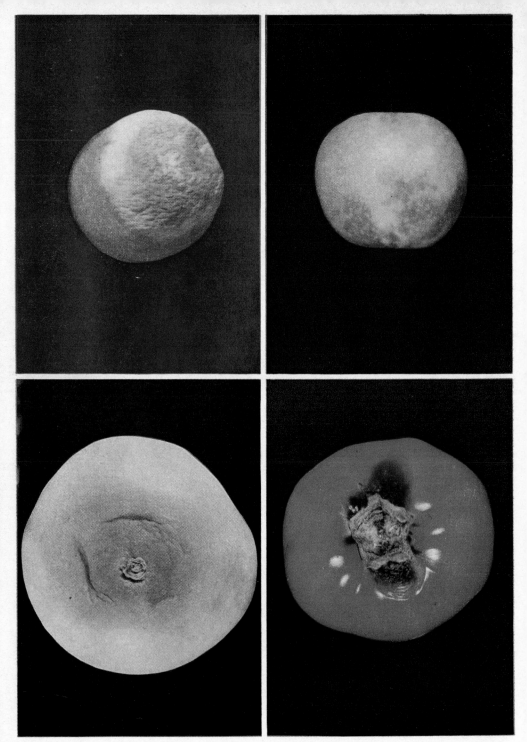

Upper left: Green mold, a common storage decay that affects oranges. Upper right: Apple scald, an important storage trouble that causes much loss of fruit. Lower left: Stem-end rot of grapefruit, a fungus disease affecting the fruit on the trees and in transit. Lower right Phoma spot of tomato, a storage and transportation problem.

Upper left: Black rot, a destructive disease of grapes. Upper right: Grape downy mildew is a serious disease in many vineyards. Lower left: Red stele, a fungus disease of the strawberry that affects the root system. Lower right: Powdery mildew can cover the leaves, fruits, and stems with powdery white spots of fungus growth.

Upper left: Brown rot on sour cherry. Upper right: Leaf spot, a destructive cherry disease. Lower left: Brown rot on peach. This is the most common disease of peaches in the more humid sections of the United States. It destroys many bushels yearly. Lower right: Pear black spot, a disease common on unsprayed pear leaves and fruit.

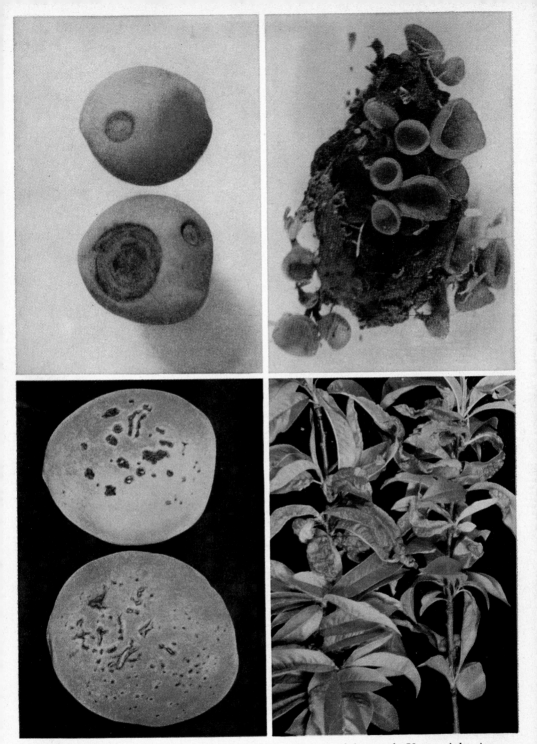

Upper left: Anthracnose, a relatively new fungus disease of the peach. Upper right: Apothecia of the brown rot fungus. Spores from these goblet-shaped bodies are shot into the air during the blossom period and start the new cycle of infection. Lower left: Bacterial spot on peaches. Lower right: Leaf curl, a springtime leaf disease.

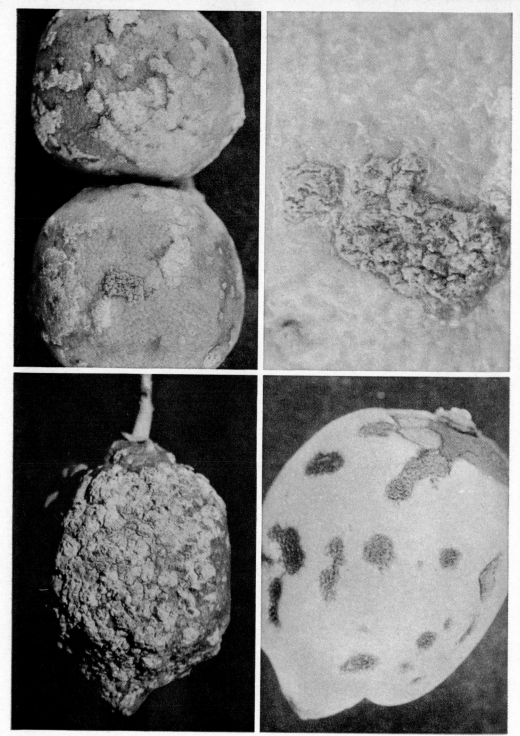

Upper left: Sour orange scab on limes. The fruit at bottom also shows citrus canker spot. Upper right: Typical citrus canker on limes—a serious disease that apparently has been eradicated in the United States. Lower left: A young lemon injured by sour orange scab. Lower right: Septoria spot on lemon.

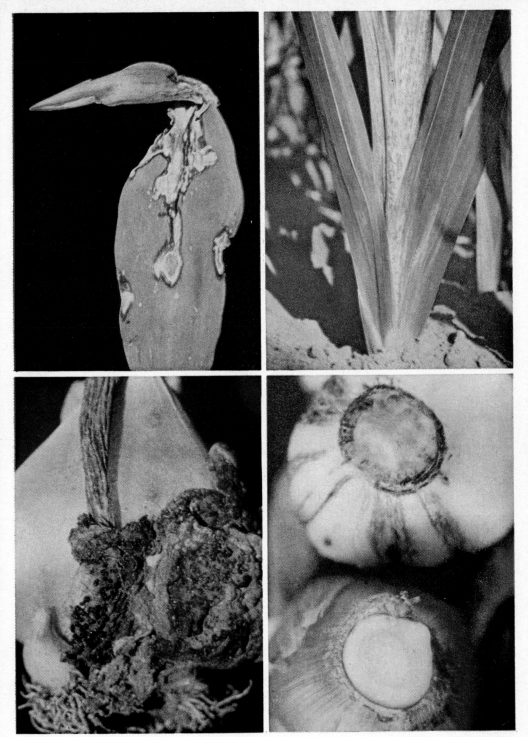

Upper left: Botrytis blight in a tulip leaf; large blight lesions generally develop gray mold spores. Upper right: White streak in gladiolus leaves, a virus disease. Lower left: Botrytis sclerotia on the dry tulip bulb carry the fungus into old and new fields. Lower right: Iris bulbs attacked by the bulb and stem nematode.

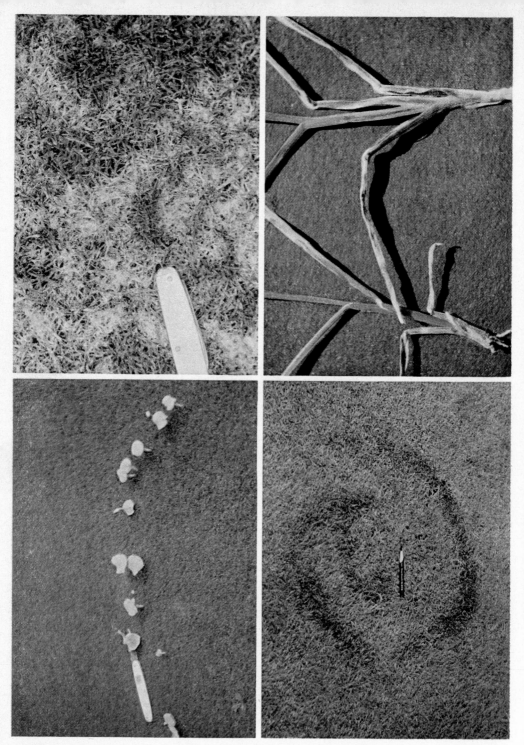

Upper left: Dollar spot injury of creeping bent, caused by *Sclerotinia homeocarpa.* Upper right: Leaf spot injury of Kentucky bluegrass, caused by *Helminthosporium vagans.* Lower left: Fairy ring, caused by the mushroom *Marasmius oreades.* Lower right: Brown patch injury on Colonial bent, caused by *Pellicularia filamentosa.*

Upper left: The streaks in a normally pink gladiolus result from a virus disease. Upper right: Streaked color pattern in a normally red tulip indicates virus disease. Lower left: A virus infection causes the yellow and green rings in a camellia leaf. Lower right: The fungus *Curvularia* blights leaves, stems, and flowers of gladiolus.

Upper: Enlarged cysts of golden nematode of potato. The cysts are naturally about the size of a pinhead. This destructive pest has recently come to us from abroad. Lower: Rose black spot. The ragged margin of the spots, yellowing, and leaf drop are characteristic symptoms of this serious and widely distributed rose disease.

Upper: Black shank attacks the roots of tobacco plants. In the bare patches plants wilted and died early. The fungus causing the disease survives for years in the contaminated soil. Lower: Tobacco plants affected by mosaic and wildfire. Wildfire caused spotting and dead areas on lower leaves; mosaic caused mottling of top leaves.

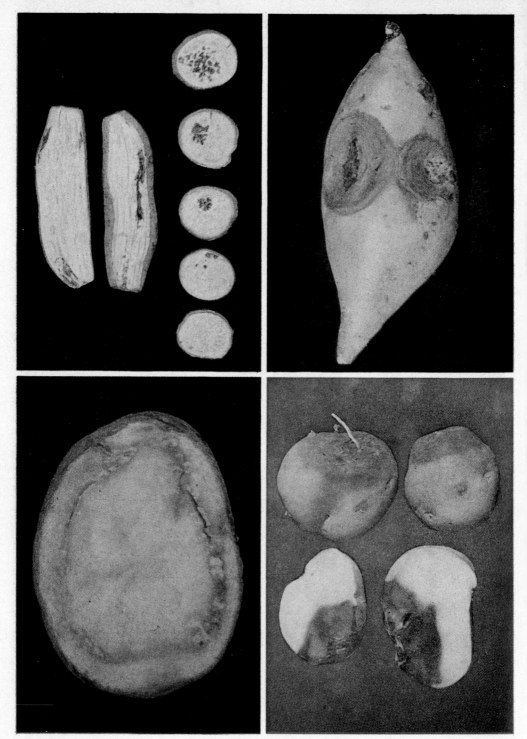

Upper left: Sections of sweetpotato roots affected with internal cork, caused by a virus. Upper right: Black rot of sweetpotato—principally a storage rot. Lower left: Potato tuber infected with ring rot, a bacterial disease. Lower right: Fusarium tuber rot of Irish potato, a destructive disease in the United States.

Upper left: Stem anthracnose on lima bean pods. Upper right: Downy mildew on pods of lima bean. This organism requires a high humidity to cause infection. Lower left: Bacterial blight infection of pea leaves. The bacteria are spread from plant to plant by rain and hail. Lower right: Red node, a virus disease of bean.

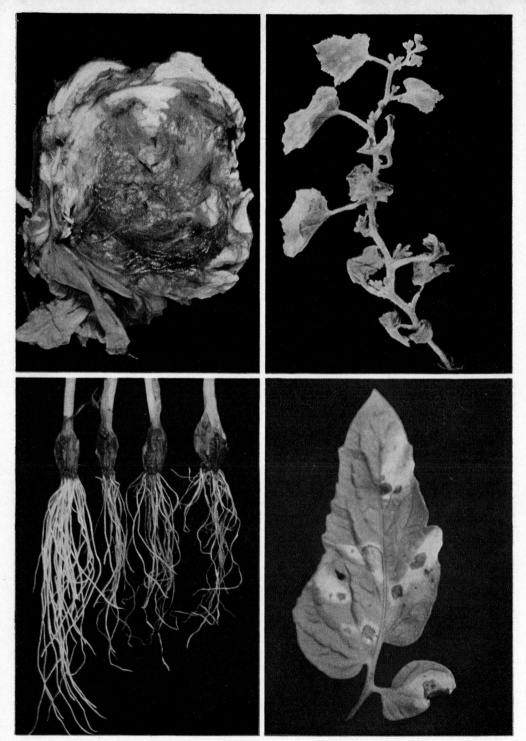

Upper left: Head lettuce affected with bacterial soft rot. Upper right: Cantaloup vine attacked by the powdery mildew fungus. The disease is important in the Imperial Valley of California. Lower left: Pink root, a disease of onion. One plant is healthy and three are diseased. Lower right: Alternaria leaf spot on tomato leaf.

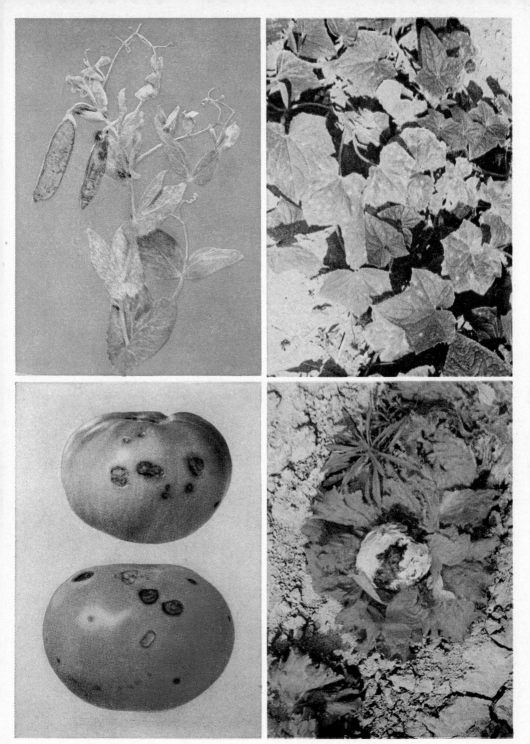

Upper left: Pea streak, caused by a virus, on pea pods. Upper right: Anthracnose of cucumber plants; the disease also affects watermelon and muskmelon growing in humid regions. Lower left: Bacterial spot of tomato on two fruits. Lower right: A plant of Great Lakes lettuce affected with rib blight, a physiologic disease.

Upper left: Scab on squash fruits; the disease affects other cucurbits, including cucumber. Upper right: Cucumber plant infected with the downy mildew fungus; the disease is important along the Atlantic coast. Lower left: Anthracnose of watermelon. Lower right: Spinach blight, caused by the common cucumber mosaic virus.

Upper left: Pepper ring spot disease, caused by a strain of the cucumber mosaic virus. Upper right: Leaf stalks of celery infected with the brown spot fungus. Lower left: White rust of spinach, caused by a fungus. The disease is frequently widespread in Texas. Lower right: Peanut leaf spot disease on runner peanut leaves.

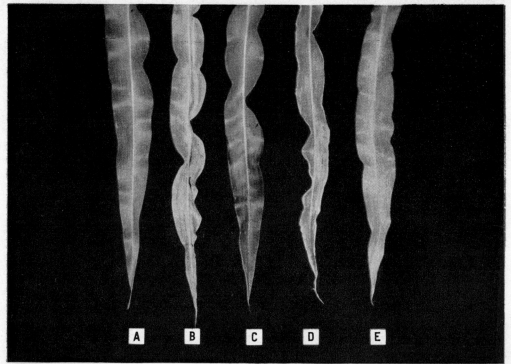

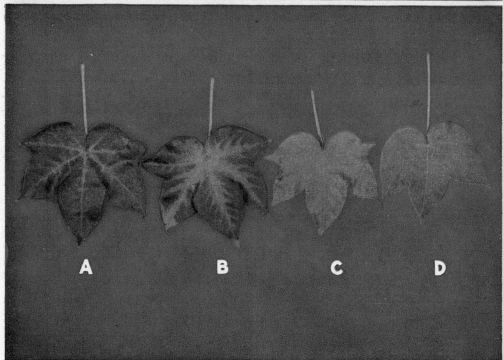

Upper: Mineral deficiency disease caused the discoloration of the old corn leaves. A, a normal leaf; B, C, D, and E lack nitrogen, phosphorus, potassium, and magnesium, respectively. Lower: Leaves from a cotton plant showing symptoms of magnesium hunger. The leaves A to D represent progressively the reactions on old to new growth.